Business Dynamics

Systems Thinking and
Modeling for a Complex World

Business Dynamics
Systems Thinking and
Modeling for a Complex World

John D. Sterman
Massachusetts Institute of Technology
Sloan School of Management

Boston   Burr Ridge, IL   Dubuque, IA   Madison, WI   New York   San Francisco   St. Louis
Bangkok   Bogotá   Caracas   Lisbon   London   Madrid
Mexico City   Milan   New Delhi   Seoul   Singapore   Sydney   Taipei   Toronto

McGraw-Hill Higher Education

A Division of The McGraw-Hill Companies

http://www.mhhe.com

For Cindy

ABOUT THE AUTHOR

John D. Sterman is J. Spencer Standish Professor of Management at the Sloan School of Management of the Massachusetts Institute of Technology and Director of MIT's System Dynamics Group. His research centers on the development of practical methods for systems thinking and dynamic modeling of complex systems, with applications to organizational learning and change, operations management, corporate strategy, and nonlinear dynamics in a wide range of systems, from supply chains to scientific revolutions. He has pioneered the development of management flight simulators of corporate and economic systems. These flight simulators are used in research to understand and improve managerial decision making in complex dynamic systems; more importantly, they are now widely used by corporations and universities around the world for teaching, problem solving, and policy design. Professor Sterman discovered system dynamics modeling in high school, studied it as an undergraduate at Dartmouth College, and received his PhD from MIT. He has been awarded the Jay W. Forrester Prize, given for the best published work in the field of system dynamics over the prior five years, and has four times won awards for teaching excellence from the students of the Sloan School.

Preface

Accelerating economic, technological, social, and environmental change challenge managers and policy makers to learn at increasing rates, while at the same time the complexity of the systems in which we live is growing. Many of the problems we now face arise as unanticipated side effects of our own past actions. All too often the policies we implement to solve important problems fail, make the problem worse, or create new problems.

Effective decision making and learning in a world of growing *dynamic complexity* requires us to become systems thinkers—to expand the boundaries of our mental models and develop tools to understand how the structure of complex systems creates their behavior.

This book introduces you to system dynamics modeling for the analysis of policy and strategy, with a focus on business and public policy applications. System dynamics is a perspective and set of conceptual tools that enable us to understand the structure and dynamics of complex systems. System dynamics is also a rigorous modeling method that enables us to build formal computer simulations of complex systems and use them to design more effective policies and organizations. Together, these tools allow us to create management flight simulators—microworlds where space and time can be compressed and slowed so we can experience the long-term side effects of decisions, speed learning, develop our understanding of complex systems, and design structures and strategies for greater success.

The field of system dynamics is thriving. Over the past decade, many top companies, consulting firms, and governmental organizations have used system dynamics to address critical issues. More innovative universities and business schools are teaching system dynamics and finding enthusiastic and growing enrollments. Hundreds of primary and secondary schools, from kindergarten to high school, are integrating systems thinking, system dynamics, and computer simulation into their curricula. Tools and methods for system dynamics modeling, the library of successful applications, and insights into the effective use of the tools with executives and organizations are all expanding rapidly.

FEATURES AND CONTENT

University and graduate-level texts, particularly those focused on business and public policy applications, have not kept pace with the growth of the field. This book is designed to provide thorough coverage of the field of system dynamics today, by examining

- Systems thinking and the system dynamics worldview;
- Tools for systems thinking, including methods to elicit and map the structure of complex systems and relate those structures to their dynamics;
- Tools for modeling and simulation of complex systems;
- Procedures for testing and improving models;
- Guidelines for working with client teams and successful implementation.

You will learn about the dynamics of complex systems, including the structures that create growth, goal-seeking behavior, oscillation and instability, S-shaped growth, overshoot and collapse, path dependence, and other nonlinear dynamics. Examples and applications include

- Corporate growth and stagnation,
- The diffusion of new technologies,
- The dynamics of infectious disease such as HIV/AIDS,
- Business cycles,
- Speculative bubbles,
- The use and reliability of forecasts,
- The design of supply chains in business and other organizations,
- Service quality management,
- Transportation policy and traffic congestion,
- Project management and product development,

and many others.

The goal of systems thinking and system dynamics modeling is to improve our understanding of the ways in which an organization's performance is related to its internal structure and operating policies, including those of customers, competitors, and suppliers and then to use that understanding to design high leverage policies for success. To do so this book utilizes

- **Process Points** that provide practical advice for the successful application of the tools in real organizations.
- Case studies of **System Dynamics in Action** that present successful applications ranging from global warming and the war on drugs to reengineering the supply chain of a major computer firm, marketing strategy in the automobile industry, and process improvement in the petrochemicals industry.

System dynamics is not a spectator sport. Developing systems thinking and modeling skills requires the active participation of you, the reader, via

- **Challenges.** The challenges, placed throughout the text, give you practice with the tools and techniques presented in the book and will stimulate your original thinking about important real world issues. The challenges range from simple thought experiments to full-scale modeling projects.

- **Simulation software and models.** The accompanying CD-ROM and web site (http://www.mhhe.com/sterman) include all the models developed in the text along with state-of-the-art simulation software to run them. There are several excellent software packages designed to support system dynamics modeling. These include ithink, Powersim, and Vensim. The CD and website include the models for the text in all three software formats. The disk also includes fully functional versions of the ithink, Powersim, and Vensim software so you can run the models using any of these packages without having to purchase any additional software.

- Additionally, the **Instructor's Manual** and instructor's section of the **web site** include suggested solutions for the challenges, additional assignments, Powerpoint files with the diagrams and figures from the text suitable for transparencies, suggested course sequences and syllabi, and other materials.

INTENDED AUDIENCE

The book can be used as a text in courses on systems thinking, simulation modeling, complexity, strategic thinking, operations, and industrial engineering, among others. It can be used in full or half-semester courses, executive education, and self-study. The book also serves as a reference for managers, engineers, consultants, and others interested in developing their systems thinking skills or using system dynamics in their organizations.

A NOTE ON MATHEMATICS

System dynamics is grounded in control theory and the modern theory of nonlinear dynamics. There is an elegant and rigorous mathematical foundation for the theory and models we develop. System dynamics is also designed to be a practical tool that policy makers can use to help them solve the pressing problems they confront in their organizations. Most managers have not studied nonlinear differential equations or even calculus, or have forgotten it if they did. To be useful, system dynamics modeling must be accessible to the widest range of students and practicing managers without becoming a vague set of qualitative tools and unreliable generalizations. That tension is compounded by the diversity of backgrounds within the community of managers, students, and scholars interested in system dynamics, backgrounds ranging from people with no mathematics education beyond high school to those with doctorates in physics.

IF YOU DON'T HAVE A STRONG MATHEMATICS BACKGROUND, FEAR NOT

This book presents system dynamics with a minimum of mathematical formalism. The goal is to develop your intuition and conceptual understanding, without sacrificing the rigor of the scientific method. You do not need calculus or differential equations to understand the material. Indeed, the concepts are presented using only text, graphs, and basic algebra. Mathematical details and references to more advanced material are set aside in separate sections and footnotes. Higher mathematics, though useful, is not as important as the critical thinking skills developed here.

IF YOU HAVE A STRONG MATHEMATICS BACKGROUND, FEAR NOT

Realistic and useful models are almost always of such complexity and nonlinearity that there are no known analytic solutions, and many of the mathematical tools you have studied have limited applicability. This book will help you use your strong technical background to develop your intuition and conceptual understanding of complexity and dynamics. Modeling human behavior differs from modeling physical systems in engineering and the sciences. We cannot put managers up on the lab bench and run experiments to determine their transfer function or frequency response. We believe all electrons follow the same laws of physics, but we cannot assume all people behave in the same way. Besides a solid grounding in the mathematics of dynamic systems, modeling human systems requires us to develop our knowledge of psychology, decision making, and organizational behavior. Finally, mathematical analysis, while necessary, is far from sufficient for successful systems thinking and modeling. For your work to have impact in the real world you must learn how to develop and implement models of human behavior in organizations, with all their ambiguity, time pressure, personalities, and politics. Throughout the book I have sought to illustrate how the technical tools and mathematical concepts you may have studied in the sciences or engineering can be applied to the messy world of the policy maker.

FEEDBACK

I welcome your comments, criticisms, and suggestions. Suggestions for additional examples, cases, theory, models, flight simulators, and so on, to make the book more relevant and useful to you are especially invited. I will update the website to incorporate user feedback and new materials. Email comments to <BusDyn@mit.edu>.

ACKNOWLEDGMENTS

This work benefited immensely from the advice, criticism, and encouragement of many colleagues, students, and friends. I owe an immeasurable debt to my first system dynamics teachers, Dana Meadows, Dennis Meadows, and Jay Forrester, for their integrity, high standards, and passionate commitment. I'm particularly indebted to the exceptional students of the MIT Sloan School of Management. They constantly challenge me to make the discipline of system dynamics relevant, useful, and exciting; I hope they've learned as much from me as I've learned from them. In addition, I thank my colleagues at the Sloan School and in the system dynamics community around the world, who helped by providing data and examples, reviewing the draft, testing early versions in their courses, and in countless other ways. This group includes (but is not limited to) the following folks and institutions:

Tarek Abdel-Hamid (Naval Postgraduate School); David Andersen, George Richardson (SUNY Albany); Ed Anderson (Univ. of Texas); Carlos Ariza, Sharon Els, Ken Cooper, Jim Lyneis, Hank Taylor (Pugh-Roberts Associates); George Backus (Policy Assessment Corporation); Bent Bakken (Norwegian Defense Research Establishment); Yaman Barlas (Bogazici University, Istanbul); Michael Bean (Powersim Corp.); Eric Beinhocker, Damon Beyer, Andrew Doman, Usman Ghani, Maurice Glucksman, Paul Langley, Norman Marshall (McKinsey and Company); Laura Black, John Carroll, Vanessa Colella, Ernst Diehl, Steve Eppinger, Charlie Fine, Mila Getmansky, Paulo Goncalves, Janet Gould Wilkinson, Jim Hines, Nan Lux, Brad Morrison, Tim Nugent, Nelson Repenning, Ed Roberts, Scott Rockart, George Roth, Ed Schein, Peter Senge (MIT); Allen and Jane Boorstein; Steve Cavaleri (Central Connecticut State Univ.); Geoff Coyle (Royal Military College of Science, UK, retired); Brian Dangerfield (Univ. of Salford); Pål Davidsen (Univ. of Bergen); Jim Doyle, Mike Radzicki, Khalid Saeed (Worcester Polytechnic Institute); Bob Eberlein, Tom Fiddaman, Dan Goldner, David Peterson, Laura Peterson (Ventana Systems); David Foley and Judy Berk; Andy Ford (Washington State Univ.); David Ford (Texas A&M University); Nathan Forrester (A. T. Kearney); Rich Goldbach (Metro Machine Corp.); Christian Haxholdt, Heather Hazard (Copenhagen Business School); Jack Homer (Homer Consulting); Jody House (Oregon Graduate Institute); Bill Isaacs (Dialogos); Sam Israelit (Arthur Andersen); Nitin Joglekar (Boston Univ. School of Management); Drew Jones (Sustainability Institute); Christian Kampmann, Erik Mosekilde (Technical Univ. of Denmark); Daniel Kim, Virginia Wiley (Pegasus Communications); Craig Kirkwood (Arizona State Univ.); Elizabeth Krahmer Keating (Northwestern Univ.); Don Kleinmuntz (Univ. of Illinois, Urbana-Champaign); David Kreutzer (GKA, Inc.); Robert Landel (Darden School of Business, Univ. of Virginia); David Lane (London School of Economics); Erik Larsen (City University, London); Winston J. Ledet, Winston P. Ledet (The Manufacturing Game, Inc.); Ralph Levine (Michigan State Univ.); Angela Lipinski (Society for Organizational Learning); Martin Großmann, Frank Maier, Peter Milling (Univ. of Mannheim, Germany); Ali Mashayekhi (Sharif Univ. of Technology, Teheran); Nathaniel Mass (GenCorp); Paul Monus (BP/Amoco), John Morecroft, Ann van Ackere, Kim Warren (London Business School); Erling Moxnes (Norwegian School of Economics and Business Administration); Rogelio Oliva (Harvard Business School); Mark Paich (Colorado College); Steve Peterson, Barry Richmond (High Performance Systems); Greg Petsch (Compaq Computer); Nick Pudar (General Motors); Jack Pugh, Julia Pugh, Roberta Spencer (System Dynamics Society), Jørgen Randers (World Wildlife Fund International); Nancy Roberts (Leslie College); Jenny Rudolph (Boston College); Jorge Rufat-Latre (Strategos); Anjali Sastry, Marshall van Alstyne (University of Michigan); Bob Stearns; Susan Sterman; Jim Thompson (Global Prospectus, LLC); John Voyer

(Univ. of Southern Maine); Lyle Wallis (Decisio, Inc.); Jim Waters (Waters Business Systems); Jason Wittenberg (Harvard Univ.); Eric Wolstenholme (Leeds Business School, UK); Pavel Zamudio Ramirez (Monitor Company); the Copenhagen Business School, The International Network of Resource Information Centers (aka the Balaton Group), McKinsey and Company, the Norwegian School of Management, Pugh-Roberts Associates, the Society for Organizational Learning, the Technical University of Denmark, and, of course, the MIT Sloan School of Management.

Special thanks to High Performance Systems, Powersim, SA, and Ventana Systems—and their great people—for providing their simulation software and translations of the models for the CD and website.

The team at Irwin/McGraw-Hill deserves special mention for their enthusiasm, patience, and editorial help, particularly Scott Isenberg, Carol Rose, Jeff Shelstad, and Gladys True.

Cara Barber and Kelley Donovan provided important secretarial support.

Kathy Sullivan went beyond the call of duty on library research, data collection, editorial changes, and graphics.

Finally, the love and support of my family have been constant and essential. Thanks, Cindy, David, and Sarah.

Table of Contents

List of Challenges

Part I

Perspective and Process

This section describes the system dynamics worldview and the process of using system dynamics to solve problems in the real world. Chapter 1 provides an overview of the characteristics of complex systems and discusses why it is so hard to learn in systems with high dynamic complexity. Chapter 2 presents three case studies showing how major companies successfully used system dynamics to solve pressing business issues. Chapter 3 describes the process of using system dynamics in more detail, emphasizing how modelers and clients work together to achieve implemented results. Chapter 4 provides a qualitative tour of dynamical theory, illustrating the major patterns of behavior that dynamic systems generate and presenting the feedback structures underlying these behaviors.

1

Learning in and about Complex Systems

Experience is an expensive school.

—Benjamin Franklin

Experience is something you get just after you need it.

—Anonymous

1.1 INTRODUCTION

The greatest constant of modern times is change. Accelerating changes in technology, population, and economic activity are transforming our world, from the prosaic—the effect of information technology on the way we use the telephone—to the profound—the effect of greenhouse gases on the global climate. Some of the changes are wonderful; others defile the planet, impoverish the human spirit, and threaten our survival. All challenge traditional institutions, practices, and beliefs. Most important, most of the changes we now struggle to comprehend arise as consequences, intended and unintended, of humanity itself. All too often, well-intentioned efforts to solve pressing problems lead to *policy resistance,* where our policies are delayed, diluted, or defeated by the unforeseen reactions of other people or of nature. Many times our best efforts to solve a problem actually make it worse.

The dizzying effects of accelerating change are not new. Henry Adams, a perceptive observer of the great changes wrought by the industrial revolution, formulated the Law of Acceleration to describe the exponential growth of technology, production, and population that made the legacy of colonial America he inherited irrelevant:

> Since 1800, scores of new forces had been discovered; old forces had been raised to higher powers . . . Complexity had extended itself on immense horizons, and arithmetical ratios were useless for any attempt at accuracy.
>
> If science were to go on doubling or quadrupling its complexities every 10 years, even mathematics should soon succumb. An average mind had succumbed already in 1850; it could no longer understand the problem in 1900. (Adams 1918, pp. 490, 496)

Adams believed the radical changes in society induced by these forces "would require a new social mind." With uncharacteristic, and perhaps ironic, optimism, he concluded, "Thus far, since 5 or 10 thousand years, the mind had successfully reacted, and nothing yet proved that it would fail to react—but it would need to jump."

A steady stream of philosophers, scientists, and management gurus have since echoed Adams, lamenting the acceleration and calling for similar leaps to fundamental new ways of thinking and acting. Many advocate the development of *systems thinking*—the ability to see the world as a complex system, in which we understand that "you can't just do one thing" and that "everything is connected to everything else." If people had a holistic worldview, it is argued, they would then act in consonance with the long-term best interests of the system as a whole, identify the high leverage points in systems, and avoid policy resistance. Indeed, for some, the development of systems thinking is crucial for the survival of humanity.[1]

The challenge facing us all is how to move from generalizations about accelerating learning and systems thinking to tools and processes that help us understand complexity, design better operating policies, and guide change in systems from the smallest business to the planet as a whole. However, learning about complex systems when you also live in them is difficult. We are all passengers on an aircraft we must not only fly but redesign in flight.

System dynamics is a method to enhance learning in complex systems. Just as an airline uses flight simulators to help pilots learn, system dynamics is, partly, a method for developing management flight simulators, often computer simulation models, to help us learn about dynamic complexity, understand the sources of policy resistance, and design more effective policies.

But learning about complex dynamic systems requires more than technical tools to create mathematical models. System dynamics is fundamentally interdisciplinary. Because we are concerned with the behavior of complex systems, system

---

[1]There are many schools of systems thinking (for surveys, see Richardson 1991 and Lane 1994). Some emphasize qualitative methods; others stress formal modeling. As sources of method and metaphor they draw on fields as diverse as anthropology, biology, engineering, linguistics, psychology, physics, and Taoism and seek applications in fields still more diverse. All agree, however, that a systems view of the world is still rare. Jay Forrester developed system dynamics in the 1950s at MIT. Richardson (1991) traces the history of the field and relates system dynamics to other systems approaches.

dynamics is grounded in the theory of nonlinear dynamics and feedback control developed in mathematics, physics, and engineering. Because we apply these tools to the behavior of human as well as physical and technical systems, system dynamics draws on cognitive and social psychology, economics, and other social sciences. Because we build system dynamics models to solve important real world problems, we must learn how to work effectively with groups of busy policy makers and how to catalyze sustained change in organizations.

This chapter discusses the skills required to develop your systems thinking capabilities, how to create an effective learning process in dynamically complex systems, and how to use system dynamics in organizations to address important problems. I first review what we know about how people learn in and about complex dynamic systems. Such learning is difficult and rare because a variety of structural impediments thwart the feedback processes required for learning to occur. Successful approaches to learning about complex dynamic systems require (1) tools to elicit and represent the mental models we hold about the nature of difficult problems; (2) formal models and simulation methods to test and improve our mental models, design new policies, and practice new skills; and (3) methods to sharpen scientific reasoning skills, improve group processes, and overcome defensive routines for individuals and teams.

1.1.1 Policy Resistance, the Law of Unintended Consequences, and the Counterintuitive Behavior of Social Systems

And it will fall out as in a complication of diseases, that by applying a remedy to one sore, you will provoke another; and that which removes the one ill symptom produces others . . .

—Sir Thomas More

The best-laid schemes o' mice an' men/ Gang aft a-gley.

—Robert Burns

Anything that can go wrong will go wrong.

—"Murphy"

We have met the enemy and he is us.

—Pogo

From Thomas More in 1516 to Pogo in the mid 20th century it has long been acknowledged that people seeking to solve a problem often make it worse. Our policies may create unanticipated side effects. Our attempts to stabilize the system may destabilize it. Our decisions may provoke reactions by others seeking to restore the balance we upset. Forrester (1971a) calls such phenomena the "counterintuitive behavior of social systems." These unexpected dynamics often lead to policy resistance, the tendency for interventions to be delayed, diluted, or defeated by the response of the system to the intervention itself (Meadows 1982).

FIGURE 1-1
Policy resistance:
Romanian birth
rates

The crude birth
rate in Romania
showing the effect
of restricting abor-
tion beginning in
1966

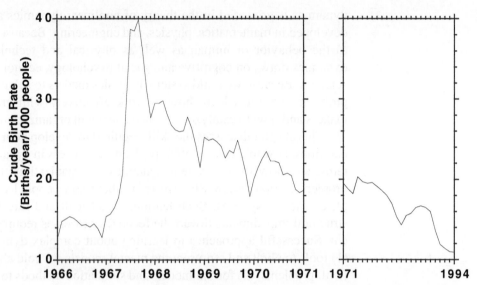

Source: 1966–1971, David and Wright (1971); 1971–1994, *Romanian Statistical Yearbook 1995,*
pp. 100–101. *Note:* 1971–1994 are annual averages.

As an example, consider the birth rate in Romania in the late 1960s. The crude
birth rate (births per year per 1000 people) was extremely low—about 15 per
thousand (Figure 1-1). For various reasons, including national pride and ethnic
identity, the low birth rate was considered to be a grave problem by the government, including the dictator Nicolau Ceausesçu. The Ceausesçu regime responded
by imposing policies designed to stimulate the birth rate. Importation of contraceptive devices was outlawed; propaganda campaigns extolling the virtues of large
families and the patriotic (matriotic would be more accurate) duty to have more
children were introduced, along with some modest tax incentives for larger families. Perhaps most important, abortion—freely available on demand since 1957
through the state health care system—was banned in October 1966 (David and
Wright 1971).

The result was immediate and dramatic. The birth rate rose sharply to nearly
40 per 1000 per year, rivaling those of the fastest growing nations. The policy appeared to be a sensational success. However, within months the birth rate began to
fall. By the end of 1970, only 4 years after the policy was implemented, the birth
rate had dropped below 20 per thousand, close to the low levels seen prior to the
intervention. Though the policy continued in force, the birth rate continued to fall,
reaching 16 per thousand by 1989—about the same low rate that led to the imposition of the policy. What happened?

The system responded to the intervention in ways the regime did not anticipate. The people of Romania found ways around the policy. They practiced alternative methods of birth control. They smuggled contraceptive pills and devices in
from other countries. Desperate women sought and found back-alley abortions.
Many of these were unsanitary or botched, leading to a near tripling of deaths due

to complications of abortion from 1965 to 1967. Most horribly, the number of neonatal deaths rose by more than 300% between 1966 and 1967, a 20% increase in the infant mortality rate (David and Wright 1971). The result: the policy was rendered completely ineffective almost immediately after implementation.

But the unanticipated consequences didn't end with the failure of the population policy. The people of Romania, among the poorest in Europe, were having small families because they couldn't afford larger ones. Child care was unavailable for some. Many others lived with their extended families in small, crowded apartments. Jobs were scarce; income was low. Many people gave children they couldn't support to state-run orphanages. The government's policy didn't prevent the people of Romania from controlling their own fertility, but it did breed intense resentment against the intrusive policies of the regime. In 1989, when the Berlin wall fell and the totalitarian regimes of Eastern Europe toppled, Romania was the only nation where the velvet revolution was violent. The hated Ceausescu and his equally hated wife were summarily executed by firing squad. Their bloody bodies were left in the courtyard of the presidential palace while the scene was broadcast on national television. The law banning abortion was the first overturned by the new government. The birth rate, already low, fell further. By the mid 1990s, the population of Romania was actually declining as births dropped below deaths.

The children of Romania suffered the most from the population policy. During the years of the population policy thousands of children were placed in the care of state orphanages, where they were kept like animals in cribs (cages, really) without attention to basic needs, much less the love that all of us need and deserve. Food was so scarce that blood transfusions were routinely given as nutritional supplements. Because needles were used repeatedly, an epidemic of AIDS spread rapidly among the children. The side effects of the failed population policy cast a shadow on the health and happiness of an entire nation, a shadow stretching over generations.

Policy resistance is not limited to dictators. It doesn't respect national borders, political ideology, or historical epoch. Consider the US government's fight against inflation in the early 1970s. Figure 1-2 shows the Consumer Price Index (CPI) for the United States between 1968 and 1976. In the early 1970s inflation had accelerated and the Nixon administration felt action had to be taken. Though a Republican, Nixon chose to implement wage and price controls. The policy was expensive: A new federal bureaucracy, the Council on Wage and Price Stability, was created to oversee the controls and enforce compliance. Wage and price controls were viewed by many in Nixon's own party as verging on socialism, costing Nixon valuable political capital. At first, the policy seemed to work, although imperfectly. During so-called Phase I of the controls, the rate of inflation fell by about half. The administration decided the controls could be relaxed. In Phase II, President Ford (who inherited the program from Nixon) launched a jawboning campaign, complete with campaign-style buttons labeled "WIN!" for "Whip Inflation Now!". Few observers expected WIN! buttons to have any effect, and most felt inflation would return to its rate prior to the start of controls. Instead, inflation actually accelerated until, by 1975, the CPI had returned to the trajectory it was on prior to the imposition of the price controls. Less than 4 years after the intervention there was

FIGURE 1-2   Policy resistance in the fight against inflation

The US Consumer Price Index (CPI) showing the Nixon/Ford wage and price controls

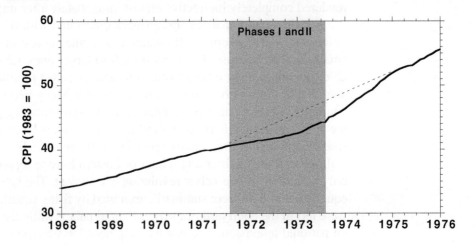

no residue of benefit. Other examples of policy resistance can be found nearly every day in the newspaper. Table 1-1 lists a few.[2]

Machiavelli, a keen observer of human systems, discussed policy resistance at length, observing in the *Discourses* that

> When a problem arises either from within a republic or outside it, one brought about either by internal or external reasons, one that has become so great that it begins to make everyone afraid, the safest policy is to delay dealing with it rather than trying to do away with it, because those who try to do away with it almost always increase its strength and accelerate the harm which they feared might come from it. (Machiavelli 1979, pp. 240–241).

I find Machiavelli's view too cynical but can sympathize with his frustration in observing his client princes (the CEOs of Renaissance Italy) take actions that only made their problems worse. A more reflective view is offered by the late biologist and essayist Lewis Thomas (1974, p. 90):

> When you are confronted by any complex social system, such as an urban center or a hamster, with things about it that you're dissatisfied with and anxious to fix, you cannot just step in and set about fixing with much hope of helping. This realization is one of the sore discouragements of our century . . . You cannot meddle with one part of a complex system from the outside without the almost certain risk of setting off disastrous events that you hadn't counted on in other, remote parts. If you want to fix something you are first obliged to understand . . . the whole system . . . Intervening is a way of causing trouble.

_____

[2]Further reading: John McPhee (1989) offers a wonderful description of policy resistance in the relationship of people with nature. McPhee brilliantly describes the unanticipated side effects and policy resistance arising from attempts to defeat three elemental forces of nature: volcanism, flood, and fire. Edward Tenner (1996) also identifies many examples of policy resistance.

TABLE 1-1

Examples of policy resistance

- "Use of Cheaper Drugs Pushes Costs Up, Not Down, Study Finds: Limiting what is prescribed, as managed-care systems do, has unintended effect of increasing costs, results show" (Headline in *LA Times,* 3/20/96, p. 1, reporting Univ. of Utah study of 13,000 patients in various HMOs).
- "Washington's biggest conservation program, which pays farmers to take soil out of cultivation for a decade to combat erosion and help the environment, is a waste of money, so says a new study of the 11-year-old program . . . For every eroding acre a farmer idles, another farmer—or sometimes the same one—simply plows up nearly as much additional erosion-prone land . . . In the Great Plains, for instance, farmers set aside 17 million acres, yet the total cultivated land dropped by only 2 million acres" (*Business Week,* 3/18/96, p. 6, reporting a Univ. of Minnesota study).
- Low tar and nicotine cigarettes actually increase intake of carcinogens, CO, etc. as smokers compensate for the low nicotine content by smoking more cigarettes per day, by taking longer, more frequent drags, and by holding the smoke in their lungs longer.
- Antilock brakes and other automotive safety devices cause some people to drive more aggressively, offsetting some of their benefits.
- Information technology has not enabled the "paperless office"—paper consumption per capita is up.
- Road building programs designed to reduce congestion have increased traffic, delays, and pollution.
- Despite widespread use of labor-saving appliances, Americans have less leisure today than 50 years ago.
- The US government's war on drugs, focusing on interdiction and supply disruption (particularly cocaine production in South America), with a cost in the billions, has had only a small impact on cocaine cultivation, production, or smuggling. Drug use in America and elsewhere remains high.
- The US policy of fire suppression has increased the size and severity of forest fires. Rather than frequent, small fires, fire suppression leads to the accumulation of dead wood and other fuels leading to larger, hotter, and more dangerous fires, often consuming the oldest and largest trees which previously survived smaller fires unharmed.
- Flood control efforts such as levee and dam construction have led to more severe floods by preventing the natural dissipation of excess water in flood plains. The cost of flood damage has increased as the flood plains were developed by people who believed they were safe.
- Imposing 200-mile territorial limits and quotas to protect fish stocks did not prevent the collapse of the Georges Bank fishery off the coast of North America. Once the world's richest, by the mid 1990s many species were commercially extinct, the fishery was shut down, the fleets were idled, and the local economies were in depression.
- Deregulation of the US Savings and Loan industry, designed to save the industry from financial problems, led to a wave of speculation followed by collapse, at a cost to taxpayers in the hundreds of billions of dollars.
- Antibiotics have stimulated the evolution of drug-resistant pathogens, including virulent strains of TB, strep, staph, and sexually transmitted diseases.
- Pesticides and herbicides have stimulated the evolution of resistant pests and weeds, killed off natural predators, and accumulated up the food chain to poison fish, birds, and possibly humans.

But how can one come to understand the whole system? How does policy resistance arise? How can we learn to avoid it, to find the high leverage policies that can produce sustainable benefit?

1.1.2   Causes of Policy Resistance

One cause of policy resistance is our tendency to interpret experience as a series of events, for example, "inventory is too high," or "sales fell this month." Accounts of who did what to whom are the most common mode of discourse, from the mailroom to the boardroom, from headlines to history books. We are taught from an early age that every event has a cause, which in turn is an effect of some still earlier cause: "Inventory is too high because sales unexpectedly fell. Sales fell because the competitors lowered their price. The competitors lowered their price because . . ." Such event-level explanations can be extended indefinitely, in an unbroken Aristotelian chain of causes and effects, until we arrive at some First Cause, or more likely, lose interest along the way.

The event-oriented worldview leads to an event-oriented approach to problem solving. Figure 1-3 shows how we often try to solve problems. We assess the state of affairs and compare it to our goals. The gap between the situation we desire and the situation we perceive defines our problem. For example, suppose sales of your organization were $80 million last quarter, but your sales goal was $100 million. The problem is that sales are 20% less than you desired. You then consider various options to correct the problem. You might cut prices to stimulate demand and increase market share, replace the vice president of sales with someone more aggressive, or take other actions. You select the option you deem best and implement it, leading (you hope) to a better result. You might observe your sales increase: problem solved. Or so it seems.

The system reacts to your solution: As your sales rise, competitors cut prices, and sales fall again. Yesterday's solution becomes today's problem. We are not puppet masters influencing a system *out there*—we are embedded in the system. The puppet master's movements respond to the position of the marionette on the strings. There is feedback: The results of our actions define the situation we face in the future. The new situation alters our assessment of the problem and the decisions we take tomorrow (see the top of Figure 1-4).

Policy resistance arises because we often do not understand the full range of feedbacks operating in the system (Figure 1-4). As our actions alter the state of the system, other people react to restore the balance we have upset. Our actions may also trigger side effects.

FIGURE 1-3
Event-oriented
view of the world

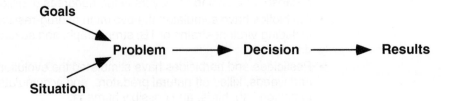

We frequently talk about side effects as if they were a feature of reality. Not so. In reality, there are no side effects, there are just *effects*. When we take action, there are various effects. The effects we thought of in advance, or were beneficial, we call the main, or intended effects. The effects we didn't anticipate, the effects which fed back to undercut our policy, the effects which harmed the system—these are the ones we claim to be side effects. Side effects are not a feature of reality but a sign that our understanding of the system is narrow and flawed.

Unanticipated side effects arise because we too often act as if cause and effect were always closely linked in time and space. But in complex systems such as an urban center or a hamster (or a business, society, or ecosystem) cause and effect are often distant in time and space. Narrow model boundaries often lead to beliefs that violate the laws of physics: in the mid 1990s California and the automobile industry debated the introduction of so-called zero emission vehicles (ZEVs) to reduce air pollution. True, the ZEVs—electric cars—would have no tailpipe. But the power plants required to make the electricity to run them do generate pollution. In reality, California was promoting the adoption of DEVs—*displaced* emission vehicles—cars whose wastes would blow downwind to other states or accumulate in nuclear waste dumps outside its borders. Electric cars may turn out to be an environmental boon compared to internal combustion. The technology is improving rapidly, and air pollution is a major health problem in many cities. But no mode of

FIGURE 1-4
The feedback view

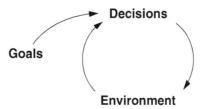

Our decisions alter our environment, leading to new decisions,

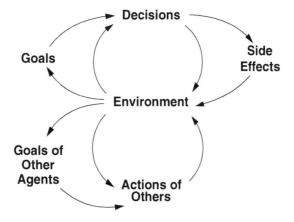

but also triggering side effects, delayed reactions, changes in goals and interventions by others. These feedbacks may lead to unanticipated results and ineffective policies.

transport or energy conversion process is free of environmental impact, and no legislature can repeal the second law of thermodynamics.[3]

To avoid policy resistance and find high leverage policies requires us to expand the boundaries of our mental models so that we become aware of and understand the implications of the feedbacks created by the decisions we make. That is, we must learn about the structure and dynamics of the increasingly complex systems in which we are embedded.

1.1.3   Feedback

Much of the art of system dynamics modeling is discovering and representing the feedback processes, which, along with stock and flow structures, time delays, and nonlinearities, determine the dynamics of a system. You might imagine that there is an immense range of different feedback processes and other structures to be mastered before one can understand the dynamics of complex systems. In fact, the most complex behaviors usually arise from the interactions (feedbacks) among the components of the system, not from the complexity of the components themselves.

All dynamics arise from the interaction of just two types of feedback loops, positive (or self-reinforcing) and negative (or self-correcting) loops (Figure 1-5). Positive loops tend to reinforce or amplify whatever is happening in the system: The more nuclear weapons NATO deployed during the Cold War, the more the Soviet Union built, leading NATO to build still more. If a firm lowers its price to gain market share, its competitors may respond in kind, forcing the firm to lower its price still more. The larger the installed base of Microsoft software and Intel machines, the more attractive the "Wintel" architecture became as developers sought the largest market for their software and customers sought systems compatible with the most software; the more Wintel computers sold, the larger the installed base. These positive loops are all processes that generate their own growth, leading to arms races, price wars, and the phenomenal growth of Microsoft and Intel, respectively.

Negative loops counteract and oppose change. The less nicotine in a cigarette, the more smokers must consume to get the dose they need. The more attractive a neighborhood or city, the greater the inmigration from surrounding areas will be, increasing unemployment, housing prices, crowding in the schools, and traffic congestion until it is no more attractive than other places people might live. The higher the price of a commodity, the lower the demand and the greater the production, leading to inventory accumulation and pressure for lower prices to eliminate the excess stock. The larger the market share of dominant firms, the more likely is government antitrust action to limit their monopoly power. These loops all describe processes that tend to be self-limiting, processes that seek balance and equilibrium.

---

[3]Even scientists suffer from these problems. I once heard a distinguished physicist argue that the solution to the energy problem was to build hundreds of huge offshore nuclear power stations, to be cooled by seawater. The warm wastewater would be pumped back in the ocean where, he said, "The waste heat would disappear." Out of sight, out of mind.

FIGURE 1-5
Positive and negative feedback loops

Positive feedback: Positive loops are self-reinforcing. In this case, more chickens lay more eggs, which hatch and add to the chicken population, leading to still more eggs, and so on. A Causal Loop Diagram or CLD (chapter 5) captures the feedback dependency of chickens and eggs. The arrows indicate the causal relationships. The + signs at the arrowheads indicate that the effect is positively related to the cause: an increase in the chicken population causes the number of eggs laid each day to rise above what it would have been (and vice versa: a decrease in the chicken population causes egg laying to fall below what it would have been). The loop is self-reinforcing, hence the loop polarity identifier **R.** If this loop were the only one operating, the chicken and egg population would both grow exponentially.

Of course, no real quantity can grow forever. There must be limits to growth. These limits are created by negative feedback.

Negative feedback: Negative loops are self-correcting. They counteract change. As the chicken population grows, various negative loops will act to balance the chicken population with its carrying capacity. One classic feedback is shown here: The more chickens, the more road crossings they will attempt. If there is any traffic, more road crossings will lead to fewer chickens (hence the negative − polarity for the link from road crossings to chickens). An increase in the chicken population causes more risky road crossings, which then bring the chicken population back down. The **B** in the center of a loop denotes a balancing feedback. If the road-crossing loop was the only one operating (say because the farmer sells all the eggs), the number of chickens would gradually decline until none remained.

All systems, no matter how complex, consist of networks of positive and negative feedbacks, and all dynamics arise from the interaction of these loops with one another.

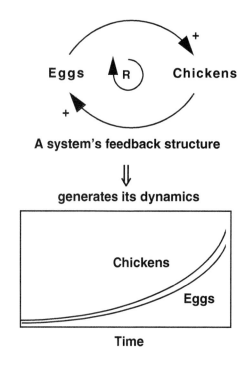

A system's feedback structure

⇓

generates its dynamics

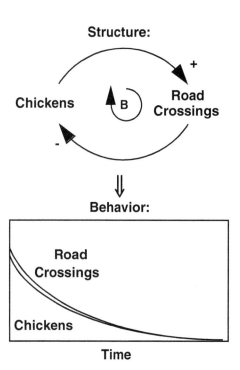

Structure:

⇓

Behavior:

1.1.4   Process Point: The Meaning of Feedback

In common parlance the term "feedback" has come to serve as a euphemism for criticizing others, as in "the boss gave me feedback on my presentation." This use of feedback is not what we mean in system dynamics. Further, "positive feedback" does not mean "praise" and "negative feedback" does not mean "criticism." Positive feedback denotes a self-reinforcing process, and negative feedback denotes a self-correcting one. Either type of loop can be good or bad, depending on which way it is operating and of course on your values. Reserve the terms positive and negative feedback for self-reinforcing and self-correcting processes, and avoid describing the criticism you give or receive to others as feedback. Telling someone your opinion does not constitute feedback unless they act on your suggestions and thus lead you to revise your view.

Though there are only two types of feedback loop, models may easily contain thousands of loops, of both types, coupled to one another with multiple time delays, nonlinearities, and accumulations. The dynamics of all systems arise from the interactions of these networks of feedbacks. Intuition may enable us to infer the dynamics of isolated loops such as those shown in Figure 1-5. But when multiple loops interact, it is not so easy to determine what the dynamics will be. Before continuing, try the challenge shown in Figure 1-6. When intuition fails, we usually turn to computer simulation to deduce the behavior of our models.

CHALLENGE

Dynamics of Multiple-Loop Systems

What are the dynamics of the chicken population when both loops are simultaneously active (Figure 1-6)? Sketch a graph showing the behavior of the chicken population over time. Assume the initial chicken population is small (but includes at least one rooster).

FIGURE 1-6
Dynamics arise from the interaction of multiple loops.

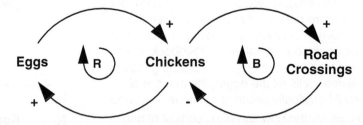

1.2   LEARNING IS A FEEDBACK PROCESS

Just as dynamics arise from feedback, so too all learning depends on feedback. We make decisions that alter the real world; we gather information feedback about the real world, and using the new information we revise our understanding of the world and the decisions we make to bring our perception of the state of the system closer to our goals (Figure 1-7).

The feedback loop in Figure 1-7 appears in many guises throughout the social sciences. George Richardson (1991), in his history of feedback concepts in the social sciences, shows how beginning in the 1940s leading thinkers in economics, psychology, sociology, anthropology, and other fields recognized that the concept of feedback developed in physics and engineering applied not only to servomechanisms but to human decision making and social settings as well. By 1961, Forrester, in *Industrial Dynamics,* asserted that all decisions (including learning) take place in the context of feedback loops. Later, the psychologist Powers (1973, p. 351) wrote:

> Feedback is such an all-pervasive and fundamental aspect of behavior that it is as invisible as the air that we breathe. Quite literally it is behavior—we know nothing of our own behavior but the feedback effects of our own outputs.

These feedback thinkers followed in the footsteps of John Dewey, who recognized the feedback loop character of learning around the beginning of the 20th century when he described learning as an iterative cycle of invention, observation, reflection, and action (Schön 1992). Feedback accounts of behavior and learning have now permeated most of the social and management sciences. Learning as an explicit feedback process has even appeared in practical management tools such as Total Quality Management, where the so-called Shewhart–Deming PDCA cycle (Plan-Do-Check-Act) lies at the heart of the improvement process in the quality improvement literature (Shewhart 1939; Shiba, Graham, and Walden 1993).

   The single feedback loop shown in Figure 1-7 describes the most basic type of learning. The loop is a classical negative feedback whereby decision makers compare information about the state of the real world to various goals, perceive discrepancies between desired and actual states, and take actions that (they believe) will cause the real world to move towards the desired state. Even if the initial choices of the decision makers do not close the gaps between desired and actual states, the system might eventually reach the desired state as subsequent decisions are revised in light of the information received (see Hogarth 1981). When driving, I may turn the steering wheel too little to bring the car back to the center of my lane, but as visual feedback reveals the error, I continue to turn the wheel until the car returns to the straight and narrow. If the current price for products of my firm is too low to balance orders with production, depleted inventories and long delivery delays may cause me to gradually raise price until I discover a price that clears the market.[4]

FIGURE 1-7
Learning is a feedback process.

Feedback from the real world to the decision maker includes all forms of information, both quantitative and qualitative.

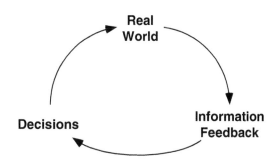

---

[4]Depending on the time delays and other elements of dynamic complexity in the system, these examples may not converge. It takes but little ice, fog, fatigue, or alcohol to cause an accident, and equilibrium eludes many industries that experience chronic business cycles.

The feedback loop shown in Figure 1-7 obscures an important aspect of the learning process. Information feedback about the real world is not the only input to our decisions. Decisions are the result of applying a decision rule or policy to information about the world as we perceive it (see Forrester 1961, 1992). The policies are themselves conditioned by institutional structures, organizational strategies, and cultural norms. These, in turn, are governed by our mental models (Figure 1-8). As long as the mental models remain unchanged, the feedback loop shown in the figure represents what Argyris (1985) calls single-loop learning, a process whereby we learn to reach our current goals in the context of our existing mental models. Single-loop learning does not result in deep change to our mental models—our understanding of the causal structure of the system, the boundary we draw around the system, the time horizon we consider relevant—nor our goals and values. Single-loop learning does not alter our worldview.

Mental models are widely discussed in psychology and philosophy. Different theorists describe mental models as collections of routines or standard operating procedures, scripts for selecting possible actions, cognitive maps of a domain, typologies for categorizing experience, logical structures for the interpretation of language, or attributions about individuals we encounter in daily life (Axelrod 1976; Bower and Morrow 1990; Cheng and Nisbett 1985; Doyle and Ford 1998; Gentner and Stevens 1983; Halford 1993; Johnson-Laird 1983; Schank and Abelson 1977; Vennix 1990). The concept of the mental model has been central to system dynamics from the beginning of the field. Forrester (1961) stresses that all decisions are based on models, usually mental models. In system dynamics, the term "mental model" includes our beliefs about the networks of causes and effects that describe how a system operates, along with the boundary of the model (which variables are included and which are excluded) and the time horizon we consider relevant—our framing or articulation of a problem.

Most of us do not appreciate the ubiquity and invisibility of mental models, instead believing naively that our senses reveal the world as it is. On the contrary,

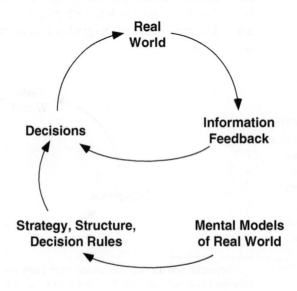

FIGURE 1-8
Single-loop learning: information feedback is interpreted by existing mental models.

The learning feedback operates in the context of existing decision rules, strategies, culture, and institutions which in turn are derived from our mental models.

Real World

Information Feedback

Decisions

Strategy, Structure, Decision Rules

Mental Models of Real World

our world is actively constructed (modeled) by our senses and brain. Figure 1-9 shows an image developed by psychologist Gaetano Kanizsa. The vast majority of people see a bright white triangle resting on top of three circles and a second triangle with black edges. The illusion is extremely powerful (try to look at the figure and "not see" the two triangles!). Research shows that the neural structures responsible for the ability to see illusory contours such as the white triangle exist between the optic nerve and the areas of the brain responsible for processing visual information.[5] Active modeling occurs well before sensory information reaches the areas of the brain responsible for conscious thought.[6] Powerful evolutionary pressures are responsible: Our survival depends so completely on the ability to rapidly interpret our environment that we (and other species) long ago evolved structures to build these models automatically. Usually we are completely unaware these mental models even exist. It is only when a construction such as the Kanizsa triangle reveals the illusion that we become aware of our mental models.

The Kanizsa triangle illustrates the necessity of active and unconscious mental modeling or construction of "reality" at the level of visual perception. Modeling of higher-level knowledge is likewise unavoidable and often equally unconscious. Figure 1-10 shows a mental model elicited during a meeting between my colleague Fred Kofman and a team from a large global corporation. The company worked with the Organizational Learning Center at MIT in the early 1990s to reduce the total cycle time for their supply chain. At that time the cycle time was 182 days and they sought to cut it in half. The company viewed reductions in cycle time as essential for continued competitiveness and even corporate survival. With the

FIGURE 1-9

Kanizsa triangle

Do you see the bright white triangle lying on top of the three dark circles and a second triangle?

---

[5]See *Science,* 256, (12 June 1992), pp. 1520–1521.

[6]Even more obviously, our ability to see a three-dimensional world is the result of extensive modeling by the visual processing system, since the retina images a planar projection of the visual field.

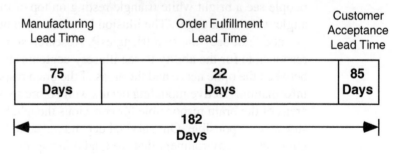

FIGURE 1-10
Mental model
revealed by
a diagram of a
company's
supply chain

The figure has
been simplified
compared to the
actual chart to
protect company-
confidential
information but is
drawn to scale.

support of senior management, they assembled a team to address these issues. At the first meeting the team presented background information, including Figure 1-10.

The figure shows the current cycle time divided into three intervals along a line: manufacturing lead time, order fulfillment lead time, and customer acceptance lead time. Order fulfillment, which then required 22 days, occupies more than half of the total length of the line, while the manufacturing lead time, then requiring 75 days (70 days due to suppliers), receives about one-fourth of the length. Customer acceptance, then requiring 85 days, occupies only about one-eighth of the total length. What the figure reveals is the prominence of order fulfillment operations in the mental models of the people on the team and the insignificance in their minds of suppliers and customers. It will come as no surprise that the members of the team all worked in functions contributing to order fulfillment. There was not a single person at the meeting representing procurement, nor a single supplier representative, nor anyone from accounting, nor a single customer. Until Fred pointed out this distortion, the members of the group were as unaware of the illusory character of their image of the supply line as we normally are of the illusory contours our brains project onto the data transmitted by our optic nerves. The distorted mental model of the supply chain significantly constrained the company's ability to reduce cycle time: Even if order fulfillment could be accomplished instantly the organization would fall well short of its goal.

The type of reframing stimulated by Fred's intervention, denoted *double-loop learning* by Argyris (1985), is illustrated in Figure 1-11. Here information feedback about the real world not only alters our decisions within the context of existing frames and decision rules but also feeds back to alter our mental models. As our mental models change we change the structure of our systems, creating different decision rules and new strategies. The same information, processed and interpreted by a different decision rule, now yields a different decision. Altering the structure of our systems then alters their patterns of behavior. The development of systems thinking is a double-loop learning process in which we replace a reductionist, narrow, short-run, static view of the world with a holistic, broad, long-term, dynamic view and then redesign our policies and institutions accordingly.

FIGURE 1-11
Double-loop
learning

Feedback from the
real world can also
stimulate changes
in mental models.
Such learning
involves new
understanding
or reframing of
a situation and
leads to new goals
and new decision
rules, not just
new decisions.

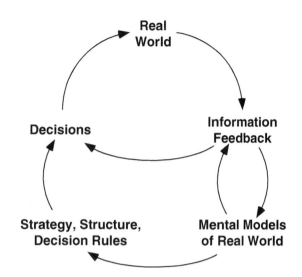

1.3   BARRIERS TO LEARNING

For learning to occur each link in the two feedback loops shown in Figure 1-11 must work effectively and we must be able to cycle around the loops quickly relative to the rate at which changes in the real world render existing knowledge obsolete. Yet in the real world, particularly the world of social action, these feedbacks often do not operate well. More than two and a half centuries elapsed from the first experiments showing that lemon juice could prevent and cure scurvy until citrus use was mandated in the British merchant marine (Table 1-2). Learning in this case was terribly slow, despite the enormous importance of the problem and

TABLE 1-2
Teaching scurvy
dogs new tricks

Total delay
in learning:
264 years.

- Prior to the 1600s, scurvy (vitamin C deficiency) was the greatest killer of seafarers—more than battle deaths, storms, accidents, and all others *combined.*
- 1601: Lancaster conducts a controlled experiment during an East India Company voyage:
  The crew on one ship received 3 tsp. of lemon juice daily; the crew on three other ships did not.
  Results: At the Cape of Good Hope 110 out of 278 sailors had died, most from scurvy. The crew receiving lemon juice remained largely healthy.
- 1747: Dr. James Lind conducts a controlled experiment in which scurvy patients were treated with a variety of elixirs. Those receiving citrus were cured in a few days; none of the other treatments worked.
- 1795: The British Royal Navy begins using citrus on a regular basis. Scurvy wiped out.
- 1865: The British Board of Trade mandates citrus use. Scurvy wiped out in the merchant marine.

Source: Mosteller (1981).

the decisive evidence supplied by controlled experiments throughout the years. You may reply that today we are much smarter and learn faster. Perhaps. Yet the rate of corporate and organizational failure remains high (for example, over one-third of the Fortune 500 largest industrial firms in 1970 had disappeared by 1983 [de Geus 1997]). Today the rate of change in our systems is much faster, and their complexity is much greater. The delays in learning for many pressing problems remain woefully long. In most settings we lack the ability to run experiments, and the delays between interventions and outcomes are much longer. As the rate of change accelerates throughout society, learning remains slow, uneven, and inadequate.

Figure 1-12 shows the main ways in which each link in the learning feedbacks can fail. These include dynamic complexity, imperfect information about the state of the real world, confounding and ambiguous variables, poor scientific reasoning skills, defensive routines, and other barriers to effective group processes, implementation failure, and the misperceptions of feedback that hinder our ability to understand the structure and dynamics of complex systems.

FIGURE 1-12
Impediments
to learning

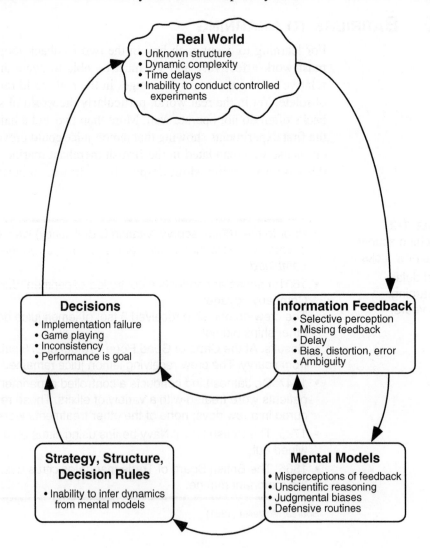

Real World
• Unknown structure
• Dynamic complexity
• Time delays
• Inability to conduct controlled experiments

Decisions
• Implementation failure
• Game playing
• Inconsistency
• Performance is goal

Information Feedback
• Selective perception
• Missing feedback
• Delay
• Bias, distortion, error
• Ambiguity

Strategy, Structure, Decision Rules
• Inability to infer dynamics from mental models

Mental Models
• Misperceptions of feedback
• Unscientific reasoning
• Judgmental biases
• Defensive routines

1.3.1   Dynamic Complexity

Much of the literature in psychology, economics, and other fields suggests learning proceeds via the simple negative feedback loops described in Figure 1-11. Implicitly, the loops are seen as swift, linear, negative feedbacks that produce stable convergence to an equilibrium or optimal outcome, just as immediate visual feedback allows you to fill a glass of water without spilling. The real world is not so simple. From the beginning, system dynamics emphasized the multiloop, multistate, nonlinear character of the feedback systems in which we live (Forrester 1961). The decisions of any one agent form but one of many feedback loops that operate in any given system. These loops react to the decision maker's actions in ways both anticipated and unanticipated; there may be positive as well as negative feedback loops, and these loops will contain many stocks (state variables) and many nonlinearities. Natural and human systems have high levels of *dynamic complexity*. Table 1-3 shows some of the characteristics of systems that give rise to dynamic complexity.

Most people think of complexity in terms of the number of components in a system or the number of combinations one must consider in making a decision. The problem of optimally scheduling an airline's flights and crews is highly complex, but the complexity lies in finding the best solution out of an astronomical number of possibilities. Such needle-in-a-haystack problems have high levels of *combinatorial* complexity (also known as *detail* complexity). *Dynamic* complexity, in contrast, can arise even in simple systems with low combinatorial complexity. The Beer Distribution Game (Sterman 1989b, chap. 17.4) provides an example: Complex and dysfunctional behavior arises from a very simple system whose rules can be explained in 15 minutes. Dynamic complexity arises from the interactions among the agents over time.

Time delays between taking a decision and its effects on the state of the system are common and particularly troublesome. Most obviously, delays reduce the number of times one can cycle around the learning loop, slowing the ability to accumulate experience, test hypotheses, and improve. Schneiderman (1988) estimated the improvement half life—the time required to cut defects in half—in a wide range of manufacturing firms. He found improvement half lives as short as a few months for processes with short delays, for example reducing operator error in a job shop, while complex processes with long time delays such as product development had improvement half lives of several years or more.[7]

Dynamic complexity not only slows the learning loop; it also reduces the learning gained on each cycle. In many cases controlled experiments are prohibitively costly or unethical. More often, it is simply impossible to conduct controlled experiments. Complex systems are in disequilibrium and evolve. Many actions yield irreversible consequences. The past cannot be compared well to current circumstance. The existence of multiple interacting feedbacks means it is difficult to hold other aspects of the system constant to isolate the effect of the variable of interest. Many variables change simultaneously, confounding the interpretation

---

[7]Sterman, Repenning, and Kofman (1997) show how these differential improvement rates led to difficulty at a leading semiconductor manufacturer.

TABLE 1-3
Dynamic
complexity

Dynamic complexity arises because systems are

- **Dynamic:** Heraclitus said, "All is change." What appears to be unchanging is, over a longer time horizon, seen to vary. Change in systems occurs at many time scales, and these different scales sometimes interact. A star evolves over billions of years as it burns its hydrogen fuel, then can explode as a supernova in seconds. Bull markets can go on for years, then crash in a matter of hours.

- **Tightly coupled:** The actors in the system interact strongly with one another and with the natural world. Everything is connected to everything else. As a famous bumper sticker from the 1960s proclaimed, "You can't do just one thing."

- **Governed by feedback:** Because of the tight couplings among actors, our actions feed back on themselves. Our decisions alter the state of the world, causing changes in nature and triggering others to act, thus giving rise to a new situation which then influences our next decisions. Dynamics arise from these feedbacks.

- **Nonlinear:** Effect is rarely proportional to cause, and what happens locally in a system (near the current operating point) often does not apply in distant regions (other states of the system). Nonlinearity often arises from the basic physics of systems: Insufficient inventory may cause you to boost production, but production can never fall below zero no matter how much excess inventory you have. Nonlinearity also arises as multiple factors interact in decision making: Pressure from the boss for greater achievement increases your motivation and effort—up to the point where you perceive the goal to be impossible. Frustration then dominates motivation and you give up or get a new boss.

- **History-dependent:** Taking one road often precludes taking others and determines where you end up (path dependence). Many actions are irreversible: You can't unscramble an egg (the second law of thermodynamics). Stocks and flows (accumulations) and long time delays often mean doing and undoing have fundamentally different time constants: During the 50 years of the Cold War arms race the nuclear nations generated more than 250 tons of weapons-grade plutonium (^{239}Pu). The half life of ^{239}Pu is about 24,000 years.

- **Self-organizing:** The dynamics of systems arise spontaneously from their internal structure. Often, small, random perturbations are amplified and molded by the feedback structure, generating patterns in space and time and creating path dependence. The pattern of stripes on a zebra, the rhythmic contraction of your heart, the persistent cycles in the real estate market, and structures such as sea shells and markets all emerge spontaneously from the feedbacks among the agents and elements of the system.

- **Adaptive:** The capabilities and decision rules of the agents in complex systems change over time. Evolution leads to selection and proliferation of some agents while others become extinct. Adaptation also occurs as people learn from experience, especially as they learn new ways to achieve their goals in the face of obstacles. Learning is not always beneficial, however.

- **Counterintuitive:** In complex systems cause and effect are distant in time and space while we tend to look for causes near the events we seek to explain. Our attention is drawn to the symptoms of difficulty rather than the underlying cause. High leverage policies are often not obvious.

- **Policy resistant:** The complexity of the systems in which we are embedded overwhelms our ability to understand them. The result: Many seemingly obvious solutions to problems fail or actually worsen the situation.

- **Characterized by trade-offs:** Time delays in feedback channels mean the long-run response of a system to an intervention is often different from its short-run response. High leverage policies often cause worse-before-better behavior, while low leverage policies often generate transitory improvement before the problem grows worse.

of system behavior and reducing the effectiveness of each cycle around the learning loop.

Delays also create instability in dynamic systems. Adding time delays to negative feedback loops increases the tendency for the system to oscillate.[8] Systems from driving a car, to drinking alcohol, to raising hogs, to construction of office buildings all involve time delays between the initiation of a control action (accelerating/braking, deciding to "have another," choosing to breed more hogs, developing a new building) and its effects on the state of the system. As a result, decision makers often continue to intervene to correct apparent discrepancies between the desired and actual state of the system even after sufficient corrective actions have been taken to restore the system to equilibrium. The result is overshoot and oscillation: stop-and-go traffic, drunkenness, commodity cycles, and real estate boom-and-bust cycles (see chapter 17.4). Oscillation and instability reduce our ability to control for confounding variables and discern cause and effect, further slowing the rate of learning.

1.3.2   Limited Information

We experience the real world through filters. No one knows the current sales rate of their company, the current rate of production, or the true value of the order backlog at any given time. Instead we receive estimates of these data based on sampled, averaged, and delayed measurements. The act of measurement introduces distortions, delays, biases, errors, and other imperfections, some known, others unknown and unknowable.

Above all, measurement is an act of selection. Our senses and information systems select but a tiny fraction of possible experience. Some of the selection is hardwired (we cannot see in the infrared or hear ultrasound). Some results from our own decisions. We define gross domestic product (GDP) so that extraction of nonrenewable resources counts as production rather than depletion of natural capital stocks and so that medical care and funeral expenses caused by pollution-induced disease add to the GDP while the production of the pollution itself does not reduce it. Because the prices of most goods in our economic system do not include the costs of resource depletion or environmental degradation, these externalities receive little weight in decision making (see Cobb and Daly 1989 for thoughtful discussion of alternative measures of economic welfare).

Of course, the information systems governing the feedback we receive can change as we learn. They are part of the feedback structure of our systems. Through our mental models we define constructs such as GDP or scientific research, create metrics for these ideas, and design information systems to evaluate and report them. These then condition the perceptions we form. Changes in our mental models are constrained by what we previously chose to define, measure,

---

[8]Technically, negative loops with no time delays are first-order; the eigenvalue of the linearized system can only be real and oscillation is impossible. Adding delays (state variables) allows the eigenvalues to become complex conjugates, yielding oscillatory solutions. Whether the oscillations of the linearized system are damped or expanding depends on the parameters. All else equal, the more phase lag in a control loop, the less stable the system will be.

and attend to. Seeing is believing *and* believing is seeing. They feed back on one another.

In a famous experiment, Bruner and Postman (1949) showed playing cards to people using a tachistoscope to control exposure time to the stimuli. Most could identify the cards rapidly and accurately. They also included some anomalous cards, such as a black three of hearts or a red ten of spades. People took on average four times as long to judge the anomalous cards. Many misidentified them (e.g., they said three of spades or three of hearts when shown a black three of hearts). Some could not identify the card at all, even with very long exposure times, and grew anxious and confused. Only a small minority correctly identified the cards. Bruner and Postman concluded, "Perceptual organization is powerfully determined by expectations built upon past commerce with the environment." Henri Bergson put it more succinctly: "The eye sees only what the mind is prepared to comprehend."

The self-reinforcing feedback between expectations and perceptions has been repeatedly demonstrated in a wide variety of experimental studies (see Plous 1993 for excellent discussion). Sometimes the positive feedback assists learning by sharpening our ability to perceive features of the environment, as when an experienced naturalist identifies a bird in a distant bush where the novice birder sees only a tangled thicket. Often, however, the mutual feedback of expectations and perception limits learning by blinding us to the anomalies that might challenge our mental models. Thomas Kuhn (1970) cited the Bruner–Postman study to argue that a scientific paradigm suppresses the perception of data inconsistent with the paradigm, making it hard for scientists to perceive anomalies that might lead to scientific revolution.[9]

As one of many examples, the history of ozone depletion by chlorofluorocarbons (CFCs) shows the mutual dependence of expectation and perception is no laboratory artifact but a phenomenon with potentially grave consequences for humanity.

The first scientific papers describing the ability of CFCs to destroy atmospheric ozone were published in 1974 (Molina and Rowland 1974; Stolarski and Cicerone 1974). Yet much of the scientific community remained skeptical, and despite a ban on CFCs as aerosol propellants, global production of CFCs remained near its all time high. It was not until 1985 that evidence of a deep ozone hole in the Antarctic was published (Farman, Gardiner, and Shanklin 1985). As described by Meadows, Meadows, and Randers (1992, pp. 151–152):

> The news reverberated around the scientific world. Scientists at [NASA] . . . scrambled to check readings on atmospheric ozone made by the Nimbus 7 satellite, measurements that had been taken routinely since 1978. Nimbus 7 had never indicated an ozone hole.

---

[9]Sterman (1985a) developed a formal model of Kuhn's theory, which showed that the positive feedback between expectations and perceptions suppressed the recognition of anomalies and the emergence of new paradigms. Sterman and Wittenberg (1999) extended the model to simulate the competition among rival theories.

> Checking back, NASA scientists found that their computers had been programmed to reject very low ozone readings on the assumption that such low readings must indicate instrument error.

The NASA scientists' belief that low ozone readings must be erroneous led them to design a measurement system that made it impossible to detect low readings that might have shown their belief to be wrong. Fortunately, NASA had saved the original, unfiltered data and later confirmed that ozone concentrations had indeed been falling since the launch of Nimbus 7. Because NASA created a measurement system immune to disconfirmation the discovery of the ozone hole and resulting global agreements to cease CFC production were delayed by as much as 7 years. Those 7 years could be significant: ozone levels in Antarctica dropped to less than one-third of normal in 1993, and current models show that even with full compliance with the ban (there is a thriving black market in CFCs), atmospheric chlorine will not begin to fall until the first decade of the 21st century, and then only slowly. Data collected near Toronto in the early 1990s showed a 5% increase in cancer-causing UV-B ultraviolet radiation at ground level, indicating that ozone depletion already affects the heavily populated and agriculturally vital northern hemisphere (Culotta and Koshland 1993). The thinning of the ozone layer is a global phenomenon, not just a problem for penguins.

1.3.3   Confounding Variables and Ambiguity

To learn we must use the limited and imperfect information available to us to understand the effects of our own decisions, so we can adjust our decisions to align the state of the system with our goals (single-loop learning) and so we can revise our mental models and redesign the system itself (double-loop learning). Yet much of the information we receive is ambiguous. Ambiguity arises because changes in the state of the system resulting from our own decisions are confounded with simultaneous changes in a host of other variables. The number of variables that might affect the system vastly overwhelms the data available to rule out alternative theories and competing interpretations. This identification problem plagues both qualitative and quantitative approaches. In the qualitative realm, ambiguity arises from the ability of language to support multiple meanings. In the opening soliloquy of *Richard III,* the hump-backed Richard laments his deformity:

> And therefore, since I cannot prove a lover
> To entertain these fair well-spoken days,
> I am determinèd to prove a villain
> And hate the idle pleasures of these days.
> (I, i, 28–31)

Does Richard celebrate his free choice to be evil or resign himself to a predestined fate? Did Shakespeare intend the double meaning? Rich, ambiguous texts, with multiple layers of meaning often make for beautiful and profound art, along with employment for literary critics, but also make it hard to know the minds of others, rule out competing hypotheses, and evaluate the impact of our past actions so we can decide how to act in the future.

In the quantitative realm, engineers and econometricians have long struggled with the problem of uniquely identifying the structure and parameters of a system from its observed behavior. Elegant and sophisticated theory exists to delimit the conditions in which one can identify a system from its behavior alone. In practice the data are too scarce and the plausible alternative specifications are too numerous for statistical methods to discriminate among competing theories. The same data often support wildly divergent models equally well, and conclusions based on such models are not robust. As Leamer (1983) put it in an article entitled "Let's Take the 'Con' Out of Econometrics":

> In order to draw inferences from data as described by econometric texts, it is necessary to make whimsical assumptions . . . The haphazard way we individually and collectively study the fragility of inferences leaves most of us unconvinced that any inference is believable.[10]

1.3.4   Bounded Rationality and the Misperceptions of Feedback

Dynamic complexity and limited information reduce the potential for learning and performance by limiting our knowledge of the real world. But how wisely do we use the knowledge we do have? Do we process the information we do get in the best way and make the best decisions we can? Unfortunately, the answer is no.

Humans are not only rational beings, coolly weighing the possibilities and judging the probabilities. Emotions, reflex, unconscious motivations, and other nonrational or irrational factors all play a large role in our judgments and behavior. But even when we find the time to reflect and deliberate we cannot behave in a fully rational manner (that is, make the best decisions possible given the information available to us). As marvelous as the human mind is, the complexity of the real world dwarfs our cognitive capabilities. Herbert Simon has best articulated the limits on human decision-making ability in his famous "principle of bounded rationality," for which he won the Nobel Memorial Prize in economics in 1979:

> The capacity of the human mind for formulating and solving complex problems is very small compared with the size of the problem whose solution is required for objectively rational behavior in the real world or even for a reasonable approximation to such objective rationality. (Simon 1957, p. 198)

Faced with the overwhelming complexity of the real world, time pressure, and limited cognitive capabilities, we are forced to fall back on rote procedures, habits, rules of thumb, and simple mental models to make decisions. Though we sometimes strive to make the best decisions we can, bounded rationality means we often systematically fall short, limiting our ability to learn from experience.

While bounded rationality affects all decision contexts, it is particularly acute in dynamic systems. Indeed, experimental studies show that people do quite poorly

---

[10]I am not arguing that econometrics should be abandoned, despite its difficulties. On the contrary, wise use of numerical data and statistical estimation is central to good system dynamics practice, and more effort should be devoted to the use of these tools in simulation model development and testing. See chap. 21.

in systems with even modest levels of dynamic complexity (Table 1-4). These studies led me to suggest that the observed dysfunction in dynamically complex settings arises from *misperceptions of feedback*. The mental models people use to guide their decisions are dynamically deficient. As discussed above, people generally adopt an event-based, open-loop view of causality, ignore feedback processes, fail to appreciate time delays between action and response and in the reporting of information, do not understand stocks and flows and are insensitive to nonlinearities that may alter the strengths of different feedback loops as a system evolves.

Subsequent experiments show that the greater the dynamic complexity of the environment the worse people do *relative to potential*. Further, the experiments show the misperceptions of feedback are robust to experience, financial incentives, experience, and the presence of market institutions (see, e.g., Diehl and Sterman 1993; Paich and Sterman 1993; Kampmann and Sterman 1998).

The robustness of the misperceptions of feedback and the poor performance they cause are due to two basic and related deficiencies in our mental model. First, our cognitive maps of the causal structure of systems are vastly simplified compared to the complexity of the systems themselves. Second, we are unable to infer correctly the dynamics of all but the simplest causal maps. Both are direct consequences of bounded rationality, that is, the many limitations of attention, memory, recall, information processing capability, and time that constrain human decision making.

TABLE 1-4 Misperceptions of feedback have been documented in many experimental studies.	• In a simple production–distribution system (the Beer Distribution Game), people, from high school students to CEOs, generate costly fluctuations (business cycles). Average costs were more than 10 times greater than optimal (Sterman 1989b). • Subjects responsible for capital investment in a simple multiplier-accelerator model of the economy generate large amplitude cycles even though consumer demand is constant. Average costs were more than 30 times greater than optimal (Sterman 1989a). • Subjects managing a firm in a simulated consumer product market generate the boom and bust, price war, and shake-out characteristic of industries from video games to chain saws (Paich and Sterman 1993). • Participants in experimental asset markets repeatedly bid prices well above fundamental value, only to see them plummet when a "greater fool" can no longer be found to buy. These speculative bubbles do not disappear when the participants are investment professionals, when monetary incentives are provided, or when short-selling is allowed (Smith, Suchanek, and Williams 1988). • In a forest fire simulation, many people allow their headquarters to burn down despite their best efforts to put out the fire (Brehmer 1989). • In a medical setting, subjects playing the role of doctors order more tests while the (simulated) patients sicken and die (Kleinmuntz and Thomas 1987).

1.3.5   Flawed Cognitive Maps

Causal attributions are a central feature of mental models. We all create and update cognitive maps of causal connections among entities and actors, from the prosaic—if I touch a flame I will be burned—to the grand—the larger the government deficit, the higher interest rates will be. Studies of cognitive maps show that few incorporate any feedback loops. Axelrod (1976) found virtually no feedback processes in studies of the cognitive maps of political leaders; rather, people tended to formulate intuitive decision trees relating possible actions to probable consequences—an event-level representation. Hall (1976) reports similar open-loop mental maps in a study of the publishing industry. Dörner (1980, 1996) found that people tend to think in single strand causal series and had difficulty in systems with side effects and multiple causal pathways (much less feedback loops). Similarly, experiments in causal attribution show people tend to assume each effect has a single cause and often cease their search for explanations when the first sufficient cause is found (see the discussion in Plous 1993).

The heuristics we use to judge causal relations lead systematically to cognitive maps that ignore feedbacks, multiple interconnections, nonlinearities, time delays, and the other elements of dynamic complexity. The causal field or mental model of the stage on which the action occurs is crucial in framing people's judgments of causation (Einhorn and Hogarth 1986). Within a causal field, people use various cues to causality including temporal and spatial proximity of cause and effect, temporal precedence of causes, covariation, and similarity of cause and effect. These heuristics lead to difficulty in complex systems where cause and effect are often distant in time and space, where actions have multiple effects, and where the delayed and distant consequences are different from and less salient than proximate effects (or simply unknown). The multiple feedbacks in complex systems cause many variables to be correlated with one another, confounding the task of judging cause. However, people are poor judges of correlation. Experiments show people can generally detect linear, positive correlations among variables if they are given enough trials and if the outcome feedback is accurate enough. However, we have great difficulty in the presence of random error, nonlinearity, and negative correlations, often never discovering the true relationship (Brehmer 1980).

A fundamental principle of system dynamics states that the structure of the system gives rise to its behavior. However, people have a strong tendency to attribute the behavior of others to dispositional rather than situational factors, that is, to character and especially character flaws rather than the system in which these people are acting. The tendency to blame the person rather than the system is so strong psychologists call it the "fundamental attribution error" (Ross 1977). In complex systems different people placed in the same structure tend to behave in similar ways. When we attribute behavior to personality we lose sight of how the structure of the system shaped our choices. The attribution of behavior to individuals and special circumstances rather than system structure diverts our attention from the high leverage points where redesigning the system or governing policy can have significant, sustained, beneficial effects on performance (Forrester 1969, chap. 6; Meadows 1982). When we attribute behavior to people rather than system structure the focus of management becomes scapegoating and blame rather than the design of organizations in which ordinary people can achieve extraordinary results.[11]

1.3.6   Erroneous Inferences about Dynamics

Even if our cognitive maps of causal structure were perfect, learning, especially double-loop learning, would still be difficult. To use a mental model to design a new strategy or organization we must make inferences about the consequences of decision rules that have never been tried and for which we have no data. To do so requires intuitive solution of high-order nonlinear differential equations, a task far exceeding human cognitive capabilities in all but the simplest systems (Forrester 1971a; Simon 1982). In many experimental studies, including Diehl and Sterman (1995) and Sterman (1989a), the participants were given complete knowledge of all structural relationships and parameters, along with perfect, comprehensive, and immediate knowledge of all variables. Further, the systems were simple enough that the number of variables to consider was small. Yet performance was poor and learning was slow. Poor performance in these tasks is due to our inability to make reasonable inferences about the dynamics of the system despite perfect and complete knowledge of the system structure.

People cannot simulate mentally even the simplest possible feedback system, the first-order linear positive feedback loop.[12] Such positive feedback processes are commonplace, from the compounding of interest to the growth of populations. Wagenaar and Sagaria (1975) and Wagenaar and Timmers (1978, 1979) showed that people significantly underestimate exponential growth, tending to extrapolate linearly rather than exponentially. Using more data points or graphing the data did not help, and mathematical training did not improve performance.

Bounded rationality simultaneously constrains the complexity of our cognitive maps and our ability to use them to anticipate the system dynamics. Mental models in which the world is seen as a sequence of events and in which feedback, nonlinearity, time delays, and multiple consequences are lacking lead to poor performance when these elements of dynamic complexity are present. Dysfunction in complex systems can arise from the misperception of the feedback *structure* of the environment. But rich mental models that capture these sources of complexity cannot be used reliably to understand the dynamics. Dysfunction in complex systems can arise from faulty mental simulation—the misperception of feedback *dynamics*. These two different bounds on rationality must both be overcome for effective learning to occur. Perfect mental models without a simulation capability yield little insight; a calculus for reliable inferences about dynamics yields systematically erroneous results when applied to simplistic models.

---

[11]Repenning and Sterman (1999) show how the fundamental attribution error arose in a major manufacturing organization, thwarting their efforts to improve operations and product development.

[12]The first-order linear positive loop is represented by the differential equation $dx/dt = gx$ and yields pure exponential growth, $x = x_o\exp(gt)$; see chap. 8.

1.3.7   Unscientific Reasoning: Judgmental Errors and Biases

To learn effectively in a world of dynamic complexity and imperfect information people must develop what Davis and Hogarth (1992) call "insight skills"—the skills that help people learn when feedback is ambiguous:

> [T]he interpretation of feedback . . . needs to be an *active* and *disciplined* task governed by the rigorous rules of scientific inference. Beliefs must be actively challenged by seeking possible disconfirming evidence and asking whether alternative beliefs could not account for the facts (emphasis in original).

Unfortunately, people are poor intuitive scientists, generally failing to reason in accordance with the principles of scientific method. For example, people do not generate sufficient alternative explanations or consider enough rival hypotheses. People generally do not adequately control for confounding variables when they explore a novel environment. People's judgments are strongly affected by the frame in which the information is presented, even when the objective information is unchanged. People suffer from overconfidence in their judgments (underestimating uncertainty), wishful thinking (assessing desired outcomes as more likely than undesired outcomes), and the illusion of control (believing one can predict or influence the outcome of random events). People violate basic rules of probability, do not understand basic statistical concepts such as regression to the mean, and do not update beliefs according to Bayes' rule. Memory is distorted by hindsight, the availability and salience of examples, and the desirability of outcomes. And so on. Hogarth (1987) discusses 30 different biases and errors documented in decision-making research and provides a good guide to the literature (see also Kahneman, Slovic, and Tversky 1982). The research convincingly shows that scientists and professionals, not only "ordinary" people, suffer from many of these judgmental biases.

Among the failures of scientific reasoning most inimical to learning is the tendency to seek evidence consistent with current beliefs rather than potential disconfirmation (Einhorn and Hogarth 1978; Klayman and Ha 1987). In a famous series of experiments, Wason and colleagues presented people tasks of the sort shown in Figure 1-13.[13] Before continuing, try the challenge shown in the figure.

CHALLENGE   ### Hypothesis Testing

You are shown these four cards. Each card has a letter on one side and a number on the other. What is the smallest number of cards you should turn over to test the rule that cards with vowels on one side have even numbers on the reverse? Which are they?

FIGURE 1-13
Wason card puzzle

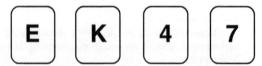

---

[13]The summary of the Wason test is drawn from Plous (1993, chap. 20).

In one version you are shown one side of four cards, each with a letter on one side and a number on the other, say E, K, 4, and 7. You are told that if a card has a vowel on it, then it has an even number on the other side. You must then identify the smallest set of cards to turn over to see if the proposed rule is correct.

Wason and Johnson-Laird (1972) found that the vast majority of subjects selected E or E and 4 as the answers. Less than 4% gave the correct answer: E and 7. The rule has the logical form *if p, then q.* Falsification requires observation of *p and not-q.* The only card showing *p* is the E card, so it must be examined (the back of the E card must be an even number for the rule to hold). The only card showing *not-q* is the 7, so it too must be examined. The K and 4 cards are irrelevant. Yet people consistently choose the card showing *q,* a choice that can only provide data consistent with the theory, but cannot test it; if the back of the 4 is a consonant, you have learned nothing, since the rule is silent about the numbers associated with consonants. Experiments show the tendency to seek confirmation is robust in the face of training in logic, mathematics, and statistics. Search strategies that focus only on confirmation of current beliefs slow the generation and recognition of anomalies that might lead to learning, particularly double-loop learning.

Some argue that while people err in applying the principles of logic, at least people are rational in the sense that they appreciate the desirability of scientific explanation. Unfortunately, the situation is far worse. The rational, scientific worldview is a recent development in human history and remains rare. Many people place their faith in what Dostoyevsky's Grand Inquisitor called "miracle, mystery, and authority," for example, astrology, ESP, UFOs, creationism, conspiracy theories of history, channeling of past lives, cult leaders promising Armageddon, and Elvis sightings. The persistence of such superstitious beliefs depends partly on the bias towards confirming evidence. Wade Boggs, former Boston Red Sox batting champion, ate chicken every day for years because he once had a particularly good day at the plate after a dinner of lemon chicken (Shaughnessy 1987). During this time Boggs won five batting championships, proving the wisdom of the "chicken theory." Consider the continued popularity of astrology, psychics, and economic forecasters, who publicize their successes and suppress their (more numerous) failures. Remember that the 40th president of the United States and first lady managed affairs of state on the basis of astrology (Robinson 1988). And it worked: He was reelected in a landslide.

Such lunacy aside, there are deeper and more disturbing reasons for the prevalence of these learning failures and the superstitions they engender. Human beings are more than cognitive information processors. We have a deep need for emotional and spiritual sustenance. But from Copernican heliocentrism through evolution, relativity, quantum mechanics, and Gödelian uncertainty, science has stripped away ancient and comforting beliefs placing humanity at the center of a rational universe designed for us by a supreme authority. For many people scientific thought leads not to enlightenment and empowerment but to existential angst and the absurdity of human insignificance in an incomprehensibly vast universe. Others believe science and technology were the shock troops for the triumph of materialism and instrumentalism over the sacred and spiritual. These antiscientific reactions are powerful forces. In many ways they are important truths. They have led to many of the most profound works of art and literature. But they can also lead to mindless new-age psychobabble.

The reader should not conclude from this discussion that I am a naive defender of science as it is practiced nor an apologist for the real and continuing damage done to the environment and to our cultural, moral, and spiritual lives in the name of rationality and progress. On the contrary, I have stressed the research showing that scientists are often as prone to the judgmental errors and biases discussed above as laypeople. It is precisely because scientists are subject to the same cognitive limitations and moral failures as others that we experience abominations such as the US government funded research in which plutonium was injected into seriously ill patients, and in which radioactive calcium was fed to retarded children, all without their knowledge or consent (Mann 1994). A central principle of system dynamics is to examine issues from multiple perspectives; to expand the boundaries of our mental models to consider the long-term consequences and "side effects" of our actions, including their environmental, cultural, and moral implications (Meadows, Richardson, and Bruckmann 1982).

1.3.8   Defensive Routines and Interpersonal Impediments to Learning

Learning by groups, whether system dynamics is used or not, can be thwarted even if participants receive excellent information feedback and reason well as individuals. We rely on our mental models to interpret the language and acts of others, construct meaning, and infer motives. However, as Forrester (1971) argues,

> The mental model is fuzzy. It is incomplete. It is imprecisely stated. Furthermore, within one individual, a mental model changes with time and even during the flow of a single conversation. The human mind assembles a few relationships to fit the context of a discussion. As the subject shifts so does the model . . . [E]ach participant in a conversation employs a different mental model to interpret the subject. Fundamental assumptions differ but are never brought into the open.

Argyris (1985), Argyris and Schön (1978), Janis (1982), Schein (1969, 1985, 1987), and others document the defensive routines and cultural assumptions people rely on, often unknowingly, to interact with and interpret their experience of others. We use defensive routines to save face, assert dominance over others, make untested inferences seem like facts, and advocate our positions while appearing to be neutral. We make conflicting, unstated attributions about the data we receive. We fail to distinguish between the sense-data of experience and the attributions and generalizations we readily form from them. We avoid publicly testing our hypotheses and beliefs and avoid threatening issues. Above all, defensive behavior involves covering up the defensiveness and making these issues undiscussable, even when all parties are aware they exist.

Defensive routines are subtle. They often arrive cloaked in apparent concern and respect for others. Consider the strategy called "easing-in:"

> If you are about to criticize someone who might become defensive and you want him to see the point without undue resistance, do not state the criticism openly; instead, ask questions such that if he answers them correctly, he will figure out what you are not saying (Argyris, Putnam, and Smith 1985, p. 83).

But easing-in often

> Creates the very defensiveness that it is intended to avoid, because the recipient typically understands that the actor is easing-in. Indeed, easing-in can be successful only if the recipient understands that he is supposed to answer the questions in a particular way, and this entails the understanding that the actor is negatively evaluating the recipient and acting as if this were not the case (Argyris, Putnam, and Smith 1985, p. 85).

Defensive behavior, in which the espoused theories we offer to others differ from our theories in use, prevents learning by hiding important information from others, avoiding public testing of important hypotheses, and tacitly communicating that we are not open to having our mental models challenged. Defensive routines often yield groupthink (Janis 1982), where members of a group mutually reinforce their current beliefs, suppress dissent, and seal themselves off from those with different views or possible disconfirming evidence. Defensive routines ensure that the mental models of team members remain ill formed, ambiguous, and hidden. Thus learning by groups can suffer even beyond the impediments to individual learning.

1.3.9   Implementation Failure

In the real world decisions are often implemented imperfectly, further hindering learning. Even if a team agreed on the proper course of action, the implementation of these decisions can be delayed and distorted as the actual organization responds. Local incentives, asymmetric information, and private agendas can lead to game playing by agents throughout a system. Obviously implementation failures can hurt the organization. Imperfect implementation can defeat the learning process as well, because the management team evaluating the outcomes of their decisions may not know the ways in which the decisions they thought they were implementing were distorted.

Finally, in the real world of irreversible actions and high stakes the need to maintain performance often overrides the need to learn by suppressing new strategies for fear they would cause present harm even though they might yield great insight and prevent future harm.

1.4   REQUIREMENTS FOR SUCCESSFUL LEARNING IN COMPLEX SYSTEMS

We face grave impediments to learning in complex systems like a nation, firm, or family. Every link in the feedback loops by which we might learn can be weakened or cut by a variety of structures. Some of these are physical or institutional features of the environment—the elements of dynamic complexity that reduce opportunities for controlled experimentation, prevent us from learning the consequences of our actions, and distort the outcome feedback we do receive. Some are consequences of our culture, group process, and inquiry skills. Still others are fundamental bounds on human cognition, particularly the poor quality of our mental maps and our inability to make correct inferences about the dynamics of complex nonlinear systems.

1.4.1   Improving the Learning Process: Virtues of Virtual Worlds

What then are the requirements for successful learning in complex systems? If we are to create useful protocols and tools for learning effectively in a world of dynamic complexity we must attend to all of the impediments to learning. Figure 1-14 shows how the learning feedbacks would operate when all the impediments to learning are addressed. The diagram features a new feedback loop created by the use of *virtual worlds*. Virtual worlds (the term is Schön's [1983]) are formal models, simulations, or "microworlds" (Papert 1980), in which decision makers can refresh decision-making skills, conduct experiments, and play. They can be physical models, role plays, or computer simulations. In systems with significant dynamic complexity, computer simulation will typically be needed (though there are notable exceptions, such as the Beer Distribution Game (Sterman 1989b) and the Maintenance Game described in section 2.4, along with role-play/computer hybrids such

FIGURE 1-14
Idealized learning process

Effective learning involves continuous experimentation in both the virtual world and real world. Feedback from both informs the development of mental models, formal models, and the design of experiments for the next iteration.

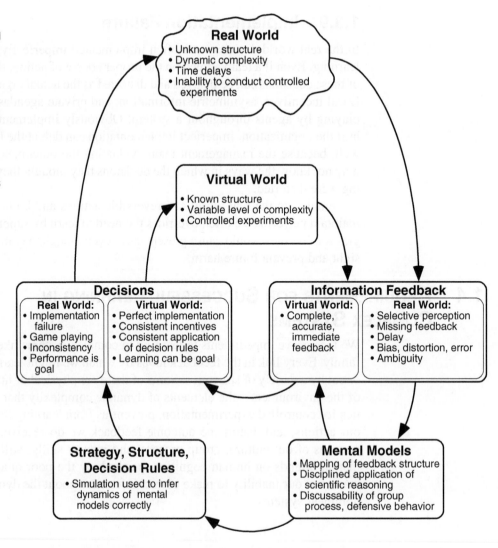

Real World
- Unknown structure
- Dynamic complexity
- Time delays
- Inability to conduct controlled experiments

Virtual World
- Known structure
- Variable level of complexity
- Controlled experiments

Decisions

Real World:	Virtual World:
• Implementation failure	• Perfect implementation
• Game playing	• Consistent incentives
• Inconsistency	• Consistent application of decision rules
• Performance is goal	• Learning can be goal

Information Feedback

Virtual World:	Real World:
• Complete, accurate, immediate feedback	• Selective perception
	• Missing feedback
	• Delay
	• Bias, distortion, error
	• Ambiguity

Strategy, Structure, Decision Rules
- Simulation used to infer dynamics of mental models correctly

Mental Models
- Mapping of feedback structure
- Disciplined application of scientific reasoning
- Discussability of group process, defensive behavior

as Fish Banks, Ltd. (Meadows, Fiddaman, and Shannon 1993). Many of the tools of system dynamics are designed to help you develop useful, reliable, and effective models to serve as virtual worlds to aid learning and policy design.

Virtual worlds have several virtues. First, they provide low-cost laboratories for learning. The virtual world allows time and space to be compressed or dilated. Actions can be repeated under the same or different conditions. One can stop the action to reflect. Decisions that are dangerous, infeasible, or unethical in the real system can be taken in the virtual world. Thus controlled experimentation becomes possible, and the time delays in the learning loop through the real world are dramatically reduced. In the real world the irreversibility of many actions and the need to maintain high performance often override the goal of learning by preventing experiments with untried possibilities ("If it ain't broke, don't fix it"). In the virtual world you can try strategies that you suspect will lead to poor performance or even (simulated) catastrophe. Often pushing a system into extreme conditions reveals more about its structure and dynamics than incremental adjustments to successful strategies. Virtual worlds are the only practical way to experience catastrophe in advance of the real thing. Thus a great deal of the time pilots spend in flight simulators is devoted to extreme conditions such as engine failure or explosive decompression.

Virtual worlds provide high-quality outcome feedback. In the *People Express Management Flight Simulator* (Sterman 1988a), for example, and similar system dynamics simulations, players receive perfect, immediate, undistorted, and complete outcome feedback. In an afternoon one can gain years of simulated experience. The degree of random variation in the virtual world can be controlled. Virtual worlds offer the learner greater control over strategy, lead to more consistent decision making, and deter implementation failure and game playing. In contrast to the real world, which, like a black box, has a poorly resolved structure, virtual worlds can be open boxes whose assumptions are fully known and can even be modified by the learner.

Virtual worlds for learning and training are commonplace in the military, in pilot training, in power plant operations, and in many other real time tasks where human operators interact with complex technical systems. Virtual worlds are also common in professions such as architecture and engineering that lend themselves to the use of physical models (Schön 1983). The use of virtual worlds in managerial tasks, where the simulation compresses into minutes or hours dynamics extending over years or decades, is more recent and less widely adopted. Yet these are precisely the settings where dynamic complexity is most problematic, where the learning feedbacks described above are least effective, and where the stakes are highest.

1.4.2 Pitfalls of Virtual Worlds

Virtual worlds are effective when they engage people in what Dewey called "reflective thought" and what Schön (1992) calls "reflective conversation with the situation." Though simulation models and virtual worlds may be necessary for effective learning in dynamically complex systems, they are not sufficient to overcome the flaws in our mental models, scientific reasoning skills, and group processes.

Obviously, while the virtual world enables controlled experimentation, it does not require the learner to apply the principles of scientific method. Many participants in system dynamics projects lack training in scientific method and awareness of the pitfalls in the design and interpretation of experiments. A commonly observed behavior among modelers and in workshops using management flight simulators is the video game syndrome in which people play too much and think too little. People often do not take time to reflect on the outcome of a simulation, identify discrepancies between the outcomes and their expectations, formulate hypotheses to explain the discrepancies, and then devise experiments to discriminate among the competing alternatives. Effective learning using system dynamics will often require training for participants in scientific method. Protocols for the use of simulations should be structured to encourage proper procedure, such as keeping laboratory notebooks, explicitly formulating hypotheses and presenting them to the group, and so on.

Defensive routines and groupthink can operate in the learning laboratory just as in the real organization. Indeed, protocols for effective learning in virtual worlds such as public testing of hypotheses, accountability, and comparison of different strategies can be highly threatening, inducing defensive reactions that prevent learning (Isaacs and Senge 1992). The use of system dynamics to stimulate learning in organizations often requires members of the client team to spend time addressing their own defensive behavior. Managers unaccustomed to disciplined scientific reasoning and an open, trusting environment with learning as its goal will have to build these basic skills before a system dynamics model—or indeed, any model—can prove useful. Developing these skills takes effort and practice.

Still, settings with high dynamic complexity can garble the reflective conversation between the learner and the situation. Long time delays, causes and effects that are distant in time and space, and the confounding effects of multiple nonlinear feedbacks can slow learning even for people with good insight and group process skills. Learning in virtual worlds can be accelerated when the modeling process also helps people learn how to represent complex feedback structures and understand their implications rather than simply presenting the results of an analysis. To learn in dynamically complex systems participants must have confidence that the model is an appropriate representation of the problem they care about. They must believe it mimics the relevant parts of the real world well enough that the lessons emerging from the virtual world apply to the real one. To develop such confidence the virtual world must be an open box whose assumptions can be inspected, criticized, and changed. To learn, participants must become modelers, not merely players in a simulation game.

In practice, effective learning from models occurs best, and perhaps only, when the decision makers participate actively in the development of the model. Modeling here includes the elicitation of the participants' existing mental models, including articulating the issues (problem structuring), selecting the model boundary and time horizon, and mapping the causal structure of the relevant system. Along with techniques developed in system dynamics, many tools and protocols for group model-building are now available, including causal loop diagrams, policy structure diagrams, interactive computer mapping, and various problem structuring and soft systems methods (see, e.g., Checkland 1981; Eden, Jones and

Sims 1983; Lane 1994; Morecroft 1982; Morecroft and Sterman 1994; Reagan-Cirincione et al. 1991; Richmond 1987, 1993; Rosenhead 1989; Senge and Sterman 1992; and Wolstenholme 1990).

1.4.3 Why Simulation Is Essential

Eliciting and mapping the participants' mental models, while necessary, is far from sufficient. As discussed above, the temporal and spatial boundaries of our mental models tend to be too narrow. They are dynamically deficient, omitting feedbacks, time delays, accumulations, and nonlinearities. The great virtue of many protocols and tools for elicitation is their ability to improve our models by encouraging people to identify the elements of dynamic complexity normally absent from mental models. However, most problem structuring methods yield qualitative models showing causal relationships but omitting the parameters, functional forms, external inputs, and initial conditions needed to fully specify and test the model. Regardless of the form of the model or technique used, the result of the elicitation and mapping process is never more than a set of causal attributions, initial hypotheses about the structure of a system, which must then be tested.

Simulation is the only practical way to test these models. The complexity of our mental models vastly exceeds our capacity to understand their implications. Typical conceptual models such as the type of causal diagram shown in Figure 1-6 are too large and complex to simulate mentally. Without simulation, even the best conceptual models can only be tested and improved by relying on the learning feedback through the real world. As we have seen, this feedback is very slow and often rendered ineffective by dynamic complexity, time delays, inadequate and ambiguous feedback, poor reasoning skills, defensive reactions, and the costs of experimentation. In these circumstances simulation becomes the only reliable way to test hypotheses and evaluate the likely effects of policies.

Some scholars argue that formal modeling can at best provide quantitative precision within preexisting problem definitions but cannot lead to fundamentally new conceptions (for various views see Dreyfus and Dreyfus 1986 and the discussion in Lane 1994). On the contrary, formalizing qualitative models and testing them via simulation often leads to radical changes in the way we understand reality. Simulation speeds and strengthens the learning feedbacks. Discrepancies between formal and mental models stimulate improvements in both, including changes in basic assumptions such as model boundary, time horizon, and dynamic hypotheses (see Forrester 1985 and Homer 1996 for philosophy and examples). Without the discipline and constraint imposed by the rigorous testing enabled by simulation, it becomes all too easy for mental models to be driven by ideology or unconscious bias.

Some argue that formalization forces the modeler to omit important aspects of the problem to preserve tractability and enable theorems to be proved or to omit soft variables for which no numerical data exist. These are indeed dangers. The literature of the social sciences is replete with models in which elegant theorems are derived from questionable axioms, where simplicity dominates utility, and where variables known to be important are ignored because data to estimate parameters are unavailable. System dynamics was designed specifically to overcome these limitations and from the beginning stressed the development of useful models; models unconstrained by the demands of analytic tractability, based on realistic assumptions about human behavior, grounded in field study of decision making, and utilizing the full range of available data, not only numerical data, to specify and estimate relationships (see Forrester 1961, 1987).

Some people don't believe that models of human behavior can be developed. Simulations of natural and technical systems such as the climate or an oil refinery are based on well-understood laws of physics, but, it is argued, there are no comparably reliable laws of human behavior. This view overestimates our understanding of nature and underestimates the regularities in human decision making. As Kenneth Boulding points out, "Anything that exists is possible." You will see many examples of models of human systems throughout this book (see also the models in Levine and Fitzgerald 1992; Roberts 1978; Langley et al. 1987; Sterman 1985a; Homer 1985; and many of the models cited in Sastry and Sterman 1993).

Is it possible to learn effectively in complex settings without simulation? Can the use of problem structuring methods, elicitation techniques, and other qualitative systems methods overcome the impediments to learning? If intuition is developed highly enough, if systems thinking is incorporated in precollege education early enough, or if we are taught how to recognize a set of "system archetypes" (Senge 1990), will we be able to improve our intuition about complex dynamics enough to render simulation unnecessary?

The answer is clearly no. It is true that systems thinking techniques, including system dynamics and qualitative methods such as soft systems analysis, can enhance our intuition about complex situations, just as studying physics can improve our intuition about the natural world.[14] As Wolstenholme (1990) argues, qualitative systems tools should be made widely available so that those with limited mathematical background can benefit from them. I am a strong advocate for the introduction of system dynamics and related methods at all levels of the educational system. Yet even if we all began serious study of physics in kindergarten and continued it through a Ph.D., it is ludicrous to suggest that we could predict the track of a hurricane or understand by intuition alone what happens when two galaxies collide. Many human systems are at least as complex. Even if children learn to think in systems terms—a goal I believe is vitally important—it will still be necessary to develop formal models, solved by simulation, to learn about such systems.

Most important, when experimentation in real systems is infeasible, simulation becomes the main, and perhaps the only, way you can discover for yourself how complex systems work. The alternative is rote learning based on the authority of the teacher and textbook, a method that dulls creativity and stunts the development of the scientific reasoning skills needed to learn about complexity.

---

[14]Such knowledge of basic physics is desperately needed. When asked the question "If a pen is dropped on the moon, will it (a) float away; (b) float where it is; (c) fall to the surface of the moon?" 48 out of 168 students in physics courses at Iowa State University gave incorrect answers. Typical student explanations were "The gravity of the moon can be said to be negligible" and "The moon's a vacuum, there is no external force on the pen. Therefore it will float where it is." (Partee, personal communication, 1992).

The implications for this book are clear. System dynamics is not a spectator sport: Throughout the book I have tried to encourage the active participation of you, the reader. You will find Challenges in each chapter—examples for you to consider and work through yourself, such as the chicken and egg causal loop diagram in Figure 1-6 and the Wason card puzzle in Figure 1-13. Some of these are followed by a suggested response. Others are not. As you work through the book, extend the examples. Build the models. Experiment with them. Apply your skills to new problems and new issues. And, most of all, have fun.[15]

1.5   SUMMARY

Complex dynamic systems present multiple barriers to learning. The challenge of bettering the way we learn about these systems is itself a classic systems problem. System dynamics is a powerful method to gain useful insight into situations of dynamic complexity and policy resistance. It is increasingly used to design more successful policies in companies and public policy settings. However, no one method is a panacea. Overcoming the barriers to learning requires a synthesis of many methods and disciplines, from mathematics and computer science to psychology and organizational theory. Theoretical studies must be integrated with field work. Interventions in real organizations must be subjected to rigorous follow-up research.

The field of system dynamics is itself dynamic. Recent advances in interactive modeling, tools for representation of feedback structure, and simulation software make it possible for anyone to engage in the modeling process. Corporations, universities, and schools are experimenting vigorously. The library of successful interventions and insightful research is growing. Much further work is needed to test the utility of the tools and protocols, evaluate their impact on individual and organizational learning, and develop effective ways to train others to use them. Never before have the challenges of our increasingly dynamic world been more daunting. Never before have the opportunities been greater. It's an exciting time to be learning in and about complex systems.

---

[15]The accompanying CD-ROM and website (http://www.mhhe.com/sterman) include the models developed in the text and simulation software you can use to run and extend them.

2

System Dynamics in Action

[System dynamics] is an approach that should help in important top-management problems . . . The solutions to small problems yield small rewards. Very often the most important problems are but little more difficult to handle than the unimportant. Many [people] predetermine mediocre results by setting initial goals too low. The attitude must be one of enterprise design. The expectation should be for major improvement . . . The attitude that the goal is to explain behavior, which is fairly common in academic circles, is not sufficient. The goal should be to find management policies and organizational structures that lead to greater success.

—Jay W. Forrester (*Industrial Dynamics,* 1961, p. 449).

This chapter presents three case studies of the successful application of system dynamics to solve important real world problems. The cases span a range of industries and issues. They illustrate different contexts for the use of system dynamics and different modeling processes, from large, data intensive models to small models, interactive management flight simulators, and role-playing games. The cases illustrate how system dynamics can be used to help solve high-stakes problems in real time. The cases illustrate the principles discussed in chapter 1 and preview many of the tools and methods discussed in subsequent chapters.

2.1 APPLICATIONS OF SYSTEM DYNAMICS

System dynamics has been applied to issues ranging from corporate strategy to the dynamics of diabetes, from the cold war arms race between the US and USSR to the combat between HIV and the human immune system. System dynamics can be applied to any dynamic system, with any time and spatial scale. In the world of business and public policy, system dynamics has been applied to industries from aircraft to zinc and issues from AIDS to welfare reform.[1]

Developing an insightful model is difficult enough; using modeling to help change organizations and implement new policies is even harder. The greatest potential for improvement comes when the modeling process changes deeply held mental models. Yet the more fundamental the mental model you challenge, the more defensive the client may be. To resolve the dilemma the clients must discover the insights for themselves by active participation in the modeling process.

This chapter presents three case studies illustrating the process. Each addressed an important real world issue. Each involved a different context and therefore used a different approach. Yet each also succeeded in involving the clients as partners in the modeling process, in changing long-established mental models, and in generating significant benefit.

2.2   AUTOMOBILE LEASING STRATEGY: GONE TODAY, HERE TOMORROW[2]

In the 1990s a new way to buy cars emerged in the United States—the used car superstore. National chains like CarMax and AutoNation offered a large selection of clean, low mileage late model cars with warranties, roadside assistance plans, and other amenities traditionally available only to new car buyers. Superstore sales grew from nothing in 1992 to more than $13 billion in 1998. Internet car vendors began to spring up as well. Many analysts believed the combination of superstores and internet sales heralded a revolution in the retail auto market.

In 1995 some senior managers at General Motors were concerned about the impact of the superstores on new car sales. Would they cut into GM's core market? Would they force prices down? How could GM respond? Ron Zarella, then vice president and group executive for North American vehicle sales, service, and marketing (VSSM) and later promoted to president of GM's North American region, needed a way to examine these issues.

There was little research on the used car market available to help. For many decades the new and used car markets were only loosely coupled because people tended to keep their cars a long time. Market research in the early 1990s showed new car buyers were keeping their cars an average of more than 6 years. The bulk of used cars offered for sale were 4 or more years old and were poor substitutes for new cars. The prevailing mental model in the auto industry, including GM, was

---

[1]Richardson (1996), Roberts (1978), and Morecroft and Sterman (1994), among others, provide examples of the application of system dynamics to important problems in a wide range of industries and public policy issues. Mosekilde (1996) describes applications in physics and biology. Ford (1999) describes environmental applications.

[2]This case is based on the work of the General Motors Strategy Support Center, led by Nick Pudar. I'm grateful to Nick and GM for permission to present the case and to Nick and Mark Paich for help in its preparation.

that auto companies were in the business of selling new cars; the vehicles people traded in were old and effectively disappeared into a separate system, the used car market. "There are really two markets—new and used," the executive director of sales operations at Ford told *The Wall Street Journal* in 1994 (3 June, p. B1).

Zarella contacted Vince Barabba, then general manager of corporate strategy and knowledge development in the VSSM organization, and described his concerns. Barabba, former head of the US Census Bureau, also headed up the Decision Support Center (DSC) and asked Nick Pudar, then a senior business analyst in the DSC, to work on the superstore issue. The DSC is an internal group GM formed to help business units and project teams throughout the company develop and implement strategy. The DSC uses a variety of analytical tools, including system dynamics. More than simply a group of analytical modelers, the DSC developed a sophisticated approach, the dialogue decision process, designed to build consensus that leads to action, not merely analysis and reports. Barabba and Pudar (1996) describe the dialogue decision process as

> a disciplined decision making process which involves a series of structured dialogues between two groups responsible for reaching a decision and implementing the resulting action plan. The first group (Decision Review Board) consists of the decision-makers, who generally represent different functions. What they have in common is the authority to allocate resources: people, capital, materials, time, and equipment . . . The second group (Core Team), consists of . . . those with a stake in the implementation.
>
> The dialogue between the two groups, which involves sharing and learning for both, takes place in four sequential stages: 1) framing the problem; 2) developing alternatives; 3) conducting the analysis; and 4) establishing connection. Each of these four steps is completed by the Core Team and supported by facilitators equipped with decision analytic tools. At the end of each phase, they have a dialogue session with the Decision Review Board where they jointly review the progress. In an atmosphere of inquiry . . . senior leadership converses with a cross-functional team of managers on a topic of mutual strategic importance.

Pudar told Zarella he would need to commit to a several hour meeting each week for a month "to be sure we are working on the right problem." While Zarella's schedule was extremely tight he offered to meet with Barabba and Pudar the next day.

Pudar, working with Mark Paich, an external system dynamics consultant and professor of economics at Colorado College, Darren Post of the DSC, and Tom Paterson (another consultant to the DSC) scrambled to develop an initial model of the issue. That afternoon they developed a simple diagram representing the stocks and flows of cars through the new and used markets and some of the feedbacks that might couple them. They deliberately kept it very simple, both to be sure they could complete it in time and so they could explain it clearly.

That night Pudar developed a simple, working simulation model of the interactions between the new and used markets. The model included sectors for new and used cars (divided into GM and non-GM vehicles) and tracked vehicles from production through initial sale or lease, trade-in, the used car market, and, ultimately, scrapping. It also tracked the flows of customers moving into and out of the market and included a simple consumer choice model for the new/used purchase decision. Pudar used data at hand and his judgment to estimate parameters.

Figure 2-1shows a simplified diagram of the initial model. The structure in black captures the prevailing mental model focused on the new car market. The left side tracks the stocks and flows of vehicles. Starting at the top, the inventory of unsold new cars is increased by production and drained by new car sales. New car sales add to the stock of late model cars on the road. People sell or trade in their car and buy a new one with a frequency defined by the average trade-in time.

Figure 2-1 also shows the main feedbacks operating in the new car market. Manufacturers and dealers pay close attention to the stock of new cars. Inventory coverage of about 45 days provides a good balance between the selection available on dealer lots and carrying costs. Low coverage hurts sales because cars aren't available; high inventories slash dealer and automaker profits as carrying costs balloon. If inventory coverage rises above normal, carmakers cut production, which helps reduce inventories back to normal. The response of production to inventories forms the negative (balancing) Production Control feedback loop, B1. However, automakers are reluctant to cut production and in any case, it takes time. The delay in adjusting production means inventories tend to fluctuate around desired levels as demand varies.

The second main response to excess inventories is lower prices. When inventory coverage is high, dealers are more willing to cut their margins and manufacturers offer incentives such as cash-back and low annual percentage rates (APRs) on loans financed through their credit divisions. Lower prices make new cars more attractive relative to the cars people already own. People trade in their old cars sooner, boosting new car sales until inventories fall back to normal (the negative Pricing loop, B2).

2.2.1   Dynamic Hypothesis

Challenging the conventional wisdom, the team expanded the stock and flow structure to include late model used cars. Instead of disappearing, trade-ins add to inventories of late model used cars on dealer lots or available for auction. When these cars are purchased, they reenter the stock of late model cars on the road. The sum of the cars on the road and cars on dealer lots is the total stock of late model vehicles (shown by the large rectangle in Figure 2-1); these cars gradually age into the population of older cars and are eventually scrapped. The model used an "aging chain" to keep track of the cars on the road and in used car inventories by 1-year cohorts. The aging chain (chapter 12) allowed the team to examine how the number of 1-, 2-, and 3-year-old cars on the road and for sale changed in response to sales.

The stock and flow perspective motivated the modeling team to ask where the superstores got the large inventories of attractive late model cars they required. Part of the answer was the growing quality of new cars. Stimulated by the high quality of foreign cars, particularly the Japanese imports, all manufacturers had

FIGURE 2-1   A simple model of the automobile market

Rectangles represent stocks of cars; pipes and valves represent flows between categories (chapter 6). Arrows and polarities (+ or −) indicate causal influences: An increase in New Car Inventory leads to an increase in Inventory Coverage (and a decrease leads to a decrease); an increase (decrease) in Inventory Coverage causes new car prices to decrease (increase); see chapter 5. Gray structure was not captured in the prevailing industry mental model in which new and used car markets do not interact.

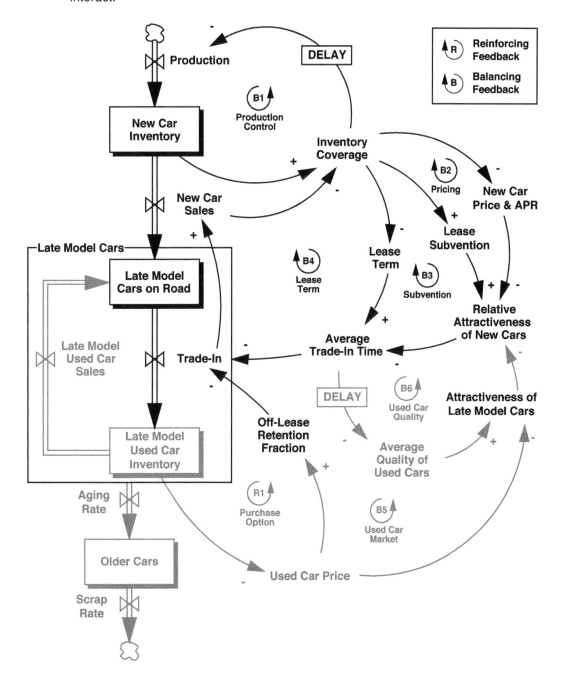

invested in major quality programs. Though there was still room for improvement, by the 1990s the quality and durability of new cars was significantly higher than in the 1980s.

But quality improvement alone could not explain the rise of the superstores. By the time most cars are traded in they are too old to compete against new cars and are unsuitable for the superstores. Quality improvements might even lengthen the trade-in cycle time, reducing the supply of late model used cars.

The answer was leasing. In the early 1990s leasing was the hot new marketing tool in the automobile industry. Leasing offered what seemed to be a sure-fire way to boost sales. Rising quality meant the market value of 2-, 3-, and 4-year-old cars was much higher relative to new cars than in the past. The higher the residual value at the end of a lease, the lower the lease payments. Leases also give customers the option to buy the car when the lease expires at the specified residual value, transferring the risk of fluctuations in the market value of used vehicles from the customer to the carmaker. Most important to the manufacturers, typical lease terms are 2 to 4 years, stimulating sales by cutting the trade-in cycle time. Leasing increased from 4.1% of all new car sales in 1990 to more than 22% in 1997.

From the perspective of the prevailing mental model, leasing was a boon. First, it stimulated sales. Whenever inventories rise carmakers could increase incentives for leasing through lease subvention. Subvention lowers lease payments by assuming higher residuals, lower interest rates, or lower initial capitalization; typically carmakers would raise residual values above guidebook values for used cars. Lower lease payments boost the attractiveness of new cars and induce some people to trade their current car for a new leased vehicle (forming the balancing Lease Incentive loop B3 in Figure 2-1). Second, the shorter the average lease term, the shorter the trade-in time and the greater the sales (the balancing Lease Term loop B4). If all new car buyers switched to leases with an average term of 3 years, the trade-in cycle time would be cut in half and new car sales would double—*all else equal.*

The modeling team quickly challenged the assumption that all else was equal. While a 6-year old car is a poor substitute for a new car, a 1- to 3-year-old car with low mileage might be attractive to many people. As the growing volume of leases expired the used car market could be flooded with high-quality nearly new cars. Used car prices might plummet. Some people who might have traded their current cars for new ones opt instead for off-lease vehicles, raising the average trade-in time and returning more late model used cars to the stock of cars on the road (the balancing Used Car Market loop, B5). Leasing also shortens the average trade-in cycle time, raising the average quality of used cars for sale. More people opt for off-lease vehicles instead of buying new. The average trade-in time for the population as a whole rises, forming the balancing Used Car Quality loop, B6. Even more interesting, the used market could feed back to affect the fraction of customers who choose to buy their car when their lease expires. If, at lease end, used car prices are higher than the residual value written into the lease, the customer can purchase the car below market value. The customer retention fraction would rise. If, however, used car prices dropped below residual values, the retention fraction would fall as more customers turned their cars back to the lessor. The inventory of late model cars would rise and used car prices would drop still more, in a vicious cycle, the positive (self-reinforcing) Purchase Option loop, R1.[3]

However, the feedbacks shown in gray operate with a long delay (roughly equal to the average lease term) and were poorly understood in the industry. Leasing stimulates sales in the short-run. Unaware of the structure shown in gray in Figure 2-1, the experience of the early 1990s taught carmakers that leasing *works*—and they diverted still more marketing dollars to subvention and shorter terms.

Initial results suggested, however, that leasing would eventually create a glut of high-quality nearly new cars, depressing late model used car prices. New car sales would suffer as more consumers opted for cheap off-lease vehicles. The carmakers' credit companies (General Motors Acceptance Corporation [GMAC], Ford Credit Corporation, and Chrysler Credit Corporation) would face losses as market values fell short of the residual value they had booked and as fewer consumers exercised their option to buy, turning the car back to the lessors instead.

The following day Pudar and his team presented these results to Zarella, including the structure of the initial model and simulations showing the problems aggressive leasing could cause. By shortening trade-in cycle times through leasing and fleet sales, carmakers were creating a glut of high-quality used cars at attractive prices. Superstores were simply the market response to the opportunity the manufacturers themselves had created.

Used car superstores were only the symptom of a deeper problem—the leasing policies of the carmakers. Leasing increased sales in the short run but set in motion feedbacks that caused sales to slump when the leased vehicles reentered the market. In the old days, people kept their cars long enough that trade-ins effectively disappeared from concern. But in a world of short-term leases, new cars are gone today, here tomorrow.

The realization that superstores were an endogenous consequence of the carmakers' own actions dramatically redefined the focus of the work. Initial model analysis suggested GM should de-emphasize leasing, exactly counter to industry trends.

These effects may seem obvious (especially now that you have read the description of the model above), and auto industry executives did know that some off-lease cars would reenter the market. However, most discounted the possibility of any problems. In 1994, *USA Today* quoted a General Motors leasing executive who said, "The demand for cars coming off leases is triple the supply. Lease-end cars have 'not created a bottleneck in the industry'" (2 November). A Detroit-area

---

[3]The Purchase Option loop is partially offset because customers turning their cars back to lessors purchase another vehicle. If lease customers used their purchase option to make a pure arbitrage play when used car prices fell below residual values by turning their cars in and immediately buying identical ones at the lower market price, then the net effect of changes in the retention fraction would be zero. However, some customers turning their cars back to lessors will buy a new car or different used car, possibly from a competitor. On net a lower retention fraction for a given make and model will tend to push prices for that car down still more, triggering even lower retention. These effects were captured in the full model but for clarity are not shown in Figure 2-1.

Cadillac dealer dismissed any linkage between the new and used markets for high-end cars, scoffing, "You'll never get a luxury buyer to take a car with 30,000 miles on it" (*The Wall Street Journal,* 3 June 1994). In the same article, *The Journal* went on to note that Ford's executive director of sales operations

> argues that the industry has had a chronic shortage of good two-year-old cars to sell . . . "This [short-term leasing] brings the cars back at just the right time, when demand is highest," he says. Moreover, the used-car market is at least twice as big as the new-car market and can easily absorb the projected volumes.
>
> The underlying strength in used-car demand will safely absorb the volume of used vehicles coming off lease, without cannibalizing new-car sales," predicts . . . [an] auto securities analyst at Salomon Bros.

There appeared to be ample evidence to support these views. Used car sales grew from 37.5 million in 1990 to nearly 42 million in 1995 while 1995 new car sales were about 15 million, a rise of only about a million vehicles/year since 1990. Used car prices rose more than 6%/year between 1990 and 1995, much faster than inflation. With rising used car prices, more and more people opted to keep their vehicle when their lease expired. Many in the industry, including GM, argued that strong demand and rising used car values justified even higher residual values, allowing lower lease payments and boosting new car sales still more.

While the initial results were intriguing, more work was needed before credible policy recommendations could be made, much less any action taken. Even if leasing was a devil's bargain, every carmaker felt strong pressure to match the terms and prices of its competitors. Once all major manufacturers were offering short lease terms with aggressive subvention, unilaterally backing away from leasing might risk too much market share. Zarella asked the team to continue the modeling to address these questions. The DSC formed a decision review board, chaired by Zarella and Barabba, to oversee the project and the modeling team then began to refine the model and gather the data needed to calibrate it. They had 20 days.

2.2.2   Elaborating the Model

The modeling team interviewed people throughout the organization to understand the issues and gather data. Through the meetings of the core and modeling teams they opened up the model to critical review and presented interim results for discussion.

One area for improvement was the treatment of the competition and segmentation of the market into different vehicle types. Some argued for explicit treatment of every major manufacturer and market segment. Brand loyalty is important: People who bought GM cars last time are more likely to buy another GM car than non-GM owners. They also argued that GM customers were different from Ford or Honda customers and that markets for luxury cars, family sedans, sport utility vehicles, and so on were all different. The team countered that the data requirements for such a detailed model would be enormous and would delay development of a useful model. They preferred an iterative approach, with more limited disaggregation; if sensitivity analysis showed that further segmentation was needed they could then revise the model to include more detail. The team agreed to separate the market into GM and non-GM vehicles but to represent only a single aggregate vehicle type.

Another important area of discussion was disaggregation of the customer base. Parallel to the flow of cars between the "on the road" and "for sale" stocks are stocks and flows of drivers. Every car traded in moves a customer from "on the road" to "in the market;" every new or used car sold puts a driver on the road again. Changes in the relative attractiveness of new and used cars shift the proportion of drivers in the market opting for a new car. The choice between new and used vehicles also depends on their past behavior. The chance a customer will lease, buy new, or buy used depends on whether he or she leased, bought new, or bought used last time. Some members of the organization pointed out that the company, through extensive market research, already knew a lot about consumer behavior in the new car market. They insisted that the dynamic model incorporate these data so the DSC could speak with one voice and avoid the need to reconcile conflicting models.

To address the brand loyalty and consumer behavior issues the modeling team disaggregated the customer base into several categories: those who leased a new car, purchased a new car, or purchased used cars of various ages. Figure 2-2 shows a simplified representation of the resulting transition matrix. Each entry in the matrix is the probability that buyers coming from a particular category shown in a row will, when they next trade in, move to the categories shown in the columns. The actual matrix had twice as many categories as it included probabilities for each purchase option for both GM and non-GM vehicles.

The transition probabilities in the matrix were not constant but changed as the prices of new and used cars changed. Lower payments on GM leases increase

FIGURE 2-2
The matrix shows the probability p(i, j) that customers in each category shown in row i will, on trade-in, move to the category in column j.
The transition probabilities in the full model are variable and depend on relative prices. The full matrix disaggregates GM and non-GM vehicles.

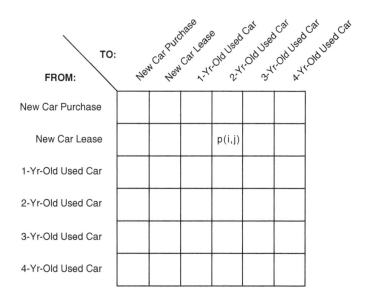

Source: Adapted from GM Decision Support Center diagram. Used with permission.

the proportion opting for a GM lease, while lower used car prices increase the share of people buying used cars at the expense of new purchases and leases. The response to such changes differed for each category of customer.

The disaggregation of the model was not accomplished in one step but in several iterations. At each stage modeling team members made sure they understood the structure and behavior of the model and presented it to Zarella and his team for comment and review. Each iteration they incorporated the criticisms and suggestions they received. Even with the limited disaggregation of the model the data challenges were formidable. Given the 20-day deadline, the team had to use data already available in various parts of the organization. The market research data for new cars were excellent. Data on leasing, a relatively new phenomenon, were sketchy. And consistent with the prevailing mental model that downplayed the used car market, there was almost no research describing how people traded off new and late model used vehicles. They drew on the best data sources available and used judgment and qualitative data where numerical data were not available.

At the end of the 20 days the team met again with Zarella and his team. Instead of presenting the model and results, they configured the model as an interactive management flight simulator. A "dashboard" contained dials and gauges reporting standard accounting information such as inventory levels, sales volumes, prices, market share, and profitability. Players set production targets, incentives, lease terms, and so on. By clicking a button on the screen players could get additional information including the structure and assumptions of the model.

By playing the game instead of listening to a presentation, Zarella and his team explored the dynamics of leasing for themselves. They could try various strategies, from aggressive subvention of leases to pulling out of the lease market altogether, and see the impact on sales and profits in the short run and the long run. They discovered that the full impact of leasing decisions took up to 5 years to play out. While leasing did provide a lift to sales in the short run, it often caused problems when the off-lease cars returned to the market.

After 20 days the modeling process revealed the challenges leasing posed for the company and indicated preliminary policy recommendations. However, before any consensus for action could be developed, the process had to be broadened to include other key decision makers throughout North American Operations (NAO).

The modeling team began to work with the Leasing Strategy Implementation Team, a task force including people from marketing, finance, and other functions. Their mandate was to boost market share and profitability. They didn't think a model was necessary, didn't trust the modeling approach, and opposed the initial recommendations. Viewed through the lens of their mental model, this position was entirely rational. The success of leasing and strength of the used car market provided ample evidence that competitive leasing was essential to GM's strategy.

Working with your critics is often the best way to improve your understanding of complex issues. Over the next few months the modeling team refined the model structure, improved the data and calibration, and tested the model over a wide range of conditions. They met with the leasing team about once a month to present interim results and listen to critiques.

2.2.3 Policy Analysis

As their confidence in the formulations and calibration of the model grew, the team turned to policy analysis. Policy levers include lease terms and subvention levels, along with purchase incentives, fleet sales, and various decision rules for production. The impact of each policy combination depended on the policies of the competitors and a host of market uncertainties, from changes in the economy, demographics, gasoline prices, and interest rates to changes in the unit costs of each carmaker, car quality, and brand loyalty.

The combination of policies and market scenarios define a policy matrix. The team used the model to find the optimal lease policies for each cell in the matrix. Figure 2-3 shows a sample illustrating the net present value of GM profits as a function of leasing policy (no leasing vs. 2-, 3-, or 4-year terms) for each combination of competitor lease terms and economic growth scenario (stable, boom, or recession).

The policy analysis showed that there was no going back: Profits without leasing were consistently negative, reflecting the attractiveness of leasing to consumers and the prisoner's dilemma that unilaterally stopping leasing while competitors continued to offer it dramatically reduced GM sales.

The analysis also showed that GM's profits were consistently higher with 4-year lease terms. Four-year terms were superior over a wide range of competitor strategies and uncertainties. Longer terms have two main beneficial effects. First, though shorter terms do shorten the trade-in cycle, the resulting glut of nearly new cars depresses used prices so much that the substitution of used for new purchases offsets their benefit. In terms of Figure 2-1, the Used Car Market, Used Car Quality, and Purchase Option loops overwhelm the benefit of the Lease Term and Lease

FIGURE 2-3
Policy analysis

The policy matrix shows the simulated net present value (NPV) of GM profits as a function of GM's leasing policy (no leasing or 2- to 4-year terms) for each combination of economic scenario and competitor strategy.

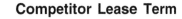

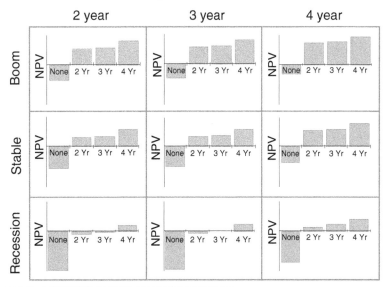

Source: Adapted from GM DSC diagram. Used with permission.

Incentive loops. Four-year terms mean the cars coming off lease are less attractive substitutes for new cars, while still speeding the trade-in cycle somewhat.

The second benefit of longer terms is a more subtle, disequilibrium effect. By increasing the substitutability between new and nearly new used cars, short-term leases increased the vulnerability of earnings to industry downturns. Rather than showing complex diagrams such as Figure 2-1 to explain why, Pudar developed Figure 2-4, showing the stock of late model vehicles as a bathtub. The bathtub diagram uses a simple metaphor to illustrate the dynamics of leasing. The stock of new and new-car substitutes is increased by production and the flow of late model used cars coming off lease (and out of rental car fleets). Sales drain the tub.

During recessions, auto sales drop. The water level in the tub rises. Carmakers come under pressure to cut prices and subsidize leases to drain cars out of the tub faster and also cut production to stop the inflow. However, the flow of new car substitutes into the market from expiring leases cannot be turned off. When a recession hits, leases sold during the preceding boom continue to expire, boosting the level in the tub. Lower used car prices and concerns over future income lead more people to turn their off-lease cars back to the lessor rather than exercising their option to buy. The larger the share of new cars sold through leasing, the larger the unstoppable flow of returning vehicles. Prices are forced down even farther, and production cuts must be even deeper, significantly eroding profits.

The team used the bathtub diagram in presentations to senior managers throughout the firm, including all brand managers. Of course the formal analysis, model structure, and other details were presented, but the bathtub provided a powerful metaphor to communicate an important dynamic insight and helped in the difficult process of changing mental models.

FIGURE 2-4
Bathtub diagram to illustrate the impact of leasing

Why do short-term leases make us more vulnerable during an economic downturn?

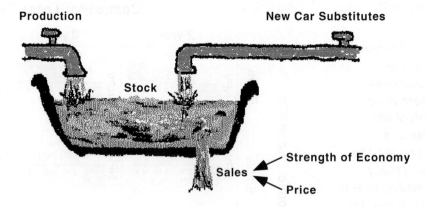

- When industry demand falls, the flow of returning lease cars cannot be stopped:
  - Prices of used cars will be driven down;
  - New car transaction prices will be forced down;
  - Some returning lessees will opt for cheap used cars.

- Price does not alter the supply of new car substitutes

Source: GM Decision Support Center. Used with permission.

Pudar and his team made two main recommendations to Zarella and other senior managers in NAO. First, GM should shift incentives to favor longer leases and move the mix of the leasing portfolio toward a higher average term. Second, they recommended that all proposals for new pricing and marketing programs formally include analysis of their impact on the used car market and its feedback to the new car market. They recommended the market research organization create new clinics to assess new/used/lease consumer choice behavior so that up-to-date data would be available on an ongoing basis. They also supported changing the incentives and metrics for managers of the car groups to include the profit or loss GMAC realized as a result of leasing.

Many brand managers and brand analysts were initially opposed to these recommendations. They argued that consumers had been conditioned to prefer short-term leases. Competition was intense and GM's market share had been slipping. Ford, in particular, was aggressively pushing 2-year leases with significant subvention; unless GM responded in kind, they argued, market share would suffer more. Given the tremendous pressure they faced to stay competitive, they were not willing to sacrifice market share and profits today to avoid the possibility that leasing might lead to problems in a few years. Brand managers and the sales organization put strong pressure on the senior management of NAO to increase residual levels. They pointed to strong used car demand and rising used car prices to justify increased residuals. They also argued that subvention levels should be increased even further above the higher residuals they were recommending. Finally, they argued for a decrease in the fraction of off-lease vehicles GM predicted it would have to take back at lease end. The costs of subvention are deferred because they are only realized when cars come off lease. Accounting rules require carmakers to set aside reserves to cover the expected cost of subvention; these reserves reduce current period earnings. The amount set aside in reserves depends on the fraction of cars they expect to be returned. If customers exercise their option to buy when their lease expires then GMAC never has to pay the difference between the subvented residual and market value. Many brand managers believed that the strong used car market meant reserves were too high and could safely be cut, allowing the car divisions to show higher current period profits while increasing market share. They supported their case with spreadsheets in which recent trends toward higher used car prices and higher customer retention of off-lease vehicles were assumed to continue, that is, in which all feedbacks between the new and used markets were cut.

The dynamic model, in contrast, suggested that used car prices would soon decline as the large volume of leased and fleet vehicles sold in the last few years reentered the market. The team's analysis suggested some of the surge in used car prices was a temporary blip generated by the used car superstores as they bought heavily to stock their lots. When that period of inventory building ended, used car sales would slump while the flow of cars coming off lease continued. As used prices fell below the contracted residuals, more customers would terminate their leases early and fewer would exercise their option to buy, decreasing the retention fraction and boosting the supply of late model used cars still more. GM would have to take a significant charge against earnings for residual reconciliation, and new car sales would suffer as customers opted for late model off-lease vehicles.

Senior managers at NAO decided to focus on 36- to 48-month terms and eliminated 2-year leases. They also chose not to increase residual values and moved to full accrual of residual risk in calculating reserves. These decisions made subvention much more expensive to brand managers and raised lease payments.

2.2.4   Impact and Follow-up

In 1997 a flood of off-lease vehicles inundated the market. Used car prices fell significantly (Figure 2-5). The data show the aggregate for all used cars; the drop for late model vehicles was much steeper and was most severe in the segments in which leasing had grown most rapidly.

As prices fell, fewer customers opted to keep their cars. The Consumer Banking Association reported that the fraction of vehicles from expiring full-term leases returned to lessors jumped from 29% in 1997 to 39% in 1998. About three-quarters of all off-lease vehicles returned to lessors incurred losses; the average loss in 1998 was $1878 per vehicle, 220% more than the average for 1993.

GM's early action helped it avoid these losses, while other carmakers found themselves facing huge reconciliation charges. Profits at Ford Credit Corporation fell $410 million in 1997 compared to 1996, a 28% drop, largely due to losses on off-lease vehicles. At GMAC, net income from automotive financing operations fell only $36 million, less than 4%, and overall GMAC profits rose more than 6%.

In 1997 several carmakers, including Ford and Nissan USA, attempted to prop up wholesale prices for their cars by paying dealers to keep off-lease cars instead of returning them to the manufacturer for sale at auction. Ford paid dealers $700 to $6000 (depending on the model) for each 2-year old off-lease vehicle the dealer agreed to keep, dipping into its residual reserves for the first time to do so. This policy reduced the number of 2-year-old cars sold at auction, but of course, since retention of these cars added to dealer inventories, the number of these cars dealers bought at auction fell by the same amount, so wholesale prices continued to slide.

In 1998 GE Capital dropped its partnership with Chrysler to finance leases because, as *Automotive News* (24 August, p. 1) reported,

FIGURE 2-5
Used car prices,
1989–1999

Index shows the used car and truck component of the US Consumer Price Index, seasonally adjusted.

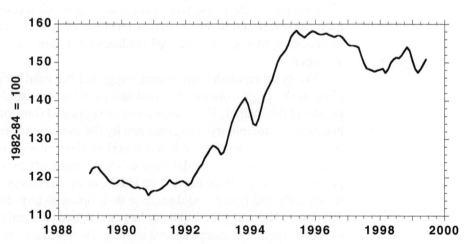

Source: US Bureau of Labor Statistics, series CUSR000SETA02.

GE Capital Auto Financial Services got burned on residual-value losses in 1997. Much of that was due to off-lease products from Chrysler . . . GE Capital cited residual losses as one reason for the decline in operating profits for Consumer Services, the GE unit that includes Auto Financial Services. Profits fell from $1.3 billion in 1996 to $563 million [in 1997].

In 1998 net income at Ford Credit rose $53 million over the depressed level of 1997 but remained 25% below the net for 1996.[4] GMAC's net on auto financing rose $74 million over 1997, a rise of 4% over 1996, and total GMAC profit for 1998 rose $181 million over 1996, a gain of 15%. In 1998 Ford and other carmakers belatedly followed GM's lead and began to move away from short-term leasing.

Since 1996 the leasing model has been updated several times, disaggregated further to separate the car and light truck segments, and used to examine issues such as sales of fleet vehicles. The model is now used on an ongoing basis by NAO's Portfolio Pricing Team, the group responsible for review and approval of all pricing and incentive programs in North America.

Pudar, now Director of the DSC (renamed the Strategy Support Center [SSC]), reports that the SSC continues to apply system dynamics, in combination with other analytic methods, to a wide range of issues, from negotiating joint ventures with foreign governments to designing business plans for new products, services, and business units.

2.3 ON TIME AND UNDER BUDGET: THE DYNAMICS OF PROJECT MANAGEMENT[5]

In 1970, Ingalls Shipbuilding of Pascagoula, Mississippi, won a major contract to build a fleet of 30 new destroyers for the US Navy. Combined with its 1969 contract for 9 LHAs (an amphibious assault/aircraft carrier), Ingalls found itself in the happy position of landing two of the largest shipbuilding programs in the world and looked forward to healthy sales and profits for years to come. By the mid-1970s, however, Ingalls was in deep trouble, facing cost overruns projected to exceed $500 million. With annual sales in the mid-1970s of $500–800 million, the overrun threatened to sink Ingalls, and its parent Litton Industries, altogether. Adjusted for inflation the overrun would exceed $1.5 billion in 1999 dollars.

Both contracts were awarded as total package procurement projects with a firm fixed-price contract structure in which Ingalls "was provided only with the performance specifications, and was thereafter solely responsible for all system design, detailed design, materials procurement, planning, testing, and construction" (Cooper 1980, p. 22).

Both programs involved innovative and technically sophisticated new designs. The DD class multimission destroyers were twice as large as earlier "tin cans." The

---

[4]Excluding one-time income from asset sales.

[5]This section is based on Cooper (1980) and personal communication with Ken Cooper (president, Pugh–Roberts Associates), Rich Goldbach (formerly with Ingalls/Litton Industries and currently president, Metro Machine Corporation), and many others at Pugh–Roberts Associates. I'm grateful for their help.

LHA was also an entirely new design. More than 20 stories high and three football fields long, each LHA carries a complement of 2000 battle-ready Marines and 200 combat vehicles that can be deployed by landing craft and several dozen helicopters. The DD and LHA contracts required a massive mobilization of Ingalls' resources. Already one of the largest shipyards in the world, Ingalls doubled its workforce to more than 20,000. During this time there were shortages of some skilled trades and critical materials. Ingalls also had to create new organizational structures to manage the two programs.

Large-scale projects are among the most important and consistently mismanaged endeavors in modern society. Large-scale projects include the design and construction of civil works and infrastructure (e.g., bridges, tunnels, power plants, and telecommunications networks), military systems (e.g., aircraft, ships, and weapons systems), and new products in every industry (e.g., software, automobiles, semiconductor chip design, and wafer fab construction).

Projects of all types routinely experience cost overruns, delays, and quality problems. Cooper and Mullen (1993) examined a sample of large civilian and military projects (averaging 130,000 person-hours of planned work over about a year for the civilian projects and 170,000 person-hours of planned work over more than 2 years for the military projects). They found commercial projects cost 140% and took 190% as long as originally scheduled, while defense projects cost 310% of the original estimates and took 460% as long to complete.

Delays, cost overruns, and quality problems in commercial new product development can kill a company, particularly in high-velocity industries such as software and high technology. Overruns and delays in civil works and military projects can affect the economic vitality of a region and the ability of a nation to defend itself.

2.3.1   The Claim

The Navy and Ingalls disagreed sharply over the causes of the delays and cost overrun. Ingalls believed the majority of the cost overrun was caused by the actions of the Navy. As is common in large, lengthy projects, the technologies and systems to be used in the DD and LHA ships were not mature at the time the contracts were awarded. Technologies for navigation, intelligence, communications, and weapons systems, for example, were advancing rapidly, and the Navy naturally sought to incorporate the most up-to-date systems in the ships. Rich Goldbach, then a senior manager at Ingalls and one of the key participants in the claim, commented that "Ingalls was convinced that the government interfered with the design for the LHA from the start by micro-managing the design process." As high-level design, detailed design, and even construction proceeded, Ingalls received many thousands of design changes from the Navy. Ingalls believed that much of the overrun was caused by the imposition of these design changes. After the Navy repeatedly refused to compensate Ingalls for these costs, Ingalls brought a claim against the Navy to recover the $500 million in losses it expected.

Suing your customers is always tricky. In the case of Ingalls it was particularly delicate. Ingalls brought the claim early, while the two programs still had many years to run. Ingalls had to continue to manage the two programs and maintain a good working relationship with the Navy while simultaneously pursuing the claim. Further, since commercial shipbuilding was in decline in the US, the Navy was Ingalls' most important customer and would be for the indefinite future.[6]

The Navy conceded that it had generated the design changes but argued that their impact was limited to the direct cost of reissuing the specifications and reworking the affected engineering drawings. The total cost of these direct impacts was a small fraction of the total claim. Ingalls countered that a design change could create much larger costs, for example, by altering the sequence of tasks and requiring overtime and unscheduled hiring that interfered with other phases of the work, diluted experience, and reduced productivity even in work phases not directly affected by change orders. Ingalls believed such ripple effects could multiply the direct impact of a change notice many times, leading to significant overall "delay and disruption."

The Navy countered that the supposed delay and disruption were actually the result of contractor mismanagement or deliberate underbidding to win the contract. Disputes over the delay and disruption component of prior claims throughout the defense industry often dragged out over many years. The Navy had never paid a significant delay and disruption claim.

2.3.2   Initial Model Development

Ingalls spent several years pursuing the claim, but traditional project management tools did not provide a means to quantify the ripple effects. Ingalls turned to system dynamics to quantify the delay and disruption created by Navy design changes. The model, developed by Pugh–Roberts Associates of Cambridge, Massachusetts, simulated all phases of the DD and LHA projects, from the award of the contract to the delivery of the last ship, then 5 years in the future.

The model ultimately contained many thousands of equations, a very large model indeed (especially considering the state of computer technology at the time). It began, however, as a much smaller model designed to illuminate the basic feedbacks that might be responsible for ripple effects. The modeling team worked closely with Ingalls' claim management organization, including managers from all major phases of each program and key attorneys. Lead modeler Ken Cooper described the process this way (1980, pp. 26-27):

> The Ingalls project team guided and reviewed the decision of what elements to include in the model, and with what measures and in what detail to include them . . . [D]ozens of individuals in all stages of shipbuilding, from workers through vice presidents, were interviewed. They offered qualitative and quantitative observations on ship design and construction. As the design of the model began to gel, the numerical data requirements were clarified; a massive data collection effort, in concert with other elements of the claim, was undertaken. These data and information provided enough material to assemble a preliminary mathematical model of a single work phase. The equations, parameters, and detailed output were reviewed by the project team, and several model modifications made.

---

[6]Due in part to the problems encountered in the program, the number of LHAs utlimately built was cut to 5. LHA5, the USS Peleliu, was completed in mid 1980, as was the last DD class destroyer, USS Fletcher.

2.3.3   Dynamic Hypothesis

A full description of the feedback structure of the model is beyond the scope of this discussion; this section provides only a few illustrations of the type of ripple effects the model addressed.

Figure 2-6 shows a highly simplified stock and flow structure for the flow of work within a single project phase. The tasks could be high-level systems design tasks, preparation of detailed engineering drawings, or construction of a vessel. The rectangles and valves represent the stock and flow structure of the system.[7] The stocks represent the accumulations of work in different categories; the valves represent the flow of tasks through the system. Initially all tasks are in the stock of Work to be Done. Completing a task requires resources such as a productive labor force with appropriate skills; the number and productivity of the labor force vary over time as project conditions change. Tasks can be done correctly or incorrectly, depending on the quality of the work. Tasks done correctly add to the stock of Work Really Done while tasks containing errors of various types add to the stock of Undiscovered Rework. Work quality is often quite low, as new-product development and large-scale projects usually involve new technologies, materials, and systems and often involve unique new circumstances. Cooper and Mullen (1993)

FIGURE 2-6
Stock and flow structure of a project phase

Rectangles represent the stock of tasks, straight lines and valves represent flows of tasks between categories (chapter 6). Quality is the fraction of tasks done correctly. The diagram is highly simplified and omits several task categories and flows included in the full model.

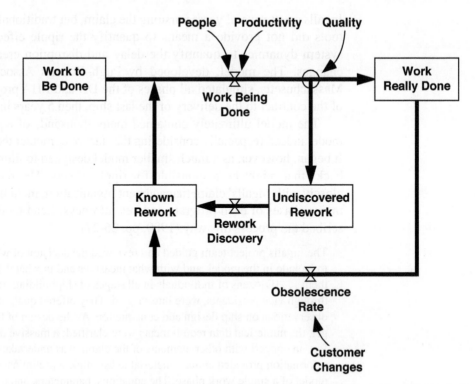

Source: Adapted from a diagram developed by Pugh–Roberts Associates, Cambridge, MA. Used with permission.

---

[7]Mathematically, each stock is the integral of the flows in less the flows out. Stocks and flows are discussed in chapters 6 and 7.

found the average fraction of work done correctly the first time in their sample to be 68% for commercial projects and just 34% for defense projects.

Uncovering errors takes time and resources. Often, errors are only detected by a downstream phase, as when a design flaw is discovered during the construction phase. Tasks in the stock of undiscovered rework are therefore perceived to be complete and are treated as done by the organization. Discovery of errors by quality assurance, testing, or a downstream phase moves the imperfectly done tasks to the stock of Known Rework. Cooper and Mullen (1993) found average rework discovery delays of about 9 months for both civil and military projects, a significant fraction of scheduled project duration.

Changes in customer specifications have effects similar to the discovery of errors. Specification changes make some work previously done correctly obsolete, moving those tasks from the stock of Work Really Done to the stock of Known Rework. The affected phase must recall work it previously released to other phases and upon which those downstream phases have based their own work. The organization must then increase the resources and attention devoted to rework, slowing completion of remaining basework tasks and potentially disrupting the entire project.[8]

Obviously customer changes that make completed design work obsolete are costly because the affected tasks must be reworked; these are the direct impacts of changes the Navy was willing to pay for. But the indirect effects can be many times larger. Figure 2-7 shows a few of the feedbacks that explain how the indirect effects of customer changes could be amplified.

As a project falls behind contractors have only a few choices. They can put the existing workforce on overtime, thus increasing the effective number of people working on the project. This negative or balancing feedback is the intended effect of overtime and is shown in the diagram by solid lines. However, excessive or extended overtime causes fatigue and burnout. Productivity and quality fall, reducing progress and increasing the stock of undiscovered rework. Burnout also leads to absenteeism and attrition as employees request transfers or quit, reducing the number of people on the project. These unintended effects, shown as dashed lines, form positive (self-reinforcing) feedbacks that act as vicious cycles to undercut the progress-enhancing effect of overtime. To avoid the side effects of overtime more people can be hired (another balancing loop). But rapid hiring dilutes the experience base of the employees. If the pool of qualified workers in the region is small relative to hiring needs, accelerated hiring lowers the average quality of available candidates. Recruiting standards often erode so vacancies can be filled quickly. All these effects lower productivity and quality and slow progress even as management seeks to boost headcount and speed progress.

---

[8]Most large military and civilian projects specify deadlines for delivery. Failure to meet the deadline leads to penalties, known as liquidated damages (LDs), for every day the project is late; LDs can rapidly mount to many millions. In disputes such as discussed here the LDs form the primary basis for the customer's counterclaim against the contractor. In several cases for which system dynamics models have been used the difference between the contractor delay and disruption claim and the customer's counterclaim was several billion dollars. Even when LDs do not apply, as for in-house commercial product development projects, every day the project is late erodes the competitiveness of the product and the sales and profits it can generate.

FIGURE 2-7   Side effects of corrective measures lead to vicious cycles

As customer changes cause a project to fall behind, management can accelerate the
schedule, use overtime, and hire more people, forming negative feedbacks designed
to get the project back on track (solid lines). However, each of these negative loops triggers side effects that undercut the intended effects, forming vicious cycles (positive feedbacks, shown by the dashed lines).

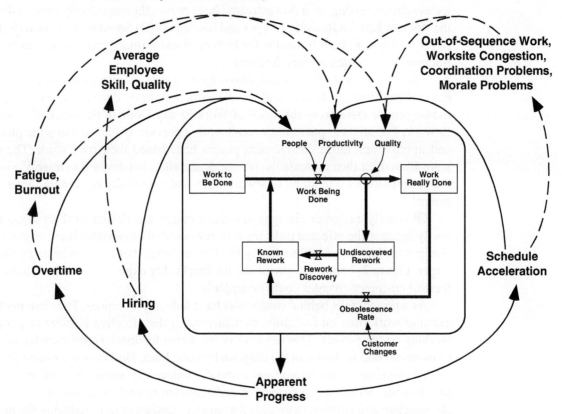

Source: Adapted from a diagram developed by Pugh–Roberts Associates, Cambridge, MA. Used with permission.

As a project falls behind schedule management often pressures employees to
work harder and compresses the schedule by overlapping activities that should be
done in sequence. Apparent productivity rises, but there are also unanticipated side
effects. Schedule compression forces people to do work out of sequence, meaning
important information or materials from upstream phases are not available.
Detailed design may start before system design is mature and stable. Prototype
builds may begin before component specifications are complete.[9] Schedule compression also leads to work site congestion, be it overloaded CAD/CAM facilities
in engineering or a crowded construction site. Managers and supervisors find their

---

[9]Many organizations today have adopted concurrent engineering practices designed to shorten
development cycle times. Successful deployment of concurrent engineering is difficult and even in
highly concurrent programs the degree of overlap between different phases can be too aggressive,
leading to excessive rework. See Ford and Sterman (1998a) and (1998b) for system dynamics
models of concurrent engineering, with applications to semiconductor design. See also section 14.5.

time is increasingly consumed by meetings to work out conflicts arising from the accelerated schedule and ad hoc, last-minute coordination of out-of-sequence activities. Stress from work pressure, increased fire fighting, and constant changes in schedules can lead to morale problems that cut productivity and quality and increase absenteeism and attrition. These effects are further multiplied by the rework cycle. Lower quality means more tasks contain errors. Because many errors are not discovered immediately, subsequent work begins using designs, materials, and information that appear to be correct at the time but are later recalled for rework.

Thus customer changes can disrupt and delay upstream activities such as system design. These phases must then recall some previously released work, so delays and quality problems cascade to downstream phases such as detailed design, materials procurement, and construction. The downstream phases must then redo much of their job, often at great expense (particularly when construction has already begun). To the extent different projects such as the DD and LHA programs share resources such as work sites, workers, support infrastructure, and management, problems in one can spill over to another.

The diagrams above are highly simplified, and many other important feedbacks captured in the full model are omitted (how many other such effects can you identify from your own experience?). But they illustrate how apparently small changes in customer specifications can snowball into much larger delay and disruption despite management's best efforts to get the project back on track. The model augmented traditional project analysis through the explicit recognition of the rework cycle, variable staff productivity and quality, and the bane of most development projects—undiscovered rework. Conventionally, any indirect effects were viewed as a small additional percentage over the direct costs. Explicit recognition of the feedback structure described here helped explain how the indirect effects of customer changes could be many times larger than the direct effects.

2.3.4 The Modeling Process

The modeling team assembled the full model by replicating the generic project phase module to represent each phase for each ship in each program. The major activities (system design, detailed design, procurement, construction, etc.) were disaggregated further where necessary; for example, construction was divided into several major activities (e.g., hull, piping, electrical, etc.) and the construction workforce was disaggregated by major crafts (e.g., steelworkers, electricians, etc.). Construction progress for each ship was represented separately. Each instance of the generic phase module was calibrated to the particular activity it represented. The individual activities, phases, and programs were linked by additional structure representing overall program management, progress monitoring, scheduling, hiring, resource allocation, and so on.

A model of this scope could never be built, calibrated, maintained, or understood if such a modular architecture were not used. To represent such a diverse array of activities the generic module had to be extremely robust. Considerable effort went into extreme conditions tests to ensure that the model behaved appropriately under any conceivable combination of inputs or conditions (see chapter 21). The team worked to ensure the model was consistent with all available information, including the qualitative assessments gleaned from interviews and observations in the field, not only the numerical data.

Early on the team compared the output of the model to the history of the projects to date. The purpose of the comparison to historical behavior was not to prove to Ingalls that the model was right, but rather to identify areas where the model required improvement. These comparisons sometimes identified omissions and problems, leading to revisions in model structure and parameters. Other times, discrepancies between model and data suggested the data were inconsistent or incomplete, leading to additional data collection, interviews, and refinement of the values and justification for parameters. This process led to three major and many minor iterations in the model.

The model ultimately replicated the historical performance of the projects quite well. But, as discussed in chapter 21, it is quite easy to fit a model to a set of data. It is also necessary that the model replicate the data for the right reasons, reasons the modelers and Ingalls' management understand and can explain in plain language. While particularly important in the adversarial setting of a large lawsuit, these are important in any modeling project. Ultimately the clients for any modeling project will take action only to the extent their mental models have changed. In turn, the clients' mental models are unlikely to change unless they have confidence in the integrity and appropriateness of the formal model. Developing that confidence requires a modeling process that gives the clients the opportunity to delve as deeply into the details as they want, to question any assumption, and to challenge any result. Opening the model to review by the clients is also essential for the modelers to ensure it addresses the issues the client cares most deeply about and to generate the best model for that purpose.

To uncover model flaws and create opportunities for the Ingalls team to challenge the model the modeling team used several other procedures. Cooper (1980, p. 27) explains:

> First, we established at the outset explicit limits of reasonableness for each numerical parameter in the model; these would not be violated in order to achieve a more "accurate" simulation. Further, the numerical parameters in different sections of the model were required to be consistent with one another in terms of relative magnitude. These guidelines . . . were never violated. The model was also subjected to a series of "shock tests" to assess robustness in responding as the company would to radically different circumstances. Finally, several different plausible combinations of equations and parameters were tested to explore "alternative models" that might accurately represent Ingalls operations.

As time passed the model-generated projections for schedule and costs turned out to be quite close to what actually happened, further boosting confidence in the ability of the model to capture the underlying structure of the projects.

The modeling team assessed the systemwide effects of the Navy's design changes by comparing two simulations. The "as-built" case was the historical simulation including all the Navy design changes; this was compared to the "would have" case in which the design changes were removed. The difference in total costs and completion times represented the cumulative impact of the design changes. Sensitivity analysis then placed confidence bounds around the estimated cost of the delay and disruption.

The model also allowed Ingalls to estimate the role of its own management decisions in the overrun. Simulations of alternative policies showed how much lower project costs and duration might have been if Ingalls had managed the project more effectively. The ability to quantify the contribution of customer interference and contractor mismanagement to the delays and cost overrun was a critical part of the process. Goldbach (personal communication, 1999) described the dispute resolution process prior to the development of the system dynamics model as

> just a bunch of finger-pointing. A contractor would say "Here's what the government did wrong" and blame all their problems on that. Then the government would send the GAO [General Accounting Office] in to find all the things the contractor did wrong. It went nowhere.
>
> The problem was that with the [project management] technologies available at the time there was no way to separate the impact of government and contractor problems or examine the synergy between them. In the end we had to have the ability to say "here are the things the contractor didn't do well and here are the things the government didn't do well, and here's how much each contributed to costs and time."

The adversarial setting of a large dispute accentuates the need for a robust, well-understood model whose parameters and assumptions can be justified with independent data. As part of the discovery process in the lawsuit Ingalls had to turn the model, documentation, analysis, and supporting data over to the Navy, which hired its own experts to try to debunk it. A common criticism of such models, and one used by the Navy, is that the parameters and assumptions are "cooked" to achieve a preselected outcome. "Garbage in, garbage out," they would say, and argued that the model was merely a complicated ruse designed to impress the court.

The Navy's outside experts examined and criticized the model. After they delivered their reports, the modeling team, along with Ingalls management and their attorneys, Navy officials, the government's attorneys, and the Navy's outside experts met for several days in a large conference room to discuss the critique. Each issue was discussed in detail, from high-level issues of modeling methodology and model architecture to specific equations and parameters. Ingalls and the modeling team then had a chance to respond. They revised the model to address the criticisms leveled by the Navy's experts. In the next round of meetings, they showed the Navy team how they had modified the model to incorporate the changes the Navy's experts wanted. Repeating the comparison of the as-built to would have cases, the modeling team found that the fraction of the overrun and delay caused by the Navy's design changes had actually increased.[10]

The Navy clearly expected that incorporating the critiques and parameter estimates of its experts into the model would show more of the overrun was due to contractor mismanagement. The counterintuitive result that the claim value

---

[10]Given the technology of the time (mainframe computers operating with time-sharing, teletype printers, and 100 baud acoustic coupler modems) it was not feasible to run the model live in the meetings. The model developers painfully recall overnight sessions running the model on the largest computer then available. Today it is possible to bring the model to such meetings on a laptop and make many changes in assumptions on the spot, slashing the cycle time for experimentation and greatly increasing client involvement.

increased demonstrated to all that it is actually quite difficult to engineer a model to generate a preselected result. Goldbach commented, "For the first time the Navy saw that Ingalls had a credible case." Intensive negotiations then began at the highest levels of Litton and the Navy. In June 1978 the parties settled out of court. Ingalls received $447 million.

Thus the clients for the modeling work were not only Ingalls' management and attorneys but also the court and the Navy. It may seem counterintuitive to include the opposing side among the client group for a model used in a lawsuit. And indeed the Navy attempted to discredit the model and have it excluded from the proceedings. However, to the extent the model became the focus, even through the critique of the Navy experts, the structures in the model and the dynamics they generated started to become the common framework for discussion of the claim by all parties. The process of changing mental models was well underway. This process has since been observed in many other conflicts (see, e.g., Weil and Etherton 1990, Reichelt and Sterman 1990). Experience shows that the better the oppositions' understanding of the model, the more likely it will be influential in the resolution of the dispute.

Though the setting here was a lawsuit, the process applies to any modeling project. Even when the clients for the work are all from the same management team, there will always be different sides and factions, proponents and opponents of each policy. Only the intensive involvement of the clients in the modeling process can create the understanding of the issues needed to change entrenched mental models and lead to consensus for action.

2.3.5   Continuing Impact

The system dynamics model was the sole technical basis for the delay and disruption component of Ingalls' claim against the Navy. Estimates from the attorneys and Ingalls management "place the model's dollar contribution to the settlement between $170–350 million" (Cooper 1980, pp. 28). But these sums, large as they are, underestimate the benefits of the modeling process. The lawsuit itself can be viewed as a large project that generated its own ripple effects. By achieving a settlement a little over 2 years after beginning the modeling process (a very short interval in such large disputes),

> The direct dollar costs of continuing the claim effort were avoided [legal fees and court costs]. Even more significant, however, was the vast amount of managerial and professional time and talent (an entire "claim organization" of over 100 Ingalls personnel) that would have continued to be spent on something other than ship design and construction . . . Above all, the elimination of the adversary relationship between Ingalls and its best customer was a milestone achievement (Cooper 1980, p. 28).

Since this groundbreaking work Pugh–Roberts and other firms have gone on to apply system dynamics to disputes totaling many billions of dollars. These range from other military and commercial shipbuilding projects to aerospace and weapons systems, power plants, civil works such as the cross-channel tunnel, and software projects. In most cases contractors use the models in actions against their customers. In each case the defendants have sought to debunk the models and exclude them from the allowable expert testimony but each time the models have been allowed and have contributed to favorable settlements.

While the dollar value of these actions is impressive and of undoubted benefit to the plaintiffs, the damage (the cost overrun) has already been done, and the dispute is only over who pays. The real leverage lies in using these models proactively so overruns and delays are avoided in the first place. Since the first Ingalls model, many organizations have gone on to apply similar models to the management of large-scale projects in a wide range of industries (for examples see sections 6.3.4 and 14.5).[11] Ingalls itself has used descendants of that first model to help manage virtually every program since the LHA and DD. The benefits of such proactive modeling are harder to quantify but likely outweigh the value of dispute settlements many times.

As one illustration, Rich Goldbach left Ingalls in the late 1970s to head up Metro Machine, a shipyard in Norfolk, Virginia. Then small and struggling, Metro today is a highly successful yard specializing in repair and refitting work for the Navy with about 700 employees and sales of about $90 million/year. Goldbach introduced a wide range of innovative management practices including employee involvement. The firm is 100% employee owned, with universal participation in the employee stock ownership plan. Metro has won several awards for the high quality of their work, including National Small Business Prime Contractor of the Year and the US Navy AEGIS Excellence Award "for superior performance in quality, reliability, delivery and cost"—the first ever given to a repair yard.

Models continue to play an important role. Goldbach commissioned the development of a simulation model to project the financial consequences of various decisions for up to 10 years. Metro uses the model to assess acquisitions, capital investment decisions, new ventures, and all aspects of bidding for jobs.

> We built the model to a spec[ification] I provided based on what I learned from the Ingalls model. The model helps the government understand our bids better. It lets the DCAA [Defense Contract Audit Agency, a Department of Defense agency that audits defense contractor bids and assesses their ability to do the work] look at alternative scenarios. We use the model interactively with them. There is an on-site DCAA auditor who knows the model. She can ask us to run any set of assumptions, and we usually get the answer back in an hour (Goldbach, personal communication, 1999).

The financial simulation has been very effective, but far more important, Goldbach says, are the lessons he learned about the challenges of managing complex systems:

> For the [shipbuilding] industry I thought I was a pretty sophisticated manager, but it changed my whole perspective. I never had the ability I think I got from working with system dynamics to ask "how will this decision ripple out?" I got to the point that I had the mental self-discipline to fight my impulses and not just do the macho thing when there's a problem. The playing field changes while you're playing the

---

[11]See also Abdel-Hamid and Madnick (1989a–c, 1990, 1991); Cooper (1993a–c, 1994); Cooper and Mullen (1993); Ford and Sterman (1998a–b); Homer et al. (1993); Weil and Etherton (1990); and Yourdon (1993).

game. Now I ask how customers, employees, suppliers and so on will react to what we might do. Sometimes I get it right and sometimes I don't.

It permeates every aspect of my thinking. I'm a different person than I was before.

2.4   PLAYING THE MAINTENANCE GAME[12]

In 1991, Winston Ledet, then a manager in Gulf Coast Regional Manufacturing Services at Du Pont, reflected on the results of an in-house benchmarking study documenting a large gap between Du Pont's maintenance record and those of the best-practice companies in the global chemicals industry.

The benchmarking study revealed an apparent paradox: Du Pont spent more on maintenance than industry leaders but got less for it. Du Pont had the highest number of maintenance employees per dollar of plant value yet its mechanics worked more overtime. Spare parts inventories were excessive yet the plants relied heavily on costly expedited procurement of critical components. Most disturbing, Du Pont spent 10–30% more on maintenance per dollar of plant value than the industry leaders, while at the same time overall plant uptime was some 10–15% lower.

Many people found the results of the benchmarking study to be counterintuitive. Their mental models suggested that equipment quality should suffer and uptime should be low in a company that spends little on maintenance, while spending more on maintenance should yield high-quality equipment and high uptime. How could Du Pont be spending more and getting less?

Many people blamed the problem on the difficult competitive environment. The chemicals industry is mature and intensely competitive. Because there is little product differentiation for bulk (commodity) feedstocks, chemical manufacturers compete on other dimensions, mostly cost and delivery reliability. Since the early 1970s the industry was hit by one crisis after another: Two severe energy crises wreaked havoc with input and operating costs. Always cyclical, the three worst recessions since the Great Depression caused widespread excess capacity. New competitors from the Pacific rim and the oil-rich nations of the Middle East entered the market. Environmental concerns and regulations were growing.

Ledet knew all this; he had lived through it during his 25 years with Du Pont. But blaming outside forces for the problems, while psychologically safe, didn't provide any leverage to improve. Ledet felt that the explanation of the paradox lay not in the outside pressures the company had faced during two turbulent decades but in its response to those pressures.

Ledet and his team needed a way to explore the ways in which different parts of the maintenance system interacted, explain why past attempts to improve had failed, and assist in the design of new policies. And they needed to explain these complex dynamics to the experienced plant operations and maintenance people who had to take action.

---

[12]I'm indebted to Winston P. Ledet and Winston J. Ledet (principals, The Manufacturing Game), Paul Monus (BP Chemicals), and Mark Paich (Colorado College) for permission to present their work and their assistance in the preparation of the material. Thanks also to Tony Cardella, Mark Downing, Vince Flynn, and the rest of the Du Pont team.

Ledet and his team began the development of a simulation model to capture the systemwide, dynamic benefits and costs of different maintenance initiatives. They developed the model with the assistance of an experienced modeler, Mark Paich. The model was developed interactively, with the participation of Ledet and other key team members. The role of the expert modeler was more of a coach and facilitator, and the modeling process involved extensive hands-on workshops in which the model was discussed, tested, and changed in real time as members of the modeling team identified problems or areas needing improvement.

Du Pont, like most large firms, already used a number of maintenance planning tools. These tools tend to focus on the detail complexity of the maintenance challenge, for example, databases to track the maintenance history of each individual piece of equipment, statistical models to optimize maintenance schedules, scheduling systems to assign mechanics to planned and reactive work, and so on. These tools are important for the day-to-day management of large plants but they don't capture the dynamic complexity of the maintenance system. Where the detailed planning and scheduling models tracked each pump and motor in the plant separately, the dynamic model divided all equipment into just three categories: operable, broken down, or taken down for planned maintenance. But where the existing models assumed failure rates and repair costs and durations were exogenous, the dynamic model treated these factors endogenously. It encompassed technical issues such as equipment characteristics; logistical issues such as spare parts availability, maintenance scheduling, and mechanic assignments; human resources issues such as mechanic skill, training, and motivation; and financial issues including maintenance budgets, resource allocation, and overall plant performance. The system dynamics model was a complement to, and not a replacement for, existing planning and scheduling tools.

2.4.1 Dynamic Hypothesis

Using the model as a laboratory to design and test different policies, the team gradually developed an appreciation for the dynamic complexity of the maintenance system. The dynamic hypothesis they developed explained the paradox that Du Pont spent more on maintenance and got less for it in terms of uptime and equipment reliability.

The modeling process led to several important conceptual shifts in the way they viewed maintenance. Prior to the modeling work maintenance was largely seen as a process of defect correction (repair of failed equipment) and the maintenance function was viewed as a cost to be minimized. The first conceptual shift was to change the focus from defect correction to defect prevention and defect elimination. The model therefore centered on the physics of breakdowns rather than the cost minimization mentality that prevailed throughout the organization. Equipment fails when a sufficient number of latent defects accumulate in it. Latent defects are any problem that might ultimately cause a failure. They include leaky oil seals in pumps, dirty equipment that causes bearing wear, pump and motor shafts that are out of true and cause vibration, poorly calibrated instrumentation, and so on. A pump with a leaky oil seal or dirty bearings can still run but will eventually fail unless these latent defects are eliminated.

The total number of latent defects in a plant's equipment is a stock (Figure 2-8). Defects are created by operations (normal wear and tear) and by collateral damage arising from breakdowns (when the oil leaks out of the pump bearing and the bearing seizes, the shaft may be bent, the motor may overheat, and the vibration may break couplings and pipes, introducing new problems). More subtly, maintenance activity can create new defects, through mechanic errors or the use of poor quality replacement parts. The lower the intrinsic design quality of the equipment, the more defects these activities create.

The stock of defects is drained by two flows: reactive maintenance (repair of failed equipment) and planned maintenance (proactive repair of operable equipment).[13] Each of these activities forms a balancing feedback loop. As defects accumulate, the chance of a breakdown increases. Breakdowns lead to more reactive

FIGURE 2-8   Defect creation and elimination

The diagram is simplified. In the full model equipment was divided into operable, broken down, and taken down for planned maintenance, with an associated stock of latent defects for each category.

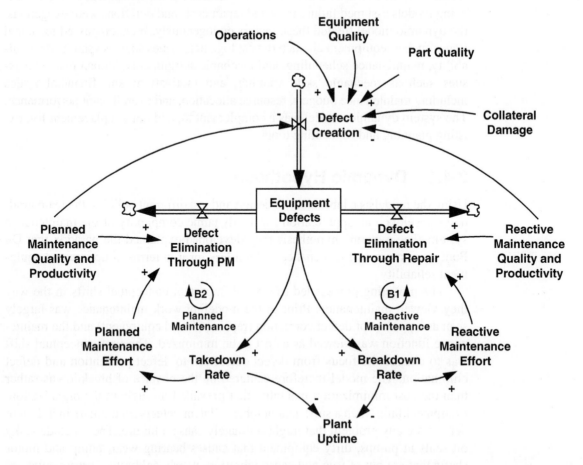

<hr />

[13]Planned maintenance includes preventive (time-based) work, e.g., replace worn parts on pumps every n months, and predictive (condition-based) work, e.g., replace worn parts on a pump if vibration exceeds a certain tolerance.

maintenance, and, after repair, the equipment is returned to service and the stock of defects is reduced (the Reactive Maintenance loop B1). Similarly, scheduled maintenance or equipment monitoring may reveal the presence of latent defects (a vibrating pump, an oil leak). The equipment is then taken out of service and the defects are corrected before a breakdown occurs (the Planned Maintenance loop B2).

Obviously breakdowns reduce plant uptime. In addition, most planned maintenance activity also reduces uptime since planned maintenance frequently requires operable equipment be taken out of service so the needed work can be done. Figure 2-8 shows only the most basic physics of defect accumulation. The two negative feedbacks regulating the stock of defects appear to be symmetrical: Defects can be eliminated either by planned maintenance or repair of failed equipment. The full system is more complex, however, and includes a number of positive, self-reinforcing feedbacks (Figure 2-9).

FIGURE 2-9 Positive feedbacks undercutting planned maintenance

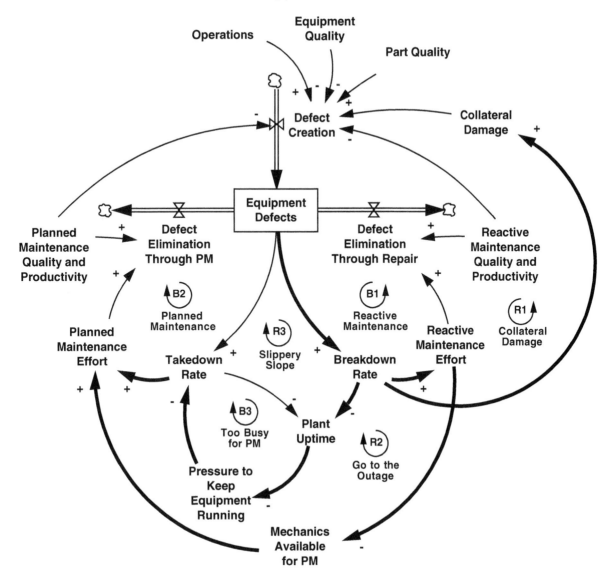

Consider the impact of the first oil crisis in late 1973. Input and operating costs skyrocketed. But the severe recession that began in 1974 meant chemical producers could not pass the entire cost increase on to consumers. Under intense financial pressure, all plants and functions had to cut costs. If maintenance departments are asked to cut expenses nearly all of the cut has to come from activities such as planning and preventive maintenance: When critical equipment breaks down, it must be fixed. At the same time, financial pressure leads to other actions (e.g., postponing replacement of older, less reliable equipment or running equipment longer and more aggressively than original design specifications indicate), which increase the maintenance workload. With resources for planned maintenance diminishing and maintenance needs increasing, the stock of defects grows. Breakdowns increase. Breakdowns cause collateral damage, directly increasing the stock of defects further and leading to still more breakdowns in a vicious cycle (the positive loop R1). Because the total number of mechanics is limited, more breakdowns necessarily pull mechanics off planned work as management reassigns mechanics to repair work. But many mechanics also prefer repair work. A planned maintenance manager in one plant commented, "We've had several people who say they want to get involved in preventive work but when an outage comes and [they] have a chance to work 14–16 hours per week overtime they say 'to hell with this vibration [monitoring] stuff, I'm going to the outage area.'" With less planned work, breakdowns increase still more, forming the reinforcing Go to the Outage loop R2.

The rising breakdown rate means more critical equipment will be out of service awaiting repair. Plant uptime falls. Plant operators find it harder to meet demand. When a mechanic or maintenance supervisor requests that a certain piece of equipment be taken off line to correct latent defects, the harried line manager is likely to shout something like "I can barely meet demand as it is and you want me to take this line down? No way. If you maintenance people were doing your job, I wouldn't have so many down pumps in the first place. Now get out of here, I've got a plant to run." The balancing Too Busy for PM loop (B3) means operators are less willing to take working equipment down for planned maintenance when uptime is low. The side effect of that policy, however, is a further increase in defects and breakdowns and still lower uptime. The plant slowly slides down the slippery slope (reinforcing loop R3) into a trap of high breakdowns and low uptime, with nearly all maintenance resources devoted to crisis management, fire fighting, and repair work.

The positive feedbacks R1 to R3 operate fairly quickly but are not the only vicious cycles that can drag a plant into the trap of low reliability and high costs. The operational feedbacks in Figure 2-9 are embedded in a larger system shown in Figure 2-10.

A higher breakdown rate increases costs (due to overtime, the nonroutine and often hazardous nature of outages, the need to expedite parts procurement, collateral damage, etc.). The resulting pressure to cut costs leads to a reduction in the quality of parts, increasing the stock of equipment defects and leading to still more breakdowns and still higher costs (the Part Quality loop R4). Cost pressure also reduces investment in equipment upgrades and other design improvements, so breakdowns increase further (the Design Improvement loop R5). As costs rise training for maintenance workers is cut, particularly training in planned

FIGURE 2-10 Additional positive feedbacks leading to a reactive maintenance culture

The contents of the rounded rectangle represent the structure in Figure 2-9.

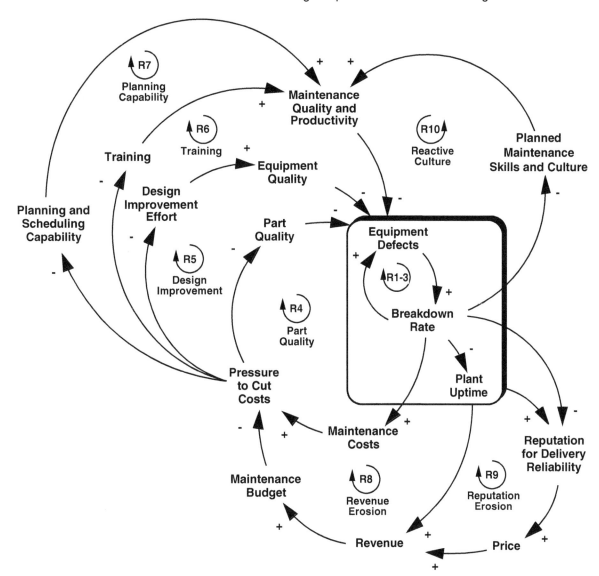

maintenance techniques (the Training loop R6). Cost pressure also forces the maintenance department to downsize. The first to go are the planners and schedulers—unlike mechanics, they don't actually fix anything, and with less and less planned maintenance going on there is less for them to do. Without advance planning, part kits, equipment histories, and engineering drawings for maintenance work are less available, lowering the quality of work still more (the Planning Capability loop R7).

A parallel set of self-reinforcing feedbacks operate to reduce the maintenance budget even as costs rise. Lower uptime directly constrains production and therefore revenue, forcing budget cuts throughout the organization. Worse, high breakdown rates and low uptime mean the plant is less able to meet its delivery commitments. As it develops a reputation for poor delivery reliability the price it can charge and volume of business it attracts decline, further eroding revenue and profit and forcing still more budget cuts. Cost pressure rises still further, accelerating the part quality, training, design improvement, and planning capability loops. These loops are summarized as the Revenue Erosion and Reputation Erosion loops (R8 and R9).

After years of cost pressure, Du Pont had developed a culture of reactive maintenance. Unreliable equipment and frequent breakdowns had become an accepted occurrence. Organizational norms and routines for writing up work orders, scheduling maintenance effort, and ordering parts had come to reflect a world of frequent breakdowns. Mechanics spent most of their time fighting fires. Mechanics who were scheduled for planned maintenance were routinely pulled off to do reactive work. Mechanics knew they could work overtime on a regular basis and considered overtime pay a part of their regular income. The knowledge that equipment was unreliable had even led to installation of backup pumps in many sites, embedding the low-reliability culture in the physical layout and capital costs of the plants. As the years passed the workforce increasingly consisted of people who had never experienced anything other than the reactive regime. For them, the equipment was intrinsically unreliable, low uptime was normal, and reactive maintenance was business as usual (the Reactive Culture loop R10).

As the model developed they calibrated it to represent a typical plant. In the early 1990s a typical Du Pont chemical plant was valued at $400 million and spent about 3–3.5% of its value annually on maintenance, or $12 to $14 million/year. The spare parts store stocked more than 60,000 parts. It employed about 90 maintenance mechanics who might complete as many as 25,000 work orders per year. Average uptime was 83.5%. Maintenance expenses accounted for 15–40% of direct production costs, depending on the process and product. The amount of money Du Pont spent companywide on maintenance in the late 1980s was about $1 billion/year, a significant fraction of net income.

Once the model was adequately calibrated to the historical data, the next step was to design high leverage policies to escape from the reactive regime. The team simulated the impact of different policies, including those that had been tried in the past and failed. Table 2-1 shows the results of selected simulations.

Optimizing the use of scheduling alone, within the traditional cost-minimization mindset, had only a modest impact. Through better scheduling the plant could still meet its traditional uptime of 83.5% with 10% fewer mechanics, generating savings of $350,000/year. Implementing a full suite of proactive maintenance policies, including better planning systems, parts, reliability engineering, and so on, allowed the plant to achieve the traditional uptime with only 61 mechanics, saving $1.2 million/year.

However, deploying the same suite of proactive policies without downsizing allowed uptime to rise above 93% and generated $9 million/year in additional profit. Why the difference? The cost-minimization approach means any improvement in productivity generated by the adoption of improved maintenance techniques is immediately harvested as headcount reduction. Resources for planned maintenance remain constrained. The organization continues to fight fires and

TABLE 2-1
Results from
selected policy
simulations

Cases 1 and 2:
Minimize
maintenance
costs subject to
uptime ≥ initial
uptime.
Case 3: Maximize
plant profit subject
to mechanic
headcount ≤
initial headcount.

Policy Mix	Head Count	Uptime	Change in Profit ($ million/year)
0. Typical plant under existing policies	91	83.5	0.00
1. Use scheduling to minimize maintenance costs	82	83.5	0.35
2. Minimize costs via full suite of proactive maintenance policies	61	83.5	1.20
3. Maximize plant profit via full suite of proactive maintenance policies	91	93.3	9.00

Source: Winston Ledet, Mark Paich, Tony Cardella, and Mark Downing (1991), "The Value of Integrating the CMLT Key Pursuits," Du Pont internal report.

focus on reactive maintenance but does so more efficiently. In contrast, implementing the new policies without downsizing frees up resources that can be reinvested in still more planned maintenance. As breakdowns fall, still more mechanics are released from fire fighting and outages to do even more planned work. Maintenance expenses drop, releasing resources that can be invested in training, parts quality, reliability engineering, planning and scheduling systems, and other activities that cut defects and breakdowns still more. Higher uptime yields more revenue and provides additional resources for still more improvement. For example, upgrading to a more durable type of pump seal improves reliability, allowing maintenance intervals to be lengthened and inventories of replacement seals to be cut.

All the positive loops that once acted as vicious cycles to drag reliability down become virtuous cycles, progressively and cumulatively reducing breakdowns and improving uptime. The result is a tremendous synergy, with the combined effect of the individual policies greatly exceeding the sum of their impacts when implemented individually.

The model also revealed an important insight about the transition path following implementation of the new policies. The simulation results in Table 2-1 show that proactive maintenance policies with reinvestment of the results ultimately lowers maintenance costs and boosts uptime. Immediately after implementation, however, maintenance costs increase and uptime falls. Why? It takes time for the planned work to cut the breakdown rate; in the short run the plant must bear the cost of both the repair work and the additional planned maintenance effort. Uptime falls because additional operable equipment must be taken off-line so planned maintenance can be performed. Only later, as the stock of latent defects starts to fall, does the breakdown rate drop. As it does, expenses fall and uptime rises. This worse-before-better behavior is quite common in complex systems. However, if managers do not understand why it occurs or how long it might last, they may interpret the short-run deterioration in performance as evidence that the policies don't work and then abandon them.

2.4.2   The Implementation Challenge

Ledet and his colleagues felt that the new perspectives they developed on the maintenance problem could improve the contribution of Du Pont's maintenance program to corporate profitability. Now their challenge was to implement the needed changes. The team wrote a white paper detailing the results of the modeling study and gave presentations throughout the organization. The result? Nothing happened. People would say, "We already know that planned maintenance is a good idea," "We tried those policies and they didn't work," or "Your model doesn't account for x."

Ledet realized that the client group for the project—the group of people whose behavior had to change for any results to be realized—was far broader than the management team responsible for maintenance. Nothing could happen without the cooperation and willing participation of huge numbers of line managers, equipment operators, and maintenance mechanics. The client group numbered in the thousands. Reflecting on their own learning process, modeling team members realized that their views had changed radically because they had participated in an iterative process of modeling. They had seen the model evolve, had challenged and questioned it, had seen their concerns addressed, and had gone through the process of working out the feedback structures that explained the dynamics of the system. Somehow they had to recreate that learning process throughout the plants, from top management to the lowest-grade mechanics.

It was obviously impossible for the thousands of people they had to reach to participate in modeling workshops or even to give them the model so they could work with it themselves. None had training in system dynamics or computer modeling. Line supervisors and maintenance mechanics are action oriented and have little patience for presentations with lots of charts and graphs.

Ledet was familiar with the Beer Distribution Game, a role-playing management flight simulator of a manufacturing supply chain developed by the MIT System Dynamics Group as an introduction to systems thinking.[14] Working with his son, Ledet converted the maintenance model into an interactive role-play simulation that they called the Manufacturing Game (see Ledet 1999). The game was embedded in a 2-day workshop or learning laboratory designed to be highly interactive, to put people at ease, and to create an environment for learning that addressed emotional as well as cognitive issues.

The game simulates a typical plant. There are three roles: operations manager, maintenance manager, and spare parts stores manager. The operations manager is charged with meeting demand and has equipment, represented by chips, to do so. As production proceeds, red markers representing latent defects are placed on the equipment chips. When enough red markers accumulate, the equipment breaks down and capacity falls. The maintenance manager must then allocate mechanics to repair the equipment and must go to the spare parts store to see if the needed

---

[14]The Beer Distribution Game is an enjoyable and effective introduction not only to supply chain management but also to the principles of systems thinking in general (see chapter 17; also Sterman 1989b, 1992 and Senge 1990 for descriptions, but not until after you have played the game).

parts (determined by a roll of the dice) are available. If the parts are in stock, the equipment is repaired. If not, the mechanics must wait until they are available or pay to have delivery expedited. Alternatively, the maintenance manager can schedule planned work, ordering the needed parts and allocating mechanics in advance. Planned maintenance can only be done, however, if the operations manager agrees to take operating equipment out of service. Each round the participants make decisions such as how much equipment to take down for planned maintenance, how to allocate mechanics and maintenance resources, and how many spare parts to order. Revenue and cost are recorded, along with production, uptime, inventories, and so on. While the game is highly simplified compared to real plants, and even compared to the original simulation model, it realistically captures the time delays, costs, and other parameters characterizing a plant.

Despite its many simplifications the game rapidly becomes in many ways a real plant, with real emotions and conflicts among players. Initialized with high breakdowns and low uptime, the maintenance manager's attempts to increase planned maintenance are often rebuffed by the operations manager, who faces intense pressure to meet demand, just as in the real world.

Teams who stick with the prevailing cost-minimization, reactive maintenance policies are able to keep costs low for a while. But as defects build up they find their uptime slowly sinking and costs gradually rising. Teams who do follow through with a planned maintenance strategy immediately find costs rising and uptime falling as equipment is taken off line for planned maintenance. Soon, however, costs begin to fall and uptime rises. By compressing time the game allows people to experience the worse-before-better dynamic in a few hours instead of a few months.

Two members of the implementation team at Du Pont's Washington Works complex in Parkersburg, West Virginia, described how they used the game to catalyze a broad-based improvement program:

> The team was initiated with a two-day learning lab . . . learning the concepts of defect elimination and experiencing the Manufacturing Game . . . The basic concepts are presented in different manners so that all learning modes are utilized—visual, auditory and kinesthetic. The material is presented in the form of lectures, skits and participative exercises in an off-site environment. Posters and music are used. The atmosphere is much different than routine plant meetings or training, to open up their thinking . . . Through interactive exercises, the team develops their personal aspirations for improving the area where they have chosen to work . . . [Then] they . . . develop an action plan to immediately start working.[15]

The game and learning laboratory proved popular throughout the company. But playing it once with a small group of managers wasn't enough. The team found that they had to run several workshops for a given plant before a critical mass of people emerged to lead action teams that put proactive maintenance policies into practice. Often the plant needed to develop its own capability to run the game and workshop so it could be done on demand by local people, with their site-specific

---

[15]Tewksbury, R., and R. Steward (1997) Improved Production Capability Program at Du Pont's Washington Works, Proceedings of the 1997 Society for Maintenance and Reliability annual conference.

experience and authority. Ledet's team thus had to develop a group of trained facilitators and a training process so that the quality of the workshop could be maintained as it spread into the plants. The demand for the workshop grew slowly at first, but as favorable word of mouth about the experience and results spread, more and more plants asked Ledet's group to run the program for them. The surge in demand stressed the number of skilled facilitators, which lagged behind. By the end of 1992 some 1200 people had participated in the workshop and more than 50 facilitators had been certified.

2.4.3　Results

By 1994 a number of plants throughout the Gulf Coast region had adopted the learning lab and associated policies. Figure 2-11 shows the direct maintenance cost savings for a particular plant after implementation of the program. Just as seen in the model and the game, the first effect of the new policies is an increase in costs. Only after several months did the cost savings begin to accumulate.

Among plants that implemented the program by the end of 1993, the mean time between failure (MTBF) for pumps (the focus of the program) rose by an average of 12% each time cumulative operating experience doubled, while direct maintenance costs had fallen an average of 20%. In 23 comparable plants not implementing the program the learning rate averaged just 5% per doubling of cumulative experience and costs were *up* an average of 7% (Carroll, Sterman, and Marcus 1998). The program at Washington Works boosted net production capability 20%, improved customer service 90%, and cut delivery lead time by 50%, all with minimal capital investment and a reduction in maintenance costs. It is difficult to estimate the total benefit of the program for the company as a whole, but conservative estimates exceed $350 million/year in avoided maintenance costs.

The story does not end here, however. Success creates its own challenges. What happens to a plant after it succeeds in improving MTBFs and cutting maintenance expenditures? One issue related to the persistence of the cost-saving

FIGURE 2-11

Worse-before-better behavior of maintenance costs at a typical plant

Graph shows direct cost savings after implementation of the learning laboratory and new maintenance policies at a particular plant. Vertical axis disguised.

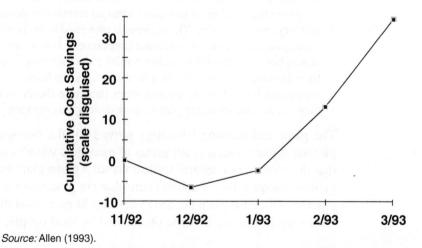

Source: Allen (1993).

mentality. A member of the modeling team commented, "As soon as you get the problems down, people will be taken away from the effort and the problems will go back up." In fact, cost-cutting programs mandated by corporate headquarters did cause significant downsizing throughout the entire company and limited their ability to expand the program.

Another problem for Du Pont was rewarding the modeling team. Ledet believed the game and learning laboratory had great potential to stimulate improvement in a wide range of companies and industries. He began to receive inquiries from other firms interested in using the game. Ledet acquired the rights to the game from Du Pont, took early retirement, and became an entrepreneur, working with other companies to implement the approach. These firms include other chemicals manufacturers along with firms in the energy, automotive, and high-tech sectors.

2.4.4   Transferring the Learning: The Lima Experience

One of the organizations that adopted the maintenance game and other system dynamics tools was British Petroleum (BP).[16] BP's Lima, Ohio, refinery was built in 1886 by John D. Rockefeller to supply fuel and petrochemicals to the Midwest. Once the "Queen of the Fleet," cost cutting during the 1980s had led to the same spiral of increasing breakdowns, declining performance, and still more cost cutting that had plagued Du Pont. By the early 1990s it was a poor performer and lagged well behind other US refineries. A number of improvement programs were tried, with little success, and BP began to think about selling or closing the facility while trying to cut costs.

In 1994 the Lima facility introduced the maintenance learning lab and game along with some other tools of system dynamics such as the Beer Distribution Game. This was not a top management intervention: The game was initially championed by an equipment specialist, a maintenance training supervisor, and an engineer, Paul Monus, then working in continuous improvement. Successful pilot projects led refinery management to run 80% of all employees through the program. Soon dozens of improvement teams were in place. During the first 6 months maintenance costs ballooned by 30%. Management was prepared for this worse-before-better dynamic, however, and focused on the improvements generated by the action teams. Momentum began to build.

In January 1996 BP announced that it intended to sell the Lima refinery and stepped up its cost cutting and downsizing. A few months later BP stunned the employees by announcing that it could not find a buyer at a satisfactory price and would therefore close the refinery.

The announcement was a deep blow to the workers and the city. The Lima facility was one of the most important employers in the community, occupying 650 acres of prime real estate and generating 400 jobs with payroll, utility, and other payments pumping more than $60 million/year into Lima's depressed economy.

---

[16]BP merged with Amoco in 1998, after the work described here was done.

Some employees became discouraged and questioned the value of continuing the program of defect elimination and proactive maintenance. A few transferred to other BP facilities or left altogether. Winston Ledet described what happened next:

> For those who decided to stay with the ship, a new spirit emerged. They realized that they needed a future in Lima and should take responsibility for creating that future. The first step was to ensure that the exit of many experienced people did not throw them back in the reactive mode. This heightened the sense of urgency to do defect elimination. It actually created a clearer focus for the people who remained. They were all there because they had chosen to be there.[17]

Soon the cumulative impact of the new maintenance policies and attitudes was clearly visible in the performance of the plant. Table 2-2 highlights some of the results.

The dramatic improvements in the refinery did not go unnoticed. On July 2, 1998, the banner headline of the *Lima News* announced "Oil Refinery Rescued." Clark USA, a privately held Fortune 500 company with refining and distribution interests, agreed to buy the Lima refinery from BP for $215 million and keep it operating as a refinery. Many people and organizations contributed to the rescue of the refinery. Yet without the dramatic improvements in refinery operations stimulated by the systems thinking intervention it is unlikely Clark, or any buyer, would have offered enough for the facility to keep it running.

TABLE 2-2
Improvement at the Lima refinery

1. Lima Refinery pump MTBF up from 12 to 58 months (pump failures down from more than 640 in 1991 to 131 in 1998). Direct savings: $1.8 million/year.
2. Total flare-off of hydrocarbon down from 1.5% to 0.35%. Direct savings: $0.27/barrel. Improved environmental quality.
3. On-line analyzer uptime improvement from 75% and not trusted to 97% and trusted, permitting real-time optimization of product flow. Savings: $0.10–0.12/barrel.
4. Thirty-four production records set.
5. Safety incidents and lost hours cut by factor of 4.
6. Cash margin improved by $0.77 per barrel of oil processed.
7. Total new value created: $43 million/year. Total cost: $320,000/year. Ratio: 143:1.
8. BP wide learning initiative under way for all other refineries and plants. Over 2000 people from sites in the US, UK, Australia, North Sea, Alaska, and Europe had participated in the workshop and game by 1998.

Source: Paul Monus, personal communication; Monus, P. (1997) "Proactive Manufacturing at BP's Lima Oil Refinery," presented at National Petroleum Refiners Association Maintenance Conference, 20–23 May 1997, New Orleans; and Griffith, J., D. Kuenzli, and P. Monus (1998) "Proactive Manufacturing: Accelerating Step Change Breakthroughs in Performance," NPRA Maintenance Conference, MC-98-92.

---

[17]*TMG News,* 15 September 1998.

The success of the learning laboratory and maintenance game illustrates the real purpose of the modeling process. The model, game, and workshop don't teach anyone how to maintain a pump better or how to do vibration monitoring. Du Pont, BP, and other organizations already have plenty of technical tools and knowledge. Instead, the game and learning laboratory enable people to experience the long-term organizationwide consequences of their actions, to enact a future in which old ways of behaving are changed, and to experience emotionally as well as cognitively what it might be like to make the transition to a high-performing plant.

The Lima experience illustrates the power of a shift in mental models. The BP team reduced butane flare-off to zero, generating annual savings of $1.5 million/year and reducing pollution as well. The effort took 2 weeks and cost $5000, a return on investment of 30,000%/year. What had stopped them from implementing this improvement long ago? Members of the team knew about the problem and how to solve it for 8 years. They already had all the engineering know-how they needed to solve the problem and most of the equipment and materials were already on site. The only barriers were the mental models through which employees came to believe that they were powerless, that the problem was imposed by external forces beyond their control, and that a few people could never make a difference.

These entrenched mental models changed in four essential ways. The belief that the problem was out there had to change from "our equipment is lousy and there's nothing we can do about it" to "our equipment performs poorly as a result of our own past policies—if we change our behavior, the equipment will respond." The focus on defect correction through repairs had to shift to a focus on defect prevention and elimination. The focus on minimizing maintenance costs had to shift to maximizing overall organizational performance. And they had to realize that escaping the trap of reactive maintenance necessarily involved a worse-before-better tradeoff.

The formal model was essential, as it led to the initial insights into the dynamics of process improvement and the synergistic effects of high leverage policies. The model also allowed the modeling team to develop the game and helped make it realistic. Ultimately implementation success required the modeling team to embed their insights into a learning environment that involved the active participation of the people on the front lines, that enabled people to discover those insights for themselves, and that spoke not only to their heads but also to their hearts.

2.5   SUMMARY: PRINCIPLES FOR SUCCESSFUL USE OF SYSTEM DYNAMICS

Though the projects described above differed in many ways, they all illustrate a number of principles for effective development and implementation of system dynamics models (see chapter 3; see also Forrester 1961; Roberts 1977/1978; and Morecroft and Sterman 1994):

1. **Develop a model to solve a particular problem, not to model the system.**
   A model must have a clear purpose and that purpose must be to solve the problem of concern to the client. Modelers must exclude all factors not

relevant to the problem to ensure the project scope is feasible and the results timely. The goal is to improve the performance of the system as defined by the client. Focus on results.

2. **Modeling should be integrated into a project from the beginning.**
The value of the modeling process begins early on, in the problem definition phase. The modeling process helps focus diagnosis on the structure of the system rather than blaming problems on the people making decisions in that structure.

3. **Be skeptical about the value of modeling and force the "why do we need it" discussion at the start of the project.**
There are many problems for which system dynamics is not useful. Carefully consider whether system dynamics is the right technique for the problem. Modelers should welcome difficult questions from the clients about how the process works and how it might help them with their problem. The earlier these issues are discussed, the better.

4. **System dynamics does not stand alone. Use other tools and methods as appropriate.**
Most modeling projects are part of a larger effort involving traditional strategic and operational analysis, including benchmarking, statistical work, market research, etc. Effective modeling rests on a strong base of data and understanding of the issues. Modeling works best as a complement to other tools, not as a substitute.

5. **Focus on implementation from the start of the project.**
Implementation must start on the first day of the project. Constantly ask, How will the model help the client make decisions? Use the model to set priorities and determine the sequence of policy implementation. Use the model to answer the question, How do we get there from here? Carefully consider the real world issues involved in pulling various policy levers. Quantify the full range of costs and benefits of policies, not only those already reported by existing accounting systems.

6. **Modeling works best as an iterative process of joint inquiry between client and consultant.**
Modeling is a process of discovery. The goal is to reach new understanding of how the problem arises and then use that understanding to design high leverage policies for improvement. Modeling should not be used as a tool for advocacy. Don't build a client's prior opinion about what should be done into a model. Use workshops where the clients can test the model themselves, in real time.

7. **Avoid black box modeling.**
Models built out of the sight of the client will never lead to change in deeply held mental models and therefore will not change client behavior. Involve the clients as early and as deeply as possible. Show them the model. Encourage them to suggest and run their own tests and to criticize the model. Work with them to resolve their criticisms to their satisfaction.

8. **Validation is a continuous process of testing and building confidence in the model.**

    Models are not validated after they are completed nor by any one test such as their ability to fit historical data. Clients (and modelers) build confidence in the utility of a model gradually, by constantly confronting the model with data and expert opinion—their own and others'. Through this process both model and expert opinions will change and deepen. Seek out opportunities to challenge the model's ability to replicate a diverse range of historical experiences.

9. **Get a preliminary model working as soon as possible. Add detail only as necessary.**

    Develop a working simulation model as soon as possible. Don't try to develop a comprehensive conceptual model prior to the development of a simulation model. Conceptual models are only hypotheses and must be tested. Formalization and simulation often uncover flaws in conceptual maps and lead to improved understanding. The results of simulation experiments inform conceptual understanding and help build confidence in the results. Early results provide immediate value to clients and justify continued investment of their time.

10. **A broad model boundary is more important than a great deal of detail.**

    Models must strike a balance between a useful, operational representation of the structures and policy levers available to the clients while capturing the feedbacks generally unaccounted for in their mental models. In general, the dynamics of a system emerge from the interactions of the components in the system—capturing those feedbacks is more important than a lot of detail in representing the components themselves.

11. **Use expert modelers, not novices.**

    While the software available for modeling is easily mastered by a high school student or CEO, modeling is not computer programming. You cannot develop a qualitative diagram and then hand it off to a programmer for coding into a simulation model. Modeling requires a disciplined approach and an understanding of business, skills developed through study and experience. Get the expert assistance you need. Use the project as an opportunity to develop the skills of others on the team and in the client organization.

12. **Implementation does not end with a single project.**

    In all three cases the modeling work continued to have impact long after the initial project was over. Models and management flight simulators were applied to similar issues in other settings. The modelers developed expertise they applied to related problems and clients moved into new positions and new organizations, taking the insights they gained and, sometimes, a new way of thinking, with them. Implementation is a long-term process of personal, organizational, and social change.

3

The Modeling Process

Perhaps the fault [for the poor implementation record for models] lies in the origins of managerial model-making—the translation of methods and principles of the physical sciences into wartime operations research . . . If hypothesis, data, and analysis lead to proof and new knowledge in science, shouldn't similar processes lead to change in organizations? The answer is obvious—NO! Organizational changes (or decisions or policies) do not instantly flow from evidence, deductive logic, and mathematical optimization.
—Edward B. Roberts[1]

In chapter 1 the concept of a virtual world was introduced as a way to speed the learning process, and chapter 2 showed how models became virtual worlds to help solve problems in three different situations. How can virtual worlds (models) be used most effectively? How can useful virtual worlds be created? Modeling takes place in the context of real world problem solving, with all its messiness, ambiguity, time pressure, politics, and interpersonal conflict. The purpose is to solve a problem, not only to gain insight (though insight into the problem is required to design effective policies). Modeling, as a part of the learning process, is iterative, a continual process of formulating hypotheses, testing, and revision, of both formal and mental models. Experiments conducted in the virtual world inform the design and execution of experiments in the real world; experience in the real world then leads to changes and improvements in the virtual world and in participants' mental

---

[1]Roberts, E. (1977), "Strategies for effective implementation of complex corporate models," Interfaces 7(5); also chapter 4 in Roberts (1978). The paper remains a succinct and still relevant statement of the need for an implementation focus from the very start of any modeling project.

models. This chapter discusses the purpose of modeling, describes the process of system dynamics modeling, the role of the client, and the modeler's professional and ethical responsibilities.

3.1   THE PURPOSE OF MODELING: MANAGERS AS ORGANIZATION DESIGNERS

Jay Forrester often asks, Who are the most important people in the safe operation of an aircraft? Most people respond, The pilots. In fact, the most important people are the designers. Skilled, well-trained pilots are critical, but far more important is designing an aircraft that is stable, robust under extreme conditions, and that ordinary pilots can fly safely even when stressed, tired, or in unfamiliar conditions. In the context of social and business systems, managers play both roles. They are pilots, making decisions (who to hire, what prices to set, when to launch the new product) and they are designers, shaping the organizational structures, strategies, and decision rules that influence how decisions are made. The design role is the most important but usually gets the least attention. Too many managers, especially senior managers, spend far too much time acting as pilots—making decisions, taking control from subordinates—rather than creating an organizational structure consistent with their vision and values and which can be managed well by ordinary people (see Forrester 1965).

Today designing a new aircraft is impossible without modeling and simulation. Managers seeking to enhance their organizational design skills, however, continue to design by trial and error, by anecdote, and by imitation of others, though the complexity of their organizations rivals that of an aircraft. Virtual worlds provide an important tool for managers in both the operation and especially the design of their organizations.

There is clearly a role for models that help managers pilot their organizations better, and system dynamics is often useful for these purposes. But the real value of the process comes when models are used to support organizational redesign. In *Industrial Dynamics,* Forrester calls for courage in the selection of problems, saying, "The solutions to small problems yield small rewards . . . The goal should be to find management policies and organizational structures that lead to greater success." Focus your modeling work on the important issues, on the problems where your work can have lasting benefit, on the problems you care most deeply about.

3.2   THE CLIENT AND THE MODELER

Modeling does not take place in splendid isolation. It is embedded in an organization and social context. Even before the modeling process per se begins, the modeler must gain access to the organization and identify the client. The client is not the person who brings you in to an organization or champions your work, nor even the person who pays for the modeling study, though it is helpful to have contacts, champions, and cash. Your clients are the people you must influence for your work to have impact. They are those people whose behavior must change to solve the problem. Your client can be a CEO or a machine operator on the factory floor. Clients can be individuals, groups, or entire communities. The client for a modeling study can be your academic colleagues, the public at large, or even your-self. In the discussion that follows, I will focus on modeling projects conducted for organizations. The process, however, is similar for these other contexts as well.

To be effective the modeling process must be focused on the clients' needs. The clients for a modeling project are busy. They are embroiled in organizational politics. They are looking out for their own careers. Their concern is solving a problem and taking action in the real world. They care little for the elegance of your theory or cleverness of your model. Modeling is done to help the client, not for the benefit of the modeler. The client context and real world problem determine the nature of the model, and the modeling process must be consistent with the clients' skills, capabilities, and goals. The purpose is to help the clients solve their problem. If the clients perceive your model does not address their concerns or lose confidence in it, you will have little impact. Focus your modeling work on the problems that keep the clients up at night.

The political context of modeling and the need to focus on the clients' problem does not mean modelers should be hired guns, willing to do whatever the clients want. Modelers should not automatically accede to clients' requests to include more detail or to focus on one set of issues while ignoring others, just to keep the clients on board. A good modeling process challenges the clients' conception of the problem. Modelers have a responsibility to require their clients to justify their opinions, ground their views in data, and consider new viewpoints. When the clients ask you to do something you think is unnecessary or misguided, you must work with them to resolve the issue.

Unfortunately, far too many clients are not interested in learning but in using models to support conclusions they've already reached or as instruments to gain power in their organizations. Sadly, far too many consultants and modelers are only too eager to oblige. As a modeler you have an ethical responsibility to carry out your work with rigor and integrity. You must be willing to let the modeling process change your mind. You must "speak truth to power," telling the clients that their most cherished beliefs are wrong, if that is what the modeling process reveals, even if it means you will be fired. If your clients push you to generate a result they've selected in advance or that is not supported by the analysis, push back. If your clients' minds are closed, if you can't convince them to use modeling hon-estly, you must quit. Get yourself a better client.[2]

3.3   STEPS OF THE MODELING PROCESS

In practice, as a modeler you are first brought into an organization by a contact who thinks you or your modeling tools might be helpful. Your first step is to find out what the real problem is and who the real client is. Your initial contact may not be the client, but only serve as a gatekeeper who can introduce you to the client. As the modeling project proceeds, you may find the client group expands or changes. Assume that you've successfully negotiated entry to the organization and

---

[2]Wallace (1994) provides a good collection of articles addressing the ethical issues facing modelers.

1. **Problem Articulation (Boundary Selection)**
   - **Theme selection:** What is the problem? Why is it a problem?
   - **Key variables:** What are the key variables and concepts we must consider?
   - **Time horizon:** How far in the future should we consider? How far back in the past lie the roots of the problem?
   - **Dynamic problem definition (reference modes):** What is the historical behavior of the key concepts and variables? What might their behavior be in the future?

2. **Formulation of Dynamic Hypothesis**
   - **Initial hypothesis generation:** What are current theories of the problematic behavior?
   - **Endogenous focus:** Formulate a dynamic hypothesis that explains the dynamics as endogenous consequences of the feedback structure.
   - **Mapping:** Develop maps of causal structure based on initial hypotheses, key variables, reference modes, and other available data, using tools such as
     - Model boundary diagrams,
     - Subsystem diagrams,
     - Causal loop diagrams,
     - Stock and flow maps,
     - Policy structure diagrams,
     - Other facilitation tools.

3. **Formulation of a Simulation Model**
   - **Specification** of structure, decision rules.
   - **Estimation** of parameters, behavioral relationships, and initial conditions.
   - **Tests** for consistency with the purpose and boundary.

4. **Testing**
   - **Comparison to reference modes:** Does the model reproduce the problem behavior adequately for your purpose?
   - **Robustness under extreme conditions:** Does the model behave realistically when stressed by extreme conditions?
   - **Sensitivity:** How does the model behave given uncertainty in parameters, initial conditions, model boundary, and aggregation?
   - **. . . Many other tests** (see chapter 21).

5. **Policy Design and Evaluation**
   - **Scenario specification:** What environmental conditions might arise?
   - **Policy design:** What new decision rules, strategies, and structures might be tried in the real world? How can they be represented in the model?
   - **"What if . . ."** analysis: What are the effects of the policies?
   - **Sensitivity analysis:** How robust are the policy recommendations under different scenarios and given uncertainties?
   - **Interactions of policies:** Do the policies interact? Are there synergies or compensatory responses?

identified the (initial) clients. How do you proceed to develop a model which can be helpful to them?[3]

There is no cookbook recipe for successful modeling, no procedure you can follow to guarantee a useful model. Modeling is inherently creative. Individual modelers have different styles and approaches. Yet all successful modelers follow a disciplined process that involves the following activities: (1) articulating the problem to be addressed, (2) formulating a *dynamic hypothesis* or theory about the causes of the problem, (3) formulating a simulation model to test the dynamic hypothesis, (4) testing the model until you are satisfied it is suitable for your purpose, and (5) designing and evaluating policies for improvement. Table 3-1 lists these steps along with some of the questions each step addresses and the principal tools used in each (see also Randers 1980).

3.4   MODELING IS ITERATIVE

Before discussing each of these steps in more detail, it is important to place the modeling process in context with the ongoing activities of the people in the system. Modeling is a feedback process, not a linear sequence of steps. Models go through constant iteration, continual questioning, testing, and refinement. Figure 3-1 recasts the modeling process shown in Table 3-1 more accurately as an iterative cycle. The initial purpose dictates the boundary and scope of the modeling effort, but what is learned from the process of modeling may feed back to alter our basic understanding of the problem and the purpose of our effort. Iteration can occur from any step to any other step (indicated by the interconnections in the center of the diagram). In any modeling project one will iterate through these steps many times.[4]

FIGURE 3-1

The modeling process is iterative.

Results of any step can yield insights that lead to revisions in any earlier step (indicated by the links in the center of the diagram).

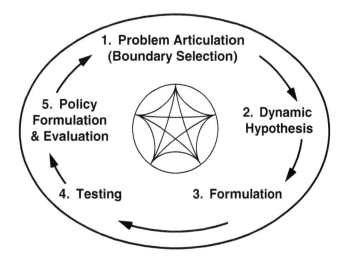

---

[3]There is a huge literature on methods for planned organizational change and group interventions. See particularly Argyris and Schön (1996), Beckhard and Harris (1987), Dyer (1995), Michael (1997), and Schein (1987, 1988).

[4]Homer (1996) provides an excellent discussion of the value of iteration and rigor in system dynamics, not only in academic research but also in consulting work, with a variety of examples.

Most importantly, modeling is embedded in the larger cycle of learning and action constantly taking place in organizations (and described in chapter 1). Pilots step into an aircraft flight simulator and learn more quickly, effectively, and safely how to operate the real aircraft, then put these skills to use in the real thing. They feed back what they learn flying the real thing to the simulator designers so the simulators can be continually improved. What pilots and designers learn in the simulator is used in the real world. And what they learn in the real world is used to change and improve the virtual world of the simulator. So it is with management flight simulators and system dynamics models. Figure 3-2 shows the modeling process embedded in the single- and double-loop learning feedbacks discussed in chapter 1. Simulation models are informed by our mental models and by information gleaned from the real world. Strategies, structures, and decision rules used in the real world can be represented and tested in the virtual world of the model. The experiments and tests conducted in the model feed back to alter our mental models and lead to the design of new strategies, new structures, and new decision rules. These new policies are then implemented in the real world, and feedback about their effects leads to new insights and further improvements in both our formal and

FIGURE 3-2

Modeling is embedded in the dynamics of the system.

Effective modeling involves constant iteration between experiments and learning in the virtual world and experiments and learning in the real world.

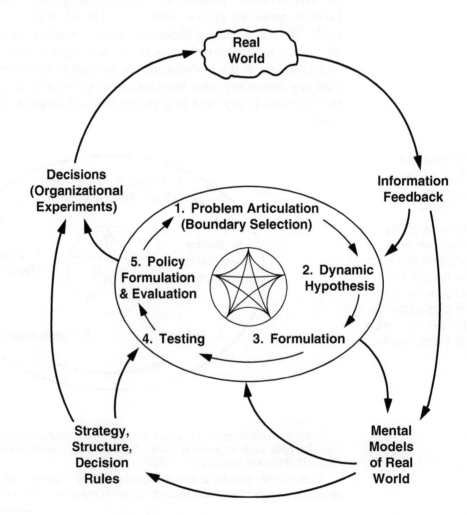

mental models. Modeling is not a one-shot activity that yields The Answer, but an ongoing process of continual cycling between the virtual world of the model and the real world of action.

3.5   OVERVIEW OF THE MODELING PROCESS

3.5.1   Problem Articulation: The Importance of Purpose

The most important step in modeling is problem articulation. What is the issue the clients are most concerned with? What problem are they trying to address? What is the real problem, not just the symptom of difficulty? What is the purpose of the model?

A clear purpose is the single most important ingredient for a successful modeling study. Of course, a model with a clear purpose can still be misleading, unwieldy, and difficult to understand. But a clear purpose allows your clients to ask questions that reveal whether a model is useful in addressing the problem they care about.

Beware the analyst who proposes to model an entire business or social system rather than a problem. Every model is a representation of a system—a group of functionally interrelated elements forming a complex whole. But for a model to be useful, it must address a specific problem and must simplify rather than attempt to mirror an entire system in detail.

What is the difference? A model designed to understand how the business cycle can be stabilized is a model of a problem. It deals with a specific policy issue. A model designed to explore policies to slow fossil fuel use and mitigate global warming is also a model of a problem; it too addresses only a limited set of issues. A model that claims to be a representation of the entire economy is a model of a whole system. Why does it matter? The usefulness of models lies in the fact that they simplify reality, creating a representation of it we can comprehend. A truly comprehensive model would be just as complex as the system itself and just as inscrutable. Von Clausewitz famously cautioned that the map is not the territory. It's a good thing it isn't: A map as detailed as the territory would be of no use (as well as being hard to fold).

The art of model building is knowing what to cut out, and the purpose of the model acts as the logical knife. It provides the criteria to decide what can be ignored so that only the essential features necessary to fulfill the purpose are left. In the example above, since the purpose of the comprehensive model would be to represent the entire economic system, nothing could be excluded. To answer all conceivable questions about the economy, the model would have to include an overwhelming array of variables. Because its scope and boundary are so broad, the model could never be completed. If it were, the data required to use it could never be compiled. If they were, the model's underlying assumptions could never be examined or tested. If they were, the model builders could never understand its behavior and the clients' confidence in it would depend on the authority of the modeler and other nonscientific grounds. Mihailo Mesarovic, a developer of early global simulations, captured the impossibility of building models of systems when he said, "No matter how many resources one has, one can envision a complex enough model to render resources insufficient to the task." (Meadows, Richardson, and Bruckmann 1982, p. 197).

A model designed for a particular purpose such as understanding the business cycle or global climate change would be much smaller, since it would be limited to those factors believed to be relevant to the question at hand. For example, the business cycle model need not include long-term trends in population growth, resource depletion, or climate change. The global warming model could exclude short-term dynamics related to interest rates, employment, and inventories. The resulting models could be simple enough so that their assumptions could be examined. The relation of these assumptions to the most important theories regarding the business cycle and climate change could then be assessed to determine how useful the models were for their intended purposes. Of course even models with well-defined purposes can be too large. But without a clear purpose, there is no basis to say "we don't need to include that" when a member of the client team makes a suggestion. In sum: Always model a problem. Never model a system.

Usually the modeler develops the initial characterization of the problem through discussion with the client team, supplemented by archival research, data collection, interviews, and direct observation or participation. There are many methods available to work with a group to elicit the information needed to define the problem dynamically while still keeping the conversation focused firmly on the clients and their problem.[5] Two of the most useful processes are establishing *reference* modes and explicitly setting the *time horizon*.

Reference Modes

System dynamics modelers seek to characterize the problem dynamically, that is, as a pattern of behavior, unfolding over time, which shows how the problem arose and how it might evolve in the future. You should develop a *reference mode,* literally a set of graphs and other descriptive data showing the development of the problem over time. Reference modes (so-called because you refer back to them throughout the modeling process) help you and your clients break out of the short-term event-oriented worldview so many people have. To do so you and the clients must identify the time horizon and define those variables and concepts you consider to be important for understanding the problem and designing policies to solve it.

Time Horizon

The time horizon should extend far enough back in history to show how the problem emerged and describe its symptoms. It should extend far enough into the future to capture the delayed and indirect effects of potential policies. Most people dramatically underestimate the length of time delays and select time horizons that

---

[5]See the references in note 9 for modeling tools that are effective for real time modeling with organizations and teams including eliciting and structuring the mental models of a group to define the problem.

are far too short. A principal deficiency in our mental models is our tendency to think of cause and effect as local and immediate. But in dynamically complex systems, cause and effect are distant in time and space. Most of the unintended effects of decisions leading to policy resistance involve feedbacks with long delays, far removed from the point of decision or the problem symptom. Work with your clients to think about the possible reactions to policies and how long they might take to play out and then increase the time horizon even further. A long time horizon is a critical antidote to the event-oriented worldview so crippling to our ability to identify patterns of behavior and the feedback structures generating them.

The choice of time horizon dramatically influences your perception of the problem. Figure 3-3 shows production, consumption, and imports of petroleum in the United States from 1986 to 1996. The historical time horizon is 10 years, already a long time relative to most discussion of energy policy (the oil shocks of the 1970s are considered ancient history in most policy debate today). The graphs show production slowly trending down, consumption trending slowly up, and therefore imports growing modestly. Prices fluctuate in a narrow band between $14 and $23 per barrel, lower than any time since the first oil crisis in 1973 (though prices did spike to $40/barrel after the Iraqi invasion of Kuwait, they soon fell back). The energy system appears to be relatively stable; there is little evidence of a long-term problem.

FIGURE 3-3
US oil production, consumption, imports, and price over a 10-year time horizon

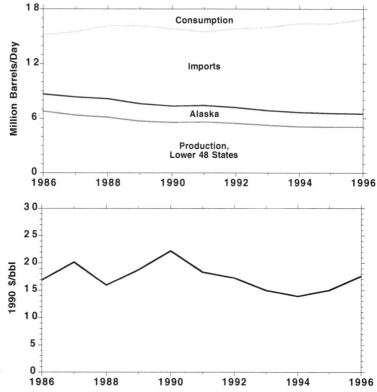

Source: EIA (US Energy Information Agency) Annual Energy Review.

Now consider Figure 3-4, showing the same variables from near the beginning of the oil era (the petroleum industry began in earnest in 1859 with Colonel Drake's famous well in Titusville, Pennsylvania). The impression is completely different. The history of the oil industry in the United States is divided into two regimes. From 1920 through 1973, consumption grew exponentially at an average rate of 4.3%/year. Production nearly kept pace, as exploration and better drilling techniques more than offset depletion. Starting in the 1950s, imports grew slightly, stimulated by the availability of cheap foreign oil. Prices fluctuated, often dramatically, but along a slowly declining trend as technology improved. All this changed in 1970. In 1970, domestic production of oil peaked. It's been falling ever since, despite the intense exploration stimulated by the much higher prices of the 1970s and early 1980s. US production from the lower 48 states and adjacent offshore area in 1996 stood at only 54% of its peak level. Even the addition of Prudhoe Bay and the trans-Alaska pipeline did not halt the slide, and Alaskan production peaked in 1988. Higher prices following the 1970s oil shocks, along with the deepest recessions since the Great Depression, cut the growth of consumption, but imports nevertheless reached 61% of total oil consumption by 1996.

Changing the time horizon completely changes the assessment of the problem. Viewed with a time scale consistent with the life of the resource, it is clear that the petroleum problem wasn't solved in the 1980s but has been steadily getting worse.

FIGURE 3-4
US oil production, consumption, imports, and price over a 130-year time horizon

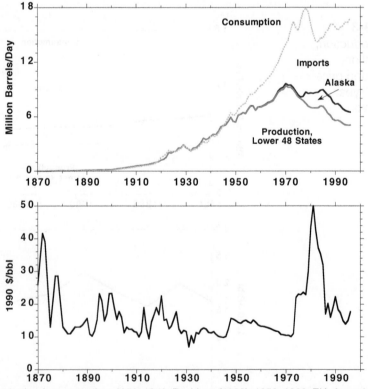

Source: Production & consumption: 1870–1949, Davidsen (1988); 1950–1966, EIA *Annual Energy Review.* Price: 1880–1968, Davidsen (1988); 1968–1996, EIA *Annual Energy Review,* Refiners Acquisition Cost.

Petroleum is a finite nonrenewable resource. In the US, depletion began to dominate finding rates in the 1960s, leading to an inevitable decline in production, a decline that began in 1970. The United States is the most heavily explored and densely drilled region of the world. The very success of early wildcatters in finding oil means there is less left to find now. While not all the petroleum in the US has been found or recovered, consumption continues to exceed the rate at which what remains is found. Consequently, imports continue to grow, leading to still greater dependency on the unstable Persian Gulf region, still more political and economic power for the oil exporting countries and less for the US, and, eventually, higher oil prices, either at the pump or in the defense budget.[6]

The oil industry illustrates the dangers of selecting a time horizon too short to capture the important dynamics and feedbacks creating them. Of course, one can err too far in the other direction. Figure 3-5 shows a graph developed by the late petroleum geologist M. King Hubbert. Hubbert invented the most successful technique for forecasting fossil fuel production ever created. In 1956 he estimated the ultimate recoverable petroleum resources of the US to be between 150 and 200 billion barrels and forecast that "the peak in production should probably occur within the interval 1966-1971" (Hubbert 1975, p. 371). His prediction of decline came at a time when the US Geological Survey projected ultimate recoverable resources nearly three times as large and claimed "the size of the resource base would not limit domestic production capacity 'in the next 10 to 20 years at least, and probably [not] for a much longer time' " (Gillette 1974). The actual peak occurred in 1970 at almost the precise value Hubbert had predicted, one of the most accurate long-term forecasts on record. Hubbert's success lay in explicitly modeling oil as a nonrenewable resource. Production could grow exponentially in the early phases

FIGURE 3-5
The fossil fuel era shown with a time horizon of 15,000 years

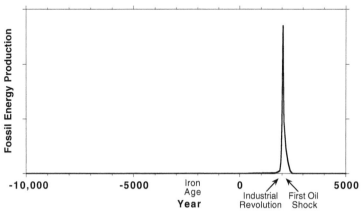

Source: Adapted from Hubbert (1962).

---

[6]There is a large literature of energy modeling in system dynamics, originating with work in Meadows et al. (1974). See, e.g., Backus (1996), Bunn and Larsen (1997), Fiddaman (1997), Ford (1990, 1997, 1999), Ford and Bull (1989), Naill (1977, 1992), and Naill et al. (1992) for work on national and global energy markets, electric utilities, global climate change, and other energy policy issues.

of its life cycle but had to fall to zero as it was depleted, forcing a transition to renewable energy sources.[7] To emphasize the transitory nature of fossil fuel civilization, Hubbert showed the production of fossil fuels on a time scale from the beginning of the agricultural revolution 10,000 years ago to 5000 years in the future. Against this backdrop, the fossil fuel era is seen as a transitory spike—a unique period during which humanity lives extravagantly off a rich inheritance of irreplaceable natural capital. The picture is sobering. But Hubbert's pimple, as it was called by critics, takes a time horizon too long to be useful to policy makers who influence public policy or corporate strategy affecting energy prices, regulations, capital investment, and R&D.

The choice of time horizon can dramatically influence the evaluation of policies. In the early 1970s a US government agency concerned with foreign aid sponsored a model focused on the Sahel region of sub-Saharan Africa. The Sahel was then experiencing rapid population growth at the same time the desert was expanding southward, reducing grazing land for the nomadic herders' cattle. The purpose of the model was to identify high leverage policies to spur economic development in the region. The model was used to assess the effects of many of the policies then in use, such as drilling bore holes to increase the water supply for cattle by tapping deep aquifers or subsidizing crops such as sorghum and ground nuts. Running the model to the year 2000, a round number several decades in the future at the time, showed that the policies led to improvement. Subsidies increased agricultural output. Bore holes permitted cattle stocks to grow, increasing the supply of milk and meat and the wealth of the herders. However, running the model into the first decades of the 21st century showed a different outcome: larger stocks of cattle began to outstrip the carrying capacity of the region. As the cattle overbrowsed and trampled the grasslands, erosion and desertification increased. The cattle population dropped sharply, creating a food deficit in the region. Selecting a time horizon too short to capture these feedbacks favored adoption of policies counter to the long-term interests of the region's people and the mission of the client organization.[8]

Modelers must guard against accepting the client's initial assessment of the appropriate time frame. Often these are based on milestones and round numbers having little to do with the dynamics of the problem, such as the end of the fiscal year, or the next 5-year planning cycle. A good rule of thumb is to set the time horizon several times as long as the longest time delays in the system, and then some.

3.5.2   Formulating a Dynamic Hypothesis

Once the problem has been identified and characterized over an appropriate time horizon, modelers must begin to develop a theory, called a *dynamic hypothesis,* to

---

[7]Sterman and Richardson (1985), Sterman et al. (1988), and Sterman, Richardson, and Davidsen (1990) model the world and US petroleum life cycles and study the evolution of estimates of the resource base, showing why Hubbert was so accurate while other estimation methods proved so wildly overoptimistic.

[8]Picardi and Seifert (1976) describe one of several models of the Sahel region (the model described above was not published).

account for the problematic behavior. Your hypothesis is dynamic because it must provide an explanation of the dynamics characterizing the problem in terms of the underlying feedback and stock and flow structure of the system. It is a hypothesis because it is always provisional, subject to revision or abandonment as you learn from the modeling process and from the real world.

A dynamic hypothesis is a working theory of how the problem arose. It guides modeling efforts by focusing you and your clients on certain structures. Much of the remainder of the modeling process helps you to test the dynamic hypothesis, both with the simulation model and by experiments and data collection in the real world.

In practice, discussion of the problem and theories about the causes of the problem are jumbled together in conversation with client teams. Each member of a team likely has a different theory about the source of the problem; you need to acknowledge and capture them all. Many times the purpose of the model is to solve a critically important problem that has persisted for years and generated great conflict and not a little animosity among members of the client team. All will tenaciously advocate their positions while deriding the views of others in the group. Early in the modeling process, the modeler needs to act as a facilitator, capturing these mental models without criticizing or filtering them. Clarifying and probing questions are often useful, but the modeler's role during this early phase is to be a thoughtful listener, not a content expert. A variety of elicitation techniques and diagramming tools have been developed to assist you in facilitating a productive conversation to elicit people's theories about the causes of the problem.[9] Your goal is to help the client develop an endogenous explanation for the problematic dynamics.

Endogenous Explanation

System dynamics seeks endogenous explanations for phenomena. The word "endogenous" means "arising from within." An endogenous theory generates the dynamics of a system through the interaction of the variables and agents represented in the model. By specifying how the system is structured and the rules of interaction (the decision rules in the system), you can explore the patterns of behavior created by those rules and that structure and explore how the behavior might change if you alter the structure and rules. In contrast, a theory relying on exogenous variables (those "arising from without," that is, from outside the boundary of the model) explains the dynamics of variables you care about in terms of other variables whose behavior you've assumed. Exogenous explanations are really no explanation at all; they simply beg the question, What caused the exogenous variables to change as they did? The focus in system dynamics on endogenous explanations does not mean you should never include any exogenous variables in your models. But the number of exogenous inputs should be small, and each candidate for an exogenous input must be carefully scrutinized to consider whether

[9]The literature on group model building is growing rapidly. Reagan-Cirincione et al. (1991), Morecroft and Sterman (1994), Vennix (1996), and Vennix et al. (1997) provide good overviews of tools and techniques to elicit and capture the mental models of teams and client groups.

there are in fact any important feedbacks from the endogenous elements to the candidate. If so, the boundary of the model must be expanded and the variable must be modeled endogenously.

The consequences of narrow model boundaries and reliance on exogenous variables are often serious. A typical example is provided by the Project Independence Evaluation System (PIES) model, a hybrid model based on linear programming, econometrics, and input/output analysis used in the 1970s by the US Federal Energy Administration (FEA) and later by the US Department of Energy. As described by the FEA, the purpose of the model was to evaluate different energy policies according to the following criteria: their impact on the development of alternative energy sources; their impact on economic growth, inflation, and unemployment; their regional and social impacts; their vulnerability to import disruptions; and their environmental effects.

Surprisingly, considering the stated purpose, the PIES model treated the economy as exogenous. The model economy (including economic growth, interest rates, inflation, world oil prices, and the costs of unconventional fuels) was completely unaffected by the energy situation (including prices, policies, and production). In the model, even a full embargo of imported oil or a doubling of oil prices would have no impact on the economy.

Treating the economy exogenously made the PIES model inherently contradictory. Because it assumed high rates of economic growth and low price elasticities, it projected huge increases in energy demand, requiring even greater increases in the capital requirements of the energy sector as cheap domestic oil was consumed. In the model, these huge investments in energy production were satisfied without reducing investment or consumption in the rest of the economy and with no impact on interest rates or inflation. In effect, the model let the economy have its pie and eat it too.

In part because it ignored the feedbacks between the energy sector and the rest of the economy, the PIES model consistently proved to be overoptimistic. In 1974 the model projected that by 1985 the US would be well on the way to energy independence: energy imports would be only 3.3 million barrels per day and production of shale oil would be 250,000 barrels per day. Furthermore, these developments would be accompanied by oil prices of about $22 per barrel (1984 dollars) and by vigorous economic growth. It didn't happen. Imports in the late 1980s were about 5.5 million barrels per day and grew to more than half of oil consumption by the mid 1990s. Shale oil and other exotic synfuels never materialized. This situation prevailed despite huge reductions in oil demand caused by oil prices in the early 1980s greater than $30/bbl and the most serious recession since the Great Depression.

A broad model boundary that captures important feedbacks is more important than a lot of detail in the specification of individual components. It is worth noting that the PIES model provided a breakdown of supply, demand, and price for dozens of fuels in each region of the country yet its aggregate projections weren't even close. What purpose was served by the effort devoted to forecasting the demand for jet fuel or naphtha in the Pacific Northwest when the basic assumptions were so palpably inadequate and the main results were so woefully erroneous?

Mapping System Structure

System dynamics includes a variety of tools to help you communicate the boundary of your model and represent its causal structure. These include model boundary diagrams, subsystem diagrams, causal loop diagrams, and stock and flow maps.

Model boundary chart.   A model boundary chart summarizes the scope of the model by listing which key variables are included endogenously, which are exogenous, and which are excluded from the model.

To illustrate, Table 3-2 shows a model boundary diagram for a model designed to study the feedbacks between the energy system and the economy (Sterman 1983). Partly in reaction to the limitations of existing models such as PIES, the Department of Energy in the late 1970s sought to develop dynamic models with a broader boundary (Naill 1977, 1992). The purpose of the model was to explore the impact of higher energy prices on economic growth, unemployment, inflation, and interest rates and how these macroeconomic considerations might constrain the development of new energy sources. The time horizon of the model was quite long (1950-2050) to capture the full transition from fossil fuels to renewable or other energy sources and consistent with the long time delays in the development, construction, and useful life of energy-producing and energy-consuming capital stocks.

In contrast to nearly all models used to address these issues at the time, the model had a broad boundary, with all major macroeconomic variables generated endogenously. Unlike the PIES model, the capital, labor, and energy requirements

TABLE 3-2
Model boundary chart for a long-term model of energy-economy interactions

Endogenous	Exogenous	Excluded
GNP	Population	Inventories
Consumption	Technological change	International trade
Investment	Tax rates	(except with OPEC)
Savings	Energy policies	Environmental constraints
Prices (real and nominal)		Nonenergy resources
Wages (real and nominal)		Interfuel substitution
Inflation rate		Distributional equity
Labor force participation		
Employment		
Unemployment		
Interest rates		
Money supply		
Debt		
Energy production		
Energy demand		
Energy imports		

Source: Sterman (1983).

of the energy industries were endogenous and the energy industry had to compete against other sectors for these resources. The model still contained several exogenous variables. These include population, the rate of overall technological progress, and the price of imported oil. Were these exogenous variables acceptable? Population growth and the overall rate of technical progress might be affected by changes in energy prices and consequent changes in the rate of economic growth. However, these feedbacks seemed likely to be small. The decision to model the price of imported oil exogenously is more problematic. Clearly the price of oil affects both the demand for and supply of energy in the United States, determining the quantity imported. As a major importer, changes in US oil imports can dramatically alter the supply/demand balance of the oil exporting nations, feeding back to the price of oil in the world market. Treating import prices exogenously cuts an important feedback loop. In discussing the boundary of the model I argued that there were in fact important feedbacks between the US energy system and the world oil market. But I also argued that the dynamics of the world price were so complex that incorporating them endogenously was beyond the scope and purpose of the project. I had previously helped build a model of the world oil market for the US Department of Energy and hoped that ultimately the two models could be joined. The model boundary chart alerted the clients to a questionable assumption so they could evaluate what the effect of the missing feedback might be.

The list of excluded concepts also provides important warnings to the model user. The model omitted inventories of goods and materials (and hence short-term business cycles)—no problem in such a long-term model. International trade was excluded, except for the flows of oil, goods, capital, and money between the US and the oil exporting nations. The petrodollars flowing to OPEC and their recycling as exports or foreign investment had to be included, but to include nonenergy trade would have expanded the model into a global macroeconomic system, and I would probably still be working on it. Environmental constraints and nonenergy resources such as water that might limit new energy sources like synfuels were excluded, meaning conclusions about the rate of development of these exotic energy sources would be overoptimistic. The model also treated the energy system in a fairly aggregate fashion, so interfuel substitution (oil vs. gas, for example), was not considered, another optimistic assumption. Finally, the model did not consider income distribution, even though some energy policies such as gasoline taxes are regressive unless offset by changes in the income tax code. The purpose of listing all these omissions from the model was to help model users decide for themselves whether the model was appropriate for their purpose.

Model boundary diagrams are surprisingly useful and shockingly rare. Often, models are used not as tools of inquiry but as weapons in a war of advocacy. In such cases modelers seek to hide the assumptions of their models from potential critics. But even when the modelers' motives are benign, many feel uncomfortable listing what they've left out, see the omissions as flaws and prefer to stress the strengths of their model. While this tendency is natural, it undercuts the utility of your model and weakens the ability of people to learn from and improve your work. By explicitly listing the concepts you have chosen not to include, at least for now, you provide a visible reminder of the caveats to the results and limitations of the model. Without a clear understanding of the boundary and assumptions, models constructed for one purpose are frequently used for another for which they are ill-suited, sometimes producing absurd results. All too often models with completely inappropriate and even bizarre assumptions about exogenous and excluded variables are used in policy making because the model users are unable to examine the boundary of the models themselves and the modelers have not provided that information for them (chapter 21 provides examples; see also Meadows and Robinson 1985).

Subsystem diagram.
A subsystem diagram shows the overall architecture of a model. Each major subsystem is shown along with the flows of material, money, goods, information, and so on coupling the subsystems to one another. Subsystems can be organizations such as the firm and the customer or organizational subunits such as operations, marketing, and product development. Subsystem diagrams convey information on the boundary and level of aggregation in the model by showing the number and type of different organizations or agents represented. They also communicate some information about the endogenous and exogenous variables.

In the 1960s Jay Forrester served on the boards of several successful high-tech companies and became interested in the dynamics of corporate growth. To help him think about the strategic issues facing these firms, Forrester (1964, p. 32) created a model designed "to show how the differing kinds of corporate growth patterns can be created by different corporate policies and management attitudes and by the interactions between a company and its market." Figure 3-6 shows the reference mode. Forrester (pp. 32-33) explained:

> The very rare company grows smoothly, as in curve A, and eventually reaches a healthy sustained plateau of mature life. More frequently, the company follows a pattern, as in curve B, where it appears to succeed at first and then encounters a severe crisis that leads to bankruptcy or merger. Often, the pattern is growth stagnation, as in curve C, marked by neither success nor failure. Of those companies which do show a long-term growth trend, the most common pattern is that in curve D, where growth is accompanied by repeated crisis.

FIGURE 3-6
Patterns of
corporate growth

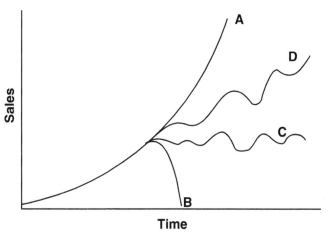

Source: Adapted from Forrester (1964).

Forrester argued that "contrary to first impressions, one cannot explain these differences on the basis of the particular industry or the type and design of products... One must therefore look deeper into the structure of information flows and the policies which guide operating decisions" (p. 33). To do so the model consisted of two subsystems, the company and the market (Figure 3-7).

The two subsystems are coupled by the obvious flows of orders, product, and money: The firm receives orders from the market, ships product, and receives payment. But in addition, the firm sends signals to the market including the price of the product, its availability (measured by the delivery delay), its functionality, quality, suitability to customer needs, and other intangible attributes of the company's reputation. The market responds to these signals through the order rate and through customer feedback about price, quality, service, product features, and so on. The diagram elegantly presents the essential feedback processes coupling a firm to its market, stresses that orders depend on much more than price, and begins to suggest the structure which must be captured within each subsystem. Forrester reflected on the importance of this conceptual framework in his thinking:

> Defining the system boundary and the degree of aggregation are two of the most difficult steps in successful modeling. In this particular study, part-time effort for about two years was devoted to false starts before arriving at the point shown in [Figure 3-7]. Thereafter, only eight weeks were required to create the entire system of some 200 equations.

Chapter 15 presents a simple version of this model, Forrester's "market growth model," and shows how different management policies can create the patterns of growth described in Figure 3-6.

A more detailed subsystem diagram is shown in Figure 3-8. The diagram shows the architecture for a model of a semiconductor manufacturer (Sterman, Repenning, and Kofman 1997). The purpose of the model was to explore the dynamics of process improvement programs. The firm had implemented a very

FIGURE 3-7
Subsystem diagram for Forrester's corporate growth model

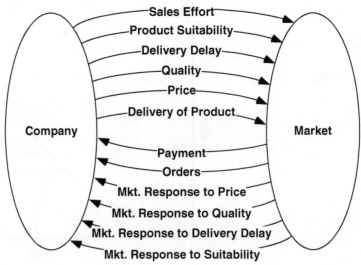

Source: Adapted from Forrester (1964).

successful quality improvement program. However, despite dramatic improvements in quality, productivity, and customer responsiveness, operating profit and the stock price fell, leading to layoffs. Exploring this paradox required a model with a broad boundary both within the representation of the firm and in interactions of the firm with its environment. Besides the usual subsystems for manufacturing, product development, and accounting, the model includes a process improvement sector and a sector labeled "Financial Stress." The Financial Stress subsystem is not an organizational subunit but represents top management decisions regarding layoffs, investment, and the attention given to process

FIGURE 3-8   Subsystem diagram for model of a semiconductor firm and its quality improvement Σprogram

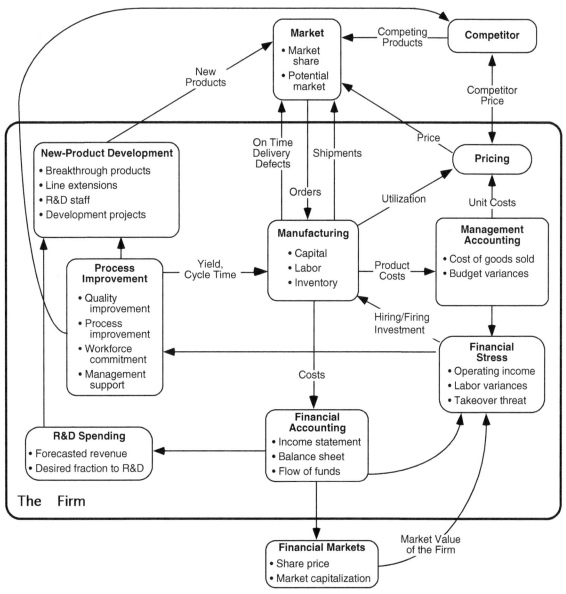

Source: Adapted from Sterman, Repenning, and Kofman (1997).

improvement. These decisions were affected by the firm's financial health and the threat of takeover (as influenced by the market value of the firm relative to book value and cash flow). The diagram also shows that the firm's sales and market share are endogenous, as is competitor behavior (note that competitors respond not only to the firm's price but also to its quality improvement efforts). The stock price and market valuation of the firm are also endogenous.

Subsystem diagrams are overviews and should not contain too much detail. The diagram in Figure 3-8 is quite complex; subsystem diagrams should generally be simpler. Multiple subsystem diagrams can be used to convey the hierarchical structure of large models.

Causal loop diagrams.   Model boundary charts and subsystem diagrams show the boundary and architecture of the model but don't show how the variables are related. Causal loop diagrams (CLDs) are flexible and useful tools for diagramming the feedback structure of systems in any domain. Causal diagrams are simply maps showing the causal links among variables with arrows from a cause to an effect. Chapter 2 provides examples; chapter 5 covers the rules for their construction and interpretation in depth.

Stock and flow maps.   Causal loop diagrams emphasize the feedback structure of a system. Stock and flow diagrams emphasize their underlying physical structure. Stocks and flows track accumulations of material, money, and information as they move through a system. Stocks include inventories of product, populations, and financial accounts such as debt, book value, and cash. Flows are the rates of increase or decrease in stocks, such as production and shipments, births and deaths, borrowing and repayment, investment and depreciation, and receipts and expenditures. Stocks characterize the state of the system and generate the information upon which decisions are based. The decisions then alter the rates of flow, altering the stocks and closing the feedback loops in the system. Chapter 2 shows examples; chapters 6 and 7 discuss the mapping and behavior of stocks and flows.

Policy structure diagrams.   These are causal diagrams showing the information inputs to a particular decision rule. Policy structure diagrams focus attention on the information cues the modeler assumes decision makers use to govern the rates of flow in the system. They show the causal structure and time delays involved in particular decisions rather than the feedback structure of the overall system. Chapter 15 provides examples; see Morecroft (1982) for details.

3.5.3   Formulating a Simulation Model

Once you've developed an initial dynamic hypothesis, model boundary, and conceptual model, you must test them. Sometimes you can test the dynamic hypothesis directly through data collection or experiments in the real system. Most of the time, however, the conceptual model is so complex that its dynamic implications are unclear. As discussed in chapter 1, our ability to infer correctly the dynamics of a complex model is extremely poor. Further, in many situations, especially human systems, it is difficult, dangerous, unethical, or simply impossible to conduct the real world experiments that might reveal the flaws in a dynamic hypothesis. In the majority of cases, you must conduct these experiments in a virtual world. To do so, you must move from the conceptual realm of diagrams to a fully specified formal model, complete with equations, parameters, and initial conditions.

Actually, formalizing a conceptual model often generates important insight even before it is ready to be simulated. Formalization helps you to recognize vague concepts and resolve contradictions that went unnoticed or undiscussed during the conceptual phase. Formalization is where the real test of your understanding occurs: computers accept no hand waving arguments. Indeed, the most experienced modelers routinely write some equations and estimate parameters throughout the modeling process, even in the earliest phases of problem articulation and conceptualization—often with the clients—as a way to resolve ambiguity and test initial hypotheses. System dynamics practice includes a large variety of tests one can apply during the formulation stage to identify flaws in proposed formulations and improve your understanding of the system.

3.5.4 Testing

Testing begins as soon as you write the first equation. Part of testing, of course, is comparing the simulated behavior of the model to the actual behavior of the system. But testing involves far more than the replication of historical behavior. Every variable must correspond to a meaningful concept in the real world. Every equation must be checked for dimensional consistency (so you aren't adding apples and oranges). The sensitivity of model behavior and policy recommendations must be assessed in light of the uncertainty in assumptions, both parametric and structural.

Models must be tested under extreme conditions, conditions that may never have been observed in the real world. What happens to the GDP of a simulated economy if you suddenly reduce energy supplies to zero? What happens in a model of an automaker if you raise the price of its cars by a factor of one billion? What happens if you suddenly increase dealer inventories by 1000%? Even though these conditions have never and could never be observed, there is no doubt about what the behavior of the system must be: Without energy, the GDP of a modern economy must fall nearly to zero; with a price one billion times higher, the demand for the firm's cars must fall to zero; with a huge surplus of cars on dealer lots, production should soon fall to zero but cannot become negative. You might imagine that models would never fail to pass such obvious tests, that production without energy, demand for goods that cost more than the total wealth of many nations, and negative production would never arise. But you'd be wrong. Many widely used models in economics, psychology, management, and other disciplines violate basic laws of physics, even though they may replicate historical behavior quite well (see section 9.3.2 and chapter 21). Extreme conditions tests, along with other tests of model behavior, are critical tools to discover the flaws in your model and set the stage for improved understanding.

3.5.5 Policy Design and Evaluation

Once you and the client have developed confidence in the structure and behavior of the model, you can use it to design and evaluate policies for improvement.

Policy design is much more than changing the values of parameters such as a tax rate or markup ratio. Policy design includes the creation of entirely new strategies, structures, and decision rules. Since the feedback structure of a system determines its dynamics, most of the time high leverage policies will involve changing the dominant feedback loops by redesigning the stock and flow structure, eliminating time delays, changing the flow and quality of information available at key decision points, or fundamentally reinventing the decision processes of the actors in the system.

The robustness of policies and their sensitivity to uncertainties in model parameters and structure must be assessed, including their performance under a wide range of alternative scenarios. The interactions of different policies must also be considered: Because real systems are highly nonlinear, the impact of combination policies is usually not the sum of their impacts alone. Often policies interfere with one another; sometimes they reinforce one another and generate substantial synergies.

3.6   SUMMARY

This chapter described the modeling process. While there are certain steps all modelers go through, modeling is not a cookbook procedure. It is fundamentally creative. At the same time, modeling is a disciplined, scientific, and rigorous process, challenging the modeler and client at every step to surface and test assumptions, gather data, and revise their models—both formal and mental.

Modeling is iterative. No one ever built a model by starting with step 1 and progressing in sequence through a list of activities. Modeling is a continual process of iteration among problem articulation, hypothesis generation, data collection, model formulation, testing, and analysis. There are revisions and changes, blind alleys and backtracking. Effective modeling continually cycles between experiments in the virtual world of the model and experiments and data collection in the real world.

Models must be clearly focused on a purpose. Never build a model of a system. Models are simplifications; without a clear purpose, you have no basis for excluding anything from your model and your effort is doomed to failure. Therefore the most important step in the modeling process is working with your client to articulate the problem—the real problem, not the symptoms of the problem, the latest crisis, or the most recent fad. Of course, as the modeling process leads you to deeper insight, your definition and statement of the problem may change. Indeed, such radical reframings are often the most important outcome of modeling.

The purpose of modeling is to help the clients solve *their* problem. Though the modeling process often challenges the clients' conception of the problem, ultimately, if the client perceives that your model does not address their concern, you can have little impact. The modeler must not grow attached to a model, no matter how elegant or how much time has been invested in it. If it doesn't help the clients solve their problem, it needs to be revised until it does.

Modeling takes place in an organizational and social context. The setting may be a business but can also be a government agency, a scientific community, a public policy debate, or any other organization. Modelers are inevitably caught up in the politics of the community and personalities of its members. Modelers require both first-rate analytical skills and excellent interpersonal and political skills.

Finally, modelers have an ethical responsibility to pursue the modeling process with rigor and integrity. The fact that modeling is embedded in an organizational context and subject to political pressures does not relieve you of your responsibility to carry out your work with the highest standards of scientific inquiry and professional conduct. If your client is not willing to pursue the modeling process honestly, quit and find yourself a better client.

4

Structure and Behavior of Dynamic Systems

Like all systems, the complex system is an interlocking structure of feedback loops . . . This loop structure surrounds all decisions public or private, conscious or unconscious. The processes of man and nature, of psychology and physics, of medicine and engineering all fall within this structure.
—Jay W. Forrester, *Urban Dynamics* (1969), p. 107.

The behavior of a system arises from its structure. That structure consists of the feedback loops, stocks and flows, and nonlinearities created by the interaction of the physical and institutional structure of the system with the decision-making processes of the agents acting within it. This chapter provides an overview of dynamics focusing on the relationship between structure and behavior. The basic modes of behavior in dynamic systems are identified along with the feedback structures generating them. These modes include growth, created by positive feedback; goal seeking, created by negative feedback; and oscillations (including damped oscillations, limit cycles, and chaos), created by negative feedback with time delays. More complex modes such as S-shaped growth and overshoot and collapse arise from the nonlinear interaction of these basic structures. The chapter also illustrates the concept of *reference modes* to capture dynamic behavior and *causal loop diagrams* as a method to represent feedback structure.

4.1   FUNDAMENTAL MODES OF DYNAMIC BEHAVIOR

Change takes many forms, and the variety of dynamics around us is astounding. You might imagine that there must be a correspondingly huge variety of different feedback structures to account for such a rich array of dynamics. In fact, most dynamics are instances of a fairly small number of distinct patterns of behavior, such as exponential growth or oscillation. Figure 4-1 shows the most common modes of behavior.

The most fundamental modes of behavior are exponential growth, goal seeking, and oscillation. Each of these is generated by a simple feedback structure: growth arises from positive feedback, goal seeking arises from negative feedback, and oscillation arises from negative feedback with time delays in the loop. Other common modes of behavior, including S-shaped growth, S-shaped growth with overshoot and oscillation, and overshoot and collapse, arise from nonlinear interactions of the fundamental feedback structures.

4.1.1   Exponential Growth

Exponential growth arises from positive (self-reinforcing) feedback. The larger the quantity, the greater its net increase, further augmenting the quantity and leading to ever-faster growth (Figure 4-2). The paradigm cases are compound interest and the growth of populations. The more money you have invested, the more interest you earn, so the greater your balance and the greater still the next interest payment will be. The larger the population, the bigger the net birth rate, adding to the population and eventually leading to still more births, in an ever-accelerating spiral. Pure exponential growth has the remarkable property that the *doubling time* is constant: the state of the system doubles in a fixed period of time, no matter how large.

FIGURE 4-1   Common modes of behavior in dynamic systems

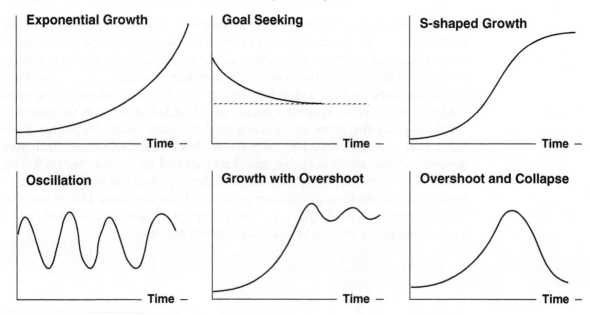

It takes the same length of time to grow from one unit to two as it does to grow from one million to two million. This property is a direct consequence of positive feedback: the net increase rate depends on the size of the state of the system (see chapter 8). Positive feedback need not always generate growth. It can also create self-reinforcing decline, as when a drop in stock prices erodes investor confidence which leads to more selling, lower prices, and still lower confidence.

What about linear growth? Linear growth is actually quite rare. Linear growth requires that there be no feedback from the state of the system to the net increase rate, because the net increase remains constant even as the state of the system changes. What appears to be linear growth is often actually exponential, but viewed over a time horizon too short to observe the acceleration.

Figure 4-3 shows some examples of exponential growth. Growth is never perfectly smooth (due to variations in the fractional growth rates, cycles, and perturbations), but in each case exponential growth is the dominant mode of behavior. Though the doubling times vary widely (from about 40 years for world population to about 2 years for semiconductor performance), these systems all exhibit the same enormous acceleration caused by positive feedback.

Process Point: When a Rate Is Not a Rate

In dynamic modeling, the term "rate" generally refers to the absolute rate of change in a quantity. The population growth example above states, "the larger the

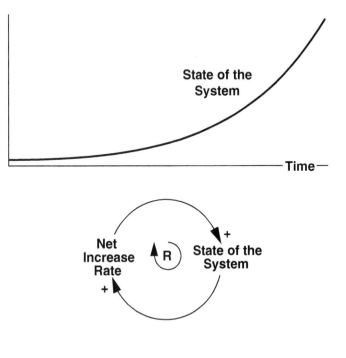

FIGURE 4-2

Exponential growth: structure and behavior

The *causal loop diagram* in the bottom half of the figure shows the feedback structure that generates exponential growth. Arrows indicate the direction of causal influences. Here, State of the System determines Net Increase Rate (the lower arrow), and Net Increase Rate adds to State of the System (the upper arrow). Signs at arrow heads (+ or −) indicate the polarity of the relationship. A positive polarity, indicated by +, means an increase in the independent variable causes the dependent variable to rise above what it would have been (and a decrease causes a decrease). Negative signs (see Figure 4-4) mean an increase (decrease) in the independent variable causes the dependent variable to decrease (increase) beyond what it would have been. Loop identifiers show the polarity of the loop, either positive (self-reinforcing, denoted by R) or negative (balancing, denoted by B; see Figure 4-4). Chapter 5 discusses causal loop diagrams in depth.

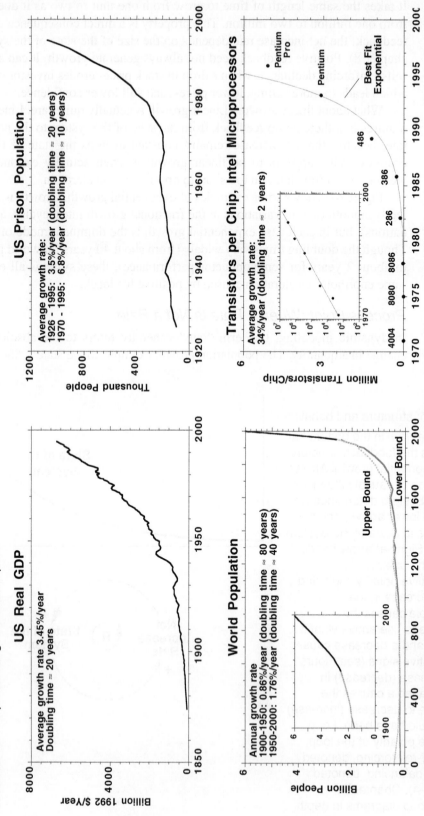

FIGURE 4-3 Exponential growth: examples

US Real GDP

Average growth rate 3.45%/year
Doubling time ≈ 20 years

Billion 1992 $/year

1850 · 1900 · 1950 · 2000

US Prison Population

Average growth rate:
1926 - 1995: 3.5%/year (doubling time ≈ 20 years)
1970 - 1995: 6.8%/year (doubling time ≈ 10 years)

Thousand People
1200 · 800 · 400 · 0

1920 · 1940 · 1960 · 1980 · 2000

World Population

Annual growth rate
1900-1950: 0.86%/year (doubling time ≈ 80 years)
1950-2000: 1.76%/year (doubling time ≈ 40 years)

Billion People
6 · 4 · 2 · 0

Upper Bound
Lower Bound

400 · 800 · 1200 · 1600 · 2000

Transistors per Chip, Intel Microprocessors

Average growth rate:
34%/year (doubling time ≈ 2 years)

Million Transistors/Chip
6 · 3 · 0

Pentium Pro
Pentium
Best Fit Exponential
486
386
286
8086
8080
4004

1970 · 1975 · 1980 · 1985 · 1990 · 1995 · 2000

Sources: Real GNP: Prior to 1929, Historical Statistics of the US. Real GDP, 1929-present: Survey of Current Business, Bureau of Economic Analysis. State and Federal Adult Prison Population: 1926-1970, Historical Statistics of the US; 1970-1980, Kurian (1994); 1980-1995, US Dept. of Justice. World Population: Prior to 1950, US Census Bureau summary of various estimates; 1950-present, US Census Bureau. Inset shows performance: Joglekar (1996). Curve is best fit exponential function. Inset shows performance on semi-log scale.

population, the greater the birth rate." The term "birth rate" here refers to the number of people born per time period. For example, the birth rate in a city of one million people might be 20,000 people per year. Often, however, the term "rate" is used as shorthand for the *fractional* rate of change of a variable. For example, the birth rate is often interpreted as the number of births per year per thousand people (also known as the crude birth rate). The crude birth rate in the city of one million would be 20 births per year per thousand people, or 2%/year. Similarly, we commonly speak of the interest rate or the unemployment rate. The word "rate" in these cases actually means "ratio": the interest rate is the ratio of the interest payments you must make each period to the principal outstanding; the unemployment rate is the ratio of the number of unemployed workers to the labor force.

You must carefully distinguish between absolute and fractional rates of change and between rates of change and ratios. Select variable names that minimize the chance for confusion. Be sure to check the units of measure for your rates. The units of measure for rates of flow are units/time period; the units of measure for fractional rates of flow are units per unit per time period = 1/time periods. For example, the interest rate on your credit card is not, say, 12%, but 12% *per year,* or, equivalently, 1% *per month* (0.12/year or 0.01/month). The economy doesn't grow at, say, 3.5%, but at a fractional rate of 3.5%/year.

4.1.2 Goal Seeking

Positive feedback loops generate growth, amplify deviations, and reinforce change. Negative loops seek balance, equilibrium, and stasis. Negative feedback loops act to bring the state of the system in line with a goal or desired state. They counteract any disturbances that move the state of the system away from the goal. All negative feedback loops have the structure shown in Figure 4-4. The state of

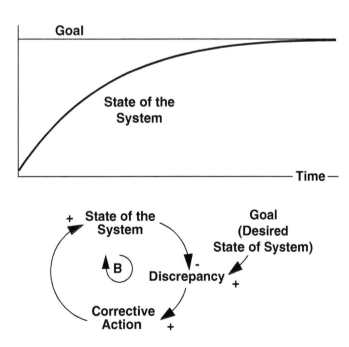

the system is compared to the goal. If there is a discrepancy between the desired and actual state, corrective action is initiated to bring the state of the system back in line with the goal. When you are hungry, you eat, satisfying your hunger; when tired, you sleep, restoring your energy and alertness. When a firm's inventory drops below the stock required to provide good service and selection, production increases until inventory is once again sufficient.

Every negative loop includes a process to compare the desired and actual conditions and take corrective action. Sometimes the desired state of the system and corrective action are explicit and under the control of a decision maker (e.g., the desired level of inventory). Sometimes the goal is implicit and not under conscious control, or under the control of human agency at all. The amount of sleep you need to feel well rested is a physiological factor not under your conscious control. The equilibrium surface temperature of the earth depends on the flux of solar energy and the concentration of greenhouse gases in the atmosphere, among other physical parameters. And a cup of coffee cools via negative feedback until it reaches room temperature.

In most cases, the rate at which the state of the system approaches its goal diminishes as the discrepancy falls. We do not often observe a constant rate of approach that suddenly stops just as the goal is reached. The gradual approach arises because large gaps between desired and actual states tend to generate large responses, while small gaps tend to elicit small responses. The flow of heat from your coffee cup to the air in the room is larger when the temperature gap between them is large and diminishes as the gap falls. When coffee and room temperatures are equal, there is no net heat flow between them.

When the relationship between the size of the gap and the corrective action is linear, the rate of adjustment is exactly proportional to the size of the gap and the resulting goal-seeking behavior is *exponential decay*. As the gap falls, so too does the adjustment rate. And just as exponential growth is characterized by its doubling time, pure exponential decay is characterized by its *half life*—the time it takes for half the remaining gap to be eliminated (see chapter 8).

Figure 4-5 shows examples of goal-seeking behavior. The top left panel shows the rate of defect generation in the wafer fabrication process of a major semiconductor manufacturer. In 1987, the company began a process improvement program using principles of Total Quality Management. The goal of the program was zero defects. In 4 years the defect rate declined from 1500 ppm to about 150 ppm. Note that as the defect rate fell, the rate of improvement declined. The top right panel shows the average load factor (up time) for two Finnish nuclear power plants started up in 1978. The fraction of the year the plants operated increased rapidly at first, then more slowly, until a maximum of about 94% was reached. The bottom left panel shows the share of all advertising dollars spent on television in the US. Growth was rapid in the 1950s, but reached a fairly steady level of about 20-25% by 1980. The bottom right panel shows the roughly exponential decline in automobile-related fatalities in the US per 100 million vehicle miles driven. Despite the substantial decline in death risk per mile, the number of miles driven has grown exponentially, so the total number killed on the roads each year has fluctuated between about 30 and 50 thousand since the 1930s.

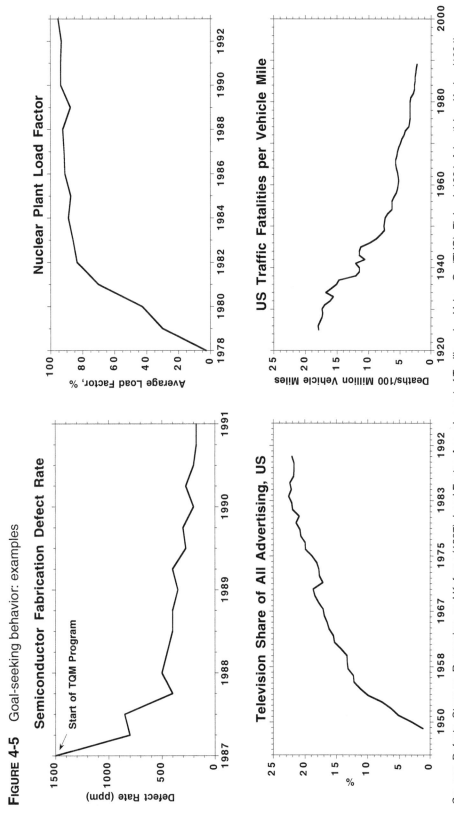

FIGURE 4-5 Goal-seeking behavior: examples

Sources: Defects: Sterman, Repenning, and Kofman (1997); Load Factor: Annual report of Teollisuuden Voima Oy (TVO), Finland, 1994; Advertising: Kurian (1994); Fatalities: Historical Statistics of the US, Statistical Abstract of the US.

4.1.3   Oscillation

Oscillation is the third fundamental mode of behavior observed in dynamic systems. Like goal-seeking behavior, oscillations are caused by negative feedback loops. The state of the system is compared to its goal, and corrective actions are taken to eliminate any discrepancies. In an oscillatory system, the state of the system constantly overshoots its goal or equilibrium state, reverses, then undershoots, and so on. The overshooting arises from the presence of significant time delays in the negative loop. The time delays cause corrective actions to continue even after the state of the system reaches its goal, forcing the system to adjust too much, and triggering a new correction in the opposite direction (Figure 4-6).

Oscillations are among the most common modes of behavior in dynamic systems. There are many types of oscillation, including damped oscillations, limit cycles, and chaos (see section 4.3.3). Each variant is caused by a particular feedback structure and set of parameters determining the strengths of the loops and the lengths of the delays. But every type of oscillation has, at its core, a negative feedback loop with delays.

Oscillations can arise if there is a significant delay in any part of the negative loop. As shown in Figure 4-6, there may be delays in any of the information links making up the loop. There may be delays in perceiving the state of the system caused by the measurement and reporting system. There may be delays in initiating corrective actions after the discrepancy is perceived due to the time required

FIGURE 4-6
Oscillation: structure and behavior

Delays can exist in any of the causal links in a negative feedback loop. Oscillation can occur if there are delays in at least one of the links in a negative loop.

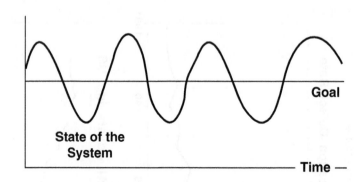

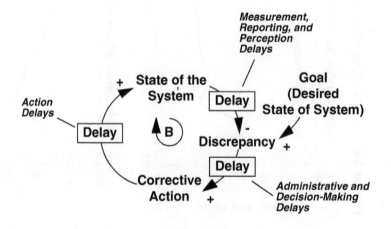

to reach a decision. And there may be delays between the initiation of a corrective action and its effect on the state of the system. It takes time for a company to measure and report inventory levels, time for management to meet and decide how much to produce, and more time while raw materials procurement, the labor force, and other needed resources respond to the new production schedule. Sufficiently long delays at any one of these points could cause inventory to oscillate.

Figure 4-3 showed real GDP in the US. The dominant mode of behavior in the data is exponential growth. But the growth is not smooth. Output fluctuates around the growth trend. In the top panel of Figure 4-7 these oscillations are revealed by detrending the GDP data (removing the best fit exponential function). After the exponential growth is removed, the business cycle is clearly visible as a fluctuation averaging about 5% in amplitude and with an average period of about 4 years. A longer and larger fluctuation in real production is also apparent, with peaks relative to trend around 1910 and 1970—the so-called economic long wave.[1] The bottom panels of Figure 4-7 show two critical business cycle indicators—capacity utilization in the US manufacturing sector and the civilian unemployment rate. The amplitude of the business cycle in these important variables is quite large. Utilization typically fluctuates 15 points from peak to trough (nearly 20% of its average value), while unemployment during the postwar period in the US has ranged from under 3% to nearly 11% of the labor force, with much higher values in Europe.

Note that the business cycle (and most real world oscillations) is not perfectly regular. You should not expect it to be. Many people think a cycle must be as predictable as the dawn, as regular as the orbits of the planets, as smooth and symmetric as the swing of a pendulum clock. But these paradigms of periodicity are special systems. The planets interact mainly with the sun and only weakly with one another.[2] A pendulum clock has been carefully designed to generate a regular motion by isolating its components from the environment. Biological, social, and economic systems, in contrast, involve huge numbers of interactions among tightly coupled elements. They are continuously bombarded by perturbations that cause their motion to be somewhat irregular, a (usually nonlinear) combination of their endogenous dynamics and these exogenous shocks (see section 4.3.2).

---

[1]The long wave, or Kondratiev cycle, has an average period of about 60 years and, as seen in the data, an amplitude much larger than the short-term business cycle. Sterman (1986) and Forrester (1977, 1983) present theory and evidence for the existence and feedback structure generating the long wave. Sterman (1985b) presents a simple model of the long wave; Sterman 1989a reports an experimental test of the model, and Sterman (1989c) shows that many of the decision rules characterizing human subjects in the experiment generate chaotic dynamics.

[2]Actually, the apparent regularity of the solar system is illusory. The length of the day is increasing as tidal and frictional forces dissipate the earth's rotational energy. Recent research shows that the orbits of most of the planets are chaotic and that chaotic resonances among the planets can hurl meteorites and asteroids from distant orbits into trajectories that cross the earth's orbit, perhaps accounting for the impacts now believed to have caused the major extinctions. It is only our short (by heavenly standards) record of observations that causes us to perceive the solar system to be stable and predictable. Peterson (1993) provides an excellent nontechnical treatment of chaotic dynamics in the solar system; Diacu and Holmes (1996) cover the origins of chaos in theories of celestial mechanics. Jack Wisdom of MIT pioneered computer simulations that revealed the chaotic character of the solar system (see Wisdom 1987 for a review). See section 4.3.3 for more on chaos.

FIGURE 4-7
Oscillation:
examples

The business
cycle in the
United States.

Top: Deviation
of real GDP
from long-term
exponential trend.

Middle: Capacity
utilization.

Bottom: Civilian
unemployment.

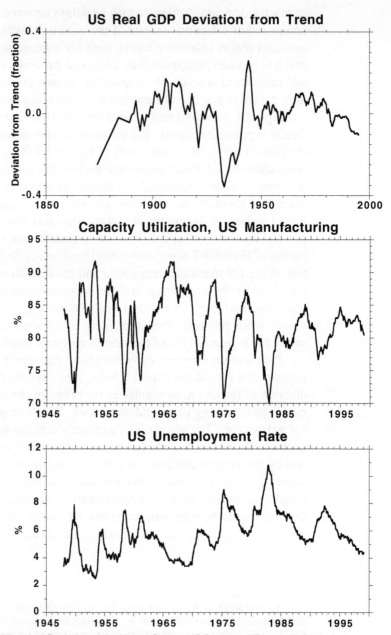

Source: Historical Statistics of the United States, US Bureau of Economic Analysis.

4.1.4   Process Point

The connection between structure and behavior provides a useful heuristic for the conceptualization process. Any time you observe exponential growth in a variable, you know there is at least one positive feedback in which the variables of interest participate (and possibly more). There will, of course, be many negative loops present as well. However, if the system is exhibiting exponential growth, then you know that positive loops are dominant (at least during the regime in which growth occurs). You can then guide the discussion among the client group toward the identification of self-reinforcing processes. Typically, the group will be able to identify many positive loops involving the variables of interest. Of course, it is not possible to tell which of these candidate loops are active and contributing to the behavior, nor their relative strengths, without recourse to data and/or model simulations. But focusing on the connection between structure and behavior helps generate fruitful hypotheses about the key loops.

Similarly, any time you observe the other core modes of behavior, you immediately know what types of loop must be dominant, guiding your initial search for the structures responsible. Oscillation, for example, must mean there is an important negative feedback with significant time delays. You can then ask about the decision processes by which the variable is regulated and the time delays in the perception of the state of the system, in the decision process, and in the response of the system to the corrective actions of the decision makers.

A caveat: This heuristic helps in the identification of the feedback structures responsible for the observed behavior. In addition, it is essential to consider what structures exist but have not yet played a significant role in the history of the system or left a trace in the available data. As the system evolves these latent feedbacks may become dominant, dramatically changing the dynamics, shifting trends and patterns, and altering the system's response to policies. Identifying potential shifts in loop dominance arising from latent structures is a valuable function of modeling.

To illustrate, return to the case of exponential growth. No real quantity can grow forever. Eventually, one or more negative loops will become dominant as various limits to growth are approached. Immediately after identifying some positive loops potentially responsible for observed growth, you should ask, What negative loops might stop the growth? Most people can easily generate a wide range of potential limits and constraints to the growth of the system. Identifying the potential constraints to growth is a powerful way to identify possible future bottlenecks and limits, even if there is no evidence of a slowdown in the data. As with the identification of positive loops, empirical investigation and modeling are required to determine which negative loops are strongest, what limits to growth they reflect, and whether those limits can be relaxed or tightened by other feedbacks or through policy interventions (see section 4.2.1).

| CHALLENGE | ## Identifying Feedback Structure from System Behavior |

1. Identify the positive loops responsible for the growth in the examples shown in Figure 4-3. Sketch a causal loop diagram to capture the loops you identify. Identify as many negative feedbacks that might halt growth in these systems as you can.

2. Identify the negative loops that might be responsible for the goal-seeking behaviors shown in Figure 4-5. Identify the state of the system, the goal, and the corrective action(s) for each case. What counterforces might prevent the state of the system from reaching its goal?

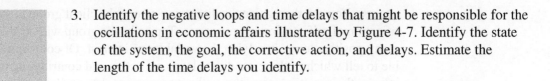

3. Identify the negative loops and time delays that might be responsible for the oscillations in economic affairs illustrated by Figure 4-7. Identify the state of the system, the goal, the corrective action, and delays. Estimate the length of the time delays you identify.

4.2   INTERACTIONS OF THE FUNDAMENTAL MODES

The three basic modes of behavior—exponential growth, goal seeking, and oscillation—are caused by three basic feedback structures: positive feedback, negative feedback, and negative feedback with delays. Other, more complex patterns of behavior arise through the nonlinear interaction of these structures with one another.

4.2.1   S-shaped Growth

As discussed above, no real quantity can grow (or decline) forever: eventually one or more constraints halt the growth. A commonly observed mode of behavior in dynamic systems is *S-shaped growth*—growth is exponential at first, but then gradually slows until the state of the system reaches an equilibrium level. The shape of the curve resembles a stretched-out "S" (Figure 4-8). To understand the structure underlying S-shaped growth it is helpful to use the ecological concept of *carrying capacity*. The carrying capacity of any habitat is the number of organisms of a particular type it can support and is determined by the resources available in the

FIGURE 4-8
S-shaped growth: structure and behavior

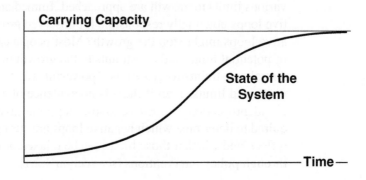

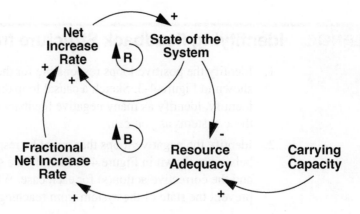

environment and the resource requirements of the population. As a population approaches its carrying capacity, resources per capita diminish thereby reducing the fractional net increase rate until there are just enough resources per capita to balance births and deaths, at which point the net increase rate is zero and the population reaches equilibrium. Any real quantity undergoing exponential growth can be interpreted as a population drawing on the resources in its environment. As the capacity of the environment is approached, the adequacy of the required resources diminishes, and the fractional net increase rate must decline. The state of the system continues to grow, but at a slower rate, until resources are just scarce enough to halt growth. In general, a population may depend on many resources, each creating a negative loop which might limit growth. The constraint that is most binding determines which of the negative loops will be most influential as the state of the system grows.

The carrying capacity concept is subtle and complex. While it is appropriate to consider the carrying capacity of an environment to be constant in some situations, in general the carrying capacity of an environment is intimately intertwined with the evolution and dynamics of the species it supports. We humans alter the carrying capacity of the planet in ways both intended and unintended, through the development of technology enabling greater utilization of resources, through changes in cultural practices and norms for consumption of resources per capita, and through consumption, depletion, and erosion of the various resources upon which we depend. Even so-called lower species interact with their environment to alter the carrying capacity. The co-evolution of flowers and pollinating insects permitted greater population densities for both. Similarly, all businesses and organizations grow in the context of a market, society, and physical environment that imposes limits to their growth. As with natural populations, these limits can increase or decrease, both exogenously and, more importantly, endogenously, as the organization interacts with its customers, competitors, suppliers, regulators, and other entities in the system. In general, one must model the various resources that together determine the carrying capacity—for a species or an organization—as an endogenous element of the system.

Despite the dynamic character of the carrying capacity, there is, at any moment, a limit to the size of the population (the current carrying capacity), which, if exceeded, causes the population to fall. Further, the carrying capacity itself cannot grow forever. The laws of thermodynamics dictate an absolute limit to the carrying capacity of the earth, though there is no agreement among scholars as to what that level is, how it is changing, whether population should grow to the carrying capacity or be voluntarily stabilized below it, or whether a population as large as the carrying capacity would enable a reasonable quality of life or provide only the bare minimum for subsistence.[3]

A system generates S-shaped growth only if two critical conditions are met. First, the negative loops must not include any significant time delays (if they did, the system would overshoot and oscillate around the carrying capacity; see section

---

[3]For good discussion of the uncertainty in definitions and estimates of the earth's carrying capacity, see Cohen (1995). For system dynamics models in which the carrying capacity of the earth is treated endogenously and dynamically, see Meadows, Meadows, and Randers (1992).

FIGURE 4-9
S-shaped growth: examples

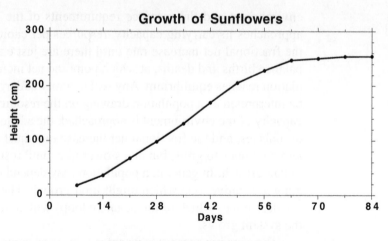

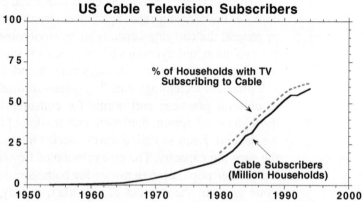

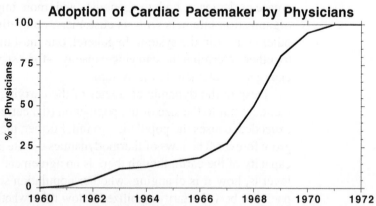

Source: Sunflowers: Lotka (1956, p. 74); Cable TV: Kurian (1994), Statistical Abstract of the US; Pacemaker adoption: Homer (1983, 1987).

4.2.2). Second, the carrying capacity must be fixed. It cannot be consumed by the growth of the population, lest the population exhaust its resources and force itself into extinction, as a population of yeast consumes the sugar in a cask of wine, ultimately causing fermentation to stop (see section 4.2.3).

A key aspect of the structure generating S-shaped growth is that the interaction of the positive and negative loops must be nonlinear. At first, when the state of the system is small relative to the resource base, the limits to growth are distant and the positive loops dominate. An additional unit added to the state of the system contributes more to the net increase rate than it decreases the fractional net increase rate by reducing resource adequacy. The state of the system grows exponentially. However, as a direct consequence of that growth, the adequacy of the resource base falls. As the limits to growth are approached, the negative loops grow stronger and stronger, until they begin to dominate the dynamics. The inflection point in the curve is the point where the system, though still growing, shifts from acceleration to deceleration. The inflection marks the point at which there is a shift in loop dominance. It is the point at which an additional unit added to the state of the system reduces the fractional net increase rate more than it adds to the total population driving the growth.

Figure 4-9 shows some examples of S-shaped growth. Whether the growth of a plant, the diffusion of a new product or service such as cable television, or the adoption of a new idea or technology like the cardiac pacemaker, growth always confronts limits.

4.2.2   S-Shaped Growth with Overshoot

S-shaped growth requires the negative feedbacks that constrain growth to act swiftly as the carrying capacity is approached. Often, however, there are significant time delays in these negative loops. Time delays in the negative loops lead to the possibility that the state of the system will overshoot and oscillate around the carrying capacity (Figure 4-10). Figure 4-11 shows some examples of S-shaped growth with overshoot and oscillation.

FIGURE 4-10
S-shaped growth with overshoot and oscillation: structure and behavior

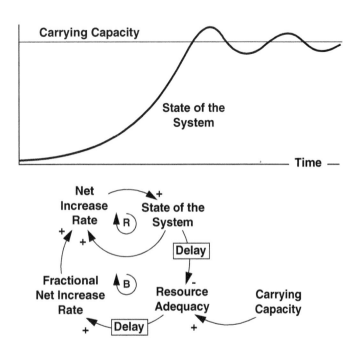

FIGURE 4-11
S-shaped growth
with overshoot
and oscillation:
examples

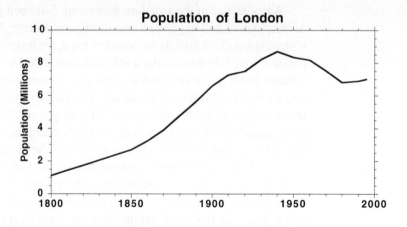

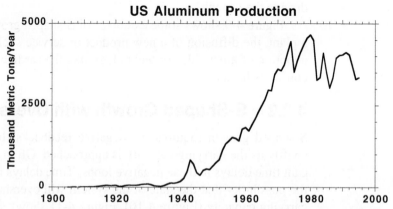

Source: London Population: 1800-1960, Mitchell (1975, p. 77); 1970-1995, 1997 Annual Abstract of
Statistics, UK Office for National Statistics. Aluminum Production: USGS; http://minerals.er.usgs.gov/
minerals/pubs/commodity/

CHALLENGE | # Identifying the Limits to Growth

What are the limits to growth for the population of a city and the rise in production
of commodities such as aluminum? Identify the negative feedbacks that halt the
growth in each case. Identify the time delays responsible for the overshoot and
fluctuation.[4]

---

[4]In *Urban Dynamics,* Forrester (1969) presents a model of urban growth and stagnation, showing how many urban renewal policies actually accelerate the decay of the inner city. Mass (1975)
and Schroeder, Sweeney, and Alfeld (1975) extend and apply the results of *Urban Dynamics,* and
Alfeld and Graham (1976) build up a simplified version of the *Urban Dynamics* model suitable for
teaching.

4.2.3   Overshoot and Collapse

The second critical assumption underlying S-shaped growth is that the carrying capacity is fixed. Often, however, the ability of the environment to support a growing population is eroded or consumed by the population itself. For example, the population of deer in a forest can grow so large that they overbrowse the vegetation, leading to starvation and a precipitous decline in the population. Figure 4-12 shows the feedback structure and typical behavior for the overshoot and collapse behavior mode.

Consumption or erosion of the carrying capacity by the population creates a second negative feedback limiting growth. Population growth now cuts resource adequacy two ways: by reducing the resources available per capita and by reducing total resources. As in the S-shaped growth case, when resources are initially ample the positive growth loop dominates and the state of the system grows exponentially. As it grows, resource adequacy drops. The negative loops gradually gain in strength. At some point, the net increase rate falls to zero, and the population reaches its maximum. But unlike the S-shaped growth case, the system does not reach equilibrium. When the population reaches its peak, the rate of decline of the carrying capacity is at its maximum. The carrying capacity continues to drop, resources per capita fall further, and the net increase rate of the population becomes negative. The state of the system declines. Even as it declines, the remaining population continues to consume the carrying capacity, so resources per capita remain

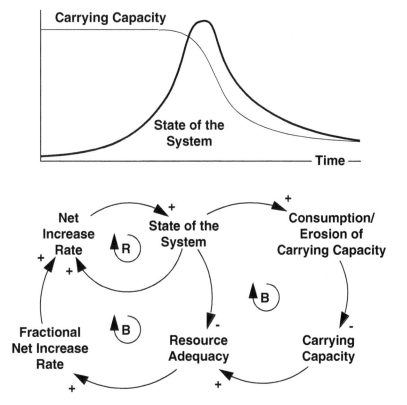

FIGURE 4-12
Overshoot and collapse: structure and behavior

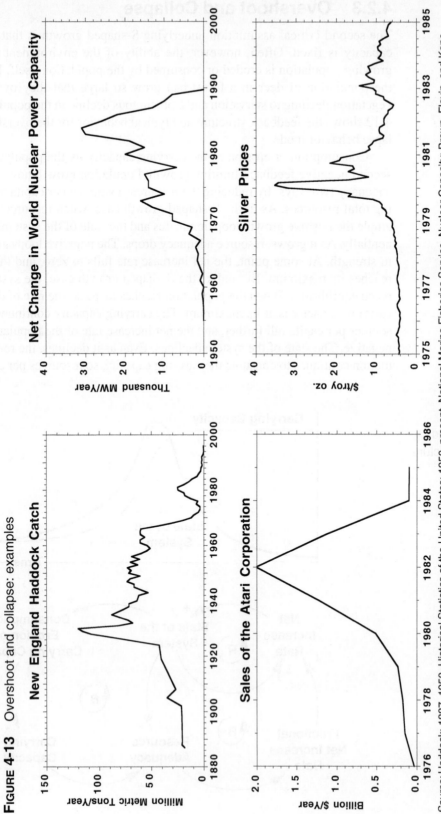

FIGURE **4-13** Overshoot and collapse: examples

Source: Haddock: 1887–1950, Historical Statistics of the United States; 1950–present, National Marine Fisheries Service. Nuclear Capacity: Brown, Flavin, and Kane (1992). Atari: Paich and Sterman (1993). Silver Prices: Cash Price, Datastream database.

insufficient and the population keeps falling. If there is no regeneration of the carrying capacity (if it is strictly nonrenewable), the equilibrium of the system is extinction: any nonzero population continues to consume the resource base, forcing it to zero, and with it, the population. If the carrying capacity can be regenerated or supplemented with renewable resources, a nonzero equilibrium can be sustained.

Figure 4-13 shows some examples of overshoot and collapse. The New England Haddock fishery collapsed due to overfishing of Georges Bank, once one of the world's richest fishing areas. Overfishing has also shut down the Canadian and US cod fishery, and similar overexploitation is common in fisheries around the world.[5] Nuclear power construction ground to a halt in the 1980s as high-level waste—and public concern over safety—accumulated and as the costs of nuclear power steadily escalated. The Atari Corporation was the leader of the first wave of home and arcade video games in the late 1970s. Sales doubled roughly every year from 1976 through 1982. Abrupt saturation of the market—depletion of the stock of potential customers—led to a precipitous drop in sales from $2 billion per year in 1982 to $100 million per year in 1984. The company lost about $600 million during the collapse. Silver experienced a classic speculative bubble in the late 1970s, with prices rising tenfold in a year, then collapsing even more precipitously.

The interplay between population and carrying capacity leading to overshoot and collapse is illustrated in Figure 4-14, which shows the population of Easter Island (Rapa Nui in the local language) and a measure of the carrying capacity derived from pollen cores indicating the extent of tree cover.

Easter Island, one of the most remote spots on earth, is a small island of about 160 km² located in the eastern Pacific. Easter Island is most famous for the giant stone statues, known as moai, that dot the island. Radiocarbon dating puts the arrival of the first settlers, intrepid sailors of Polynesian origin, at about the year 400 and not later than 690. Population is estimated to have grown slowly until about 1100, when growth accelerated dramatically, perhaps doubling about every century, until about the year 1400. Pollen counts from soil cores and other records show that prior to the arrival of the first humans, Easter Island was lushly forested and supported a diverse set of fauna, particularly birds (Bahn and Flenley 1992; Steadman 1995). However, as the human population grew, the forests were progressively cut to provide wood and fiber for boats, structures, ropes, and tools, as well as to provide firewood. The Polynesian rat, which arrived with the original settlers, hastened the decline by killing birds and eating the seeds and nuts of the native palm.

By about the year 1400, deforestation was nearly complete. The loss of tree cover dramatically reduced the island's carrying capacity. There is clear stratigraphic evidence that soil erosion increased with deforestation as rain washed away the unprotected soil. Without tree cover, wind speeds at ground level increased, carrying still more valuable soil into the sea. The erosion was so severe

---

[5]The "Fishbanks" simulation (Meadows, Fiddaman, and Shannon 1993) is a wonderful role-play management flight simulator illustrating the dynamics of renewable resources such as fisheries.

FIGURE 4-14

Estimated population and tree cover of Easter Island

Top: Population estimates for Easter Island are highly uncertain. The graph shows the likely range of population based on data in Bahn and Flenley (1992, pp. 80, 178ff).

Bottom: Pollen records from soil core at Rano Kau, Easter Island, showing decline in the fraction of pollen from trees and shrubs, indicating the deforestation of the island (remainder of pollen from grasses, sedges, herbs, and ferns). Deforestation was essentially complete by about 1400.

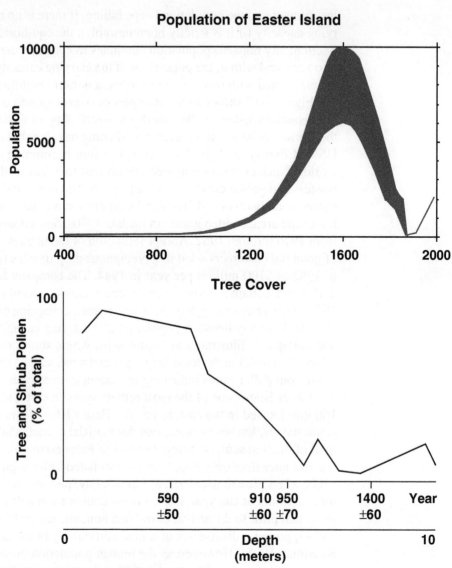

Note: Time axes for top and bottom graphs differ.

Source: Bahn and Flenley (1992, p. 174).

that sediment washed from the higher elevations eventually covered many of the moai, so that European visitors thought the giant statues were just heads, when in fact they were complete torsos averaging 20 feet in height. Deforestation also increased evaporation from the soil and may have reduced rainfall. The few streams on the island dried up, further reducing food production and the fresh water supply. Eventually, fishing, the other main source of food, also fell, as boats, lines, and hooks, all made from wood, could no longer be replaced. When the first Europeans arrived, the islanders prized wood above all other items offered in trade. Most of the bird species living on Easter Island became at least locally extinct. Only 1 of about 25 indigenous species still nests on the island today (Steadman 1995).

As the carrying capacity declined, population growth slowed, reaching a peak generally estimated to be between 6000 and 10,000 people around the year 1600. A precipitous decline in population had set in by about 1680, accompanied by major changes in social, political, and religious structures. Spear points and other tools of war appeared for the first time, and there is evidence of large battles among competing groups. Some scholars believe there is evidence of cannibalism during this period. The first Europeans known to visit Easter Island arrived in 1722 and found a small and poor population. Scholars generally accept an estimate of 2000 people in 1786. After Peruvian slave raids and a subsequent smallpox epidemic the population fell to 111 in 1877. The population recovered to about 2100 by the early 1990s, largely the result of immigration and settlement from Chile, which has governed the island since 1888.

The overshoot and collapse of Easter Island is but one of many similar episodes documented in the history of island biogeography (see Kirch 1997). In each case, population growth led to deforestation, the extinction of native species, and unfavorable changes in local climate, rainfall, and agricultural productivity, followed by starvation, conflict, and, often, population collapse.[6]

4.3   OTHER MODES OF BEHAVIOR

Growth, goal seeking, oscillation, and their combinations: are these the only patterns of behavior systems can exhibit? No, but they cover the vast majority of dynamics. There are other patterns, for example: (1) stasis, or equilibrium, in which the state of the system remains constant over time; and (2) random variation.

4.3.1   Stasis, or Equilibrium

Constancy arises either because dynamics affecting the state of the system are so slow that change is imperceptible or because there are powerful negative feedback processes keeping the state of the system nearly constant even in the face of environmental disturbances. In the former case, change is too slow relative to your time horizon to be meaningful. In the latter case, constancy is an example of highly effective goal-seeking behavior. The firmness and reliability with which you remain in contact with the ground when standing reflects the equilibrium caused by a powerful negative feedback loop: as gravity causes you to sink into the earth, the electrons in the atoms of the ground exert greater and greater upward force on the electrons in the atoms of your feet until the force of their mutual electrostatic repulsion just offsets the force of gravity, at which point you come to rest.

4.3.2   Randomness

Many variables appear to vary randomly. In most situations, randomness is a measure of our ignorance, not intrinsic to the system. (Except in quantum mechanics,

---

[6]The Easter Island data above are drawn primarily from Bahn and Flenley (1992), Kirch (1984), and Van Tilburg (1994). These works, along with Kirch (1997) and Steadman (1995), provide a good survey of recent research on the biological and human history of Rapa Nui and other island ecosystems.

where Einstein's famous lament "God does not play dice with the universe!" appears to be wrong. However, the random behavior of elementary particles near the Planck scale has little if any bearing on the dynamics of macroscopic systems such as a company). When we say there are "random" variations in, say, the demand for a firm's product, what we actually mean is that we don't know the reasons for these variations. We are revealing the limitations of our understanding, not characterizing a feature of reality. The demand for a firm's product may be growing and may also experience a seasonal cycle. The firm may understand and can perhaps even forecast the trend and seasonal cycle with some accuracy. But after accounting for these sources of change, people tend to call the residual variation random as if the customers were somehow rolling dice to decide whether to buy the product. People generally have reasons for behaving as they do, but the managers of the firm are not aware of either their decision rules or the information they use to make their decisions. The managers' model of customer behavior is imperfect. If the firm could, through additional modeling and fieldwork, discover those rules and their inputs, they could explain more of the total variation in demand, and some of what was formerly deemed random would now be resolved into their theory of the system structure.

As a practical matter, no one can never know all the local conditions and idiosyncrasies causing a customer to place an order today or wait until tomorrow or cause a machine to break down now instead of 3 hours from now. The aggregate impact of the individual deviations from average behavior means systems are bathed in a continuous rain of random shocks. Engineers term these random perturbations "noise," after the distortion heard on telephone lines caused by thermal fluctuations of the atoms in the wires. Of course, the rain of random shocks includes the occasional downpour, or even flood (for example, note the impact of WWII on economic output in the US, Figure 4-3).

The rain of random noise falling on our systems does play an important role in dynamics, however. By constantly knocking systems away from their current trajectory, noise can excite modes of behavior that otherwise would lie dormant. A pendulum swinging in the air will tend towards equilibrium as friction dissipates its energy; eventually the bob of the pendulum comes to rest, straight down. However, perturb the bob with small, random jolts, and soon it will begin swinging, somewhat irregularly, with a rhythm close to its natural frequency. The structure of the system has the potential to oscillate, but energy from some external source such as high-frequency random noise is required to excite its latent dynamics (chapters 18-20 provide examples). Random noise can also unfreeze systems that are stuck on local optima, sending them into a new neighborhood where the dynamics are quite different, and can determine which of many equally attractive paths a system takes, contributing to path dependence (see chapter 10). These disturbances can be modeled as random variations around the average behavior given by the equations capturing the feedback structure of the system. Other times it is more appropriate to model the individual elements and actors in the system, in which case nonaverage behavior arises from the heterogeneity of the population of agents. These roles for random perturbations will be explored in later chapters.

4.3.3   Chaos

In recent years chaos has become a ubiquitous buzz word in the popular press and management literature. Books and articles by a host of new age management gurus warn companies to "manage at the edge of chaos" or be overtaken by more nimble competitors. Extravagant claims have been made that chaos is a new and radically different science, one which is fundamentally nonlinear and complex, one that can't be explained without some mysterious new theory. Actually, the term "chaos" has a narrow and precise technical meaning in dynamical theory. Unfortunately, the hunger for the latest fad in the business world, reinforced by marketing hype attending the development of chaos and complexity theory, has led to the misappropriation and dilution of the term. To explain chaos I first describe some more common types of oscillations.

Damped Oscillations: Local Stability

One important characteristic of oscillations is damping: if an oscillatory system is perturbed once and then left undisturbed, will the fluctuations die out? If so, the cycle is damped. Many systems are damped oscillators. The classic example is a pendulum like a child's swing: Given a single push, the arc traversed by the swing steadily diminishes as friction dissipates its energy, until it eventually comes to rest. If you could reduce the frictional energy losses of the pendulum, damping would be weaker and it would take longer and longer for equilibrium to be reestablished after a shock. In the (unattainable) limit of zero friction, a single shock would cause a perpetual oscillation at a constant amplitude.

The equilibrium of the damped pendulum is said to be *locally stable:* perturbations will cause the system to oscillate, but it will eventually return to the same equilibrium. The qualifier "locally" is important. Real systems are nonlinear, meaning that the feedback loops and parameters governing the dynamics vary depending on the state of the system (where the system is operating in state space—the space created by the state variables of the system).[7] Local stability means the perturbations have to be small relative to nonlinearities that might cause other dynamics to emerge, as when the pendulum is swung so hard it breaks.

Many real world oscillators are damped, but the oscillations never die away because the systems are continually bombarded with noise. Many models suggest that the short-term business cycle (Figure 4-7) is a damped, locally stable oscillation (chapter 19). The oscillatory structure is a set of negative feedback loops through which firms adjust production to control their inventories of products and raw materials. These loops are oscillatory because of the lags in the adjustment of production to changes in demand and inventory, particularly delays in hiring and

---

[7]In a simple pendulum, there are two state variables: the position of the pendulum and its momentum. These two states define a two-dimensional space, and the state of the system is defined at any time by the point in that space corresponding to the position and momentum of the pendulum. As the pendulum swings through its arc, its trajectory traces out a curve in state space. More complex systems have high-dimensional state spaces, but the concept of a trajectory in state space remains the same.

materials acquisition (Forrester 1961; Mass 1975). In these models, both the persistence and irregularity of the business cycle are caused by the excitation of the economy by random shocks, just as the simple pendulum discussed above fluctuates somewhat irregularly when perturbed by noise.

Figure 4-15 shows an example of damped oscillation in a simple model of a firm based on the Beer Distribution Game (Sterman 1989b, chap. 17). The game represents the supply chain in a typical manufacturing industry. The supply chain has four sectors: a retailer, wholesaler, distributor, and factory. Each stage is identical and managed by a different person. The managers strive to minimize their costs by controlling inventories as they seek to meet incoming demand. The simulation shows the response of the factory order rate to a one-time change in customer orders. The decision rule used by each agent in the simulation was estimated from the behavior of actual players. In response to the shock in demand, factory orders exhibit a damped oscillation which returns the system to equilibrium after about 70 weeks. Here the negative loop is the process by which each stage in the supply chain manages its inventory: ordering more when inventories are inadequate and less when they are high. The delays arise from the time required to process orders and produce and deliver the beer.

Expanding Oscillations and Limit Cycles

While many oscillatory systems are damped, the equilibria of other systems are locally unstable, meaning that small disturbances tend to move the system farther away from the equilibrium point. Imagine a ball balanced on top of a hill. As long as the ball is exactly balanced on the hilltop, it remains in equilibrium. But the slightest breeze pushes the ball down the hill ever so slightly, leading to a still greater force downhill, in a positive feedback. The equilibrium is unstable. While an equilibrium may be locally unstable, any real system must be globally stable. Global stability means the trajectories of the system do not diverge to infinity: the trajectories are bounded because the positive feedbacks leading to the accelerating flight from the balance point must ultimately be limited by various negative loops. The ball cannot accelerate indefinitely, but will come to rest at the bottom of the hill.

FIGURE 4-15

Damped oscillation in a model of the Beer Distribution Game

Note the nonlinearity: between weeks 30 and 45 there is a large surplus of inventory but orders are constrained to be nonnegative.

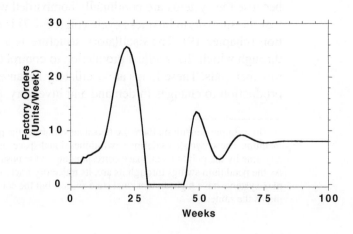

If an oscillatory system with a locally unstable equilibrium is given a slight nudge off its equilibrium point, its swings grow larger and larger until they are constrained by various nonlinearities. Such oscillations are known as *limit cycles,* to denote the nonlinear limits restricting their amplitude. In limit cycles, the states of the system remain within certain ranges (they are limited to a certain region of state space). In the steady state, after the effects of any initial perturbations have died out, a limit cycle follows a particular orbit (closed curve) in state space. The steady state orbit is known as an attractor, since trajectories near enough to it will move toward it, just as the bob of the damped pendulum is attracted to its stable equilibrium point.

Figure 4-16 shows an example of a limit cycle from the Beer Distribution Game. The situation in the figure is the same as described above for the damped oscillation except that the parameters of the ordering decision rule are slightly different. As in the case of the damped oscillation, the parameters characterize the behavior of an actual player. Again, there is a one-time change in customer demand. Instead of dying out, the cycle persists indefinitely, even though the environment is completely unchanging. The figure shows the cycle both as a time series and as a so-called phase plot with orders on the vertical axis and inventory on the horizontal axis, showing the closed orbit perpetually traced by the system.

Of course, limit cycles are not perpetual motion machines. The energy required to maintain the cycle must be provided from a source outside the oscillator. Limit cycles are quite common. Your life depends on them—your heartbeat and respiration are limit cycles. The circadian rhythms (daily fluctuations in alertness, hormone production, and a host of other physiological parameters) observed in almost all organisms, from bacteria to people, are limit cycles. Many cycles in the biological world also appear to be limit cycles, including cycles in predator-prey populations, cycles in the mass fruiting of certain plant species such as Piñon pines and some bamboos, and the periodic population explosions of certain insects such as the 17-year cicada (see Murray 1993). Many models suggest that very long-term

FIGURE 4-16   A limit cycle generated in the Beer Distribution Game

Left: Time series of factory orders. The cycle repeats indefinitely without any external variation.
Right: The orbit of the system is a closed curve, shown here with factory orders plotted against net factory inventory (inventory less backlog).

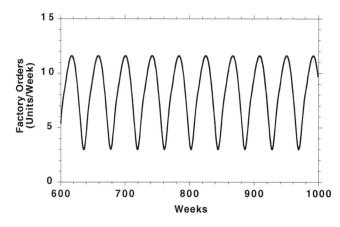
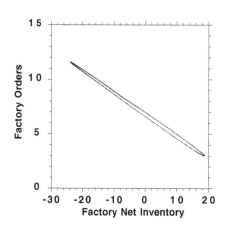

fluctuations in the world economy known as "long waves" are self-perpetuating limit cycles (Sterman 1985; Forrester 1983). Sterman (1989a) reports an experiment in which people managed a simple economic model; the vast majority generated long waves much like the behavior of the model. Sterman (1989c) shows that many of the decision rules characterizing the human subjects generate chaos and various forms of limit cycle.

Chaotic Oscillations

Chaos, like damped fluctuations and limit cycles, is a form of oscillation. However, unlike limit cycles, a chaotic system fluctuates irregularly, never exactly repeating, even though its motion is completely deterministic. The irregularity arises endogenously and is not created by external, random shocks. Like a limit cycle, the path of a chaotic system is bounded to a certain region of state space. Because chaotic systems are bounded, chaos, like limit cycles, can only arise in nonlinear systems. However, unlike linear systems or limit cycles, chaotic dynamics do not have a well-defined period, as does the simple pendulum discussed above. The motion of a chaotic system never repeats; instead, the orbits of the system approach what is known as a strange attractor—a set of closely related but slightly different orbits rather than a single closed curve. Furthermore, chaotic systems have the property known as sensitive dependence on initial conditions. Two nearby trajectories, no matter how close, will diverge exponentially until the state of one provides no more information about the state of the other than any randomly chosen trajectory. Sensitive dependence means that the prediction horizon for chaotic systems—the length of time over which forecasts of future behavior are accurate—is likely to be short even if our model of the system structure and parameter estimates are perfect. Further, the cost of increasing the prediction horizon a fixed amount by improving our knowledge of the current state of the system increases exponentially.

Figure 4-17 shows chaotic behavior in a simulation of the Beer Distribution Game. Only the parameters of the decision rule for orders have been altered; again,

FIGURE 4-17   Chaos in the Beer Distribution Game
Left: Time series showing factory orders. *Right:* Phase plot showing orders vs. net factory inventory (inventory less backlog).

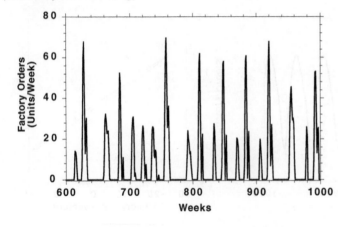
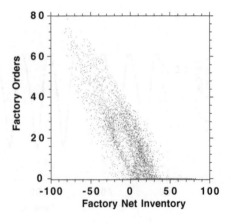

these parameters were estimated from the behavior of an actual player. Like the limit cycle, orders fluctuate indefinitely, in this case with an amplitude ranging from 0 to about 50 units per week and an average period of about 20 weeks. Unlike the limit cycle, the oscillation does not have a regular amplitude, periodicity, or shape, even though the environment is completely constant and the system is completely free of random shocks. The trajectory of the system in state space follows a well-defined path, but one which never closes on itself.[8]

In all three of these cases, damped oscillation, limit cycle, and chaos, the feedback structure and decision rules are the same. The only differences are in the parameters of the ordering rule such as the size of desired inventory and the aggressiveness with which managers react to the discrepancy between desired and actual inventory.

4.4   SUMMARY

The feedback structure of a system generates its behavior. Most dynamics observed in the real world are examples of a small set of basic patterns or modes of behavior. Three of these modes are fundamental: exponential growth, goal seeking, and oscillation. Each of these modes is generated by a particular underlying feedback structure. Exponential growth is generated by positive feedback processes, goal seeking is generated by negative feedback, and oscillation is generated by negative feedback with delays. More complex patterns of behavior such as S-shaped growth, growth with overshoot, and overshoot and collapse result from the nonlinear interaction of these basic feedback structures.

The principle that the structure of a system generates its behavior leads to a useful heuristic to help modelers discover the feedback loop structure of a system. Whenever a particular pattern of behavior is observed, you know which of the basic feedback structures must have been dominant during the period covered by the data. Observing that a variable of interest has been fluctuating, for example, implies the existence of (at least) one negative feedback loop with significant time delays, which helps to guide the search for the particular structures, decision processes, and time delays that comprise the negative loop. While this heuristic is useful as an aid to the initial conceptualization process, modelers must also take care to search for and include in their models the feedback loops and structures that have not been important in generating the dynamics to date but that may become active as the system evolves.

---

[8]Mosekilde (1996) provides an excellent treatment of chaotic and other nonlinear dynamics in the Beer Distribution Game and a wide variety of other physical, technical, and biological systems. Strogatz (1994) provides an excellent mathematical introduction to nonlinear dynamics and chaos.

Part II

Tools for Systems Thinking

This section introduces and develops the basic tools of systems thinking and system dynamics. Chapter 5 presents causal loop diagrams, a technique for mapping the feedback loop structure of systems. Chapter 6 introduces the concept of stocks and flows, showing how the stock and flow structure of systems can be mapped and how stock and flow structure can be integrated with feedback loop structure to yield additional insights into dynamics. Chapter 7 discusses the dynamics of stocks and flows. Here the intuitive concepts behind the calculus are developed so that modelers can understand the relationship between structure and behavior of systems without requiring the use of advanced mathematics. Chapter 8 combines stock and flow structure and feedback to derive the behavior of the simplest feedback systems, showing how exponential growth arises from positive feedback and how negative feedback processes produce adjustment to a goal. These structures form the building blocks from which all more complex systems are developed. Mastering these tools is essential for all systems thinkers, whether they intend to build formal simulation models or only qualitative conceptual maps.

5

Causal Loop Diagrams

We shape our buildings; thereafter, our buildings shape us.

—Winston Churchill

Feedback is one of the core concepts of system dynamics. Yet our mental models often fail to include the critical feedbacks determining the dynamics of our systems. In system dynamics we use several diagramming tools to capture the structure of systems, including causal loop diagrams and stock and flow maps. This chapter focuses on causal loop diagrams, including guidelines, pitfalls, and examples.

5.1 CAUSAL DIAGRAM NOTATION

Causal loop diagrams (CLDs) are an important tool for representing the feedback structure of systems. Long used in academic work, and increasingly common in business, CLDs are excellent for

- Quickly capturing your hypotheses about the causes of dynamics;
- Eliciting and capturing the mental models of individuals or teams;
- Communicating the important feedbacks you believe are responsible for a problem.

The conventions for drawing causal diagrams are simple but should be followed faithfully. Think of causal diagrams as musical scores. Neatness counts, and idiosyncratic symbols and styles make it hard for fellow musicians to read your score. At first, you may find it difficult to construct and interpret these diagrams. With practice, however, you will soon be sight-reading.

A causal diagram consists of variables connected by arrows denoting the causal influences among the variables. The important feedback loops are also identified in the diagram. Figure 5-1 shows an example and key to the notation.

Variables are related by *causal links*, shown by arrows. In the example, the birth rate is determined by both the population and the fractional birth rate. Each causal link is assigned a polarity, either positive $(+)$ or negative $(-)$ to indicate how the dependent variable changes when the independent variable changes. The important loops are highlighted by a loop identifier which shows whether the loop is a positive (reinforcing) or negative (balancing) feedback. Note that the loop identifier circulates in the same direction as the loop to which it corresponds. In the example, the positive feedback relating births and population is clockwise and so is its loop identifier; the negative death rate loop is counterclockwise along with its identifier.

Table 5-1 summarizes the definitions of link polarity.

FIGURE 5-1
Causal loop
diagram notation

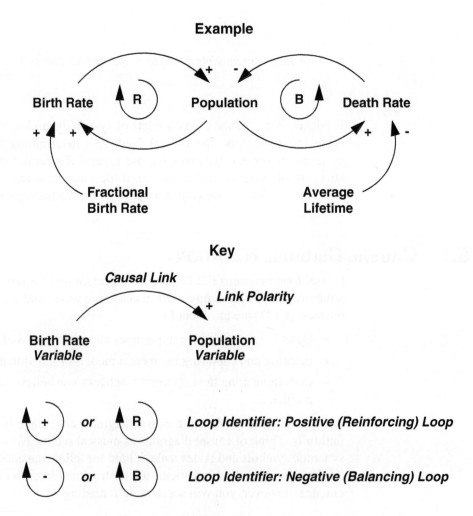

Example

Birth Rate   R   Population   B   Death Rate

Fractional
Birth Rate

Average
Lifetime

Key

Causal Link

Link Polarity

Birth Rate
Variable

Population
Variable

+) or R)   *Loop Identifier: Positive (Reinforcing) Loop*

-) or B)   *Loop Identifier: Negative (Balancing) Loop*

A positive link means that if the cause **increases,** the effect **increases** *above what it would otherwise have been,* and if the cause **decreases,** the effect **decreases** *below what it would otherwise have been.* In the example in Figure 5-1 an increase in the fractional birth rate means the birth rate (in people per year) will increase above what it would have been, and a decrease in the fractional birth rate means the birth rate will fall below what it would have been. That is, if average fertility rises, the birth rate, given the population, will rise; if fertility falls, the number of births will fall. When the cause is a rate of flow that accumulates into a stock then it is also true that the cause adds to the stock. In the example, births add to the population (see chapter 6 for more on stocks and flows).

A negative link means that if the cause **increases,** the effect **decreases** *below what it would otherwise have been,* and if the cause **decreases,** the effect **increases** *above what it would otherwise have been.* In the example, an increase in the average lifetime of the population means the death rate (in people per year) will fall below what it would have been, and a decrease in the average lifetime means the death rate will rise above what it would have been. That is, if life expectancy increases, the number of deaths will fall; and if life expectancy falls, the death rate will rise.

Link polarities describe the structure of the system. They do not describe the behavior of the variables. That is, they describe what would happen **IF** there were a change. They do not describe what actually happens. The fractional birth rate might increase; it might decrease—the causal diagram doesn't tell you what *will* happen. Rather, it tells you what *would* happen if the variable were to change.

Note the phrase *above (or below) what it otherwise would have been* in the definition of link polarity. An increase in a cause variable does not necessarily mean the effect will actually increase. There are two reasons. First, a variable often has more than one input. To determine what actually happens you need to know how all the inputs are changing. In the population example, the birth rate depends

TABLE 5-1   Link polarity: definitions and examples

Symbol	Interpretation	Mathematics	Examples
X $\xrightarrow{+}$ Y	All else equal, if X increases (decreases), then Y increases (decreases) above (below) what it would have been. In the case of accumulations, X adds to Y.	$\partial Y/\partial X > 0$ In the case of accumulations, $Y = \int_{t_0}^{t} (X + \ldots)\,ds + Y_{t_0}$	Product Quality $\xrightarrow{+}$ Sales Effort $\xrightarrow{+}$ Results Births $\xrightarrow{+}$ Population
X $\xrightarrow{-}$ Y	All else equal, if X increases (decreases), then Y decreases (increases) below (above) what it would have been. In the case of accumulations, X subtracts from Y.	$\partial Y/\partial X < 0$ In the case of accumulations, $Y = \int_{t_0}^{t} (-X + \ldots)\,ds + Y_{t_0}$	Product Price $\xrightarrow{-}$ Sales Frustration $\xrightarrow{-}$ Results Deaths $\xrightarrow{-}$ Population

on both the fractional birth rate and the size of the population (that is, Birth Rate = Fractional Birth Rate * Population). You cannot say whether an increase in the fractional birth rate will actually cause the birth rate to rise; you also need to know whether the population is rising or falling. A large enough drop in the population may cause the birth rate to fall even if the fractional birth rate rises. When assessing the polarity of individual links, assume all other variables are constant (the famous assumption of *ceteris paribus*). When assessing the actual behavior of a system, all variables interact simultaneously (all else is not equal) and computer simulation is usually needed to trace out the behavior of the system and determine which loops are dominant.

Second, and more importantly, causal loop diagrams do not distinguish between stocks and flows—the accumulations of resources in a system and the rates of change that alter those resources (see chapter 6). In the population example, the population is a stock—it accumulates the birth rate less the death rate. An increase in the birth rate will increase the population, but a decrease in the birth rate does not decrease the population. Births can only increase the population, they can never reduce it. The positive link between births and population means that the birth rate adds to the population. Thus an increase in the birth rate increases the population above what it otherwise would have been and a decrease in the birth rate decreases population below what it otherwise would have been.

Similarly, the negative polarity of the link from the death rate to population indicates that the death rate subtracts from the population. A drop in the death rate does not add to the population. A drop in deaths means fewer people die and more remain alive: the population is higher *than it would otherwise have been.* Note that you cannot tell whether the population will actually be increasing or decreasing: Population will be falling even if the birth rate is rising if the death rate exceeds births. To know whether a stock is increasing or decreasing you must know its net rate of change (in this case, births less deaths). It is always true, however, that if the birth rate rises, population will rise above what it would have been in the absence of the change in births, even if the population continues to fall. Population will be falling at a slower rate than it otherwise would. Chapters 6 and 7 discuss the structure and behavior of stocks and flows.

Process Point: A Note on Notation

In some of the system dynamics literature, especially the systems thinking tradition (see, e.g., Senge et al. 1994 and Kim 1992), an alternate convention for causal diagrams has developed. Instead of + or − the polarity of a causal link is denoted by **s** or **o,** respectively (denoting the **s**ame or **o**pposite relationship between independent and dependent variables):

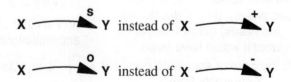

The link denoted with an **s** is read as "X and Y move in the *same* direction" while the link denoted with an **o** is read as "X and Y move in the *opposite* direction." Thus Product Quality and Sales tend to move in the same direction while Product Price and Sales tend to move in the opposite direction.

The **s** and **o** notation was motivated by a desire to make causal diagrams even easier to understand for people with little mathematical background. Which notation is better is hotly debated. Richardson (1997) provides strong arguments against the use of **s** and **o.** He notes that the statement "X and Y move in the same direction" is not in general correct, for the reasons stated above. The correct statement is, "If X increases, Y increases *above what it would have been.*" That is, a causal link is a contingent statement of the individual effect of a hypothesized change. The variables X and Y may be positively linked and yet Y may fall even as X increases, as other variables also affect Y. The **s** and **o** definitions also don't work for stock and flow relationships. Births and population do not move in the same direction: a decrease in births does not cause population to decrease because the birth rate is an inflow to the stock of population. The correct definition is given in Table 5-1: for positive link polarity, if X increases, Y will always be higher than it would have been; for negative polarity, if X increases, Y will always be lower than it would have been. In this book I will use the + and − signs to denote link polarity. As a modeler you should know how to interpret the **s** and **o** notation when you see it, but you should use the + and − notation to denote link polarity.

5.2   GUIDELINES FOR CAUSAL LOOP DIAGRAMS

5.2.1   Causation versus Correlation

Every link in your diagram must represent (what you believe to be) causal relationships between the variables. You must not include correlations between variables. The Latin root of the word simulate, *simulare,* means "to imitate." A system dynamics model must mimic the structure of the real system well enough that the model behaves the same way the real system would. Behavior includes not only replicating historical experience but also responding to circumstances and policies that are entirely novel. Correlations among variables reflect the past *behavior* of a system. Correlations do not represent the *structure* of the system. If circumstances change, if previously dormant feedback loops become dominant, if new policies are tried, previously reliable correlations among variables may break down. Your models and causal diagrams must include only those relationships you believe capture the underlying causal structure of the system. Correlations among variables will emerge from the behavior of the model when you simulate it.

Though sales of ice cream are positively correlated with the murder rate, you may not include a link from ice cream sales to murder in your models. Instead, as shown in Figure 5-2, both ice cream sales and murder rise in summer and fall in winter as the average temperature fluctuates. Confusing correlation with causality can lead to terrible misjudgments and policy errors. The model on the left side of Figure 5-2 suggests that cutting ice cream consumption would slash the murder rate, save lives, and allow society to cut the budget for police and prisons.

FIGURE 5-2
Causal diagrams
must include
only (what you
believe to be)
genuine causal
relationships.

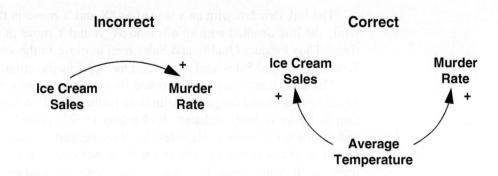

While few people are likely to attribute murders to the occasional double-dip cone, many correlations are more subtle, and it is often difficult to determine the underlying causal structure. A great deal of scientific research seeks the genuine causal needles in a huge haystack of correlations: Does vitamin C cure the common cold? Can eating oat bran reduce cholesterol, and if it does, will your risk of a heart attack drop? Does economic growth lead to lower birth rates, or is the lower rate attributable to literacy, education for women, and increasing costs of child rearing? Do companies with serious quality improvement programs earn superior returns for stockholders? Scientists have learned from bitter experience that reliable answers to such questions are hard to come by and require dedication to the scientific method—controlled experiments, randomized, double-blind trials, large samples, long-term follow-up studies, replication, statistical inference, and so on. In the social and human systems we often model, such experiments are difficult, rare, and often impossible. Modelers must take extra care to consider whether the relationships in their models are causal, no matter how strong the correlation, how high the R^2, or how great the statistical significance of the coefficients in a regression may be. As the English economist Phelps-Brown (1972, p. 6) noted, "Where, as so often, the fluctuations of different series respond in common to the pulse of the economy, it is fatally easy to get a good fit, and get it for quite a number of different equations . . . Running regressions between time series is only likely to deceive."

5.2.2   Labeling Link Polarity

Be sure to label the polarity of every link in your diagrams. Label the polarity of the important feedback loops in your diagrams, using the definitions in Table 5-1 to help you determine whether the links are positive or negative. *Positive feedback* loops are also called *reinforcing* loops and are denoted by a + or **R**, while *negative* loops are sometimes called *balancing* loops and are denoted by a − or **B** (Figure 5-3).

FIGURE 5-3
Label link and loop polarities.

Note that all links are labeled and loop polarity identifiers show which loops are positive and which are negative. Loop identifiers are clockwise for the clockwise loops (and vice versa).

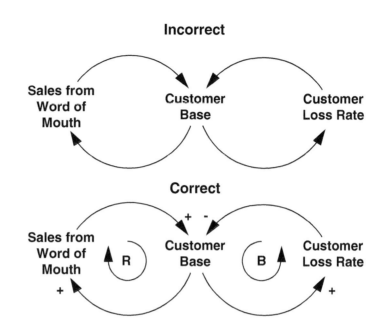

CHALLENGE	## Assigning Link Polarities

Consider the attractiveness of a product to customers as it depends on various attributes of the product (Figure 5-4). Assign link polarities. What feedback loops might be created as product attractiveness changes the demand for the firm's product? Add these to the diagram, labeling the link and loop polarities.

FIGURE 5-4
The attractiveness of a product as it depends on various attributes

5.2.3   Determining Loop Polarity

There are two methods for determining whether a loop is positive or negative: the fast way and the right way.

The Fast Way: Count the Number of Negative Links

The fast way to tell if a loop is positive or negative is to count the number of negative links in the loop. If the number of negative links is even, the loop is positive; if the number is odd, the loop is negative. The rule works because positive loops reinforce change while negative loops are self-correcting; they oppose disturbances. Imagine a small disturbance in one of the variables. If the disturbance propagates around the loop to reinforce the original change, then the loop is positive. If the disturbance propagates around the loop to oppose the original change, then the loop is negative. To oppose the disturbance, the signal must experience a net sign reversal as it travels around the loop. Net reversal can only occur if the number of negative links is odd. A single negative link causes the signal to reverse: an increase becomes a decrease. But another negative link reverses the signal again, so the decrease becomes an increase, reinforcing the original disturbance. See "Mathematics of Loop Polarity" below for a formal derivation of this rule.

The fast method always works . . . except when it doesn't. Why might it fail? In a complex diagram it is all too easy to miscount the number of negative links in a loop. And it is easy to mislabel the polarity of links when you first draw the diagram. Counting the number of negative signs is unlikely to reveal these errors. The right method, carefully tracing the effect of a disturbance around the loop, will often reveal a wrongly labeled polarity and will help you and your audience to grasp the meaning and mechanism of the loop. Assigning loop polarity the right way rather than the fast way saves time in the long run.

The Right Way: Trace the Effect of a Change around the Loop

The right way to determine the polarity of a loop is to trace the effect of a small change in one of the variables as it propagates around the loop. If the feedback effect reinforces the original change, it is a positive loop; if it opposes the original change, it is a negative loop. You can start with any variable in the loop; the result must be the same. In the market loops shown in Figure 5-3, assume sales from word of mouth increase. Because the link from sales from word of mouth to the customer base is positive, the customer base increases. Because the link from the customer base back to sales from word of mouth is positive, the signal propagates around the loop to increase sales from word of mouth still further. The feedback effect reinforces the original change, so the loop is positive. Turning to the other loop, assume a small increase in the customer loss rate. If customer losses increase, the customer base falls. With a lower customer base, there are fewer customers who can drop out. The feedback effect opposes the original change, so the loop is negative.

This method works no matter how many variables are in a loop and no matter which variable you start with. (Identify the loop polarities for the example starting with customer base instead of sales from word of mouth: you should get the same result). You may also assume an initial decrease in a variable rather than an initial increase.

CHALLENGE   **Identifying Link and Loop Polarity**

Identify and label the polarity of the links and loops in the examples shown in Figure 5-5.

FIGURE 5-5
Feedback
loop
examples

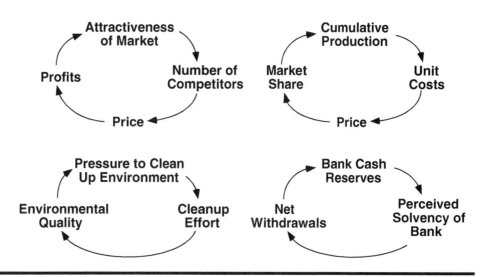

Mathematics of Loop Polarity

When you determine loop polarity, you are calculating what is known in control theory as the sign of the open loop gain of the loop. The term "gain" refers to the strength of the signal returned by the loop: a gain of two means a change in a variable is doubled each cycle around the loop; a gain of negative 0.5 means the disturbance propagates around the loop to oppose itself with a strength half as large. The term "open loop" means the gain is calculated for just one feedback cycle by breaking—opening—the loop at some point. Consider an arbitrary feedback loop consisting of n variables, $x_1, \ldots, x_n$. You can calculate the open loop gain at any point; let x_1 denote the variable you choose. When you break the loop, x_1 splits into an input, x_1^I, and output, x_1^O (Figure 5-6). The open loop gain is defined as the (partial) derivative of x_1^O with respect to x_1^I, that is, the feedback effect of a small change in the variable as it returns to itself. The polarity of the loop is the sign of the open loop gain:

$$\text{Polarity of loop} = \text{SGN}(\partial x_1^O / \partial x_1^I) \tag{5-1}$$

where SGN() is the signum or sign function, returning $+1$ if its argument is positive and -1 if the argument is negative (if the open loop gain is zero, the SGN function $= 0$: there is no loop). The open loop gain is calculated by the chain rule from the gains of the individual links, $\partial x_i / \partial x_{i-1}$:

$$\text{SGN}(\partial x_1^O / \partial x_1^I) = \text{SGN}[(\partial x_1^O / \partial x_n)(\partial x_n / \partial x_{n-1})(\partial x_{n-1} / \partial x_{n-2}) \cdots (\partial x_2 / \partial x_1^I)] \tag{5-2}$$

FIGURE 5-6
Calculating the
open-loop gain
of a loop

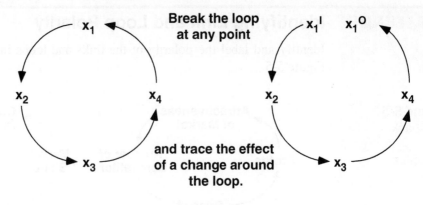

Break the loop
at any point

and trace the effect
of a change around
the loop.

$$\text{Polarity} = \text{SGN}(\partial x_1^O / \partial x_1^I)$$

$$\partial x_1^O / \partial x_1^I = (\partial x_1^O / \partial x_4)(\partial x_4 / \partial x_3)(\partial x_3 / \partial x_2)(\partial x_2 / \partial x_1^I)$$

Since the sign of a product is the product of the signs, loop polarity is also given by:

$$\text{SGN}(\partial x_1^O / \partial x_1^I) = \text{SGN}(\partial x_1^O / \partial x_n) * \text{SGN}(\partial x_n / \partial x_{n-1}) * \text{SGN}(\partial x_{n-1} / \partial x_{n-2})$$
$$* \cdots * \text{SGN}(\partial x_2 / \partial x_1^I) \tag{5-3}$$

Using the right method to determine loop polarity by tracing the effect of a small change around a loop is equivalent to calculating equation (5-3). Equation (5-3) also explains why the fast method works: Since the product of two negative signs is a positive sign, negative open loop polarity requires an odd number of negative links in the loop.

All Links Should Have Unambiguous Polarities

Sometimes people say a link can be either positive or negative, depending on other parameters or on where the system is operating. For example, people often draw the diagram on the left side of Figure 5-7 relating a firm's revenue to the price of its product and then argue that the link between price and company revenue can be either positive or negative, depending on the elasticity of demand. If demand is highly elastic, a higher price means less revenue because a 1% increase in price causes demand to fall more than 1%. The link would have negative polarity. If demand is inelastic, then a 1% increase in price causes demand to drop less than 1%, so revenues rise. The link would be positive. It appears no single polarity can be assigned.

When you have trouble assigning a clear and unambiguous polarity to a link it usually means there is more than one causal pathway connecting the two variables. You should make these different pathways explicit in your diagram. In the example, price has at least two effects on revenue: (1) it determines how much revenue is generated per unit sold and (2) it affects the number of units sold. That is, Revenue = Price * Sales, and (Unit) Sales depend on Price (presumably the demand curve is downward sloping: Higher prices reduce sales). The proper diagram is

FIGURE 5-7
Causal links must have unambiguous polarity.

Apparently ambiguous polarities usually indicate the presence of multiple causal pathways that should be represented separately.

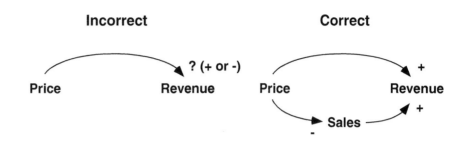

shown on the right side of Figure 5-7. There is now no ambiguity about the polarity of any of the links.

The price elasticity of demand determines which causal pathway dominates. If demand is quite insensitive to price (the elasticity of demand is less than one), then the lower path in Figure 5-7 is weak, price raises unit revenue more than it decreases sales, and the net effect of an increase in price is an increase in revenue. Conversely, if customers are quite price sensitive (the elasticity of demand is greater than one), the lower path dominates. The increase in revenue per unit is more than offset by the decline in the number of units sold, so the net effect of a price rise is a drop in revenue. Separating the pathways also allows you to specify different delays, if any, in each. In the example above, there is likely to be a long delay between a change in price and a change in sales, while there is little or no delay in the effect of price on revenue.

Separating links with apparently ambiguous polarity into the underlying multiple pathways is a fruitful method to deepen your understanding of the causal structure, delays, and behavior of the system.

CHALLENGE

Employee Motivation

Your client team is worried about employee motivation and is debating the best ways to generate maximum effort from their people. They have drawn a diagram (Figure 5-8) and are arguing about the polarity of the links. One group argues that the greater the performance shortfall (the greater the gap between Required Performance and Actual Performance), the greater the motivation of employees will be. They argue that the secret of motivation is to set aggressive, even impossible goals (so-called stretch objectives) to elicit maximum motivation and effort. The other group argues that too big a performance shortfall simply causes frustration as people conclude there is no chance to accomplish the goal, so the link to employee motivation should be negative. Expand the diagram to resolve the apparent conflict by incorporating both theories. Discuss which links dominate under different circumstances. Can you give some examples from your own experience where these different pathways were dominant? How can a manager tell which pathway is likely to dominate in any situation? What are the implications for goal setting in organizations? Actual and required performance are not exogenous but part of the feedback structure. How does motivation feed back to performance, and how might actual performance affect the goal? Indicate these loops in your diagram and explain their importance.

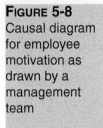

FIGURE 5-8
Causal diagram
for employee
motivation as
drawn by a
management
team

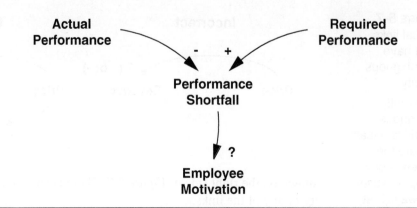

5.2.4   Name Your Loops

Whether you use causal diagrams to elicit the mental models of a client group or to communicate the feedback structure of a model, you will often find yourself trying to keep track of more loops than you can handle. Your diagrams can easily overwhelm the people you are trying to reach. To help your audience navigate the network of loops, it's helpful to give each important feedback a number and a name. Numbering the loops R1, R2, B1, B2, and so on helps your audience find each loop as you discuss it. Naming the loops helps your audience understand the function of each loop and provides useful shorthand for discussion. The labels then stand in for a complex set of causal links. When working with a client group, it's often possible to get them to name the loop. Many times, they will suggest a whimsical phrase or some organization-specific jargon for each loop.

Figure 5-9 shows a causal diagram developed by engineers and managers in a workshop designed to explore the causes of late delivery for their organization's design work. The diagram represents the behavior of the engineers trying to complete a project against a deadline. The engineers compare the work remaining to be done against the time remaining before the deadline. The larger the gap, the more Schedule Pressure they feel. When schedule pressure builds up, engineers have several choices. First, they can work overtime. Instead of the normal 50 hours per week, they can come to work early, skip lunch, stay late, and work through the weekend. By burning the Midnight Oil, they increase the rate at which they complete their tasks, cut the backlog of work, and relieve the schedule pressure (balancing loop B1). However, if the workweek stays too high too long, fatigue sets in and productivity suffers. As productivity falls, the task completion rate drops, which increases schedule pressure and leads to still longer hours: the reinforcing Burnout loop R1 limits the effectiveness of overtime. Another way to complete the work faster is to reduce the time spent on each task. Spending less time on each task boosts the number of tasks done per hour (productivity) and relieves schedule pressure, thus closing the balancing loop B2. Discussion of the name for this loop was heated. The managers claimed the engineers always gold-plated their work; they felt schedule pressure was needed to squeeze out waste and get the engineers to focus on the job. The engineers argued that schedule pressure often rose so high that they had no choice but to cut back quality assurance and skip documentation

FIGURE 5-9
Name and number your loops to increase diagram clarity and provide memorable labels for important feedbacks.

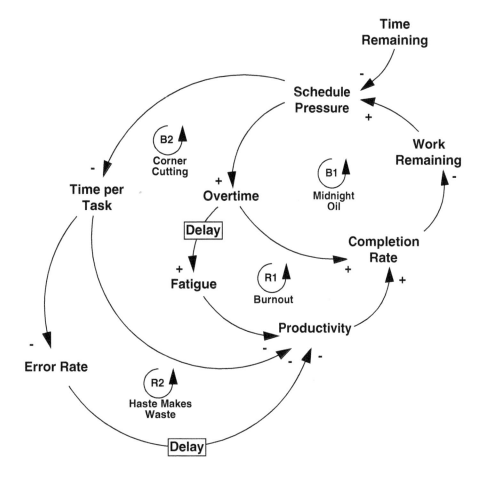

of their work. They called it the Corner Cutting loop (B2). The engineers then argued that corner cutting is self-defeating because it increases the error rate, which leads to rework and lower productivity in the long run: "Haste makes waste," they said, and schedule pressure rises further, leading to still more pressure to cut corners (loop R2).

The full model included many more loops (section 5.1 provides a closely related example; see also section 2.3). The names given to the loops by one group (engineers) communicated their attitudes and the rationale for their behavior to the managers in a clear and compelling way. The conversation did not degenerate into ad hominem arguments between managers shouting that engineers just need to have their butts kicked and engineers griping that getting promoted to management turns your brain to [fertilizer]—the mode of discourse most common in the organization prior to the intervention. Participants soon began to talk about the Burnout Loop kicking in and the nonlinear relationships between schedule pressure, overtime, fatigue, and errors. The names for the loops made it easy to refer to complex chunks of feedback structure. The concepts captured by the names gradually began to enter the mental models and decision making of the managers and engineers in the organization and led to change in deeply ingrained behaviors.

5.2.5   Indicate Important Delays in Causal Links

Delays are critical in creating dynamics. Delays give systems inertia, can create oscillations, and are often responsible for trade-offs between the short- and long-run effects of policies. Your causal diagrams should include delays that are important to the dynamic hypothesis or significant relative to your time horizon. As shown in chapter 11, delays always involve stock and flow structures. Sometimes it is important to show these structures explicitly in your diagrams. Often, however, it is sufficient to indicate the presence of a time delay in a causal link without explicitly showing the stock and flow structure. Figure 5-10 shows how time delays are represented in causal diagrams.

When the price of a good rises, supply will tend to increase, but often only after significant delays while new capacity is ordered and built and while new firms enter the market. See also the time delays in the Burnout and Haste Makes Waste loops in Figure 5-9.

Example: Energy Demand

The response of gasoline sales to price involves long delays. In the short run, gasoline demand is quite inelastic: if prices rise, people can cut down on discretionary trips somewhat, but most people still have to drive to work, school, and the supermarket. As people realize that prices are likely to stay high they may organize carpools or switch to public transportation, if it is already available. Over time high prices induce other responses. First, consumers (and the auto companies) wait to see if gas prices are going to stay high enough and long enough to justify buying or designing more efficient cars (a perceptual and decision-making delay of perhaps a year or more). Once people have decided that the price won't drop back down any time soon, the auto companies must then design and build more efficient cars (a delay of several years). Even after more efficient cars become available, the vast majority of cars on the road will be inefficient, older models which are only replaced as they wear out and are discarded, a delay of about 10 years. If prices stay high, eventually the density of settlement patterns will increase as people abandon the suburbs and move closer to their jobs. Altogether, the total delay in the link between price and demand for gasoline is significantly more than a decade. As the stock of cars on the road is gradually replaced with more efficient cars, and as (perhaps) new mass transit routes are designed and built, the demand for gasoline would fall substantially—long-run demand is quite elastic. Figure 5-11 makes these different pathways for the adjustment of gasoline demand explicit.

Explicitly portraying the many delays between a change in price and the resulting change in demand makes it easier to see the worse-before-better behavior of expenditures on gasoline caused by a price increase. The bottom of Figure 5-11 shows the response of gasoline demand and expenditures to a hypothetical

FIGURE 5-10
Representing delays in causal diagrams

unanticipated step increase in the price of gasoline. In the short run gasoline demand is rather inflexible, so the first response to an increase in the price of gas is an increase in gasoline expenditures. As the high price persists, efficiency

FIGURE 5-11   Different time delays in the response of gasoline demand and expenditures to price

Top: The short run response to higher prices is weak, while the long run response is substantial as the stock of cars is gradually replaced with more efficient models, and as lifestyles change.

Bottom: Response to a hypothetical permanent unanticipated increase in gasoline price. Consumption slowly declines due to the long delays in adjusting the efficiency of automobiles and in changing settlement patterns and mass transit routes. Expenditures therefore immediately rise and only later fall below the initial level: a worse-before-better trade-off for consumers. Of course, as demand falls, there would be downward pressure on price, possibly lowering expenditures still more, but also discouraging further efficiency improvements. The feedback to price is deliberately ignored in the diagram.

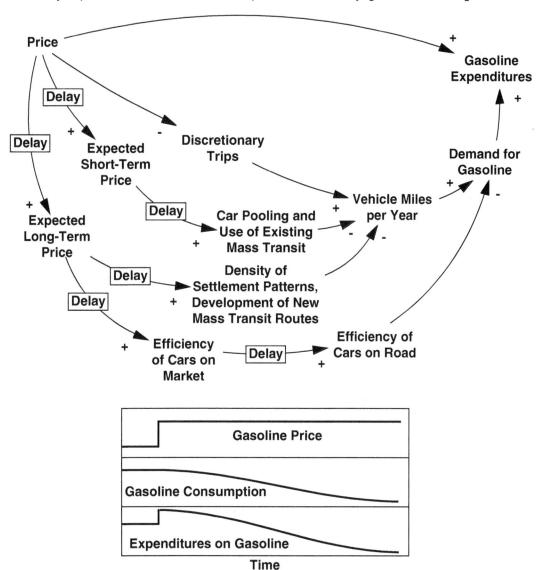

improvements gradually cut consumption of gasoline per vehicle mile, and eventually, settlement patterns and mass transit availability will adjust to reduce the number of vehicle miles driven per year. In the long run, demand adjustments more than offset the price increase and expenditures fall. From the point of view of the consumer, this is a worse-before-better situation. The time delays and the trade-off they create help explain why it has proven so difficult, in the United States at least, to increase gasoline taxes. Although the long-run benefits outweigh the short-run costs, even in net present value terms, they only begin to accrue after many years. Government officials focused on the next reelection campaign judge the short-run costs to be politically unacceptable. In turn, they make this judgment because the public is unwilling to sacrifice a little today for larger benefits tomorrow.

5.2.6 Variable Names

Variable Names Should Be Nouns or Noun Phrases

The variable names in causal diagrams and models should be nouns or noun phrases. The actions (verbs) are captured by the causal links connecting the variables. A causal diagram captures the structure of the system, not its behavior—not what has *actually* happened but what *would* happen if other variables changed in various ways. Figure 5-12 shows examples of good and bad practice.

The correct diagram states: **If** costs rise, **then** price rises (above what it would have been), but **if** costs fall, **then** price will fall (below what it would have been). Adding the verb "rises" to the diagram presumes costs will only rise, biasing the discussion towards one pattern of behavior (inflation). It is confusing to talk of a decrease in costs rising or a fall in price increases—are prices rising, rising at a falling rate, or falling?

Variable Names Must Have a Clear Sense of Direction

Choose names for which the meaning of an increase or decrease is clear, variables that can be larger or smaller. Without a clear sense of direction for the variables you will not be able to assign meaningful link polarities.

On the left side of Figure 5-13 neither variable has a clear direction: If feedback from the boss increases, does that mean you get more comments? Are these

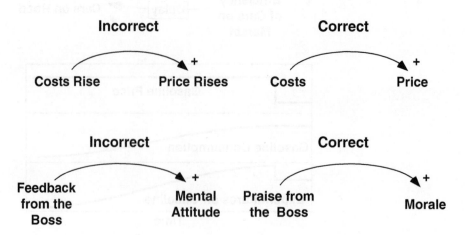

FIGURE 5-12
Variable names should be nouns or noun phrases.

FIGURE 5-13
Variable names should have a clear sense of direction.

Incorrect — Costs Rise → Price Rises +   Correct — Costs → Price +

Incorrect — Feedback from the Boss → Mental Attitude +   Correct — Praise from the Boss → Morale +

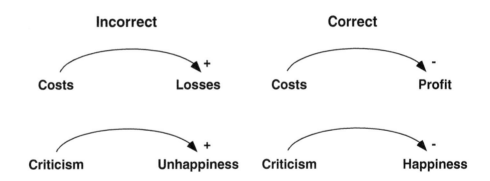

FIGURE 5-14
Choose variables
whose normal
sense of direction
is positive.

comments from the boss good or bad? And what does it mean for mental attitude to increase? The meaning of the right side is clear: More praise from the boss boosts morale; less praise erodes it (though you should probably not let your self-esteem depend so much on your boss' opinion).

Choose Variables Whose Normal Sense of Direction Is Positive

Variable names should be chosen so their normal sense of direction is positive. Avoid the use of variable names containing prefixes indicating negation (non, un, etc.; Figure 5-14).

Standard accounting practice is Profit = Revenue − Costs, so the better variable name is Profit, which falls when costs rise and rises when costs fall. Likewise, criticism may make you unhappy, but it is confusing to speak of rising unhappiness; a better choice is the positive happiness, which may fall when you are criticized and rise when criticism drops. Though there are occasional exceptions, decreasing noncompliance with this principle will diminish your audience's incomprehension.

5.2.7   Tips for Causal Loop Diagram Layout

To maximize the clarity and impact of your causal diagrams, you should follow some basic principles of graphic design.

1. Use curved lines for information feedbacks. Curved lines help the reader visualize the feedback loops.
2. Make important loops follow circular or oval paths.
3. Organize your diagrams to minimize crossed lines.
4. Don't put circles, hexagons, or other symbols around the variables in causal diagrams. Symbols without meaning are "chart junk" and serve only to clutter and distract. An exception: You will often need to make the stock and flow structure of a system explicit in your diagrams. In these cases the rectangles and valves around the variables tell the reader which are stocks and which are flows—they convey important information (see chapter 6).
5. Iterate. Since you often won't know what all the variables and loops will be when you start, you will have to redraw your diagrams, often many times, to find the best layout.

FIGURE 5-15
Make intermediate
links explicit to
clarify a causal
relationship.

If your audience was confused by

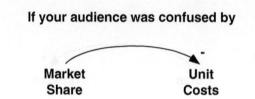

Market   Unit
Share   Costs

you might make the intermediate concepts explicit as follows:

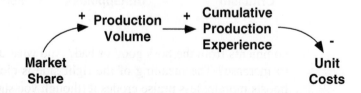

5.2.8   Choose the Right Level of Aggregation

Causal loop diagrams are designed to communicate the central feedback structure
of your dynamic hypothesis. They are not intended to be descriptions of a model at
the detailed level of the equations. Having too much detail makes it hard to see the
overall feedback loop structure and how the different loops interact. Having too little detail makes it hard for your audience to grasp the logic and evaluate the plau-
sibility and realism of your model.

   If your audience doesn't grasp the logic of a causal link, you should make
some of the intermediate variables more explicit. Figure 5-15 shows an example.
You might believe that in your industry, market share gains lead to lower unit costs
because higher volumes move your company down the learning curve faster. The
top panel compresses this logic into a single causal link. If your audience found
that link confusing, you should disaggregate the diagram to show the steps of your
reasoning in more detail, as shown in the bottom panel.

   Once you've clarified this logic to the satisfaction of all, you often can
"chunk" the more detailed representation into a simple, more aggregate form. The
simpler diagram then serves as a marker for the richer, underlying causal structure.

5.2.9   Don't Put All the Loops into
One Large Diagram

Short-term memory can hold 7 ± 2 chunks of information at once. This puts a
rather sharp limit on the effective size and complexity of a causal map. Presenting
a complex causal map all at once makes it hard to see the loops, understand which
are important, or understand how they generate the dynamics. Resist the temptation to put all the loops you and your clients have identified into a single comprehensive diagram. Such diagrams look impressive—My, what a lot of work must
have gone into it! How big and comprehensive your model must be!—but are not
effective in communicating with your audience. A large, wall-filling diagram may
be perfectly comprehensible to the person who drew it, but to the people with

whom the author seeks to communicate, it is indistinguishable from a Jackson Pollock and considerably less valuable.

How then do you communicate the rich feedback structure of a system without oversimplifying? Build up your model in stages, with a series of smaller causal loop diagrams. Each diagram should correspond to one part of the dynamic story being told. Few people can understand a complex causal diagram unless they have a chance to digest the pieces one at a time. Develop a separate diagram for each important loop. These diagrams can have enough detail in them to show how the process actually operates. Then chunk the diagrams into a simpler, high-level overview to show how they interact with one another. In presentations, build up your diagram piece by piece from the chunks (see sections 5.4 and 5.6 for examples).

5.2.10   Make the Goals of Negative Loops Explicit

All negative feedback loops have goals. Goals are the desired state of the system, and all negative loops function by comparing the actual state to the goal, then initiating a corrective action in response to the discrepancy. Make the goals of your negative loops explicit. Figure 5-16 shows two examples. The top panel shows a negative loop affecting the quality of a company's product: the lower the quality, the more quality improvement programs will be started, and (presumably) the deficiencies in quality will be corrected. Making goals explicit encourages people to ask how the goals are formed. The goals in most systems are not given exogenously but are themselves part of the feedback structure. Goals can vary over time and respond to pressures in the environment. In the example, what determines the

FIGURE 5-16
Make the goals of negative loops explicit.

Human agency or natural processes can determine goals.

Top: The goal of the loop is determined by management decision.

Bottom: The laws of thermodynamics determine the goal of the loop.

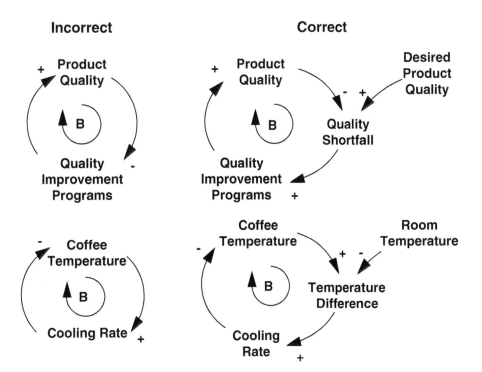

desired level of product quality? The CEO's edict? Benchmarking studies of competitor quality? Customer input? The company's own past quality levels? When the goal is explicit these questions are more likely to be asked and hypotheses about the answers can be quickly incorporated in the model.

Making the goals of negative loops explicit is especially important when the loops capture human behavior. But often it is important to represent goals explicitly even when the loop does not involve people at all. The second example portrays the negative feedback by which a cup of coffee cools to room temperature. The rate of cooling (the rate at which heat diffuses from the hot coffee to the surrounding air) is roughly proportional to the difference between the coffee temperature and room temperature. The cooling process stops when the two temperatures are equal. This basic law of thermodynamics is made clear when the goal is shown explicitly.

There are exceptions to the principle of showing the goals of negative loops. Consider the death rate loop in Figure 5-1. The goal of the death rate loop is implicit (and equal to zero: in the long run, we are all dead). Your models should not explicitly portray the goal of the death loop or the goals of similar decay processes such as the depreciation of capital equipment.

5.2.11   Distinguish between Actual and Perceived Conditions

Often there are significant differences between the true state of affairs and the perception of that state by the actors in the system. There may be delays caused by reporting and measurement processes. There may be noise, measurement error, bias, and distortions. In the quality management example shown in Figure 5-16, there may be significant delays in assessing quality and in changing management's opinion about product quality. Separating perceived and actual conditions helps prompt questions such as How long does it take to measure quality? To change management's opinion about quality even after the data are available? To implement a quality improvement program? To realize results? Besides the long time delays, there may be bias in the reporting system causing reported quality to differ systematically from quality as experienced by the customer. Customers don't file warranty claims for all problems or report all defects to their sales representative. Sales and repair personnel may not report all customer complaints to the home office. There may be bias in senior management's quality assessment because subordinates filter the information that reaches them. Some auto executives are provided with the latest models for their personal use; these cars are carefully selected and frequently serviced by company mechanics. Their impression of the quality of their firm's cars will be higher than that of the average customer who buys off the lot and keeps the car for 10 years. The diagram might be revised as shown in Figure 5-17. The diagram now shows how management, despite good intentions, can come to hold a grossly exaggerated view of product quality, and you are well positioned for a discussion of ways to shorten the delays and eliminate the distortions.

Figure 5-17
Distinguish
between actual
and perceived
conditions.

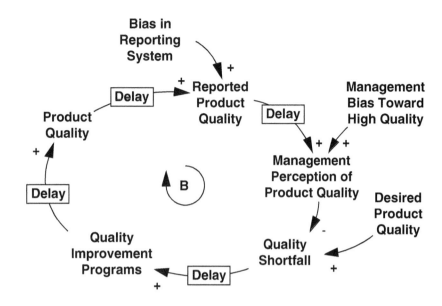

5.3   Process Point:
Developing Causal Diagrams from Interview Data

Much of the data a modeler uses to develop a dynamic hypothesis comes from interviews and conversations with people in organizations. There are many techniques available to gather data from members of organizations, including surveys, interviews, participant observation, archival data, and so on. Surveys generally do not yield data rich enough to be useful in developing system dynamics models. Interviews are an effective method to gather data useful in formulating a model, either conceptual or formal. Semistructured interviews (where the modeler has a set of predefined questions to ask but is free to depart from the script to pursue avenues of particular interest) have proven to be particularly effective.

Interviews are almost never sufficient alone and must be supplemented by other sources of data, both qualitative and quantitative. People have only a local, partial understanding of the system, so you must interview all relevant actors, at multiple levels, including those outside the organization (customers, suppliers, etc.). Interview data is rich, including descriptions of decision processes, internal politics, attributions about the motives and characters of others, and theories to explain events, but these different types of information are mixed together. People both know more than they will tell you and can invent rationales and even incidents to justify their beliefs, providing you with "data" they can't possibly know (Nisbett and Wilson 1977). The modeler must triangulate by using as many sources of data as possible to gain insight into the structure of the problem situation and the decision processes of the actors in it. An extensive literature provides guidance in techniques for qualitative data collection and analysis; see, for example, Argyris et al. (1985), Emmerson et al. (1995), Glaser and Strauss (1967), Kleiner and Roth (1997), March et al. (1991), Morecroft and Sterman (1994), Van Maanen (1988), and Yin (1994).

Once you've done your interviews, you must be able to extract the causal structure of the system from the statements of the interview subjects. Formulate variable names so that they correspond closely to the actual words used by the person you interviewed, while still adhering to the principles for proper variable name selection described above (noun phrases, a clear and positive sense of direction). Causal links should be directly supported by a passage in the transcript. Typically, people will not describe all the links you may see and will not explicitly close many feedback loops. Should you add these additional links? It depends on the purpose of your diagram.

If you are trying to represent a person's mental model, you must not include any links that cannot be grounded in the person's own statements. However, you may choose to show the initial diagram to the person and invite him or her to elaborate or add any missing links. People will often mention the motivation for a decision they made, with the feedback effect on the state of the system implicitly understood. For example, "Our market share was slipping, so we fired the marketing VP and got ourselves a new ad agency." Implicit in this description is the belief that a new VP and agency would lead to better ads and an increase in market share, closing the negative loop.

If the purpose of your interviews is to develop a good model of the problem situation, you should supplement the links suggested by the interviews with other data sources such as your own experience and observations, archival data, and so on. In many cases, you will need to add additional causal links not mentioned in the interviews or other data sources. While some of these will represent basic physical relationships and be obvious to all, others require justification or explanation. You should draw on all the knowledge you have from your experience with the system to complete the diagram.[1]

CHALLENGE   ## Process Improvement

The following two quotes are actual interview transcripts developed in fieldwork carried out in an automobile company in the United States. The managers, from two different component plants in the same division of the company, describe why the yield of their lines was persistently low and why it had been so difficult to get process improvement programs off the ground (Repenning and Sterman 1999):

> In the minds of the [operations team leaders] they had to hit their pack counts [daily quotas]. This meant if you were having a bad day and your yield had fallen . . . you had to run like crazy to hit your target. You could say, "You are making 20% garbage, stop the line and fix the problem," and they would say, "I can't hit my pack count without running like crazy." They could never get ahead of the game.
> —*Manager at Plant A*

> Supervisors never had time to make improvements or do preventive maintenance on their lines . . . they had to spend all their time just trying to keep the line going,

---

[1]Burchill and Fine (1997) illustrate how causal diagrams can be developed from interview data in a product development context.

but this meant it was always in a state of flux . . . because everything was so unpredictable. It was a kind of snowball effect that just kept getting worse.

—Supervisor at Plant B

Develop a single causal diagram capturing the dynamics described by the interviews. Name your loops using terms from the quotes where possible. Explain in a paragraph or two how the loops capture the dynamics described. Build your diagram around the basic physical structure shown in Figure 5-18. The Net Throughput of a process (the number of usable parts produced per time period, for example, the number of usable parts produced per day) equals Gross Throughput (the total number produced per time period) multiplied by the process Yield (the fraction of gross throughput that passes inspection and is usable). The remainder, Gross Throughput * (1 − Yield), are defective.

FIGURE 5-18
The net throughput of any process is gross throughput times process yield.

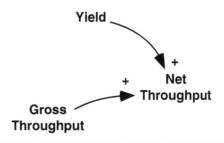

5.4   CONCEPTUALIZATION CASE STUDY: MANAGING YOUR WORKLOAD

This section illustrates the use of causal diagrams to model an issue. The example shows how causal diagramming can be an aid to the development of a dynamic hypothesis, along with identifying variables and developing a reference mode showing the dynamics of the variables over the relevant time horizon.

5.4.1   Problem Definition

Consider the process of managing your workload. You might be an engineer in a product development organization, a consultant, or a CEO. To keep it concrete, focus on a student managing his or her workload. A student (imagine yourself) must balance classes and assignments with outside activities, a personal life, and sleep. During the semester you attend classes, do the readings, and hand in assignments as they are due, at least occasionally. You probably try to work harder if you think your grades are lower than you desire and take more time off when you are sleep-deprived and your energy level falls. There are two basic policies you can follow: (1) The ant strategy—never put off until tomorrow what you can do today; or (2) the grasshopper strategy—never do today what can be put off until tomorrow.

   The ant works steadily throughout the semester as work is assigned and never builds up a large backlog of assignments. As a result, the ant avoids the end of semester crunch, keeps the workweek under control, and is able to stay well rested. Because the ant gets enough sleep, productivity is high, and the ant has plenty of time to participate in outside activities. The ant's grades improve steadily through-out the term.

The grasshopper, in contrast, defers the work until the last minute. The grasshopper's workweek is low at the beginning of the term, providing lots of time for parties and outside activities. The grasshopper can stay reasonably well rested despite a heavy social schedule because the workweek is low. But because the grasshopper doesn't do the work as fast as it is assigned, the assignment backlog steadily builds up. Eventually, it's crunch time, and the grasshopper starts putting in long hours, perhaps pulling a few all-nighters. Unfortunately, as sleep suffers, energy and productivity fall. The rate and quality of work suffers. Grades plummet, and the term ends before the grasshopper can finish all the work, perhaps leading the grasshopper to plead for extensions from the faculty.

5.4.2   Identifying Key Variables

The description above suggests several variables important in a model of student workload management (units of measure are given in parentheses):

Assignment rate: the rate at which professors assign work throughout the term (tasks/week).

Work completion rate: the rate at which tasks are completed (tasks/week).

Assignment backlog: the number of tasks that have been assigned but not yet completed (tasks).

Grades: the grade received for work handed in (0-100 scale).

Workweek: the number of hours spent on academic work, including classes, reading, homework, projects, etc. (hours/week).

Energy level: measures how well rested the student is. Arbitrary scale from 0–100% where 100% = fully rested and 0 = comatose).

Other variables could be added, but this set provides a reasonable starting point for conceptualization of the feedback structure governing the dynamics. As you proceed, you may find you need to revise the list.

5.4.3   Developing the Reference Mode

Figure 5-19 translates the written descriptions of the ant's behavior into graphical form (Figure 5-20 shows the grasshopper strategy). These graphs constitute the reference mode characterizing the problem. Some items to note:

1. The time horizon is explicitly stated. Here, the semester is 13 weeks long.
2. Several different graphs are used to avoid clutter. The time axes of each graph are aligned so that the timing of events can be directly compared.
3. Variables with the same units are plotted on the same axis. For example, the assignment and completion rates are both measured in tasks/week and are plotted together.
4. You don't need quantitative data to capture the dynamics in the reference modes. When numerical data are unavailable you should estimate the

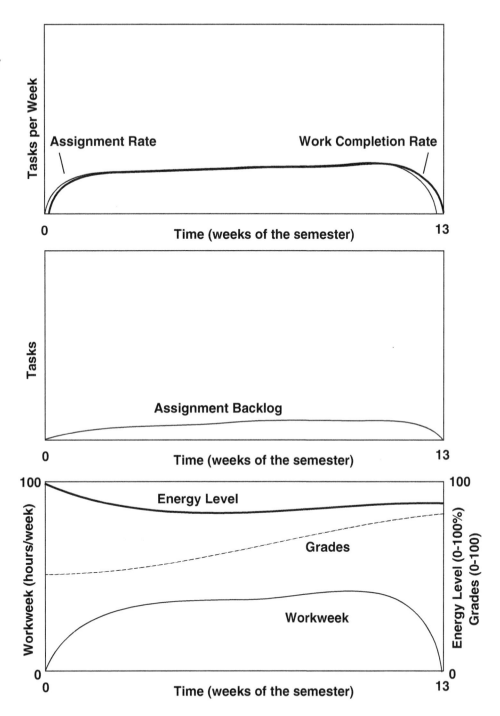

FIGURE 5-19
Reference mode
for the ant strategy

behavior of the variables from the written description and other qualitative information. Scales and rough magnitudes are provided where possible, as they are for the workweek, grades, and energy level. Of course, when quantitative data are available, they should be used. But don't omit important variables simply because they haven't been measured yet or because the data aren't readily available. An important goal of the modeling

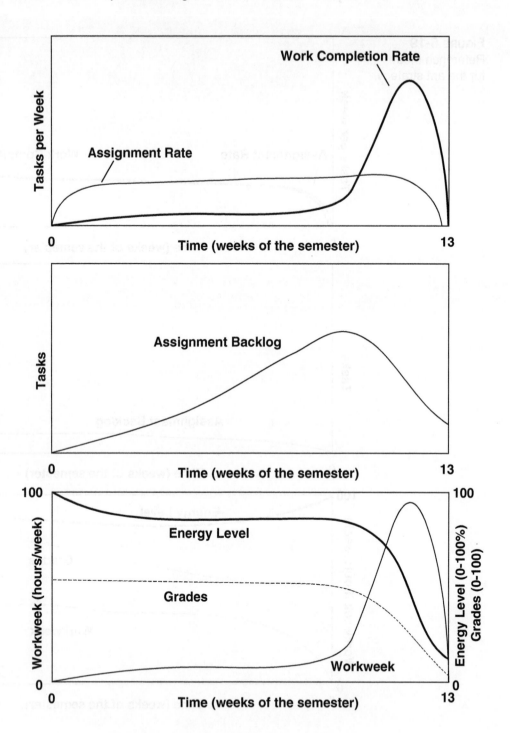

FIGURE 5-20
Reference
mode for the
grasshopper
strategy

process is the identification of variables that should be measured so the
necessary empirical work can be done.

5. There should be a basis in the data (numerical or written) for each feature of
the reference mode. For example, the graph of the ant's grades rises because
the description of the ant strategy states that the ant's grades improve
steadily throughout the term. Likewise, for the grasshopper the "term ends

before the grasshopper can finish all the work" so the assignment backlog, though falling, remains positive even as the term ends.

6. The magnitudes and timing of variables should be consistent with your knowledge of the system even if the description available does not specify these features. Details matter. For example, consider the grasshopper strategy. The work completion rate must depend on the student's work effort (workweek), so these move together. However, because energy and productivity are falling at the end, the completion rate does not rise as much as the workweek during the end of semester crunch. To make this even more obvious, you might define the variable Productivity explicitly (try sketching its dynamics from the description above).

7. Make sure your graphs are consistent with any stock and flow relationships among the variables. Since the assignment backlog accumulates the rate of assignments less the rate of work completion, it must be rising whenever the assignment rate exceeds the completion rate, and vice versa. The relationship between the backlog and its flows is most clearly seen in the grasshopper strategy. Until week 10, the assignment rate exceeds the completion rate, so the backlog builds up. At week 10, the grasshopper is handing in work just as fast as new work is assigned, and the backlog reaches its peak. After week 10, the completion rate exceeds the assignment rate and the backlog falls.

5.4.4   Developing the Causal Diagrams

Next you must use the description of the system and reference modes to develop a causal map of the feedback processes you believe are responsible for the dynamics.

Consider Figure 5-21. The Assignment Rate is assumed to be exogenous: Once a student has signed up for a set of courses, the assignment rate is determined. Classes can sometimes be dropped, but this possibility is ignored for now. The Assignment Backlog is increased by the Assignment Rate and decreased by the Completion Rate. Completion Rate (tasks/week) is Workweek (hours per week) times Productivity (tasks completed per hour of effort) times the Effort Devoted to Assignments. Effort Devoted to Assignments is the effort put in by the student compared to the effort required to complete the assignment with high quality. If work pressure is high, the student may choose to cut corners, skim some reading, skip classes, or give less complete answers to the questions in assignments. For example, if a student works 50 hours per week and can do one task per hour with high quality but only does half the work each assignment requires for a good job, then the completion rate would be $(50)(1)(.5) = 25$ task equivalents per week.

Work Pressure determines the workweek and effort devoted to assignments. Work pressure depends on the assignment backlog and the Time Remaining to complete the work: The bigger the backlog or the less time remaining, the higher the workweek needs to be to complete the work on time. Time remaining is of course simply the difference between the Due Date and the current Calendar Time. The two most basic options available to a student faced with high work pressure are to (1) work longer hours, thus increasing the completion rate and reducing the

FIGURE 5-21   Basic control loops for the assignment backlog

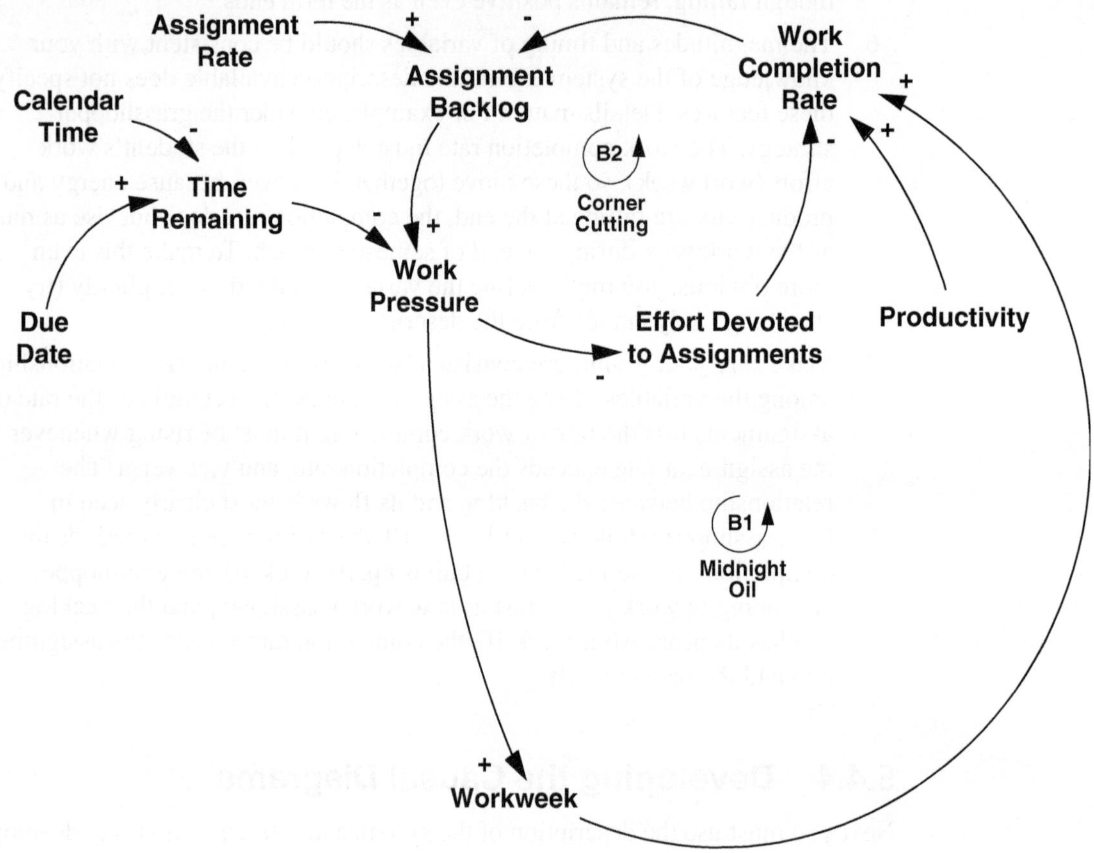

backlog (the Midnight Oil loop B1), or (2) work faster by spending less time on each task, speeding the completion rate and reducing the backlog (the Corner Cutting loop B2). Both are negative feedbacks whose goal is to reduce work pressure to a tolerable level.

However, each of these negative feedbacks has side effects. Consider Figure 5-22. Sustained high workweeks cut into sleep and the satisfaction of other needs (eating, exercise, human companionship, etc.), causing the student's Energy Level to fall. As energy level falls, so too do concentration and focus. Errors rise. Productivity drops, reducing the completion rate—a tired student must spend longer than a well-rested one to complete a task with a given level of quality. As the completion rate falls, the backlog remains higher than it would otherwise be and work pressure intensifies, leading to still higher workweeks and still lower energy and productivity. If the self-reinforcing Burnout loop, R1, dominates the balancing Midnight Oil loop, an increase in workweek would actually lower the completion rate as the extra hours are more than offset by the increase in errors and reduction in productivity.

Reducing the effort devoted to each assignment also has side effects. Putting less effort into each task does allow assignments to be completed in less time but reduces the Quality of Work, lowering the student's Grades. When grades fall

FIGURE 5-22 The burnout loop

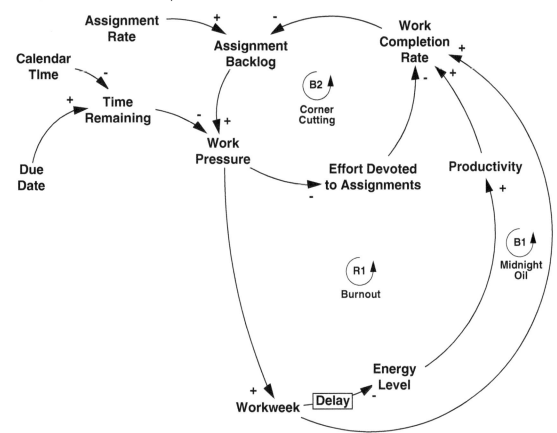

relative to the student's aspirations, there is pressure to boost the effort put into each task. The negative Quality Control loop B3 prevents effort and quality from falling too far even when work pressure is high (Figure 5-23). However, the effort to maintain quality also creates an insidious positive feedback. As work pressure forces the workweek up, energy level eventually falls (note the delay), reducing grades. The student responds by increasing the effort put into each task in an attempt to boost grades back up through the quality control loop. But increasing the time spent on each task lowers the completion rate. The backlog of work rises, intensifying work pressure and leading to still more overtime, still lower energy, and still lower grades. When the exhausted student is Too Tired to Think, the positive loop R2 operates as a vicious cycle—efforts to boost grades only succeed in creating more work pressure, longer hours, even lower energy, and still lower quality work.

You may wonder why anyone would keep working when their efforts not only yielded diminishing returns but negative returns. Wouldn't the grasshoppers realize their efforts were actually counterproductive? It is precisely when people are exhausted that their judgment is most impaired. How many times have you continued to work on a project when, at least in retrospect, you should have called it a day?

FIGURE 5-23   The "too tired to think" loop

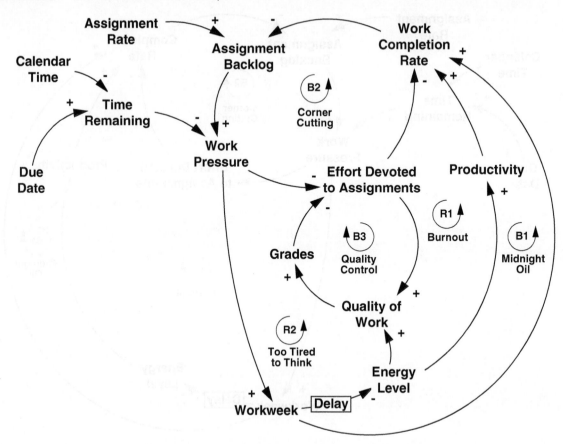

If all else fails, the exhausted student can appeal to the faculty for relief, generating Requests for Extensions (Figure 5-24). Usually, such requests are accompanied by stories of bad luck and hardship beyond the student's control: "My dog ate my homework," "My hard disk crashed," "My roommate had a nervous breakdown." If the faculty are moved by these tales of tragedy and woe (a big if), the due date is slipped, making more time available and reducing work pressure. Because faculty rarely give extensions unless there are genuine extenuating circumstances, the negative My Dog Ate My Homework loop B4 is quite weak. Note that slipping the deadline, because it lowers work pressure, may actually cause the workweek to fall and the effort devoted to each assignment to rise, both reducing the completion rate and causing work pressure to build up again. These feedbacks are responsible for Parkinson's (1957) famous law: "Work expands to fill the time available for its completion."

While there are many other loops you could add to the framework, these six feedbacks jointly explain most of the dynamics created by the ant and grasshopper strategies.

5.4.5   Limitations of the Causal Diagram

Causal diagrams can never be comprehensive (and you shouldn't try: modeling is the art of simplification). They are also never final, but always provisional. The

FIGURE 5-24   My dog ate my homework—Parkinson's Law

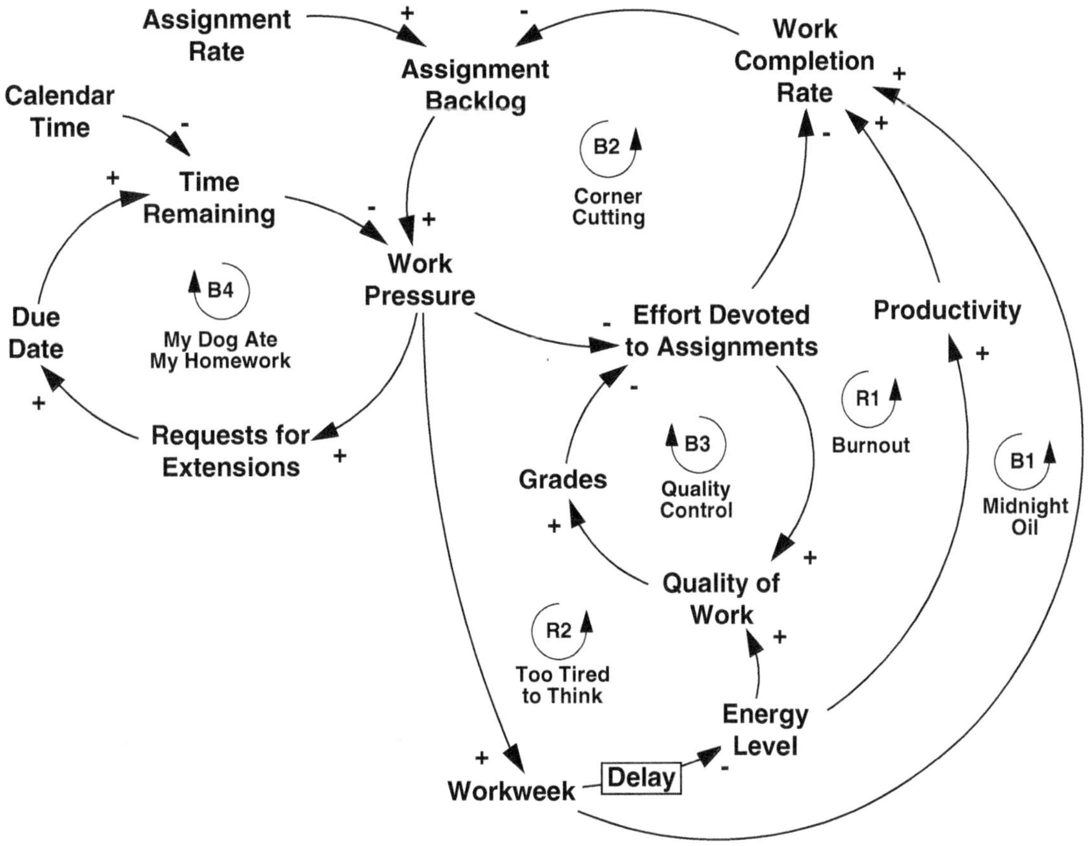

maps evolve as your understanding improves and as the purpose of the modeling effort evolves. The account of workload management above is far from perfect. Here are some issues to consider:

First, the diagram does not distinguish between stocks and flows. In particular, it would be helpful to show the stock and flow structure of the assignment backlog. What other variables in this model are stocks?

Second, some loops could be specified in more detail. For example, the quality control loop assumes that effort increases when grades fall relative to the student's aspirations. It would be clearer to specify those aspirations explicitly, for example, by creating a variable Desired Grade Point Average (GPA). Effort would then be affected by the student's Satisfaction with Grades, which measures the gap between desired and actual grades. An explicit goal for grades makes it easier to explore the dynamics for students with different aspirations and attitudes about the importance of grades. Making the goal explicit also motivates questions such as What determines aspirations for academic achievement?—that is, what feedback processes might cause the desired GPA to vary over time?

A variety of pressures for achievement, external to the workload management model, put upward pressure on grade aspirations. Such pressures arise from observations of the grades your peers receive (or claim to have received), from parents,

FIGURE 5-25
Making the goal of a loop explicit
Adding the desired GPA and its determinants.

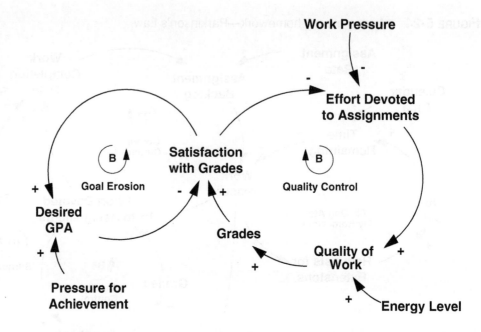

or from the (perceived) requirements of future employers or graduate school admissions officers. Figure 5-25 shows another important determinant of student goals: Aspirations adjust to past actual achievement, forming the negative Goal Erosion loop. Many people judge what is possible, at least in part, from what has been achieved. Eroding your goals in the face of a persistent discrepancy between aspiration and achievement is a common way to reduce what Festinger (1957) called "cognitive dissonance" and has been amply documented in many situations. The goal erosion loop can be an important learning process or may create a harmful self-fulfilling prophecy. For example, most students admitted to elite universities were at the top of their high school class. Once enrolled in the Ivy League or MIT, however, half of them will be in the bottom half of their class. The adjustment of grade aspirations to a new situation prevents perpetual disappointment, stress, and self-doubt. On the other hand, overly flexible goals can lead to underachievement. Some grasshoppers, reflecting on how much midnight oil they burned at the end of the term and the disappointing grades those hours led to, may conclude they aren't A or even B students and lower their aspirations to relieve the dissonance between expectations and achievement. Sadly, this lesson may be entirely erroneous: Fewer hours of effort, if they were well rested, may easily have led to higher grades.

CHALLENGE

Policy Analysis with Causal Diagrams

The boundary of the student workload model could be extended to include many other feedback processes. Modify the student workload diagram to include the following issues:

1. Dropping classes in response to high work pressure, low grades, or low energy.

2. Drinking coffee or taking stimulants to stay awake when energy level is low.

3. Cheating on assignments to boost the completion rate and raise grades.

4. Other loops you believe to be important.

As you expand the boundary of the model, ask yourself: Does the ability of the model to explain the dynamics change? Does the response of the model to policies change? Are the conclusions of the earlier analysis robust to changes in the boundary of the model?

5.5   ADAM SMITH'S INVISIBLE HAND AND THE FEEDBACK STRUCTURE OF MARKETS

Adam Smith's invisible hand is one of the most famous metaphors in the English language. Smith realized that a free market creates powerful negative feedback loops that cause prices and profits to be self-regulating. While Smith lacked modern tools such as causal diagrams and simulation models, the feedback loops in his description of the functioning of markets are clear. In *The Wealth of Nations* Smith argued that for any commodity there was a "natural" price which is just "sufficient to pay the rent of the land, the wages of the labour, and the profits of the [capital] stock employed in raising, preparing, and bringing [the commodity] to market . . ." At the natural price, a "commodity is then sold precisely for what it is worth, or for what it really costs the person who brings it to market . . ." In contrast, the actual market price "may either be above, or below, or exactly the same with its natural price"—that is, markets may at any time be out of equilibrium.

Smith then noted how prices respond to the balance between demand and supply:

> The market price of every particular commodity is regulated by the proportion between the quantity which is actually brought to market, and the demand of those who are willing to pay the natural price of the commodity . . . When the quantity of any commodity which is brought to market falls short of the effectual demand, all those who are willing to pay the whole value . . . cannot be supplied with the quantity which they want. Rather than want it altogether, some of them will be willing to give more. A competition will immediately begin among them, and the market price will rise more or less above the natural price.

Similarly, when supply exceeds demand, "[t]he market price will sink more or less below the natural price."

But supply in turn responds to the market price:

> If . . . the quantity brought to market should at any time fall short of the effectual demand, some of the component parts of its price must rise above their natural rate. If it is rent, the interest of all other landlords will naturally prompt them to prepare more land for the raising of this commodity; if it is wages or profit, the interest of all other labourers and dealers will soon prompt them to employ more labour and stock in preparing and bringing it to market. The quantity brought thither will soon be sufficient to supply the effectual demand. All the different parts of its price will soon sink to their natural rate, and the whole price to its natural price.

FIGURE 5-26

The invisible hand: the feedback structure of markets

Demand responds to the relative value of the commodity compared to substitutes; higher relative value increases demand, bidding prices up and lowering relative value. Supply expands when profits rise; profit depends on price relative to production costs including the required return on capital. Greater supply bids prices down, lowering profits. The price of substitutes and the cost of production determine what Adam Smith called the "natural price" of the commodity—the equilibrium price at which supply and demand are equal.

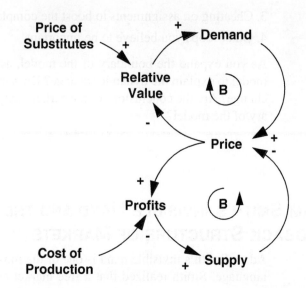

A simple representation of the feedback structure Smith describes is shown in Figure 5-26. When the price of a commodity rises above the natural price, fewer buyers "will be willing to give more" and more will be forced to "want it altogether." That is, as price rises relative to the price of substitutes, including all substitute uses for the funds available to the buyer, consumers will seek substitutes or find themselves simply priced out of the market. As demand falls prices will be bid down, forming a negative loop. At the same time, higher prices increase the profit suppliers can realize, which attracts new entrants to the market and encourages existing producers to increase output. As the supply increases, prices are bid downwards. These two negative feedback loops cause price to adjust until, in the absence of further external shocks, the market reaches equilibrium, with production equal to consumption and price equal to its natural level. Smith concludes:

> The natural price, therefore, is, as it were, the central price, to which the prices of all commodities are continually gravitating. Different accidents may sometimes keep them suspended a good deal above it, and sometimes force them down even somewhat below it. But whatever may be the obstacles which hinder them from settling in this centre of repose and continuance, they are constantly tending towards it.

Smith's great insight was to realize that when prices rise above the natural level, producers who seek to maximize their own gain will continue to enter the market until the price is bid down to the point where the return on their capital is no higher (today we would add "on a risk adjusted basis") than that available elsewhere, resulting in competitive prices and an efficient allocation of resources throughout society. He famously concludes:

> Every individual endeavors to employ his capital so that its produce may be of greatest value. He generally neither intends to promote the public interest, nor knows how much he is promoting it. He intends only his own security, only his own gain. And he is in this led by an invisible hand to promote an end which was no part of his intention. By pursuing his own interest he frequently promotes that of society more effectually than when he really intends to promote it.

Smith was thus one of the first systems thinkers to show how the local, intendedly rational self-interested behavior of individual people could, through the feedback processes created by their interactions, lead to unanticipated side effects for all.

Of course, Smith's concept of the invisible hand is far more famous as the credo of modern free market capitalism. It is the core of the faith that markets know best. Smith himself, however, was careful to note the limits of the market feedbacks in equilibrating demand and supply at the natural price. "This at least would be the case" Smith notes, "where there was perfect liberty"—that is, under conditions of perfect competition (free entry and exit, free mobility of the factors of production, and free exchange of information on demand, supply, costs, and profits). Where there are monopolies, trade secrets, government regulations, barriers to trade, restrictions on immigration and capital mobility, or other feedbacks outside the simple negative loops coupling supply and demand, Smith notes that prices and profits may rise above the natural level for many years, even decades.

The feedback structure for competitive markets shown in Figure 5-26 is quite useful. Beginning with the general framework, one can disaggregate to show the specific adjustment processes at work in any particular market for both demand and supply. Additional feedbacks besides the demand and supply loops can be added, both positive and negative, and their implications assessed. The time delays, if any, in the reaction of demand and supply to higher prices can be estimated, and the implications for the stability of the market explored. If either the demand or supply loop operates strongly and swiftly (high short-run elasticities), then the market will rapidly return to equilibrium if perturbed. However, if there are long delays or weak responses in the loops (low short-run elasticity and high long-run elasticity), then the market will be prone to persistent disequilibrium and instability; random shocks in demand or production will excite the latent oscillatory behavior of the market (see chapters 4 and 20).

Not all markets clear through price alone. Few products are pure commodities for which price is the only consideration: Products and services are increasingly differentiated and companies compete to offer the best availability, delivery reliability, service, functionality, terms of payment, aftermarket support, and so on. In many markets prices do not change fast enough to equilibrate supply and demand and other competitive variables such as availability become important in clearing the market. Prices may be sluggish due to government regulation, the costs and administrative burden of frequent price changes, or considerations of fairness. For example, most people consider it unfair for hardware stores to raise the price of snow shovels after a storm, even though demand may have increased (see Kahneman, Knetsch, and Thaler 1986; Thaler 1991).

In many institutional settings price does not mediate markets at all. Most organizations, for example, have no price-mediated markets for offices, parking spaces, senior management attention, and many other scarce resources. In these cases, supply and demand are still coupled via negative feedbacks, but resources are allocated on the basis of availability, politics, perceived fairness, lottery, or other administrative procedures. Figure 5-27 shows examples of non-price-mediated markets. In each case the feedback structure is a set of coupled negative loops which regulate the demand for and supply of a resource. As in the case of price-mediated markets, there may be substantial delays in the adjustments, leading to persistent disequilibria.

FIGURE 5-27   Feedback structure of non-price-mediated resource allocation systems

Left: Availability is an important competitive variable in many product markets, and firms regulate production in response to inventory adequacy and delivery delay.

Right: In service settings, higher service quality stimulates demand, but greater demand erodes service quality as waiting time increases, and accuracy, friendliness, and other experiential aspects of the service encounter deteriorate.

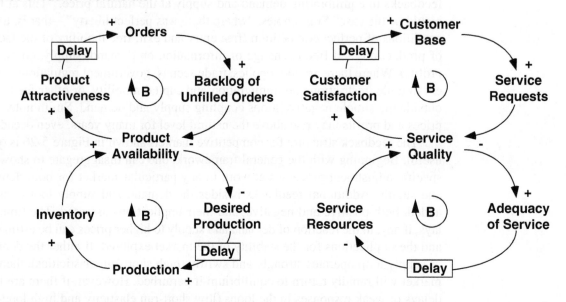

CHALLENGE	## The Oil Crises of the 1970s

In 1973 the first OPEC oil shock stunned the industrial world. Oil prices more than tripled in a matter of months as many Arab oil producers embargoed shipments to western nations to retaliate for their support of Israel in the Yom Kippur war. Many analysts believed market forces would bring the price of oil back to pre-embargo levels in a matter of months, or at most a year or two, as demand and supply reacted. Instead, prices remained high, then rose even higher as Iranian production fell in the wake of the 1979 revolution. By the early 1980s, many analysts predicted that oil prices were headed even higher and would never return to the low levels of the early 1970s. But after reaching nearly $50 per barrel (in 1990 dollars), the price of oil collapsed in the mid 1980s. Many oil exploration and alternative energy projects were canceled; bankruptcy was common. In the US, gasoline prices in real terms fell below their pre-embargo level—gasoline in the late 1990s was often one-fourth the price of designer water.

Starting with the basic market feedback structure (Figure 5-26), develop a causal diagram to explain (1) the failure of market forces to bring prices back to equilibrium soon after the first oil shock (that is, How could prices remain so high so long?) and (2) why prices collapsed in the mid 1980s and remained below the equilibrium level for so long (that is, Why didn't prices stay high?). To help, Figure 5-11 shows some of the causal links on the demand side of the market. Figure 3-4 shows US petroleum production, consumption, and real prices over the relevant

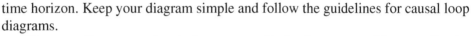

time horizon. Keep your diagram simple and follow the guidelines for causal loop diagrams.

Use your diagram to sketch the pattern of behavior you would expect for the rate of oil production and the rate of drilling of new wells from 1970 to 1990. Also plot capacity utilization for both activities (that is, what fraction of existing wells are pumping, and what fraction of existing drill rigs are operating, at any given time). What does your diagram suggest about the likely dynamics of the world oil price over the next few decades?

CHALLENGE

Speculative Bubbles

Not all markets consist of negative feedbacks alone. In many markets the locally rational behavior of individual entrepreneurs creates positive feedbacks as they interact with one another and with the physical structure of the system. One common example is the speculative bubble. There have been many dozens of major speculative bubbles in the past few centuries, from the infamous tulip mania of 1636 and South Sea bubble of 1720 to the manias and crashes of the past few decades, including gold, silver, real estate, impressionist paintings, and internet stocks.[2]

John Stuart Mill distilled the essence of the dynamics of speculation in the following passage from his famous text *Principles of Political Economy,* originally published in 1848:

> When there is a general impression that the price of some commodity is likely to rise, from an extra demand, a short crop, obstructions to importation, or any other cause, there is a disposition among dealers to increase their stocks, in order to profit by the expected rise. This disposition tends in itself to produce the effect which it looks forward to, a rise of price: and if the rise is considerable and progressive, other speculators are attracted, who, so long as the price has not begun to fall, are willing to believe that it will continue rising. These, by further purchases, produce a further advance: and thus a rise of price for which there were originally some rational grounds, is often heightened by merely speculative purchases, until it greatly exceeds what the original grounds will justify. After a time this begins to be perceived; the price ceases to rise, and the holders, thinking it time to realize their gains, are anxious to sell. Then the price begins to decline: the holders rush into market to avoid a still greater loss, and, few being willing to buy in a falling market, the price falls much more suddenly than it rose.

Develop a reference mode for Mill's description of a speculative bubble. Beginning with the basic two-loop structure for a market (Figure 5-26), develop a causal diagram grounded in Mill's text which explains the dynamics he describes. Explain briefly how the feedback structure corresponds to Mill's description and how it explains the behavior. Give examples of the phenomenon.

---

[2]Perhaps the best treatment of speculative bubbles is Charles Kindleberger's (1978) *Manias, Panics, and Crashes.* See also Galbraith's (1988) *The Great Crash* on the 1929 stock market crash.

CHALLENGE

The Thoroughbred Horse Market

Figure 5-28 shows the price of top yearling thoroughbreds in the US from 1965 through 1990. From 1974 to 1984 nominal prices for these elite horses increased by almost a factor of 10, to about $450,000. Even after removing the effects of inflation, the real price of a top thoroughbred increased by more than a factor of 4. Prices then collapsed, falling by nearly 50% in just 4 years (in real terms). Adapt your diagram of speculative bubbles to the thoroughbred horse market. Add sufficient detail to specify the particular biological and institutional features of the market. For example, what are the motivations for owning a top race horse? (You can consider a race horse to be an investment like a common stock, with an uncertain future payoff depending on the horse's performance on the track, but this is only one of the reasons people own race horses, and expected cash flow rarely justifies such a risky investment). How is the supply of horses increased? What time delays are involved?

Use your causal diagram to explain the dynamics of the thoroughbred price during the 1970s and 80s. Why did the market rise so dramatically? Why did it crash even faster? In 1965 about 18,000 thoroughbreds were born in North America. Using your model, sketch the likely behavior of the birth rate of North American thoroughbreds through 1990.

FIGURE 5-28
Real and nominal price of top thoroughbred yearlings in the US

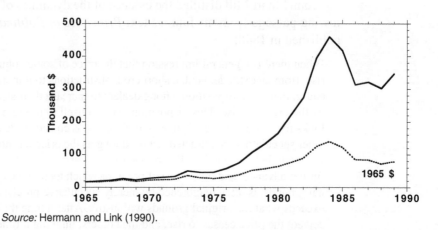

Source: Hermann and Link (1990).

5.5.1   Market Failure, Adverse Selection, and the Death Spiral

Many real world markets are imperfect due to limitations of information, costs of entry and exit, and inflexibility of resources. These imperfections create feedbacks that sometimes overwhelm the negative loops normally balancing supply and demand, leading to inefficiency or even the complete failure of the market. One source of market failure is *adverse selection*.

Adverse selection can arise when sellers and buyers in a market have different information. A classic example, first developed by Akerlof (1970), considers the used car market. To illustrate how adverse selection works, Akerlof assumed that the owners of used cars know the true quality of their cars while potential buyers do not. At any given market price, owners, knowing the true quality of their cars, will offer for sale only those cars actually worth less than the market price (the "lemons") while keeping any car actually worth more (the "peaches"). Therefore, the only cars offered for sale will be lemons. Potential buyers, realizing this, refuse to buy. Akerlof showed that in equilibrium no one will be willing to buy a used car—the market will not exist, even though there are buyers and sellers who would be willing to trade if both knew which were lemons and which were peaches.[3] Each person, behaving rationally given the information available to them, causes an outcome undesirable for all. Akerlof's result was a breakthrough in economics. Not only did his model form the foundation for the important field of information economics, a field of immense importance in economics today, but he also demonstrated that the workings of free markets were not always benign, even without monopoly power or collusive agreements among producers. Adam Smith celebrated market forces for creating an invisible hand leading individuals to "promote an end which was no part of [their] intention," an end which "frequently promotes [the interests] of society." Akerlof showed that rational self-interest could lead individuals to promote, though unintentionally, an end harmful to the interests of society—and themselves.

However, Akerlof's theory, like most economic models, is an equilibrium model and does not address the dynamics of the process. To examine the dynamics of adverse selection in an important public policy context, consider the market for health insurance.

Since the 1950s, health care costs in the US have grown much faster than GDP and have long been the highest in the world, both in absolute expenditures per capita and as a percent of national income. As costs rose, so too did health insurance premiums. Federal programs such as Medicare (for the elderly) and Medicaid (for the poor) were created to provide a safety net for these groups. But rising health care costs soon outstripped federal benefits, and forced the elderly to seek private insurance to supplement Medicare. As the costs of private insurance rose, however, many were frozen out of the market. To prevent health care from bankrupting them, many states required health insurers to offer so-called medigap insurance to senior citizens in return for the privilege of underwriting other business in their state. In Massachusetts, insurers were required to offer at least one medigap plan providing unlimited coverage for prescription drugs, one of the highest costs for the elderly. At first, the program was very successful. In the 1980s, a wide range of insurers offered medigap coverage in Massachusetts, capturing a large share of the total senior citizen market. The largest program, Medex, offered by

---

[3]Of course, there is a used car market. Akerlof's assumption that buyers have no knowledge of quality was a simplifying assumption to make the example clear. The real used car market has evolved various means to prevent market failure. Buyers can gain some information on quality through test drives and by having their own mechanic look at the car, and regulations such as lemon laws and implied warranty doctrine reduce the buyer's risk. Information on the past quality of cars offered by used car dealers deters some from selling lemons to unwitting buyers. The cost (in time and money) of these activities is a measure of the impact of the adverse selection problem in the used car market.

Blue Cross/Blue Shield of Massachusetts, covered about one-third of all senior citizens in the state in 1987. Premiums were low, about $50/month. In the late 1980s, health care cost inflation accelerated, and underwriters had to raise premiums, including the premiums for medigap and Medex. In response, some of the elderly were forced to drop their medigap coverage. Others found they could get lower rates with other carriers or by signing up for plans offering fewer benefits or which capped benefits for items such as prescriptions. However, only the healthiest seniors were eligible for these other, cheaper plans. The sickest of the elderly, those suffering from chronic illnesses, those with a history putting them at high risk—those with so-called pre-existing conditions—were not eligible for less expensive coverage or health maintenance organizations (HMOs) and had no choice but to stay with medigap. In many cases, the cost of prescriptions alone for those elderly covered by Medex exceeded their premiums by hundreds of dollars each year. As medigap losses mounted, premiums grew. But higher premiums forced still more of the comparatively healthy elderly to opt out of medigap as they found coverage elsewhere or simply did without, bearing the risk of illness themselves. Those remaining with the plan were, on average, sicker and costlier, forcing premiums up further. Figure 5-29 shows the evolution of the Medex subscriber base and premiums. Total subscribers fell from nearly 300,000 in 1988 to about 158,000 in 1997, while subscribers of the premium Medex Gold option, which provided unlimited coverage for prescriptions, fell even faster, from about 250,000 in 1988 to about 65,000 in 1997. Over the same 10 years premiums rose from about $50/month to $228/month, with further increases projected. As the customer base shrank and losses grew, underwriters began to withdraw from the market. In the early 1990s half a dozen insurers wrote medigap coverage in Massachusetts; by 1997 only Medex remained. A consumer activist lamented, "As healthier people continue to drop out and sicker people stay in, premiums continue to go up, and you create a death spiral." (*Boston Globe,* 20 January 1998, A12).

CHALLENGE   # The Medigap Death Spiral

1. Develop a causal loop diagram capturing the death spiral as depicted in section 5.5.1. Your diagram should explain not only the dynamics of the subscriber base and premiums, but also the profitability of the medigap market, the number of carriers offering coverage, and the health status of those in the program. Note any important delays in your diagram. Use your diagram to analyze the impact of the following policies:

    a. Requiring all carriers doing business in the state to insure all qualified applicants, regardless of age or health.

    b. Requiring all medigap plans (all the versions of Medex) to provide unlimited coverage for prescription drugs. The goal is to pool healthier seniors who generally use fewer drugs and choose the less expensive Medex plans with the sicker seniors who use more drugs and opt for Medex Gold.

    c. Provide a subsidy to lower medigap premiums, funded by the state.

d.   Allowing BC/BS to drop Medex, effectively eliminating all medigap coverage in the state of Massachusetts.

In assessing the impact of the policies, consider their effects on the insurers, on the elderly (insured and uninsured), and on society at large.

2.   What assumptions about information availability and consumer behavior underlie the theory captured in your causal loop diagram of the health insurance market? How might the validity of these assumptions be altered, for example, by advances in information technology which might make a person's entire health history available to insurers, or advances in genetic screening which might reveal which people were at increased risk for the development of particular illnesses?

3.   What other examples of adverse selection can you identify? Map their feedback structure.

FIGURE 5-29   The death spiral: subscribers and premiums for medigap insurance

Medex is medigap insurance for the elderly offered by Blue Cross/Blue Shield of Massachusetts. Medex Gold covers unlimited prescription drugs with a small copayment. Other Medex plans limit total benefits. Figures are for December 1 of each year. * indicates proposed rate for 1998 of $278/month.

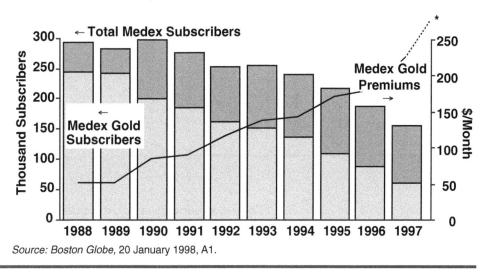

Source: Boston Globe, 20 January 1998, A1.

5.6   EXPLAINING POLICY RESISTANCE: TRAFFIC CONGESTION

By showing the network of feedback loops in which policies are embedded, causal diagrams are often an effective way to show how event-oriented, open-loop mental models lead to policy resistance. Consider the problem of traffic congestion. America's roads are choked with traffic. In 1995 there were nearly 200 million vehicles registered in the US. The 1990 census reported that about 100 million people, 87% of all workers, traveled to work by motor vehicle, 85% of them alone. Only 5% used public transportation. In 1960 64% commuted by motor vehicle. Since 1970 the number of registered vehicles grew by 70% and annual vehicle miles grew by 90%, both much faster than the growth in population or households, while public transportation stagnated (Figure 5-30). More and more of the average person's day is spent inside a car: The government estimates Americans spend 8 billion hours per year stuck in traffic. The cost of driving includes about $6000 per car per year in direct costs and up to another $9400 in indirect, externalized costs. Estimates of lost productivity due to traffic congestion range from $43 to $168 billion per year. The economy and culture of the US (and of other auto-rich nations) have adapted themselves to the dominance of the auto, from the $40 billion spent annually in the US to market automobiles to the rise of drive-through fast foods, especially foods you can eat with one hand (while the other steers). Road rage is increasingly recognized as a common mental disorder, and frustrated drivers have taken to shooting those who cut them off on the so-called freeway. What went wrong?[4]

5.6.1   Mental Models of the Traffic Problem

The traditional solution to traffic jams and congestion has been road building. Figure 5-31 shows the open-loop perspective on the problem: The problem is highway congestion; the solution is to build more roads.

FIGURE 5-30
More roads,
more traffic

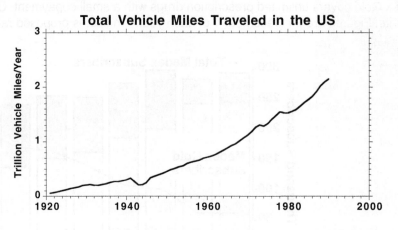

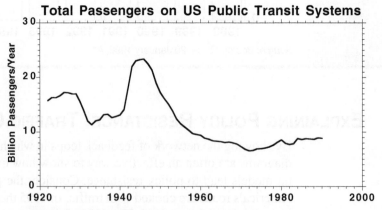

Sources: Historical Statistics of the US; Kurian (1994).

---

[4]Some of these data appear in Kay (1997), whose book *Asphalt Nation* discusses a broad range of social, cultural, economic, and environmental effects of automobile addiction. See also Downs (1992), Hansen (1995), and Gibbs (1997).

FIGURE 5-31
Open-loop view of
traffic congestion

But what happens when new roads are built? And where should you begin the development of a causal diagram to show the feedback effects of road construction? It's usually best to begin by capturing the physical structure of the system. Systems consist of both a physical structure and the decision rules used by the people in the system (the behavioral structure). The physical structure is often easier to visualize and represent than the decision-making structure. Additionally, conceptualization is often part of a group process in which people must share their own mental models and reach agreement over a single representation. It is usually easier to gain agreement about the physical structure. The behavioral structure is often more controversial; if you start there your group process may grind to a halt before you've really begun.

A good place to start for the traffic congestion case is congestion itself. A good model requires a variable that has operational meaning and can be measured. One good summary measure of congestion is average travel time (for the typical trip in a particular region). What determines travel time? Travel time depends on the balance between the capacity of the highways to handle traffic and the number of vehicles using the roads, denoted Traffic Volume in Figure 5-32.

As the number of vehicles on the roads increases, given the highway capacity, the average trip will take longer. As highway capacity rises, given the vehicle volume, the average travel time will fall. Highway capacity is altered by construction of new roads. Road construction here includes not only new roads but also improvements to existing roads such as adding lanes or increasing capacity by changing the flow of traffic, for example by converting a four-way intersection into a cloverleaf. Any project that augments the capacity of the roads to carry traffic would be included in the notion of road construction, at least in this first version of

FIGURE 5-32
Determinants of
travel time

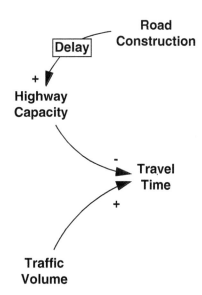

the model (later you could disaggregate the construction of new roads from widening of existing roads, if that was deemed to be necessary for the purpose). Since highway projects take time, the delay between the initiation of a construction project and the increase in highway capacity is explicitly noted.

When developing a causal map it is helpful to consider the units of measure for the constructs in your diagram. Having consistent units is often a great aid to clear thinking about the definitions of and relationships among the variables. Specifying units and checking for dimensional consistency is useful even when your model is purely conceptual and you do not intend to develop a formal simulation. Travel time would be measured in minutes per trip (for the average trip in the region). Highway Capacity and Traffic Volume are measured in vehicle-miles per day (a vehicle mile is one mile traveled by one vehicle).

Having specified the physical structure of road building and highway construction, next ask what drives highway construction programs. The primary motivation is congestion: as travel time rises, as traffic jams become the norm, as the rush hour expands from dawn through dusk, political pressure to build will build. Figure 5-33 adds the link from travel time to road construction.

Congestion creates pressure for new roads; after the new capacity is added, travel time falls, relieving the pressure. The Capacity Expansion loop (B1) acts to reduce travel time to acceptable levels. Note that the goal of the loop, the desired travel time, has been made explicit. Desired travel time is the travel time drivers consider acceptable (on average), perhaps 20 minutes for the commute from home to work. The 1990 census found average one-way commuting times for all modes and all workers of about 22 minutes, though more than 17 million people spent more than 40 minutes getting to work and nearly 2 million spent more than 90 minutes.

FIGURE 5-33
Congestion leads to political pressure to build more roads, reducing congestion via the negative Capacity Expansion feedback.

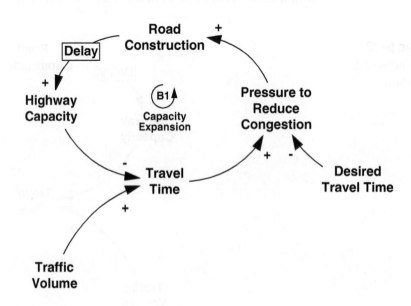

5.6.2   Compensating Feedback: The Response to Decreased Congestion

So far traffic volume is considered to be exogenous. This assumption is an accurate reflection of the mental models of many politicians, city planners, and transportation officials, for whom traffic volume grows as the population of the region grows and as the local economy develops. They see their job as building enough roads to keep travel time at the acceptable level, so political pressure stays low, so they can be reelected, and so they can serve special interests such as construction firms, real estate developers, and the business community who benefit from road building and who often provide lucrative jobs for them when they leave office.

If the capacity expansion loop were the only feedback operating in the system, then the policy of road building to relieve congestion would work well: whenever traffic volume rose, leading to congestion and pressure from the community, a road building program would be started and highway capacity would expand until the pressure was relieved.

However, traffic volume is not exogenous. To formulate the causal structure determining traffic flow it is again helpful to consider the physics of the system and the units of measure for the variables. What determines the volume of traffic? To have traffic, there must be . . . cars. No cars, no traffic. So the number of cars in the region must be a determinant of traffic volume. Traffic volume is measured in vehicle-miles per day. Total traffic volume must therefore equal the number of vehicles in the region multiplied by the number of miles each vehicle travels per day. In turn, the number of miles each vehicle travels per day is the product of the number of trips each vehicle makes per day and the length of each trip. Thus, averaging over the vehicle population,

Traffic Volume   = Vehicles * Average Trips per Day * Average Trip Length
Vehicle Miles/Day = Vehicles *   Trips/Day   *   Miles/Trip

The number of trips per day and the average trip length are not constant but depend on the level of congestion. If traffic is light, people are more likely to take additional and longer trips. When congestion is heavy, people will forego or defer trips and make shorter trips, skipping that quick run to the video shop and buying what they need at the closest store rather going on to the mall. Likewise, the number of cars in the region is not constant. The number of vehicles in the region can be thought of as the product of the population of the region and the number of cars per person: The more people in the region (and the more businesses), the more vehicles there will be. The number of vehicles per person or business in turn is not constant but depends on the attractiveness of driving. The attractiveness of driving depends on the level of congestion (Figure 5-34).

Adding these relationships to the model closes three negative feedback loops, all of which act to *increase* congestion whenever new roads are built. Suppose new roads are built to relieve congestion. In the short run, travel time falls—the number of cars in the region hasn't changed and people's habits haven't adjusted to the new, shorter travel times. As people notice that they can now get around much faster than before, they will take more Discretionary Trips (loop B2). They will

FIGURE 5-34   Traffic volume depends on congestion, closing several negative loops that cause traffic to increase whenever new roads are built.

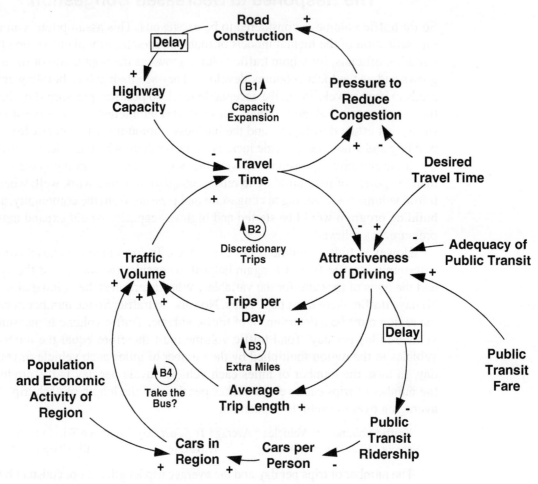

also travel Extra Miles (loop B3). Over time, seeing that driving is now much more attractive than other modes of transport such as the public transit system, some people will give up the bus or subway and buy a car. The number of cars per person (and business) rises as people ask why they should Take the Bus? (loop B4).

All three of these loops compensate for any new road construction by increasing traffic flow. But road construction stimulates other long-term feedbacks. The population of the region is not exogenous but is affected by the accessibility of the outlying districts. As the road network expands, as new freeways and ring roads link the countryside with the center city, the size of the region within a reasonable travel time grows. Of course, average travel time has a negative effect on the size of the accessible region: The greater the congestion, the smaller the radius accessible within, say, a 30-minute drive of the city (Figure 5-35).

The links to the population of the region close two more feedbacks. People begin to Move to the Suburbs (B5). As the population of the suburbs grows, the auto population rises as well. The roads begin to fill. Traffic volume grows further and

FIGURE 5-35 Reduced travel time and an expanded highway network increase the size of the region accessible from the center, which expands the population and leads to still more traffic.

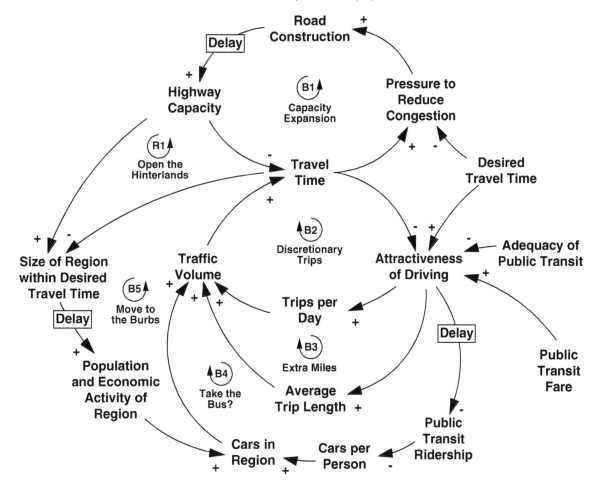

travel time rises until the resulting congestion makes the suburbs sufficiently unattractive to stop further inmigration and development.

The combined effect of the four negative feedbacks B2 through B5 is to compensate strongly for any decrease in travel time caused by new roads. If new highways were built and then all construction stopped, there would be an immediate drop in travel time. But as people respond to their newfound ease of travel, more, longer trips would be taken. More people would abandon the bus and buy cars to commute to work. The population of the suburbs would grow. These adjustments continue until travel time rises enough to stop the expansion of the suburbs because the commute required is too long. The delays in these negative loops could cause congestion to overshoot the desirable level.

But road construction doesn't stop. As new highways Open the Hinterlands (loop R1), it becomes possible to live in the countryside and commute to work in the town or city. What was once remote farm country or woods now becomes a 20 minute drive from the city, with its jobs, culture, and nightlife. Whole new communities spring up, communities where the people have to drive not only to work but also to the market, to school, to the homes of their friends and their children's friends. The burgeoning population brings new development. Shops, strip malls, and other businesses spring up, turning countryside to condo development, pasture to parking lot. All the while, the number of cars on the road grows. After some years, traffic congestion in these formerly quiet towns becomes a terrible problem. Political pressure grows and still more roads are built.

Route 128, a ring road around Boston built in the 1950s to relieve congestion by diverting long-haul traffic around the center city, rapidly attracted local drivers and soon proved inadequate. To relieve the congestion it was widened, from four to eight, and in places, even more lanes. In stretches the breakdown lane was opened to traffic during rush hour (not a few hapless motorists have been killed when they had the temerity to use the breakdown lane for a breakdown). Traffic soon filled these new lanes, and today during rush hour the cars crawl along bumper to bumper through long stretches of route 128. A second ring road, Interstate 495, was then built another 15 to 20 miles farther out. The expanded network made even more countryside accessible, and another round of population growth and economic development began. This self-reinforcing process leads to more and more new roads, pushing ever farther into the countryside, in a vain attempt to ease congestion. The story is similar for other cities in the US, including the paradigm case of congestion—Los Angeles—as well as London, Paris, Istanbul, Cairo, Tokyo, Bangkok, and countless other cities around the world.

The model clearly shows the futility of attempts to reduce traffic congestion through road building. It may take some years, but, in an automotive version of Parkinson's Law, traffic always expands to fill the highways available for its travel. Traffic volume grows until congestion is just bad enough to deter people from taking that additional trip, from driving to work instead of riding public transit, or from moving just a little farther out into the suburbs.[5] Traffic engineers call this reaction "road generated traffic." Hansen's (1995) econometric study of US metropolitan areas showed that the elasticity of traffic volume with respect to highway capacity was 0.9 after just 5 years, that is, a 10% increase in capacity led to a 9% increase in traffic within 5 years. Many of the feedbacks identified in the model operate over even longer periods, fully negating the effect of road construction on congestion. Some analysts even argue that by "adding capacity to a crowded [highway] network you could actually slow things down" (Kay 1997, p. 15), a phenomenon known as Braess' Law after the operations research analyst who first coined it. For example, the M25, London's ring road, was designed to carry long distance traffic around London. Instead, it is actually used primarily for short trips by local residents and commuters. It soon became the busiest highway in Europe and has long been known as 'the longest parking lot in the world', though commuters on the Long Island Expressway, Paris' Peripherique, and the San Diego Freeway might disagree. In response, the M25 has been steadily widened, all to no avail. Studies typically find, as the London *Times* reported (10 November 1997), that

---

[5]The analogy with Parkinson's Law ("work expands to fill the time available for its completion") is more than casual: Parkinson's Law arises through a negative feedback loop structure quite similar to that governing traffic congestion. See section 5.4.

Traffic congestion on a widened section of the M25 is now greater than before the improvement took place, a motoring survey suggests. The widening of a stretch of the motorway at junction 15, west of London, was intended to curb congestion, but the survey showed that jams on the stretch were now commonplace, although last year traffic was generally free-flowing.

5.6.3   The Mass Transit Death Spiral

Standard economic analysis suggests that a decline in the attractiveness of a good or service should lead people to switch to substitutes. Why, then, as congestion builds up, don't people turn to mass transit? Part of the answer is shown in Figure 5-36.

As lower travel time caused by new roads increases the attractiveness of driving, ridership and revenue of the public transit system fall. Costs don't fall very much, since most of the costs are the fixed costs of providing service: the buses must run whether they are full or empty. If the transit authority tries to close its deficit by Cost Cutting (loop B6), service and quality erode. Routes are closed and the frequency of service is cut. The relative attractiveness of driving rises and mass transit ridership falls still more. The deficit widens, leading to still more cuts in the public transit network as the self-reinforcing Route Expansion loop R2 operates as a vicious cycle of decreasing ridership, greater cuts, and still fewer riders.

Raising fares to balance the transit authority budget is little better: Higher fares increase the relative attractiveness of driving, and more people abandon mass transit for cars. Ridership falls, and fares must be raised again, Choking off Ridership (loop R3). Because mass transit systems have a high proportion of fixed costs, they are highly vulnerable to these self-reinforcing feedbacks. As road construction and auto use accelerated in America, particularly after the late 1940s, people abandoned trolleys, trains, and buses. These positive loops became a death spiral of higher fares, reduced service, and declining quality until in many cities only the poorest people, those who cannot afford to move to the suburbs or own a car, are left to ride the public transit system. Attempts to build up the mass transit network to offset the positive loops that erode ridership through Mass Transit Capacity Expansion (loop B7) often fight a losing battle due to their long delays and high costs.

One final positive feedback is worth adding: The adequacy of a public transit system depends not only on the scope of the network and the frequency of service but also on the size and population density of the region. As the countryside is developed, the locus of activity shifts away from the area served by existing mass transit. As population density falls, fewer and fewer people live near a bus or subway route. Public transit becomes less and less useful because You Can't Get There on the Bus, leading to still more driving and still lower mass transit ridership, in another vicious cycle, loop R4 (Figure 5-37). The suburbs grow and the adequacy of public transit falls much faster than mass transit capacity can be added.

The model above is still incomplete (as all models always are). One could add many more feedbacks. For example, the spread of population into the less densely populated suburbs increases the average length of trips, forming additional channels by which congestion rises to offset any gains caused by new highways. The model does not explore other side effects of the automobile's rise to dominance,

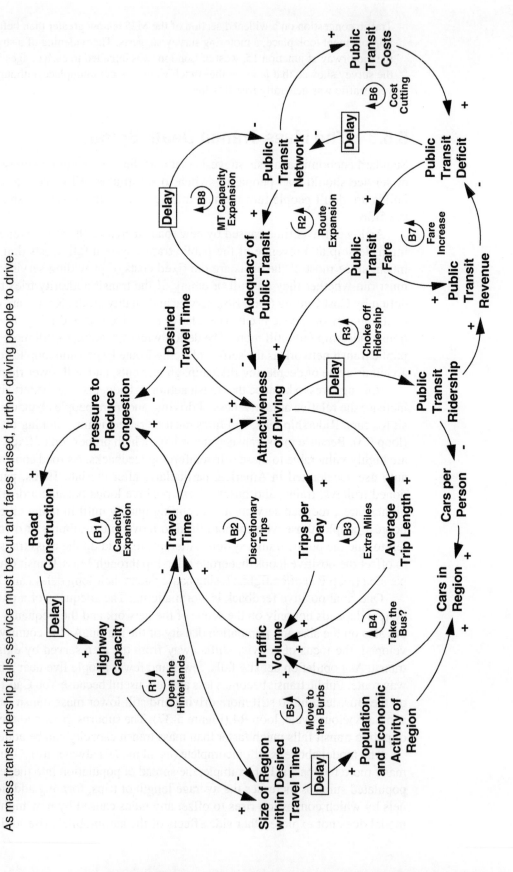

FIGURE 5-36 The high fixed costs of mass transit lead to a death spiral. As mass transit ridership falls, service must be cut and fares raised, further driving people to drive.

FIGURE 5-37 You can't get there on the bus.

As the size of the populated region expands, the adequacy of public transit declines. The result is more driving, more congestion, and still more road construction rather than an expansion of the public transit network.

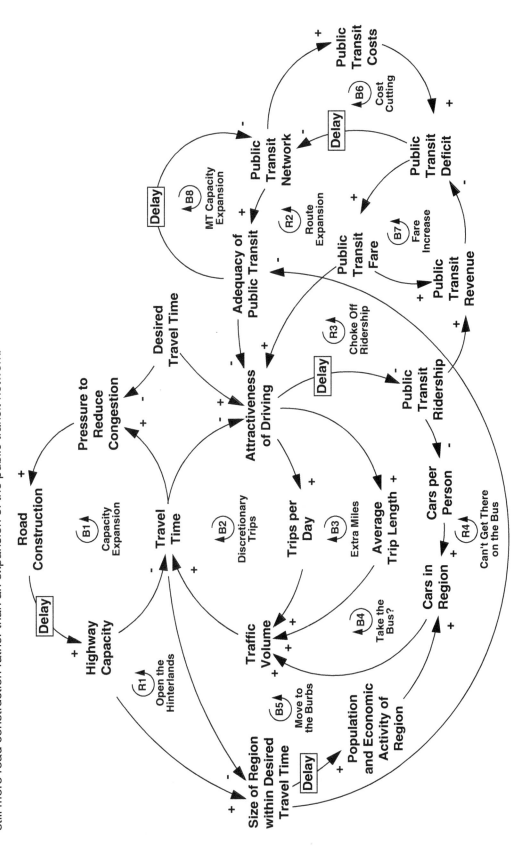

including the deaths, injuries and costs of accidents, the health effects of smog and ozone production, greenhouse gas generation, the solid waste problem posed by the discard of millions of vehicles each year (see chapter 6), and the dependence of the highly automotive nations on insecure supplies of imported oil. What other feedbacks and side effects do you see?

5.6.4   Policy Analysis: The Impact of Technology

Despite its limitations and omissions, the model provides a rich explanation for the persistent failure of road-building programs to alleviate traffic congestion. You can now use the model to assess the likely effect of other policies.

In the 1970s and 1980s, a popular solution was HOV lanes (high-occupancy vehicle, or carpool lanes). These lanes are restricted to cars with at least two occupants (sometimes only during rush hour). The result? To the extent drivers joined carpools, the number of trips per day fell, reducing traffic volume slightly. The resulting reduction in congestion, however, simply encouraged others to take to the roads instead of mass transit, to take additional trips they might otherwise have foregone, and to leave for work a little later. The total volume of traffic during rush hours didn't change and more people were now on the highways than before, further eroding mass transit ridership. And some enterprising but immoral motorists took to riding with inflatable dummies in the passenger seat to fool the police and illegally take advantage of the HOV lane.

Despite the persistent failure of road building and innovations such as HOV lanes, many transportation planners continue to pin their hopes on technological solutions to the congestion problem. The latest of these is so-called intelligent vehicle-highway systems. Many clever technologies are under development, from sensors to detect the distance to the car ahead and automatically adjust your car's speed, to transponders or magnets embedded in the road surface to automatically steer your car. Already sensors embedded in some highways transmit real time traffic data to cars equipped with special receivers. Technologists look forward to the day when the internet, GPS, and real time vehicle controls will allow your car to pick the optimal route to your destination and drive you there while you relax or read a book. Some of these technologies are designed to increase highway safety. Many are motivated by the need to increase highway capacity in cities where building new roads and adding new lanes is no longer possible: under computer control, the technologists promise, cars could zip safely along at 70 miles per hour only inches apart, greatly expanding the capacity of existing highways.

The model shows the futility of these hopes. There is no technological solution to the congestion problem. The more effectively these technologies increase highway capacity, the more trips will be taken, the more people will buy cars, the less attractive public transit will be, and the more countryside will be developed into bedroom communities for commuters. The volume of traffic will swiftly rise to absorb all the new capacity technology can yield. We might zip along the freeway at seventy, but we'll be stuck in much longer lines at the entrance ramp and on secondary routes. On the roadways of the future we may ride more safely and more comfortably, but we won't ride more swiftly.

Economists generally suggest the solution is to charge tolls that increase as congestion rises (Downs 1992). While some regions are experimenting with time-of-day tolls and congestion-based pricing using real time sensing equipment, there is considerable political resistance to the notion of paying for the freeway, and some concern over the regressive impact of tolls. Worse, drivers tend to switch to secondary roads and city streets where tolls are infeasible.

Some nations have come to understand these dynamics and are moving to reduce traffic and the attendant pollution, accidents, and destruction of open land it causes by *increasing* travel times. In September 1997 Sweden's parliament adopted "Vision Zero", a policy aimed at eliminating all traffic fatalities by permitting towns to *reduce* speed limits to 30 kilometers per hour and install speed bumps and other flow restricting devices. The model suggests these policies will, in addition to saving lives, encourage people to use other modes such as bus, train, and bicycle, thus reducing the pressure for road building and the growth in traffic.

5.6.5   Compensating Feedback: The Source of Policy Resistance

The feedbacks affecting traffic clearly show that attempts to control congestion through road building are vain. Any reduction in congestion leads to more trips and more cars, swiftly building congestion back up. What road construction actually controls is the size of the metropolitan area and the number of cars on the road. Road construction causes the dramatic expansion of the urbanized and suburbanized area, the growth of strip malls and parking lots, and the decline of farm, forest, and field.

The causal structure of the traffic problem illustrates how policy resistance arises in a wide range of complex systems. Road-building programs are typical of policies directed at the symptom of difficulty. Policies directed at alleviating the symptoms of a problem usually fail because they trigger *compensating feedbacks,* feedbacks that undercut the intended effects of the policy. The compensating loops arise because other actors, with their own goals, respond to changes in the state of the system in such a way as to offset the intended effects of the policy. While each individual loop may be weak, the combined effect can often compensate completely for any policy directed at a symptom of a problem. Directing policies at the symptoms of a problem is like trying to squeeze a balloon to make it smaller. Whenever you squeeze, the air pressure increases, expanding some other part of the balloon so its volume remains about the same.

Why then do so many policies focus on alleviating the symptoms of difficulty? We focus on symptoms because so much of our experience is with simple systems in which cause and effect are closely related in time and space, in which symptom and cause are obvious. Most of our experience is with systems in which there is a single, dominant negative feedback, as when you reach out to grasp an object by assessing the gap between the position of the object and your hand. We then extrapolate these everyday experiences with simple systems into the management of complex systems. But, as Jay Forrester (1969, pp. 9–10) notes

In the complex system the cause of a difficulty may lie far back in time from the symptoms, or in a completely different and remote part of the system. In fact, causes are usually found, not in prior events, but in the structure and policies of the system . . . Conditioned by our training in simple systems, we apply the same intuition to complex systems and are led into error. As a result we treat symptoms, not causes. The outcome lies between ineffective and detrimental . . . If the attempted solution intensifies the problem, wrongly attributed to another source, the organization likely will redouble its "corrective" action, producing more difficulty and pressure for still more remedial action. A destructive spiral becomes established.

CHALLENGE   ## Identifying the Feedback Structure of Policy Resistance

1. Consider the failed Romanian population policy described in chapter 1. Develop a causal loop diagram explaining the failure of the government's efforts to increase the birth rate.

2. Table 1-1 lists a number of common examples of policy resistance in social, business, and economic systems. Develop simple causal diagrams for each. Use your diagrams to explain why each policy failed.

5.7   SUMMARY

Causal diagrams are a powerful tool to map the feedback structure of complex systems. Causal diagrams can be helpful to you in the early phases of a project, when you need to work with the client team to elicit and capture their mental models. They are helpful in presenting the results of your modeling work in a nontechnical fashion. To be effective, you should follow the rules for causal diagrams, including selection of variable names, layout, and assignment of link and loop polarities. It is best to build up diagrams in steps: resist the urge to create a single, comprehensive diagram. As in learning to read music, practice is everything. Develop your skills in mapping the feedback structure of systems by sketching causal diagrams to capture the feedbacks you recognize as you read the newspaper or the great works of literature.

6

Stocks and Flows

I'm very good at integral and differential calculus,
I know the scientific names of beings animalculous;
In short, in matters vegetable, animal, and mineral,
I am the very model of a modern Major-General.
                        —W. S. Gilbert, *The Pirates of Penzance,* Act 1.

This chapter introduces the concept of stocks and flows, a central idea in dynamics. It presents the conceptual and mathematical definitions of stocks and flows, the diagramming tools for mapping networks of stocks and flows, and case studies of the use of stocks and flows in modeling projects including automobile recycling and the construction of pulp and paper mills. Developing facility in identifying, mapping, and interpreting the stock and flow networks of systems is a critical skill for any modern systems modeler.

6.1 STOCKS, FLOWS, AND ACCUMULATION

Causal loop diagrams are wonderfully useful in many situations. They are well suited to represent interdependencies and feedback processes. They are used effectively at the start of a modeling project to capture mental models—both those of a client group and your own. They are also used to communicate the results of a completed modeling effort.

However, causal loop diagrams suffer from a number of limitations and can easily be abused. Some of these are discussed in chapter 5. One of the most important limitations of causal diagrams is their inability to capture the stock and flow structure of systems. Stocks and flows, along with feedback, are the two central concepts of dynamic systems theory.

Stocks are accumulations. They characterize the state of the system and generate the information upon which decisions and actions are based. Stocks give systems inertia and provide them with memory. Stocks create delays by accumulating the difference between the inflow to a process and its outflow. By decoupling rates of flow, stocks are the source of disequilibrium dynamics in systems.

Stocks and flows are familiar to all of us. The inventory of a manufacturing firm is the stock of product in its warehouses. The number of people employed by a business is a stock. The balance in your checking account is a stock. Stocks are altered by inflows and outflows. A firm's inventory is increased by the flow of production and decreased by the flow of shipments (and possibly other outflows due to spoilage or shrinkage). The workforce increases via the hiring rate and decreases via the rate of quits, layoffs, and retirements. Your bank balance increases with deposits and decreases as you spend. Yet despite everyday experience of stocks and flows, all too often people fail to distinguish clearly between them. Is the US federal deficit a stock or a flow? Many people, including politicians responsible for fiscal policy, are unclear. Failure to understand the difference between stocks and flows often leads to underestimation of time delays, a short-term focus, and policy resistance.

6.1.1   Diagramming Notation for Stocks and Flows

System dynamics uses a particular diagramming notation for stocks and flows (Figure 6-1).

- Stocks are represented by rectangles (suggesting a container holding the contents of the stock).
- Inflows are represented by a pipe (arrow) pointing into (adding to) the stock.
  Outflows are represented by pipes pointing out of (subtracting from) the stock.
- Valves control the flows.
- Clouds represent the sources and sinks for the flows. A source represents the stock from which a flow originating outside the boundary of the model arises; sinks represent the stocks into which flows leaving the model boundary drain. Sources and sinks are assumed to have infinite capacity and can never constrain the flows they support.

The structure of all stock and flow structures is composed of these elements. As the example in the figure shows, a firm's inventory is a stock that accumulates the inflow of production and is reduced by the outflow of shipments. These are the only flows considered in the model: unless explicitly shown, other possible flows into or out of the stock, such as inventory shrinkage or spoilage, are assumed to be zero. The clouds indicate that the stock of raw materials never starves the production rate and the stock of product shipped to customers never grows so high that it blocks the shipment rate.

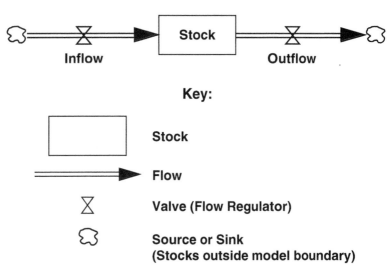

FIGURE 6-1
Stock and flow
diagramming
notation

General Structure:

Key:

- Stock
- Flow
- Valve (Flow Regulator)
- Source or Sink
(Stocks outside model boundary)

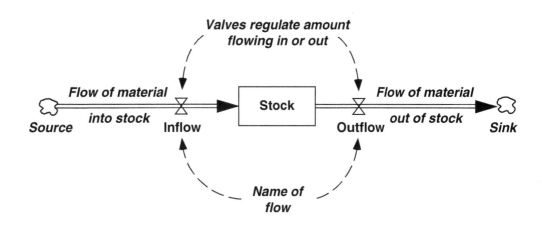

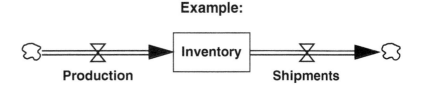

Example:

6.1.2   Mathematical Representation of Stocks and Flows

The stock and flow diagramming conventions (originated by Forrester 1961) were based on a hydraulic metaphor—the flow of water into and out of reservoirs. Indeed, it is helpful to think of stocks as bathtubs of water. The quantity of water in your bathtub at any time is the accumulation of the water flowing in through the tap less the water flowing out through the drain (assume no splashing or evaporation). In exactly the same way, the quantity of material in any stock is the accumulation of the flows of material in less the flows of material out. Despite the prosaic metaphor the stock and flow diagram has a precise and unambiguous mathematical meaning. Stocks accumulate or *integrate* their flows; the net flow into the stock is the rate of change of the stock. Hence the structure represented in Figure 6-1 above corresponds exactly to the following integral equation:

$$\text{Stock(t)} = \int_{t_0}^{t} [\text{Inflow(s)} - \text{Outflow(s)}]ds + \text{Stock}(t_0) \qquad (6\text{-}1)$$

where Inflow(s) represents the value of the inflow at any time s between the initial time t_0 and the current time t. Equivalently, the net rate of change of any stock, its derivative, is the inflow less the outflow, defining the differential equation

$$d(\text{Stock})/dt = \text{Inflow(t)} - \text{Outflow(t)}. \qquad (6\text{-}2)$$

In general, the flows will be functions of the stock and other state variables and parameters. Figure 6-2 shows four equivalent representations of the general stock and flow structure. The bathtub and stock and flow diagrams may appear to be less rigorous than the integral or differential equation representations, but they are precisely equivalent and contain exactly the same information. From any system of integral or differential equations we can construct the corresponding stock and flow map; from any stock and flow map we can generate the corresponding integral or differential equation system.

FIGURE 6-2
Four equivalent representations of stock and flow structure

Each representation contains precisely the same information.

Hydraulic Metaphor:

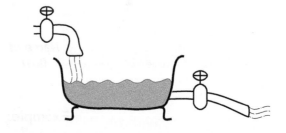

Stock and Flow Diagram:

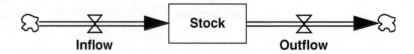

Integral Equation:

$$\text{Stock(t)} = \int_{t_0}^{t} [\text{Inflow(s)} - \text{Outflow(s)}]ds + \text{Stock }(t_0)$$

Differential Equation:

$$d(\text{Stock})/dt = \text{Net Change in Stock} = \text{Inflow(t)} - \text{Outflow(t)}$$

Process Point: Notation for Accumulation

The traditional notation used in calculus and shown in Figure 6-2 is often confusing to many people. In this book, I will generally represent the process of accumulation with the INTEGRAL() function:

$$Stock = INTEGRAL(Inflow - Outflow, Stock_{t_0}) \tag{6-3}$$

The INTEGRAL() function is exactly equivalent to equation (6-1) and represents the concept that the stock accumulates its inflows less its outflows, beginning with an initial value of $Stock_{t_0}$.

6.1.3   The Contribution of Stocks to Dynamics

Stocks are critical in generating the dynamics of systems for the following reasons (Mass 1980):

1. **Stocks characterize the state of the system and provide the basis for actions.**
   The stocks in a system tell decision makers where they are, providing them with the information needed to act. A pilot must know the state of the aircraft including position, heading, altitude, and fuel level. Without knowledge of these states, the pilot is flying blind and won't survive long. Likewise, a firm can't set its production schedule appropriately without knowledge of the order backlog, the stock of inventory, the parts stocks, the labor force, and other stocks. A balance sheet characterizes the financial health of a corporation by reporting the values of stocks such as cash, inventory, payables, and debt. Information about these stocks affects decisions such as issuing new debt, paying dividends, and controlling expenses via layoffs.

2. **Stocks provide systems with inertia and memory.**
   Stocks accumulate past events. The content of a stock can only change through an inflow or outflow. Without changes in these flows, the past accumulation into the stock persists. The stock of lead in the paint of America's inner city housing remains high today even though lead paint was banned in 1978. Once the stock of lead paint accumulated, the only way to eliminate it is through expensive deleading or the eventual demolition of the housing itself. Even then the lead remains, either safely sequestered or more likely dispersed into the environment as dust, chips, or lead leaching from landfills into water supplies. Likewise, the stock of ozone-destroying chlorine generated by CFCs will remain in the atmosphere for decades even after the production rate of CFCs falls to zero because the rate at which chlorine is scrubbed from the stratosphere is very low. Stocks don't have to be tangible. Memories and beliefs are stocks that characterize your mental states. Your beliefs persist over time, generating inertia and continuity in your attitudes and behavior. If you have a bad experience on an airline and never fly on that carrier again, your belief about the low quality of their service remains even if they've improved.

3. **Stocks are the source of delays.**
    All delays involve stocks. A delay is a process whose output lags behind its
    input. The difference between the input and output accumulates in a stock of
    material in process. There is a lag between the time you mail a letter and the
    time it is received. During this interval, the letter resides in a stock of letters
    in transit. Even email accumulates in stocks of undelivered packets and
    messages residing in the memory of various computers between the sender
    and receiver. There is a lag of several years between the decision to build
    new office buildings and the time they are ready for occupancy. During this
    interval there is a supply line of buildings under development, including a
    stock of proposed projects and a stock of buildings under construction.

    By definition, when the input to a delay changes, the output lags behind
    and continues at the old rate for some time. During such adjustments, the
    stock accumulating the difference between input and output changes. If you
    mail wedding invitations to 1000 of your closest friends all at once, while the
    rate at which other mail is deposited remains constant, the stock of letters in
    transit jumps by 1000 and remains at the new level as the letters make their
    way to their destinations. Only as the invitations begin to arrive does the
    stock of letters in transit start to fall. The delivery rate exceeds the mailing
    rate, shrinking the stock of mail in transit, until all the invitations have been
    delivered, at which point the delivery rate once again equals the rate at which
    mail is deposited and the stock of letters in transit returns to its original level.

    Perception delays also involve stocks though these stocks do not involve
    any material flows. For example, the belief of managers in a company's
    Taiwan headquarters about the shipment rate from their Silicon Valley plant
    lags behind the true shipment rate due to measurement and reporting delays.
    Measurement of a rate such as shipments always involves a stock. Due to
    unpredictable variations in customer orders, product availability, and
    transportation, shipments can vary significantly from hour to hour, day to
    day, or over even longer periods. Shipments must be accumulated for some
    period of time such as a day, week, or month to provide a meaningful
    measurement of the rate. If shipments are highly volatile, the firm will have
    to accumulate them over longer intervals to filter out the short-term noise and
    provide a meaningful average managers can use to make decisions. In
    addition there are reporting delays involving a stock of shipment information
    waiting to be uploaded to and downloaded from the firm's computer system.
    There may be further delays in the adjustment of the executives' beliefs even
    after they see the latest data. Chapter 11 describes the structure and dynamics
    of delays in detail.

4. **Stocks decouple rates of flow and create disequilibrium dynamics.**
    Stocks absorb the differences between inflows and outflows, thus permitting
    the inflows and outflows to a process to differ. In equilibrium, the total
    inflow to a stock equals its total outflow so the level of the stock is
    unchanging. However, inflows and outflows usually differ because they are
    often governed by different decision processes. Disequilibrium is the rule
    rather than the exception.

The production of grain depends on the yearly cycle of planting and harvest, along with unpredictable natural variations in weather, pest populations, and so on. Consumption of grain depends on how many mouths there are to feed. The difference between grain production and consumption rates accumulates in grain stocks, stored throughout the distribution system from field to grain elevator to processor inventories to market to kitchen cupboard. Without a stock of grain to buffer the differences between production and consumption, consumption would necessarily equal production at all times and people would starve between harvests. Thus Joseph advised Pharaoh to stockpile grain during the 7 good years in anticipation of the 7 lean years during which consumption would exceed harvests. While on average the production of grain balances consumption (and losses) as farmers respond to market prices and inventory conditions in determining how much to plant, and as consumers adjust consumption in response to prices and availability, production and consumption are rarely equal.

Whenever two coupled activities are controlled by different decision makers, involve different resources, and are subject to different random shocks, a buffer or stock between them must exist, accumulating the difference. As these stocks vary, information about the size of the buffer will feed back in various ways to influence the inflows and outflows. Often, but not always, these feedbacks will operate to bring the stock into balance. Whether and how equilibrium is achieved cannot be assumed but is an emergent property of the whole system as its many feedback loops interact simultaneously. Understanding the nature and stability of these dynamics is often the purpose of a system dynamics model.

6.2   Identifying Stocks and Flows

The distinction between stocks and flows is recognized in many disciplines. Table 6-1 shows some common terms used to distinguish between stocks and flows in various fields. In mathematics, system dynamics, control theory, and related engineering disciplines, stocks are also known as *integrals* or *state variables*. Flows are also known as *rates* or *derivatives*. Chemists speak of *reactants* and *reaction products* (the stocks) and *reaction rates* (the flows). In manufacturing settings, stocks and flows are also called *buffers* and *throughput*. In economics, stocks are also known as *levels* and flows as *rates*. For example, the capital stock of an economy is its level of wealth (measured in, say, dollars) while the GDP is the aggregate rate of national output (measured in \$/year). In accounting, balance sheet items are stocks, such as cash, the book value of inventory, long-term debt, and shareholder equity (all measured in, e.g., dollars). Items appearing on the income statement or flow of funds report are flows which alter the corresponding stocks on the balance sheet, such as net receipts, the cost of goods sold, long-term borrowing, and the change in retained earnings. These flows are measured in \$/year. Physiological models often lump different stocks into a small number of *compartments* or boxes connected by diffusion rates (the flows). For example, the stock of glucose in a human can be represented by a three compartment model:

Field	Stocks	Flows
Mathematics, physics and engineering	Integrals, states, state variables, stocks	Derivatives, rates of change, flows
Chemistry	Reactants and reaction products	Reaction rates
Manufacturing	Buffers, inventories	Throughput
Economics	Levels	Rates
Accounting	Stocks, balance sheet items	Flows, cash flow or income statement items
Biology, physiology	Compartments	Diffusion rates, flows
Medicine, epidemiology	Prevalence, reservoirs	Incidence, infection, morbidity and mortality rates

glucose in the digestive system, glucose in the bloodstream, and glucose in the intracellular matrix. In epidemiology, *prevalence* measures the number or stock of people who have a particular condition at any given time, while *incidence* is the rate at which people come down with the disease or condition. In December 1998 the prevalence of HIV/AIDS worldwide was estimated by the United Nations AIDS program to be 33.4 million and the incidence of HIV infection was estimated to be 5.8 million/year. That is, a total of 33.4 million people were estimated to be HIV-positive or to have AIDS; the rate of addition to this stock was 5.8 million people per year (16,000 new infections per day). The net change in the population of HIV-positive individuals was estimated to be 3.3 million people per year due to the death rate from AIDS, estimated to be 2.5 million people per year in 1998.

How can you tell which concepts are stocks and which are flows? Stocks are quantities of material or other accumulations. They are the states of the system. The flows are the rates at which these system states change. Imagine a river flowing into a reservoir. The quantity of water in the reservoir is a stock (measured in, say, cubic meters). If you drew an imaginary line across the point where the river enters the reservoir, the flow is the rate at which water passes the line—the rate of flow in cubic meters per second.

6.2.1   Units of Measure in Stock and Flow Networks

The units of measure can help you distinguish stocks from flows. Stocks are usually a quantity such as widgets of inventory, people employed, or Yen in an account. The associated flows must be measured in the same units *per time period*, for example, the rate at which widgets are added per week to inventory, the hiring rate in people per month, or the rate of expenditure from an account in ¥/hour. Note that the choice of time period is arbitrary. You are free to select any measurement system you like as long as you remain consistent. You can measure the flow of production into inventory as widgets per week, widgets per day, or widgets per hour. The statement "The current rate of production is 1200 widgets per day" is exactly equivalent to the statement that production is proceeding at a rate of 8400 widgets per week, 50 widgets per hour, 5/6 widgets per minute, or even 43,800,000 widgets per century. All are statements about how many widgets are being produced *right now—at this instant.* Whether the cumulative number of widgets produced in any given interval such as a day, week, or century is equal to 1200, 8400, or 43,800,000 depends on whether the current rate stays constant over that interval (or averages out to the current rate). Most likely it won't.

6.2.2   The Snapshot Test

Stocks characterize the state of the system. To identify key stocks in a system, imagine freezing the scene with a snapshot. Stocks would be those things you could count or measure in the picture, including psychological states and other intangible variables. You can estimate the stock of water in a reservoir from a set of satellite images and topographic data, but you cannot determine whether the water level is rising or falling. Your bank statement tells you how much money is in your account but not the rate at which you are spending it now. If time stopped, it would be possible to determine how much inventory a company has or the price of materials but not the net rate of change in inventory or the rate of inflation in materials prices. The snapshot test applies also to less tangible stocks. The plant manager's expectation of the customer order rate at any instant or perception of the size of inventory are stocks, even though they are mental and not physical stocks. A snapshot of people's mental states, however, does not indicate how fast they are revising their beliefs.

Figure 6-3 lists some common concepts and identifies them as stocks or flows, showing their stock and flow structure and units of measure. Population, Employees, and Debt are straightforward. Why is the price of a product a stock? Prices characterize the state of the system, in this case how much you must pay per unit. A price posted on an item remains in effect until it is changed, just as the number of widgets in an inventory remains constant until it is changed by a flow of production or shipments. Even the bids and offers called out in a trading pit at a financial market are stocks, albeit short-lived ones: a bid or offer remains in effect until the trader withdraws or alters it by crying out another.

Why is the expected customer order rate for a product a stock? Clearly, the actual customer order rate is a flow. The flow of customer orders accumulates in a backlog or stock of unfilled orders until the product can be delivered. However, a manager's belief about the rate at which customer orders are booked is a stock—it is a state of the system, in this case a mental state. No one knows the true current or future order rate. The manager's belief about orders can, and usually does, differ from the true order rate (the belief can be wrong). Managers' beliefs about the customer order rate will tend to remain the same until they become aware of new information and update their beliefs. The Change in Expected Order Rate is the rate at which the belief is updated. Note the units of measure for the expected order rate. Like the actual order rate, the expected order rate is measured in widgets per time period (say weeks). The units of measure for the rate at which the belief about customer orders is updated are (widgets/week)/week.

FIGURE 6-3
Examples of
stocks and flows
with their units of
measure

The choice of time
unit for the flows
(e.g., days, weeks,
years) is arbitrary
but must be
consistent within a
single model.

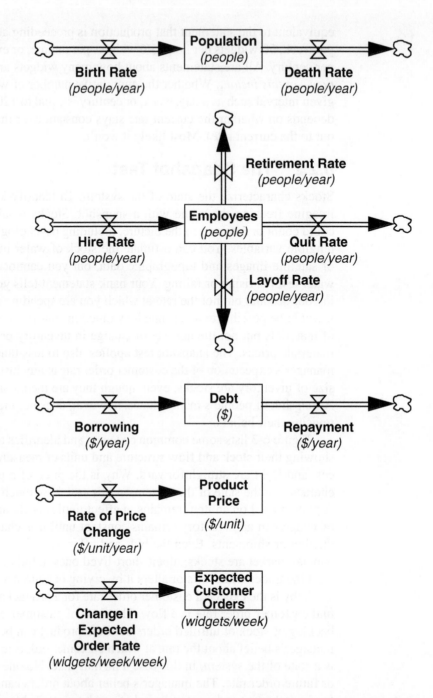

Note that the rate of price change and the change in the expected order rate can
be positive or negative (prices and demand forecasts can rise or fall). Any flow into
or out of a stock can be either positive or negative. The direction of the arrow
(pointing into or out of a stock) defines the sign convention for the flow. An inflow
adds to the stock when the flow is positive; if the flow is negative it subtracts from
the stock. When the outflow is positive, the flow subtracts from the stock.

CHALLENGE

Identifying Stocks and Flows

Are the following concepts stocks or flows? Draw a stock and flow map for each and give their units of measure.

1. Interest rate (e.g., the prime interest rate or rate on the 30-year US Treasury bond).
2. Unemployment rate.

Hint: What does the word "rate" mean in these settings?

6.2.3   Conservation of Material in Stock and Flow Networks

A major strength of the stock and flow representation is the clear distinction between the physical flows through the stock and flow network and the information feedbacks that couple the stocks to the flows and close the loops in the system. The contents of the stock and flow networks are *conserved* in the sense that items entering a stock remain there until they flow out. When an item flows from one stock to another the first stock loses precisely as much as the second gains. Consider the stock and flow structure representing the accounts receivable of a firm (Figure 6-4). The stock of receivables is increased by billings and decreased by payments received and by defaults. The flow of billings is conserved in the sense that once a customer is billed, the invoice remains in the stock of receivables until it explicitly flows out when the receivables department records the customer's payment or acknowledges that the customer has defaulted and writes off the account. In contrast, information about the stock of receivables is not conserved. The corporate accounting system makes the value of the receivables stock available to many throughout the organization. Accessing and using this information does not use it up or make it unavailable to others.

Note also that while the units of accounts payable are dollars and the billing, payment, and default flows are measured in dollars per time period, the contents of the stock are not actually dollars. Rather, the content of the receivables stock is information, specifically, a ledger or database consisting of records of invoices outstanding. To see why, imagine trying to exchange your firm's stock of receivables for cash—you can sell them to a collection agency, but only for much less than 100 cents on the dollar. Though the contents of the stock of receivables is information and not a material quantity, it is nevertheless conserved—you cannot sell a given stock of receivables more than once (not legally, anyway). Stocks can represent information as well as more tangible quantities such as people, money, and materials. Stocks can also represent intangible variables including psychological states, perceptions, and expectations such as employee morale, the expected rate of inflation, or perceived inventory.

FIGURE 6-4

Stock and flow structure of accounts receivable

The material flowing through the network is actually information about customers and the amounts they owe. This information is conserved—the only way a receivable, once billed, is removed from the stock is if the customer pays or defaults. Information about the size and composition of accounts payable, however, can be made available throughout the system and is not depleted by usage.

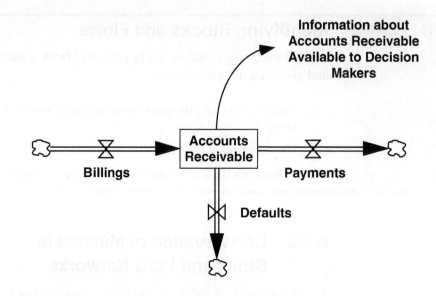

6.2.4 State-Determined Systems

The theory of dynamic systems takes a state-determined system or state variable approach. The only way a stock can change is via its inflows and outflows. In turn, the stocks determine the flows (Figure 6-5).

Systems therefore consist of networks of stocks and flows linked by information feedbacks from the stocks to the rates (Figure 6-6). As shown in the figure, the determinants of rates include any constants and exogenous variables. These too are stocks. Constants are state variables that change so slowly they are considered to be constant over the time horizon of interest in the model. Exogenous variables are stocks you have chosen not to model explicitly and are therefore outside the model boundary. For example, in a model of the demand for a new video game, the size of the potential market might depend on the population between, say, ages 4 and 20. The product life cycle will last a few years at most. Over this time horizon the population between 4 and 20 years of age is not likely to change significantly and can reasonably be assumed constant. Alternatively, you could model the stock of children in the target age group as an exogenous variable, using census data and projections to estimate its values. Making population constant or exogenous is acceptable in this case since there are no significant feedbacks between sales of video games and birth, death, or migration rates.

6.2.5 Auxiliary Variables

As illustrated in Figure 6-6, mathematical description of a system requires only the stocks and their rates of change. For ease of communication and clarity, however, it is often helpful to define intermediate or *auxiliary variables*. Auxiliaries consist of functions of stocks (and constants or exogenous inputs). For example, a population model might represent the net birth rate as depending on population and the fractional birth rate; fractional birth rate in turn can be modeled as a function of food per capita. The left side of Figure 6-7 shows the structure and equations for

State-determined
systems

Systems evolve
by feedback of
information from
the state of the
system to the
flows that alter
the states.

Left: Causal loop
representation in
which the stock
and flow
structure is not
explicit.

Right: Explicit
stock and flow
structure for the
same feedback
loop.

The equations
correspond to the
stock and flow
map. The net
rate of change
of the stock is a
function of the
stock itself,
closing the
feedback loop.

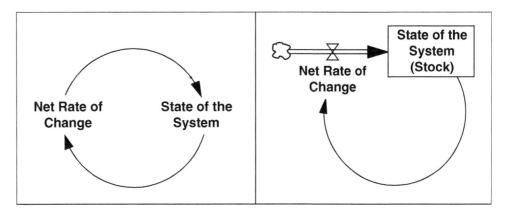

State of the System = INTEGRAL(Net Rate of Change, State of the System$_{t_0}$)

Net Rate of Change = f (State of the System)

the model. The Net Birth Rate accumulates in the Population stock. The auxiliary variables Fractional Birth Rate and Food per Capita are neither stocks nor flows. They are functions of the stocks (and exogenous inputs, in this case Food). Population participates in two feedback loops: a positive loop (more people, more births, more people) and a negative loop (more people, less food per person, lower fractional net birth rate, fewer births). The inclusion of the auxiliary variables distinguishes the two loops and allows unambiguous assignment of link and loop polarities.

The auxiliaries can always be eliminated and the model reduced to a set of equations consisting only of stocks and their flows. By substituting the equation for Food per Capita into the equation for Fractional Birth Rate and then substituting the result into the equation for Net Birth Rate, you can eliminate the auxiliaries, reducing the model to one with only Net Birth Rate and Population. The right side of Figure 6-7 shows this model and its equations. Though the model is mathematically equivalent to the model with auxiliaries, it is harder to explain, understand, and modify. Note that in the reduced form model population enters the equation for the rate of change of population in both the numerator and denominator. The polarity of the causal link between Population and Net Births is now ambiguous, and it is not possible to distinguish the two feedback loops involving population and births.

The process of creating the reduced form model by substitution of intermediate variables into their rates is a general one and can be carried out on any model. However, the use of auxiliary variables is critical to effective modeling. Ideally, each equation in your models should represent one main idea. Don't try to economize on the number of equations by writing long ones that embed multiple concepts. These long equations will be hard for others to read and understand. They will be hard for *you* to understand. Finally, equations with multiple components and ideas are hard to change if your client disagrees with one of the ideas.

FIGURE 6-6   Networks of stocks and flows are coupled by information feedback.

Stocks accumulate their rates of flow; information about the stocks feeds back to alter the rates, closing the loops in the system. Constants are stocks changing too slowly to be modeled explicitly; exogenous variables are stocks outside the model boundary (shown by the rectangle with rounded corners).

Equation representation: The derivatives of the stocks in dynamic systems are, in general, nonlinear functions of the stocks, the exogenous variables, and any constants. In matrix notation, the rates of change d$\mathbf{S}$/dt are a function f() of the state vector $\mathbf{S}$, the exogenous variables $\mathbf{U}$ and the constants $\mathbf{C}$:

$$d\mathbf{S}/dt = f(\mathbf{S}, \mathbf{U}, \mathbf{C}) \tag{6-4}$$

For the diagram below, the equation for the rate of change of S_4 is

$$dS_4/dt = f_4(S_3, S_4, U_3, C_3) \tag{6-5}$$

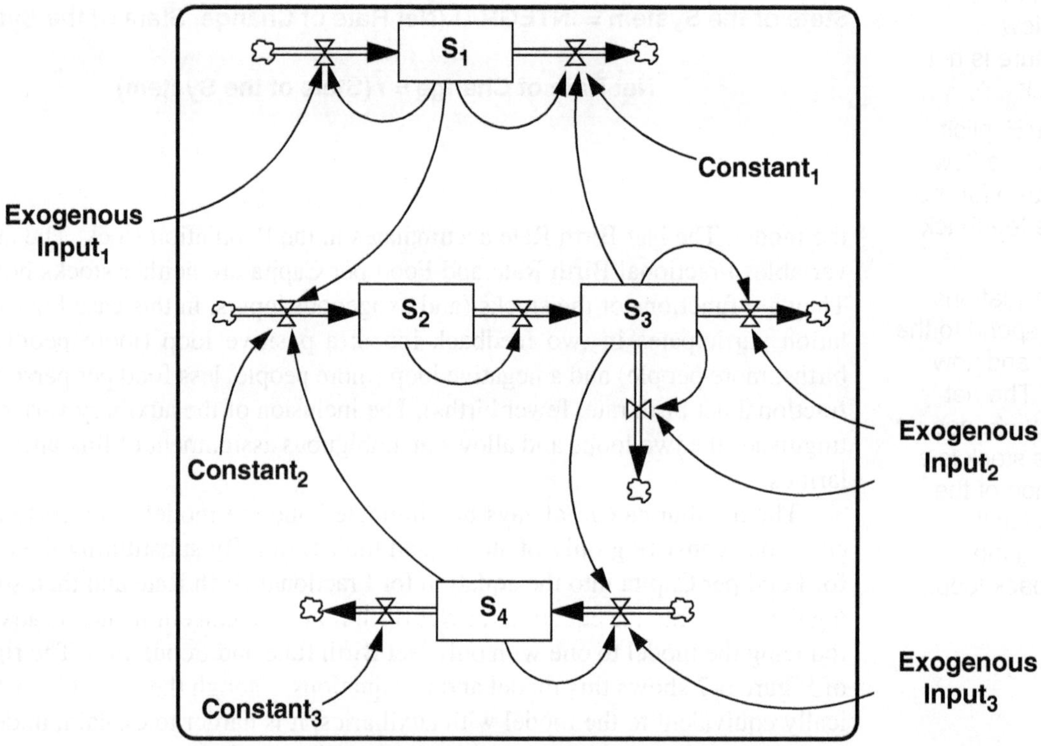

6.2.6   Stocks Change Only Through Their Rates

Stocks change only through their rates of flow. There can be no causal link directly into a stock. Consider a model for customer service. Customers arrive at some rate and accumulate in a queue of Customers Awaiting Service. The queue could be a line at a fast food restaurant, cars awaiting repair at a body shop, or people on hold calling for airline reservations. When the service is completed customers depart from the queue, decreasing the stock of customers waiting for service. The rate at which customers can be processed depends on the number of service personnel, their productivity (in customers processed per hour per person), and the number of hours they work (the workweek). If the number of people waiting for service increases, employees increase their workweek as they stay an extra shift, skip lunch, or cut down on breaks.

FIGURE 6-7 Auxiliary variables

Left: A simple population model with auxiliary variables. Fractional Birth Rate and Food per Capita are neither stocks nor flows, but intermediate concepts added to the model to aid clarity.

Right: The same model with the auxiliary variables eliminated by substitution into the rate equation. The link from Population to Net Birth Rate now has an ambiguous sign, a poor practice.

Correct

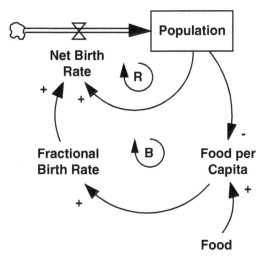

Incorrect

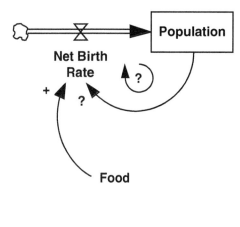

Population = INTEGRAL(Net Birth Rate, Population$_{t_0}$)

Net Birth Rate = Population * Fractional Birth Rate

Fractional Birth Rate = *f*(Food per Capita)

Food per Capita = Food/Population

Population = INTEGRAL(Net Birth Rate, Population$_{t_0}$)

Net Birth Rate = Population * *f*(Food/Population)

I have often seen people in workshops draw the diagram shown in the top of Figure 6-8. They correctly recognize that the rate at which customers are processed is the product of Service Staff, Productivity, and Workweek and that higher queues of waiting customers lead to longer hours and hiring of additional staff, forming two balancing feedbacks. But often people draw information feedbacks directly from the workweek and service staff to the stock of Customers Awaiting Service, assigning them a negative polarity. They reason that an increase in the workweek or staff level decreases the number of customers remaining in the queue, thus closing the negative feedback loops.

The correct diagram is shown in the lower panel of Figure 6-8. The only way customers can exit the stock is via the departure rate. The departure rate is the product of the number of staff, their workweek, and their productivity. An increase in any of these inputs boosts the rate at which customers are processed and leave the queue. The balancing feedbacks are still present: A longer queue of waiting customers leads to longer hours and more staff and an increase in the processing rate. The valve controlling the outflow from the stock of waiting customers opens wider, and customers depart the queue at a higher rate. The polarities of the information links in the feedback loop are all positive, but an increase in the customer departure rate causes a reduction in the stock of waiting customers because the departure rate is an outflow from the stock.

FIGURE 6-8

Stocks change only through their rates.

Top: Incorrect stock and flow map of a service operation. Workweek, Service Staff,and other variables cannot directly alter the stock of Customers Awaiting Service.

Bottom: Corrected diagram. The Workweek, number of Service Staff, and Productivity drive the Customer Departure Rate, which decreases the stock of Customers Awaiting Service.

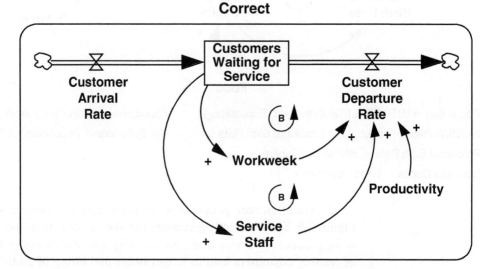

6.2.7   Continuous Time and Instantaneous Flows

The stock and flow perspective (and its equivalent integral or differential equation structure) represents time as unfolding continuously. That is, as our experience suggests, time progresses smoothly and continuously. In system dynamics we almost always represent time as continuous. Events can happen at any time; change can occur continuously; and time can be divided into intervals as fine as one desires.[1]

---

[1]In numerical simulation time is divided into discrete intervals. However, these intervals must be small enough that the numerical solution is a good approximation of the underlying continuous dynamics, and model dynamics cannot depend on the length of the solution interval (cutting it in half, e.g., should not affect any of your conclusions). In discrete time or difference equation systems the time interval is an irreducible minimum time delay in every feedback loop and often has a large impact on the dynamics. Appendix A discusses numerical integration and the selection of an appropriate time step for your simulations.

A flow at any time is defined to be its instantaneous value—the rate at which water is flowing into your bathtub *right now*. Mathematically, the net flow to a stock (inflows less outflows) is the instantaneous rate of change of the stock—its derivative (this is the meaning of equation 6-2). No one can measure the instantaneous value of any flow. The government does not and cannot report the GDP at a particular moment but instead reports the average rate of production over some prior, finite interval of time (typically a quarter of a year). Likewise, quarterly reports of a firm's sales are the cumulative sales during the quarter, not the instantaneous sales rate at the end of the quarter. During the quarter sales likely varied substantially. Sales reports at more frequent intervals such as monthly or even daily are better approximations of the instantaneous sales rate but still represent averages taken over some prior, finite interval. Similarly, the speedometer of a car does not measure its instantaneous velocity. Because the components of the velocity sensor and instrumentation have inertia, the speedometer indicates an average of the velocity over a (short) prior interval.

As the length of the measurement interval shrinks, the reported average rate becomes a better approximation of the instantaneous rate. Most speedometers respond quickly relative to the rate of change of the car's true velocity, so for practical purposes the average velocity reported on the instrument panel is the same as the actual, current velocity. On the other hand, the delays in reporting the state of the economy or the profits of a company are often long relative to their rates of change and dramatically influence the stability of the system. Though we might develop instruments for our physical and social systems that shrink the delays in measuring and reporting rates of flow, we can never measure the instantaneous value of the flows affecting any stock.

6.2.8   Continuously Divisible versus Quantized Flows

Just as time can be represented as unfolding continuously or in discrete intervals, so too the units flowing into and out of stocks can be thought of either as continuously divisible or as a discrete numbers of items. Most flows are actually quantized, meaning they consist of collections of individual items which cannot be divided into arbitrarily small units. Oil tankers are commissioned one at a time—it is not meaningful to speak of launching half a tanker. Company hiring consists of a whole number of people. Even the flow in a river consists of an (astronomically large) integer number of water molecules. The stock and flow concept and the four equivalent notations shown in Figure 6-2 apply whether the flow is conceived to be infinitely divisible or quantized. The metaphor of the flow of water into a bathtub emphasizes our everyday experience of water as a continuously divisible substance—we aren't concerned with the identity of the individual water molecules. However, if it were important to our purpose, we could just as easily imagine that the tub is filled by a lumpy flow of individual ice cubes. Whether continuous or quantized, the quantity in the stock is always the accumulation of the inflows to the stock less its outflows.

In many models it is appropriate and useful to approximate the flow of individual items as a continuous stream. In modeling the cash flow of a large organization you usually do not need to track individual payments; it is a perfectly acceptable approximation to consider the flow of revenue and expenditures as continuous in time and continuously divisible (though of course the accounting department must track individual payments). Similarly, though organizations hire discrete, whole individuals, it is usually acceptable to assume the flows of people are continuously divisible. Some clients are troubled by the fractional people your model will generate, but almost always the error is insignificant compared to the measurement error in parameters including the number of employees the firm actually has. Since people can be hired part time, work in job-sharing situations, or be assigned to multiple projects, it is quite meaningful to speak of fractional employees, measured in FTE (Full-Time Equivalent) people.

When the purpose of the model requires tracking the individual people, for example modeling the behavior of people entering the line at the supermarket to determine the optimal number of checkout counters, then people can be modeled as discrete individuals arriving at discrete points; this is a classic modeling paradigm in queuing theory (Prabhu 1997; Gross and Harris 1998; Papadopoulos 1993). Yet even in many queuing applications, the continuous time, continuous flow approximation works extremely well and the errors it introduces are often small compared to measurement error and parameter uncertainty in the real system. The decision to represent stocks and flows as continuous or discrete always depends on the purpose of the model. For example, if your purpose is to understand the dynamics of price and the origin of cycles in the oil tanker market (see chapter 20), it is fine to assume that the rates of tanker ordering, construction, and scrappage are continuous in time and continuously divisible. In contrast, if your purpose were to model the arrival and offloading of tankers to optimize port facilities you would have to model the ships as discrete entities.

6.2.9   Which Modeling Approach Should You Use?

The choice of modeling technique and software will depend on which assumptions about the stocks and flows in your system are appropriate to your purpose. In all cases make sure your modeling software and method can include the feedback processes you consider important. In modeling the behavior of people in line at the supermarket, for example, you might choose to use a discrete time, quantized flow representation and select a stochastic modeling package, or even use a spreadsheet. Be sure, however, that your tools allow you to capture behavioral feedbacks such as the feedback from the length of the line to the rate at which people join the line. Some models and a great many of the theorems in queuing theory assume that the rate of arrivals to a queue such as the checkout line is exogenous. People actually choose to enter a line based on its length (more precisely, their estimate of expected waiting time). A long line will cause people to switch to another, defer their shopping to a less crowded time of day, or even go to a different store. Such *balking* creates a powerful negative feedback loop: The longer the line, the smaller the arrival rate. Omitting such feedback processes from your model in the interests of analytical tractability or programming convenience will often lead to a fatal flaw in your analysis and policy conclusions.

6.2.10   Process Point:
Portraying Stocks and Flows in Practice

Each of the stock and flow representations in Figure 6-2 (the bathtub, stock and flow diagram, integral equation, and differential equation) contains precisely the same information. They are exactly equivalent. Which should you use to develop and present your models, especially when you are working in a team?

The answer depends on the context of the modeling project you are doing and the background of your client team. While many mathematically sophisticated modelers scoff at the idea of explaining a complex model using bathtubs and pipes, I have many times seen otherwise brilliant modeling efforts founder because the analyst tried to explain a model using differential equations and mathematical notation—or the simulation code—to a client team with little technical background. One of the worst things a consultant can do is humiliate the client. Showing off your mathematical knowledge by using differential equations, lots of Greek letters, and other notation the client never studied or forgot a long time ago is a sure-fire way to convince your clients you care more for the elegance of your equations than for helping them solve their problem.

Stock and flow diagrams contain the same information as the more mathematically formal notation but are easier to understand and to modify on the fly. Still, some team members consider even the stock and flow diagram format to be too abstract. I have often seen clever graphics of tanks, pipes, and valves used to excellent effect with client teams. For example, a consulting project with a multinational chemicals firm represented the flows of production, inventories, shipments, and customer stocks—along with capacity, cash, and even equipment defects—as a series of pipes, valves, and tanks. The team members were able to grasp the stock and flow structure readily since they were all familiar with the tanks and pipes carrying materials in their plants. In fact, most of the client team were engineers by training and had plenty of background in mathematics. Yet several commented that they never really understood how the business worked until they saw the chart showing its stock and flow structure as tanks and pipes.

What if your clients have even less technical training than these chemical company executives? The bathtub metaphor is often used to good effect, as illustrated by the case of automobile leasing (see Figure 2.4). What if the stocks and flows in your model aren't as tangible as barrels of oil or automobiles? Get creative. In a management flight simulator of insurance claims processing (Kim 1989; Diehl 1994), a flow of letters arriving to an inbox represented the addition of new claims to the stock of unresolved claims. Letters containing checks flowed out to the customers as claims were settled. Icons of people represented the stock and flow structure of claims adjusters (Figure 6-9). Participants in workshops using the model were able to understand the system structure much better than if the more abstract symbols had been used.

I am not recommending that you keep the equations or stock and flow diagrams hidden from your client. Never hide your model from a curious client. You should always look for and create opportunities for client team members to learn more about the modeling process; you should always be prepared to explain the workings of your model.

FIGURE 6-9

Stocks and flows
of claims and
claims adjusters
in an insurance
company

Hiring   Adjusters   Turnover

Claims   Claims   Claims
Received   Outstanding   Settled

Source: Kim 1989.

And while I caution the mathematically sophisticated modeler against overly technical presentation, the opposite problem can also arise: some clients are offended by what they consider to be simplistic cartoon diagrams and prefer what they view as the more professional presentation of stock and flow diagrams or even equations. As always, you must get to know your client deeply and early in the modeling process.

Finally, a caution for those with less technical training and mathematical background: Clients may not need to understand the deep relationship between their bathtub and the mathematics underlying stocks and flows, but you do. While you don't need to be able to solve differential equations to be a successful modeler, you do need to understand the structure and dynamics of stocks and flows thoroughly and rigorously.

6.3   MAPPING STOCKS AND FLOWS

6.3.1   When Should Causal Loop Diagrams Show Stock and Flow Structure?

Causal diagrams can be drawn without showing the stock and flow structure of a system. Or, as shown in Figure 6-8, they can include the stock and flow structure explicitly. When should you include the stock and flow structure, and when can you omit it? Generally, you should include stock and flow structures representing physical processes, delays, or stocks whose behavior is important in the dynamics you seek to explain. For example, consider the flow of a product through a supply chain from producer to consumer. The product travels through a network of stocks (inventories) and flows (shipment and delivery rates). The stock and flow representation for this process is shown in the top panel of Figure 6-10.

Production starts add to the stock of work in process (WIP) Inventory. The Production Completion Rate reduces the stock of WIP and increases the stock of

FIGURE 6-10   Stock and flow vs. causal diagram representations

Stock and Flow Representation of a Manufacturing Process

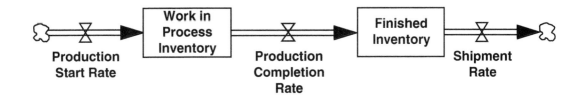

Causal Loop Diagram Representation of the Manufacturing Process

Finished Inventory. Shipments to customers deplete Finished Inventory. Equivalently, the stock of WIP accumulates production starts less completions, and the stock of finished inventory accumulates production completions less shipments.

The causal diagram representation is shown in the bottom panel of Figure 6-10. While technically correct, the causal diagram makes it hard to see the physical flow of product through the system and the conservation of material in the stock and flow chain. It is often confusing to interpret the polarities of the causal links when they involve stocks and flows. An increase in the Production Completion Rate causes Finished Inventory to rise above what it would have been otherwise (it rises at a faster rate), hence the polarity of the link is positive. A decrease in production completions, however, does not cause finished inventory to fall. Rather, a decrease in the production completion rate causes finished inventory to be less than it would have been. You cannot say whether finished inventory will be rising or falling based on the behavior of the production rate alone. Inventory will rise only when production completions exceed the shipment rate; that is, inventory rises only when we add to it faster than we remove units from it. You need to know the values of all the flows affecting a stock to determine its behavior. Richardson (1986a, 1997) carefully documents the pitfalls of causal diagrams, most of which involve the failure of causal diagrams to show the stock/flow distinction.

CHALLENGE   ## Adding Stock and Flow Structure to Causal Diagrams

Consider the causal loop diagrams in chapter 5. For each, redraw the diagram showing the important stock and flow structure along with the feedback structure shown in the diagram. In particular, identify the main stocks and flows in the following conceptualization case studies presented in chapter 5:

1. The workload management example.
2. The oil industry and horse racing examples.
3. The traffic congestion example.

In each case, consider whether the explicit representation of the main stocks and flows enhances your ability to understand the dynamics of the system or merely clutters the diagram.

CHALLENGE

Linking Stock and Flow Structure with Feedback

Often understanding the dynamics of a system requires linking the feedback loop structure with the stock and flow structure. As an example, consider the gasoline shortages of the 1970s. In 1979 the United States (and some other industrialized nations) experienced a severe gasoline shortage. Iran's exports of oil dropped in the wake of the revolution there, and petroleum prices on the world market increased sharply. Within weeks, a shortage of gasoline began. Some service stations found their tanks emptied before the next delivery. Drivers, remembering the first oil embargo in 1973 and worried that they wouldn't be able to get gas, began to top off their tanks, instead of filling up only when the gas gauge fell toward empty. Soon, long lines of cars were seen idling in front of gas stations, and "Sorry—No Gas" signs sprouted along the highways of America as station after station found its underground tanks pumped dry. The shortage was the top story on the evening news—aerial footage of cars lined up around the block, close-ups of "No Gas" signs, and interviews with anxious drivers dominated the news. In some states, mandatory rationing was imposed, including limiting purchases to, for example, no more than $10 worth of gas. California imposed odd/even purchase rules: Drivers were allowed to buy gas only every other day, based on whether their license plate number was odd or even. It seemed that the supply of gasoline had been slashed.

Curiously, the impact of the Iranian revolution on the flow of oil to the US was small. True, US oil imports from the Persian Gulf (including Iran) fell by 500,000 barrels per day between 1978 and 1979, about 3% of US consumption, but imports from other nations increased by 640,000 barrels per day, so imports in 1979 actually *increased* by 140,000 barrels per day. Domestic production fell by 150,000 barrels per day, so total supply was essentially constant, while consumption fell by about 330,000 barrels per day, a drop of 2% from 1978. Plainly, for the year as a whole, there was no shortage. But if the flow of oil into the US was essentially constant, what caused the shortage? Where did the gas go?

First, develop a stock and flow map for the gasoline distribution system. You need not consider the entire supply chain for gasoline but can focus on retail distribution. Your diagram should begin with the flow of gasoline to service stations, then represent the stock and flow structure for its subsequent storage, sale, and eventual combustion.

Once you've mapped the stock and flow structure, identify the information inputs to the rates of flow in your diagram. Assume that the rate at which gasoline is delivered to service stations is exogenous. By identifying the information inputs to the flows in your stock and flow map, you will be closing some feedback loops, loops which should help explain why the shortage occurred and answer the question, Where did the gas go? Be sure to ask how individual drivers would learn about the shortage and what their behavior would then be.

Finally, using your diagram, assess the likely effectiveness of the maximum purchase and odd/even policies. Do policies of this type help ease the shortage or make it worse? Why? What policy would you recommend to ease the shortage? Explain why you think your policy would be effective in terms of the stock/flow and feedback structure of the system.

6.3.2 Aggregation in Stock and Flow Mapping

The ability to map the stocks and flows in a system is critical to effective modeling. Usually it is wise to identify the main stocks in a system and then the flows that alter those stocks. You must select an appropriate level of aggregation and boundary for these stock and flow maps. The level of aggregation refers to the number of internal categories or stocks represented. The boundary refers to how far upstream and downstream one chooses to represent the flows of materials and other quantities in the model.

To illustrate, consider the manufacturing process discussed above in which material flows from production starts through WIP inventory to finished inventory and finally shipment to the customer. All the various parts, components, and subassemblies are aggregated together into a single stock of WIP. And though the firm may carry tens of thousands of SKUs (stock keeping units), these individual items are all aggregated into a single stock of finished inventory. For many purposes the aggregate picture is sufficient. However, the model purpose might require more detail. If the purpose involved a closer look at the manufacturing process, you could disaggregate the stock of work in process serially to represent the different stages, such as part fabrication, assembly, and testing (Figure 6-11).

The sum of the three intermediate stocks is the total work in process inventory, but now the model tracks throughput at a finer level of resolution and can represent more potential bottlenecks in the production process. Note that in both the original, aggregate diagram and in this more detailed diagram there is no provision for rework or scrap. All units started are eventually completed—the flow of widgets through the system is conserved. Note also that as material flows through the system it is transformed from parts to finished product. To maintain consistent units of measure we might measure parts in widget equivalents—that is, a widget's worth of parts. If necessary for the purpose, you can further disaggregate the stock and flow structure.

CHALLENGE ### Modifying Stock and Flow Maps

1. Modify the diagram in Figure 6-11 to represent the case where units that fail testing are scrapped.

2. Modify your diagram to represent the case where items failing testing are returned to assembly for rework.

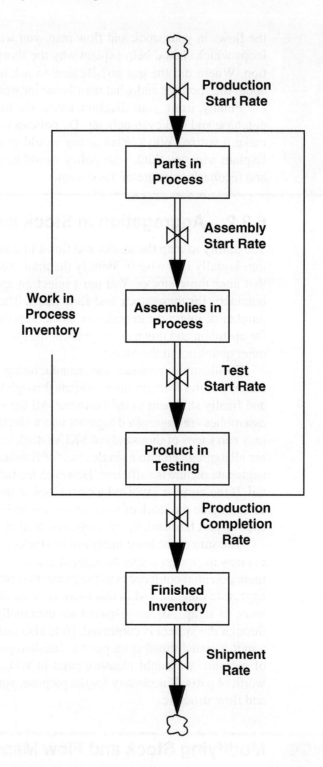

FIGURE 6-11
Disaggregated
stock and flow
map for a
manufacturing
process

CHALLENGE   ## Disaggregation

Each of the three stages of WIP identified in Figure 6-11 consists of other steps,
each with its own stock and flow structure. Suppose you learn that part fabrication

at the plant you are modeling actually requires several operations: welding, grinding, and painting. Observation of the grinding operation reveals that workers draw parts ready for grinding from a buffer generated by the welding operation. When grinding is completed, the parts are placed in a bin which then goes on to the next operation (painting). The welding and paint shops are similar. Draw the disaggregated stock and flow map for the part fabrication step to show the welding, grinding, and painting operations explicitly.

Up to now the discussion has focused on *serial* disaggregation: how finely to break down the stages of processing. Throughout, the many different parts and products produced by a typical firm are aggregated into a single chain of stocks and flows. In many situations the process occurs not only in series but also involves parallel activities. You could of course replicate the main stock and flow chain for each product (many simulation software packages support array structures for this purpose). When there are multiple, parallel activities you must make a decision not only about the number of stages of the process to represent but also how much to aggregate the different parallel processes together. For example, the assembly process for automobiles involves integrating the chassis and engine. Each subassembly is built on a separate line, often in plants far from the final assembly point. Suppose the client argues that you can't aggregate all subcomponents into a single flow of parts, but must separate chassis and engine fabrication (omit the body for simplicity). The stock and flow map for the assembly process might be shown as in Figure 6-12.

There are now three distinct stock and flow chains, one each for engines, chassis, and assembled cars. Because the three chains are separate, each can be measured in different units: engines, chassis, and cars. The three chains are linked because each car beginning the final assembly process requires one engine from the stock of completed engines and one chassis from the stock of completed chassis. The information arrows from the assembly rate to the engine and chassis use rates show these links. The number of engines and chassis available also determine the maximum assembly start rate, which in turn constrains actual assembly starts: If either component buffer falls to zero, assembly must cease.[2] These links (not shown) define two balancing feedbacks that regulate the outflows from the stocks of components and couple the stock and flow networks. The diagram does not represent many other information flows that must exist in the system (such as the determinants of the chassis start and completion rates); try adding these to the map.

You could of course continue to disaggregate. The process can be broken down into more steps: The paint process, for example, actually consists of multiple activities separated by buffers such as part preparation (solvent bath), drying, spraying the first coat, drying in the oven, spraying the second coat, drying, and so on, with various inspections along the way. You could also continue the parallel disaggregation by splitting the engine or chassis assembly processes into their

---

[2]Firms can sometimes build incomplete units and add the missing components later. When a 1997 strike shut down a critical supplier, Ford continued to assemble its popular Explorer, storing the nearly completed cars until the missing parts became available and could be retrofitted (try modifying the diagram in Figure 6-12 to accommodate such retrofitting).

FIGURE 6-12   Disaggregating parallel activities

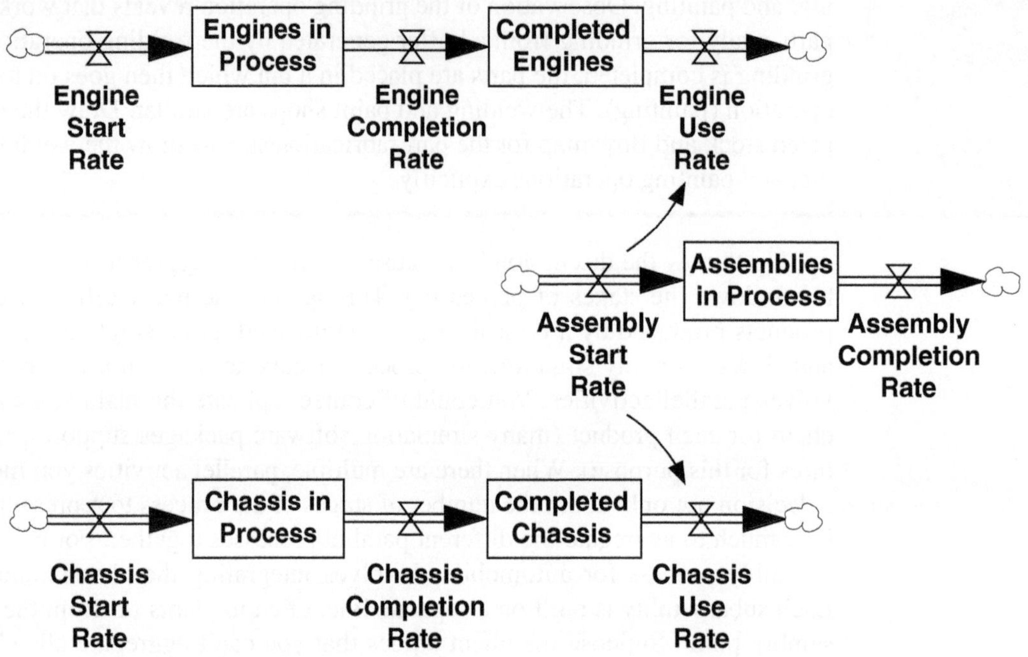

subassemblies. In the limit each and every part and operation would be represented separately. Obviously such a model would be just as complex as the real system, at least as hard to understand, and quite useless.

Where should you stop? How much detail is necessary? This is always a matter of judgment to be made by considering the model purpose and the needs of the client. If the purpose is representing the lag in the response of the manufacturing system to changes in demand as part of a larger model of firm strategy, the simpler representation is probably fine. If you seek to reengineer the flow of material through the production line, a more detailed representation is required. It is better to start with a high-level, aggregate representation and add detail if needed to address the purpose. Beginning with detailed process maps often leads to paralysis due to their complexity, data requirements, and rapid obsolescence rates. The aggregate map showing only production starts, WIP, production, and finished inventory is quite stable and remains appropriate even as the details of the production process change, while a detailed map may become obsolete as new products, tooling, or process technologies are introduced.

6.3.3   Guidelines for Aggregation

When is it appropriate to aggregate different activities together? To determine whether activities taking place serially can be aggregated, consider the average residence time of items in each stock (the average time between entering and exiting the stock). Stocks with short residence times relative to the time scale for the dynamics of interest generally do not need to be represented explicitly and can either be omitted or lumped into adjacent stocks. For example, in the long-term planning models of the US energy system developed by the US Department of Energy (Naill 1992), various stocks of undiscovered petroleum and known reserves are explicitly represented because their lifetimes range from years to decades (at current production rates). However, stocks of crude oil and refined products in the petroleum supply chain represent only a few months of consumption. In a long-term model these stocks are too short-lived to require explicit treatment. They fluctuate around their equilibrium values as producers, refiners, and distributors react to changes in inventory. In a model of short-term movements in spot petroleum prices, however, these stocks are critically important. A good model would represent the key stocks in the petroleum supply chain explicitly, perhaps even including a separate stock for the inventory of gasoline at retail service stations and the inventory of gasoline in the tanks of cars on the road. On the other hand, a short-term spot price model need not include petroleum reserves or undiscovered resources, as these stocks change too slowly to influence the spot market over a time horizon of a year.

Parallel activities can legitimately be aggregated together if the individual flows are governed by similar decision rules and if the time the different items spend in the individual stocks is similar. For example, it is often appropriate to aggregate the many parts required to manufacture a product into a small number of categories since they are usually ordered using the same procedures and their delivery lead times and residence times in parts inventories generally don't differ too much. In contrast, plant and equipment sometimes must be disaggregated. Their lifetimes are very different, and the decision rules for new green-field facilities differ substantially from those used to order equipment for existing facilities due to differences in lead times, costs, financing, permitting, and regulatory issues.

As a rule of thumb, clients generally want to see more detail in a model than the modeler thinks is needed, and modelers, in turn, generally overestimate the detail necessary to capture the dynamics of interest. Of course, the amount of detail needed to capture the dynamics relevant to the client's purpose and the amount of detail needed to give the client confidence in the results are two different things. Roberts (1977/1978) estimated that clients often require twice as much detail as the modeler feels is needed to feel comfortable with and accept a model as a basis for action, and in my experience this is often an underestimate. Success requires you to include the detail necessary to satisfy the client. But this does not mean you should acquiesce to all client demands for more detail—you will end up with an expensive and useless black box. You must work with the client to understand why excessive detail is often unnecessary. Often, models end up with too much detail, but as the client gains confidence and understanding of the important feedbacks driving the dynamics, the excess structure can be eliminated, resulting in a simpler, more easily maintained, and more useful model (Randers 1980). Still, Roberts is correct: "You must provide the level of detail that causes [the client] to be persuaded that you have properly taken into account his issues, his questions, his level of concerns. Otherwise he will not believe the model you have built, he will not accept it, and he will not use it" (p. 80).

6.3.4   System Dynamics in Action: Modeling Large-Scale Construction Projects

Aggregation of multiple serial and parallel activities is well illustrated in a model of large construction projects developed by Jack Homer (Homer et al. 1993). The client was a multinational forest products company, specifically the division of the company that designs and builds pulp and paper mills. Competition for the small number of mills built each year was intensifying as the industry globalized, and the firm, already a leader, saw that to remain strong they had to dramatically reduce the time required to design and build mills. Their goal was to reduce significantly the total cycle time, from the handshake with a customer to the handoff of a working mill, without increasing costs. They knew traditional project management techniques were not adequate: the design and construction process is exceedingly complex, with tight couplings among the phases, and they had already done all the easy things. They decided to develop a system dynamics model of the entire engineering, procurement, and construction (EPC) process.

Early meetings of the project team focused on the model boundary and aggregation, in particular, descriptions of the stock and flow structure of a typical project. Many issues were raised: Is there a typical project? How much detail is needed? What activities could be aggregated together? One member of the client team argued that the model couldn't be useful if it didn't represent every engineering drawing, every purchase order, and every component installed at the site. Obviously, such a model could never be built or made useful. Other members of the client team argued for a simpler approach. They already had highly disaggregate scheduling and planning models based on traditional project management tools to manage the detail complexity of the projects. They lacked a tool to manage the dynamic complexity and interdependencies among the phases and activities of the projects.

After extensive discussion, an initial model boundary and level of aggregation were set (Figure 6-13). The figure is a high-level subsystem diagram showing how projects were aggregated into a reasonable number of phases. The overall project was divided into two main stock and flow chains representing P&E (process and equipment) and construction. Each activity goes through design preparation, review, and design revisions. Next suppliers are selected and purchase orders are issued. The suppliers then fabricate the materials needed for each activity. On the construction side, the client felt it was acceptable to aggregate all construction materials (e.g., structural steel, concrete forms, rebar) into a single category. The process and equipment side, however, was divided into three categories: reactor vessels, major equipment (e.g., large tanks, pipelines, and conveyors), and minor equipment (e.g., pumps, motors, valves, and instrumentation). The design, procurement, and construction of these types of equipment are sufficiently different in scope, duration, and cost that they could not reasonably be lumped together. The reactor vessels, in particular, had to be modeled in more detail as they are the largest subassembly, almost always fall on the critical path, and are frequently a bottleneck constraining construction progress. During construction, reactor vessels, other equipment, and site preparation such as foundations and grading all

FIGURE 6-13   Building a pulp and paper mill

Subsystem diagram showing flows of engineering, procurement, and construction work in a model of a pulp mill construction project. The diagram illustrates the sector boundaries and level of aggregation without showing all details. Each block represents a project phase, modeled with a generic module with roughly the same structure. An internal gate captures the constraints on work available within a phase as a function of the work completed. For example, foundations cannot be completed until surveying and site preparation are done; see section 14.5.

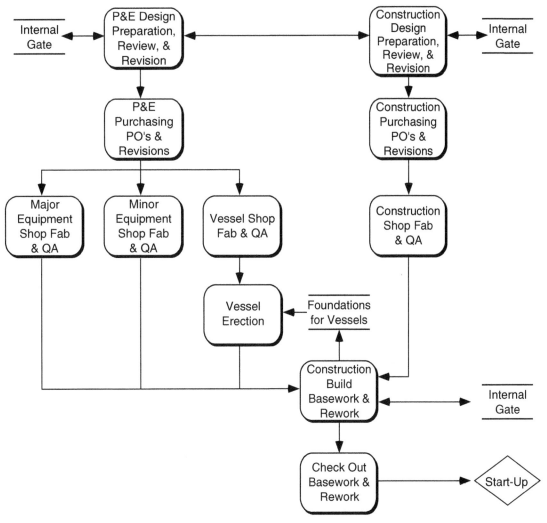

Source: Homer et al. (1993).

must come together, followed by a functionality check out, start-up and, finally, handoff to the customer.

Each block in Figure 6-13 represents a project phase. The model consisted of a generic project phase module, replicated for each block and linked as shown. Each module contained a stock and flow structure including the flows of tasks within the phase along with scheduled deadlines, the labor force dedicated to the phase, worker productivity, fatigue levels, error rates, and costs. The stock and flow structure for tasks within a phase models the progression of tasks from basework through completion (Figure 6-14). In general the tasks to be completed in a phase can only be done as upstream tasks upon which they depend are completed (the rate at which basework tasks become available). For example, the reactor vessels cannot be erected on site until their foundations are completed. Likewise, not all tasks within a given phase can be done concurrently. For example, the detailed design of conveyors and pipelines between the chippers, reactor vessels, and paper machines cannot be done until the high-level physical design of the plant is completed. These within- and between-phase dependencies were modeled explicitly. The flow of work from the stock of tasks awaiting completion to the stock of tasks requiring rework represents those tasks completed incorrectly or rendered obsolete by changes in other subsystems. Generally, errors are not detected immediately and the delay in the discovery of rework can be substantial, as when a design error is not detected until construction in the field is underway. The discovery of rework moves tasks thought to be complete back into the stock of tasks awaiting completion (see Ford and Sterman 1998b for a detailed and fully documented model of a multiphase project similar to the one used here; see also the shipbuilding project model described in section 2.3).

The model was substantially simpler than the client firm's detailed project planning model, which included literally thousands of individual activities (high detail complexity) but no feedback loops (no dynamic complexity). It was disaggregated enough to capture important interdependencies among design, procurement, and construction activities and between construction and the various types of

FIGURE 6-14
Stock and flow structure of tasks in a project phase

Simplified representation of the stock and flow structure of a phase in the pulp mill project model. Determinants of the flows and couplings among the different phases are not shown.

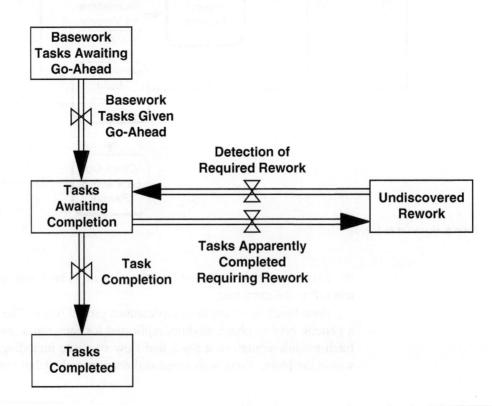

equipment. The model could capture shifts in the critical path that might result from policies accelerating the fabrication of the reactor vessels, a policy favored by some client team members.

It is important to note that the process of developing the final level of aggregation involved a number of iterations and revisions. And though the model represents the project at a high level of aggregation, the modeling team developed many more detailed diagrams. These more detailed maps helped the modeler and client team discover flaws in their thinking, estimate parameters better, and deepen their understanding of the process. And they developed confidence that the more aggregate representation in the simulation model was acceptable for their purpose so these more detailed stock and flow structures did not have to be incorporated into the model.

The level of detail selected also permitted the model to be calibrated against a wide range of data collected on one of the company's current EPC projects. The model successfully (that is, to the satisfaction of the client) reproduced all relevant project activities, including the various workforces and labor hours, overtime and rework rates, purchase order volumes and revision rates, vendor shipments, and the progress of vessel erection and construction (Figure 6-15 shows an example).

While the clients prefer not to disclose the details of policy recommendations, they viewed the model as credible and useful and developed confidence, shared among the team, that the model did a good job of representing their EPC projects. They used the model to analyze many policies and identified several which, while previously appearing to be desirable, in fact generated harmful side effects. The model also helped identify policies that reduced project delivery times by at least 30% within a few years. Several of the policies were not apparent to the client team or were hotly debated prior to the modeling effort. The modeling process helped build understanding of and consensus around these controversial initiatives, helping the firm successfully implement many of the recommendations.

FIGURE 6-15   Sample comparison of historical and simulated behavior of the pulp mill model

P&E = process and equipment.

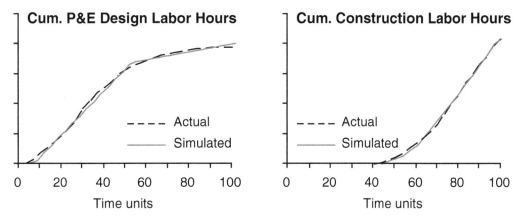

Note: Time is expressed as time units to protect client confidential information.

Source: Homer et al. (1993).

6.3.5   Setting the Model Boundary: "Challenging the Clouds"

Mapping the stock and flow structure of a system involves important decisions about the boundary of the model. In reality, flows of material, people, and money into a stock have to come from somewhere; the flows out have to go somewhere. To keep your models manageable, you must truncate these chains using sources and sinks, represented in the stock and flow maps by "clouds"; see Figure 6-1. Sources and sinks represent the stocks supplying material to or absorbing material from the modeled system. Sources and sinks are assumed to have infinite capacity and can never constrain the flows they support. In the real world, the stocks supplying or absorbing flows have finite capacity and do influence the flows. When you truncate a stock and flow chain with a cloud you are setting the boundary of the model—stocks and flows beyond this point are ignored; you exclude all possible feedbacks from or interactions with the stocks outside the boundary.

As a modeler you must critically examine these boundary assumptions; you must, in the words of Barry Richmond (1993, p. 132), "challenge the clouds." Is it appropriate for your purpose to exclude the stocks outside the boundary of the model? What feedbacks ignored by your model might exist in the real world, and might they affect your policy recommendations? Can the sources for the flows be depleted and constrain the inflow? Can the sinks be filled and block the outflows, backing up the system like a clogged drain?

Consider the automobile industry. A stock and flow map for automobile production might begin with production starts, WIP inventory, production, finished inventory, and shipments (Figure 6-16). Drawing the map with a source for the production start flow presumes that the supply of parts is unlimited and can never constrain the production start rate. Likewise, because shipments flow to a sink, the modeler has assumed stocks of product in the hands of dealers and customers have no effect on shipments. In challenging the clouds you ask whether these assumptions are reasonable. For the auto industry they are not. Production starts require the automaker to have an adequate stock of parts. Yet parts stocks may easily be depleted. Suppliers cannot respond instantly to changes in parts orders. Large orders may outstrip supplier capacity, leading to shortages. A strike at a supplier may interrupt the flow of parts to the firm. At the other end, shipments of new cars to dealers depend on the size of dealer stocks. Dealers generally try to maintain about 40 to 60 days of inventory on their lots; this is enough to provide good selection for consumers without carrying excessive and costly inventory. If stocks are low relative to their targets, dealers order more from the manufacturers; if stocks are high, they cut back. Figure 6-17 expands the model boundary to capture these effects. The model now represents three distinct organizational entities—suppliers, manufacturers, and dealers. The inventory of parts held by the manufacturer is now explicit. The supplier has the same basic structure as the automaker: a stock of finished inventory and a stock of work in process. At the shipment end, manufacturer shipments no longer disappear into a sink but flow into dealer stocks, allowing you to model the purchase rate as a function of the dealer inventory and sales to customers.

FIGURE 6-16

Initial stock and flow map for the automobile industry, showing the model boundary

The sources and sinks for the flows through the system are assumed to be infinite and can have no impact on the dynamics.

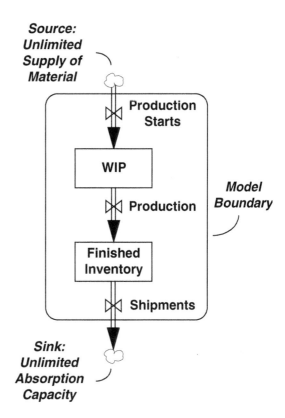

You could and should continue to challenge the boundary of the model. The model now allows you to represent supplier order processing, inventory management, and delivery, including the possibility that suppliers can become a bottleneck and starve automobile production. But now the suppliers are assumed to have unlimited parts and raw materials availability. Is this appropriate? It depends on the model purpose. You could continue to expand the model boundary by adding the suppliers to the suppliers, and their suppliers, and so on, until you reached the point where it is acceptable to assume that the supply of materials to the farthest upstream supplier is unlimited. Alternatively, you could represent the entire upstream supply chain by a single aggregate supplier stage.

The map shown in Figure 6-17 also assumes that dealer sales flow into a sink so there is no feedback from the stock of cars on the road to purchases of new cars. This is obviously a bad assumption: Sales of new cars depend on the number and age of the cars people already have relative to their needs. People who have just acquired a new car are unlikely to buy another for several years, until their loan is paid off, their lease expires, or their car is involved in an accident and must be replaced (see section 2.2). Figure 6-18 expands the downstream end of the stock and flow map to include the stock of cars on the road.

You can continue to challenge the model boundary. What happens to the cars when they are scrapped? In the current map, they simply disappear. In reality, they don't. In North America some 10 to 12 million vehicles are scrapped per year. Roughly 94% are shredded and the steel and some nonferrous metals are

FIGURE 6-17

Challenging the clouds

Adding a supplier and dealer sector to the stock and flow chain for automobile production. Rectangles with rounded corners denote the boundaries between different organizational entities and decision-making units.

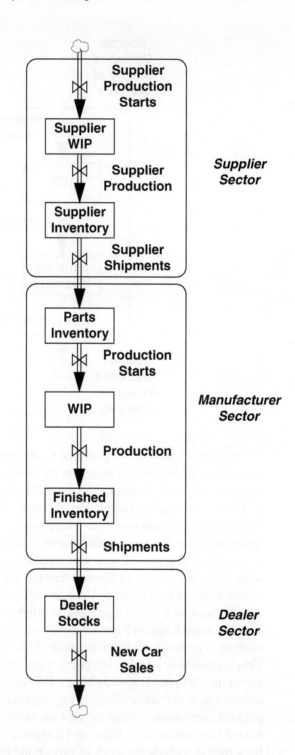

recovered, one of the highest recycling fractions of any industry. However, some cars end up abandoned as dangerous eyesores on the side of the road. And much of the plastic, glass, and other nonmetal materials end up in landfills, constituting a significant source of pollution (more than two billion discarded tires, most sitting in huge piles across the country, have already accumulated in the US).

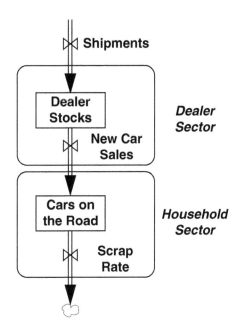

FIGURE 6-18

Expanded automobile model

The boundary now includes the stock of cars on the road, which feeds back to influence sales of new cars.

6.3.6   System Dynamics in Action: Automobile Recycling

By the mid 1990s, as landfills filled and environmental awareness grew, pressure built to recycle more of the material in cars. Germany debated a law that would require auto manufacturers to take back their old cars when people deregistered them. Pushed by these forces, the auto industry, first in Europe and then in the US, began to study ways to increase the recovery of parts and the recycling of materials from cars.

Pavel Zamudio-Ramirez (1996) modeled part recovery and the materials recycling in the US auto industry to help the industry think about a future of enhanced auto recycling. Figure 6-19 shows a simplified stock and flow structure adapted from the model. Old or wrecked cars can either be scrapped legally (sold to a junkyard or dismantler) or illegally abandoned. The stock of abandoned, often burned-out, cars is a blight on the landscape and significant source of pollution. There are two outflows from the stock of illegally abandoned cars: Dismantlers will process them if the value of the recoverable parts and materials is high enough. Alternatively, illegally dumped cars can be collected (say by local governments) and taken to shredders for proper disposal. Both these flows are relatively small, so the stock of abandoned cars can build up to high levels even if the abandonment rate is low.

Cars held in the dismantlers' inventories are stripped of those parts whose value exceeds the cost of recovery. These parts enter a used parts stock and are then sold to repair shops and used to replace worn or damaged parts on operating cars. In this map, the part usage rate flows into a sink. In actuality, these parts are installed in cars still on the road and eventually flow again through the scrap or abandonment rate. Since the number of recovered parts is very small relative to the total flow of materials through the system, this omission is probably reasonable.

FIGURE 6-19   Stock and flow map for a model of automobile recycling

The stock and flow structure for the development of new vehicle platforms, defining the mass and materials composition of cars and level of design for disassembly, is not shown. The model includes a parallel stock and flow structure (co-flow) tracking each of these properties as vehicles age and are eventually retired, dismantled, and shredded. See chapter 12.

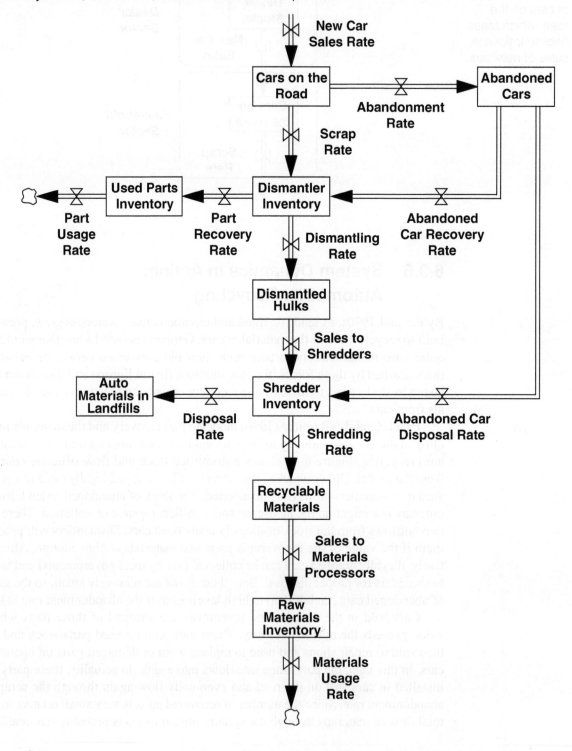

After all parts worth recovering are removed, the gutted car, now called a hulk, is sold to a shredder. In the mid 1990s there were about 200 shredders in the US who processed roughly 94% of all deregistered cars. After shredding, the valuable materials (principally steel and some nonferrous metals) are separated out for recycling. If the prices of the recovered materials don't justify the cost, shredders can take hulks directly to a landfill and cut their purchases from dismantlers. What remains after shredding and separation is a mixture of plastics, glass, elastomers, and some unrecovered metal called automotive shredder residue (ASR) or "fluff," which is then landfilled. ASR is one of the major environmental concerns generated by the disposal of old cars.

The recyclable materials accumulate in an inventory and are eventually sold to materials processors such as steel mills. The inventory of raw materials is then used to manufacture new products, including automobiles, thus helping to create a closed material flow and cutting the use of nonrenewable resources. As in the case of parts, the materials usage rate flows into a sink since the flow of recovered materials relative to the total flow of virgin materials is small.

Zamudio-Ramirez's model included a rich feedback structure representing the behavior of the various actors in the system, including the automakers, car owners, dismantlers, and shredders. Markets for recovered materials were explicit. The stock and flow structure for autos began at the design stage for new models and platforms and tracked key properties of the cars including their mass, materials composition (ferrous, nonferrous, plastics), and the level of design for disassembly built into the design. These attributes were tracked as the cars embodying them moved from the design stage to market, age, and are then retired, dismantled, and shredded.

To gather the required data, Zamudio-Ramirez conducted interviews with various actors, including carmakers, dismantlers, shredders, and industry analysts and made extensive use of various auto and recycling industry databases. Some of the data required, such as age-dependent scrap rates for cars, were relatively easy to gather. Other key parameters were not. Two critical relationships in the model are the supply curves for recovered parts and recovered materials. That is, how will the number of parts recovered by dismantlers vary as the price they can get and the costs of recovery vary?

Estimating the parts supply curve is a daunting problem. The principal cost of recovery is the labor time required to remove a part. But the time required to remove a given part depends on how many other parts must be removed first. These precedence relationships depend on the design of the car and the value of the intervening parts (can the seat be ripped out quickly to get at a valuable part under it or must it be removed carefully? Should workers get at a part from in front or behind?). To estimate these relationships Zamudio-Ramirez worked at the Vehicle Recycling Partnership, a consortium of the Big Three US automakers, dismantlers, and the recycling industry. The Vehicle Recycling Partnership assembled a comprehensive database of part removal times by completely disassembling a variety of late model cars. Zamudio-Ramirez and his colleague Andrew Spicer then developed an optimization model to estimate the supply curve for parts recovery as functions of part and materials prices, labor costs, and the design of the vehicles. The optimization model determined the number of parts worth recovering and the optimal dismantling order for any set of prices, labor costs, and design parameters—the supply curve for recovered parts. The results of the optimization model were then embedded in the simulation model. As the design parameters for cars change and the removal time for key parts falls, the estimated supply curve responds by realistically increasing the number and types of parts recovered.

Though the stock and flow structure in Figure 6-19 is simplified and does not show any of the feedback structure determining the various flows from the full model, it illustrates the response of the automobile and materials markets to policies designed to increase recycling of cars.

First consider the effect of a design for disassembly (DFD) program designed to increase the part recovery rate and reduce the amount of fluff ending up in landfills. DFD can reduce the labor cost of part recovery through better design, different choice of part fasteners, improved selection and labeling of materials, and other techniques. The first effect is...nothing. There is a lag of at least several years between the time an automaker starts a DFD program and the time the first cars designed to those specs roll off the assembly line. The average car in the United States stays on the road for about a decade, and new cars have very low scrap rates (most of these are wrecks declared total losses by insurance companies). Only after a delay of many years will the stock of recycling-ready cars be large enough and old enough for them to constitute a significant fraction of the scrapped cars purchased by dismantlers.

What then happens? Manufacturers expected DFD would eventually cause part and material recovery to rise, permanently reducing the flow of materials to landfills. Instead, the model suggests the next effect will be a glut of used parts, as the part recovery rate rises above the used parts usage rate. As parts inventories build, the price dismantlers can get for used parts falls. The number of parts that can be economically recovered drops, and the dismantling rate drops back. Prices continue to fall until the number of parts recovered falls enough to balance the used parts usage rate. The part usage rate may rise, stimulated by lower prices, but unless the demand for used parts is highly price elastic, the part recovery rate will drop back close to its original rate prior to DFD. The demand for used parts is likely to be rather insensitive to price. Automakers and third-party producers of replacement parts will be reluctant to lose the lucrative parts market and may be able to prohibit the use of recovered parts by authorized service centers or for warranty repairs or compete on price. If the demand for used parts is inelastic, the principal effect of DFD might simply be to depress the price of used parts, offsetting most of the benefit of improved design.

Now consider the effect of a trend toward smaller, lighter cars with significantly higher plastic content and less steel and metal. Such changes are promoted to improve fuel economy, increase part recoverability, and decrease the quantity of fluff ending up in landfills. However, the stock and flow structure may cause the impact of such policies to be counter to their intent. The auto industry is a significant consumer of steel. When new cars begin to use less, the recovery of steel from shredding of old hulks continues at the prior rate. The price of scrap metal will fall, reducing shredder profitability. The number of hulks shredded and the quantity of metals recovered may fall, and the volume of fluff disposed in landfills may actually rise. Further, once the scrap rate of cars with reduced steel content increases, shredder profit can fall further. With less steel and nonferrous content, shredder revenue per hulk falls, while the fixed costs of shredding remain the same. Zamudio-Ramirez found that a sustained increase in the plastic content of cars, as expected, would increase the fraction of materials recovered by dismantlers. But cars with less recyclable metal could also depress hulk prices enough to cut shredder profit, decrease the shredding rate, and actually increase the number of abandoned cars and the amount of fluff buried in landfills.

The stock and flow map helps illustrate the long delays between a change in the design of cars and the flows of old cars to landfills. By making the stocks of recovered parts and materials explicit, it is easier to see that there is imperfect coordination between inflows and outflows, leading to potential imbalances and changes in prices that invalidate the assumptions behind recycling programs. Institutional structures such as requirements that service centers use new replacement parts can overwhelm the logic of the market. Market mechanisms, even when present, are not likely to work smoothly, possibly leading to instability and inefficiency. Similar dynamics have already been observed in the market for recycled paper (Taylor 1999). Supply side steps to increase recyclability alone are not likely to be effective unless matched by policies to increase the usage of recovered parts and materials. The collection of recyclable materials and the actual recycling of those materials aren't the same thing.

6.4   SUMMARY

This chapter introduced the stock and flow concept. Stocks accumulate their inflows less their outflows. Stocks are the states of the system upon which decisions and actions are based, are the source of inertia and memory in systems, create delays, and generate disequilibrium dynamics by decoupling rates of flow. The diagramming notation for stocks and flows can be used with a wide range of audiences and makes it easier to relate a causal diagram to the dynamics of the system. Stocks accumulate (integrate) their inflows less their outflows. Equivalently, the rate of change of a stock is the total inflow less the total outflow. Thus a stock and flow map corresponds exactly to a system of integral or differential equations. However, stock and flow maps are much easier to work with and explain.

There are several ways to identify the stocks in systems. In the snapshot test you imagine freezing the system at a moment of time—the measurable quantities (physical, informational, and psychological) are the stocks, while flows are not instantaneously observable or measurable. Units of measure can also help identify stocks and flows. If a stock is measured in units, its flows must be measured in units per time period.

Stocks existing in series in a network can be aggregated together if they are short-lived relative to the time horizon and dynamics of interest. Multiple parallel activities can be aggregated into a single stock and flow network if the activities are governed by similar decision processes and utilize similar resources and if the residence times of the items in the stocks is similar enough for the purpose of your model.

Sources and sinks for the flows in a system have infinite capacity, unlike stocks in the real world, and thus represent the boundary of the model. Modelers should always challenge these boundary assumptions, asking if the assumption of infinite supply for sources and infinite absorption capacity for sinks is appropriate relative to the model purpose.

7

Dynamics of Stocks and Flows

Nature laughs at the difficulties of integration.

—Pierre-Simon de Laplace (1749–1827)

The successes of the differential equation paradigm were impressive and extensive. Many problems, including basic and important ones, led to equations that could be solved. A process of self-selection set in, whereby equations that could not be solved were automatically of less interest than those that could.

—Ian Stewart (1989, p. 39).

Chapter 6 introduced the stock and flow concept and techniques for mapping the stock and flow networks of systems. This chapter explores the behavior of stocks and flows. Given the dynamics of the flows, what is the behavior of the stock? From the dynamics of the stock, can you infer the behavior of the flows? These tasks are equivalent to integrating the flows to yield the stock and differentiating the stock to yield its net rate of change. For people who have never studied calculus, these concepts can seem daunting. In fact, relating the dynamics of stocks and flows is actually quite intuitive; it is the use of unfamiliar notation and a focus on analytic solutions that deters many people from study of calculus.

What if you have a strong background in calculus and differential equations? It is generally not possible to solve even small models analytically due to their high order and nonlinearities, so the mathematical tools many people have studied are of little direct use. If you have more mathematical background you will find this chapter straightforward but should still do the graphical integration examples and challenges to be sure your intuitive understanding is as solid as your technical knowledge. Modelers, no matter how great or small their training in mathematics, need to be able to relate the behavior of stocks and flows intuitively, using graphical and other nonmathematical techniques. The chapter also illustrates how stock and flow dynamics give insight into two important policy issues: global warming and the war on drugs.

7.1   RELATIONSHIP BETWEEN STOCKS AND FLOWS

Recall the basic definitions of stocks and flows: the net rate of change of a stock is the sum of all its inflows less the sum of all its outflows. Stocks accumulate the net rate of change. Mathematically, stocks integrate their net flows; the net flow is the derivative of the stock.

7.1.1   Static and Dynamic Equilibrium

A stock is in equilibrium when it is unchanging (a *system* is in equilibrium when *all* its stocks are unchanging). For a stock to be in equilibrium the net rate of change must be zero, implying the total inflow is just balanced by the total outflow. If water drains out of your tub at exactly the rate it flows in, the quantity of water in the tub will remain constant and the tub is in equilibrium. Such a state is termed a *dynamic equilibrium* since the water in the tub is always changing. *Static equilibrium* arises when all flows into and out of a stock are zero. Here not only is the total volume of water in the tub constant, but the tub contains the same water, hour after hour. The number of members of the US senate has been in dynamic equilibrium since 1959 when Hawaii joined the union: the total number of senators remains constant at 100 even as the membership turns over (albeit slowly). The stock of known Bach cantatas is in static equilibrium since we are unlikely to lose the ones we know of, the odds of discovering previously unknown cantatas are remote, and Bach can't write any new ones.

7.1.2   Calculus without Mathematics

To understand dynamics, you must be able to relate the behavior of the stocks and flows in a system. Given the flows into a stock, what must the behavior of the stock be? Given the behavior of the stock, what must the net rate of change have been? These questions are the domain of the calculus. Calculus provides rules to answer these questions mathematically provided you can characterize the behavior of the stocks or flows as mathematical functions. Calculus is one of the most beautiful and useful branches of mathematics but one far too few have studied. Happily, the intuition behind the relationship between stocks and flows is straightforward and does not require any mathematics. If you are shown a graph of the behavior of the flows over time, you can always infer the behavior of the stock. This process is known as *graphical integration*. Likewise, from the trajectory of the stock you can always infer its net rate of change, a process known as *graphical differentiation*. Integration and differentiation are the two fundamental operations in the calculus. Table 7-1 provides the definitions graphically and in plain language.

The amount added to a stock during any time interval is the area bounded by the curve defining its net rate of change. Why? Consider the bathtub metaphor

TABLE 7-1   Integration and differentiation: definitions and examples

Integration	Differentiation
Stocks accumulate or *integrate* their net flow. The quantity added to a stock over any interval is the area bounded by the graph of the net rate between the start and end of the interval. The final value of the stock is the initial value plus the area under the net rate curve between the initial and final times.	The slope of a line tangent to any point of the trajectory of the stock equals the net rate of change for the stock at that point. The slope of the stock trajectory is the *derivative* of the stock. In the example below, the slope of the stock trajectory at time t_1 is R_1, so the net rate at $t_1 = R_1$. At time t_2, the slope of the stock is larger, so the net rate at $t_2 = R_2$ is greater than R_1. The
In the example below, the value of the stock at time $t_1 = S_1$. Adding the area under the net rate curve between times t_1 and t_2 increases the stock to S_2.	stock rises at an increasing rate, so the net rate is positive and increasing.

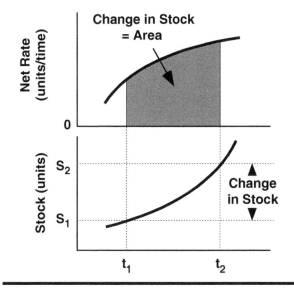

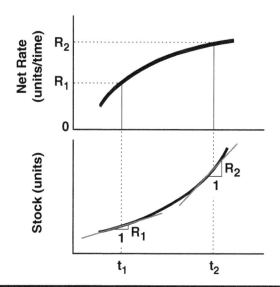

again. How much water is added to the tub in any time interval, such as between time t_1 and t_2 in Table 7-1? Divide the entire interval into a number of smaller segments, each small enough that the net flow of water is not changing significantly during the segment (Figure 7-1). The length of each segment is called "dt" for "delta time." How much water flows in during each small interval of duration dt? The quantity added is the net flow during the interval, say R, multiplied by the length of the interval, that is, the area of the rectangle dt periods wide and R units/period high:

$$\text{Quantity added during interval of length dt} = \quad R \quad * \quad dt$$
$$\text{(Units)} \qquad\qquad = \text{(Units/Time)} \quad \text{(Time)} \qquad (7\text{-}1)$$

Note the units of measure: The flow in units per time, accumulated for a period of time yields the quantity added to the stock.

To use a concrete example, suppose $t_1 = 1$ minute and $t_2 = 2$ minutes. The question is how much water flows into the tub during that minute. Divide the

FIGURE 7-1

Graphical integration

Divide time into small intervals of length dt. Each rectangle repre-sents the amount added during the interval dt, assum-ing the net rate R_i at that time re-mains constant during the interval. The area of each rectangle is $R_i dt$. The total added to the stock between t_1 and t_2 is then the sum of the areas of the rectangles. Dividing time into smaller increments increases the accuracy of the approximation.

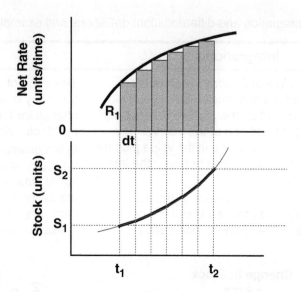

minute up into six 10-second intervals and assume the flow is constant throughout each of these intervals. If at the start of the first interval the flow was 6 liters per minute (that is, 0.1 liters/second), then the amount added would be (0.1 liters/sec-ond)(10 seconds) = 1 liter. At the start of the second 10-second interval, the flow has increased, perhaps to 7 liters/minute, or about 0.117 liters/second. The area of the second rectangle is then 1.17 liters. Calculating the area of all six rectangles and adding them together gives an approximation of the total volume of water added during the minute. The approximation isn't perfect because the net flow is actually changing during each 6-second interval. In Figure 7-1, the flow is actually rising, so the calculated value of the stock will be too small. To increase the accu-racy of the approximation, simply divide time into even finer intervals, increasing the number of rectangles. Computer simulations integrate the stocks in the model in precisely this fashion; the modeler must choose the time step dt so that the ap-proximation is acceptable for the purpose.[1] In the limit, as the time interval be-comes infinitesimal, the sum of the areas of all the rectangles becomes equal to the total area under the net rate curve. Calculus provides formulas that give the exact area under the net rate—provided the net rate can be expressed as a certain type of mathematical function. But whether the net rate can be integrated analytically or not, the amount added to a stock is always the area under the net rate. Graphical in-tegration is the process of estimating that area from a graph of the net rate.

7.1.3   Graphical Integration

To illustrate graphical integration, consider the most basic stock and flow system: a single stock with one inflow and one outflow. Assume the flows are exogenous—there are no feedbacks from the stock to either flow. Suppose the outflow from the

---

[1]The procedure described above is known as Euler integration and is the most commonly used method for numerical simulation. Other methods such as Runge-Kutta integration use more sophis-ticated methods to estimate the area and select the time step. See Appendix A.

FIGURE 7-2

Graphical integration: example

While the rate steps up and steps down, the stock rises and remains at a higher level. Note the different units of measure for the rate and stock.

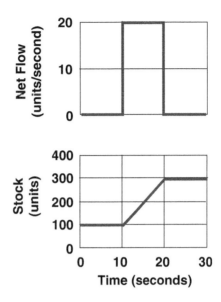

stock is zero. Suppose also that the inflow to the stock follows the pattern shown in Figure 7-2. The inflow begins at zero. At time 10 the inflow suddenly increases to 20 units/second, remains at that level for 10 seconds, then steps back down to zero. If the initial level of the stock is 100 units, how much is in the stock at time 30, and what is the behavior of the stock over time?

Table 7-2 shows the steps involved in graphical integration. Applying these steps to Figure 7-2, first make a set of axes for the stock, lined up under the graph for the flows. Next calculate the net rate. Since there is only one inflow and one outflow, and since the outflow is zero at all times, the net rate of change of the stock (Total Inflow − Total Outflow) simply equals the inflow. Initially, the stock has a value of 100 units. Between time 0 and time 10, the net flow is zero units/ second, so the stock remains constant at its initial value. At time 10, the net rate jumps to 20 units/second and remains there for 10 seconds. The amount added is the area under the net rate curve (between the net rate curve and the zero line). Since the rate is constant, the area is a rectangle 20 units/second high and 10 sec- onds long, so the stock rises by 200 units, giving a total level of 300 units by time 20. Because the net rate is positive and constant during this interval, the stock rises linearly at a rate 20 units/second (the slope of the stock is 20 units/second).

At time 20, the inflow suddenly ceases. The net rate of change is now zero and remains constant, and the stock is again unchanging, though now at the level of 300 units.

Note how the process of accumulation creates inertia: though the rate rises and falls back to its original level, the stock does not return to its original level. Instead, it remains at its maximum when the net rate falls back to zero. In this fashion, stocks provide a memory of all the past events in a system. The only way for the stock to fall is for the net rate to become negative (for the outflow to exceed the in- flow). Note also how the process of accumulation changed the shape of the input. The input is a rectangular pulse with two discontinuous jumps; the output is a smooth, continuous curve.

TABLE 7-2

Steps in graphical integration

1. Calculate and graph the total rate of inflow to the stock (the sum of all inflows). Calculate and graph the total rate of outflow from the stock (the sum of all outflows).

2. Calculate and graph the net rate of change of the stock (the total inflow less the total outflow).

3. Make a set of axes to graph the stock. Stocks and their flows have different units of measure (if a stock is measured in units its flows are measured in units per time period). Therefore stocks and their flows must be graphed on separate scales. Make a separate graph for the stock under the graph for the flows, with the time axes lined up.

4. Plot the initial value of the stock on the stock graph. The initial value must be specified; it cannot be inferred from the net rate.

5. Break the net flow into intervals with the same behavior and calculate the amount added to the stock during the interval. Segments might be intervals in which the net rate is constant, changing linearly, or following some other pattern. The amount added to or subtracted from the stock during a segment is the area under the net rate curve during that segment. For example, does the net flow remain constant from time t_1 to time t_2? If so, the rate of change of the stock during that segment is constant, and the quantity added to the stock is the area of the rectangle defined by the net rate between t_1 and t_2. If the net rate rises linearly in a segment, then the amount added is the area of the triangle. Estimate the area under the net rate curve for the segment and add it to the value of the stock at the start of the segment. The total is the value of the stock at the end of the segment. Plot this point on the graph of the stock.

6. Sketch the trajectory of the stock between the start and end of each segment. Find the value of the net rate at the beginning of the segment. Is it positive or negative? If the net flow is **positive,** the stock will be **increasing** at that time. If the net flow is **negative,** the stock will be **decreasing.** Then ask whether it is rising or falling at an increasing or decreasing rate, and sketch the pattern you infer on the graph.

    If the net rate is **positive** and *increasing,* the stock **increases** at an *increasing* rate (the stock accelerates upward).

    If the net rate is **positive** and *decreasing,* the stock **increases** at a *decreasing* rate (the stock is decelerating but still moving upward).

    If the net rate is **negative** and its *magnitude is increasing* (the net rate is becoming more negative), the stock **decreases** at an *increasing* rate.

    If the net rate is **negative** and its *magnitude is decreasing* (becoming less negative), the stock **decreases** at a *decreasing* rate.

7. Whenever the net rate is zero, the stock is unchanging. Make sure that your graph of the stock shows no change in the stock everywhere the net rate is zero. If the net rate remains zero for some interval, the stock remains constant at whatever value it had when the net rate became zero. At points where the net rate changes from positive to negative, the stock reaches a maximum as it ceases to rise and starts to fall. At points where the net rate changes from negative to positive, the stock reaches a minimum as it ceases to fall and starts to rise.

8. Repeat steps 5 through 7 until done.

FIGURE 7-3   The accumulation process creates delays.
Note the one-quarter cycle lag between the peaks of the net flow and the peaks of the stock.

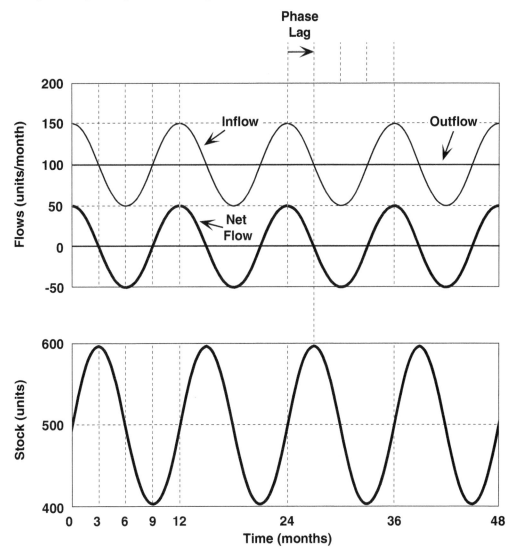

Now consider the flows specified in the top panel of Figure 7-3. The outflow is constant at 100 units/month, but the inflow fluctuates around an average of 100 with a period of 12 months and an amplitude of ±50 units/month. At the start, the inflow is at its maximum. Assume the initial value of the stock is 500 units.

Since the outflow is constant, the net inflow is a fluctuation with amplitude ±50 units/month and a mean of zero. The stock begins at its initial value of 500 units, but since the inflow is at its maximum, the stock initially rises with a slope of 50 units/month. However, the net flow falls over the first 3 months, so the stock increases at a decreasing rate. At month 3 the net flow reaches zero, then goes negative. The stock must therefore reach a maximum at month 3. The amount added to the stock in the first 3 months is the area under the net rate curve. It is not easy to estimate the area from the graph because the net rate curve is constantly changing. You could estimate it by approximating the area as a set of rectangles, as described above, though this would take time. Using simulation to carry out the accumulation shows that a little less than 100 units are added to the stock by the time the net rate falls to zero at month 3.

From month 3 to month 6, the net rate is negative. The stock is therefore falling. Just after month 3, the net rate is just barely negative, so the rate of decline of the stock is slight. But the magnitude of the net rate increases, so the stock falls at an increasing rate. At 6 months, the net rate has reached its minimum (most negative) value of −50 units/month. The stock is declining at its maximum rate; there is an inflection point in the trajectory of the stock at month 6.

How much did the stock lose between month 3 and month 6? Assuming the fluctuation in the net rate is symmetrical, the loss just balanced what was gained in the first 3 months, reducing the stock back to its initial level of 500 units.

From month 6 to month 9, the net flow remains negative, so the stock continues to fall, but now at a decreasing rate. By month 9 the net flow again reaches zero, so the stock ceases to fall and reaches its minimum. Again using the assumption of symmetry, the quantity lost from months 6 to 9 is equal to the quantity lost from months 3 to 6, so the stock falls to a level just above 400 units.

From months 9 to 12 the net flow is positive, so the stock is rising. During this time the net rate rises, so the stock increases at an increasing rate, ending with a slope of 50 units/month as the net rate reaches its maximum. Again, the stock gains the same amount, recovering its initial level of 500 units exactly at month 12. Beyond month 12 the cycle repeats.

The example illustrates the way in which the process of accumulation creates delays. The input to the system is a fluctuation with a 12-month period reaching its peak at time = 0, 12, 24, . . . months. The stock, or output of the system, also fluctuates with a 12-month period but lags behind the net inflow rate, reaching its peaks at t = 3, 15, 27, . . . months. The lag is precisely one-quarter cycle. The lag arises because the stock can only decrease when the net flow is negative. If the net flow is positive and falls to zero, the stock increases and reaches its maximum.

Analytical Integration of a Fluctuation

The example in Figure 7-3 can be made precise using a little basic calculus. The stock S is the integral of the net rate R. Assuming the net flow is a cosine with period 12 months and amplitude 50 units/month, $R = 50\cos(2\pi t/12)$, then

$$S = \int R\,dt = \int 50\cos(2\pi t/12)dt = 50(12/2\pi)\sin(2\pi t/12) + S_{t_0} \qquad (7\text{-}2)$$

The stock follows a sine wave with the same period and amplitude $(12/2\pi)$ times that of the net flow. The delay caused by the accumulation process is easily seen since $\sin(\theta) = \cos(\theta - \pi/2)$:

$$S = 50(12/2\pi)\cos(2\pi t/12 - \pi/2) + S_{t_0} \qquad (7\text{-}3)$$

The stock follows the same trajectory as the net flow but with a phase lag of $\pi/2$ (one-quarter cycle). Equation (7-2) also shows that the amplitude of the stock is (50 units/month) * (12 months/2π) $\approx$ 96 units, so the stock fluctuates between about 404 and 596, as seen in the figure.

CHALLENGE

Graphical Integration

Consider a stock with a single inflow rate R_1 and single outflow rate R_2. Draw the behavior of the stock given the rates R_1 and R_2 shown in each panel of Figure 7-4. The initial value of the stock is 100 units in both cases. Do not use a computer. The point is to develop your intuition about stocks and flows and your ability to relate their behavior. Using simulation defeats that purpose and will take longer as well.

FIGURE 7-4
Inflows and outflows for a hypothetical stock

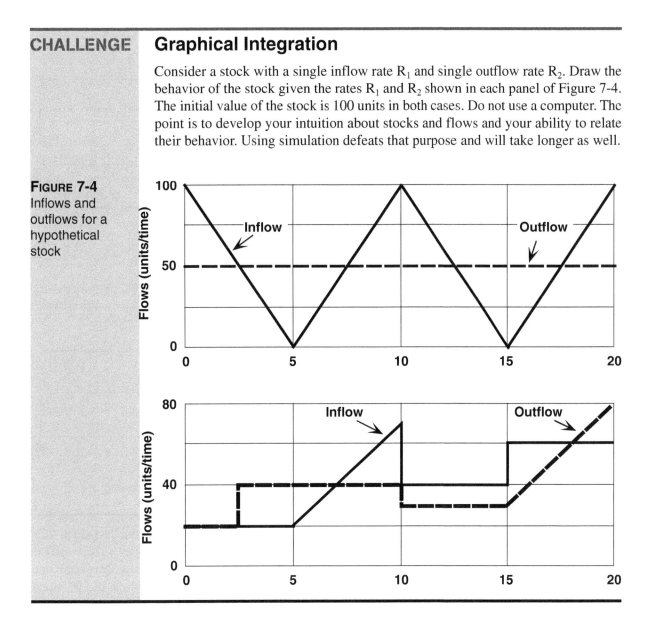

7.1.4   Graphical Differentiation

The inverse of integration is differentiation, the calculation of the net rate of change of a stock from its trajectory. Given a graph of a stock, it is always possible to infer the net rate of change and plot it. As in the case of integration, there are analytic methods to calculate the net rate of a stock if the function describing the stock's path is known. However, in most dynamic models no analytic function for the stocks is known, so you must develop the skill of graphical differentiation.

Graphical differentiation is straightforward. Simply estimate the slope of the stock at each point in time and plot it on a graph of the net rate. Figure 7-5 provides an example.

FIGURE 7-5
Graphical
differentiation

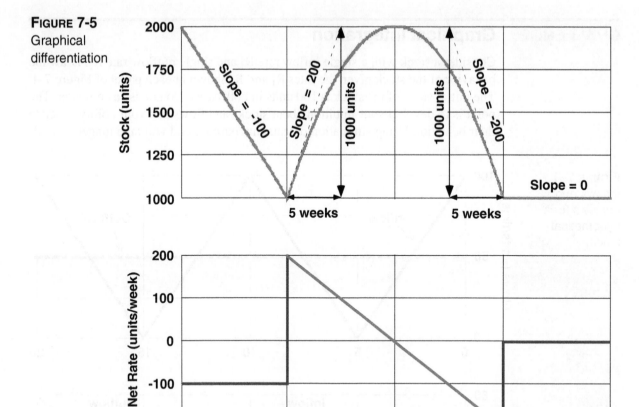

The initial stock is 2000 units. For the first 10 weeks the stock declines linearly, so the net rate during this interval is negative and constant. The stock falls from 2000 to 1000 units in 10 weeks, so the net rate (the slope of the stock) is −100 units/week. At week 10 the stock suddenly starts increasing. Drawing a line tangent to the stock curve at time 10 gives an estimate of the slope of 200 units/week. The net rate therefore steps up from −100 units/week the instant before the start of week 10 to +200 units/week just after it starts. From weeks 10 to 20 the stock increases at a decreasing rate, so the net rate is positive but falling. At time 20 the stock reaches a maximum so the net rate is zero. There are no kinks or bumps in the stock trajectory, implying a steady, linear decline in the net rate from 200 units/week in week 10 to zero in week 20. From week 20 to week 30 the stock is falling. By week 30 it is falling rapidly; the slope of a line tangent to the stock trajectory at week 30 has a slope of −200 units/week. Again, there are no kinks in the trajectory, so the net rate declines linearly from zero in week 20 to −200 units/week in week 30. At week 30 the stock suddenly stops changing and remains constant afterwards. The net rate suddenly steps up from −200 to zero units/week and remains at zero thereafter.

Graphical differentiation of a stock reveals only its net rate of change. If the stock has multiple inflows and outflows it is not possible to determine their individual values from the net rate alone: a firm's stock of cash remains constant whether revenues and expenditures both equal $1 million per year or $1 billion per year.

CHALLENGE

Graphical Differentiation

The trajectory of a stock is shown in Figure 7-6. Determine the behavior of its net rate by graphical differentiation. Do not use a computer.

FIGURE 7-6
Behavior of a
hypothetical stock

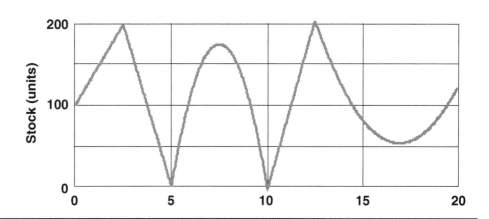

7.2   SYSTEM DYNAMICS IN ACTION: GLOBAL WARMING

Much of the power of the system dynamics perspective comes from understanding how the process of accumulation creates dynamics, even before considering the feedbacks coupling the stocks and their flows. To illustrate, consider global warming.

Is the earth warming? Is the warming caused by emissions of greenhouse gases (GHGs) caused by human activity? How much warming is likely over the next century? What changes in climate patterns, rainfall, growing season, storm incidence and severity, and sea level might ensue, and how much damage would these changes cause to humanity and to other species? These questions are difficult to answer, and legitimate scientific debates about the impact of anthropogenic GHG emissions continue.

Despite the scientific uncertainty, several facts are not in dispute. The temperature at the earth's surface—the land, lower atmosphere, and surface layer of the ocean (the so-called mixed layer, the top 50 to 100 meters, where most sea life exists)—is primarily determined by the balance of the incoming solar radiation and the outgoing reradiated energy. The earth is a warm mass surrounded by the cold of space and like all such masses emits so-called black body radiation whose frequency distribution and intensity depends on its surface temperature. The warmer the mass, the more energy it radiates. Incoming solar energy warms the earth. As it warms, more energy is radiated back into space. The temperature rises until the earth is just warm enough for the energy radiated back to space to balance the incoming solar energy.

The amount of energy radiated back into space depends on the composition of the atmosphere. GHGs such as carbon dioxide and methane trap some of the energy radiated by the earth, instead of allowing it to escape into space. Thus an increase in GHGs causes the earth to warm. The earth heats up until the energy escaping through the atmosphere to space rises enough to again balance the incoming solar energy. Greenhouse gases reduce the emissivity of the atmosphere enough to warm the surface of the earth (including the oceans) to a life-sustaining average of about 15°C (59°F). Without GHGs in the atmosphere, the mean global temperature would be about -17°C (1°F) and a blanket of ice would perpetually cover the earth.

Natural processes have caused the concentration of carbon dioxide (CO_2) in the atmosphere to fluctuate significantly over geological time, and surface temperatures have fluctuated with it. Human activity has now reached a scale where it can affect these processes. As shown in Figure 7-7, the rate of anthropogenic GHG emissions has been growing exponentially since the beginning of the industrial age. Atmospheric concentrations of CO_2 and other GHGs including nitrous oxide (N_2O), methane (CH_4), chlorofluorocarbons (CFCs), hydrofluorocarbons (HFCs), perfluorinated carbons (PFCs), and others have been growing exponentially, with concentrations of CO_2, N_2O, and CH_4 up by 30, 15, and 145%, respectively, since 1800. Mean global surface temperature has been rising, though not in a steady pattern. Compared to the late 1800s, average global temperatures are about 0.5 to 1°C warmer today. By comparison, the mean global temperature during the last ice age, when sheets of ice 1000 feet thick covered much of the northern hemisphere, was about 5°C colder than today.

Debate continues about the dynamics of the global climate system, its response to forcing by human activity, and the consequences of a rise in global mean temperature. The public discussion has been polarized by well-financed campaigns to discount the science. Nevertheless, consensus is emerging. In 1995, the UN sponsored Intergovernmental Panel on Climate Change (IPCC) concluded that global warming was indeed occurring, and that human activity was responsible, stating "The balance of evidence suggests a discernible human influence on climate" (IPCC 1996). Through the UN Framework Convention on Climate Change (UNFCCC) various nations are negotiating limits to GHG emissions, though compliance remains elusive.

Simulation models of various types are the primary research tool to explore these issues. The enormously detailed general circulation models (GCMs) calculate climate at finely spaced intervals covering the entire surface of the earth, but take GHG emissions as exogenous inputs. At the other extreme, so-called integrated climate–economy models close some of the feedbacks among the human economy, carbon emissions, and global climate but treat the carbon cycle and climate as global aggregates with a small number of stocks. Tom Fiddaman (1997) analyzed many of the most widely used climate–economy models, identifying a number of problems and inconsistencies in them. For example, the widely cited DICE model (Nordhaus 1992a, 1992b) violates the law of conservation of mass by assuming that a significant fraction of carbon emissions simply disappear (Nordhaus assumed they flow into a sink outside the model boundary). Fiddaman (1997)

FIGURE 7-7
GHG emissions,
concentration,
and global mean
temperature

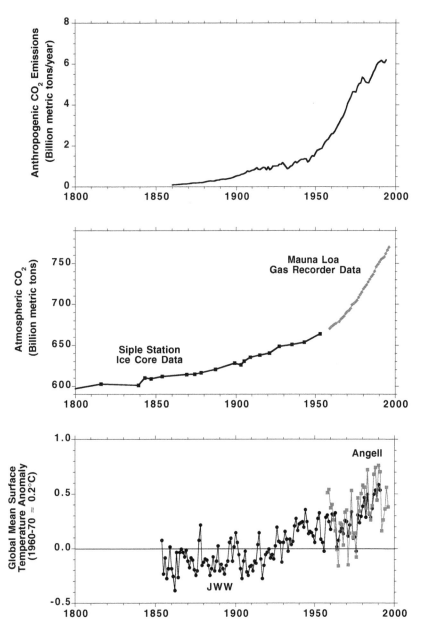

Sources: Data from the Carbon Dioxide Information Analysis Center (CDIAC), Oak Ridge National Laboratory (http://cdiac.esd.ornl.gov/trends/trends.htm). Emissions: Keeling (1997). Emissions include carbon from burning fossil fuels only and excludes other GHGs and changes in carbon flux from, e.g., deforestation. CO_2 in atmosphere: Siple Station ice core data (Neftel et al. 1994). Mauna Loa gas recorder data (Keeling et al. 1997); concentration in ppmv converted to billion tons in total atmosphere. Global mean surface temperature anomaly: Jones, Wigley, and Wright (1997) and Angell (1997); rescaled so 1960-70 ≈ 0.2°C.

developed a model that corrects these and other defects in common climate–economy models and linked it to a model of the economy and energy system. The model sectors were based on the relevant scientific knowledge of the global carbon cycle and climate system and carefully calibrated to the available data.

Despite the differences among the models, all show the climate system to possess enormous inertia. Changes in GHG emissions only slowly show up in changes in global temperature and climate, and the changes persist for many decades. To illustrate, Figure 7-8 shows an extreme conditions test using Fiddaman's model. In the simulation, anthropogenic CO_2 emissions follow their historical path through the mid 1990s, remain constant until 2000, and then fall to zero after 2000. Surprisingly, though the rate of CO_2 emissions falls to zero in the year 2000, mean global temperature continues to rise for about three more decades. It then falls very slowly.

The stock and flow structure responsible for the counterintuitive result that temperature rises even though emissions fall to zero is shown in Figure 7-9. The left side of the figure portrays the global carbon cycle; the right side portrays the global heat balance. Burning fossil fuels adds CO_2 to the atmosphere. There are several outflows from the stock of atmospheric CO_2. Higher atmospheric CO_2 concentration increases the rate at which CO_2 is consumed by aquatic life or dissolves into the mixed layer of the ocean. Eventually, CO_2 taken up by the surface layer diffuses to deeper waters, both through ocean currents and as detritus from aquatic life sinks. The transfer of carbon to the depths is slow, and mixing between the surface and abyssal waters is weak, so many carbon cycle models disaggregate the water column into a number of distinct states and model the transfer of carbon between adjacent layers explicitly. Fiddaman's model utilizes 10 layers, enough to capture the slow adjustment of abyssal CO_2 concentrations to changes in CO_2 in the mixed layer.

Increased atmospheric CO_2 concentration also stimulates uptake of carbon by terrestrial plants (the flux of CO_2 to biomass). Carbon in biomass can be released back into the atmosphere through respiration and metabolic activity of animal and bacterial life and by fire (natural and human-caused). As biomass decays, the stock of carbon stored in soil increases (the flux of carbon from biomass to soil humus). The carbon in humus can be taken up directly into biomass as plants grow or can be released into the atmosphere through decay.

Note that the model represents the inflow of CO_2 to the atmosphere from the burning of fossil fuels as flowing from an unlimited source when in fact the flow draws down the carbon sequestered in global stocks of fossil fuels. Similarly, the model does not capture the conversion of carbon in humus or the abyssal layer of the ocean into new stocks of fossil fuels. Although the dynamics of global warming will play out over the next several centuries, this time horizon is so short relative to the millions of years required to form oil, gas, and coal that these carbon flows can be safely ignored.

The right side of Figure 7-9 shows the stock and flow structure for the heat balance of the earth's surface, atmosphere, and oceans. The surface and atmosphere, including the surface layer of the ocean, absorb incoming solar energy and radiate heat back into space. Heat is also transferred between the surface layer and the deep ocean, though at slow rates. The rate of heat transfer between surface and deep ocean depends on the temperature differential between the different layers, creating two negative feedbacks which seek to equilibrate the temperatures of the different layers. Similarly, net radiative forcing is the difference between the incoming solar energy and the energy radiated from the warm earth back into space.

FIGURE 7-8

Global temperature rises well after GHG emissions fall to zero.

Simulated emissions fall to zero in 2000. Mean surface temperature continues to rise for roughly 20 years.

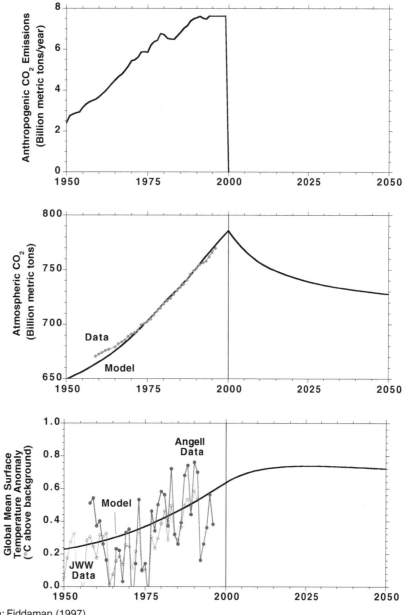

Source: Fiddaman (1997).

The warmer the surface, the more energy is radiated back into space, cooling the earth and forming another negative loop. The concentration of CO_2 and other GHGs increases net radiative forcing by reducing the rate at which energy is radiated back into space for any given surface temperature.

The diagram (though not the full model) deliberately omits many additional feedbacks affecting the rates of carbon flow and heat exchange as well as couplings to other biogeochemical cycles. Knowledge of the nature and strength of the many feedbacks coupling climate, carbon cycle, and human activity is still evolving. Some of these feedbacks are negative and may offset GHG emissions or

FIGURE 7-9   Stock and flow diagram of global carbon cycle and heat balance

Burning fossil fuels adds CO_2 to the atmosphere, increasing net radiative forcing until the temperature of the land, ocean surface, and atmosphere rises enough to balance reradiation of energy into space with incoming insolation. The diagram deliberately omits many of the feedbacks, both positive and negative, among the carbon stocks and global mean temperature. Flows with arrowheads at both ends can be positive or negative (e.g., Net Radiative Forcing can be an inflow of heat to the atmosphere or an outflow). The solid arrowhead indicates the positive direction of two-way flows.

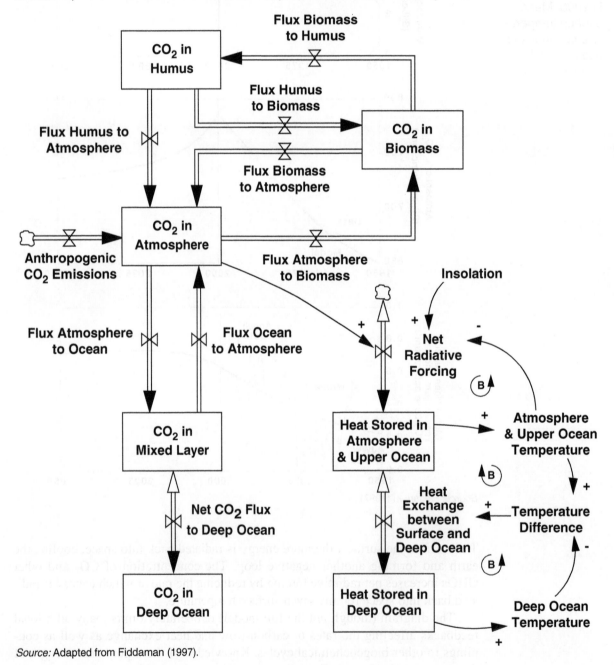

Source: Adapted from Fiddaman (1997).

warming. These include increased carbon uptake by biomass, stimulated by higher CO_2 concentrations, and increased cloud cover from enhanced evaporation, reflecting more incoming sunlight to space. Particulate aerosols from fossil fuel consumption (air pollution and smog) also increase reflection of incoming solar radiation and may account for the slower than expected rate of temperature rise observed in the Northern Hemisphere.

Among the positive feedbacks driving climate change are changes in surface albedo: Warming reduces the winter snow cover and shrinks the highly reflective polar ice caps, thus increasing heat absorption and leading to further melting, less snow cover, and still greater absorption. Scientists expect this positive loop will cause much greater warming at the poles than in the tropics and more warming in winter than summer. Thawing of permafrost may release large quantities of methane from decay of organic matter, increasing the concentration of GHGs and leading to further warming in another positive loop. Increased evaporation from warmer land and surface waters may be self-reinforcing since water vapor is a powerful GHG. At present it is not known whether the negative or positive feedbacks dominate the dynamics nor how the dominance of the loops might change as various nonlinearities come into play. However, Goulden et al. (1998) studied the northern boreal forest of Canada and found that warming has resulted in net carbon flux to the atmosphere as CO_2 released from decay of thawed biomass outweighed increased carbon uptake by plants. For that biome, at least, the positive feedbacks appear to dominate the negative loop of increased biotic activity.

The impact of warming on sea level may also be driven by positive feedback. The huge West Antarctic Ice Sheet (WAIS) consists of a floating tongue attached to a larger ice mass so heavy it rests on bedrock below sea level. The WAIS holds a lot of water: "If it melted away in a greenhouse-warmed world, it would raise all the world's oceans by 5 meters" (Kerr 1998, p. 17). If warmer seas cause the WAIS to thin, it will rise farther off the sea bed, exposing more of the ice to melting and accelerating thinning in a positive loop. As the edge thins, the higher ice on the Antarctic land mass flows faster into the sea, where it is exposed to the warmer waters, further speeding melting in another positive feedback. Rignot (1998) notes that a glacier with "[t]his configuration is theoretically unstable because a retreat of its grounding line (where the glacier starts to float) would be self-perpetuating and irreversible" and shows that the grounding line of the Pine Island glacier feeding the WAIS is retreating at 1.2 ± 0.3 kilometers per year. Ice cores show that within the past 1.3 million years, "at a time perhaps not much warmer than today, the WAIS wasted away to a scrap and flooded the world's coasts" (Kerr 1998, p. 17). Ice core data from Greenland also suggest the paleoclimate repeatedly warmed and cooled, with corresponding changes in snowfall, over time scales of only decades. These rapid changes suggest positive feedbacks may have dominated climate dynamics in geologically recent times.

It will take years of research to discover all the feedbacks that drive the climate and determine the likely effects of greenhouse warming. Nevertheless, the stock and flow structure of the global carbon cycle and heat budget explains some basic features of the dynamics. The stock and flow structure shows how it is possible for the global temperature to rise even after human GHG emissions fall to zero. When emissions fall to zero the inflows to the stock of atmospheric carbon fall below the outflows. Therefore the stock of CO_2 in the atmosphere peaks and begins to fall. The concentration of CO_2 in the atmosphere falls only slowly, however. First, the uptake of carbon by biomass falls as the concentration of CO_2 in the atmosphere declines, while CO_2 continues to flow into the air from burning and decay of biomass and humus stocks. Second, as atmospheric CO_2 falls, the flux of carbon from the air to the mixed layer of the ocean falls, while the flux of carbon from the ocean to the air increases. These compensatory responses slow the decline of atmospheric CO_2 so that 50 years after human emissions stop completely, the concentration of CO_2 in the model atmosphere has fallen back only to its 1990 level.

The heat content of the surface layer rises as long as incoming radiation exceeds the heat radiated back to space or transferred to the deep ocean. Though falling after the year 2000, global atmospheric CO_2 concentrations remain high enough to reduce the energy radiated back to space below incoming insolation. Declining atmospheric CO_2 after 2000 means global mean temperature grows at a diminishing rate. By about 2030 the surface has warmed enough and the concentration of CO_2 in the atmosphere has fallen enough for insolation to be balanced again by the earth's black-body radiation and the rate of heat transfer to the deep ocean. Note that global mean temperature falls only slowly after 2030. First, the slow decline of GHG concentrations after 2000 slows the increase in radiative emissivity. Second, during the warmest decades when the surface temperature exceeded the temperature of the deep ocean, heat flowed from the surface layer to the deep. As the surface layer cools, heat stored in the deep ocean now flows back to the surface, slowing atmospheric cooling.

The stock and flow structure of the carbon cycle and heat balance explains the seemingly paradoxical result that temperatures can rise even when emissions fall. There are several lessons. First, global warming cannot be proven or disproven by correlating emissions and temperature: the dynamics are too complex for such naive commonsense approaches. Second, the full impact of past emissions has not yet been observed. The oceans and terrestrial carbon stocks have been absorbing carbon out of the atmosphere at higher rates, suppressing the rise in atmospheric CO_2 concentrations. And as these stocks increase, their absorption capacity diminishes. The impact of future emissions on atmospheric CO_2 may well be larger than that observed in the past. Third, the inertia of the system means further warming and climate change are already underway. Action to halt warming must be taken decades before we can know what the consequences of warming will be and before scientific certainty about the dynamics of the global climate can be gained.

Most important, the stock and flow structure of the global climate means stabilizing emissions near current rates will not stabilize the climate. Figure 7-10 shows a simulation in which emissions are stabilized in 1995. The concentration of atmospheric CO_2 continues to rise, more than doubling by 2300. Global mean surface temperature rises by about 3°C. Many industrialized nations agreed at the Rio conference on the environment to stabilize their GHG emissions at 1990 levels, and 38 industrialized nations agreed at the 1997 Kyoto conference of the UNFCCC to reduce emissions by 2012 to about 95% of 1990 rates. But the US Senate declared the treaty dead on arrival. Implementation remains elusive; signing a treaty

FIGURE 7-10

Stabilizing GHG emissions does not stabilize the climate.

Stabilizing GHG emissions at 1995 levels causes atmospheric CO_2 concentrations to double by 2300, while mean global surface temperature increases about 3°C. Even under the proposed Kyoto agreement, global emissions are likely to increase substantially over the next several decades.

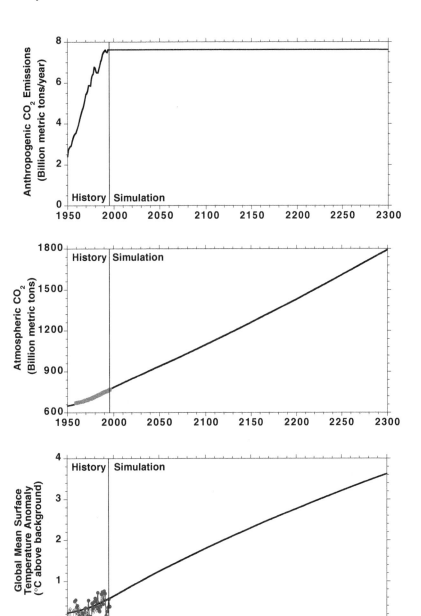

Source: Fiddaman (1997).

is one thing, actually reducing emissions another. Most troubling, the emissions of rapidly developing nations such as China continue to grow at high exponential rates. The US Energy Information Administration forecast in 1997 that GHG emissions from developing nations would nearly double by 2015, accounting for the large majority of the world total (Malakoff 1997).

While different climate models differ in their details and in their estimates of future warming, all agree that stabilizing emissions near current levels will not stabilize the climate. Mitigating the risk of climate change from global warming requires a substantial decline in the rate of GHG emissions. The world has yet to face up to the inexorable logic of the stocks and flows of the global climate system.

7.3   SYSTEM DYNAMICS IN ACTION: THE WAR ON DRUGS

In the 1980s the use of cocaine increased dramatically. As cocaine spread, crime, violence, and health problems grew exponentially. The United States declared a war on drugs. A new federal agency, the White House Office of National Drug Control Policy (ONDCP), headed by the "drug czar," was appointed to oversee the campaign. Penalties for possession, sale and use of drugs were stiffened. Billions were spent to increase enforcement, especially to reduce the flow of cocaine into the US, estimated by the ONDCP to be 550 to 660 metric tons in 1989. The focus of the war on drugs was primarily the supply side: slashing the production of cocaine, choking off smuggling into the US, and stiffening penalties for possession and sale. On the demand side, kids were told to "Just say NO."

Did it work? In the late 1980s the data told a conflicting story. Some drug data showed improvement. Through the "National Household Survey" (NHS) and "High School Senior Survey" (HSSS), the government regularly asks people about their use of alcohol and drugs. To assess trends in incidence and prevalence, the surveys ask whether people have ever used cocaine, whether they've used it in the last year, and whether they've used it in the last month. Figure 7-11 shows NHS data for the fraction of people responding that they have used cocaine in the past month. According to the surveys, cocaine use was falling sharply, with less than 1% of the population reporting past month cocaine use in 1990, down from 3% in 1985. The drop in reported use coincided with a sharp increase in the seizure rate, to more than 75 metric tons per year (Figure 7-11). The war on drugs seemed to be working; citing these data, the administration called for even more money to finish the job.

However, other indicators showed the problem was getting worse. Arrests for possession and sale of cocaine, the number of emergency room visits associated with cocaine, and the number of cocaine-related deaths all showed exponential increases, while the purity of cocaine on the street was growing and the street price was falling (Figure 7-11). By these measures, cocaine use was up sharply and availability was growing. Critics, citing the failure of prohibition in the 1920s and 1930s, argued that interdiction could never work and called for stronger demand-side measures (MacCoun and Reuter 1997 review the debate). Others argued that decriminalization would eliminate the crime problem caused by use of illegal drugs and allow the government to regulate purity to prevent accidental overdoses.

Much of the debate focused on which data series were right and which were wrong. The stakes were high: Besides the issues of public health and safety, the drug war was prosecuted and data series were collected by an alphabet soup of federal and state agencies, including the FBI, DEA, SAMHSA, NIJ, NIDA, DEPB, ONDCP, and CIA.[2] Each argued for the primacy and correctness of its data and

---

[2]Federal Bureau of Investigation, Drug Enforcement Agency, Substance Abuse and Mental Health Services Administration of the Department of Health and Human Services, National Institute of Justice, National Institute on Drug Abuse, Drug Enforcement Policy Board, Office of National Drug Control Policy, and Central Intelligence Agency.

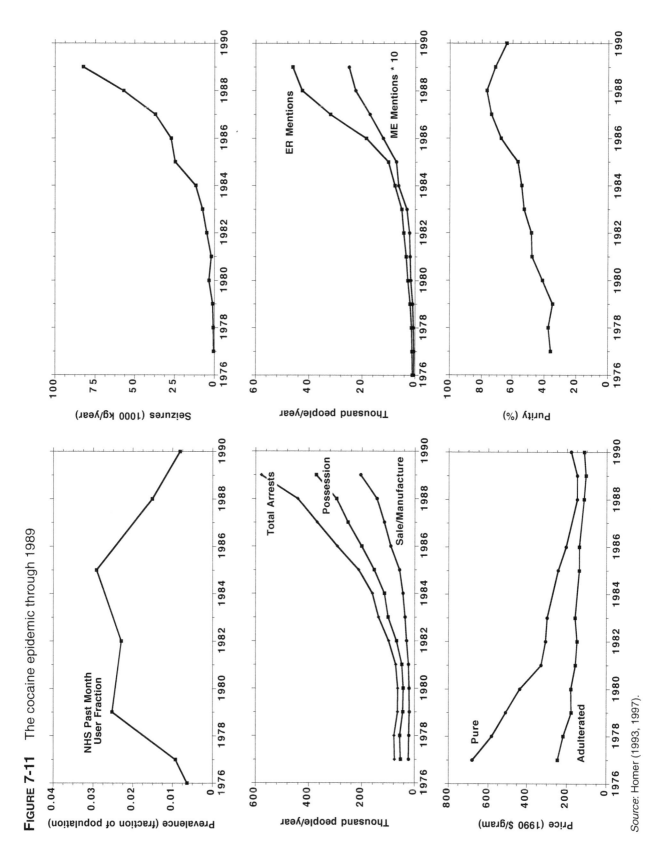

FIGURE 7-11 The cocaine epidemic through 1989

Source: Homer (1993, 1997).

251

drug-enforcement programs as they struggled to gain a larger share of more than $10 billion per year devoted to the war on drugs.

Supporters of the interdiction strategy argued that the survey data directly measured what counts—the use of drugs—while other indicators were indirect. They argued that rising arrest rates and seizures reflected greater enforcement, not greater drug use, and were therefore a sign of success; falling prices, rising purity, and the surge in medical emergencies and deaths simply reflected the substitution of more potent crack for the less pure powder form. Critics of interdiction and the survey data argued that drug users are less likely than law-abiding citizens to be selected for or participate in the surveys. Many cocaine users are likely to deny they use drugs when the government asks. Defenders of the surveys pointed to the sophisticated sampling methods they used to account for possible underrepresentation of certain subpopulations. They guaranteed anonymity to survey respondents and claimed that while "[t]he value of self-reports obviously depends on the honesty and memory of sampled respondents[, r]esearch has supported the validity of self-report data in similar contexts" (SAMHSA 1994).

In the late 1980s the National Institute of Justice commissioned a study to resolve the apparent paradox of declining measures of cocaine use and rising consumption, crime, arrests, and deaths. As part of the study, a system dynamics model was developed to integrate the demand and supply sides of the market (Homer 1993, 1997). The full model consisted of several hundred equations and included a detailed representation of the stock and flow structure of users, along with the feedbacks among different market actors, the market, and the criminal justice system.

Figure 7-12 shows a simplified representation of the stock and flow structure for the different categories of drug users represented in the model. The NHS considers all persons age 12 and over to be potential drug users. As people in this age group first experiment with cocaine they move from the "never used" population to the stock of active casual users (those who have used cocaine in the past month but are not addicted). Some casual users find they cannot control their cocaine consumption and become compulsive users. Active users, both casual and compulsive, can stop, becoming "transitional users" (those who have used cocaine in the past year, but not in the past month). Transitional users can relapse, becoming active users again. After a year without any cocaine use, transitional users are reclassified as ex-users. Some ex-users relapse, becoming active users again. Others quit permanently. There are, of course, death rates out of each stock, both from drug-related causes and all other sources.

The full model has a more complex stock and flow structure than shown in Figure 7-12, explicitly distinguishing between casual and compulsive transitional and ex-users and between users of powder and crack cocaine. The model accounted for escalation from casual to compulsive use and for switching between powder and crack. This disaggregation was necessary because the probabilities of moving from one state to another depend on the form and intensity of use. Compulsive users are less likely to quit and more likely to relapse, and crack users are more likely to escalate from casual to compulsive use and suffer higher relapse rates.

FIGURE 7-12
Cocaine use:
stocks and flows

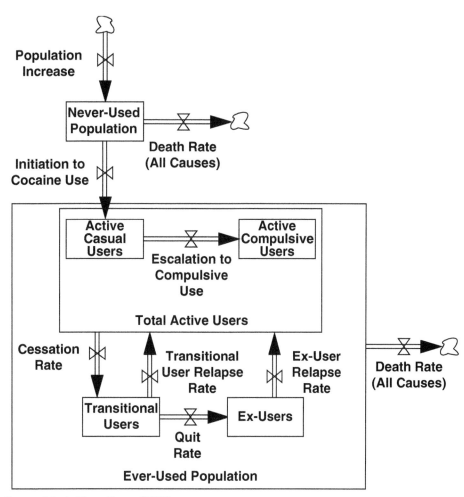

Source: Adapted from Homer (1993).

Note that the categories of use in the model can be directly compared to those used in the surveys. The total number of active users, both casual and compulsive, for both powder and crack, is the number of people who have actually used cocaine in the past month. The sum of the active users and the transitional users is the total number who actually used cocaine in the past year. Finally, the sum of active, transitional, and ex-users is the total number who have ever used cocaine.

What are the determinants of the initiation rate—what causes people to use cocaine for the first time? Studies show most people begin using drugs through peer influence—by observing others using drugs and through their membership in social networks in which others use drugs (that is, by hanging with the wrong crowd). As more people start using cocaine, the social networks of users expand, bringing still more nonusers into contact with the drug, in a positive feedback process analogous to the spread of an infectious disease (chapter 9). The strength of the social exposure feedback depends on the social aura of the drug: how chic cocaine is perceived to be (is this the drug the opinion leaders, the beautiful people, are using this year?). The positive feedback also depends on whether current and potential users view the drug as benign—is it perceived to offer a good high without negative effects such as addiction, bad trips or the risk of sudden death? Price has a comparatively modest effect, at least in higher socioeconomic groups, because high price and scarcity confer social status on those who can provide the drug for friends at parties or in the workplace. In the mid 1970s, as the cocaine epidemic began, cocaine was viewed as a benign, nonaddictive drug posing little health risk. It became the in-group drug of choice among certain professional elites. The entertainment industry reinforced the chic image of the drug. All these self-reinforcing processes are captured by the Word of Mouth loop R1 in Figure 7-13.

The dynamics of the market reinforced the growth of the epidemic. As consumption increased, the supply side of the market became much more efficient. Price declined and purity increased. The growing scale of the industry created huge incentives for technological and organizational innovation by producers and smugglers. The introduction of crack cocaine in 1981 was the most important, but far from the only, technical innovation in the market. As in many legitimate industries, growth led to production and especially distribution scale economies. Horizontal and vertical market integration through the cocaine cartels cut costs and led to more consistent product quality. Growing experience led to a substantial learning curve as harvesting, production, smuggling, distribution, and money laundering operations were improved. These scale and learning effects created additional positive feedbacks leading to wider availability, greater purity, and lower prices, making cocaine affordable and accessible to all (loop R2).

As long as people perceived the health and legal risks of cocaine to be small, these positive feedbacks dominated the system. Cocaine use mushroomed, spreading gradually from middle and upper income, trend-conscious populations on the east and west coasts to every social and income level in every state of the country.

Why then did the data show such a large drop in the incidence of current cocaine use after 1985? Supporters of the interdiction strategy credited the administration's supply-side policy. They argued that enhanced enforcement increased the fraction of cocaine seized, cutting the availability of the drug (the balancing Supply Disruption loop B1) and that aggressively arresting and incarcerating pushers and users helps clean up the Streets (the balancing loop B2). Both these negative loops, it was argued, cut drug use, as indicated by the survey data.

However, stock and flow structure for drug users showed that the survey data *could not be correct* and were substantially understating the prevalence of drug use. In addition to asking about past month use, the NHS asks respondents if they have used cocaine in the past year and if they have ever used cocaine. Homer carefully disaggregated the user population into stocks corresponding to these categories so the model could be directly compared to the data.

Figure 7-14 shows the NHS data for the fraction of the population who responded affirmatively when asked if they had ever used cocaine. Note that the reported ever-used-cocaine population peaks in 1982 at about 12% and falls to about 10% by 1988.

The lifetime cocaine prevalence data in Figure 7-14 is the ratio of the ever-used population to the total population (those who never used plus those who ever used). The inflow to the total stock of people who have actually used cocaine is the

FIGURE 7-13 Feedback structure of the cocaine epidemic

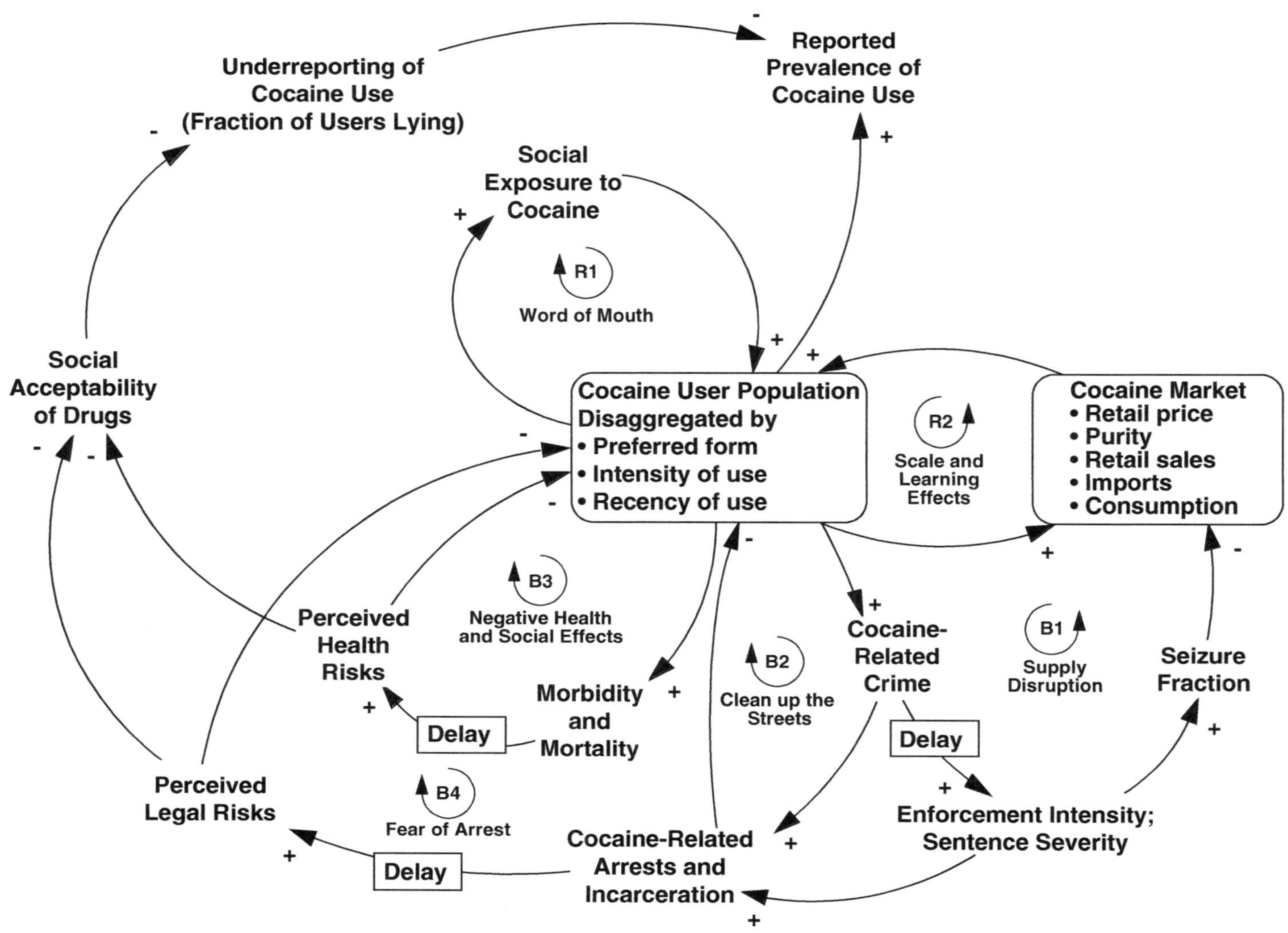

Source: Adapted from Homer (1993).

FIGURE 7-14
Survey estimates
of lifetime cocaine
prevalence

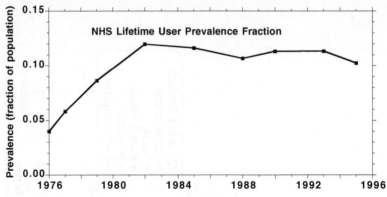

Source: National Household Survey, Homer (1993, 1997).

initiation rate. The only outflow is death. The only way the stock of people who have ever used cocaine can decline is for the death rate of current and past users to exceed the initiation rate of new users.[3] Yet the survey data reported a 3.2% drop in the number of people who have ever used cocaine from 1982 to 1988. Even if the rate at which people tried cocaine for the first time fell to zero in 1985—even if every man, woman, and child in the US who had never used cocaine just said NO!, something not even the administration believed—mortality rates of the ever-used population are too small to cause the reported decline in the number of people who have ever tried cocaine. Even with the most optimistic estimates for the decline in the initiation rate, it is physically impossible for the stock of people who have ever used cocaine to fall as quickly as the surveys suggested.[4]

Why then did the reported incidence of use fall so dramatically after 1985? There are two main reasons. First, the surveys presume that their samples are properly stratified, that is, that the representation and response rates of subpopulations (such as different geographic, ethnic, racial, and socioeconomic groups) are adjusted to match the proportion of these groups in the overall population and that any underrepresentation is constant through time. Heavy drug users, however, are much less likely to be interviewed for the survey. Though the NHS methodology attempted to adjust for this underrepresentation, they cautioned that

> Prevalence estimates for specific subgroups are sometimes based on modest to small sample sizes, which may lead to substantial sampling error . . . [T]his report does not present estimates for some segments of the US population that may contain a substantial proportion of drug users, such as transients not residing in shelters

---

[3]In principle, the lifetime prevalence fraction could fall if those in the ever-used population emigrated from the US to other countries at a rate much higher than that of those who have never used cocaine. These rates, however, are negligible. For the survey to be correct the required outmigration of drug users would greatly exceed all outmigration from the US.

[4]The problem in the survey data is worse. The NHS reported a drop in the *fraction* of the population that has ever used cocaine. The decline in relative lifetime prevalence would require the death rate of former cocaine users to greatly exceed the death rate of those who have never used cocaine. The difference in death rates, however, is very small, partly due to the low excess mortality of active users and largely because most members of the ever-used population no longer use cocaine and experience mortality rates about the same as the never-used population.

(e.g., users of soup kitchens or residents of street encampments) and those incarcerated in county jails or State and Federal prisons (SAMHSA 1994).

That is, few federal workers are willing to knock on the doors of a crack house to ask the occupants whether they use illegal drugs. Consequently, active and especially compulsive users are underrepresented in the surveys. Because these populations grew rapidly in the 1980s, the surveys systematically underestimated the growth in cocaine use.

Second, and more importantly, increasing legal risks caused a larger fraction of current and especially former users to deny they ever used cocaine. In plain language, more people lied about their past cocaine use. The changing distribution of cocaine users and declining social acceptance of cocaine led to systematic underestimation of cocaine prevalence in the survey data.

By integrating all the available data into a consistent and unified framework, the model provided more accurate estimates of drug use than were available previously. Model estimates of the ever-used population (along with the other categories of drug use) were derived to be consistent with other demographic, crime, health, price, and purity data, constrained by the stock and flow structure of the population and epidemiological and medical data on health risks. Understanding the dynamics of the stocks and flows of users helps reconcile the apparently contradictory data. Figure 7-15 compares the model's behavior for reported lifetime use against the survey data, along with the model's estimate of the actual ever-used population. The actual population of past users must have continued to grow because the number of people trying cocaine for the first time exceeded the death rate of those who had ever tried it. The availability, purity, and use of cocaine were in fact increasing throughout the late 1980s despite the billions spent on enforcement and supply reduction.

In hindsight it seems quite obvious that the stock of people who have ever used cocaine cannot decline as rapidly as the data suggested, so the survey data should immediately have been challenged. But hindsight is always crystal clear. The fact remains that the data were not challenged. Instead, the government used the survey data to take credit for winning the drug war, to justify intervention in the affairs of other nations, and to lobby for tougher penalties, greater powers for law enforcement agencies, more prisons, and more resources to defend the borders of the US against the threat of foreign drugs.

Perhaps the administration knew the data overstated the reduction in drug use and used it cynically to manipulate public opinion and the congress. Even if true, it immediately begs the question of why others in government, along with the media, policy analysts, and the public at large did not recognize the flaw in the data.

The administration, congress, and the media all focused on the data showing recent use—the NHS past month or past week data, along with the HSSS—rather than lifetime use. Recent use provides a better snapshot of current drug trends, and showed the largest decline, making the case most favorable to the administration. However, the data showing decline in recent use confounded the actual decline in use with the increase in underreporting. The two sources of decline cannot be disentangled from the recent-use data because the recent user stock can drop as people quit; likewise, past users age out of the high school senior population. It is

FIGURE 7-15
Simulated vs. actual population of lifetime cocaine users

Note that while the survey data show a drop in the ever-used population after 1982, the model estimates for the actual population of those who have ever used cocaine continue to rise, though at a diminishing rate. Increasing legal risks led to a large increase in the fraction of former users who denied their cocaine use.

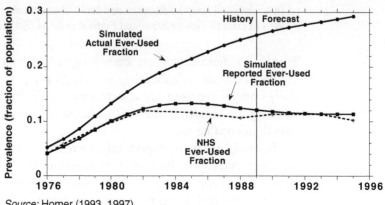

Source: Homer (1993, 1997).

only by explicitly accounting for the stock and flow structure of drug use—for the inexorable accumulation of users into the ever-used population—that the two competing sources of decline in current use data can be separated. Unfortunately, the ability to understand basic stock and flow relationships is far too rare in our society today, even among many professional policy analysts.

7.3.1   The Cocaine Epidemic after 1990

The model showed persuasively that the survey data significantly underestimated cocaine use and highlighted the failure of the supply-side strategy. As MacCoun and Reuter (1997, p. 47) put it, "The probability of a cocaine or heroin seller being incarcerated has risen sharply since about 1985 but that has led neither to increased price nor reduced availability." However, a close look at the simulation in Figure 7-15 shows that by the late 1980s the number of people who had ever used cocaine, though still rising, was growing at a diminishing rate. Therefore the initiation rate must have been falling. By the mid 1990s, the epidemic began to abate: the growth of cocaine-related medical emergencies and deaths slowed; arrests fell slightly. The ONDCP estimated net imports in 1995 at between 421 and 513 metric tons, with 98 metric tons seized, leaving net cocaine available on the streets of America at about three-quarters the 1989 level. The model, originally developed in the late 1980s, forecast these dramatic shifts in cocaine use quite well (Figure 7-16).

Note that the point-by-point fit of the model in the 1990s isn't perfect, and you should not expect it to be. Simulated arrests are too high, and the model does not track the temporary dip in cocaine related medical emergencies in 1990-91. Nevertheless, the model's ability to capture the turning point in the epidemic, from exponential growth to gradual decline, is quite remarkable, considering that the simulations shown in Figure 7-16 were based on data available only through 1989. The only exogenous inputs affecting model behavior after 1990 are the target population (those age 12 and over) and the prevalence of marijuana use (a proxy for social tolerance of drugs). Changes in data-reporting systems and definitions were not included.

FIGURE 7-16
Simulated vs.
actual cocaine
epidemic

Dashed lines,
data; solid lines,
model.

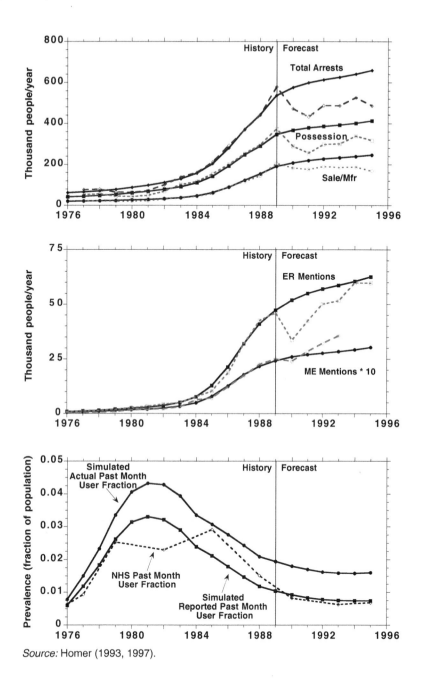

Source: Homer (1993, 1997).

Adding additional exogenous inputs could improve the fit to the data. But models should not be tuned to fit data by introducing exogenous variables whose sole function is to improve the correspondence of model output to data. Exogenous variables must be justified by significant real world evidence independent of their potential contribution to historical fit. Further, variables involved in any feedback loops judged to be potentially significant relative to the model purpose must be captured as part of the model's endogenous structure and cannot be used as exogenous inputs to improve historical fit.

While the model shows that the survey data overestimated the decline in cocaine use, model-generated estimates of the actual number of active users, while remaining significantly higher than the estimates reported in the surveys, do show a decline. The field research and model results showed the drop in cocaine use was not caused primarily by the Supply Disruption Loop B1 in Figure 7-13 or by the Clean up the Streets loop B2, as supporters of the interdiction policy claimed. Rather, the exponential growth of cocaine use was eventually halted by two negative feedbacks involving public perceptions of cocaine's health and legal risks. First, cocaine is not the benign substance it was thought to be in the 1970s. As people began to experience or hear about the Negative Health and Social Effects of the drug, they became less likely to start and more likely to stop (balancing loop B3 in Figure 7-13). Second, growing legal risks of drug use due to higher arrest rates and longer sentences decreased the willingness of people to start and increased the quit rate—the Fear of Arrest reduced usage (balancing loop B4). As the population of active users began to fall, the social exposure of nonusers also fell, weakening the reinforcing Word of Mouth loop (R1).

Unfortunately, both of these negative loops involve long delays. First, there is a lag between growth in cocaine use and the incidence of harmful health and legal effects. As the initiation rate grew exponentially, so did the stock of active casual users. The stock of compulsive users also rose exponentially, though with a substantial lag. The lag in the growth of the compulsive user population is important because compulsive users are more likely to experience severe health effects (especially as they turn to crack) and more likely to commit drug-related crimes including pushing the drug to finance their own habits. Thus the exponential growth in cocaine-related crime, arrests, medical emergencies, and deaths lags behind the growth of the casual user population, which in turn lags behind the initiation rate.

There is a further lag in the perception by the public of the true health effects of cocaine. Most people don't read the *New England Journal of Medicine* or the *Annals of Addiction* to learn about the health risks of illegal drugs. Instead, public perceptions of risk are strongly conditioned by personal experience, personal acquaintance with someone harmed by cocaine, and media reports of high-profile individuals who were arrested for, injured by, or died from cocaine use, such as the comedian Richard Pryor, who was severely burned while freebasing, or the University of Maryland basketball star Len Bias, who died of acute heart failure while doing cocaine to celebrate his selection as a top draft pick by the Boston Celtics of the National Basketball Association.

The strength of all these channels of public awareness therefore lags behind the population of active users driving the growth of the epidemic. Exponential growth in cocaine use did eventually reduce the social acceptability of the drug and thus the initiation rate. However, the stock of active users lags well behind the initiation rate. The stock of active users will rise as long as initiation exceeds the rate at which people stop using, and the stock of compulsive users increases as long as the escalation rate exceeds the rate at which compulsive users stop. The dynamics of the stock and flow structure inevitably mean that the population of drug users, especially the compulsive users responsible for most of the crime and health effects, continues to grow even after the initiation rate peaks and falls. The delay ensures that the reinforcing social exposure and word of mouth feedbacks dominate the negative risk perception loops in the early years of the epidemic, leading to a later and higher peak for incidence and prevalence.

Still, by the late 1980s, nearly every community had experienced the arrest, injury, or death of at least one of its promising young people, slowly strengthening the negative feedbacks that slow the initiation rate. Ironically, the cocaine epidemic did not abate because interdiction made the drug less available; on the contrary, the data showed growing accessibility, purity, and affordability throughout the 1980s. Instead, the very abundance of cocaine, by leading to a large increase in personal knowledge of its harmful effects, led people to turn away from the drug. No longer chic, stripped of its social aura and benign image, those who craved escape from the world turned from cocaine to other drugs. Thus, the cocaine epidemic was ultimately self-limiting.

The feedback structure outlined in Figure 7-13 is quite general and applies to any harmful drug, legal or illegal. The positive feedbacks generating growth in usage act swiftly, while the negative feedbacks that deter usage, particularly public recognition of a drug's harmful effects, are only perceived slowly. The result is the characteristic boom and bust pattern for drug use. Each new or newly popular drug generates a wave of naive enthusiasm in which users extol its benefits, only to discover as the population of users grows and more people escalate to compulsive use that the drug isn't as benign as people were led to believe.

In fact, the cocaine epidemic of the 1980s was not the first. A similar boom and bust in cocaine use occurred in the late 1800s. It began with medicinal use, as cocaine was praised by the medical community, including Freud in his famous 1884 paper "On Coca," as a cure for opium addiction, alcoholism, fatigue, depression, nervousness, timidity, impotence, and seasickness, among other complaints. Following the classic pattern, cocaine moved into more general and recreational use, becoming an ingredient in Coca-Cola and some cigarettes. As use spread, availability and purity increased; instead of injecting or drinking the preparation, powder for snorting became popular. Soon the harmful effects began to be experienced, observed, and reported in the medical and popular press. By the early 1900s, cocaine use had spread from social elites to lower social classes. Communities across the country struggled to deal with compulsive users (known as "coke fiends"), and "by 1914 the Atlanta police chief was blaming 70 percent of the crimes [in the city] on cocaine" (Grinspoon and Bakalar 1985, p. 38). In response, legal restrictions and prohibitions grew increasingly severe; in 1922 congress defined cocaine as a narcotic and banned importation of coca; by 1931 every state had restricted its sale and most made possession a crime. Cocaine use fell from its peak and remained low as people turned to other drugs, until the current epidemic began. Similar waves of drug use have been repeatedly observed for the opiates, for psychedelics, and for various stimulants and barbiturates.

While epidemics of any particular illegal drug are ultimately self-limiting (if the drug is harmful enough) people have always sought out mind-altering substances. Even as one drug falls out of favor, new epidemics begin, centered on new drugs for which there is as yet no experience of harmful effects or on old drugs for which the hard-won knowledge of harm gained by prior generations has faded from collective memory. The modest decline in cocaine use in the 1990s led to an increase in the use of other drugs, including marijuana, methamphetamine, and most troubling, a resurgence of heroin use, more than 20 years after the last wave of heroin crested. This latest heroin epidemic was stimulated by the usual self-reinforcing word of mouth and media feedbacks, including the glorification of "heroin chic" in popular culture and Calvin Klein underwear ads.[5]

7.4   SUMMARY

This chapter showed how stocks and flows generate dynamics. The process of accumulation is equivalent to integration in calculus. The amount added to a stock in any period is equal to the area swept out by the net rate of change in the stock over that period. Conversely, the slope of the trajectory of a stock at any time is its derivative, the net rate of change. Graphical methods for integration and differentiation were introduced. Given the behavior over time for the rates affecting any stock, you can deduce the behavior of the stock; given the trajectory of the stock you can deduce its net rate of change, all without use of calculus. The ability to relate stocks and flows intuitively is essential for all modelers, even those with extensive mathematics training, because most realistic models have no analytical solutions. Examples show that understanding the dynamics of stocks and flows, even without feedback, can yield insight into important problems.

---

[5]Further reading: Shreckengost developed a model for the US CIA to estimate heroin imports by integrating prevalence, crime, price, purity, and other data (Gardiner and Shreckengost 1987). Shreckengost (1991) applies the framework to cocaine. Levin, Hirsch, and Roberts (1975), in *The Persistent Poppy*, develop a system dynamics model of heroin use and abuse in a community based on a case study of the south Bronx. They use the model to explore a variety of policy options including demand-side policies, increased enforcement, and methadone maintenance. See also Levin, Hirsch, and Roberts (1978). Richardson (1983) develops a simple model to explain why aggressive police effort to seize street supplies of heroin actually increases drug-related crime. Göluke, Landeen, and Meadows (1981a, 1981b) developed a model of addictive behavior, focusing on alcoholism. Holder and Blose (1987) develop a model of community level policy responses to alcoholism. Homer et al. (1982) present a system dynamics model of (tobacco) smoking and analyze a variety of policies.

8

Closing the Loop: Dynamics of Simple Structures

A mathematical theory is not to be considered complete until you have made it so clear that you can explain it to the first man whom you meet on the street.
—David Hilbert

I hope to show...that mathematical notation can be kept close to the vocabulary of business; that each variable and constant in an equation has individual meaning to the practicing manager; that the required mathematics is within the reach of almost anyone who can successfully manage a modern corporation.
—Jay W. Forrester (*Industrial Dynamics*, 1961, p. 9)

This chapter formalizes the connection between structure and behavior by linking feedback with stock and flow structures. The focus is the simplest feedback systems, those with one stock (known as first-order systems). Linear first-order systems (defined in this chapter) can generate exponential growth and goal-seeking behavior. Nonlinearity in first-order systems causes shifts in the dominant loops, leading for example to S-shaped growth. The chapter also introduces the concept of a *phase plot*—a graph showing how the net rate of change of a stock is related to the stock itself—and shows how dynamics can be derived from the phase plot without calculus or differential equations.

8.1 FIRST-ORDER SYSTEMS

Chapter 4 discussed the basic modes of behavior generated by complex systems and the feedback structures responsible for them. The most fundamental modes are

FIGURE 8-1   Growth and goal seeking: structure and behavior

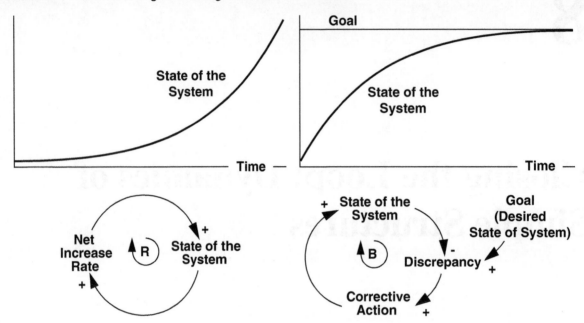

exponential growth and goal seeking. Positive feedback causes exponential growth, and negative feedback causes goal-seeking behavior (Figure 8-1).

The simplest system that can generate these behaviors is the first-order, linear feedback system. The *order* of a dynamic system or loop is the number of state variables, or stocks, it contains. A first-order system contains only one stock. *Linear* systems are systems in which the rate equations are linear combinations of the state variables and any exogenous inputs.

The term "linear" has a precise meaning in dynamics: in a linear system the rate equations (the net inflows to the stocks) are always a weighted sum of the state variables (and any exogenous variables, denoted U_j):

$$dS/dt = \text{Net Inflow} = a_1S_1 + a_2S_2 + \cdots + a_nS_n + b_1U_1 + b_2U_2 + \cdots + b_mU_m \quad (8\text{-}1)$$

where the coefficients a_i and b_j are constants. Any other form for the net inflows is nonlinear.[1]

8.2   POSITIVE FEEDBACK AND EXPONENTIAL GROWTH

The simplest feedback system is a first-order positive feedback loop. In a first-order system, there is only one state variable (stock), denoted here by S. The state of the system accumulates its net inflow rate; in turn, the net inflow depends on the

---

[1]For example, formulations for the net inflow such as $a_1 * S_1 * S_2$, $a_1 * S_1/S_2$, or $MAX(0, a_1 * S_1)$ are all nonlinear. The term "nonlinear" is often used in other senses, for example to describe the nonchronological narrative structure of novels such as Cortázar's *Hopscotch*. The term "nonlinear" in these contexts actually means "nonsequential" and has nothing to do with the technical meaning of linearity.

state of the system (for now, assume no exogenous inputs). In general, the net inflow is a possibly nonlinear function of the state of the system:

$$S = INTEGRAL(Net\ Inflow, S(0)) \tag{8-2}$$

$$Net\ Inflow = f(S). \tag{8-3}$$

If the system is linear, the net inflow must be directly proportional to the state of the system:

$$Net\ Inflow = gS \tag{8-4}$$

where the constant g has units of (1/time) and represents the fractional growth rate of the stock.[2]

Figure 8-2 shows the structure of this system as a causal diagram and also as a set of equations. As examples, consider the accumulation of interest income into a bank account or the growth of a population. The principal and prevailing interest rate determine the interest payment; population and the fractional net birth rate determine the net birth rate.[3]

What will the behavior of the system be? Section 8.2.1 uses basic calculus to solve the differential equation; the solution is the exponential function

$$S(t) = S(0)exp(gt) \tag{8-5}$$

where S(0) is the value of S at the initial time t = 0. The state of the system grows exponentially from its initial value at a constant fractional rate of g per time unit.

8.2.1   Analytic Solution for the Linear First-Order System

To solve the differential equation for the first-order linear system, dS/dt = gS, first separate variables, to obtain

$$\frac{dS}{S} = gdt \tag{8-6}$$

Now, integrate both sides

$$\int \frac{dS}{S} = \int gdt \tag{8-7}$$

to get

$$\ln(S) = gt + c \tag{8-8}$$

where c is a constant. Taking exponentials of both sides gives

---

[2]In the general case of a multistate system, the rates of change, dS/dt, are a function $f()$ of the state vector **S** and any exogenous variables **U**: dS/dt = f(**S**, **U**). In a linear system, the rates are linear combinations of the states and exogenous variables: dS/dt = **AS** + **BU** where **A** and **B** are matrices of coefficients. For good treatments of linear system theory, see, e.g., Ogata (1997) and Karnopp, Margolis, and Rosenberg (1990).

[3]Representing population growth as a first-order process assumes there is no delay between birth and the ability to reproduce, a poor assumption for mammals, but reasonable for many unicellular and other small organisms.

FIGURE 8-2   First-order, linear positive feedback system: structure and examples

General Structure

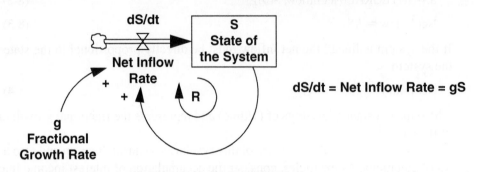

$$dS/dt = \text{Net Inflow Rate} = gS$$

Examples

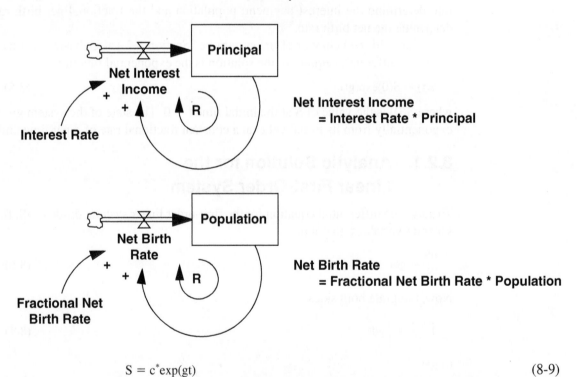

Net Interest Income
= Interest Rate * Principal

Net Birth Rate
= Fractional Net Birth Rate * Population

$$S = c^* \exp(gt) \tag{8-9}$$

where c^* is $\exp(c)$. The value of S at the initial time, when $\exp(gt) = 1$, is by definition $S(0)$, so c^* must equal $S(0)$. Substitution yields equation (8-5).

8.2.2   Graphical Solution of the Linear First-Order Positive Feedback System

You do not need calculus to solve the equation for the first-order linear system. You can also deduce its behavior graphically. Figure 8-3 shows a third representation of the structure of the system: a *phase plot*—a graph showing the net rate as a function of the state of the system. The graph shows that the net inflow rate is a straight line starting at the origin with positive slope *g*.

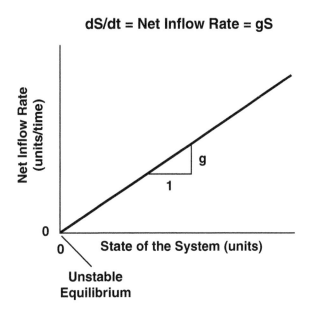

FIGURE 8-3
Phase plot for
the first-order,
linear positive
feedback system

dS/dt = Net Inflow Rate = gS

Net Inflow Rate
(units/time)

g

1

0

0   **State of the System (units)**

**Unstable
Equilibrium**

Note that if the state of the system is zero, the net inflow is also zero. Zero is an equilibrium of the system: no savings, no interest income; no people, no births. However, the equilibrium is *unstable:* add any quantity to the stock and there will now be a small, positive net inflow, increasing the state of the system a bit. The greater state of the system leads now to a slightly greater net inflow and a still larger addition to the stock. The slightest departure from the equilibrium leads to further movement away from the equilibrium, just as a ball balanced exactly at the top of a hill, if disturbed even slightly, will roll ever faster away from the balance point. The greater the state of the system, the greater the net inflow: this is precisely the meaning of the positive feedback loop coupling the stock and its net inflow. In the general case where the phase plot of a state variable can be nonlinear, the state of the system will grow whenever the net rate is an increasing function of the stock. An equilibrium is unstable whenever the slope of the net rate at the equilibrium point is positive.

Because the rate equation in the example is linear, the net increase rate grows exactly in proportion to the state of the system. Every time the state of the system doubles, so too will its absolute rate of increase. Therefore, the trajectory of the system in time shows an ever-increasing acceleration. Figure 8-4 shows the trajectory of the first-order linear positive feedback system on the phase plot and as a time series. In the figure, the growth rate g is 0.7%/time period and the initial state of the system is 1 unit. The arrows along the phase plot show that the flow of the system is away from the unstable equilibrium point. From any nonnegative starting point, the state of the system grows at an ever-accelerating rate as it moves along the line Net Inflow = gS.[4] The accelerating growth is easily seen in the time

---

[4]The system is symmetric for negative values of the state variable. If $S(0) < 0$, S will become ever more negative at exponential rates. In most systems, however, the state variables are restricted to nonnegative values (there can be no negative populations).

FIGURE 8-4   Exponential growth: structure (phase plot) and behavior (time plot)

The fractional growth rate g =0.7%/time unit. Initial state of the system = 1 unit. Points on plot show every doubling (10 time periods)

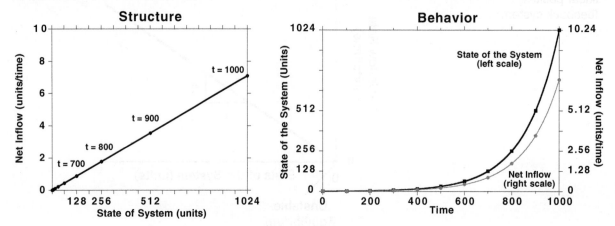

domain. The slope of the state variable at every point is exactly proportional to the quantity in the stock, and the state of the system doubles every 100 time periods (see section 8.2.3).

Note that changing the fractional growth rate changes the slope of the line Net Inflow = gS and therefore the rate of growth, but not the exponential shape of the curve.

8.2.3   The Power of Positive Feedback: Doubling Times

Before continuing, try the following challenge.

CHALLENGE   ## Paper Folding

Take an ordinary sheet of paper. Fold it in half. Fold the sheet in half again. The paper is still less than half a millimeter thick. If you were to fold it 40 more times, how thick would the paper be? If you folded it a total of 100 times, how thick would it be? Give your intuitive estimate, without using a calculator. Give your 95% upper and lower confidence bounds for your estimates (that is, a range of estimates you are 95% sure includes the right answer. Your 95% confidence bound means you believe there is only a 5% chance the correct answer falls outside the upper and lower bounds you give). Ask your friends and family to try the challenge as well, noting down their answers and confidence bands.

The Rule of 70

Positive feedback loops are the most powerful processes in the universe. Their power arises from the fact that the rate of increase grows as the state of the system grows. When the fractional net increase rate is constant, positive feedback leads to exponential growth. Exponential growth has the remarkable property that the state of the system doubles in a fixed period of time, no matter how large it is. In the example in Figure 8-4, the state of the system doubles every 100 time periods. It takes 100 time periods to grow from the initial value of 1 to 2 units and only 100 time periods to grow from 1000 to 2000 or from 1 billion to 2 billion. Any quantity that grows by positive feedback, that doubles in a fixed period of time, gets very large after just a few doublings.

You can readily determine the doubling time for any exponential growth process. To do so solve equation (8-5) for the interval of time t_d that satisfies the equation when the stock has reached twice its initial value: $2S(0) = S(0)\exp(gt_d)$. The result is

$$t_d = \ln(2)/g \tag{8-10}$$

where t_d is the doubling time.[5] The natural log of $2 = 0.6931 \ldots$ Rounding $\ln(2)$ to 0.70 and expressing the fractional growth rate in percent per time period gives the *Rule of 70:*

$$t_d = 70/(100g). \tag{8-11}$$

Thus an investment earning 7%/year doubles in value after 10 years.[6] As shown in Figure 4-2, the average growth rate of real GDP in the US over the past 100 years has been 3.4%/year, so the doubling time is roughly 20 years. The past 200 years have witnessed 10 doublings, increasing the size of the US economy by roughly a factor of one thousand ($2^{10} = 1024$).

8.2.4   Misperceptions of Exponential Growth

While the Rule of 70 is simple and easy to apply, the implications of exponential growth are difficult to grasp intuitively. Wagenaar (1978) and Wagenaar and Sagaria (1975) studied people's ability to extrapolate exponential growth processes. They found people grossly underestimated the rate of growth, tending to extrapolate linearly instead of exponentially. That is, we tend to assume a quantity increases by the same *absolute* amount per time period, while exponential growth *doubles* the quantity in a fixed period of time. When the growth rate and forecast horizon are small, linear extrapolation is a reasonable approximation to

---

[5]Dividing equation (8-5) through by S(0) yields $2 = \exp(gt_d)$. That is, the doubling time is independent of the initial size of the stock. Taking the natural log of both sides and dividing through by g gives $t_d = \ln(2)/g$.

[6]The Rule of 70 is based on the assumption that the growth process is continuous in time. In the investment example, the assumption is that interest is compounded continuously. Compounding at discrete intervals reduces the effective yield and lengthens the doubling time. In discrete time, equation (8-5) no longer holds; instead the state variable is given by $S(t) = S(0)(1+g/p)^{pt}$ where p is the compounding period (for example, $p = 12$ for monthly compounding when g is the interest rate per year). The doubling time of the discrete time process is given by $t_d = \ln(2)/(p\ln(1 + g/p))$. Since $\ln(1 + g/p) \approx g/p$ for small g/p, the Rule of 70 remains a good approximation of discrete time positive feedback processes as long as the compounding interval is relatively short compared to the doubling time. For example, a process growing at a rate of 7%/year compounded only annually doubles in 10.24 years compared to 9.90 years when compounding is continuous (using the exact value of $\ln(2)$ to calculate t_d). In the limit as $p \to \infty$, $(1 + g/p)^{(pt)} = \exp(gt)$.

exponential growth. However, as the growth rate increases or the forecast horizon lengthens, the errors become huge.

How thick did you think the sheet of paper would be after folding it 42 times? After 100 times? Most people estimate the paper will be less than a meter thick (3.3 feet) even after 100 folds. In fact, after 42 folds the paper would be 440,000 kilometers thick—more than the distance from the earth to the moon! And after 100 folds, the paper would be an incomprehensibly immense 850 *trillion* times the distance from the earth to the sun![7]

The underestimation of exponential growth is a pervasive and robust phenomenon. Wagenaar and colleagues found that the underestimation was robust to the presentation of the data in tabular vs. graphic form. Surprisingly, showing *more* data tends to *worsen* the underestimation, and training in mathematics did not help (Wagenaar and Timmers 1979).

The counterintuitive and insidious character of exponential growth can be seen by examining it over different time horizons. Figure 8-5 shows a positive feedback process growing exponentially at a constant rate of 0.7%/time period, with four different time horizons. By the Rule of 70, the doubling time $t_d = 100$ time periods. Over a time horizon of one-tenth the doubling time, growth is imperceptible. Over a time horizon of one doubling time, the growth appears to be close to linear. Over 10 doublings, the accelerating character of exponential growth is clearly visible. Over 100 doublings, it appears that nothing happens at all until about 90% of the time has passed. Many people, examining the behavior over the long time horizon, conclude that there must have been a dramatic change in the structure of the system around time 9000. In fact, the same process of accumulation powered by positive feedback is operating throughout the entire history, but only the last few doublings are noticeable.

Of course, no real quantity can grow forever. Because exponential growth doubles in a fixed time interval, positive feedback processes approach their limits rapidly and often unexpectedly. Meadows et al. (1972, p. 29) illustrate with an old French riddle:

> Suppose you own a pond on which a water lily is growing. The lily plant doubles in size each day. If the lily were allowed to grow unchecked, it would completely cover the pond in 30 days, choking off the other forms of life in the water. For a long time the lily plant seems small, and so you decide not to worry about cutting it back until it covers half the pond. On what day will that be? On the twenty-ninth day, of course. You have one day to save your pond.[8]

---

[7]Each fold doubles the thickness of the paper. A typical sheet of paper is about 0.1 mm thick. After two folds it is 0.4 mm thick; after five folds, just 3.2 mm. After 42 doublings the thickness has increased by a factor of $2^{42} \approx 4.4$ trillion. Multiplying by the initial thickness of 0.1 mm and converting to kilometers gives a thickness of 440,000 km. After 100 folds the thickness has increased by a factor of $2^{100} \approx 1.27 \times 10^{30}$. Multiplying by the initial thickness, converting to kilometers, and dividing by the mean earth-solar distance of 93 million miles = 149 million km gives a thickness of 852×10^{12} times the mean solar distance—more than 1 billion light-years. Of course, you would need a very large sheet of paper to carry the experiment through.

[8]In fact, the lily pad would be microscopic for much of the 30 days. Initially the lily covers only 9.3×10^{-8}% of the pond's area. It reaches 1% of the area only after the 23rd day.

FIGURE 8-5 Exponential growth over different time horizons

The state of the system is given by the same growth rate of 0.7%/time period in all cases (doubling time = 100 time periods).

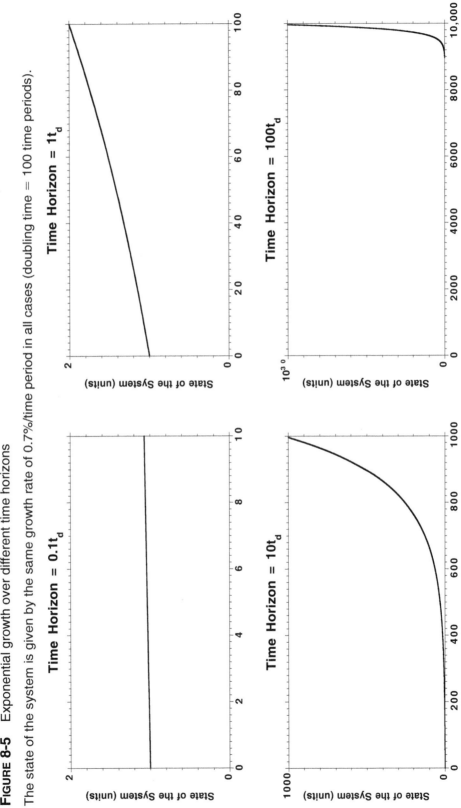

As various limits are approached, nonlinearities always weaken the positive loops and strengthen the negative feedbacks until the exponential growth halts. These nonlinear effects are illustrated by another famous story about exponential growth. As told by Meadows et al. (1972, p. 29):

> There is an old Persian legend about a clever courtier who presented a beautiful chessboard to his king and requested that the king give him in return 1 grain of rice for the first square of the board, 2 grains for the second square, 4 grains for the third, and so forth. The king readily agreed and ordered rice to be brought from his stores. The fourth square of the chessboard required 8 grains, the tenth square took 512 grains, the fifteenth required 16,384, and the twenty-first square gave the courtier more than a million grains of rice. By the fortieth square a million million rice grains had to be brought from the storerooms. The king's entire rice supply was exhausted long before he reached the sixty-fourth square.

In fact, the total quantity of rice on all 64 squares would have covered all of modern day Iran to a depth of more than 5 feet.

8.2.5   Process Point: Overcoming Overconfidence

Consider again your answers to the paper folding challenge. Not only do people underestimate the thickness of the paper, but the correct answers fall outside their 95% confidence bounds almost all the time. That is, people are grossly overconfident in their judgments.

Overconfidence is one of the most robust judgmental biases documented in the psychological literature. In a careful review, Scott Plous (1993) writes, "No problem in judgment and decision making is more prevalent and more potentially catastrophic than overconfidence."

Overconfidence means the confidence bounds people provide around their estimate of an unknown quantity are too narrow, causing an unexpectedly high rate of incorrect predictions. Lichtenstein and Fischoff (1977) found that people were 65% to 70% confident of being right in answering a variety of questions when in fact they answered correctly at only about the chance rate of 50%. Such results have been replicated in a wide range of tasks and with experts as well as novices. Lichtenstein, Fischoff, and Phillips (1982) reviewed studies totaling nearly 15,000 judgments and found that people's 98% confidence bounds contained the correct response only 68% of the time—an error rate 16 times greater than expected.

Extensive study of the relevant issue can actually worsen overconfidence. Oskamp (1965) showed that the more information people received about an issue, the more confident they became—while accuracy did not improve. Financial incentives do not reduce overconfidence: In some studies subjects were given the option of betting on their answers at the odds they estimated for being correct. They consistently lost money.

Situations in which people's confidence bounds are approximately correct are rare. Weather forecasters and professional card players are among the few groups whose judgments have been found to be well calibrated. These are narrowly bounded contexts where the relevant factors are well known. Thousands of repetitions provide feedback enabling the meteorologist and gambler to learn from experience. These conditions do not hold for most dynamically complex settings, including judgments about the likely behavior of feedback systems: the causal structure, relevant variables, and parameters are highly uncertain and largely unknown (see chapter 1). In most social and business situations the time delays are so long there is little or no chance to learn from experience; by the time feedback is available it will be too late to take effective action. Many investors and money managers during the great bull markets of the 1920s and 1980s–90s never experienced a market crash and underestimated the likelihood of declining share prices. And for issues such as global climate change the world must adopt policies regarding emissions of greenhouse gases decades before the full impact of human activity on global climate will be known. Overconfidence means you will probably buy too little insurance and are likely to wake up one day to find you have insufficient coverage. Before the Challenger explosion NASA estimated the risk of catastrophic launch failure at 1 in 100,000.[9]

As an illustration that experts are far from immune to overconfidence, consider the debate over global warming. The economist William Nordhaus (1994) conducted a survey of distinguished experts on global climate change to assess their views on the likely economic effects of global warming. Nordhaus asked the panel to estimate the loss of gross world product (GWP) caused by various amounts of warming. The results showed a huge gulf between the estimates of the scientists compared to the economists. Scientists estimated the probability of a "high-consequence event" (a catastrophic change in climate cutting GWP by 25% or more) as 20 to 30 times more likely than the economists did. Estimates of the most likely reduction in GWP were similarly bimodal, with scientists generally estimating large impacts and economists generally estimating small or even positive impacts of warming on the global economy. No one knows which group is correct. What is striking, however, is the small range of uncertainty each expert allowed. Each provided 90% confidence bands around their best estimates, yet in many cases these ranges were so small they excluded the majority of the other experts' views. Economists, who tended to predict small effects, tended to have the narrowest confidence bands. One economist wrote, "It is impossible to contemplate what society will be like a century from now as technology changes" yet estimated that a 3°C rise in global mean temperature by 2090 would produce a change in GWP ranging from −2% to +1%, one of the smallest ranges offered by any respondent.

Overcoming overconfidence requires greater humility about the limits of our expertise. Several techniques can help. List all the reasons your opinion could be wrong. Try to identify the implicit assumptions of your mental model and consider how the outcome might change if different assumptions were used. Because identifying the hidden biases in our own mental models is difficult, it is especially valuable to solicit the judgments and opinions of a diverse group of people, especially those with opposite views. Your critics will usually be far more effective in helping you calibrate and improve your judgment than your friends—seek out and welcome their views. You should be especially suspect of statements that something is absolutely certain, inevitable, without doubt, or a one in a million chance, especially if the situation involves human behavior or if people's judgments require

---

[9]Of course, NASA's estimate could have been correct and the Challenger disaster, just extraordinarily bad luck. While logically possible, careful studies of the disaster belie that view.

mental simulation of dynamically complex systems. When assessing the confidence intervals provided by formal models or statistical analysis of data, remember that the confidence bounds provided by statistical models measure only the uncertainty due to sampling error, and not that due to specification error (errors in the model boundary and in the maintained hypotheses of the statistical method). These latter sources of error are typically much larger than uncertainty due to sampling error. When formal models are available, conduct extensive sensitivity tests, not only of the response to parametric uncertainty but also to uncertainty about the model boundary, feedback structure, and other structural assumptions.

8.3   NEGATIVE FEEDBACK AND EXPONENTIAL DECAY

First-order linear positive feedback systems generate exponential growth. First-order negative feedback systems generate goal-seeking behavior. When the system is linear, the behavior is pure exponential decay.

The feedback structure responsible for exponential decay is shown in Figure 8-6. As examples, consider the death rate of a population or the depreciation of an asset. In both cases, the net outflow is proportional to the size of the stock. The equation for the net rate of change of the stock is

$$\text{Net Inflow} = -\text{Net Outflow} = -dS \qquad (8\text{-}12)$$

where d is the fractional decay rate (its units are 1/time). The reciprocal of the fractional decay rate is the average lifetime of units in the stock (see chapter 11 on delays for a proof).

To deduce the behavior of the linear, first-order negative feedback system note that equation (8-12) is the same as equation (8-4) except that the negative of the fractional decay rate replaces the fractional net increase rate. The solution is therefore given by the same exponential function, with $-d$ replacing g:

$$S(t) = S(0)\exp(-dt) \qquad (8\text{-}13)$$

Figure 8-7 shows the phase plot for the first-order linear negative loop system. The net rate of change of the stock is now a straight line with negative slope $-d$. As before, the point $S = 0$ is an equilibrium: where there are no people, there can be no deaths; when the value of an asset has declined to zero, no further depreciation can be taken. Unlike the positive feedback case, the equilibrium is stable. Increasing the state of the system increases the decay rate, moving the system back toward zero. A system with a stable equilibrium is like an orange resting at the bottom of a bowl. If you push the orange up the side of the bowl and release it, it rolls back down until it comes to rest again at the bottom. Deviations from the equilibrium are self-correcting.

Figure 8-8 shows the dynamics of the system on both the phase plot and in the time domain. The fractional decay rate in the example is 5%/time period, and the initial state of the system is 100 units. Initially, the decay rate is -5 units/time period. The decay rate is directly proportional to the state of the system, so as the state of the system declines, so too does the decay rate. The flow of the system, denoted by arrows in the phase plot, is always toward the stable equilibrium. The dots on the phase plot show the location of the system every 10 time units. Note how

FIGURE 8-6
First-order linear negative feedback: structure and examples

General Structure

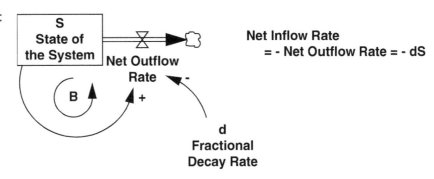

Net Inflow Rate
= - Net Outflow Rate = - dS

Examples

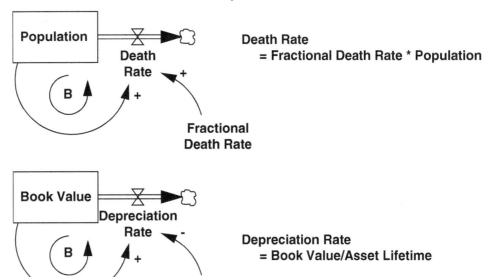

Death Rate
= Fractional Death Rate * Population

Depreciation Rate
= Book Value/Asset Lifetime

FIGURE 8-7
Phase plot for exponential decay via linear negative feedback

Net Inflow Rate = - Net Outflow Rate = - dS

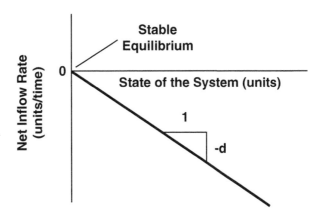

FIGURE 8-8   Exponential decay: structure (phase plot) and behavior (time plot)

The fractional decay rate d = 5%/time unit. Initial state of the system = 100 units.

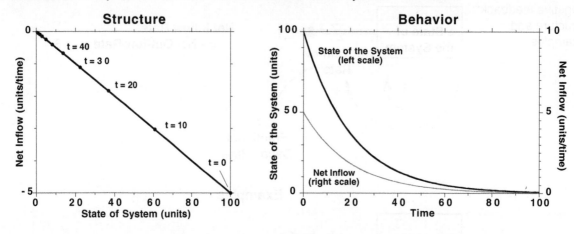

the adjustment is rapid at first and falls over time. The state of the system falls at a diminishing rate as it approaches zero.

The exponential decay structure is a special case of the first-order linear negative feedback system. As discussed in chapter 4, all negative feedback loops have goals. In the case of exponential decay, such as the death rate and depreciation examples, the goal is implicit and equal to zero. In general, however, the goals of negative loops are not zero and should be made explicit. Figure 8-9 shows the general structure for the first-order linear negative feedback system with an explicit goal. Examples include the process by which a firm adjusts its inventory or workforce to the desired level. Possible delays in changing production or hiring new workers are ignored. Including such delays would add additional stocks to the model.

In the general case, the corrective action determining the net inflow to the state of the system is a possibly nonlinear function of the state of the system, S, and the desired state of the system, S^*:

$$\text{Net Inflow} = f(S, S^*). \tag{8-14}$$

The simplest formulation, however, is for the corrective action to be a constant fraction per time period of the discrepancy between the desired and actual state of the system:

$$\text{Net Inflow} = \text{Discrepancy}/AT = (S^* - S)/AT \tag{8-15}$$

where the parameter AT is known as the *adjustment time* or *time constant* for the loop. Note the units of equation (8-15): the net inflow has dimensions of units/time period. The discrepancy between the desired and actual state of the system has dimensions of units. For example, if the desired inventory of a firm is 100 units and current inventory is only 60 units, the discrepancy is 40 units. The adjustment time represents how quickly the firm tries to correct the shortfall: if the firm seeks to correct the shortfall quickly, the adjustment time would be small. For example, the firm may set the adjustment time to AT = 1 week, meaning that they would correct

FIGURE 8-9   First-order linear negative feedback system with explicit goals

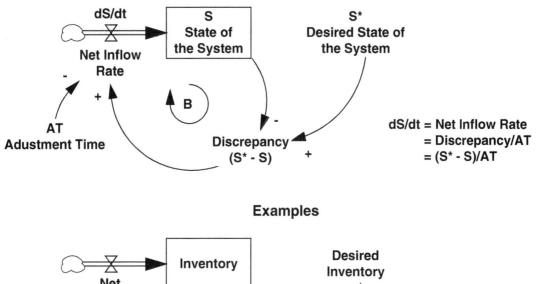

General Structure

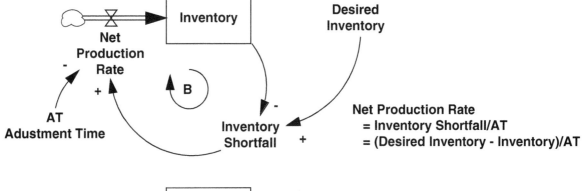

Examples

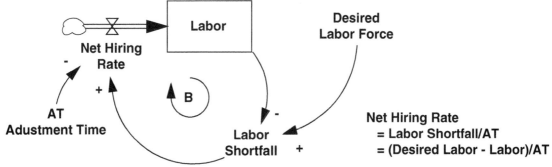

the inventory at an initial rate of 40 units/week. Being more cautious and setting AT = 2 weeks would entail an initial net inflow of 20 units/week, and an even more aggressive firm might set AT = 0.5 weeks, leading to an initial net inflow of inventory of 80 units/week. Of course, these corrective actions cause the inventory shortfall to diminish, reducing the net inflow over time until the discrepancy is eliminated. The discrepancy can be negative, as when there is excess inventory; in this case the net inflow is negative and the state of the system falls.

The reciprocal of the adjustment time has units of 1/time and is equivalent to the fractional adjustment rate, corresponding to the fractional decay rate in the exponential decay case. The phase plot for the system (Figure 8-10) shows that the net inflow rate to the state of the system is a straight line with slope $(-1/AT)$ and equals 0 when $S = S^*$. The behavior of the negative loop with an explicit goal is also exponential decay, but instead of decaying to zero, the state of the system reaches equilibrium when $S = S^*$.

If the initial state of the system is less than the desired state, the net inflow is positive and the state of the system increases, at a diminishing rate, until $S = S^*$. If the state of the system is initially greater than the goal, the net inflow is negative and the state of the system falls, at a diminishing rate, until it equals the goal. The flow of the system is always toward the stable equilibrium point at $S = S^*$ (Figure 8-11).

FIGURE 8-10
Phase plot for first-order linear negative feedback system with explicit goal

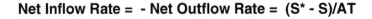
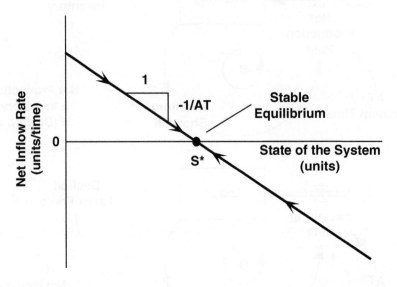

FIGURE 8-11
Exponential approach to a goal

The goal is 100 units. The upper curve begins with $S(0) = 200$; the lower curve begins with $S(0) = 0$. The adjustment time in both cases is 20 time units.

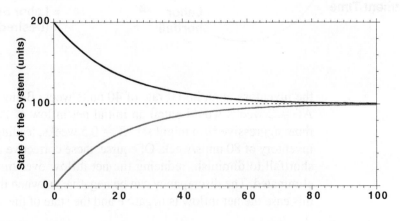

8.3.1   Time Constants and Half-Lives

Just as exponential growth doubles the state of the system in a fixed period of time, exponential decay cuts the quantity remaining by half in a fixed period of time. The half-life of an exponential decay process is calculated in the same fashion as the doubling time. The solution to equation (8-15) is

$$S(t) = S^* - (S^* - S(0))\exp(-t/AT) \tag{8-16}$$

In equation (8-16) $S^* - S(0)$ is the initial gap between the desired and actual states of the system. The term $\exp(-t/AT)$ decays from 1 to 0 as time increases; it is the fraction of the initial gap between desired and actual states remaining at any time t. The product $(S^* - S(0))\exp(-t/AT)$ is therefore the current gap remaining between the desired and actual states. When the term $\exp(-t/AT)$ has decayed to zero the state of the system equals the goal (Figure 8-12).

The half-life is given by the value of time, t_h, which satisfies

$$0.5 = \exp(-t_h/AT) = \exp(-dt) \tag{8-17}$$

where the fractional decay rate $d = 1/AT$. Solving for t_h yields

$$t_h = AT\ln(2) = \ln(2)/d \approx 0.70AT = 70/(100d) \tag{8-18}$$

The half-life is given by the same Rule of 70 characterizing exponential growth. Equivalently, the half-life is given by 70% of the adjustment time.[10]

Each time period equal to AT, the gap remaining falls to $\exp(-AT/AT) = 37\%$ of its initial value, and $1 - \exp(-AT/AT) = 63\%$ of the gap is corrected. Why isn't the entire gap corrected after one time constant has passed? From equation (8-15) the initial rate of change of the state of the system is $(S^* - S(0))/AT$, that is, the initial gap divided by the adjustment time. If the initial rate of adjustment remained constant, the entire gap would be eliminated after AT time units (note that the tangent to the state of the system at time 0 just eliminates the gap after one adjustment time; see Figure 8-12). However, the net rate of change of the state of the system does not remain constant. As the state of the system approaches the goal, the gap remaining falls, and so too does the corrective action. The negative feedback gradually reduces the adjustment rate as the goal is approached.

The table at the bottom of Figure 8-12 shows the fraction of the gap remaining for different multiples of the adjustment time. After one adjustment time, 63% of the initial gap has been corrected. After two adjustment times, the state of the system has moved 86% of the way to the goal. After three adjustment times, the adjustment is 95% complete. Technically, the gap is never fully corrected; there is always some small fraction of the gap remaining at any finite time. However, for all practical purposes adjustment is complete after three to four adjustment times have passed.[11]

---

[10]Taking logs of both sides gives $\ln(0.5) = -t_h/AT$ or $t_h = -\ln(0.5) * AT = \ln(2) * AT$.

[11]After four adjustment times, the gap remaining is just 2%, a quantity often smaller than the accuracy with which the state of the system can be measured. Control engineers speak of a system's *settling time,* defined as the time required for a system, after a shock, to settle within a small percentage of its equilibrium value.

FIGURE 8-12   Relationship between time constant and the fraction of the gap remaining

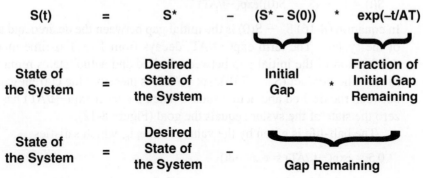

Rate equation for first order linear negative loop system:

Net Inflow Rate = – Net Outflow Rate = (S* – S)/AT

Analytic Solution:

$$S(t) \quad = \quad S^* \quad - \quad (S^* - S(0)) \quad * \quad \exp(-t/AT)$$

| State of the System | = | Desired State of the System | – | Initial Gap | * | Fraction of Initial Gap Remaining |

| State of the System | = | Desired State of the System | – | Gap Remaining |

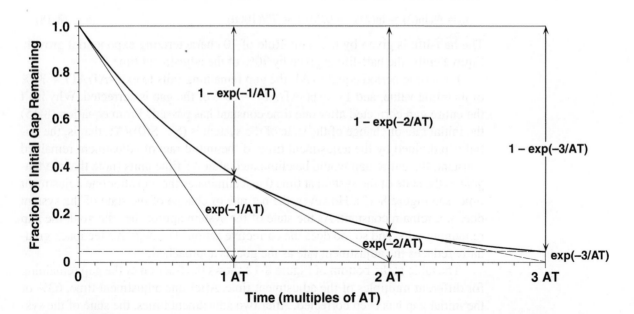

Time	Fraction of Initial Gap Remaining			Fraction of Initial Gap Corrected		
0	exp(-0)	=	1.00	1 - exp(-0)	=	0.00
AT	exp(-1)	=	0.37	1 - exp(-1)	=	0.63
2AT	exp(-2)	=	0.14	1 - exp(-2)	=	0.87
3AT	exp(-3)	=	0.05	1 - exp(-3)	=	0.95
4AT	exp(-4)	=	0.02	1 - exp(-4)	=	0.98
5AT	exp(-5)	=	0.007	1 - exp(-5)	=	0.993

CHALLENGE

Goal-seeking behavior

Consider the labor force structure in Figure 8-9. Assume the net hiring rate for a firm is proportional to the gap between the desired and actual workforce. Without using a computer or calculator, sketch the behavior of the workforce and net hiring rate for the following situations.

1.   The desired workforce increases from 1000 to 2000 at week 4, then steps down to 1500 at week 12 (Figure 8-13). Assume the workforce adjustment time AT = 4 weeks and the actual workforce initially equals the desired workforce.

2.   Repeat step 1 for the case where the labor force adjustment time AT = 2 weeks.

3.   Sketch the workforce and net hiring rate for the case where the desired workforce increases linearly beginning in week 4 (Figure 8-14). Assume the

FIGURE 8-13
Sketch the trajectory for the workforce and net hiring rate.

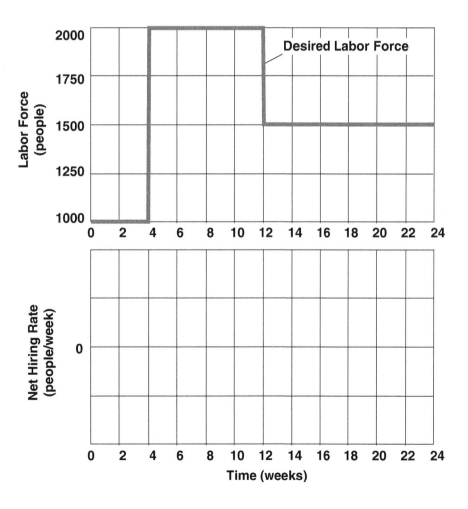

labor force adjustment time AT = 4 weeks. Does the workforce eventually equal the desired workforce? Why or why not?

FIGURE 8-14
Sketch the trajectory for the workforce and net hiring rate when the desired workforce increases linearly.

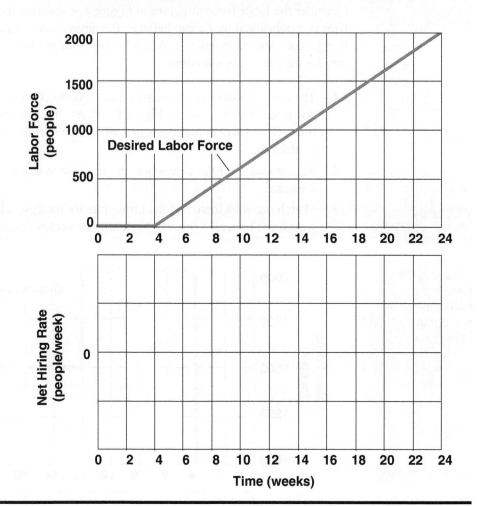

8.4   MULTIPLE-LOOP SYSTEMS

The discussion up to now treated positive and negative feedback in isolation. What is the behavior of a first-order system when the net rate of change is affected by both types of loop? Consider the example of a population (Figure 8-2). Disaggregate the net birth rate into a birth rate BR and a death rate DR. The net rate of change for the system is then

$$\text{Population} = \text{INTEGRAL}(\text{Net Birth Rate}, \text{Population}(0)) \tag{8-19}$$

$$\text{Net Birth Rate} = \text{BR} - \text{DR} \tag{8-20}$$

Consider the linear case where the fractional birth rate is a constant, denoted b, and the fractional death rate is also constant, denoted d. The net birth rate is then

$$\text{Net Birth Rate} = b\text{P} - d\text{P} = (b - d)\text{P} \tag{8-21}$$

Figure 8-15 shows the phase plot for the system. Only three behaviors are possible. If the environment contains abundant resources, births will exceed deaths (b > d), and the population grows exponentially without limit. Alternatively, births and deaths might exactly offset each other (b = d), and population is in equilibrium. Finally, the environment might be so harsh that deaths exceed births (b < d),

FIGURE 8-15
A linear first-order system can generate only growth, equilibrium, or decay.

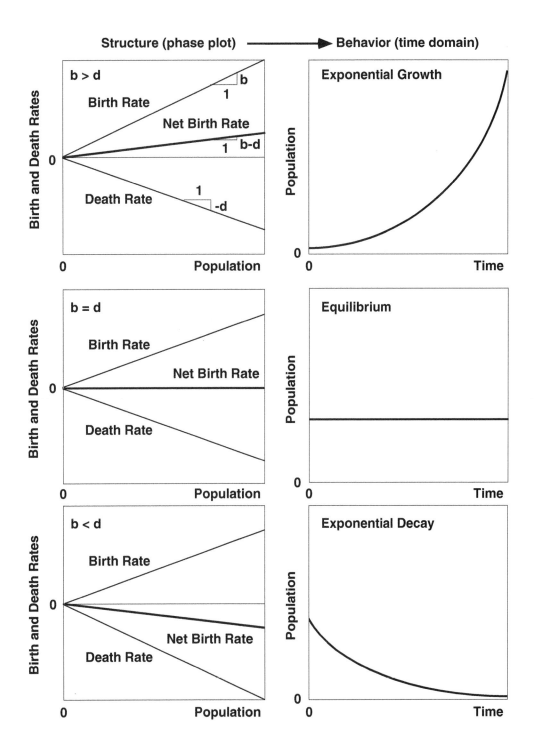

and population declines exponentially to zero. Because the system is linear, the fractional net birth rate is a constant, independent of the size of the population, fixed for all time once the values of b and d are chosen. The behavior of the system is the sum, or superposition, of the behaviors generated by the individual loops. Because the system is linear (b and d are constants), the dominance of the two loops can never change. The population will grow without bound, remain constant, or decay to extinction.

The superposition property is true of linear systems of any order and complexity. As long as all the rate equations in a system are linear, the relative importance of the different feedback loops can never change—there can be no shifts in loop dominance. Superposition means linear systems can be analyzed by reduction to their components. As a result, linear systems, no matter how complex, can be solved analytically, a distinct advantage in understanding their dynamics.

However, realistic systems are far from linear. The behavior of the linear population growth system shows why. Because the dominance of the feedback loops can never change, the population can only grow forever, remain constant, or go extinct. Real populations introduced into a new habitat with abundant resources grow at first, then stabilize or fluctuate. The relative strength of the positive and negative loops must therefore shift as a population grows relative to the carrying capacity of the environment. In real systems, there must be shifts in feedback loop dominance, and therefore there must be important nonlinearities in all real systems.

Unfortunately, many modelers have restricted their attention to models that can be expressed as linear systems so that they can apply the powerful tools of linear systems theory, while making the heroic assumption that the linear approximation is reasonable. In fairness, the reliance on linear theory and the avoidance of nonlinear systems was justifiable prior to the development of computer simulation because analytical solutions to nonlinear dynamic systems cannot in general be found. Early theorists of dynamic systems made the assumption of linearity because it was the only way to make progress. Even after the advent of computer simulation, however, too many modelers and mathematicians continued to stress linear theory and build linear models. The tendency to treat every system as a linear nail because the hammer of linear theory is so powerful has hampered the development of realistic and robust models of complexity.

Of course, the triumph of linear methods has never been complete. Even prior to the computer era several important nonlinear models were developed, most notably Verhulst's famous 1844 logistic population growth model (see section 9.1) and the equally famous Lotka-Volterra predator–prey model (Lotka 1956). And the qualitative theory of dynamic systems developed by Poincaré and others to analyze the three-body problem in celestial mechanics is fundamentally nonlinear (see Diacu and Holmes 1996 for a nontechnical treatment of the history and theory). In the past few decades there has been an explosion of interest in, theories of, and data supporting the importance of nonlinear behavior in all branches of dynamics (the rise of so-called chaos or complexity theory). Still, Yoshisuke Ueda, who discovered chaos in a nonlinear oscillator as a graduate student in the late 1950s, was unable to get his work published for over a decade because his advisors, steeped in linear theory, asserted that his measurements and analysis must be wrong because they "knew" that systems could not generate the strange nonlinear behavior (chaos) that today we recognize as ubiquitous in physical, biological, and other systems (see Ueda 1992).

Linear analysis remains an important tool. Often a system is close to linear in a certain neighborhood and can be usefully analyzed by *linearization,* that is, by approximating the nonlinear rate equations at a particular operating point (set of state variable values) with the best linear approximation. And a great deal of important intuition about dynamics comes from understanding simple, linear systems, such as the first-order linear systems responsible for exponential growth and decay. Still, understanding the dynamics of real systems requires nonlinear models.

8.5   NONLINEAR FIRST-ORDER SYSTEMS: S-SHAPED GROWTH

No real quantity can grow forever. Every system initially exhibiting exponential growth will eventually approach the carrying capacity of its environment, whether that is the food supply for a population of moose, the number of people suscepti-ble to infection by a virus, or the potential market for a new product. As the system approaches its limits to growth, it goes through a nonlinear transition from a regime where positive feedback dominates to a regime where negative feedback dominates. The result is often a smooth transition from exponential growth to equi-librium, that is, S-shaped growth (see chapter 4).

In real systems, the fractional birth and death rates cannot be constant but must change as the population approaches its carrying capacity. Hence the equation for the net birth rate becomes

$$\text{Net Birth Rate} = \text{BR} - \text{DR} = b(\text{P/C})\text{P} - d(\text{P/C})\text{P} \qquad (8\text{-}22)$$

where the fractional birth and death rates b and d are now functions of the ratio of the population P to the carrying capacity C. For now, assume the carrying capacity is fixed—neither consumed nor augmented by the activity of the population. Fig-ure 8-16 shows the causal diagram for the system.

FIGURE 8-16
Causal diagram for population growth in a fixed environment

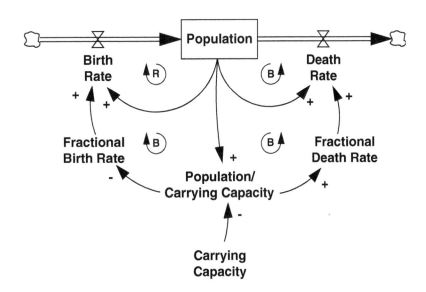

CHALLENGE

Nonlinear Birth and Death Rates

Before continuing, sketch a graph showing the likely shape of the fractional birth and death rates for a population as it approaches its carrying capacity (Figure 8-17). The carrying capacity is defined as the population that can just be supported by the environment. Be sure to consider extreme conditions (that is, what will the fractional birth and death rates be for very low or very large populations?). From your estimates, draw the fractional net birth rate (the difference between the fractional birth and death rates).

FIGURE 8-17
What is the relationship between population density and the fractional growth rate?

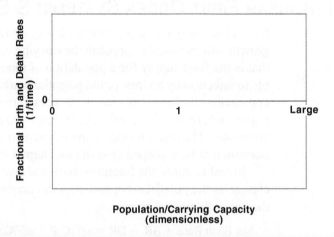

When population density (the ratio P/C) is small, both fractional birth rate and life expectancy should be at their biological maxima. As population grows, resources per capita decline. Fractional birth rate and life expectancy must fall. Do they decline immediately? In some cases, even small reductions in resources per capita could cause a decline in fertility and life expectancy. For other resources, such as food, individuals cannot consume more than a certain amount, so fractional birth and death rates should remain constant as long as resources per capita exceed the maximum each individual can consume. Reducing available food from 10 times more than needed to 5 times more than needed has no impact since each individual still gets all they can consume.[12] In this case the fractional birth and death rates remain constant—up to a point—as P/C increases. Once resources per capita fall below a certain level, the fractional birth rate falls and the fractional death rate increases. By definition, the carrying capacity is the population that can just be supported by the resources available, so the fractional birth rate must equal the

---

[12]The assumption that excess food has no impact on fertility or mortality holds only if the organisms in question eat only what they need and do not gorge themselves when a surplus is available. For the human population, in contrast, an abundant food supply and diet rich in animal protein and fat tends to lead to obesity and significantly higher morbidity and mortality. In such a case, the effect of food per capita on the fractional death rate would actually rise when food per capita exceeds a certain level.

fractional death rate when P/C = 1. If the population were to rise above the carrying capacity, the birth fraction would continue to fall and the death fraction would continue to rise. As P/C continues to increase, the birth fraction must fall to zero and the death fraction must rise to a very large value. Therefore, as shown in Figure 8-18, the fractional net birth rate will be positive for P < C, equal zero when P = C, and fall below zero at an increasing rate when population exceeds the carrying capacity of the environment. While the numerical values for these relationships would differ for different populations, their qualitative shape is not in doubt.

Next construct the phase plot for the system using these nonlinear fertility and life expectancy relationships. The birth and death rates are now curves given by the product of the population and fractional birth and death rates (Figure 8-19). First, note that the point P = 0 is an equilibrium, as in the linear system. Since the fractional birth rate remains nearly constant when population is small relative to the carrying capacity, the birth rate (in individuals/time period) is nearly linear for P ≪ C. As population density rises and the fractional birth rate falls, the birth rate, while still growing, rises with a shallower and shallower slope. At some point, the decline in the fractional birth rate reduces total births more than the increase in sheer numbers increases them, and the birth rate reaches a maximum. Since the fractional birth rate falls to zero for high population densities, so too the total birth rate must approach zero. Likewise, the death rate rises nearly linearly for P ≪ C, but as greater population density boosts the fractional death rate, the total death rate increases at an increasing rate.

Turning to the dynamics, imagine the initial population is small relative to the carrying capacity. The net birth rate rises nearly linearly for P ≪ C. The behavior of the system in this regime will be nearly pure exponential growth. As population density increases, the net birth rate continues to rise, but at a shallower and shallower slope. The population continues to grow at an increasing rate, but the fractional growth rate is steadily diminishing. At some point, the net birth rate reaches a maximum. This point comes at a lower population density than the peak in the birth rate since deaths are increasing at an increasing rate. The peak of the net birth rate curve on the phase plot corresponds to the inflection point in the trajectory of

FIGURE 8-18

Nonlinear relationship between population density and the fractional growth rate

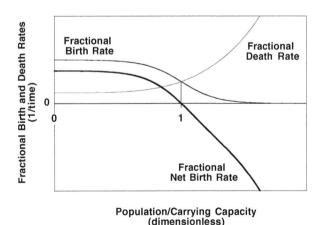

FIGURE 8-19
Phase plot for
nonlinear
population system

Arrows show di-
rection of flow.
Positive feedback
dominates the sys-
tem in the region
where the net birth
rate has positive
slope; negative
feedback is domi-
nant where the net
birth rate has neg-
ative slope. The
maximum net birth
rate occurs at the
point $(P/C)_{inf}$, the
inflection point in
the trajectory of
population.

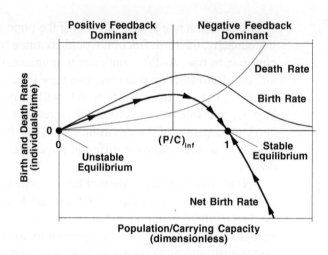

population in the time domain (the point at which the population is rising at its maximum rate). Beyond the inflection point, the increase in population density reduces the net birth rate more than the increase in total population size increases it. The net birth rate, while still positive, drops, falling to zero just when the population equals the carrying capacity. If the population exceeded the carrying capacity, resources per capita would be so scarce that deaths would exceed births, and the population would fall back toward the carrying capacity. The equilibrium at $P = C$ is therefore stable.

Figure 8-20 shows the behavior of the system over time for two cases: (1) when the initial population is much smaller than the carrying capacity and (2) when the initial population is much larger than the carrying capacity. When $P(0) \ll C$, the net birth rate is increasing in the population. As long as the slope of the net birth rate curve in the phase plot is positive, the system is dominated by the positive feedback loop and population grows exponentially. Unlike the linear system, however, the slope of the net birth rate curve is not constant, so the growth is not a pure exponential. Instead, the fractional growth rate falls as population grows. Population growth reaches its maximum when the population reaches the value denoted $(P/C)_{inf}$, the inflection point in the trajectory of the population. At that point the slope of the net birth rate curve is zero; the positive and negative loops exactly offset one another. As population continues to grow, the slope of the net birth rate curve in the phase plot becomes negative; for $P/C > (P/C)_{inf}$, the system is dominated by negative feedback. Because the net birth rate has a negative slope in this region, the equilibrium point at $P = C$ is stable. A population less than the carrying capacity will grow at a diminishing rate until it reaches the carrying capacity; a population larger than the carrying capacity will fall until it reaches the carrying capacity from above.

8.5.1   Formal Definition of Loop Dominance

The phase plot shows the origin of the terms positive and negative feedback. Positive feedback dominates whenever the rate of change of the state variable is

FIGURE 8-20

Nonlinear population growth: time domain

Top: P(0) ≪ C; Population follows an S-shaped trajectory, with inflection point at (P/C)$_{inf}$.

Bottom: P(0) ≫ C, the population rapidly decays back to the stable equilibrium at P = C.

The time axis in both simulations is the same; vertical scales differ.

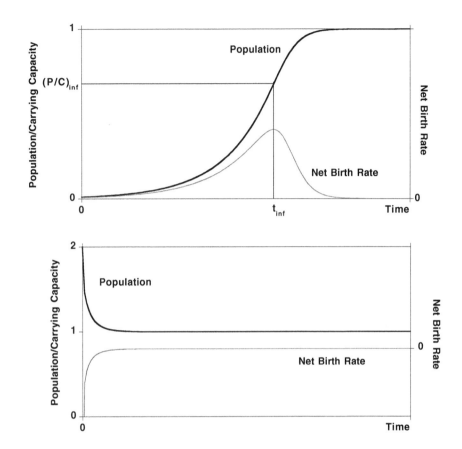

increasing in the state variable, that is, as long as the slope of the net rate of change as a function of the state variable is positive. Negative feedback dominates whenever the net rate of change is decreasing in the state variable, that is, as long as the slope of the net rate is negative.

This observation leads to a formal definition of loop dominance for first-order systems (Richardson 1986b, 1995):

$$\frac{\partial \dot{S}}{\partial S} \begin{cases} > 0 \Rightarrow \text{Positive feedback dominant} \\ = 0 \Rightarrow \text{No net feedback from state to rate} \\ < 0 \Rightarrow \text{Negative feedback dominant} \end{cases} \tag{8-23}$$

where

$$\dot{S} = \frac{dS}{dt}$$

Determining whether a system is dominated by positive or negative feedback is more difficult in higher-order systems because a loop with time delays can have a weak short-run but large long-run effect. Kampmann (1996) provides some methods to determine the dominant loops in multiloop, high-order systems; see also N. Forrester (1982) and Mojtahedzadeh (1997).

8.5.2   First-Order Systems Cannot Oscillate

As a final observation on the general nonlinear first-order system, consider whether a first-order system can oscillate. Section 8.4 demonstrated that the linear first-order system can generate only exponential growth, decay, or equilibrium. Nonlinear first-order systems generate more complex dynamics, but can never oscillate, no matter the form of the nonlinearity. To see why, consider the phase plot for the first-order system in Figure 8-19. To oscillate, the state variable must go through periods of increase followed by periods of decrease. Therefore, the net rate of change in the phase plot must cross from positive to negative values, at least in one place. However, any point where the net rate of change is zero is an equilibrium of the state variable. Since first-order systems have only one state variable, every such point is an equilibrium for the system as well. Every equilibrium point is either stable (the slope of the net rate curve in the neighborhood of the equilibrium is negative) or unstable (positive slope in the neighborhood of the equilibrium point).[13] If a first-order system is disturbed from an unstable equilibrium, it will diverge from it, either without bound (not oscillating) or until it approaches a stable equilibrium point where all change ceases. Therefore to oscillate, a system must be at least second order, meaning there must be a feedback loop with at least two stocks in it.[14]

8.6   SUMMARY

This chapter explored the dynamics of simple systems, specifically, first-order linear systems—systems with only one stock (state variable) and in which the rates of flow are linear functions of the system state. These simple systems are the building blocks out of which all models are built and from which more complex dynamics emerge. First-order linear positive feedback systems produce pure exponential growth. Exponential growth has the remarkable property that the state of the system doubles in a fixed period of time, no matter how large it is. The doubling time characterizes the strength of the positive loop. Similarly, first-order linear negative feedback systems generate exponential decay to a goal. The decay rate is characterized by the half-life, the time required for the gap between the state of the system and the goal to be cut in half. The chapter also introduced the phase

---

[13]If the net rate of change is zero over a finite interval in state space, these points have neutral stability; a disturbance (within that range) causes neither a restorative nor divergent change in the net rate, just as a ball placed anywhere on a flat surface will remain at that point.

[14]Technically, first-order systems cannot oscillate provided time is treated continuously. First-order systems in discrete time can oscillate. For example, the logistic map, the first-order nonlinear discrete time map $x(t + 1) = kx(t)(1 - x(t))$, where $0 \leq k \leq 4$ and $0 < x(0) < 1$, not only oscillates for certain values of k, but generates period doubling and chaos as well. However, the statement that oscillation requires a feedback loop with at least two stocks is still valid: in discrete time models, the time step between iterations constitutes an irreducible time delay in every feedback loop. Every time lag contains a stock which accumulates the inflow to the delay less its outflow. Every discrete dynamic system can be converted into an equivalent continuous time system by introducing a lag equal to the time step at every state variable, increasing the order of the system (see Low 1980 for an example).

plot, a useful tool to analyze the dynamics of systems graphically, without the use of calculus.

Analysis of the phase plots for first-order systems shows that in systems with more than one feedback loop, the dynamics depend on which loop is dominant. In linear systems, the dominance of the different loops can never change. Thus linear first-order systems can only exhibit three behaviors: exponential growth (when the positive loops dominate), exponential decay (when the negative loops dominate), and equilibrium (when the loops exactly offset one another). Nonlinear first-order systems can exhibit S-shaped growth because the dominant feedback loops shift as the system evolves. As the population approaches its carrying capacity the positive loops driving growth weaken and the negative loops restraining growth strengthen, until the system is dominated by negative feedback, and the population then smoothly approaches a stable equilibrium at the carrying capacity.

Part III

The Dynamics of Growth

*Growth and differentiation are fundamental to businesses, societies, and all living
systems. All growth and differentiation processes are generated by positive feedback.
The growth of a population or business, the spread of infectious disease, and the adoption
of innovations and new ideas are all driven by self-reinforcing feedbacks. Chapter 9
discusses S-shaped growth, developing a series of models to represent infectious diseases
of various types and a wide range of innovation diffusion processes such as the growth
of the market for new products. Chapter 10 discusses path dependence, which arises
in the presence of positive feedbacks that progressively differentiate a population
into distinct subsets. Path dependence and positive feedback help explain how certain
products and companies come to dominate their industries and how systems can lock in
to a particular path even when all paths are initially equally attractive.*

9

S-Shaped Growth: Epidemics, Innovation Diffusion, and the Growth of New Products

Everything that rises must converge.

—Flannery O'Connor

As seen in chapter 8, positive feedback creates exponential growth. But no real quantity can grow forever. Every system initially dominated by positive feedbacks eventually approaches the carrying capacity of its environment. As the limits to growth approach, there is a nonlinear transition from dominance by positive feedback to dominance by negative feedback. Under certain conditions, the result is S-shaped growth, where the growing population smoothly approaches equilibrium. This chapter shows how S-shaped growth can be modeled, with applications to the diffusion of innovations, the spread of infectious diseases and computer viruses, the growth of the market for new products, and others. A variety of important and widely used models of S-shaped growth are introduced and analyzed, the use of these models for forecasting is discussed, and extensions to the models are presented. Cases examined include the spread of mad cow disease and HIV and the growth of the markets for high-tech products such as computers and consumer services such as cable television.

9.1 MODELING S-SHAPED GROWTH

The nonlinear population model developed in chapter 8 is quite general. The population in the model can be any quantity that grows in a fixed environment, for example, the number of adopters of an innovation, the number of people infected by a disease, the fraction of any group adhering to an idea or purchasing a product, and so on. If the population is driven by positive feedback when it is small relative to its limits, then the resulting behavior will be S-shaped growth, provided there are no significant delays in the negative feedbacks that constrain the population. If there are delays in the response of the population to the approaching carrying capacity, the behavior will be S-shaped growth with overshoot and oscillation; if the carrying capacity is consumed by the growing population, the behavior will be overshoot and collapse (see chapter 4). Conversely, whenever you observe a system that has experienced S-shaped growth, you know that initially the behavior was dominated by positive feedback loops, but as the system grew, there was a nonlinear shift to dominance by negative feedback.

9.1.1 Logistic Growth

As illustrated in the nonlinear population growth example in chapter 8, the net fractional growth rate of the population P must fall from its initial value, pass through zero when the population equals the carrying capacity C, and become negative when $P > C$. Consequently, the phase plot of the net birth rate must have a shape roughly like an inverted bowl: Net births are zero when the population is zero, rise with increasing population up to a maximum, fall to zero at the carrying capacity, and continue to drop, becoming increasingly negative, when population exceeds the carrying capacity. However, there are an infinite number of fractional net birth rate curves, and hence phase plots, satisfying these general constraints. An important special case of S-shaped growth is known as *logistic* growth, or Verhulst growth, after François Verhulst who first published the model in 1838 (see Richardson 1991).

The logistic growth model posits that the net fractional population growth rate is a (downward sloping) linear function of the population. That is,

$$\text{Net Birth Rate} = g(P, C)P = g^*(1 - P/C)P \qquad (9\text{-}1)$$

where $g(P, C)$, the fractional growth rate, is a function of the population and carrying capacity and g^* is the maximum fractional growth (the fractional growth rate when the population is very small). The logistic model conforms to the requirements for S-shaped growth: the fractional net growth rate is positive for $P < C$, zero when $P = C$, and negative for $P > C$. The logistic model has some additional characteristics. Rearranging equation (9-1) gives

$$\text{Net Birth Rate} = g^*(1 - P/C)P = g^*P - g^*P^2/C \qquad (9\text{-}2)$$

The first term g^*P is a standard first-order linear positive feedback process; the second term, $-g^*P^2/C$, is nonlinear in the population and represents the ever-stronger negative feedback caused by the approach of the population to its carrying capacity.

When does the net growth rate reach its maximum? In the logistic model the net birth rate given by equation (9-2) is an inverted parabola which passes through zero at the points $P = 0$ and $P = C$. Because a parabola is symmetric around its peak, the maximum net birth rate occurs when

$$P_{inf} = C/2 \tag{9-3}$$

where P_{inf} is the value of population where the net growth rate is at a maximum and therefore the inflection point in the trajectory of the population.[1] The maximum net growth rate occurs precisely halfway to the carrying capacity. Figure 9-1 plots the fractional growth rate, phase plot, and time domain behavior for the logistic model.

The logistic model is important for several reasons. First, many S-shaped growth processes can be approximated well by the logistic model, despite the restriction that the inflection point occurs at precisely C/2. Second, the logistic model can be solved analytically. Finally, the logistic model, though intrinsically nonlinear, can be transformed into a form that is linear in the parameters so it can be estimated by the most common regression technique, ordinary least squares (see section 9.3.1).

9.1.2 Analytic Solution of the Logistic Equation

Though it is nonlinear, the logistic model shown in equation (9-1) can be solved analytically. First separate the variables, then integrate:

$$\int \frac{dp}{\left(1 - \frac{P}{C}\right)P} = \int g^* dt \tag{9-4}$$

Rearranging the left-hand side gives

$$\int \frac{Cdp}{(C - P)P} = \int \left[\frac{1}{P} + \frac{1}{(C - P)}\right]dP = \int g^* dt \tag{9-5}$$

Integrating both sides yields

$$\ln(P) - \ln(C - P) = g^* t + c \tag{9-6}$$

where c is a constant. Since by definition $P(t) = P(0)$ when $t = 0$,

$$\ln(P) - \ln(C - P) = g^* t + \ln(P(0)) - \ln[C - P(0)]. \tag{9-7}$$

Taking exponentials yields

$$\frac{P}{(C - P)} = \frac{P(0)\exp(g^* t)}{C - P(0)} \tag{9-8}$$

which can be rearranged as

$$P(t) = \frac{C}{1 + \left[\frac{C}{P(0)} - 1\right]\exp(-g^* t)} \tag{9-9}$$

---

[1] The maximum net birth rate, and therefore the infection point in the population, occurs when

$$\partial[g(P, C) * P]/\partial P = g^* - 2g^* P/C = 0.$$

Solving for P yields $P_{inf} = C/2$.

FIGURE 9-1

The logistic model

Top: The fractional growth rate declines linearly as population grows. *Middle:* The phase plot is an inverted parabola, symmetric about (P/C) = 0.5. *Bottom:* Population follows an S-shaped curve with inflection point at (P/C) = 0.5; the net growth rate follows a bell-shaped curve with a maximum value of 0.25C per time period. The time axis is scaled so that 1 unit = 1/g*, with the inflection point centered at time h = 0.

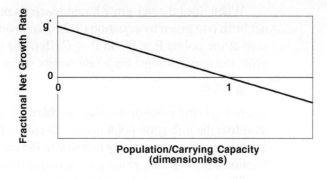

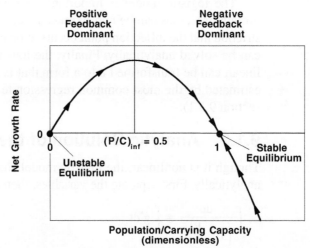

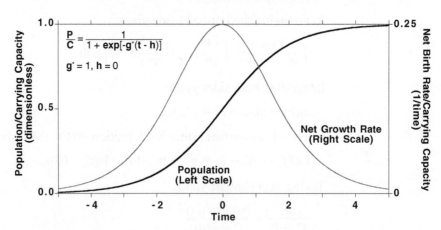

or equivalently as

$$P(t) = \frac{C}{1 + \exp[-g^*(t - h)]} \tag{9-10}$$

where h is the time at which the population reaches half its carrying capacity; setting P(h) = 0.5C in equation (9-10) and solving for h yields h = ln[(C/P(0)) − 1]/g*. Equations (9-9) and (9-10) are two forms of the analytic solution to the equation for logistic growth given by equation (9-1).

9.1.3   Other Common Growth Models

Due to its simplicity and analytic tractability, the logistic model is the most widely used model of S-shaped growth. However, there are many other models of S-shaped growth. These models relax the restrictive assumption that the fractional growth rate declines linearly in the population. These growth curves are in general not symmetric.

The Richards curve is one commonly used model (Richards 1959). In Richards' model the fractional growth rate of the population is nonlinear in the population:

$$\text{Net Birth Rate} = \frac{dP}{dt} = \frac{g^*P}{(m-1)}\left[1 - \left(\frac{P}{C}\right)^{m-1}\right] \tag{9-11}$$

When m = 2, the Richards model reduces to the logistic. Other values of m cause the fractional growth rate to be nonlinear in the population (try sketching the fractional growth rate as a function of population for different values of m). The solution of the Richards model is

$$P(t) = C(1 - k\exp(-g^*t))^{1/(1-m)} \tag{9-12}$$

where k is a parameter that depends on the initial population relative to the carrying capacity.

A special case of the Richards model is the Gompertz curve, given by the Richards model in the limit when m = 1. Note that while equation (9-12) is undefined when m = 1,

$$\lim_{a \to 0} \frac{(x^a - 1)}{a} = \ln(x) \tag{9-13}$$

so the Gompertz curve is given by

$$P(t) = C\exp(-k\exp(-g^*t)). \tag{9-14}$$

In the Gompertz model, the fractional growth rate declines linearly in the logarithm of the population, and the maximum growth rate occurs at $P/C = 0.368$.

Another commonly used growth model is based on the Weibull distribution:

$$P(t) = C\{1 - \exp[-(t/b)^a]\} \tag{9-15}$$

where a, b > 0 are known as the shape and scale parameters, respectively. The case a = 2 is known as the Rayleigh distribution.

The Richards and Weibull models provide the modeler with analytically tractable growth functions that can represent a variety of nonlinear fractional net increase rates. However, there is no guarantee that the data will conform to the assumptions of any of the analytic growth models. Fortunately, with computer simulation, you are not restricted to use the logistic, Gompertz, Richards, Weibull, or any other analytic model. You can specify any nonlinear relationship for the fractional birth and death rates supported by the data and then simulate the model to explore its behavior over time.

9.1.4   Testing the Logistic Model

To illustrate the use of the logistic model, consider the examples of S-shaped growth in Figure 4-9. Figure 9-2 shows the result of fitting the logistic model to the data for the growth of sunflowers. The best fit logistic model matches the sunflower data reasonably well, though it underestimates the growth in the first month and overestimates it later. These differences suggest a better fit might be gained through use of a different growth model, such as the Richards model, in which the fractional growth rate is nonlinear in the population. Section 9.3.1 provides additional examples.

9.2   DYNAMICS OF DISEASE: MODELING EPIDEMICS

Epidemics of infectious diseases often exhibit S-shaped growth. The cumulative number of cases follows an S-shaped curve while the rate at which new cases occur rises exponentially, peaks, then falls as the epidemic ends. Figure 9-3 shows the course of an epidemic of influenza at an English boarding school in 1978. The epidemic began with a single infected student (patient zero). The flu spreads through contact and by inhalation of virus-laden aerosols released when infected individuals cough and sneeze. The flu spread slowly at first, but as more and more students fell ill and became infectious, the number they infected grew exponentially. Due to the close quarters and thus high rate of exposure, about two-thirds of the population eventually became ill, and the epidemic ended due to the depletion of the pool of susceptible people. Figure 9-3 also shows the course of an epidemic of plague in Bombay in 1905–6. The behavior is quite similar, despite the differences in time frame, mortality, and other aspects of the situation. The pathogen does not have to be a biological agent—epidemics of computer viruses follow similar dynamics.

9.2.1   A Simple Model of Infectious Disease

Figure 9-4 shows a simple model of infectious disease. The total population of the community or region represented in the model is divided into two categories: those susceptible to the disease, S, and those who are infectious, I (for this reason the

FIGURE 9-2

The growth of sunflowers and the best fit logistic model

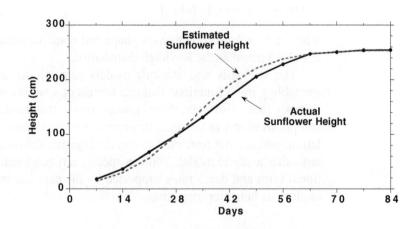

model is known as the SI model). As people are infected they move from the susceptible category to the infectious category. The SI model invokes a number of simplifying assumptions; section 9.2.2 develops a more realistic model. First,

FIGURE 9-3
Dynamics of epidemic disease

Top: Influenza epidemic at an English boarding school, January 22–February 3, 1978. The data show the number of students confined to bed for influenza at any time (the stock of symptomatic individuals).

Source: British Medical Journal, 4 March 1978, p. 587.

Bottom: Epidemic of plague, Bombay, India 1905–6. Data show the death rate (deaths/week).

Source: Kermack and McKendrick (1927, p. 714). For further discussion of both cases, see Murray (1993).

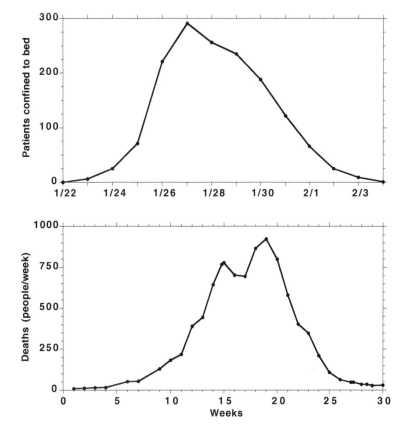

FIGURE 9-4
Structure of a simple model of an epidemic

Births, deaths, and migration are omitted so the total population is a constant, and people remain infectious indefinitely.

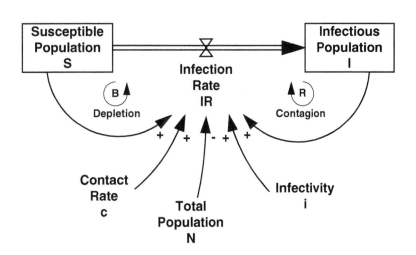

births, deaths, and migration are ignored. Second, once people are infected, they remain infectious indefinitely, that is, the model applies to chronic infections, not acute illness such as influenza or plague.

The SI model contains two loops, the positive Contagion loop and the negative Depletion loop. Infectious diseases spread as those who are infectious come into contact with and pass the disease to those who are susceptible, increasing the infectious population still further (the positive loop) while at the same time depleting the pool of susceptibles (the negative loop).

The infectious population I is increased by the infection rate IR while the susceptible population S is decreased by it:

$$I = \text{INTEGRAL}(IR, I_0) \tag{9-16}$$

$$S = \text{INTEGRAL}(-IR, N - I_0) \tag{9-17}$$

where N is the total population in the community and I_0 is the initial number of infectious people (a small number or even a single individual). To formulate the infection rate, consider the process by which susceptible people become infected.

People in the community interact at a certain rate (the Contact Rate, c, measured in people contacted per person per time period, or 1/time period). Thus the susceptible population generate Sc encounters per time period. Some of these encounters are with infectious people. If infectious people interact at the same rate as susceptible people (they are not quarantined or confined to bed), then the probability that any randomly selected encounter is an encounter with an infectious individual is I/N. Not every encounter with an infectious person results in infection. The infectivity, i, of the disease is the probability that a person becomes infected after contact with an infectious person. The infection rate is therefore the total number of encounters Sc multiplied by the probability that any of those encounters is with an infectious individual I/N multiplied by the probability that an encounter with an infectious person results in infection:

$$IR = (ciS)(I/N) \tag{9-18}$$

The dynamics can be determined by noting that without births, deaths, or migration, the total population is fixed:

$$S + I = N \tag{9-19}$$

Though the system contains two stocks, it is actually a first-order system because one of the stocks is completely determined by the other. Substituting $N - I$ for S in (9-18) yields

$$IR = (c)(i)I(1 - I/N) \tag{9-20}$$

Equation (9-20) is identical to equation (9-1), the net birth rate in the logistic model. An epidemic, in this model, grows exactly like a population in a fixed environment. The carrying capacity is the total population, N. In the SI model, once an infectious individual arrives in the community, every susceptible person eventually becomes infected, with the infection rate following a bell-shaped curve and the total infected population following the classic S-shaped pattern of the logistic curve (Figure 9-1). The higher the contact rate or the greater the infectivity, the faster the epidemic progresses.

The SI model captures the most fundamental feature of infectious diseases: the disease spreads through contact between infected and susceptible individuals. It is the interaction of these two groups that creates the positive and negative loops and the nonlinearity responsible for the shift in loop dominance as the susceptible population is depleted. The nonlinearity arises because the two populations are multiplied together in equation (9-18); it takes both a susceptible and an infectious person to generate a new case.

9.2.2 Modeling Acute Infection: The SIR Model

While the SI model captures the basic process of infection, it contains many simplifying and restrictive assumptions. The model does not represent births, deaths, or migration. The population is assumed to be homogeneous: all members of the community are assumed to interact at the same average rate (there are no subcultures or groups that remain isolated from the others in the community or whose behavior is different from others). The disease does not alter people's lifestyles: infectives are assumed to interact at the same average rate as susceptibles. There is no possibility of recovery, quarantine, or immunization.

All these assumptions can be relaxed. The susceptible population can be disaggregated into several distinct subpopulations, or even represented as distinct individuals, each with a specific rate of contact with others. An additional stock can be added to represent quarantined or vaccinated individuals. Birth and death rates can be added. Random events can be added to simulate the chance nature of contacts between susceptibles and infectives.

The most restrictive and unrealistic feature of the logistic model as applied to epidemics is the assumption that the disease is chronic, with affected individuals remaining infectious indefinitely. Consequently, once even a single infectious individual arrives in the community, every susceptible eventually becomes infected. While the assumption of chronic infection is reasonable for some diseases (e.g., herpes simplex), many infectious diseases produce a period of acute infectiousness and illness, followed either by recovery and the development of immunity or by death. Most epidemics end before all the susceptibles become infected because people recover faster than new cases arise. Kermack and McKendrick (1927) developed a model applicable to such acute diseases. The model contains three stocks: The Susceptible population, S, the Infectious population, I, and the Recovered population, R (Figure 9-5). Long known as the SIR model, the Kermack–McKendrick formulation is widely used in epidemiology. Those contracting the disease become infectious for a certain period of time but then recover and develop permanent immunity. The assumption that people recover creates one additional feedback—the negative Recovery loop. The greater the number of infectious

FIGURE 9-5   Structure of the SIR epidemic model

People remain infectious (and sick) for a limited time, then recover and develop immunity.

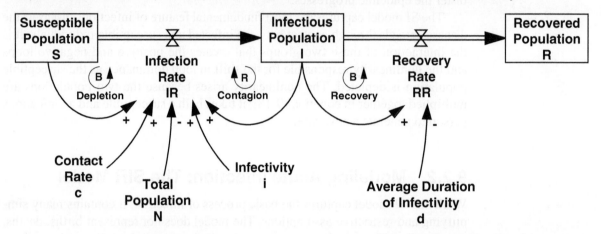

individuals, the greater the recovery rate and the smaller the number of infectious people remaining. All other assumptions of the original SI model are retained.[2]

The susceptible population, as in the SI model, is reduced by the infection rate. The infectious population now accumulates the infection rate less the recovery rate RR and the recovered population R accumulates the recovery rate:

$$S = \text{INTEGRAL}(-IR, N - I_0 - R_0) \tag{9-21}$$

$$I = \text{INTEGRAL}(IR - RR, I_0) \tag{9-22}$$

$$R = \text{INTEGRAL}(RR, R_0) \tag{9-23}$$

The initial susceptible population is the total population less the initial number of infectives and any initially recovered and immune individuals.

The recovery rate can be modeled several ways. In the SIR model, the average duration of infectivity, d, is assumed to be constant and the recovery process is assumed to follow a first-order negative feedback process:

$$RR = I/d. \tag{9-24}$$

The average duration of infectivity, d, represents the average length of time people are infectious. The assumption that the recovery rate is a first-order process means

---

[2]In the SIR model the recovered population is often termed "Removals" and the recovery rate is then called the removal rate. Many applications of the model interpret the removal rate as the sum of those recovering from the disease and those who die from it. However, this interpretation is incorrect, since those who die reduce the total population, while in the SIR model the total population is constant. The aggregation of deaths and recoveries into a single flow of removals and a single stock of cumulative removals is usually justified by arguing that mortality is often a small fraction of the total population. Even when this is true, it is bad modeling practice to aggregate the living with the dead, since their behavior is often quite different. In this case, those who recover continue to interact with the remaining susceptible and infectious populations, while those who die usually do not.

people do not all recover after exactly the same time, but rather a given population of infectious individuals will decline exponentially, with some people recovering rapidly and others more slowly.[3] The infection rate is formulated exactly as in the SI model in equation (9-18).

9.2.3   Model Behavior: The Tipping Point

Unlike the models considered thus far, the system is now second-order (there are three stocks, but since they sum to a constant, only two are independent). However, it is still possible to analyze its dynamics qualitatively. First, unlike the SI model, it is now possible for the disease to die out without causing an epidemic. If the infection rate is less than the recovery rate, the infectious population will fall. As it falls, so too will the infection rate. The infectious population can therefore fall to zero before everyone contracts the disease.

Under what circumstances will the introduction of an infectious individual to the population cause an epidemic? Intuitively, for an epidemic to occur, the infection rate must exceed the recovery rate; if so, the infectious population will grow, leading to still more new cases. If, while each person was infectious they passed the disease on to exactly one more person, then the stock of infectives would remain constant since the infection rate would be just offset by the recovery rate. Therefore, for an epidemic to occur, each infective must, on average, pass the disease on to more than one other person prior to recovering.

The question of whether an epidemic will occur is really a question about which feedback loops are dominant when the disease arrives in a community. If the positive contagion loop dominates the recovery and depletion loops, then the introduction of even a single infective individual to a community triggers an epidemic. The infection rate will exceed the recovery rate, causing the infection rate to grow still further, until depletion of the pool of susceptibles finally limits the epidemic. If, however, the positive loop is weaker than the negative loops, an epidemic will not occur since infectious people will recover on average faster than new cases arise. The number of new cases created by each infective prior to their recovery, and therefore the strength of the different loops, depends on the average duration of infection and the number of new cases each infective generates per time period. The higher the contact rate or the greater the infectivity of the disease, the stronger the positive loop. Likewise, the larger the fraction of the total population susceptible to infection, the weaker the depletion loop. Finally, the longer the

---

[3]While the assumption that removals are first-order is reasonable in the simple SIR model, the course of many diseases is more complex and the delay between infection and removal is often not exponential (if a group were all infected at once, the removal rate would be small initially, then build to a peak before tapering off). Chapter 11 discusses how different types of delays can be modeled in depth and shows how modelers can select robust formulations for delays to match the data for different distributions.

average duration of infection, the weaker the negative recovery loop and the more likely an epidemic will be.[4]

For any given population of susceptibles, there is some critical combination of contact frequency, infectivity, and disease duration just great enough for the positive loop to dominate the negative loops. That threshold is known as the *tipping point*. Below the tipping point, the system is stable: if the disease is introduced into the community, there may be a few new cases, but on average, people will recover faster than new cases are generated. Negative feedback dominates and the population is resistant to an epidemic. Past the tipping point, the positive loop dominates. The system is unstable and once a disease arrives, it can spread like wildfire— that is, by positive feedback—limited only by the depletion of the susceptible population.

Figure 9-6 shows a simulation of the model where the system is well past the tipping point. The population of the community is 10,000 and initially everyone is susceptible to the disease. At time zero, a single infective individual arrives in the community. The average duration of infection is 2 days, and infectivity is 25%. The average contact frequency is six people per person per day. Each infective therefore generates 1.5 new cases per day and an average of three new cases before they recover. The positive loop therefore dominates and the epidemic quickly spreads. The infection rate peaks at more than 2000 people per day around day nine, and at its peak more than one-quarter of the population is infectious. The susceptible population falls rapidly, and it is this depletion of potential new cases that halts the epidemic. By the tenth day, the number of susceptibles remaining is so low that the number of new cases declines. The infectious population peaks and falls as people now recover faster than new cases arise. The susceptible population continues to fall, though at a slower and slower rate, until the epidemic ends. In less than 3 weeks, a single infectious individual led to a massive epidemic involving nearly the entire community. Note that a few lucky individuals never contract the disease. Unlike the chronic infection model in which everyone eventually contracts the disease, in the SIR model the epidemic ends before the susceptible population falls to zero. The stronger the positive loop, however, the fewer susceptibles remain at the end of the epidemic. Also note that unlike the logistic model, the behavior is not symmetric: the infectious population rises faster than it falls.

---

[4]The SI and SIR models were originally formulated as deterministic systems representing the average contact rate and abstracting from the individual encounters among members of the population. Keep in mind that the deterministic formulation is a modeling assumption, appropriate in some situations and not appropriate in others (particularly, when the populations are small or the variance in the distribution of contact rates, infectivity, and recovery time is large). The models are easily generalized to incorporate stochastic encounters, infectivity, and recovery, either by adding random variation to the rate equations of the SIR model or by representing the members of the population as discrete individuals and specifying decision rules for their interaction (an agent-based model). Incorporating these random effects means there will be a distribution of possible outcomes for any set of parameters. The sharp boundary between an epidemic and stability defined by the tipping point in the deterministic models becomes a probability distribution characterizing the chance an epidemic will occur for any given average rates of interaction, infectivity, and recovery. Likewise, the SI and SIR models assume a homogeneous and well-mixed population, while in reality it is often important to represent subpopulations and the spatial diffusion of an epidemic. For spatial models of the spread of disease and other refinements, see Murray (1993).

To illustrate the tipping point, Figure 9-7 shows the susceptible population in several simulations of the model with different contact rates. The other parameters are identical to those in Figure 9-6. At the tipping point (two contacts per person per day), the number of new cases each infective generates while infectious is just equal to one (2 contacts per person per day * 0.25 probability of infection * 2 days of infectivity). Contacts at a rate less than two per person per day do not cause an

FIGURE 9-6

Simulation of an epidemic in the SIR model

The total population is 10,000. The contact rate is 6 per person per day, infectivity is 0.25, and average duration of infectivity is 2 days. The initial infective population is 1, and all others are initially susceptible.

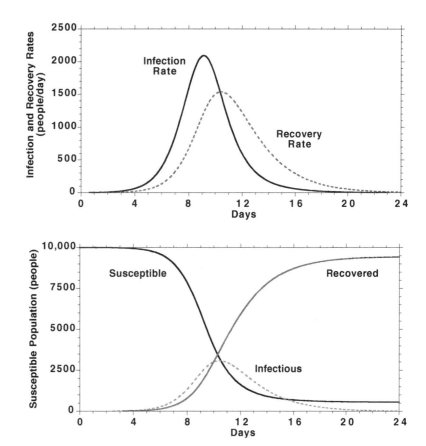

FIGURE 9-7

Epidemic dynamics for different contact rates

The contact rate is noted on each curve; all other parameters are as in Figure 9-6.

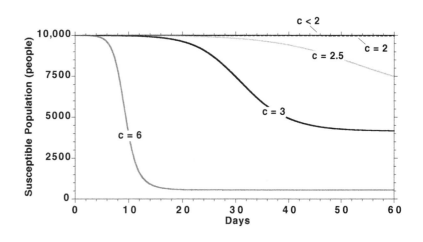

epidemic. When the contact rate rises above the critical threshold of two, the system become unstable, and an epidemic occurs. The higher the contact rate, the stronger the positive contagion loop relative to the negative recovery loop, and the faster the epidemic progresses. Further, the stronger the positive loop, the greater the population ultimately contracting the disease. Any change that increases the strength of the positive loops will yield similar results. An increase in infectivity strengthens the positive loop and is identical in impact to an increase in contact frequency. An increase in the duration of the infectious period weakens the recovery loop and also pushes the system farther past the tipping point.

CHALLENGE   ## Exploring the SIR Model

Simulate the SIR model under various combinations of parameters. What determines whether an epidemic will occur? What determines the fraction of the population remaining uninfected in equilibrium? Why?

The exact tipping point in the SIR model can easily be calculated. For an epidemic to occur, the infection rate must exceed the recovery rate:

$$IR > RR \Rightarrow ciS(I/N) > I/d \tag{9-25}$$

or equivalently,

$$cid\left(\frac{S}{N}\right) > 1 \tag{9-26}$$

In equation (9-26), the product of the contact rate and infectivity is the number of infectious contacts per time period each infectious person generates. Multiplying by the average duration of infection, d, yields the dimensionless ratio cid, known as the *contact number*. However, not all these contacts will be with susceptibles, so not all will result in a new case. The number of infectious contacts that actually result in the infection of a susceptible person depends on the probability that the infectives encounter susceptibles. Assuming the population is homogeneous, the probability of encountering a susceptible is given by the prevalence of susceptibles in the population, S/N. The expression cid(S/N) is also known as the *reproduction rate* for the epidemic. Equation (9-26) therefore defines the tipping point or threshold at which an epidemic occurs in a population and is known as the threshold theorem in epidemiology.

   Note that the contact number can be large if infectivity is high or if the duration of infection is long. The duration of the infectious period for diseases such as measles and chicken pox is very short, a matter of days, but these diseases have high contact numbers because they are easily spread through casual contact. In contrast, the contact rate and infectivity of HIV are much lower (HIV cannot be spread through casual contact but only through sexual contact or exchange of blood or blood products). Nevertheless, the contact number for HIV is high among those who engage in risky behaviors because the duration of infection is so long. The incubation period prior to the development of clinical symptoms of AIDS averages about 10 years (see section 9.2.7).

Figure 9-8 shows how the tipping point depends on the parameters. The curve is the boundary between stable and unstable regimes. To the left of the curve, the system is stable and there is no epidemic because the infectivity, contact rate, duration of infection, and fraction of susceptibles in the population are too low. To the right of the curve, the system is unstable, and there is an epidemic.

9.2.4   Immunization and the Eradication of Smallpox

The existence of the tipping point (equation (9-26)) means it is theoretically possible to completely eradicate a disease. Eradication does not require a perfect vaccine and universal immunization but only the weaker condition that the reproduction rate of the disease fall and remain below one so that new cases arise at a lower rate than old cases are resolved. The stock of infectious people will then decline, further reducing the infection rate, until the population becomes disease-free. For many diseases, it is difficult or impossible to achieve or maintain this condition due to high infectivity, the existence of reservoirs of the disease outside the human population (as in malaria or Lyme disease, both of which have animal hosts), or the rapid influx of susceptible people through births, migration, or the decay of immunity.

Smallpox, however, is different. Smallpox was once one of the most deadly diseases and endemic throughout the world. The infectivity of smallpox is high, but the duration of infection is short. Survivors acquired long-lived immunity. Most important, the smallpox virus cannot survive outside a human host—there are no animal or other reservoirs to harbor the virus. These conditions meant that the development of an effective vaccine, deployed sufficiently broadly, could reduce the infection rate below the recovery rate and eliminate the virus, even if not every person could be immunized.

The history of smallpox eradication is well known: Edward Jenner developed the first effective vaccine in 1796. Despite the success of Jenner's vaccine, it took many years for vaccination to be accepted; smallpox was still a major cause of death at the start of the 20th century. By the 1950s, due to improvements in public health programs and in the effectiveness and shelf-life of the vaccine, smallpox

FIGURE 9-8
Dependence of the tipping point on the contact number and susceptible population

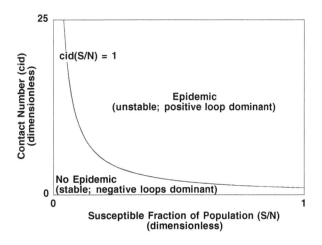

had been eradicated in most of the industrialized world. In the mid-1960s, the World Health Organization (WHO) coordinated a vigorous worldwide campaign to track the disease, immunize the susceptible, and quarantine the sick. The last known naturally occurring case was reported in 1977 in Somalia. In 1978, some smallpox virus escaped from a research lab in England and caused two cases, one fatal. Since then no further cases have been reported, and, in one of the greatest triumphs in the history of medicine, the nations of the world declared in 1980 that smallpox had been eradicated from the earth.

Almost. During the Cold War, both the US and Soviet Union maintained stocks of smallpox virus as part of their biological warfare programs. Though both nations signed the 1972 Biological Weapons Convention banning bioweapons and biowarfare research, they continued to maintain their stocks of smallpox, and the Soviet Union continued biowarfare research in violation of the Convention. While these smallpox stocks are maintained in the highest security biocontainment labs, there is natural concern that the virus might escape, accidentally, through terrorism, or in war. A WHO panel, after long and sometimes acrimonious debate, recommended in 1994 that all US and Russian stocks of the virus be destroyed by June 1999. However, many analysts believe terrorists or nations such as Iraq and North Korea may have acquired smallpox from the former Soviet Union. Because people no longer receive smallpox vaccinations, and because the immunity conferred by childhood vaccination decays, much of the world's population today is susceptible. The release of smallpox from these stocks could trigger a massive pandemic. In response, President Clinton ordered US smallpox stocks be preserved for research, and WHO suspended its attempt to have declared stocks of smallpox destroyed.

CHALLENGE ## The Efficacy of Immunization Programs

Equation (9-26) and Figure 9-8 show how the vulnerability of a population to epidemic depends on the parameters of the SIR model. Many infectious diseases are highly contagious and it is not feasible to reduce the contact number. Immunization, where vaccines are available, can be highly effective not only in protecting the immunized individuals but also in moving an entire population below the tipping point. For example, polio has all but vanished in nations with strong public health programs and WHO hopes to eradicate it worldwide within a few years.

1. **Effectiveness of immunization.**
    The contact number for polio is estimated to be roughly 5 to 7 (Fine 1993). What fraction of the population must be vaccinated to ensure that no epidemic will occur? Assume the vaccine is 100% effective. Now consider measles and pertussis (whooping cough), diseases whose contact numbers are estimated to be 12 to 18 (Fine 1993). What fraction of the population must be vaccinated to ensure no epidemic will occur? What fraction must be vaccinated if the vaccine is only 90% effective? Why do measles and pertussis persist while polio has been effectively eliminated?

    Next, simulate the SIR model with the parameters in Figure 9-6 (c = 6, i = 0.25, d = 2, N = 10,000), but assume that 50% of the population has been immunized (set the initial recovered population to half the total population). What is the effect on the course of the epidemic? What fraction of the population must be immunized to prevent an epidemic?

2. **Effectiveness of quarantine.**

Examine the effectiveness of quarantine as a policy to prevent an epidemic. To do so, modify the SIR model to include a stock of quarantined individuals.

(i)   Assume people are quarantined only after they exhibit symptoms, so the quarantine rate (the rate of inflow to the quarantined population) flows from the infectious population to the quarantined population. Formulate the quarantine rate as follows. Assume it takes a certain period of time, denoted the Quarantine Time, to identify infectious people and move them to a quarantine area. Further, assume only a fraction of the infectious population, denoted the Quarantine Fraction, is identified as infectious and willing or able to be quarantined. Be sure your formulation for the quarantine rate is dimensionally consistent. Assume quarantined individuals recover from the disease with the same average duration of infectivity as those not quarantined.

(ii) Quarantined individuals are not completely removed from contact with the rest of the population (during an epidemic of smallpox in 18th century Boston, for example, the sick were quarantined but still permitted to attend church on Sunday). Modify the equation for the infection rate to include the possibility that quarantined people come in contact with susceptibles at a certain rate, denoted the Quarantine Contact Rate. Assume the infectivity of quarantined individuals is the same as that for other infectives. How does the addition of a stock of quarantined individuals alter the feedback structure of the SIR model?

(iii) Assume the Quarantine Time is half a day, and use the parameters for the simulation in Figure 9-6 (c = 6, i = 0.25, d = 2, N = 10,000). Assume the quarantine is perfect, so that the Quarantine Contact Rate is zero. Run the model for various values of the Quarantine Fraction and explain the resulting behavior. What fraction of the infectious population must be quarantined to prevent an epidemic? Now assume that the contact rate of quarantined individuals is half the normal contact rate. What fraction must now be sequestered to prevent an epidemic and how fast must people be moved to quarantine once they become infectious? Explore the response to other parameters, including partial immunization of the population. Compare the efficacy of immunization to quarantine in preventing or slowing epidemics. What policy considerations would influence your choice of these policies in different situations?

3. **Loss of immunity.**

For some diseases, immunity is not permanent, but decays over time, leaving formerly immune people susceptible to reinfection. Modify the model to incorporate loss of immunity. Assume immunity decays at a rate determined by a constant average duration of immunity. Run the model for different

values of the average duration of immunity. What is the impact on the dynamics? Under what conditions will the disease become endemic in the population? What is the equilibrium reached, and why? What impact does loss of immunity have on the effectiveness of immunization? On the ability to eradicate a disease? Why?

9.2.5   Herd Immunity

In the real world, a population is repeatedly challenged by exposure to different diseases. Infectious individuals, unwittingly carrying the disease, may arrive from other communities. The spread of the black death in 14th century Europe was accelerated by extensive trade networks with other regions, the high rate of travel of pilgrims, and by the flight of the terrified and unknowingly infected to towns as yet unexposed. Susceptible individuals can also come into contact with other reservoirs of the disease, such as contaminated drinking water (as in cholera), or animals (bubonic plague is not only transmitted from person to person but by fleas who pass the plague bacillus from infected rats to people). Some pathogens mutate and cross the so-called species barrier, jumping from animal reservoirs to human populations (as occurs in influenza and likely occurred with HIV, outbreaks of the Ebola virus, and apparently with Bovine Spongiform Encephalopathy (BSE)—mad cow disease). If the contact rate, infectivity, and duration of infection are small enough, the system is below the tipping point and stable. Such a situation is known as herd immunity (Fine 1993) because the arrival of an infected individual does not produce an epidemic (though a few unlucky individuals may come in contact with any infectious arrivals and contract the disease, the group as a community is protected). However, changes in the contact rate, infectivity, or duration of illness can push a system past the tipping point.

Figure 9-9 shows how changes in the reproduction rate can dramatically change the response of a population to exposure. In the simulation, the population is challenged every 50 days by the arrival of a single infected individual. The population, infectivity, and duration of infection are identical to those in Figure 9-6 (10,000, 0.25, and 2 days, respectively). However, the contact rate is assumed to increase linearly over time, beginning at zero. The contact rate might increase as population density grows or as changes in social structures or cultural practices bring people into more frequent contact. The rapid urbanization of the industrial revolution, for example, increased the contact rate and incidence of epidemics for many diseases.

During the first 500 days, the reproduction rate (the number of new cases generated by each infective prior to recovery) is less than one, the negative loops dominate, and the system is below the tipping point. There is no epidemic: Every 50 days an infectious individual arrives, but any people infected by this person recover before they can replace themselves in the pool of infectives. The population enjoys herd immunity. At day 500 the tipping point is crossed. Now the contagion loop dominates, and the next infectious person to arrive triggers an epidemic. The epidemic ends after the susceptible population falls enough for the depletion and recovery loops to overpower the contagion loop. By about day 600 the decline in

FIGURE 9-9

Successive epidemic waves created by increasing contact rate

Every 50 days the population is challenged by the arrival of a single infectious individual. At first, the population has herd immunity. The contact rate increases linearly from zero, increasing the relative reproduction rate and eventually causing a wave of epidemics.

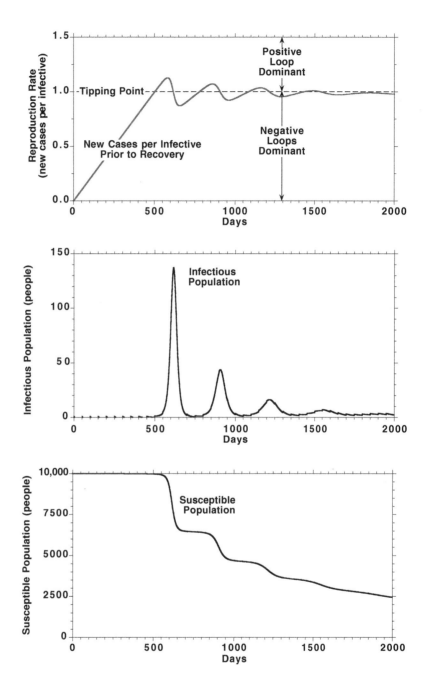

the susceptible population reduces the reproduction rate below one and the negative loops once again dominate the positive contagion loop. Though infected individuals continue to arrive at 50-day intervals, the system has become stable again. However, the contact rate keeps rising, increasing the strength of the contagion loop. By day 800, the contagion loop is once again dominant. The arrival of the next infectious person triggers another epidemic. Since there are even fewer susceptibles this time around, it is a bit milder. By day 1100 the depletion of the susceptible pool has once again overwhelmed the contagion loop and the reproduction rate falls below one. The community is once again resistant to epidemic, until the contact rate rises enough to push the reproduction rate above one again, triggering the third wave of infection.

In this simple example the periodic epidemics arise from the assumed steady rise in the contact rate. Successive waves of epidemics are in fact observed for many infectious diseases, perhaps most notably measles. Prior to the introduction of mass immunization in the 1960s, industrialized nations such as the US and UK experienced large amplitude measles epidemics about every 2 years. Due to immunization programs, the amplitude of the cycles is much reduced today, but the tendency toward cyclic waves of measles persists. In contrast to the example above, the contact rate for measles remains reasonably constant. The cyclic character of the epidemics arises from the interaction of herd immunity with population growth. Each epidemic increases the immune fraction of the population enough to confer herd immunity, preventing another epidemic the following year. However, during this time the population of susceptibles increases as children are born. Eventually, the susceptible fraction of the population rises enough to push the system past the tipping point again, and the next epidemic begins. The SIR model can easily be extended to include the age structure of the population, including births and deaths (see chapter 12). With realistic parameters these models generate persistent oscillations in disease incidence as the system repeatedly cycles above and below the tipping point.

The reproduction rate for an infectious disease is not solely a matter of the virulence and other biological attributes of the pathogen. It is strongly influenced by social structures and the physical infrastructure of a community. The contact rate obviously represents the nature of social structures in the community: The contact rate in rural communities with low population densities is lower than that of highly urbanized populations. The infectivity of a disease is only partly determined by biological factors. Casual contact and inhalation can spread influenza, while HIV can only be contracted through exchange of blood or other body fluids (a biological factor). But infectivity is also strongly affected by social practices and public health policies, such as the availability of clean water, the prevalence of hand washing, or the frequency of condom use.

9.2.6   Moving Past the Tipping Point: Mad Cow Disease

The epidemic of BSE or mad cow disease in Great Britain during the 1990s illustrates how changes in technical and social structures can push a population past the tipping point. Prior to the epidemic, the incidence of BSE and related degenerative neurological diseases such as scrapie (in sheep) and Cruetzfeldt-Jacob Disease (CJD, in humans) was extremely low. But between 1985 and 1997, approximately 170,000 cases of BSE were confirmed in the UK, and almost one million cattle out of a total livestock population of about 11 million were estimated to be infected (Prusiner 1997). BSE, scrapie, and CJD progressively and, at present, irreversibly destroy brain tissue; symptoms include uncontrollable tremor, disorientation, loss of motor and cognitive function, and ultimately death.

The cause of BSE is still debated. Most scientists believe BSE is caused by prions, abnormal proteins that are hypothesized to replicate even though they do not contain any DNA or RNA. Biologist Stanley Prusiner received the 1997 Nobel Prize for his pioneering (and still controversial) work on prions (see Prusiner 1997 for further details on prions and BSE). Others believe BSE, scrapie, and CJD are caused by an as yet undetected and possibly novel type of virus.

Since BSE is not thought to be directly communicable from animal to animal, the positive contagion feedback did not exist under traditional animal husbandry practices. How then did the epidemic arise? To reduce costs over the past few decades, cattle producers began to supplement the diets of their herds with meat and bone meal (MBM) prepared from the offal of slaughtered livestock, including sheep, cattle, pigs, and chickens. To reduce costs further, a new process for preparation of MBM was introduced in the late 1970s. The new process involved lower temperatures for rendering offal into feed pellets and left more fat in the product. It is thought that this change allowed BSE to enter the UK cattle population through MBM made from sheep infected with scrapie. In its search for lower costs the livestock industry converted its herds from herbivores to unwitting cannibals and created a pathway for infected cattle to "contact" susceptibles, thus closing the contagion loop. The practice of feeding MBM to cattle dramatically boosted the reproduction rate for BSE in the cattle population and pushed it well above the tipping point. Further, whereas most diseases are communicated only by close contact between infected and susceptible individuals so that epidemics tend to be geographically localized, MBM was distributed all over the UK, allowing a single infected animal to pass BSE to others hundreds of miles away.

The epidemic (Figure 9-10) spread rapidly, much faster than medical knowledge of it or the reactions of public health authorities. By the mid 1980s British public health officials knew there was a new disease afflicting the cattle industry. BSE was first identified as the culprit only in 1986. There was a further delay of several years before the UK banned the use of MBM as a feed supplement. Due to

FIGURE 9-10
Mad cow disease—the epidemic of BSE in the United Kingdom

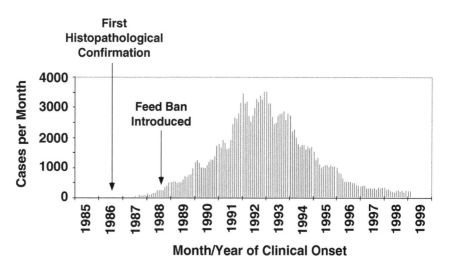

Source: UK Ministry of Agriculture, Fisheries, and Food, <www.maff.gov.uk/animalh/bse/
bse-statistics/level-4-epidem.html>, 3 August 1999.

the long incubation delay, however, confirmed cases continued to rise through 1992, declining only as animals in infected herds were destroyed. By then, however, British beef was banned by the European Union and shunned throughout the world. Worse, many scientists fear that BSE has been passed from contaminated beef or milk to the human population. By 1998, 23 confirmed and up to a dozen possible cases of a new variant of CJD (nvCJD) had been identified, all in the UK or France. The new variant, unlike traditional CJD, primarily strikes young people. Because CJD has a very long incubation time (years to decades), it is not yet known whether these nvCJD cases represent an isolated group or the first cases of a human epidemic caused by consumption of BSE contaminated beef. Many scientists fear that BSE has crossed over from the livestock to the human population and may now begin to spread through exchange of blood products. In July 1998 the UK government authorized its National Health Service to import blood plasma from nations apparently free of BSE after it was discovered that two of the victims of nvCJD were blood donors, potentially threatening the integrity of UK blood supplies and vaccines prepared from blood products.

CHALLENGE ## Extending the SIR Model

The SIR model, useful as it is, invokes a number of restrictive assumptions. Like the SI model of chronic infection, the SIR model does not incorporate births, deaths, or migration; assumes the population is homogeneous; does not distinguish between persons removed from the infectious population by recovery and the development of immunity or by death; and assumes immunity is permanent.

Most importantly, the model assumes there is no incubation period. Individuals infected with a disease in the SIR model immediately become infectious. In reality, most diseases have a latency, or incubation period, and people become infectious before exhibiting any symptoms of illness. People exposed to chicken pox become highly infectious several days prior to the emergence of symptoms, some 14 to 21 days after initial exposure. Many people infected with Hepatitis A start to exhibit symptoms about a month after infection but become highly infectious about 2 weeks earlier. The average incubation period for HIV (the time between infection with HIV and the development of AIDS) for adults not receiving treatment is about 10 years. The latency period between infection and the appearance of symptoms for Hepatitis C is even longer—averaging perhaps 15 years. Some four million people are thought to be infected with Hepatitis C in the US, and while about 15% spontaneously recover, in many other cases the disease eventually produces irreversible and often fatal liver damage. Hepatitis C is spread by exchange of blood products but only rarely through sexual contact.

Modify the SIR model by disaggregating the stock of infectious individuals into two categories: Asymptomatic Infectives and Symptomatic Infectives. The infection rate moves people from the susceptible category into the asymptomatic infective population, that is, people who are infected with the disease but do not yet exhibit any symptoms. After the incubation period, people begin to exhibit symptoms (typically while remaining infectious) and move into the symptomatic infective category. Assume that the rate at which people become sick is a first-order process with a constant average incubation period.

Susceptible people can contract the disease by coming into contact with either symptomatic or asymptomatic infectives. The contact rate and infectivity for asymptomatic and symptomatic individuals often differ. Once people fall ill (become symptomatic) they often reduce their contact rate with the outside world, either to avoid infecting others or simply because they are too sick to follow their normal routine. Asymptomatic individuals, in contrast, usually do not know they are infected, do not exhibit any symptoms, and continue to contact others at their normal rate. Similarly, the infectivity of a disease prior to the emergence of symptoms is often different from the infectivity after symptoms appear. In measles, for example, people are most infectious from 5 days prior to 5 days after the appearance of the characteristic rash. Modify the formulation for the infection rate to capture the differing contact rates and infectivities of the symptomatic and asymptomatic infective populations.

Run the model for a hypothetical disease with an incubation period similar to chicken pox. Because the incubation period for chicken pox is 14 to 21 days, assume an average of 18 days. Assume the average duration of illness is 4 days. Set the contact rate for asymptomatic infectives to four per person per day, but because those exhibiting symptoms remain in bed in self-imposed quarantine, set the contact rate for the symptomatic population to only one per person per day. Assume infectivity is 0.25 for both asymptomatic and symptomatic populations. Also assume an initial population of 10,000, all of whom are initially susceptible except for one asymptomatic infective person.

Run the model and describe the results. How does the inclusion of an incubation period affect the dynamics? By the time 1% of the population exhibits symptoms, what fraction of the susceptible population remains uninfected? How many susceptibles remain by the time 10% of the population has become sick? What is the impact of an incubation period on the effectiveness of quarantine? You can simulate a perfect quarantine policy by setting the contact rate for the symptomatic population to zero or include the quarantine structure developed above. Explore the response of the epidemic to different incubation times and infectivities. What is the effect of a long incubation period on the course of an epidemic and the ability of a population to enjoy herd immunity?

Policy Analysis: Just-in-Time Immunization

Evaluate the effectiveness of a policy of "just-in-time (JIT) vaccination," that is, vaccinating people only after evidence of an epidemic appears. Many people only get flu shots when they believe the flu in their area is particularly severe that year. Similarly, some vaccines are so expensive relative to the incidence of infection that they are not routinely given. When previously unknown diseases strike, vaccines cannot be made until after the disease emerges and is identified. The appearance of new computer viruses leads to frantic efforts by programmers to come up with countermeasures, but the resulting "vaccines" are not available until after the virus is identified. The British government's ban on the use of MBM as a feed supplement for cattle is roughly equivalent to a policy of JIT immunization. The ban reduced the number of infectious contacts by removing the vector for BSE from the diet of the cattle at risk only after the scientific evidence that MBM was the source of the epidemic became compelling enough, and the public outcry great enough, to overcome the political resistance of the cattle industry.

To model a JIT vaccination policy, create an Immunization Rate that transfers people from the susceptible population to a new stock, the Immunized Population. (Keeping the immunized population separate from the recovered population makes it easy to determine how many people ultimately get the disease.) Formulate the immunization rate so that the vaccination program is deployed only after a certain number of cases have been diagnosed:

$$\frac{\text{Immunization}}{\text{Rate}} = \begin{cases} 0 \text{ if Symptomatic Population } < \\ \quad \text{Threshold for Vaccination Program} \\ \text{Vaccination Rate * Vaccine Effectiveness} \quad \text{otherwise} \end{cases} \tag{9-27}$$

$$\text{Vaccination Rate} = \text{Fraction Vaccinated} * \frac{\text{Susceptible Population}}{\text{Time to Deploy Vaccine}} \tag{9-28}$$

The immunization rate (the actual rate at which people develop immunity from the vaccine) differs from the vaccination rate by the effectiveness of the vaccine. Once the program is deployed, it takes a certain amount of time, the Time to Deploy Vaccine, to carry out the program. The vaccination program may only reach a fraction of the population as well. Note that because the susceptibles cannot be distinguished from the asymptomatic infectives or recovered populations, the entire population would have to be immunized (with the possible exception of the symptomatic infectives for whom vaccination would not be effective). Consequently, the costs of the program depend on the total number vaccinated. However, those who have already recovered from the disease remain immune so they stay in the pool of recovered individuals. The formulation also assumes that the vaccine is ineffective for those who have already been infected, so there is no flow from the asymptomatic infective population to the immunized population.

To test the effectiveness of a JIT immunization program, make the strong assumptions that a vaccine with 100% effectiveness is available and that the fraction of the population vaccinated is 100%. Further, assume that the entire population can be vaccinated in just 2 days, once the threshold has been reached and the decision to deploy the vaccine has been made. These conditions are unlikely to be achieved in reality but provide a strong test of the potential for JIT vaccination strategies to address acute infectious disease.

Explore the effectiveness of the JIT vaccination policy by running the model for various thresholds, starting with a threshold of 5% of the total population. What fraction of the total population eventually gets the disease? How does that compare to the case without JIT vaccination? What if the threshold were just 1% of the total population (100 cases)? What is the effectiveness of JIT vaccination when the vaccine is only 95% effective, only 80% of the population is immunized, and if the delay in deploying the vaccination program is 1 week? Comment on the types of diseases for which JIT vaccination is likely to be effective and those situations in which it will be ineffective. Be sure to consider the social as well as biological determinants of compliance with a crash vaccination program.

9.2.7   Modeling the HIV/AIDS Epidemic

So far the hypothetical diseases examined have been highly infectious, acute infections (similar to chicken pox or measles) that generate rapid, short-lived epidemics. Over the course of such an epidemic, it is reasonable to assume that the contact rate and other parameters are constants—the epidemic develops too fast for significant changes in people's behavior or for research on prevention or treatment to come to fruition. These assumptions are not appropriate for diseases such as HIV/AIDS where the incubation time is long. Figure 9-11 shows the incidence and mortality of AIDS in the US from 1984 through 1996; Figure 9-12 shows the prevalence of AIDS among adults in the US.[5]

The data show important shifts in the dynamics of the epidemic in the US. Incidence of clinical AIDS (indicated by the AIDS-OI curve in Figure 9-11) grew steadily until about 1995 and has declined significantly since. Mortality closely follows incidence and exhibits an even larger decline. The decline in mortality exceeds that in incidence due to the development of therapies including AZT and, most importantly, the so-called multidrug cocktails or HAART (highly active anti-retroviral therapy). Overall incidence has declined due to a reduction in new cases transmitted by male homosexual contact and sharing of dirty needles by intravenous drug users (incidence among women and due to heterosexual contact was still rising as I wrote this). Note that even before the introduction of HAART, however, the growth of the epidemic was not a pure exponential, as would be expected if the contact rate or infectivity were constant. Instead, the fractional growth rate of AIDS incidence declined as the epidemic spread.

Despite the great strides in treatments, the improving outlook for the HIV epidemic in the wealthy nations is only part of the story. There is as yet no effective vaccine, and the long-run effectiveness and side effects of HAART remain unknown. More importantly, HAART is exceedingly costly and, in many nations, simply unavailable. The incidence of HIV infection globally continues to rise and in many nations has long since passed the crisis point. The scale of the epidemic is almost impossible to comprehend. The WHO estimated that in 1997 about one-quarter of the entire population of Zimbabwe was infected with HIV; incidence in much of Africa and some other developing nations is estimated to exceed 10%. Ten million people have already died of AIDS in sub-Saharan Africa, and without dramatic changes in access to treatment and drugs, 20 million more people are projected to die. Mortality and morbidity from HIV and AIDS in many of these nations have overwhelmed the health care systems. The WHO estimates that in 1990 there were fewer than 200 hospitals and 1400 doctors in all of Zimbabwe, a nation of more than 11 million. Life expectancy is falling. Despite the decline in AIDS-related mortality in some of the affluent nations of the world, the HIV/AIDS pandemic is far from over. The WHO reported that in 1998 AIDS was the fourth largest cause of death worldwide, up from seventh in 1997.

---

[5]Despite the massive effort and careful work of the CDC, the data are highly uncertain and are adjusted in several ways to overcome various limitations in the US surveillance and reporting system. The definitions of AIDS have changed over the years as understanding of the disease has improved. Data on HIV incidence and prevalence are even less complete and reliable. Readers are urged to consult the full HIV/AIDS Surveillance Reports and references therein for details.

FIGURE 9-11

Incidence and mortality of AIDS in the US

"Estimated incidence of AIDS, AIDS-opportunistic illness (AIDS-OI), and deaths in persons with AIDS, adjusted for delays in reporting, by quarter-year of diagnosis/death, United States, 1984–1996 [quarterly data reported at annual rates].

Estimated incidence of AIDS includes persons diagnosed using the 1993 expanded surveillance case definition [which counts HIV+ persons with severely suppressed immune systems even though they do not yet suffer from opportunistic infections; the old definition is now tracked by the incidence of AIDS-OI, which provides a more consistent estimate of incidence over time]. . . . Points on the figure represent quarterly incidence [rescaled to annual rates]; lines represent smoothed incidence. Estimated incidence of AIDS, estimated AIDS-OIs, and deaths are all adjusted for delays in reporting. Estimates are not adjusted for incomplete reporting of cases."

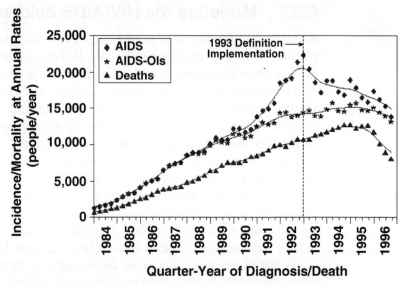

Source: US Centers for Disease Control and Prevention, *HIV/AIDS Surveillance Report,* Midyear 1997 edition, vol. 9 (no. 1), figure 6 and caption, p. 19.

To interpret the data and develop a model, it is useful to review the nature and course of HIV and AIDS. The progression of HIV/AIDS can be divided roughly into the following categories: After initial infection with HIV, the virus replicates rapidly, stimulating an immune response including the production of HIV-specific antibodies. The common clinical test for HIV does not detect the presence of the virus itself but rather the antibodies indicating the presence of sufficient virus to trigger the immune response. There is a delay of several weeks to 6 months before the body produces sufficient antibodies to yield a positive result from an HIV test. Prior to seroconversion (the point at which an infected person begins to test positive), infected people can transmit the virus to others but will not test positive. After seroconversion, there is a long latency period during which there are no clinical symptoms. The length of the incubation period varies widely. The median incubation period is estimated to be about 10 years in previously healthy adults, though it is shorter for children, the elderly, and those with prior health problems (Cooley, Myers, and Hamill 1996). Eventually, the virus compromises the immune system so severely that the patient begins to suffer from a wide range of opportunistic infections such as pnuemocystis pnuemonia and Kaposi's sarcoma, which lead to the diagnosis of AIDS.

Prior to the development of HAART, the mortality rate was extremely high. About 93% of all those diagnosed prior to 1986 in the US had died by the end of 1996. The mean survival time from the time of diagnosis, in the absence of treatment with HAART, is about 10 to 12 months, though, as with incubation, survival times vary widely.[6] The long-run effectiveness of HAART is still unknown. While it can reduce the viral load below detectable levels in some patients, HAART does

---

[6]The clinical and epidemiological literature on HIV/AIDS is enormous and evolves rapidly. A good source of information and references is available at the HIV InSite website developed by the University of California at San Francisco, <http://hivinsite.ucsf.edu>.

FIGURE 9-12
Prevalence of AIDS in the United States

"Adults/ adolescents living with AIDS, by quarter, January 1988 through June 1996, adjusted for reporting delays, United States"

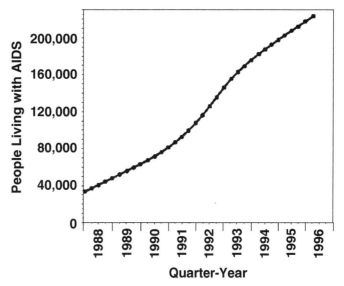

Source: US Centers for Disease Control and Prevention, *HIV/AIDS Surveillance Report,* 1996, vol. 8 (no. 2), p. 1.

not completely eliminate HIV from the body (Cohen 1998). People who discover they are HIV$^+$ can begin HAART and other treatments prior to the emergence of symptoms and are more likely to alter their behavior. Not all those who are at risk are tested, of course, so for many people the first indication that they are HIV$^+$ comes when they develop symptoms of AIDS.

CHALLENGE

Modeling HIV/AIDS

A. Stock and flow structure of the HIV/AIDS epidemic.
Based on the description above, develop a stock and flow diagram representing the progression of individuals from susceptible through the various stages of HIV infection and AIDS. Include a stock of cumulative deaths. In the SIR model the population is assumed to be homogeneous, a very poor assumption for modeling HIV/AIDS. Many epidemiological models of HIV/AIDS disaggregate the population into several categories that represent the different modes of transmission (primarily homosexual contact, heterosexual contact, and intravenous drug use), as well as gender, age, socioeconomic status, region, and perhaps other categories.[7] These groups overlap and interact, creating an intricate feedback structure and a very complex model. For the purpose of this challenge, do not disaggregate the population. After you develop a single aggregate model, you can consider disaggregation to capture the different risky behaviors and their interactions.

---

[7]There are dozens of published epidemiological models of HIV/AIDS and other sexually transmitted diseases. Good starting points include Anderson (1994), Garnett and Anderson (1996), Heidenberger and Roth (1998), and Roberts and Dangerfield (1990). The entire May-June 1998 issue of *Interfaces* (28[3]) was devoted to modeling AIDS, including policy issues such as needle exchanges, vaccine development, and HIV screening.

B.   Feedback structure of the HIV/AIDS epidemic.

Once you have developed the stock and flow map, add the feedback structure for the rates by following the assumptions of the extended SIR model above, including the infection rate, rate of seroconversion, AIDS diagnosis rate, and death rate.

Over the time frame for the development of the AIDS epidemic, the parameters of the SIR model such as the mortality rate and the contact rate between susceptibles and the various categories of HIV$^+$ individuals cannot be considered constant. Modify your causal diagram to incorporate feedbacks you believe are important. Be sure to consider the following:

1.   The average contact rate may fall as people become aware of the risk of HIV and the ways in which it can be transmitted; that is, some people may reduce or abstain from use of intravenous drugs or sexual contact.

2.   The infectivity of contacts depends on people's behavior. Safer sex practices and the use of clean needles by IV drug users can reduce the infectivity of those contacts that do occur. The use of safer sex practices and clean needles in turn depends on people's awareness of the risk of HIV infection and its consequences and on the availability of information and resources about these practices. In turn, the availability of information about safer sex and the importance of needle cleaning, along with condoms and clean needles, depends on social attitudes and public health programs in the media, schools, and other community organizations.

3.   Research and development into treatments such as HAART can reduce the mortality rate. The availability of these treatments depends on the extent to which they are reimbursable through health insurance and on the willingness of people to get tested for HIV. Many people are unwilling to be tested even if they know they are at risk, out of fear, frequently well founded, that they may be stigmatized, including the possibility they might lose their jobs, homes, and friends.

In representing changes in people's behavior (e.g., changes in contact rates and infectivity), consider how people might become aware of the existence, severity, and risks of HIV and different behaviors. Do they read the *New England Journal of Medicine* or get their information through word of mouth or personal acquaintance with someone suffering from AIDS? How do people judge the risk of infection and the consequences of infection? People are much more likely to contract the common cold than HIV, but a cold does not inspire the dread HIV does. What information sources are ordinary people exposed to, and how persuasive are these in inducing changes in behavior? What is the role of social attitudes toward the behaviors through which HIV can be transmitted? What is the role of government policies? Be sure to consider the time delays in the feedbacks you identify.

Use your causal diagram to explain the dynamics of the AIDS epidemic in the US. In particular, explain, in terms of the feedback structure of the system, why the fractional growth rate of the epidemic fell in the early years. Explain the decline in incidence beginning about 1995 and the even steeper decline in mortality. Explain why the number of people living with AIDS continues to increase (Figure 9-12).

Treatments such as HAART hold the promise to convert HIV infection from a death sentence to a chronic infection with low mortality. Based on your diagram, what changes in behavior might arise as a side effect of the development of HAART? How might these changes affect the contact rate or infectivity? Would these feedbacks increase or decrease the incidence of HIV infection? Explain. What are the public health implications of successful treatments such as HAART?

C. Simulating the HIV/AIDS epidemic.
Develop a formal model of the HIV/AIDS epidemic based on the structure you identify above. To do so you will need to use a number of nonlinear behavioral functions (e.g., to capture the way perceptions of risk alter the contact rate or infectivity). Guidelines for the development of such nonlinear functions are found in chapter 14. Work (at least initially) with a single aggregate stock and flow structure, and do not disaggregate your model into subpopulations. Simulate your model under at least two conditions: (1) on the assumption of no behavioral change and no improvement in treatments and (2) including the feedbacks you identified in part B that might lead to changes in the contact rate, in infectivity, and in mortality. Explain the results. Test the policy recommendations you identified in part B. Discuss the policy implications.[8]

9.3 INNOVATION DIFFUSION AS INFECTION: MODELING NEW IDEAS AND NEW PRODUCTS

The diffusion and adoption of new ideas and new products often follows S-shaped growth patterns. What are the positive feedbacks that generate the initial exponential growth of a successful innovation, and what are the negative feedbacks that limit its growth? Consider the spread of cable television (Figure 4-9). The growth of the population of cable television subscribers cannot be explained by the birth of children to existing cable subscribers, though the offspring of heavy TV viewers do tend to grow up to be couch potatoes. What then are the positive loops responsible for the growth of the cable industry?

The spread of rumors and new ideas, the adoption of new technologies, and the growth of new products can all be viewed as epidemics spreading by positive feedback as those who have adopted the innovation "infect" those who have not. The concept of positive feedback as a driver of adoption and diffusion is very general and can be applied to many domains of social contagion (e.g., the feedback structure of the cocaine epidemic described in section 7.3). A rumor spreads as those who have heard it tell those who have not, who then go on to tell still others. New ideas spread as those who believe them come into contact with those who do not

---

[8]For the purpose of this challenge it is acceptable to model the transitions from one category of infected individual to the next as first-order processes. More realistic models represent the incubation and mortality distributions derived from empirical studies more accurately through the use of higher-order delays (see chapter 11).

and persuade them to adopt the new belief. The new believers in turn then persuade others. As early adopters of new technology and early purchasers of a new product expose their friends, families, and acquaintances to it, some are persuaded to try it or buy it themselves. In all these cases, those who have already adopted the product, idea or technology come into contact with those who have not, exposing them to it and infecting some of them with the idea, or the desire to buy the new product and further increasing the population of adopters. Any situation in which people imitate the behavior, beliefs, or purchases of others, any situation in which people jump on the bandwagon, describes a situation of positive feedback by social contagion. Of course, once the population of potential adopters has been depleted, the adoption (infection) rate falls to zero.[9]

In the cable television case, important factors in a household's decision to subscribe (assuming cable is available in the community) include favorable word of mouth from those who already subscribe and positive experiences viewing cable at the homes of friends and family. People hear about programs only available on cable and feel they must subscribe to be hip and knowledgeable among their peers in school or at the workplace. Additionally, people may subscribe to keep up with the Joneses, that is, to maintain or enhance their status (or their perception of their status) among their peer group. All of these channels of awareness and motivations for adoption create positive feedbacks analogous to the contagion loop in the basic epidemic model.

Figure 9-13 adapts the SI epidemic model (section 9.2.1) to the case of innovation diffusion. The infectious population now becomes the population of adopters, A—those who have adopted the new idea or purchased the new product. The susceptible population becomes the pool of potential adopters, P. Adopters and potential adopters encounter one another with a frequency determined by the contact rate, c. Unlike infectious diseases, word of mouth encounters that might lead to adoption could occur by telephone, mail, email, or other remote means and do not require physical proximity. As in infectious disease, not every encounter results in infection. The proportion of contacts that are sufficiently persuasive to induce the potential adopter to adopt the innovation is termed here the adoption fraction and denoted i (since the adoption fraction is analogous to the infectivity of a disease in the epidemic model).

The equations for the simple innovation diffusion model are identical to those for the SI model of chronic infection described in 9.2.1. Using the terminology in Figure 9-13, the model is

$$A = INTEGRAL(AR, A_0) \tag{9-29}$$

$$P = INTEGRAL(-AR, N - A_0) \tag{9-30}$$

$$AR = ciP(A/N) \tag{9-31}$$

As in the SI model, the total population N is constant:

$$P + A = N \tag{9-32}$$

---

[9]The literature on diffusion of new products and of social and technical innovations is huge. A good place to start is Everett Rogers (1995), *Diffusion of Innovations,* a classic originally published in 1962. For diffusion models applied to the sales of new products, see Parker (1994) and Mahajan, Muller, and Bass (1990).

FIGURE 9-13

Adoption of a new idea or product as an epidemic

Potential adopters come into contact with adopters through social interactions. A fraction of these contacts result in infection, that is, adoption of the new idea or purchase of the new product. Compare to Figure 9-4.

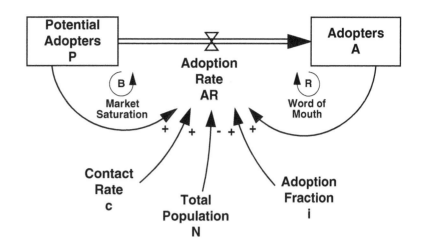

The interpretation is the same as in the SI model. People in the relevant community come into contact at a rate of c people per person per day. The total rate at which contacts are generated by the potential adopter pool is then cP. The proportion of adopters in the total population, A/N, gives the probability that any of these contacts is with an adopter who can provide word of mouth about the innovation. Finally, the adoption fraction, i, is the probability of adoption given a contact with an adopter. As before, these equations constitute an example of the logistic growth model discussed in section 9.1.1. The behavior of the model is the classic S-shaped growth of the logistic curve (Figure 9-1).

9.3.1   The Logistic Model of Innovation Diffusion: Examples

The diffusion of many new products follow roughly logistic trajectories. As an example, Figure 9-14 shows sales of the Digital Equipment Corporation VAX 11/750 minicomputer in Europe (Modis 1992). The VAX series was a very successful line of minicomputers. They sold for about $100,000 to $150,000 a unit, depending on which peripherals (such as tape drives) were included, an excellent value compared to the mainframes of the day. Typical customers were large companies, research organizations, and universities, who used them for data processing applications and to support scientific and engineering computation in R&D labs, product development departments, and academic research. The 11/750 was introduced in 1981. Sales follow the classic bell-shaped product life cycle, peaking in mid 1984. The product was withdrawn from the market around 1989. Accumulated sales follow an S-shaped path. Since the useful lifetime of the VAX is long compared to the time horizon for the product life cycle, it is reasonable to assume that few units were discarded prior to 1989 when the product was withdrawn from the market. Therefore cumulative sales is a good measure of the installed base.

To fit the logistic product diffusion model to the VAX sales data, assume the total population N = cumulative sales by 1989 (about 7600 units). The remaining parameter of the model, representing the product of the contact rate and adoption

FIGURE 9-14

Sales of the Digital Equipment Corporation VAX 11/750 in Europe

Top: Sales rate (quarterly data at annual rates). *Bottom:* Cumulative sales (roughly equal to the installed base).

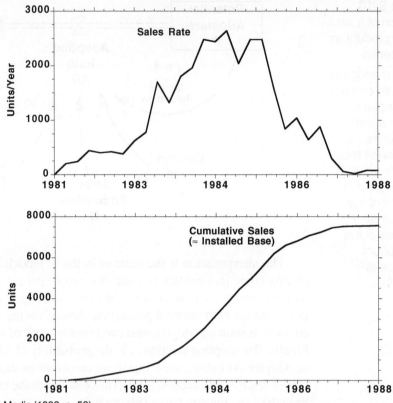

Source: Modis (1992, p. 58).

fraction (ci), can be estimated easily by linear regression.[10] First, recall from equation (9-8) that the solution to the logistic equation can be expressed (using the variable names for the innovation diffusion model above) as

$$\frac{A}{(N - A)} = \frac{A_0}{(N - A_0)} \exp(g_0 t) \tag{9-33}$$

where A is the number of adopters (the installed base), A_0 is the initial installed base, N is the total equilibrium or final value of adopters, and g_0 is the initial fractional growth rate of the installed base, which at the initial time when there are very few adopters is equal to the number of infective contacts (ci). Taking the natural log of both sides,

$$\ln\left[\frac{A}{(N - A)}\right] = \ln\left[\frac{A_0}{(N - A_0)}\right] + g_0 t \tag{9-34}$$

yields a relationship that is linear in the parameters and can be estimated by ordinary least squares. Note that since N − A = P (the difference between the total

---

[10]Since the adoption rate depends on the product of the contact rate and infectivity, ci, these parameters cannot be estimated separately from sales data. However, market research techniques such as test markets, focus groups, surveys, and so on can help the modeler develop estimates of the adoption fraction and contact rate. For forecasting purposes, only the product ci is needed.

population and the number of adopters is the number of potential adopters), equation (9-34) can be written more intuitively as a function of the ratio of adopters to potential adopters (A/P):

$$\ln\left(\frac{A}{P}\right) = \ln\left(\frac{A_0}{P_0}\right) + g_0 t \tag{9-35}$$

Equation (9-34) or (9-35) is known as the logistic (or simply, logit) transformation. Figure 9-15 shows the logit transformation of the VAX sales data, along with the estimated linear regression. The data are close to linear, which indicates excellent correspondence to the logistic model. The bottom panels of Figure 9-15 compare the estimated logistic curve to the sales and installed base data.

While the logistic innovation diffusion model fits the VAX sales data quite well, the estimation of the model was retrospective: the entire sales history was used, and the estimation method required knowledge of the final value of the installed base. In most business situations, however, the clients want to know the likely growth path prospectively, when the market potential is not known, so they can decide whether the market will be big enough to justify entry and plan strategy for capacity acquisition, pricing, marketing, and so on. One way to fit the logistic growth model to data prior to saturation is to estimate the rate at which the fractional growth rate declines with growing population. Recall from equation (9-1) that the fractional growth rate of the logistic model declines linearly as the population grows. Figure 9-16 shows the fractional growth rate in cable television subscribers in the US, along with the best linear fit (calculated by ordinary least squares). As expected, the fractional growth rate declines as the population grows, though there is considerable variation around the best linear fit. The logistic growth path implied by these parameters fits the data well through 1994 and predicts a maximum of about 74 million households subscribing to cable, reached shortly after 2010.

There is, however, considerable uncertainty in this prediction. First, there is uncertainty regarding the best fitting linear fractional growth rate. The actual fractional growth rate varies substantially around the best fit; other parameters for the straight line will fit nearly as well yet yield large differences in the maximum number of subscribers and time to saturation. Second, the best fit was estimated for the period 1969–1994; prior to 1969 the fractional growth rate was much higher. This is typical of growth processes: The fractional growth rate early in the history of a new product or innovation is often very high since the population of adopters is so small (and of course, when a new product is introduced the growth rate for the first reporting period is infinite). Changing the historical period over which the logistic model is estimated will therefore change the best fit parameters and the forecast. Third, the logistic model presumes a linear decline in the fractional growth rate as the population grows. There is, however, no compelling theoretical basis for linearity. Other shapes for the fractional growth rate curve will yield very different predictions. To illustrate, Figure 9-17 shows the cable television data against the best fit of both the logistic and Gompertz curves (equation (9-14)). The Gompertz curve fits the data about as well as the logistic curve but suggests continued growth to nearly 150 million subscribers in 2020, double the final level predicted by the logistic model.

FIGURE 9-15

Fitting the logistic model of innovation diffusion

Top: Applying the logit transformation (equation (9-35)) shows that the log of the ratio of adopters to potential adopters over time is very close to linear. The best fit is found by linear regression. *Middle:* Estimated and actual installed base (adopters) using the estimated parameters. *Bottom:* Estimated and actual sales (adoption rate) using the estimated parameters.

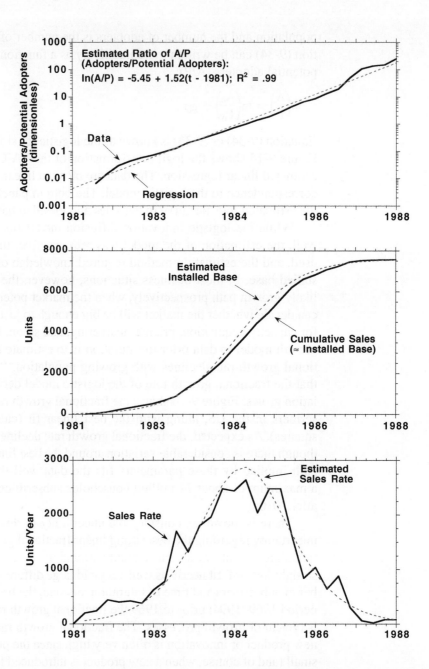

Estimated Ratio of A/P (Adopters/Potential Adopters):
$$\ln(A/P) = -5.45 + 1.52(t - 1981); R^2 = .99$$

9.3.2   Process Point: Historical Fit and Model Validity

The logistic model is widely used to explain and predict the diffusion of innovations, the growth of populations, and many other phenomena. Marchetti (1980) and Modis (1992), among many others, have fit the logistic curve to a wide range of data, from the compositions of Mozart to the construction of Gothic cathedrals. The logistic curve can fit data for a wide range of growth processes reasonably well. But you should not use the logistic model—or any model—as a curve fitting procedure for black box (atheoretical) forecasting. The logistic model often works well because it includes the two feedback processes fundamental to every growth

FIGURE 9-16

Fitting the logistic model to data for US cable TV subscribers

Top: Estimated and actual fractional growth rate of cable subscribers. *Bottom:* Actual subscribers vs. subscribers projected from the estimated growth rate.

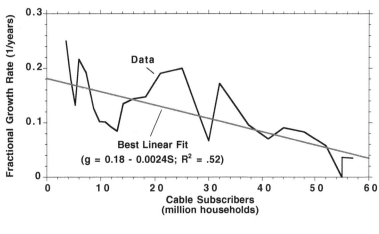

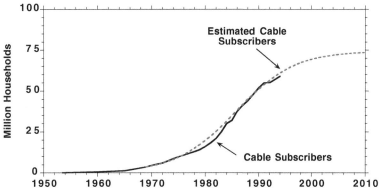

FIGURE 9-17

Predicted cable subscribers differ greatly depending on the growth model used.

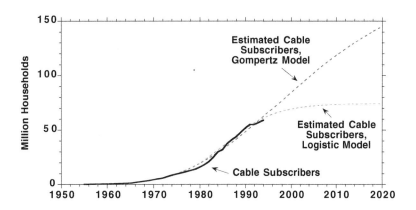

process: a positive loop that generates the initial period of accelerating growth and a negative feedback that causes the growth to slow as the carrying capacity is approached. Any system growing by positive feedback must include these two types of loops, coupled nonlinearly; any growth model must be characterized by a fractional growth rate that ultimately declines to zero as the population approaches its carrying capacity. However, as discussed above, the logistic model makes restrictive assumptions about the nature of the growth process. Advocates of the logistic model often present evidence selectively to show how well the model fits certain data but omit the many other growth processes for which it does not. The same considerations apply to all other single equation growth models such as the Richards or Weibull family.

The ability of the logistic model to fit a wide range of growth processes also illustrates several important lessons about the validity of models in general. First, the contrast between the forecasts of the logistic and Gompertz models for the cable television case shown in Figure 9-17 shows that different diffusion models can produce wildly different predictions while fitting the data equally well. The ability to fit the historical data does not, therefore, provide a strong basis for selecting among alternative hypotheses about the nature or strength of different feedbacks that might be responsible for a system's dynamics.

Second, getting more data does not solve the problem. Estimating the parameters of different growth models, and hence the trajectory of growth, by econometric techniques requires a long enough set of time series data to provide stable parameter estimates and to discriminate among the different growth models. In a review of innovation diffusion models for new product sales forecasting, Mahajan, Muller, and Bass (1990) note that "by the time sufficient observations have developed for reliable estimation, it is too late to use the estimates for forecasting purposes." By the time cable television has progressed far enough to discriminate between the logistic and Gompertz (and possibly other) models, so much of the diffusion life cycle will be past that the model will no longer be useful. The wildly different forecasts of cable diffusion are generated 40 years after the introduction of cable, after about half the households in the US had already adopted it, and well after the entry to the industry of formidable competitors.

Third, a main purpose of modeling is to design and test policies for improvement. To do so, the client must have confidence that the model will respond to policies the same way the real system would. Fitting the logistic curve (or any model) to a data set does not identify the specific feedback processes responsible for the dynamics. The ability of a model to fit the historical data by itself provides no information at all about whether its response to policies will be correct.

To illustrate, note that the logistic model, like all first-order growth models, presumes that the adopter population or installed base moves steadily upward. The number of adopters can never decline. Yet the history of new products and new technologies is replete with innovations whose pattern of emergence is boom and bust or fluctuation. It is easy to imagine credible scenarios in which, for example, cable television use declines, including rising prices, declining quality of programming, increasing competition from new technologies such as digital satellite broadcasts and the internet, and even a decline in television viewing (well, perhaps that last one isn't credible). Yet the logistic model, and all first order models, can never generate anything but growth. These models do not include the rich feedback structure needed to generate more complex and realistic patterns such as overshoot and oscillation or overshoot and collapse.

Innovation diffusion usually involves many positive feedbacks driving growth besides word of mouth (see chapter 10 for examples). For example, the availability of third-party software is a powerful driver of product attractiveness for computers. In turn, third-party developers will write software for those platforms they believe have the greatest market potential. Thus the larger the installed base of a particular computer (such as the VAX), the more software will be written for it, the more attractive it becomes to potential customers, and the larger the installed base will be. The positive software availability loop (and many others) can stimulate growth just as the word of mouth loop can. Because these other positive loops are omitted from the simple innovation diffusion model, statistical estimates of the strength of the word of mouth loop will reflect the impact of all positive loops contributing to the growth. The importance of word of mouth will be greatly overestimated while at the same time the strength of all the omitted loops is assumed to be zero. The model would indicate that a good policy to stimulate the early growth of the market would be to strengthen word of mouth (say, by sponsoring conferences or hiring key opinion leaders as spokespeople). However, the best policy may actually be to stimulate software availability by partnering with third-party developers. Such a model will not yield reliable policy recommendations despite the excellent historical fit. A model may fit the data perfectly for the wrong reasons.

Is it difficult to overemphasize the implications for modelers and clients. The ability of a model to replicate historical data does not, by itself, indicate that the model is useful. And failure to replicate historical data does not necessarily mean a model should be dismissed. The utility of a model cannot be judged by historical fit alone but requires the modeler to decide whether the structure and decision rules of the model correspond to the actual structure and decision rules used by the real people with sufficient fidelity for the client's purpose. To do so requires the modeler and client to examine the assumptions of the model in detail, to conduct field studies of decision making, and to explore the sensitivity of model results to plausible alternative assumptions (among other tests). Determining whether a model provides a sound basis for decision making is never a matter only of statistical testing or historical fit but is essentially and unavoidably a value judgment the modeler and client must make.

Unfortunately, clients and modelers frequently give historical fit too much weight. Judging the appropriateness of the model's structure, its robustness, and its sensitivity to assumptions takes time, while historical fit can be demonstrated quickly. Graphs showing a close fit between data and model are dramatic and compelling. Clients are too easily swayed by such graphs and by impressive tables of R^2 and other statistics. Modelers, even when they know better, too often overemphasize statistics showing how well their models fit the data to persuade the audience that the strong historical fit of the model means it must be correct.

You should not conclude from this discussion that historical fit is unimportant or that you do not need to compare your models to the numerical data. On the contrary, comparing model output to numerical data is a powerful way to identify limitations or flaws in model formulations. But there is a profound difference between using historical data to identify flaws so your models can be improved and using historical fit to assert the validity of your model. In the latter case, showing how well the model fits the data is a defensive maneuver designed to protect a model and the modeler from criticism and seals the client—and modeler—off from learning. In the former case, the historical fit is used to find problems and stimulate learning. Examining historical fit should be part of a larger process of testing and model improvement designed to yield a model suitable for policy design and decision making (see chapter 21).

9.3.3   The Bass Diffusion Model

One of the flaws in the logistic model of innovation diffusion is the startup problem. In the logistic (and the other simple growth models including the Richards and Weibull families), zero is an equilibrium: the logistic model cannot explain the genesis of the initial adopters. Prior to the introduction of cable television, the number of cable subscribers was zero; prior to the first sales of the VAX minicomputer, the installed base was zero. When growth processes begin, positive feedbacks depending on the installed base are absent or weak because there are no or only a few adopters. Initial growth is driven by other feedbacks outside the boundary of the simple diffusion models. There are several channels of awareness that can stimulate early adoption of new innovations besides word of mouth and related feedback effects that depend on the size of the adopter population. These include advertising, media reports, and direct sales efforts.

Frank Bass (1969) developed a model for the diffusion of innovations that overcomes the startup problem. The Bass diffusion model has become one of the most popular models for new product growth and is widely used in marketing, strategy, management of technology, and other fields. Bass solved the startup problem by assuming that potential adopters become aware of the innovation through external information sources whose magnitude and persuasiveness are roughly constant over time.

The original Bass model was introduced primarily as a tool for forecasting sales of new products, and Bass did not specify the nature of the feedbacks at the operational level. The positive feedback is usually interpreted as word of mouth (social exposure and imitation) and the external sources of awareness and adoption are usually interpreted as the effect of advertising (Figure 9-18 shows the feedback structure of the model with this interpretation).[11]

In Figure 9-18 the total adoption rate is the sum of adoptions resulting from word of mouth (and implicitly other positive feedbacks driven by the population of adopters or the installed base of the product) and adoptions resulting from advertising and any other external influences. Adoptions from word of mouth are formulated exactly as in the logistic innovation diffusion model (equation (9-31)). Bass assumed the probability that a potential adopter will adopt as the result of exposure to a given amount of advertising and the volume of advertising and other external influences each period are constant. Therefore the external influences cause a constant fraction of the potential adopter population to adopt each time period. Hence the adoption rate, AR, is

$$AR = \text{Adoption from Advertising} + \text{Adoption from Word of Mouth} \qquad (9\text{-}36)$$

$$\text{Adoption from Advertising} = aP \qquad (9\text{-}37)$$

---

[11]The original model, in continuous time, was specified as $dA/dt = AR = aP + bPA$, where a and b were parameters to be estimated statistically from the data on sales or adopters. Bass (1969) did not explicitly discuss the feedback loop structure of the model or specify what the processes of adoption were operationally, instead calling them innovation and imitation. Others refer to the two loops as external and internal influences on adoption. The model was also criticized for omitting economic and other variables that affect the adoption decision such as price or advertising effort (see the challenges below; see also Bass, Krishnan, and Jain 1994).

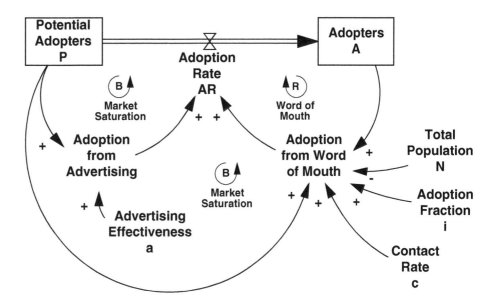

FIGURE 9-18

The Bass diffusion model

The model includes an external source of awareness and adoption, usually interpreted as the effect of advertising.

$$\text{Adoption from Word of Mouth} = ciPA/N \qquad (9\text{-}38)$$

where the parameter a, advertising effectiveness, is the fractional adoption rate from advertising (1/time period).

The two sources of adoption are assumed to be independent. Collecting terms, the model can be expressed more compactly as

$$AR = aP + ciPA/N \qquad (9\text{-}39)$$

When an innovation is introduced and the adopter population is zero, the only source of adoption will be external influences such as advertising. The advertising effect will be largest at the start of the diffusion process and steadily diminish as the pool of potential adopters is depleted.

CHALLENGE

Phase Space of the Bass Diffusion Model

Like the logistic growth model, the Bass model has two stocks. However, because $P + A = N$, only one of these stocks is independent, and the model is actually first-order. Using the fact that $P = N - A$, express equation (9-39) in terms of the adopter population A. Draw the phase plot for the model (a graph showing the adoption rate as a function of the adopter population). Draw the phase plot for three conditions: (i) advertising effectiveness is zero and all adoption occurs through word of mouth, (ii) word of mouth is zero ($ci = 0$) and all adoption occurs through advertising, and (iii) both advertising and word of mouth contribute to adoption.

Without using simulation, use the phase plot to sketch the behavior over time of the adopter population, potential adopter population, and adoption rate for each of the three cases above. How does advertising alter the point at which loop dominance shifts from positive to negative feedback? How does advertising affect the timing, symmetry, and other aspects of the dynamics compared to the logistic model?

After you have answered these questions, build and simulate the model to test your intuition. Run the model for the three cases above, and try other combinations of parameters to explore the range of behaviors the model can generate.

9.3.4   Behavior of the Bass Model

The Bass model solves the startup problem of the logistic innovation diffusion model because the adoption rate from advertising does not depend on the adopter population. When the innovation or new product is introduced, the adoption rate consists entirely of people who learned about the innovation from external sources of information such as advertising. As the pool of potential adopters declines while the adopter population grows, the contribution of advertising to the total adoption rate falls while the contribution of word of mouth rises. Soon, word of mouth dominates, and the diffusion process plays out as in the logistic diffusion model.

As an example, consider again the VAX 11/750 sales data (Figure 9-14). To model the VAX product life cycle with the logistic diffusion model it was necessary to start the simulation after the product was introduced, so that there was a nonzero installed base. A close look at Figure 9-15 shows that the pure logistic model underestimates sales during the first year and a half, and overestimates sales at the peak, consistent with the hypothesis that initial adoptions were stimulated not by word of mouth or other positive feedbacks but by external sources of awareness such as marketing effort. Figure 9-19 compares the behavior of the Bass model to the logistic diffusion model and the VAX sales data. As in the simulation of the logistic model, the total population N is assumed to be 7600 units. Advertising effectiveness, a, and the number of contacts resulting in adoption from word of mouth, c_i, were estimated by regression to be 0.011 per year and 1.33 per year, respectively. The contribution of sales from advertising to total sales is small after the first year, as seen in the bottom panel of Figure 9-19. Nevertheless, this modest change in the feedback structure of the diffusion process improves the model's ability to fit the sales data, both in the first 2 years and at the peak. Most important, the inclusion of the advertising effect solves the startup problem of the logistic model.

The Bass model is a significant and useful extension of the basic logistic model of innovation diffusion. The model itself, or variants of it, is broadly applicable to a wide range of diffusion and growth phenomena, and there is a large literature applying the Bass model and related models to innovation diffusion and sales of new products (see, e.g., Mahajan, Muller, and Bass 1990 and Parker 1994 for reviews).

CHALLENGE   **Critiquing the Bass Diffusion Model**

Even though the Bass model often works well, the model invokes a number of restrictive assumptions. List as many assumptions of the Bass model as you can. Include assumptions explicit in the formulation of the model and assumptions that are only implicit, especially those concerning aggregation and the model boundary (particularly effects and feedbacks omitted from the model).

FIGURE 9-19
The Bass
and logistic
diffusion models
compared to
actual VAX sales

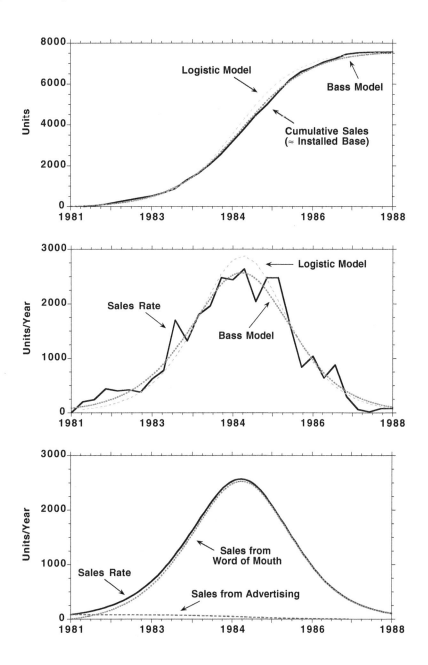

FIGURE 9-19
The Bass
and logistic
diffusion models
compared to
actual VAX sales

CHALLENGE

Extending the Bass Model

As noted above, the Bass model assumes the total size of the market (total population, N) is constant. In general, the population of a community or the number of households in a market grows over time through births, deaths, and migration. In the context of innovations with very short life cycles (e.g., the latest generation of video games) or acute diseases such as measles, the assumption of constant population is reasonable. But for innovations or diseases whose life cycles extend over many years (e.g., the diffusion of cable television or the AIDS epidemic), population growth can be significant.

A. Revise the Bass model to incorporate growth in the size of the total market.

Assume the total population size is a stock increased by a Net Population Increase Rate that aggregates births, deaths, and net migration (it is easy, but not necessary, to represent explicit birth, death, and net migration rates separately; see chapter 12). The Net Population Increase Rate is given by the total population and the Fractional Net Increase Rate, which can be assumed constant. Now you must decide how the increase in population is partitioned between potential adopters and adopters. The simplest assumption is that all increases in population size add to the pool of potential adopters. Recalling that all people or households in the population are either potential or actual adopters, reformulate the potential adopter population as $P = N - A$. Even though the potential adopter population is a stock, it is fully determined by the total population and adopter population and so can be represented as an auxiliary variable.

Apply your extended model to the cable television industry. The unit of adoption for cable television is not the individual, but households (and possibly businesses). The cable television industry in the US began in the early 1950s. At that time the number of households was about 40 million. By the late 1990s, there were nearly 100 million households, an average household formation growth rate of about 1.9%/year. Select parameters for advertising effectiveness and word of mouth that approximately replicate the pattern of cable adoption (Figure 9-16). It is not necessary to match the data exactly; an approximate fit is sufficient. Explore the sensitivity of the model to different population growth rates. What is the impact of variable population size on the dynamics?

B. Response of total market size to price.

In most markets, only a fraction of the total population will ever adopt a new innovation. The fraction of the population that might ever adopt typically depends on the benefits of the innovation relative to its cost (its price and any other associated costs, e.g., switching costs, costs of complementary assets, training costs, etc.; see Rogers 1995). Innovations are not static: their benefits often increase over time as research and product development lead to improvements in features, functionality, quality, and other attributes of product attractiveness. Similarly, the price of new products often falls significantly over time through learning curves, scale economies, and other feedbacks (see chapter 10). Modify the model you developed in part A to include the effect of product price on the size of the potential adopter pool. Assume the potential adopter population is a fraction of the total population, less the current number of adopters:

$$P = \text{Fraction Willing to Adopt} * N - A \tag{9-40}$$

where, in general, the Fraction Willing to Adopt depends on the overall attractiveness of the innovation or product (its benefits relative to costs):

$$\text{Fraction Willing to Adopt} = f(\text{Innovation Attractiveness}) \tag{9-41}$$

To keep the model simple, assume that the only feature of the innovation that varies is the price. A simple assumption is that the demand curve for the product is linear. For the case of cable television, assume that demand is a linear function of the monthly cost (ignore installation charges). Since nearly all US households have television, assume the Fraction Willing to Adopt would be 100% when cable is free and would fall to zero if the cost were $200/month.

To test the model, assume price is exogenous. First, run the model with price constant at an initial value of $100/month. To focus on the dynamics of the price effect alone, assume the Fractional Net Increase Rate for the total population is zero. Since price is constant, the total population should be constant, and the model reduces to the original Bass formulation. Simulate your model to check that it behaves appropriately when the price is constant.

Now test the impact of varying prices by assuming the price of cable falls over time. First, test the effect of a sudden drop in price, to, say, $25/month. Try the price drop at different points in the diffusion life cycle.

C. Is your model robust?

Typically, prices fall over the life cycle of a successful new product or innovation. But models must be robust and behave appropriately under all potential circumstances, not only the historical or expected behavior. A common and important way to test for robustness is the *extreme conditions test* (chapter 21). In an extreme conditions test, an input to a model is assumed to suddenly take on extreme values. The model must continue to behave appropriately even if that extreme value will never arise in reality. For example, suddenly destroying all inventory in a model of a manufacturing firm must force the shipment rate immediately to zero. If shipments do not fall to zero, the modeler (and client) immediately know there is a basic flaw in the model. As an extreme conditions test in your model, suddenly raise the price to a very large number (such as $1 million per month). If prices were to rise that much, what must happen to the potential adopter population? To the population of subscribers? Implement the price rise at various points in the life cycle. Does your model behave appropriately? What problem or problems are revealed by the test? Propose, implement, and test revisions that correct any problems you identify.

D. Interaction of diffusion and the learning curve.

The prices of many new products and services fall over time as learning, scale economies, and other effects lower costs and as competition intensifies. Make the product price an endogenous part of the model structure by incorporating a learning curve. Learning or experience curves capture the way in which producers, distributors, and others in the value chain learn to produce at lower costs as they gain experience. Usually costs are assumed to fall as cumulative experience with the product or service grows. In a manufacturing setting, cumulative experience is usually proxied by cumulative production. In a service industry, cumulative experience might better be represented as depending on the cumulative number of transactions and will depend on the adopter population and the number of transactions each adopter generates per time period. Typically, unit costs fall by a fixed percentage with every doubling of experience. Cost reductions of 10% to 30% per doubling of cumulative experience have been documented in a wide range of industries (see, e.g., Teplitz 1991; Gruber 1992; Argote and Epple 1990). To incorporate a learning curve into your innovation diffusion model, first assume that any cost reductions are fully passed into price:

$$\text{Price} = \text{Initial Price} * \text{Effect of Learning on Price} \tag{9-42}$$

$$\text{Effect of Learning on Price} = \left(\frac{\text{Cumulative Experience}}{\text{Initial Cumulative Experience}} \right)^{c} \tag{9-43}$$

$$\text{Cumulative Experience} = \text{INTEGRAL(Adoption Rate,} \\ \text{Initial Cumulative Experience)} \tag{9-44}$$

The exponent c determines how strong the learning curve is and should be negative (costs fall as cumulative experience grows). To represent a learning curve in which costs fall 30% for each doubling of experience, set $c = \log_2(0.7) \approx -0.51$.[12]

Test your model for a hypothetical manufacturing firm that introduces a new consumer durable product in the year 2000. The product has high market potential. Set the following parameters: Assume that 100% of the total population of 100 million households will purchase the product if it is free but that demand falls to zero if the price is $2500 per unit. Set the initial price to $2000/unit, and set initial experience to 10 million units (reflecting learning gained on prior products and prototypes). Research on consumer durables shows typical product life cycles last from about a year to as long as 20 years or more (Parker 1994), depending on the cost, benefits, size, trialability, novelty, and other attributes of the product, along with the role of complementary assets and other infrastructure (computers aren't valuable without software; a television is useless without programming people want to watch and networks or cable operators to distribute it). To capture the range, define the following two scenarios for the diffusion of the product: a Slow scenario, in which the product of the contact rate and adoption fraction (ci) is 1.0/year, and a Fast scenario, in which the product of the contact rate and adoption fraction ci is 3.0/year. Assume for both scenarios that 1% of the potential adopter pool will purchase as the result of advertising per year.

---

[12]For a learning curve where costs C fall by a fixed fraction per doubling of experience E, costs are given by

$C = C_0(E/E_0)^c$.

When E has doubled, costs have fallen by a fraction f, so

$(1 - f)C_0 = C_0(2E_0/E_0)^c$

or

$c = \ln(1 - f)/\ln(2) = \log_2(1 - f)$.

For a learning curve with $f = 0.30$, $c = 0.5146$. Since f, the fractional cost reduction per doubling of experience, has a more intuitive meaning than the exponent c, it is convenient to formulate c in the model as a computed constant, $c = \ln(1 - f)/\ln(2)$ and then specify the cost reduction fraction f as a constant.

Before running your model, draw a causal diagram showing the feedback structure created by the learning curve and how it interacts with the structure of diffusion. *Without simulation,* sketch the dynamics you expect for the fraction of the market willing to adopt, the potential adopter population, adoption rate, and adopter population. Also sketch the path of revenues you expect. Assume the product is purchased, not leased, and ignore revenues that may derive from sale of services or aftermarket products to the adopters (revenue depends only on the adoption rate and price).

After sketching the dynamics you expect, run the model for both the Fast and Slow cases. Describe the dynamics, and compare to your intuitive estimates. Experiment with different strengths for the learning curve relative to the diffusion process. How do diffusion processes and learning curves interact to determine the growth of a new product? What are the implications of very rapid diffusion for revenues, capacity planning, and new product development? What implications for strategy (pricing, capacity acquisition, and marketing) do you draw?

9.3.5 Fad and Fashion: Modeling the Abandonment of an Innovation

The Bass diffusion model is analogous to the SI model of chronic infection. Everyone eventually adopts the product and adopters never abandon the innovation or discontinue use of the product. These assumptions are appropriate for some innovations but do not apply to the huge category of fashions and fads.

A fad, by definition, involves the temporary adoption of a new idea or product, followed by its abandonment. In a fad, those who adopt sooner or later (usually sooner) discontinue their use of the product and no longer generate word of mouth that might lead to further adoption. Though many baby boomers wore Nehru jackets or granny dresses in the 1960s, polyester leisure suits or rainbow-colored platform shoes in the 1970s, and power suits with yellow ties or shoulder pads in the 1980s, few are seen wearing them today.[13] Fad and fashion are of course common in the apparel industry but also arise in nearly every other domain, from home furnishings, vacation destinations, cuisines, automobiles, and investments to styles in the arts and music, academic theories in the sciences and humanities, and hot new buzzwords and gurus in corporate strategy, organizational theory, and management consulting.

The Bass model cannot capture the dynamics of fads in part because adopters never discontinue their use of the innovation. Further, because the contact rate and adoption fraction are constant, the earliest adopters are just as likely to infect potential adopters as those who just purchased the product. For many innovations (not only fads), however, people's propensity to generate word of mouth, and their enthusiasm and persuasiveness, vary over time. Usually, word of mouth decays as people become habituated to the innovation. Those who have recently embraced a

---

[13]The fashion industry frequently reintroduces old fashions. The fashions of the 70s were recycled in the late 90s, including platform shoes and bellbottoms, but thankfully not polyester leisure suits.

new idea or purchased a new item are much more likely to talk about it than those who have long since adopted the innovation even if they continue to use it. Indoor plumbing can hardly be considered a passing fad, yet people do not rush out to tell their friends how wonderful flush toilets are.

In the 1980s Selchow and Righter sold tens of millions of copies of the game Trivial Pursuit. Sales boomed as Trivial Pursuit became one of the hottest products in the toy and game market. The boom was fed largely by word of mouth and social exposure as people played it at the homes of their friends. After a few years, however, sales slumped. Much of the decline can be attributed to the familiar market saturation loop: the game was so successful the company depleted the pool of people who had not yet purchased a copy. But the fading novelty of the game was also a factor. The population of adopters is still large in the sense that many people still own a copy of Trivial Pursuit. However, most of these copies are in attics and closets. The population of active adopters, those who still play the game and generate word of mouth contacts with others, is small.

Discontinuation of use and the decay of word of mouth can easily be incorporated in the innovation diffusion framework by disaggregating the adopter population into different categories, each representing different degrees of use and propensities to generate word of mouth. The simplest extension of the model is to divide the total adopter population into two categories, Active Adopters and Former Adopters. The discontinuation rate (the rate at which active adopters become former adopters) depends on the average duration of use for the innovation (the simplest assumption is that the discontinuation rate is a first-order process). Word of mouth and hence the adoption rate would be generated only by the population of active adopters.

The revised model is analogous to the SIR epidemic model. Now only active adopters (analogous to the infectious population) generate word of mouth that might induce additional adoption. Former adopters are analogous to the population of recovered individuals. Having purchased the product but no longer actively using it, the former adopters are no longer infectious to others and are also immune to reinfection—exposure to advertising or word of mouth from active adopters won't induce aging baby boomers to buy another leisure suit.[14]

The key insight from the SIR epidemic model is the concept of the tipping point: exposure to infectious individuals will not produce an epidemic if people recover and develop immunity faster than they can infect others. Similarly, new innovations might fail to take hold even if they generate positive word of mouth because active adopters discontinue usage faster than they persuade others to adopt. Though a distressingly large number of bizarre fashions and useless products are embraced by eager consumers who mindlessly allow marketers to manipulate their tastes, many more fail to take hold.

In the SIR model, the tipping point is defined by a reproduction rate of one. The reproduction rate is the number of new cases generated by each infective prior

---

[14]As in the extended SIR models developed in section 9.2, the population of adopters could be disaggregated further, for example, into cohorts of people who adopted the innovation 1, 2, . . . , n time periods ago, to capture situations where the contact rate and adoption fraction decay gradually rather than in a first-order pattern (chapter 12).

to recovery and is defined by the product of the contact number (the number of infectious contacts generated by each infective prior to recovery) and the probability of contacting a susceptible individual (equation (9-26)). Using the terminology of the innovation diffusion framework, the reproduction rate is the product of the number of persuasive word of mouth contacts generated by each active adopter prior to discontinuation and the probability of encountering a potential adopter:

$$cid\left(\frac{P}{N}\right) > 1 \tag{9-45}$$

where c is the contact rate, i is the adoption fraction, d is the average duration of active use for the innovation, P is the population of potential adopters, and N is the total population.

If the reproduction rate is greater than one, the positive word of mouth feedback dominates the system and a fad is born. The fad ends when the pool of potential adopters falls enough to bring the reproduction rate below one. If the reproduction rate is less than one, the positive word of mouth loop is dominated by the negative feedbacks and there will be no epidemic of adoption.

However, unlike the SIR model, adoption in the Bass innovation diffusion framework also arises from advertising and other external influences. In the simple Bass model the effectiveness of advertising is a constant, implying that the advertising budget is constant through time. Even when the system is below the tipping point, everyone will eventually adopt the innovation (though it may take a very long time).

In the real world, advertising is expensive and does not persist indefinitely. The marketing plan for most new products includes a certain amount for a kickoff ad campaign and other initial marketing efforts. If the product is successful, further advertising can be supported out of the revenues the product generates. If, however, the product does not take off, the marketing budget is soon exhausted and external sources of adoption fall. Advertising is not exogenous, as in the Bass model, but is part of the feedback structure of the system. There is a tipping point for ideas and new products no less than for diseases.

CHALLENGE

Modeling Fads

A. Modify the Bass model (or your extensions of it developed in section 9.3.4) by disaggregating the adopter population into active adopters and former adopters. Assume word of mouth is only generated by active adopters. Calibrate your model to represent a fad. Assume the total population is 100 million households, that the average duration of active use is 1 year, and that 1% of the potential adopters will adopt as the result of advertising each year. Assume a contact rate of 100 per person per year. Run the model for three cases: a strong word of mouth case where the adoption fraction is 0.025, an intermediate case where the adoption fraction is 0.01, and a weak case where the adoption fraction is 0.001. Contrast the behavior of the model in the three cases. How does the inclusion of adoption from advertising cause the behavior of the model to differ from the pure SIR model? Can a firm compensate for weak word of mouth by a massive advertising campaign?

B. How do most organizations set their advertising budgets? Draw a causal diagram that captures your understanding of the way in which advertising is determined. What feedback loops are created by the typical budgeting process? How might they affect the dynamics of adoption? How might such an advertising policy affect the nature of the tipping point for adoption of a new product?

C. What other processes and information sources might contribute to the dynamics of a fad? Develop a causal diagram capturing your ideas. What additional feedback loops are created? How might they affect the dynamics? Give examples.

9.3.6   Replacement Purchases

The Bass diffusion model is often described as a first-purchase model because it does not capture situations where the product is consumed, discarded, or upgraded, all of which lead to repeat purchases.

One popular way to model repeat purchase behavior is to assume that adopters move back into the population of potential adopters when their first unit is discarded or consumed. The rate at which the product is discarded and therefore the rate at which people move from the adopter population to the pool of potential adopters depends on the number of adopters and the average life of the product (Figure 9-20). Modeling replacement demand in this fashion is analogous to the loss of immunity to a disease. Now, instead of falling to zero, the potential adopter population is constantly replenished as adopters discard the product and reenter the market (Figure 9-21). The adoption rate (sales rate for a product) rises, peaks, and falls to a rate that depends on the average life of the product and the parameters determining the adoption rate. Discards mean there is always some fraction of the population in the potential customer pool. By varying the product life and strength of the word of mouth feedback, the rate of diffusion, including the height of the sales peak and the depth of the bust when the market saturates, can be varied. The model shown in Figure 9-20 assumes a first-order discard process but can easily be modified to represent any distribution of discards around the average product life using higher-order delays (chapter 11).

Because those discarding the product reenter the potential customer pool, they are treated exactly like first-time buyers and must go through another process of becoming aware of and being persuaded to buy the product through advertising or word of mouth. In some cases the lifetime of the product is so long and the attributes of the product change so much over this span that prior experience is largely irrelevant and repeat purchase decisions are reasonably similar to initial purchase decisions. But for most products, the customer has already made the decision to continue using the product and simply purchases a new one. In such cases the initial and repeat purchase decisions must be represented separately, as shown in Figure 9-22. Here the adoption process is separated from the flow of purchases. The total sales rate is the sum of initial purchases and repeat purchases. The repeat purchase rate is the product of the number of adopters and the average number of units purchased by each adopter per time period. Figure 9-23 shows typical model behavior.

FIGURE 9-20

Modeling product discard and replacement purchases

Customers discard the product with a time constant given by the Average Product Life, then return to the Potential Adopter Pool.

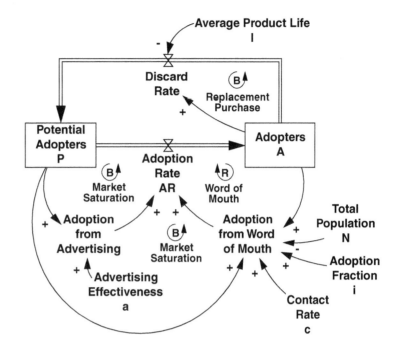

FIGURE 9-21

Behavior of the Bass model with discards and repurchases

Shows the behavior of the model in Figure 9-20 with an Average Product Life
l = 5 years,
a = 0.01, c = 100,
and i = 0.025.

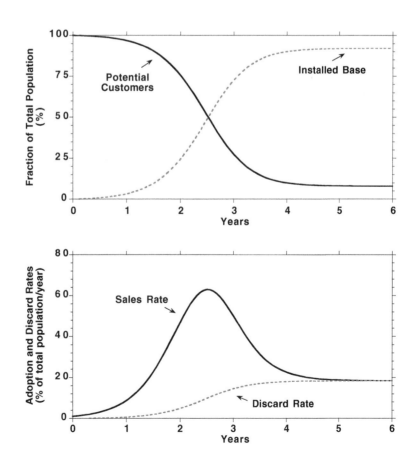

FIGURE 9-22

Modeling repeat purchases

Total sales consist of initial and repeat purchases. Each potential adopter buys Initial Sales per Adopter units when they first adopt the product and continues to purchase at the rate of Average Consumption per Adopter thereafter.

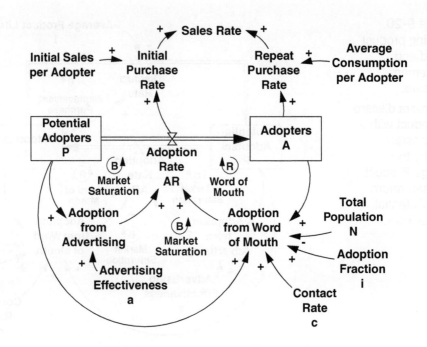

FIGURE 9-23

Behavior of the repeat purchase model

Behavior of model in Figure 9-22, with the same parameters as in Figure 9-21 and a total population of 100 million, initial purchases of 1 unit per person, and replacement purchases of 0.2 units per person per year.

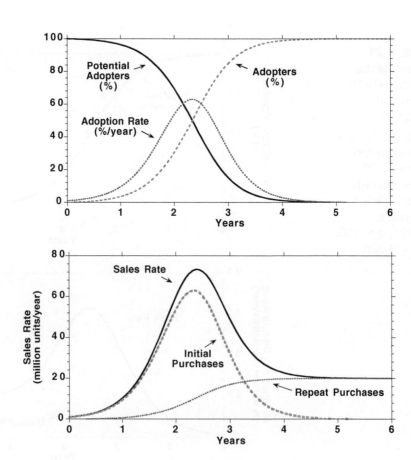

CHALLENGE	## Modeling the Life Cycle of Durable Products

The model in Figure 9-22 does not explicitly represent the stock of product held by the adopter population. Repeat purchases are modeled as depending on the current adopter population. This formulation is appropriate for nondurable consumables such as food, where the lifetime of the product is very short relative to the diffusion process and the acquisition and consumption or discard of the product do not need to be represented separately. For durable products, however, it is usually important to represent the stock of product and the discard rate explicitly.

Modify the model shown in Figure 9-22 to represent the adoption and installed base of a consumer durable such as video cassette recorders (VCRs). You may use either the simple Bass formulation or the extended model you developed in section 9.3.4 including the effect of price on the size of the market and the learning curve (when VCRs were introduced, the average price was about $2000/unit, but by the 1990s the average price had fallen to $200/unit).

The discard rate for durable products is often strongly age dependent and is not well approximated by a first-order process. To model the installed base of VCRs, create two stocks, New VCRs and Old VCRs. The stock of new VCRs is increased by the Purchase Rate. As VCRs age, they move into the stock of old VCRs. Assume the average VCR remains new for 3 years and that the aging rate is a first-order process. Though some new VCRs do break down and are discarded, for simplicity assume the discard rate of new VCRs is zero. Assume the average lifetime of old VCRs is 5 years, giving a total average life of 8 years.

What determines the purchase rate? First, households that have adopted the VCR will seek to replace those that break down and are discarded (or discard a usable unit to buy a new one with better features). Second, those households will buy more than the discard rate when the number of VCRs they collectively desire exceeds the number they actually have (and will buy less than the discard rate should they find they have more than they desire). The purchase rate is then the sum of the discard rate and an adjustment for installed base. The adjustment for the installed base is most simply formulated as a simple first-order negative feedback process:

$$\text{Adjustment for Installed Base} = \frac{(\text{Desired VCRs} - \text{Total VCRs})}{\text{Stock Adjustment Time}} \qquad (9\text{-}46)$$

where the total number of VCRs is the sum of the new and old VCR stocks, and the Stock Adjustment Time represents the average time required for people to shop for and purchase a VCR. Define the desired stock of VCRs as depending on the number of households that have adopted the VCR and the average number of VCRs desired per household. The challenge to extend the Bass model in section 9.3.4 introduced the notion that the fraction of the population willing to adopt the product depends on its overall attractiveness, including price. The growth of markets for many important products involves *both* a process of adoption by an increasing fraction of the population *and* a gradual increase in the number of units owned by each household as real prices fall and as household income rises. When they were first introduced, households "made do" with just one car, phone, TV, and computer. As prices fell, quality rose, and the importance of these products in daily life grew, the number per household grew. By explicitly representing the number of units desired per adopter the model can represent situations where adopters increase the number of units they desire as their income grows, as price declines, or as other attributes of product attractiveness improve. For now, assume the number of VCRs desired by each adopter household is one.

Note that if the desired stock of VCRs increases above the actual stock (say because prices fall so more adopting households decide to buy a second VCR), the purchase rate will rise above the discard rate and the stock will increase until the gap is closed. Should the desired stock of VCRs fall, the purchase rate will fall below the discard rate and the stock of VCRs will gradually fall.

Test the robustness of your formulation for the purchase rate. Implement an extreme conditions test in which the desired stock of VCRs suddenly falls to zero from an initial situation in which the desired and actual stocks are equal and large. Modify your formulation for the purchase rate to ensure that it behaves appropriately even if there are many more VCRs than desired.

VCRs for the home market were introduced by Sony in 1975. By the early 1990s approximately 80% of US households had at least one VCR. Select parameters for your model that are roughly consistent with these data. Use your judgment to estimate the other parameters such as the stock adjustment time. For simplicity, assume the total number of households in the US is 100 million and constant. Simulate the model and discuss the results. In particular, what is the pattern of adoption? What is the pattern of sales?

Since the introduction of the VCR the average duration of product life cycles for consumer electronics, computers, and many other products has shrunk. Life cycles of just a few years or even less are common. Simulate the model assuming the word of mouth feedback is three times as strong as the value you selected for the VCR case. How long does it now take for 80% of households to adopt the product? What are the implications for sales? Why? What difficulties do short product life cycles pose for firms?

9.4   SUMMARY

S-shaped growth arises through the nonlinear interaction of positive and negative feedback loops. Any growing quantity can be thought of as a population growing in an ecological niche with a certain carrying capacity. S-shaped growth arises when the carrying capacity is fixed and when there are no significant delays in the reaction of the population's growth rate as the carrying capacity is approached.

The structure underlying S-shaped growth applies to a wide range of growth processes, not only population growth. These include the adoption and diffusion of new ideas, the growth of demand for new products, the spread of information in a community, and the spread of diseases, including biological pathogens and computer viruses.

A number of analytically tractable models of S-shaped growth were introduced, including the logistic growth model, the SIR epidemic model, and the Bass diffusion model. Important extensions to the basic epidemic and innovation diffusion models were developed to illustrate how modelers can identify the restrictive assumptions of a model, both explicit and implicit, and reformulate the model to be more realistic.

The logistic, epidemic, and innovation diffusion models can be fit to historical data, and the fit is often excellent. However, though nonlinear growth models such as the logistic and Bass models are widely used and often fit certain data sets quite well, you should not use these (or any) models as black boxes for forecasting.

To create realistic and useful models of product diffusion and innovation adoption you must explicitly portray the feedback structure of adoption and growth, including the sources of attractiveness for the new idea or product, the competition, technical innovation, changing criteria of use, and other factors that influence adoption and growth. Many rich and insightful system dynamics models of innovation diffusion have been developed and are used successfully to anticipate growth and design policies for success (see, e.g., Homer (1987) for a model of emerging medical technologies and Urban, Hauser and Roberts (1990) for feedback models for prelaunch forecasting of new automobile models).

The historical fit of a model does *not* show that the model is "valid." Many models, each with different assumptions about the feedback structure and each generating different dynamics, can fit any set of data equally well. Ground your models in careful investigation of the physical and institutional structures and decision-making processes of the actors in the system and don't force-fit data into the assumptions of any preselected functional form or model. Models should not be used as exercises in curve fitting using the aggregate data. Only models that capture the causal structure of the system will respond accurately as conditions change and policies are implemented.

10

Path Dependence and Positive Feedback

For unto every one that hath shall be given, and he shall have abundance; but from him that hath not shall be taken away even that which he hath.

—Matthew XXV: 29

This chapter explores path dependence, a pattern of behavior in which small, random events early in the history of a system determine the ultimate end state, even when all end states are equally likely at the beginning. Path dependence arises in systems whose dynamics are dominated by positive feedback processes. The chapter explores the circumstances in which positive feedback can create path dependence, the role of random events early in the history of a path-dependent system, and the ways in which a path-dependent system can lock in to a particular equilibrium. Feedback theories of path dependence and lock in are developed for a number of important examples in business, technology, and economics.

10.1 PATH DEPENDENCE

Why do clocks go clockwise? Why do people in most nations drive on the right? Why is the diamond business in New York concentrated into the area around west 47th Street? Why do nearly all typists learn the inefficient QWERTY keyboard layout? How did Microsoft's Windows and Intel's processors come to dominate the market for personal computers? Why are there so many winner-take-all markets—

situations where success accrues to the successful, where the rich get richer and the poor get poorer? And what do these questions have to do with each other? All are examples of systems exhibiting *path dependence*. Path dependence is a pattern of behavior in which the ultimate equilibrium depends on the initial conditions and random shocks as the system evolves. In a path-dependent system, small, unpredictable events early in the history of the system can decisively determine its ultimate fate.

The eventual end state of a path-dependent system depends on the starting point and on small, unpredictable perturbations early in its history. Even when all paths are initially equally attractive, the symmetry is broken by microscopic noise and external perturbations. Positive feedback processes then amplify these small initial differences until they reach macroscopic significance. Once a dominant design or standard has emerged, the costs of switching become prohibitive, so the equilibrium is self-enforcing: the system has locked in.

The exact gauge of a railroad is of little consequence (within broad limits). At the start of the rail age, no one gauge was a better choice than any other. Yet the standard gauge used in the US and most of the world is 1.44 meters (4 feet 8.5 inches). How did this convergence arise? Early railroads, each unconnected to the others, utilized a wide range of different gauges (one early line used a 7 foot gauge!). Rolling stock was specific to each network and could not be used on lines with a different gauge. But as rail networks grew, compatibility became more and more important (when gauges differed, goods transshipped from one line to another had to be unloaded from one train and reloaded on another, greatly raising costs and slowing delivery). Railroads offering compatibility enjoyed a huge cost advantage since the same rolling stock could use any part of the network. Gradually, the smaller railroads adopted the gauge used by the largest networks. The attractiveness of that gauge was then increased still further, forming a positive feedback. Smaller railroads using incompatible gauges lost business or converted their road and rolling stock to be compatible. Soon a single gauge—with the unlikely dimensions of 1.44 meters—emerged as the dominant standard. By the 1860s, the costs of switching to another gauge (Abraham Lincoln is reported to have argued for 5 feet) were prohibitive: the system had locked in to the standard.[1]

Similar positive feedbacks are responsible for other examples of path dependence: The more typewriters with the QWERTY keyboard were sold, the more people learned to type with that layout, and the more successful QWERTY machines became, while makers of alternative keyboards lost business. As the market share of Wintel computers grew, more software was written for that platform and less developed for other platforms and operating systems. The more software available for a particular operating system, the greater the demand for computers compatible with that system, increasing Wintel market share still further.

---

[1]Some claim that the standard gauge emerged because it was the width of jigs designed originally for wagons, which in turn had those dimensions to fit the ruts on the roads, which in turn were determined by the ruts in Roman roads, which were set by the width of Roman chariots and wagons, which in turn were sized to accommodate the width of two Roman horses. If true, it illustrates the way in which positive feedback can cause a standard to persist long after the initial rationale for its selection has vanished.

What causes some systems to exhibit path dependence but not others? Path dependence arises in systems dominated by positive feedback. Figure 10-1 illustrates the difference between a system dominated by negative feedback and a path-dependent system dominated by positive feedback. First, imagine a smooth-sided bowl. The lowest point of the bowl is an equilibrium—a marble placed there will remain there. The equilibrium is stable: pushing the marble off the equilibrium creates a force opposing the displacement. A marble dropped anywhere in the bowl will eventually come to rest at the bottom (though it may roll around a while first). The equilibrium is not path dependent: the marble comes to rest at the same spot no matter where it is dropped and no matter its initial velocity (as long as it stays within the bowl—the equilibrium is only locally stable). A stable equilibrium is also called an *attractor* because all points are attracted to it. Technically, because the equilibrium is locally and not globally stable it is an attractor only for points within its *basin of attraction*. The basin of attraction is the bowl. Inside it, all points lead to the attractor at the bottom. Outside the bowl, the dynamics are different. The Dead Sea and Great Salt Lake are examples: Rain falling anywhere over these watersheds ends up in their salty brine. Rain falling over other watersheds flows to the sea.

FIGURE 10-1   Path dependence arises in systems with locally unstable equilibria.

Left: A locally stable equilibrium. The system is governed by negative feedback: the greater the displacement of the ball from the equilibrium P*, the greater the force pushing it back toward the center and equilibrium. A ball placed anywhere in the bowl eventually comes to rest at the bottom; perturbations don't affect the equilibrium reached.

Right: A locally unstable equilibrium. The system is governed by positive feedback: the greater the displacement of the ball, the steeper the hill and the greater the force pulling it away from the equilibrium at P*. The slightest disturbance causes the ball to fall off the peak. The initial perturbation determines the path taken by the ball and perhaps the ultimate destination—the system is path dependent.

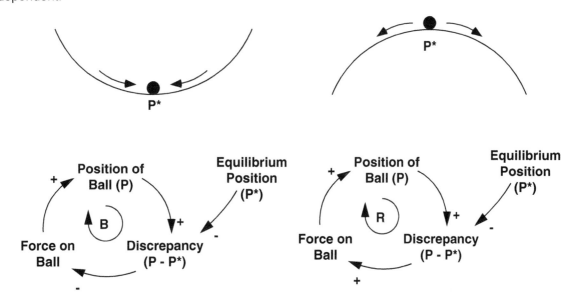

Now turn the bowl upside down. The top of the bowl is still an equilibrium—if the marble is balanced exactly at the top it will remain there. However, the equilibrium is now unstable. The slightest perturbation will cause the marble to move slightly downhill. As the slope increases, the downward force on the marble increases and it moves still further downhill, in a positive feedback. (An unstable equilibrium is also termed a *repellor* because nearby trajectories are forced away from it.) The system is path dependent because the direction taken by the ball depends on the initial perturbation: A small nudge to the left and the marble rolls to the left; an equally small shock to the right and it moves farther right. Of course, though the equilibrium at the top of the bowl is locally unstable, the system as a whole must be globally stable. The marble eventually comes to rest. But the path-dependent nature of the ball's motion near the equilibrium point means it can come to rest anywhere on the floor, and the particular spot it reaches depends on that small, initial disturbance.

Imagine rain falling near the continental divide of North America. Two raindrops fall a few inches apart, one just to the east of the divide and one just to the west. The difference in landing spot might be due to small, unobservable differences in the wind as the two drops fall from the clouds. Though they begin only inches apart, one ends up in the Pacific; the other, thousands of miles away in the Gulf of Mexico. Microscopic differences in initial conditions lead to macroscopic differences in outcomes.

The inverted bowl illustrates another important feature of path-dependent systems: *lock in.* When the ball is balanced at the top of the bowl, all equilibrium positions are equally likely. You can influence where the marble comes to rest with the slightest effort: Blow gently to the left and the marble ends up on one side of the room; blow the other way and the marble rolls to the other side. Once the ball has started to move down the slope a bit, however, it takes a great deal more energy to push it back to the top and over the other way. The farther the ball has moved and the faster it is going, the harder it is to alter its course.

At the dawn of the automobile age it didn't matter which side of the road people drove on. But as traffic density increased, the importance of a consistent standard grew. The more people drove on one side, the more likely it was new drivers in adjacent regions would drive on the same side, increasing the attractiveness of that side still further, in a positive loop. Most nations rapidly converged to one of the two standards, with Great Britain and her colonies, along with Japan and a few other nations, electing left-hand drive while most of the rest of the world converged to right-hand drive. Initially, the Swedes elected to drive on the left, as in Great Britain. As traffic and trade with the rest of Europe grew, and as the Swedish auto industry sought to increase sales in the larger right-hand drive market, it became increasingly inconvenient and costly for the Swedish system to be at odds with the prevailing standard in Europe and North America. Seeing that the Swedish road and auto system was rapidly locking in, the Swedes engineered a remarkable change. At 5 AM on September 3, 1967, the entire nation began to drive on the right. Sweden's ability to effect the switch smoothly was partly due to massive prior education and a huge public works effort to change road signage. But the success of the switch also depended on the small size and low density of the population, both human and automobile. In 1967 the total population of Sweden was less than 8 million, and there were only about 2 million cars, or 46 people and 12 cars per square mile. Most of the growth in Sweden's auto population and highway network lay ahead; the disruption and costs of the switch were small compared to the benefits. Imagine what it would cost today to switch from left- to right-hand drive in Japan. Though Japan is only about 80% as large as Sweden, in the mid 1990s it was home to about 126 million people and 40 million cars, more than 870 people and 275 cars per square mile. The disruption and cost would far outweigh any benefits. Japan has long since locked in to left-hand drive.

Path-dependent systems are more common than many of us imagine. The choice of standards such as the shape of electrical plugs, the location of the prime meridian, and the length of the standard meter in Paris are all arbitrary, but once a given choice becomes accepted, the system locks in to that choice, even though other alternatives were just as attractive early on. Path dependence and lock in are not restricted to economic, technical, or human systems. Complex organic molecules such as amino acids and the sugars in DNA can exist in two different forms, identical except each is the mirror image of the other. These *enantiomers* are known as the L (levo, or left-handed) and D (dextro, or right-handed) forms. The chirality (handedness) of the enantiomers does not matter in isolation—the physical properties of L and D molecules are the same. Yet the proteins in essentially all life on earth have levo chirality. Positive feedback and lock-in are responsible. Just as you cannot put a right handed glove on your left hand, the different three-dimensional structures of the two types mean the D-amino acids are physically incompatible with proteins built of the left-handed form. Most chemical reactions tend to produce different enantiomers in equal proportions, leading many scientists to conjecture that both left and right amino and nucleic acids were equally common in the primordial soup of the early oceans. By chance, the proteins that became the basis for life on earth were formed from left-handed amino acids. As new organisms evolved from their left-handed ancestors, the web of left-handed life grew in magnitude and complexity, while any right-handed forms became extinct. Life on earth has remained locked in to the left-handed forms ever since.[2]

CHALLENGE   ## Identifying Path Dependence

Identify as many examples of path-dependent systems as you can. Consider economic, technical, social, scientific, physical, biological, and other examples. For each case, identify at least one positive feedback process that might be responsible for the path-dependent behavior and sketch it in the form of a causal diagram.

---

[2]RNA and DNA are also chiral (one form twists left, one, right). But only the right-handed forms are stereoscopically compatible with the L-amino acids, so essentially all natural terrestrial nucleic acids have the same right-twisting chirality. Some physicists conjecture that the initial push favoring the left-handed amino acids derived from parity violations of the weak nuclear force, in which certain radioactive decay reactions favor one chiral form. However, a mechanism for preferential selection of the L-form by the weak force or other physical processes such as polarized light has not yet been demonstrated.

10.2   A SIMPLE MODEL OF PATH DEPENDENCE: THE POLYA PROCESS

You can easily construct a simple and compelling example of path dependence. Imagine a jar filled with small stones. There are black stones and white stones. Stones are added to the jar one at a time. The color of the stone added each period is determined by chance. The probability of selecting a black stone is equal to the proportion of black stones already in the jar. It is this last assumption that gives the system its unique character and creates path dependence. Suppose the jar initially contains one black and one white stone. The probability the next stone you choose will be black is then 1/2. Suppose it turns out to be black. Now there are two black and one white stones in the jar. The probability of picking black on the next draw is now 2/3. Suppose it is black. Now 3/4 of the stones are black. The preponderance of black stones means it is more likely than not that still more black stones will be added, and the jar is likely to end up with more black than white stones. But suppose on the first draw a white stone had been chosen. The likelihood of drawing a black stone on the second round would then have been 1/3 instead of 2/3. The jar is then likely to end up with more white than black stones. The trajectory of the system, and the ultimate mix of stones in the jar, depends on its history, on the particular sequence of random events. Figure 10-2 shows a causal diagram of this system, known as a Polya process after its inventor, the mathematician George Polya (1887–1985).

The Polya system contains two feedback loops, one positive and one negative, for each type of stone.[3] The greater the number of black stones, the greater the chance of adding another black stone (a positive loop). At the same time, the greater the number of black stones, the greater the total number of stones and so the smaller the impact of any new black stone added to the jar on the proportion of black stones (a negative loop).

Figure 10-3 shows 10 simulations of the Polya process. Each is 200 periods long. At first, each stone added to the jar has a large influence on the probability of choosing the next stone (the first stone added determines whether the probability of choosing a black stone is 2/3 or 1/3). The positive loop dominates. But as the number of stones grows, each new stone has a smaller and smaller effect on the proportions. The positive loop weakens relative to the negative loop. Eventually, the number of stones is so large that the next stone added has a negligible effect on the proportion of each color in the jar. The positive and negative loops are exactly balanced at that point. The proportion of each color will then stabilize, since on average stones will be added in the future in the same proportion as those already in the jar.

The ratio of black to white stones eventually reaches equilibrium, but that ratio depends on the history of the colors selected. Small random events early in the

---

[3]The process can easily be generalized to any number of colors. The probability the next stone added is any color C_i then equals the proportion of that color in the jar, $C_i/\Sigma_j C_j$ (only one color is added per period).

FIGURE 10-2 The Polya process

Every period one stone is added to the total. The probability of choosing a stone of a given color equals the proportion of that color in the total population.

The rule for adding stones of a given color is

$$\text{Black Stones Added per Period} = \begin{cases} 1 \text{ if Random Draw} < \text{Proportion of Black Stones} \\ 0 \text{ otherwise} \end{cases}$$

$$\text{White Stones Added per Period} = \begin{cases} 1 \text{ if } (1 - \text{Random Draw}) < \text{Proportion of White Stones} \\ 0 \text{ otherwise} \end{cases}$$

where the Random Draw is a number drawn at random from a uniform distribution on the interval [0,1].

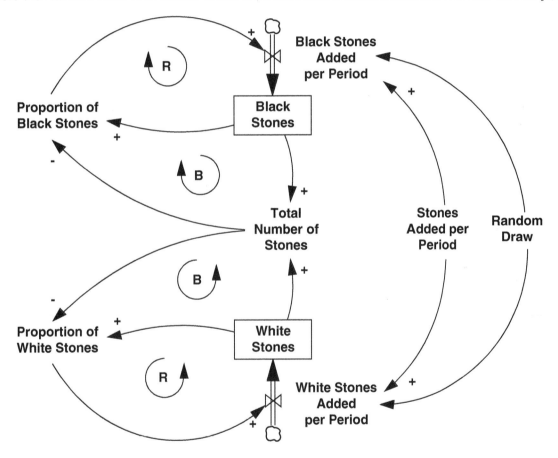

history of the system tip it toward one path rather than another. The equilibrium is path dependent. The accumulation of stones eventually locks the system in to equilibrium at a particular proportion of each color. To reverse the proportion of black stones from 2:1 to 1:2 when there are three stones in the jar requires drawing three white stones in a row, an event with a probability of 10% [P(Three White Stones|2 Black, 1 White) = (1/3)(2/4)(3/5)]. But to move from a ratio of 2:1 to 1:2 when there are 200 black and 100 white stones requires drawing 300 white stones in a row, an event with a vanishingly small probability (8.3×10^{-84} to be precise).

FIGURE 10-3
Ten realizations of
the Polya process

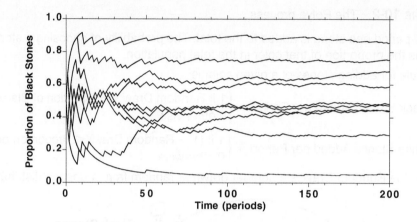

FIGURE 10-4
Equilibrium
distribution of the
Polya process

Histogram shows
the proportion of
black stones by
decile after 500
periods in 10,000
simulations. The
distribution is
quite uniform:
All proportions
are equally likely
in equilibrium.

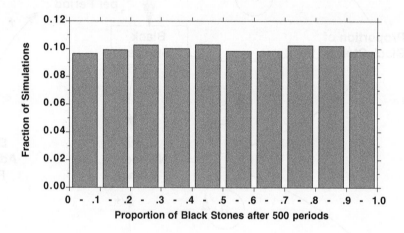

The more stones, the less likely there will be any movement away from the current proportion: the system locks in to whatever balance emerges from its early history.

Polya proved that the process will always converge to a fixed proportion of black stones, and that the particular proportion depends on the history of the random events along the way. Polya also proved the remarkable result that the distribution of final proportions is uniform, that is, the final fraction of black stones is equally likely to be anywhere between 0 and 1.[4] Figure 10-4 shows the distribution of the proportion of black stones after 500 periods in a set of 10,000 simulations. The distribution is nearly uniform: All proportions of black stones are equally likely in the long run (see Arthur 1994 for further examples).

---

[4]The distribution is uniform only for the special case where the number of stones added per period is one and the jar initially contains one white and one black stone. Other initial conditions or rules for selecting the number and type of the stones added lead to different equilibrium distributions. Johnson and Kotz (1977) provide a comprehensive treatment of urn models of this type.

FIGURE 10-5

Phase plot
for the linear
Polya process

The line shows
the probability of
adding a black
stone as a function
of the proportion
of black stones.
Every point on the
line is an equilib-
rium; every equi-
librium point has
neutral stability.

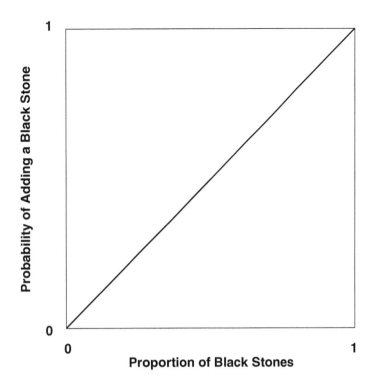

10.2.1   Generalizing the Model: Nonlinear Polya Processes

The Polya process illustrates how path dependence comes about, but it is a very
special model with a number of restrictive and unrealistic assumptions. First, the
dynamics depend on the fact that the flows are quantized: Though stones are added
with probabilities in proportion to their prevalence in the jar, each stone is either all
black or all white. Each period the proportion of each color must change. Instead
of a jar of stones, imagine filling the jar with black and white paint mixed in proportion to the current shade of gray in the jar. The shade of gray would never
change, no matter what it was initially (you can approximate the continuous time,
continuous flow situation in the model shown in Figure 10-2 by allowing fractional
stones to be added per period or reducing the time step between periods). Second,
the probability of adding a particular color is linear in the proportion of that color
(Figure 10-5). The function defining the probability of adding a ball of a given
color lies exactly on the 45° line, so every point on the line is an equilibrium. In
general, however, the decision rules determining the flows in path-dependent systems are nonlinear functions of the state variables.

   If the probability of adding a stone of a given color is a nonlinear function of
the proportion with that color, the number, location and stability of equilibria, and
the dynamics all change.

   Suppose the probability of choosing a black stone is characterized by the nonlinear function in Figure 10-6. The system now has only three equilibria (points

FIGURE 10-6
Nonlinear Polya
process

The probability of
choosing a black
stone is now a
nonlinear function
of the proportion
of black stones
in the jar. The
system has three
equilibria.

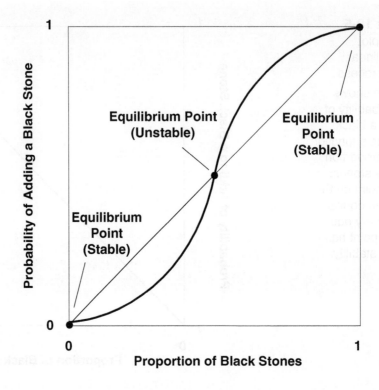

where the proportion of black stones and the probability of adding a black stone
are equal): 0, 0.50, and 1. The points zero and 100% are equilibria: If the jar is all
black or all white, it will remain so. Likewise, when the proportion of black stones
is one-half, the probability of choosing a black stone is one-half, so (on average)
the proportion of stones remains constant. When the proportion of black stones
rises above half, however, the probability of choosing black increases more than
proportionately, and when it is less than one-half, it falls more than proportionately.
The equilibrium at 0.50 is unstable: If the first stone added is black, the probability of adding more black stones increases dramatically, moving the system (on average) toward the stable equilibrium at 100% black stones. Similarly, if the first
stone is white, the probability of drawing more white stones increases sharply, and
the system will tend toward the stable equilibrium of all white stones. Of course,
since the system is stochastic, sometimes a run of one color will move the state of
the system back across the ratio 1:1.

Figure 10-7 shows 10 realizations of the nonlinear Polya process shown in Figure 10-6. All trajectories move rapidly away from the initial ratio of 1:1, and after
200 periods, the jar is nearly all one color or the other. Where the linear Polya
process has an infinite number of equilibria, this nonlinear process has only three;
of these, only two are stable. Yet the system is still strongly path dependent: which
of the two stable equilibria dominates depends entirely on the history of the random events as the system evolves. Like the linear process, the system locks in to
whichever equilibrium the positive loop reinforces, as determined by the chance

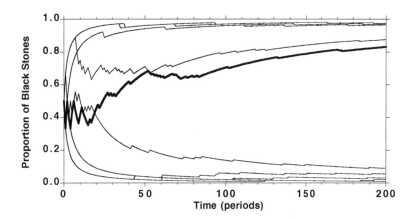

FIGURE 10-7
Dynamics of the
nonlinear Polya
process

The system tends
toward all one
color or all the
other, depending
on the early his-
tory of random
events. Note the
trajectory shown
with a heavy line
where the early
lead of white
stones is reversed
by a run of black,
leading the system
to lock in to the
predominantly
black equilibrium.
The realizations of
the random draw
in these simula-
tions are the same
as in Figure 10-3.

events early on. Note the trajectory in Figure 10-7 (shown as a bold line) where the jar is mostly white in the beginning, but due to a run of black stones, the ratio reverses after about 30 periods. The positive feedbacks then favor black stones, and the jar soon locks in to the predominantly black equilibrium.

Lock in is much swifter and stronger in the nonlinear system. In the linear case, the system has neutral stability: Every point is an equilibrium, and none of the points is better than any other. In the nonlinear example here, the two stable equilibria are strong attractors. The positive feedback continues to dominate the dynamics even as the proportion of a given color increases. Like the two rain drops falling on either side of the continental divide, trajectories on either side of the 50% point are attracted on average toward one of the stable equilibrium points. The jar ends up nearly all one color—winner take all.

10.3   PATH DEPENDENCE IN THE ECONOMY: VHS VERSUS BETAMAX

Videocassette recorders (VCRs) are ubiquitous in homes, businesses, and schools.[5] You can buy or rent videos at nearly every mall and main street. The film industry earns significant revenue from sales of video rights, and many films are made directly for the home video market, never enjoying theatrical release. Much of this success depends on the common format used by the vast majority of VCRs, known as VHS, which ensures machines made by different companies are compatible with one another and with the tapes available in the market.[6] How did VHS become the standard?

---

[5]The VCR industry data and history presented here are based in part on data collected and a model developed by Ed Anderson (personal communication, 1996). I'm grateful to Ed for permission to use his data and materials.

[6]While VHS is now the standard for 1/2 inch VCRs around the world, different regions do use incompatible signal formats. North America uses the NTSC format while Europe uses the PAL format.

VHS was actually a latecomer to the home videorecorder market. Home video recording technology came of age in 1975 when Sony introduced the Betamax system. Offering ordinary people the chance to record television broadcasts and play movies in the comfort of their own homes, VCRs soon became the hot home electronics product of the late 1970s and early 80s (Figure 10-8). As is common in consumer electronics, larger production volumes, learning effects, and increasing competition led to huge price drops for VCRs even as their features and functionality increased. Demand soared. By 1994, about 85% of US households owned at least one VCR, and sales had reached 13 million units per year in the US alone. VCR adoption in Europe and the rest of the world followed similar dynamics.

When VCRs first became available, a prime use was "time shifting"—the recording of broadcasts to be played back at a more convenient time. Time shifting also made it possible to fast-forward through commercials. Within a few years, however, the principal use of VCRs became the playing of prerecorded tapes—films, music videos, exercise tapes, and so on. Sales of prerecorded tapes in the US exploded to more than 80 million per year by 1994, and the video rental industry took off (Figure 10-8).

The data for the aggregate VCR market conceal the fight for dominance among different VCR formats. Sony's proprietary Betamax technology was the first cassette-based home video technology to reach the market, some 18 months ahead of its principal rival, the VHS standard launched by a consortium of Matsushita, JVC, and RCA (Cusumano, Mylonadis, and Rosenbloom 1992). Though Betamax and VHS technologies cost about the same, the tapes and machines were not compatible. Consumers had to choose which standard to adopt. The attractiveness of each format depends on various factors, including price, picture quality, play time, and machine features such as programmability, ease of use, size, and remote control, among others.

The most important determinant of product attractiveness is compatibility. To swap tapes with their friends and families people had to have compatible machines. As the installed base of machines of a given format increased, the attractiveness of that format to potential new buyers increased, which in turn increased the market share of that format and boosted the installed base even further. Even more importantly, people tended to buy machines compatible with the broadest selection of prerecorded tapes. Video rental shops chose to stock tapes in the most common format since these would rent more often and yield more profit. Movie studios, in turn, chose to offer their films in the format compatible with the most popular technology and the orders placed by the video stores.

These positive feedbacks mean that the format with the largest installed base of machines, all else equal, will be the most attractive to consumers and content providers. Unchecked by other loops or outside events, these positive feedbacks confer greater and greater market share advantage to the leader, until one format completely dominates the market and the other disappears. As shown in Figure 10-9, this is precisely what happened. By the late 1970s VHS had gained a market share advantage over Betamax. Soon the majority of prerecorded tapes were also coming out in the VHS format. VHS market share and sales continued to grow while the Betamax share steadily shrank. By 1988 the triumph of VHS was

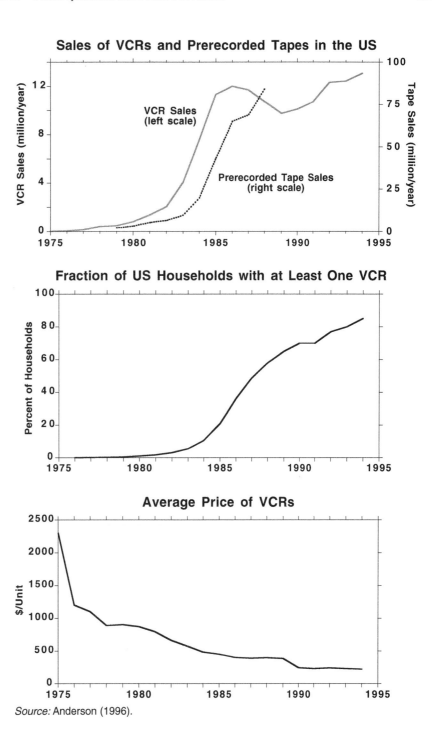

FIGURE 10-8
Diffusion of VCRs
in the US

Source: Anderson (1996).

complete. Sony was forced to abandon Betamax technology for the home market and in 1988 announced that it was switching its product line to the VHS format.

The strong effect of compatibility on product attractiveness explains how VHS rapidly achieved dominance over Betamax—once it achieved a lead in market

FIGURE 10-9
Betamax vs.
VHS formats
in the home
VCR market

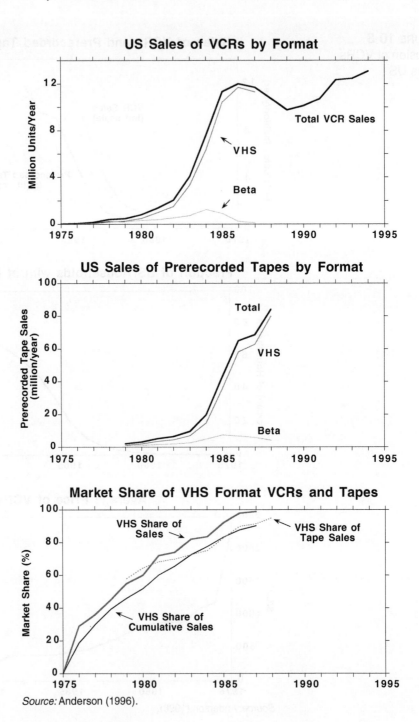

US Sales of VCRs by Format

US Sales of Prerecorded Tapes by Format

Market Share of VHS Format VCRs and Tapes

Source: Anderson (1996).

share and in the share of the installed base. But the existence of strong positive network and compatibility effects does not explain how VHS first achieved that lead. A close look at the data in Figure 10-9 shows that from its introduction through 1980, a period of 5 years, Betamax was the market share leader. As the first product to market, Betamax should have been able to use the positive network and compatibility feedbacks, along with learning curves, scale economies, and other positive feedbacks favoring the early leader, to gain a commanding advantage and prevent later entrants from succeeding. What happened?

In the Polya model of path dependence, random events early in the history of a system can tip the system toward one outcome. As seen in Figure 10-7, these random events can sometimes reverse the ratio of colored stones in the jar. Perhaps Beta's failure was just bad luck; perhaps chance led to a run of events favoring VHS, destroying Sony's early lead. Such an explanation is unsatisfying. Unlike the random selection of stones in the Polya process, electronics makers did not flip coins to determine which type of VCR to make and customers did not spin a wheel of fortune to decide which format to buy. The random shocks in a path-dependent system stand for events outside the boundary of the model—that is, those events for which we have no causal theory. A goal of modeling is to expand the boundary of our models so that more and more of the unexplained variation in the behavior of a system is resolved into the theory.

There are many theories to explain how Betamax lost its early lead. Klopfenstein (1989) notes that VHS offered longer play and record time (originally the VHS playtime was 2 hours to 1 hour for Betamax; by 1988 the ratio was 8 hours for VHS to 5.5 hours for Betamax). Longer play time, Klopfenstein argues, gave VHS the early edge. In contrast, Arthur (1994) argues that Betamax had a sharper picture than VHS and was actually the superior technology.

An early VHS price advantage is another theory but data supporting it are weak. Price data are hard to get, but suggest that while VHS machines were about 7% cheaper than Betamax machines in 1978, they were actually more expensive than Beta machines the following 3 years. Price does not seem to be a decisive factor in explaining how VHS overtook Betamax.

Cusumano, Mylonadis, and Rosenbloom (1992) point to the different business strategies employed by Sony and Matsushita. Sony, seeking to profit from their proprietary technology, was reluctant to license Betamax to other firms. In contrast, JVC and its parent Matsushita aggressively sought partners among other manufacturers, set lower licensing fees than Sony, and even delayed the introduction of VHS until they and their allies could agree on common technical standards. Matsushita also built VCRs sold under the label of other firms, speeding production ramp up. Matsushita thus gained access to the distribution channels of these firms, and also gained larger production volume than if they had kept their technology proprietary. Consequently, Matsushita enjoyed greater scale economies in distribution and production and gained experience that moved it down the learning curve more rapidly.

The development of the prerecorded tape industry played a key role. Prior to 1977, the majority of prerecorded tapes were aimed at the adult entertainment sector (similar to the early days of the worldwide web). RCA, Matsushita's largest customer in the US, sought to jump-start the market for general audience videos and thus VCR sales by offering two free VHS tapes with each VCR it sold. RCA also encouraged firms such as Magnetic Video to invest in VHS equipment to supply prerecorded tapes for the US market. Large scale production of prerecorded Betamax tapes lagged behind by about a year (Cusumano, Mylonadis, and Rosenbloom 1992). Note from Figure 10-9 that the VHS share of prerecorded tape production actually exceeds VHS's share of the installed base until 1983, which further increased the attractiveness of VHS to video rental stores and customers.

CHALLENGE	**Formulating a Dynamic Hypothesis for the VCR Industry**

Formulating a Dynamic Hypothesis for the VCR Industry

1. Using the information above (and any additional sources you wish) develop a causal loop diagram to explain the dominance of VHS in the home VCR market. Your diagram should be simple but should capture the important feedbacks described above, both positive and negative.

2. Use your diagram to explain why the market converged to a single format, and why VHS won the format battle.

3. How might Sony have altered its strategy to prevent VHS from becoming dominant?

4. Sony's Betamax format lost to VHS in the 1/2 inch home VCR market but remains the market leader in the market for professional quality 3/4 inch equipment used by television and news organizations. How do the feedback structure and strength of the various loops differ in the professional market compared to the home market? What impact do these differences have on effective strategy?

5. Since VHS became the dominant standard, other tape formats and video technologies have been introduced for the home market, especially inexpensive camcorders. A variety of camcorder tape and cassette formats coexist, including 8 mm, super or hi 8 mm, Panasonic's cassette technology, and others. None of these has become dominant. How do the uses of camcorders and the determinants of camcorder attractiveness differ compared to the home VCR market? How do these differences affect the strength of the feedback loops in your model? What is the likely impact of these differences on the dynamics and on strategies for success in the camcorder market?

10.4   POSITIVE FEEDBACK: THE ENGINE OF CORPORATE GROWTH

The network and complementary goods effects that dominated the evolution of the VCR market are but two of many positive feedbacks that can drive the growth of a business. This section surveys some of the important positive feedbacks that can cause a firm to grow. Since path dependence arises when positive feedbacks dominate a system, the prevalence of positive loops in corporate growth means that the potential for path dependence in the evolution of corporations, industries, and the economy as a whole is great.

The diagrams below present the loops in a highly simplified format, focusing on the sales of a single firm in an industry. The diagrams do not explicitly show the competitors, but all firms in a particular market are linked through competition for market share and through materials and labor markets, financial markets, distribution networks, the media, and the social fabric in general. The diagrams also omit the many negative feedbacks that can halt the growth of the firm.

10.4.1   Product Awareness

How do potential customers become aware of a firm's products? There are four principal channels: advertising, direct sales effort, word of mouth, and media attention. Each of these channels creates positive feedbacks (Figures 10-10 and 10-11).

In most firms the advertising budget (supporting ads, trade shows, and the like) grows roughly as the company and revenue grow. Larger advertising budgets have two effects: (1) more potential customers are made aware of the product and choose to enter the market (loop R1); (2) to the extent the advertising is effective, more of those who are aware and in the market are likely to buy the product offered by the company (R2). Similarly, the larger the revenue of the firm, the greater the sales budget. The more sales representatives, and the greater their skill and experience, the more calls they can make, the more time they can spend with customers, and the more effective their calls will be, increasing both total industry demand (R3) and the share of the total demand won by the firm (R4).

While a firm controls its advertising and sales budgets, word of mouth and media attention are largely outside the firm's direct control (Figure 10-11). As sales boost the installed base and the number of customers who have experience with the product, favorable word of mouth increases awareness, increasing total demand (R5) and also persuading more people to purchase the products of the firm (R6). A hot product or company will also attract media attention, which, if favorable, stimulates additional awareness and boosts market share still more (R7-9). There are many processes by which a firm or product can become hot (popular) and attract unsolicited media attention. Strongly favorable word of mouth can stimulate media coverage, especially for highly innovative new products and products

FIGURE 10-10   Advertising and direct sales effort drive awareness of the product.

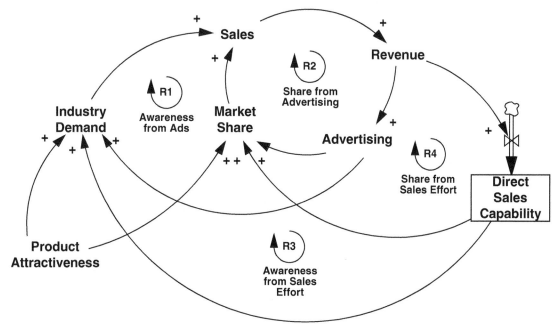

FIGURE 10-11   How word of mouth and media reports create a hot product

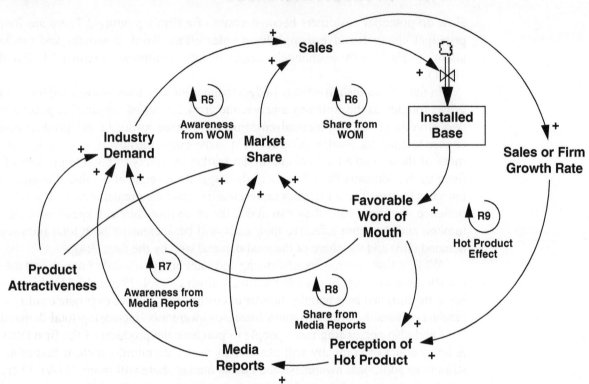

that show well on television. Rapid growth of sales, revenue, profit, or stock price can also attract media attention and turn the product into a social phenomenon. Amazon.com provides a prominent example from the late 1990s.

Product shortages—and the price gouging, profiteering, and near riots they can create—also attract media attention. Shortages are especially important in creating the impression a product is hot for consumer goods such as toys (recent examples include Beanie Babies and Furbies). Footage of frenzied shoppers trampling each other to get the last Tickle Me Elmo the week before Christmas can multiply the crowds at the mall exponentially.

The strength of these loops depends of course on the attractiveness of the product; an excellent product offered at a good price will be easier to sell and will generate more favorable word of mouth than an overpriced, poor quality product. Which of these channels of awareness dominates depends on the particular product and market, and not all firms utilize all three channels. Fast food chains do not have a direct sales force and rely instead on advertising (and word of mouth); specialty toolmakers focus their resources on direct sales effort and advertise much less.

The time delays and stock and flow structure of these four channels of awareness also differ. The delays in starting and stopping advertising campaigns are short relative to building a competent and skilled sales force. Word of mouth is weak when a new product is first launched but can grow rapidly and dominate the

FIGURE 10-12   Spreading fixed costs over a larger volume lowers price and leads to larger volumes.

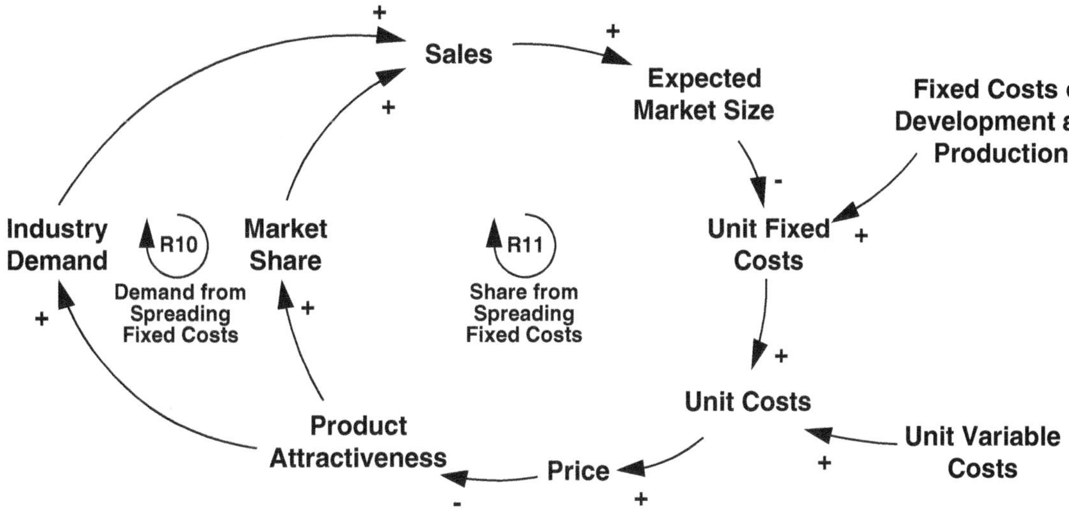

sources of information available to the market as the installed base grows. The media spotlight tends to burn very bright for a short while, then fades as the attention of editors and audience moves on to the next object of desire.

Further, while the strength of the advertising and direct sales loops are under the direct control of the firm, the word of mouth and media loops are not. Word of mouth (favorable and unfavorable) is difficult for a firm to control, though firms can stimulate communication among current and potential customers by sponsoring users' groups and conferences and by hiring opinion leaders as spokespeople. Similarly, though many firms today are highly skilled in media relations, there is no sure-fire way to get your product featured on a network magazine show or a list of hot web sites.

10.4.2   Unit Development Costs

Many products and services involve considerable up-front development and capacity acquisition costs. The greater the expected lifetime sales of the product, the lower the fixed price per unit, and the lower price can be while still achieving the required return on investment (Figure 10-12). Lower prices stimulate industry demand (R10) and lead to a greater share of that total (R11), boosting sales and cutting fixed costs per unit still more.

The larger the up-front costs of product development and production capacity, the stronger these loops will be. In a labor- and materials-intensive industry such as subsistence agriculture, fixed costs are small. In technology- and knowledge-intensive industries involving significant product development effort, nearly all the costs are incurred prior to production of the first unit. Developing a new automobile or commercial aircraft costs several billion dollars; all the design and development costs and all the costs for capacity, tooling, training, and marketing must be borne before job one rolls off the line. There's a saying in the semiconductor industry that it costs a few billion to make the first chip, but then all the rest are free. Software development is the paradigm case: As the internet expands, the marginal cost of distribution is rapidly approaching zero, while up-front development costs are rising.

The industries powering the world economy are increasingly knowledge based, and up-front costs capture a growing share of the total costs of production. In a world dominated by these positive loops, traditional rules of thumb for pricing no longer apply. Note how fixed cost per unit depends on *expected* volume. When these loops dominate the dynamics, expectations about how large lifetime volume will be can be strongly self-fulfilling. Imagine two firms with identical costs launching identical products at the same time. One expects to win about half the market and estimates market potential conservatively, believing it can lower prices as volume expands. The other expects to win the dominant share of the market and believes lower prices will greatly expand total demand for the category. The aggressive firm therefore sets prices much lower than the conservative firm and might even initially sell at a loss. The aggressive firm wins the largest share of the market, which allows it to lower prices still further, while the conservative firm finds sales of its product are disappointing. The expectations of both firms are fulfilled and their mental models are reinforced: The aggressive firm learns that pricing low, even below current unit costs, can lead to market dominance and huge profits, while managers at the conservative firm learn to be even more cautious about projecting sales; a classic example of a self-fulfilling prophecy (Merton 1948/1968).

Though not shown in the diagram, expectations of lifetime volume can depend not only on current sales, but also on forecasts of potential industry demand, market research, and knowledge about the development of complementary goods. Many of these other possible inputs to a firm's belief about market potential also close positive loops. Software sales forecasts rise as technical progress in computer hardware leads to faster and cheaper computers; lower software prices, in turn, stimulate the demand for hardware that helps make that belief a reality.

10.4.3 Price and Production Cost

Spreading up-front development costs over a larger volume is not the only way to lower unit costs. Figure 10-13 shows the positive loops created by economies of scale in production, economies of scope, learning curves, and process innovation.

Economies of scale differ from the development cost loops discussed above. In many industries, unit costs fall as the scale of production rises (at least up to a point). Larger paper mills, oil refineries, and thermal power plants are often more efficient than smaller ones. There are both thermodynamic and organizational reasons. Larger boilers (e.g., in a coal-fired power plant) have a larger ratio of volume to surface area and therefore higher thermal efficiency. In addition, every paper mill, oil refinery, and power plant requires instrumentation, safety systems, logistics capacity to handle incoming and outgoing materials, and other facilities; similarly every business must have a certain minimal amount of administrative staff and overhead. The cost of these activities usually does not rise as quickly as production volume, so firms can lower prices as they grow, which creates opportunities to increase the scale of operations further (R12). The opportunity to realize

FIGURE 10-13   Scale and scope economies, learning curves, and process improvement

Each effect creates two positive loops: One increases sales through market share gains, and one increases sales through expansion of the total size of the market.

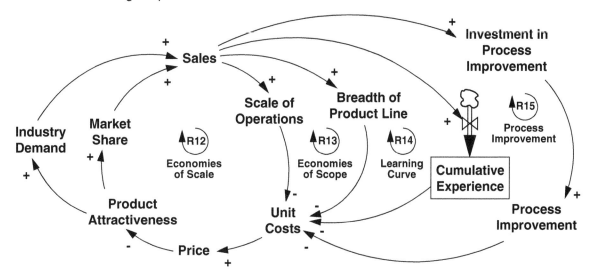

such economies of scale by consolidating general, administrative, and overhead functions is a powerful driver of mergers and acquisitions (see section 10.4.8). Another powerful source of scale economies arises from division of labor. Larger organizations can afford to divide the work into increasingly specialized tasks. It has long been observed (at least since Adam Smith's famous discussion of a pin factory in *The Wealth of Nations*) that division of labor boosts individual productivity and leads to lower unit costs (see section 10.5).

Economies of scope (R13) arise when a firm is able to share capacity, labor, technical know-how, and other resources across multiple product lines and business units. Cable television companies can offer high-speed internet access using the same cable network with low incremental capital costs. Shopping malls and so-called category killers in office supplies, toys, hardware, and other retail markets reduced unit costs dramatically by offering a huge range of products under one very large roof. These "big box" retailers also reduced search costs for their customers by providing one-stop shopping just off the freeway, which boosted product attractiveness and market share at the expense of the smaller stores on Main Street.[7]

Learning curves also create positive loops favoring the leading firm. Learning (or experience) curves have been documented in a wide range of industries, from commercial aircraft to broiler chickens (Teplitz 1991). The learning curve arises as workers and firms learn from experience. As experience grows, workers find ways to work faster and reduce errors. Typically, the unit costs of production fall by a

---

[7]The costs of malls, in terms of traffic congestion, decay of the central business district, and so on are all externalized, lowering their apparent costs below their true costs to the community.

fixed percentage every time cumulative production experience doubles.[8] For example, costs might fall 30% with each doubling of cumulative output. Learning curves with 10-30% improvement per doubling of experience are typical in many industries. Lower unit costs enable lower prices, increasing both market share and industry demand (R14) and boosting sales still more.

Finally, the larger the firm, the greater its investment in research and development leading to process innovations that lower costs (R15). Such research can include the development of more highly automated tooling, more reliable machines, and more efficient plant layout. It can also include training in process improvement techniques such as total quality management which enhance the ability of workers to detect and correct the sources of defects, thus boosting productivity and lowering costs.

The delays and stock and flow structure of scale and scope economies differ from learning curves and process improvement. Scale and scope economies depend on the current volume of sales and breadth of the firm's activities. An acquisition, for example, can quickly boost scale and scope. Similarly, if the firm shrinks, its scale and scope economies are quickly lost and the positive feedbacks reverse, speeding the decline in the firm's attractiveness. Learning by doing, R&D, and the results of process improvement are embedded in the organization's capital stock, worker knowledge, and routines. They are slower to develop. And if sales turn down, cumulative experience and process productivity tend to persist, decaying much more slowly (though to be sure, know-how and experience are often lost, depending on how the firm downsizes).

10.4.4   Network Effects and Complementary Goods

As illustrated by the VCR industry, the utility of a product often depends on how many others are also using it (the network effect; R16 in Figure 10-14) and on the availability of compatible products to use with it (the complementary good effect; R17).

Compatibility and network effects boost product attractiveness and thus expand the total size of the market (just as the growth of the internet made computer ownership more attractive, leading more people to use the internet). These loops tend to favor the market share leader within an industry, assuming competing products are incompatible. Besides VCRs, the classic example of these loops in the 1980s and 90s was the battle for control of personal computer operating systems, particularly the eclipse of the technically superior Macintosh architecture by the Wintel platform.

Just as in the case of fixed costs (section 10.4.2), the decision by third parties to produce complementary goods for a particular product depends on their expectation of the market potential, and hence the expected profitability, of that platform. Firms can shape those expectations in a variety of ways, including early sharing of technical specifications with potential third party developers and subsidies for adoption of the platform. Other strategies include consortia and joint ventures with

---

[8]Sometimes the learning curve is formulated as depending on cumulative investment rather than cumulative production, as in Arrow (1962).

FIGURE 10-14   Network and compatibility effects

Each effect creates two positive loops: one increases sales through market share gains, and one increases sales through expansion of the total size of the market.

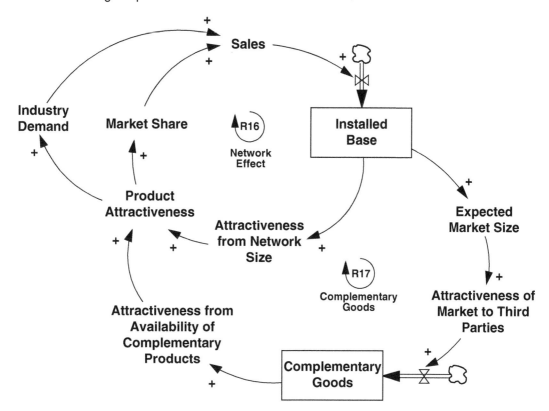

third parties (e.g., the formation by Matsushita of the VHS consortium), horizontal and vertical expansion into the markets for complementary products (e.g., Sony's purchase of film studios to control content and media for their hardware products, or IBM's purchase of Lotus), and free distribution of complementary goods (e.g., Netscape's decision to give away its web browser to stimulate sales of its server software, a strategy soon imitated by Microsoft). In the software industry, some firms strategically time the announcement of new products to preempt their rivals and influence third party developers, sometimes even announcing the near availability of vaporware (products that don't yet exist even in prototype form). When the network and complementary goods loops are strong, expectations about which platform will ultimately triumph can be strongly self-fulfilling.

10.4.5   Product Differentiation

Another set of positive feedbacks arises from the ability of firms to invest in product differentiation (Figure 10-15). As firms grow, they can invest more in activities that improve the attractiveness of their products to customers. Most products can be differentiated from those of competitors through enhanced features, functionality, design, quality, reliability, and suitability to the current and latent needs of

FIGURE 10-15   Product differentiation

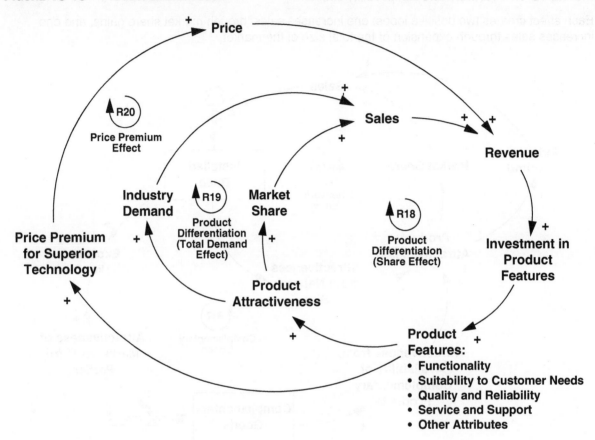

customers. Firms can also invest in superior service and customer support infrastructure. To the extent these investments increase the attractiveness of the products in the eyes of customers the firm can gain market share, boosting revenue and enabling still more investment in differentiation (R18). More capable and useful products also increase total demand (R19). Finally, companies offering clearly superior products can often charge a price premium without choking off growth. The higher margins enabled by such a price premium enable the firm to increase its investment in differentiation still further (R20).

Many high-tech firms are engaged in a technology race in which competition is primarily focused on the earliest introduction of the fastest, most powerful product with the most features. But differentiation does not have to focus on technology and product features. IBM successfully pursued the differentiation strategy for decades and dominated the computer industry from its inception through the personal computer revolution in the 1980s. IBM's differentiation investments, however, focused on product reliability and especially on customer service and support. Tom Watson, Jr., like his father, understood that the most important determinant of product attractiveness for their core market—middle managers in large corporations—was peace of mind. Especially when computers and data processing were novel, in the 1950s and 60s, these organizations were reluctant to invest in

FIGURE 10-16
New product
development
creates new
demand, boosting
development
resources.

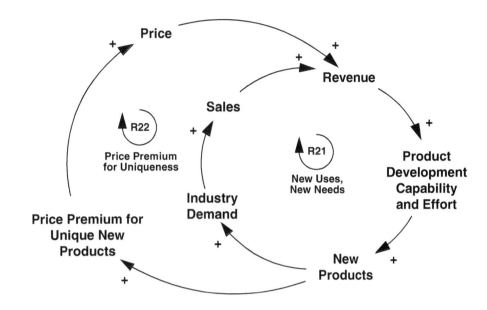

computing unless they were sure it would be highly reliable and that when something went wrong they could get it fixed quickly.

IBM focused its differentiation strategy on product quality and reliability, building the largest and most responsive sales and service organization in the business. Its success not only enabled it to gain market share and increase the size of the data processing market but also to charge the highest prices in the industry. Other firms entered the mainframe business, some created by former IBM people (e.g., Amdahl), but could never gain much market share, even though they offered lower prices for machines of comparable performance. IBM maintained its dominance of the mainframe industry by continuously investing huge sums in further development and articulation of its service and support infrastructure, even while generating consistently strong profit growth for its shareholders. Of course, while IBM's differentiation strategy was spectacularly successful for decades, all positive loops eventually encounter limits, and the company stumbled badly in the 1980s when it failed to anticipate the fundamental changes in the computer industry caused by the microprocessor and personal computer revolution.

10.4.6   New Product Development

The development of entirely new products is a core engine of growth for many firms (Figure 10-16). The greater the revenue of a firm, the larger and more effective the new product development effort can be. New products create new demand, boosting revenue and increasing investment in new product development still more (R21). And just as differentiation enables firms to charge higher prices, firms that bring novel and important products to market can often command a price premium until imitators arrive. Higher prices further increase the resources available to fund the development of still more new products (R22), so the firm can stay ahead of competitors.

Intel has successfully used these new product development loops to fend off competition from clone makers such as AMD and Cyrix who develop chips compatible with but cheaper than Intel's. Intel invests about 10% of its revenue in R&D (more than $2.3 billion in 1997), which enables it to offer the fastest and best PC-compatible chip at any time and leads to more sales growth and more R&D. Power hungry computer users are willing to pay a substantial price premium for the latest, fastest, most powerful chip.

The firms profiting most from the new uses, new needs and price premium loops are those best able to identify the latent needs of potential customers. They understand what people don't yet know they want or create a need people did not have before—and then bring products addressing those needs to market quickly, effectively, and at low cost. The capability to do so is not simply a matter of the R&D budget but depends on the size of the installed base of users and the firm's ability to collect and act on their suggestions. It is a competence built up over time through experience and through investment in product development process improvement.

The strength of these loops also depends on the ability to protect innovative new products from imitation by competitors. Patents offer an obvious method to protect such innovations and are critical to the success of the new product development loops in the pharmaceutical industry, among others. More important, however, is the ability to weaken competitors' ability to use the same loops. Intel not only charges a price premium for its latest, fastest chip but also uses the margins from these top of the line chips to lower prices on older processors as, or even before, the clone makers bring their chips to market. By cutting prices for older chips, Intel limits the margins of the clone makers, weakening their ability to use the positive differentiation loops to erode Intel's lead.

10.4.7   Market Power

The larger a firm, the more clout it has with its suppliers, workers, and customers. Such old-fashioned monopoly power enables firms to lower their unit costs and prices, leading to larger market share and sales and still more bargaining power (R23-25 in Figure 10-17).

The benefits of monopoly power do not show up only in the firm's unit costs. Suppliers will give—or be forced to give—preferential treatment to their large customers on delivery terms and payment schedules, to share technical knowledge, to respond to customer change requests, and to make other accommodations that give the firm an advantage over its smaller rivals who get the short end of the stick in terms of supplier attention and resources. For the smaller firms, the positive loops act as vicious cycles. Large firms can often receive preferential treatment from their distribution channels and customers, as for example, when the large consumer products firms demand the best shelf space in retail outlets.

Similarly, the larger a firm's share of total jobs in a community, the fewer opportunities for alternative employment there are, so job turnover may fall, reducing training costs. Firms whose workers have no alternative sources of employment not only can pay lower wages and benefits but can also save money by scrimping on investments in worker health and safety. Sweatshops are all too

FIGURE 10-17   Monopoly power over customers, suppliers, and workers is self-reinforcing.

Each effect creates two loops: one increases market share and one increases total demand.

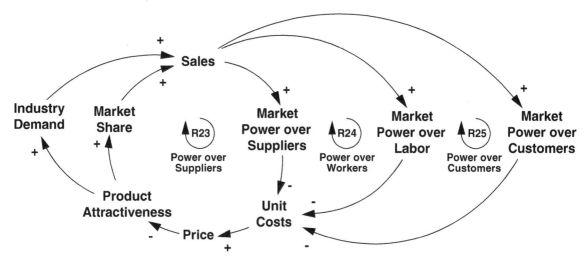

common in many industries, including the apparel industry, and not only in Indonesian sneaker plants. The company town of the 19th century was the ultimate expression of this process, where, for example, a steel or mining company not only paid low wages but also owned all the housing and stores and charged exorbitant rents and prices. Workers often fell deeply in debt, trapping them in what amounted to de facto slavery. These dominant firms also used the extra profit generated from their power over workers to hire Pinkertons and other private security forces to put down efforts to organize or strike (a strategy Andrew Carnegie employed effectively in his Pittsburgh steel mills). Such practices still exist today, in the sugar cane industry, for example. Large firms also have the resources to import workers from other regions to ensure the balance of supply and demand in the labor market continues to favor the employer, even as the firm grows. In the 19th century, the robber barons brought Chinese laborers to the American West to keep wages low while they built the railroads; today large agribusinesses import workers to harvest crops at low wages.

10.4.8   Mergers and Acquisitions

Growth can be powered by acquisitions of rival firms (horizontal expansion) and of suppliers and customers (vertical integration). The larger a firm, the more capital it can raise to finance mergers and acquisitions. If acquisitions consolidate the firm's dominant position, profits may rise through the exercise of monopoly power over labor, suppliers, and customers, enabling the firm to buy still more of its rivals (R26 in Figure 10-18). If vertical integration enables the firm to lower its costs, it can gain further market share and stimulate industry demand and grow still more (R27). Acquisitions can also enhance economies of scale and scope or permit firms to guarantee a steady flow of complementary products (see sections 10.4.3 and 10.4.4), a process important in the convergence of the film, television, entertainment, and news industries. Disney's purchase of Capital Cities/ABC in the mid

FIGURE 10-18   Self-reinforcing growth through acquisition

Each effect creates two loops: one increases market share and one increases total demand.

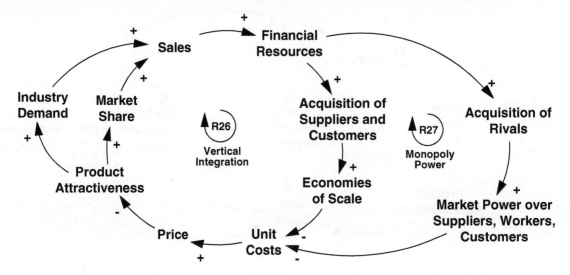

1990s provided ABC with access to content for its entertainment programming while at the same time giving Disney access to ABC's news and magazine shows to market their products, along with a network of television stations to broadcast their films, videos, and promotional specials.

Of course, the synergy often touted as the rationale for mergers can be elusive. Many acquisitions fail to lower unit costs, stimulate economies of scope, or build monopoly power. Negative loops arising from incompatible corporate cultures, overcentralization, or loss of focus can dilute the earnings of the combined firm ultimately leading to the divestiture of the disparate business units.

The consolidation of market dominance through the acquisition of weaker rivals has long been a common strategy, most famously used in the late 19th and early 20th centuries by the great trusts such as US Steel, Consolidated Tobacco, Amalgamated Copper, American Smelting and Refining, Northern Securities, and of course, Standard Oil. In 1909, according to the Census Bureau, 44% of all goods in the US were made by just 1% of the industrial firms. Many of these controlled more than half the total market in their industries. The pace of merger, acquisition, and consolidation in the late 19th century has been surpassed only in the 1980s and 1990s. The rise of the trusts in the late 19th century led to a backlash in the form of the Sherman antitrust act and trustbusters like Teddy Roosevelt (see, e.g., Mowry 1958). It remains to be seen whether these same negative feedbacks will arise once again in response to the growing consolidation of market power in the global economy today.

10.4.9   Workforce Quality and Loyalty

The ability of a firm to offer superior products and service depends on the commitment, skill, experience, and quality of its employees. The more profitable a firm, the higher the wages and benefits it can pay to recruit and retain the best and

FIGURE 10-19   Profitable growth leads to recruitment and retention of the best people.

Each effect creates two loops: one increases market share and one increases total demand.

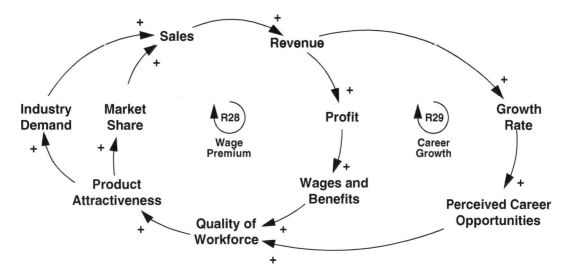

the brightest (R28 in Figure 10-19). And the faster a company grows, the greater the career opportunities and job security for employees (R29).

The strength of the wage premium loop has increased greatly in recent years as firms, especially firms with bright growth prospects, have increasingly turned to stock options as a form of compensation. Employees whose compensation is tied to profit sharing or the company's stock often work harder and longer than those on straight salary. Stock options, bonuses, and profit sharing allow firms to recruit highly qualified people while reducing base salaries, freeing additional resources that can be invested in strengthening other feedbacks driving growth, such as new product development, differentiation, or acquisitions. As growth accelerates and the stock price soars the company can pay people even less up-front.

The positive feedbacks in Figure 10-19 are highly nonlinear. It takes many years to build up a loyal, skilled, high-quality workforce, but a firm can destroy that capability very quickly. When growth stalls or the firm downsizes, opportunities for advancement and promotion quickly disappear. The best and most capable are the first to leave as they have the brightest prospects and best outside opportunities. The loss of these above-average employees further erodes the firm's capability to deliver attractive products or services, leading to still more downsizing and attrition in a vicious cycle. Firms that rely heavily on stock options are especially vulnerable to a slowdown. If the growth prospects of the company dim and the price/earnings multiple falls, people's options may become worthless, leading to demands for higher cash compensation that steal resources needed to promote growth just when they are needed most. These positive loops can speed the implosion of a declining organization.

IBM again provides an example. For decades IBM's success enabled it to offer excellent salaries and benefits, de facto lifetime employment, and excellent opportunities for promotion. Consequently, the firm was able to recruit the cream of the crop and its employees were renowned for their loyalty and commitment, qualities that greatly strengthened IBM's ability to provide the service and support its customers required. When the rise of the personal computer eviscerated the mainframe industry and growth stalled, opportunities for promotion dried up. Hiring plummeted. The company was much less successful in attracting top candidates for the few new jobs they did offer. In an attempt to preserve the decades-old no-layoff practice, there were several early retirement programs, during which many top people left for greener pastures; their departures further eroded the capabilities of the organization. Even these generous programs proved inadequate, and soon layoffs and massive reorganizations began. Morale sank further and productivity suffered as employees and managers worked to protect their job or find a new one, leaving less time and energy for the business.[9] The loss of loyalty, experience, and skill deepened and prolonged the crisis.

10.4.10   The Cost of Capital

Profitable growth leads to higher expectations of future earnings and a higher market value for the firm. The higher the market value and stock price, the lower the cost of raising new capital through the equity market (Figure 10-20). Similarly, though not shown in the figure, the greater a firm's profits and cash flow and the higher market value relative to book value, the lower the risk of default, so the lower the cost of debt as the premium over the prime interest rate falls. The lower the cost of capital, the lower the firm's costs of development and production. Lower costs increase profits and cash flow still further, leading to even higher market value and a still lower cost of capital (R30). As lower unit costs permit lower prices while maintaining healthy profit margins, market share and industry demand rise, leading to even greater market value and further cutting the cost of capital (R31). A lower cost of capital also allows the firm to increase its investment in capacity, R&D and new product development, service and support infrastructure, human resources, acquisitions, and other resources that strengthen the positive feedbacks driving growth (R32). Finally, as the capital markets respond to the greater growth rate of the firm by raising expectations of future earnings, the market value will rise even higher, further lowering the cost of capital (R33).

These loops are often quite powerful for rapidly growing high-tech firms. Initial public offerings (IPOs) of internet companies in the mid 1990s provide an example. Many of these firms were able to raise substantial capital at relatively low cost (i.e., by selling only a small fraction of their equity) relative to the risk,

---

[9]There are many examples of firms experiencing this death spiral. Sastry (1997) develops a system dynamics model addressing these issues and shows how another death spiral can be created by too-frequent reorganizations in response to poor business performance. Masuch (1985) describes a feedback model of organizations in which positive loops can lead to downsizing and decline. Case studies of these dynamics include Doman, Glucksman, and Mass (1995), who show how positive feedbacks led to different fates for two initially similar UK insurance companies; Risch, Troyano-Bermudez, and Sterman (1995), who show how these positive loops defeated a new strategy for a maker of specialty paper; and Sterman, Repenning, and Kofman's (1997) simulation model of a high-tech company where path dependence and positive feedback led to unanticipated side effects in the firm's quality improvement program.

FIGURE 10-20 Profitable growth lowers the cost of capital, stimulating further growth.

Each effect creates two loops: one increases market share and one increases total demand. Comparable loops for debt financing are not shown.

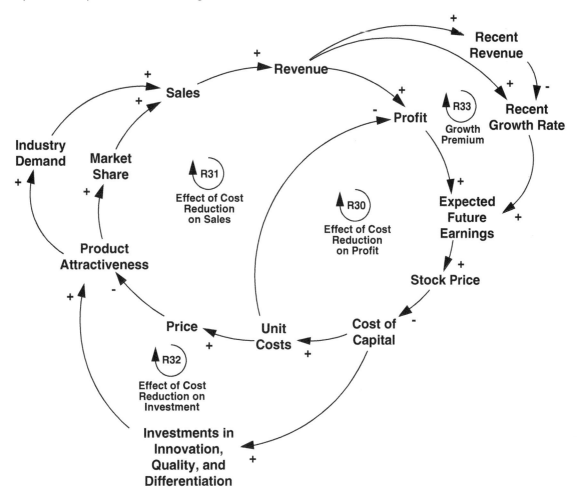

even though many had never made any money. Among the more established firms enjoying rapid growth, many are able to pay no dividends as investors prefer to let the firm reinvest its earnings in additional growth.

Because the market value of a firm is quite sensitive to recent profits and especially growth rates, the strength of these loops can change quickly. A drop in growth expectations for any reason (a sales slowdown, the entry of a strong competitor to the market) can swiftly reduce market value, effectively locking the firm out of the equity market for new capital. As market value and cash flow fall relative to current obligations, the perceived risk of debt increases, and the bond market will require a higher risk premium on any new borrowing. While these loops can give a healthy, growing firm still greater advantage over its slower growing, less profitable rivals, they can swiftly become a death spiral for an organization in financial distress.

10.4.11   The Rules of the Game

The larger and more successful an organization, the more it can influence the institutional and political context in which it operates. Large organizations can change the rules of the game in their favor, leading to still more success—and more power. Figure 10-21 shows the resulting golden rule loop R34. The golden rule loop manifests in many forms. Through campaign contributions and lobbying, large firms and their trade associations can shape legislation and public policy to give them favorable tax treatment, subsidies for their activities, protection for their markets, price guarantees, and exemptions from liability. Through overlapping boards, the revolving door between industry and government, and control of media outlets, influential and powerful organizations gain even more influence and power. In nations without a tradition of democratic government, these loops lead to self-perpetuating oligarchies where a tightly knit elite controls a huge share of the nation's wealth and income while the vast majority of people remain impoverished (e.g., the Philippines under Marcos, Indonesia under Suharto, and countless others). The elite further consolidates its control by subsidizing the military and secret police and buying high-tech weaponry and technical assistance from the developed world to keep the restive masses in check. Even in nations with strong democratic traditions these positive loops can overwhelm the checks and balances designed to ensure government of, by, and for the people.

10.4.12   Ambition and Aspirations

Another powerful positive feedback arises from the aspirations and ambitions of a firm's founders and leaders (Figure 10-22). All organizations must choose whether to eat their seed corn or plant it to seek an even larger crop next season: Firms can pay out their profits to shareholders in the form of dividends, or they can invest in the further growth of the enterprise. Which course they take depends on their aspirations for growth. Growth aspirations themselves are frequently flexible and adapt

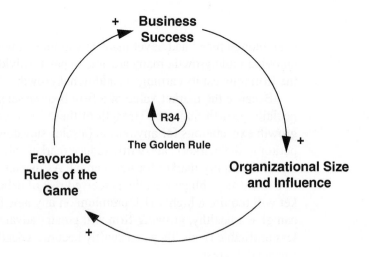

FIGURE 10-21
The golden rule:
Whoever
has the gold
makes the rules.

to actual accomplishment (see chapter 13; Cyert and March 1963/1992; Forrester 1975b; Lant 1992).

By constantly revising aspirations upward, the leadership of an organization can create perpetual pressure for greater achievement. Many top managers believe the proper way to motivate their troops is by setting aggressive stretch objectives—goals that are far above current achievement (see, e.g., Hamel and Prahalad's 1993 concept of strategy as stretch). As the organization responds and actual achievement rises, the bar is raised further. Thus business units are often given aggressive sales and profit growth goals for the coming fiscal year. These high-level goals are then translated into specific targets for the individual activities within each unit, each based on recent performance but adjusted by a stretch factor. For example, each function in the business unit might be required to cut costs by 15% next quarter while raising the quota for each sales representative 20%.

The use of floating goals based on recent performance plus a stretch factor can be highly effective. Setting goals out in front of actual accomplishment often helps people reach their ultimate potential. Athletes seek to exceed their personal best or break the most recent record; when the record falls, the goal shifts as well. As students master a subject or concept, they are given more difficult tasks. Managers set their sights on the next promotion. Politicians aspire to the next highest office.

But there are dangers. Lifting goals as accomplishment rises means there will always be tension and dissatisfaction—a hunger for more. That hunger can be a powerful motivator but it can also lead to burnout, frustration, and feelings of inadequacy (see, e.g., Homer 1985 for models of worker burnout under stretch objectives; also see Simon 1982). And it can lead to monomaniacal behavior, in which people sacrifice their friends, family, and ethics in endless pursuit of the next level.

The ability of leaders to articulate their vision and spur the best efforts of their employees depends not only on their personal charisma, but also on the size of the

FIGURE 10-22   Floating goals and stretch objectives

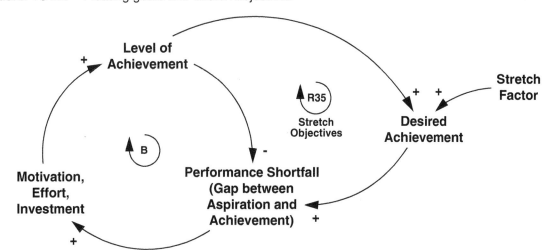

organization and the integrity of its culture, traditions, and folklore. The larger the organization and the less cohesive its culture, the harder it is for leaders to project their goals and motivate employees, creating negative feedbacks that can limit the ability of stretch objectives to generate growth.[10]

10.4.13   Creating Synergy for Corporate Growth

The preceding sections identified more than three dozen positive loops that can drive the growth of a business enterprise. How important are they? If these loops are significant, the firms (or industry groups) most successful in exploiting them should exhibit growth rates, profitability, and market shares significantly higher than average over extended periods of time. Firms where the positive loops operate as vicious cycles should yield persistently lower returns. However, traditional economic theory suggests that markets are dominated by negative feedbacks: If profits in an industry were significantly higher than average, existing firms would expand and new firms would enter the market, expanding production and pushing prices down until profits were no higher, on average, than in any other industry or for any other firm (on a risk-adjusted basis).

   The existence of persistent differences in profitability across firms and industries has been studied intensively. Mueller (1977, 1986) examined a large sample of the biggest US industrial firms and found significantly different rates of profit across firms, even for firms within the same industry group, and that these differences persist over very long time periods (at least several decades). Cubbin and Geroski (1987) document similar results for UK firms and concluded that "Whilst two-thirds of our sample converged towards a common profitability level, a solid core of firms appear able to maintain some independence from market forces more or less indefinitely." Mueller also examined the dynamics of profitability. Presumably if the negative feedbacks of traditional economics dominate, firms whose profits are far from average at any time (due to transient shocks) would tend toward the average, while those near average would tend to remain there. Mueller found just the opposite: Firms with average profitability were, over time, more likely to migrate to states of either significantly higher or significantly lower profits. Firms with high profits had higher than expected probabilities of continuing to generate high profits; the performance of firms with low profits was more likely than expected to remain disappointing. These dynamics are consistent with the differentiating, disequilibrium effects of the many positive feedbacks discussed above.

   What determines whether the positive loops will operate as virtuous cycles leading to growth and high profitability or vicious cycles trapping a firm in a self-reinforcing cycle of decline and low profit? In the most successful firms many of these loops act in concert, generating substantial synergies. Achi et al. (1995) examined the performance of the fastest growing and most profitable firms in the US—so-called growth tigers—to see if the feedbacks driving their growth could be identified. They defined a growth tiger as a firm whose sales growth rate over the

---

[10]Forrester (1975b) develops a model exploring the dynamics of goal formation in organizations addressing these issues of leadership and growth.

prior 10 years was three times greater than the average of the S&P 500 and which outperformed the S&P 500 in total return to shareholders over the prior 5 years. In a sample of more than 1200 firms, 97 met these criteria. The growth tigers were not all small startups: 1994 sales ranged from $130 million to $12.5 billion. Nor were they all high-tech firms: though 28% of the tigers were in the computer sector (including Intel, Microsoft, Compaq, 3Com, and Sun), the remainder included firms in such low-tech, mature industries as industrial equipment, business and financial services, retail, distribution and wholesaling, apparel, fashion and sports, and health care (e.g., Nike, The Home Depot, US Healthcare, Williams-Sonoma, United Asset Management, Werner Enterprises, and Nautica). Sustained growth and profitability are not merely a function of being in a hot industry (of course hot industries are hot because the positive loops driving their growth are strong).

The growth tigers generate a disproportionate share of the growth in the economy as a whole. While comprising just 8% of the firms in the sample, they created 15% of the total sales growth, 28% of the job growth, and 47% of the profit growth. Close examination showed that the tigers did not rely on any single positive loop to drive their growth but successfully used many of the positive feedbacks discussed above to create synergy. Microsoft is the paradigm case. The costs of producing software are almost entirely up-front development costs, so the reduction in unit costs as the software market exploded is a very powerful growth driver. Similarly, Microsoft's expansion from operating systems to applications, the internet, news networks, publishing, automotive computing, and other markets creates powerful scale and scope economies. Microsoft also benefits from learning curves and from substantial investment in process improvement focused on improving customer needs assessment and speeding software development. It invests heavily in product differentiation and new product development. Microsoft's financial clout enables it to preempt competition by acquiring rivals and potential rivals, often buying software start-ups and incorporating their products into Microsoft's own applications and operating systems. Microsoft's market power enables it to negotiate favorable distribution agreements and prices with computer makers. Its growth allows it to recruit the best programmers and managers and compensate them with stock options, which builds a dedicated and productive workforce and frees up resources for other investments. Microsoft's positive cash flow and high price/earnings multiple cut its cost of capital far below that of weaker rivals and risky startups. And growth is powerfully driven by the expansive aspirations of Bill Gates, a vision he has, through a well-funded public relations effort, successfully articulated not only within Microsoft but in society at large through ghost-written books and media appearances.

Most of all, Microsoft's success stems from powerful network and complementary goods effects. These feedbacks operate through many channels, linking hardware architecture and operating systems, operating systems and applications, applications and users, and software and programmers. The larger the installed base of Microsoft products, the more attractive are computers compatible with those products (powered by Intel and Intel-compatible chips). The more personal computers sold with Intel Inside, the larger Microsoft's installed base. The larger the installed base of Microsoft operating systems, the more software will be developed for those systems by third-party developers, and the more third-party software there is the greater the attractiveness of the Wintel platform. The larger the number of people using Microsoft's applications, the more important it is for others to have compatible software to exchange documents with colleagues and friends, so the greater the attractiveness of Microsoft's applications. And the larger Microsoft's share of the installed base, the greater the number and higher the quality of programmers, support personnel, and IT managers trained in those systems and the scarcer are those familiar with other operating systems and applications.

Powered by these positive feedbacks, Microsoft grew from its 1975 founding to a firm with 1997 revenues of $11.3 billion. By August 1999 its market capitalization was nearly $500 billion; by comparison, General Electric, with about 7 times more revenue and 9 times more employees than Microsoft, was worth less than $400 billion.

Bill Gates is quite aware of these positive feedbacks and their role in his success (Table 10-1).

Of course, growth cannot continue forever. Ultimately, as the limits to growth are approached, various negative feedbacks must grow stronger until they overwhelm the positive loops. If Microsoft continues to grow at its historical rate, its sales would exceed the gross domestic product of the United States by 2018, when Bill Gates will be only 63 years old, even if the US economy keeps growing at its historical rate.[11]

Some of the negative feedbacks were already apparent by the mid 1990s. Concern over Microsoft's ability to use the positive feedbacks driving growth to dominate the software market prompted its competitors to join together to promote Sun's Java. Microsoft has proven to be adept at blunting these moves through what Bill Gates calls "embracing and extending" the innovations of its competitors. It was precisely concern over Microsoft's ability to embrace and extend, to use the positive loops to dominate the emerging digital economy, that prompted the US Justice Department's 1998 antitrust suit over the bundling of Microsoft's Internet Explorer with the Windows operating system.

Not all the positive feedbacks that can drive corporate growth are compatible with one another. Pursuing the differentiation strategy by charging higher prices based on the superiority of your products and support capabilities conflicts with using low initial prices to drive the scale economy, learning curve, and network/complementary goods effects. Many long-successful firms stumbled when the positive loops driving growth in their industry changed while their strategy did not. For example, the failure of Sony's Betamax can be traced to a mismatch between their strategy and the dominant loops in the home VCR market. Sony had long pursued a strategy emphasizing product differentiation and innovation, and Sony products typically commanded a significant price premium relative to those of competitors. Sony's strategy worked very well in markets where standards were already established (such as television, stereo amplifiers, and cassette tape players) but was ineffective in a market where network effects and complementary assets

---

[11]From 1985 through 1997 Microsoft sales grew from $140 million to $11.36 billion/year, a compound growth rate of 37%/year. Over the same period, nominal US GDP grew from $4181 billion to $8079 billion, a compound growth rate of 5.5%/year. At these growth rates, the two curves intersect after 21.1 years.

TABLE 10-1
Bill Gates uses positive feedback concepts to guide Microsoft's strategy.

Comments of Bill Gates	Positive Feedbacks Referenced
"The network has enough users now that it is benefiting from the positive feedback loop; the more users it gets, the more content it gets, the more users it gets. We witnessed this same phenomena (sic) with application availability. The more applications are out there, the more attractive the device becomes, and the better the software business becomes" (Interview, *Red Herring,* Oct. 1995).	Network and Complementary Goods Effects (R16-17)
"This is a time period where now there's a broad awareness that Windows NT is by far the highest-volume general purpose server platform. The growth there continues to amaze us, and it's a positive feedback loop. As we got more applications, NT servers got more popular. As it's gotten more popular, we've got more applications" (*Computer Reseller News,* 23 Sept 1996)	
"It's all about scale economies and market share. When you're shipping a million units of Windows software a month, you can afford to spend $300 million a year improving it and still sell at a low price" (*Fortune,* 14 June 1993).	Unit Development Costs and Scale Economies Loops (R10-12)
"The biggest advantage we have is that good developers like to work with good developers" (Cusumano and Selby 1995, *Microsoft Secrets*).	Loyalty and Quality of Workforce (R28-29)
"Most people don't get millions of people giving them feedback about their products...We have this whole group of two thousand people in the US alone that takes phone calls about our products and logs everything that's done. So we have a better feedback loop, including the market" (Cusumano and Selby 1995, *Microsoft Secrets*).	Learning Curve and Process Improvement Loops (R14 and R15)

(the installed base and availability of tapes), rather than features, quality, or reputation, were the most important determinants of product attractiveness. Managers and entrepreneurs must design their growth strategy by identifying those positive loops likely to be most important in their markets, most compatible with one another, and most consistent with the capabilities and resources the firm either has or can develop.

10.5   POSITIVE FEEDBACK, INCREASING RETURNS, AND ECONOMIC GROWTH

The many positive feedbacks discussed in section 10.4 not only drive the growth of individual corporations but power the growth of entire industries and of the economy as a whole. The recognition that positive feedback is the engine of economic growth can be traced back at least to Adam Smith's *Wealth of Nations*. Smith and the other classical economists did not draw causal diagrams, but the various feedbacks are clearly seen in their writings. Smith focused on division of labor as the principal source of productivity growth. As a process is divided into a larger number of routinized operations, productivity grows because specialization enables people to learn faster, to customize their tools and capital to the specific task, and to eliminate the wasted effort that comes from moving from one operation to another. Smith noted that "the division of labor is limited by the extent of the market," recognizing the positive feedback by which economic growth enables greater specialization, which in turn leads to greater productivity and still more economic growth.

Economists generally refer to these positive loops as increasing returns. The term denotes a situation in which the output of a process increases more than proportionately as its inputs grow, in contrast to the usual situation of diminishing returns, where output saturates as inputs grow (as in agriculture, where harvests are limited by the extent and fertility of the land no matter how much fertilizer or labor are applied). Besides Adam Smith other early theories of increasing returns were developed by Alfred Marshall (in 1890) and Allyn Young (in 1928; see Buchanan and Yoon 1994 for an excellent collection of key works in the economics of increasing returns). Formal models embodying positive feedbacks include Paul Krugman's (1979) models of international trade and Paul Romer's (1990) models of endogenous economic growth.

Krugman, for example, noted that in the traditional economic theory of trade, dominated by diminishing returns (negative feedbacks), two identical economies would have no incentive to trade, since the greater transportation costs of trade would make it more efficient for each to produce the goods they need locally. However, in the presence of positive feedback it becomes advantageous for the two economies to trade even though they have identical resources, technologies, and consumer preferences. The apparently paradoxical result arises because both economies can produce more if each specializes in the production of one class of goods and trades with the other for the rest they desire—specialization boosts productivity, hence total output increases. Interestingly, in the case of initially identical economies, it doesn't matter which subset of goods each chooses to produce as long as they specialize; in practice the choice would be determined by chance events early in the history of trading relations, leading to the classical path dependence analyzed above.

The implications of positive feedback apply not only to nations engaged in international trade but also to any distinct economic entities that can exchange goods with others, including regions within a single nation, cities and towns within a region, neighborhoods within a city, or even the members of a family. When the positive feedbacks created by division of labor, scale and scope economies, learning by doing, and so on are strong, specialization and trade can quickly transform an initially identical geography into a highly variegated landscape with specialized centers of industry such as silicon valley or the New York diamond district.

Romer showed how growth for an economy as a whole could arise from some of the positive loops described above, particularly those relating to research and development, learning by doing, and other investments in human capital. Increasing returns arise because the knowledge created by R&D or employee training, for example, cannot be kept fully private. While a machine tool can only be used in one place at a time, knowledge of how to design a machine tool can be used by more than one firm at a time; knowledge is not consumed by usage the way material goods are. Consequently, a firm's investments in R&D and training, for example, not only benefit the firm but also spill over to benefit other firms. In the language of economics, these spillovers create externalities, that is, benefits external to the firm. These externalities speed economic growth because they benefit many besides the firm undertaking the investment, increasing the total size of the market and further strengthening the many positive loops that depend on the scale of activity in an industry or region. Romer also showed that because individual firms generally don't understand and can't take advantage of the benefits their knowledge investments create for the economy as a whole, there is a tendency for firms to underinvest in human capital and R&D.

10.6   DOES THE ECONOMY LOCK IN TO INFERIOR TECHNOLOGIES?

One consequence of path dependence is that random events early in the evolution of a system can push it down one path or another. These random shocks can be small and might go unnoticed at the time, or even in hindsight. They can involve chance events within the firms in the industry or spillovers from unrelated political, technical, or social events in the world at large. The positive feedbacks amplify the differences among the contenders until one emerges as the standard and dominates the industry. Success begets success. As the winner emerges, the costs of switching from one standard to another become greater and greater until the system locks in to that equilibrium. The Polya process described in section 10.2 shows how path dependence and lock in can occur when all equilibria are initially equally attractive. It doesn't matter whether we drive on the right or left or whether clocks go clockwise or counterclockwise, so long as we all choose the same direction. More controversial is the notion that path dependence can lead the economy to lock in to equilibria—to products, technologies, and ways of life—that are inferior to others that might have been chosen (see, e.g., Arthur 1994).

If the dominant determinant of product attractiveness is compatibility and the availability of complementary goods (e.g., VCRs, personal computers, keyboard layouts), then a firm might become the market leader even though its technology is inferior. Many argue that the VCR industry provides an example of lock in to an inferior technology, pointing out that Betamax offered superior picture quality and is today the standard for professional video equipment (others focus on VHS's longer play time to argue that it was after all the superior technology). The Macintosh operating system was clearly superior to Microsoft's DOS and early versions of Windows, yet Microsoft's systems became the standard while the Macintosh steadily lost market share. The QWERTY keyboard invented by Christopher Sholes in the 1870s is widely considered to be inferior to the 1936 Dvorak keyboard in terms of training time, typing speed, error rates, balance between the left and right hands, and comfort, yet nearly everyone continues to learn the QWERTY layout.[12] The irrational English system of measurement, with its feet, yards, pounds, gallons, and acres, is clearly inferior to the metric system yet continues to be used in the US.

The likelihood of locking in to an inferior technology increases with the strength of the positive loops that confer advantage to the market leader independent of the attributes of the technology itself. The stronger the network, compatibility, development cost, market power, and golden rule loops, the more likely it is the ultimate winner will be determined by factors unrelated to product quality, functionality, and features. Continued lock in to the QWERTY keyboard is due to the great importance of complementary assets, specifically, typists trained in QWERTY. The switching costs of retraining the huge installed base of typists in the Dvorak system outweigh the advantage of Dvorak, perpetuating the dominance of QWERTY.[13]

The prevalence of positive feedbacks in the economy does occasionally cause lock in to inferior technologies. But the issue is considerably more complex. Technologies evolve. An initially inferior technology might win the battle for market share and emerge as a new standard, but later improvements might overcome its initial deficiencies. Microsoft again provides an example. The DOS operating system was unquestionably inferior to the Macintosh, yet Microsoft became the industry standard while the Mac withered. Microsoft was then able to imitate the graphical interface of the Mac, incorporating many of its features in the Windows operating system. The first versions of Windows, through Windows 3.1, were still clearly inferior to the Macintosh. But Microsoft's dominance allowed it to invest heavily in further improvements. Windows 95 and 98, in the judgment of many, closed most of the gap, and further innovation will no doubt lead to still greater functionality. While the network and complementary goods loops did lead the software industry to lock in to a technology that was inferior at the time, the new product development and differentiation loops gradually erased the deficit. Of course, the Macintosh operating system would presumably have evolved at a higher rate had it won the battle and become the standard. It is entirely possible that computer users would have been better off if the initially superior technology had won. It is not possible to answer such questions definitively because we can never know how much better the losers might have become.

A more subtle issue concerns the coevolution of people's tastes with technology. People's preferences are not static; they evolve and change with experience. Your likes and dislikes adapt to your circumstances. The amount of salt or hot pepper people consider palatable, the amount of personal space people require, the

---

[12]The relative merits of QWERTY and Dvorak are still debated. Liebowitz and Margolis (1990) argue that many of the studies showing the superiority of the Dvorak layout are flawed. The preponderance of the evidence, however, suggests Dvorak's layout is more efficient than QWERTY.

[13]As another example, Moxnes (1992) develops a model showing how an economy can lock in to an inferior energy supply system; see also Fiddaman (1997). Sterman and Wittenberg (1999) develop a model of scientific revolution whose dynamics exhibit strong path dependence and find that the probability a given theory rises to dominance in its discipline is only weakly related to its intrinsic explanatory power while strongly determined by environmental conditions at the time of its founding.

amount of leisure time and access to open space people desire all vary widely across cultures. Habituation is a powerful process.

Similarly, people's evaluation of a technology can differ over time even though the technology itself may not change. Many city dwellers live more or less happily in environments noisier, more crowded, and more polluted than any their ancestors could have imagined or tolerated. Our evaluations of the attractiveness and desirability of the ensemble of technologies and social structures modern society has been locked into for the past 50 years differ from the way we would have evaluated them in 1950. Because people's preferences, tastes, and standards are malleable, technology and our assessments and reactions to it coevolve. Garud and Rappa (1994) show how such coevolution shaped the emergence of cochlear implants, a technology to provide hearing for the profoundly deaf. Rival technologies led to competing notions of what success would mean for patients receiving the technology (e.g., the ability to decode speech at a lower cost or to hear a wider spectrum of sound at a higher cost), ultimately affecting government regulations and standards for the technology.

10.7   LIMITS TO LOCK IN

The Polya model and examples of path dependence suggest that path dependent systems rapidly lock in to a stable equilibrium, which then persists indefinitely. The clockwise convention was established by the 1500s. The prime meridian continues to be located in Greenwich though the sun has long since set on the British empire. And the QWERTY keyboard has been the bane of typing students for over a century. Are all path-dependent systems perpetually trapped in the equilibria to which chance events lead them? Is there no escape?

There are many examples in which a dominant standard was overthrown. Such revolutions usually occur when the system in which the standard is dominant becomes obsolete or is itself overthrown. The dinosaurs ruled the earth for millions of years, but after a catastrophic asteroid impact caused mass extinctions throughout the plant and animal kingdoms, dinosaurs did not reemerge. The impact destroyed the ecosystem in which the dinosaurs had become the dominant standard. In terms of the Polya process, the mass extinction event removed most of the stones (species) from the jar (available ecological niches), so that the selection of new stones (the evolution of new species) was once again strongly influenced by random events. Life filled the jar once again, but different forms of life became dominant.[14]

In a process Schumpeter famously dubbed creative destruction, economic depressions can unfreeze an economy that has locked in to certain technologies. Every economy needs basic technologies for energy, transportation, and communications. An ensemble of technologies and infrastructure built around coal, steam, rail, and the telegraph dominated the industrialized world in the late 19th and early 20th centuries. Populations and industry were concentrated in large cities surrounded by farm and forest. These technologies and settlement patterns were self-reinforcing. Coal has a fairly low energy density and is difficult to handle, which

---

[14]See Gould (1990) for discussion of path dependence in evolution.

favors centralized settlement patterns and transport modes like rail and steamship. Telegraph lines were often strung along the railroad right of way, lowering the cost of infrastructure and maintenance. The coal-steam-rail-telegraph ensemble remained dominant until the Great Depression of the 1930s. The depression bankrupted many of the firms in these industries, their physical infrastructure deteriorated, and the power of their leaders waned.

When the economy began to recover from the depression in earnest after WWII, new investment did not recreate and refurbish the old networks and technologies but focused instead on a new ensemble of basic technologies. The new economy of the postwar era was built around oil, natural gas, and electricity for energy; internal combustion and electric motors for mechanical power; automobiles and aircraft for transportation; and telephone, radio, and television for communication. The suburbs emerged and industrial location patterns became less centralized. These technologies were also mutually reinforcing: catalytic cracking enabled crude oil to be refined into gasoline at low cost; gasoline is an energy-dense, easily handled fuel suitable for a large fleet of small vehicles and decentralized settlement patterns; internal combustion engines are small and powerful enough to use in aircraft; and so on. All these technologies were invented well before the 1930s, but the costs of switching were prohibitive because they were incompatible with the existing ensemble of technologies and social structures. Despite their great potential, the new inventions could not achieve widespread use until the old infrastructure—physical, social, and political—was swept away by the Great Depression and Second World War. The depression and war functioned as a mass extinction event that erased the basis for the old technologies and the firms that dominated them. Just as new forms of life evolve after every mass extinction, a new and different economy emerges with the recovery from every major depression.[15]

Great upheavals such as depressions or wars are not needed to unfreeze a system that has locked in to a particular equilibrium. Shifts in technological architecture often undermine the basis for the dominance of a particular technology, standard, or firm. The transistor made vacuum tubes obsolete, and none of the leaders in the vacuum tube industry were able to translate their dominance in the old technology into a leadership role in the solid-state world. Henderson and Clark (1990) show that dominant firms (at least in some industries) rarely maintain their leadership positions, or even survive, after such changes in product architecture. The same positive loops that confer cumulative advantage to a firm by building up networks of skills, relationships, and know-how specific to the firm's technology and market also create inertia and rigidity that make it difficult to adopt a radical and incompatible new technology (see Sastry 1997).

The architectural shifts that undermine the dominant design and dominant firms in an industry often arise from innovations created by those very firms. The computer industry provides another example. Firms such as IBM and Digital Equipment became hugely successful through exploitation of many of the positive

---

[15]For further discussion of the interaction between economic cycles and the evolution of basic technologies, see Graham and Senge (1980) and Sterman (1986).

feedbacks described above, especially the differentiation and innovation loops (sections 10.4.5 and 10.4.6). By providing superior service and support (IBM) and technically excellent products (Digital), these firms were able to charge comparatively high prices; in turn, high margins provided the resources for further investment in differentiation and innovation. These differentiation strategies worked very well during the early years of the computer industry when the costs of computers were very high, volumes were small, development and capacity costs were a modest fraction of total costs, and computers were used for a limited set of specialized functions in central data processing centers.

As computers became cheaper, more widely available, and easier to use, service and support became less important. When people buy a new PC every 2 years to keep up with technical progress, warranty terms and service capability are less important; when applications use a point and click interface, training and support are less important as employees teach themselves and each other. As the cost of manufacturing fell while the complexity of designs increased, up-front development costs became more and more important. As computing costs fell, computing became decentralized. Instead of a multimillion dollar mainframe sequestered in a cold, clean room, the employees now had a computer on their desk. Networking and compatibility became much more important. The exploding number of computers in use created lucrative markets for applications that induced third parties to enter the software market, both greatly strengthening the complementary goods feedback and reducing the hardware makers' control over these complementary goods.

The very success of the computer industry in exploiting the positive innovation and product differentiation loops caused these feedbacks to weaken, destroying the effectiveness of the strategies that had created that success. Differentiation became less and less important, while compatibility and software availability became more and more important. Success in a market dominated by compatibility, software availability, and economies of scale required aggressively lower prices to generate the volume required to offset high development costs and win the battle for market share. Mainframe and minicomputer makers like IBM, Digital Equipment, Wang Laboratories, Data General, and Prime Computer failed to recognize the shift in loop dominance they themselves helped to bring about. These firms suddenly found themselves with capabilities, resources, strategies, and cost structures grossly out of alignment with the requirements for success. Where once they rode the positive differentiation feedbacks to greater and greater success, now these loops became death spirals leading to faster and faster collapse. Some of these former industry giants survive as mere shadows while many vanished altogether.

10.8   MODELING PATH DEPENDENCE AND STANDARDS FORMATION

The linear and nonlinear Polya processes above provide simple illustrations of path-dependent systems but they do not provide realistic models of path dependence in economic or social systems such as the competition between Betamax and VHS or the triumph of the Wintel architecture over the Macintosh. This section develops a simple model of path dependence in the economy, a model with more realistic formulations for the decision rules and which can be elaborated to include the many positive feedbacks described above.

10.8.1   Model Structure

The battle for dominance between Betamax and VHS is typical of standards formation for new products in markets where the utility of the product depends on the size of the installed base and the network of users. One fax machine is not useful—fax machines only become useful when there is a network of other compatible machines. Many products depend on the availability of complementary resources: personal computers are not useful without compatible software; automobiles are not useful without networks of roads, gasoline stations, and other auto-friendly infrastructure. In such markets, the attractiveness of a product based on a given standard depends on its installed base, and market share will depend on the relative attractiveness of the different competing standards. Figure 10-23 shows the structure of a simple model to capture these feedbacks. The diagram represents two products competing to be the standard in a market. The products are assumed to be incompatible. To keep the model as simple as possible, only the most basic positive feedback, through the installed base, is represented explicitly. Prices and other determinants of product attractiveness are deliberately excluded. The challenge at the end of this section invites you to extend the model to include these variables and other important loops such as the process by which developers of complementary products choose which format to adopt.

   The installed base of each firm is increased by the sales of each firm's product (two firms i = 1, 2 are assumed in the simulations below, but the model can accommodate any number of firms). For simplicity, assume no discards and no repeat purchases, so there is no outflow from the installed base.

Installed Base Product i = INTEGRAL(Sales of Product i,
   Initial Installed Base of Product i)   (10-1)

The sales rate of each firm is the product of industry demand and its market share:

Sales of Product i = Total Demand * Market Share Product i   (10-2)

For now, assume industry demand is exogenous and constant. In reality of course there are many feedbacks to industry demand (section 10.4).

   Market share is determined by the attractiveness of each firm's products relative to the attractiveness of the other firms' products. The formulation for market share must meet several criteria. First, market share should be increasing as the attractiveness of the firm's product rises and decreasing as the attractiveness of competitors' products rises. Second, market share must be bounded between 0 and 100%. Finally, the sum of the market shares of all firms must equal 100% at all times. A useful formulation that meets these requirements is

$$\text{Market Share Product i} = \frac{\text{Attractiveness of Product i}}{\text{Total Attractiveness of All Products}} \qquad (10\text{-}3)$$

$$\text{Total Attractiveness of All Products} = \sum_{j=1}^{n} \text{Attractiveness of Product j} \qquad (10\text{-}4)$$

FIGURE 10-23 Structure for a simple model of network effects

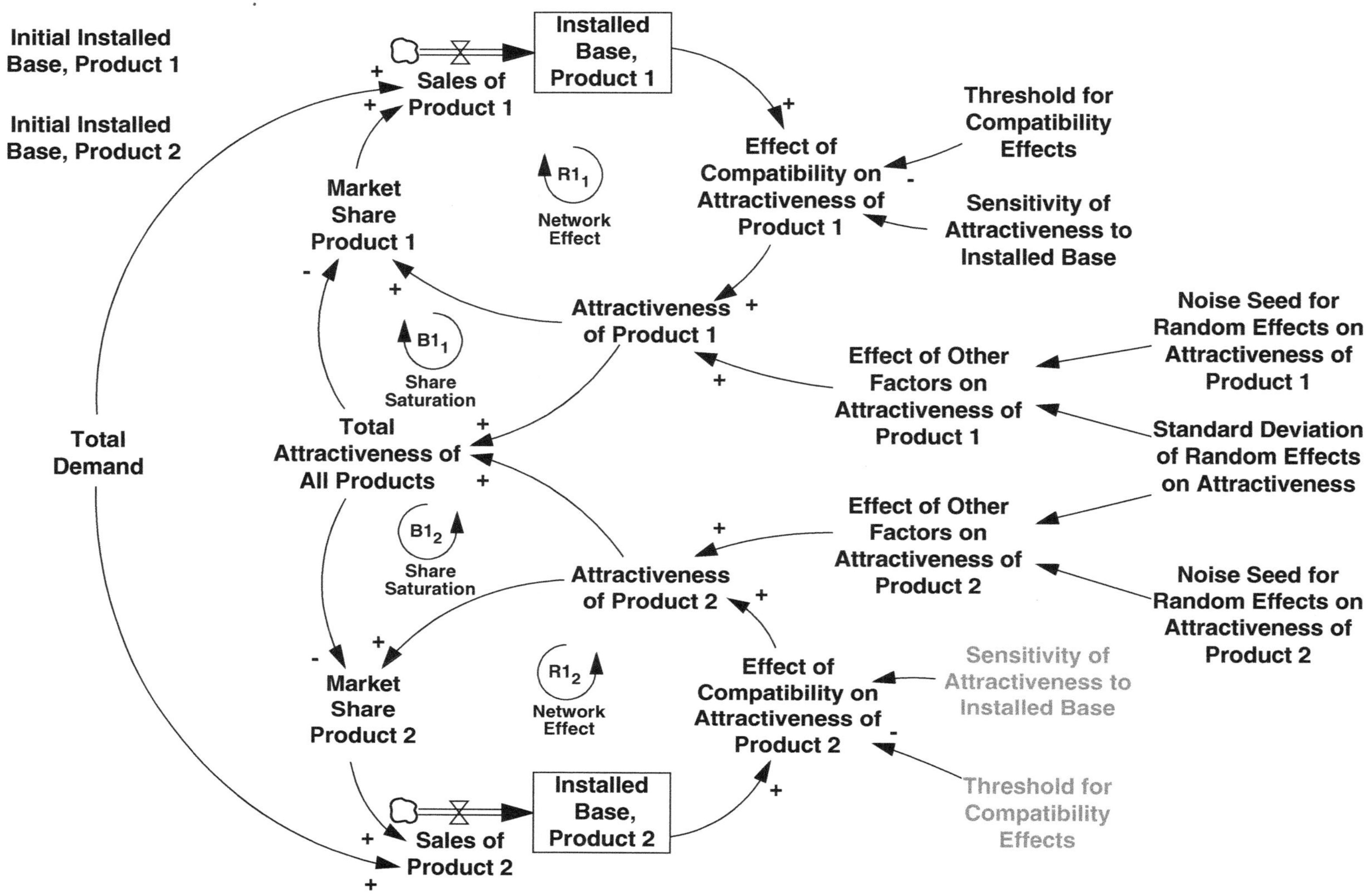

393

where n is the total number of firms. Total attractiveness is the sum of the attractiveness levels of all products in the marketplace.

How should attractiveness be specified? Attractiveness depends on a wide range of variables, including price, availability, quality, service, features, and so on. In this simple model, overall attractiveness is the product of two terms: the effect of compatibility on attractiveness (the network effect) and the effect of all other factors of attractiveness. The formulation aggregates the effects of price, features, availability, and so on into a single factor, which in this simple model is assumed to be exogenous.

$$\text{Attractiveness of Product i} = \frac{\text{Effect of Compatibility on Attractiveness of Product i}}{\text{* Effect of Other Factors on Attractiveness of Product i}} \quad (10\text{-}5)$$

The effect of compatibility on attractiveness captures the network and compatibility effects: the larger the installed base, the greater the attractiveness of that product. There are a number of plausible shapes for the relationship between installed base and attractiveness. One commonly used relationship is given by the exponential function

$$\begin{array}{l}\text{Effect of Compatibility} \\ \text{on Attractiveness} \\ \text{of Product i}\end{array} = \text{EXP}\left[\begin{array}{l}\text{Sensitivity of} \\ \text{Attractiveness} \\ \text{to Installed Base}\end{array} * \left(\dfrac{\begin{array}{c}\text{Installed Base} \\ \text{of Product i}\end{array}}{\begin{array}{c}\text{Threshold for} \\ \text{Compatibility Effects}\end{array}}\right)\right] \quad (10\text{-}6)$$

In this equation, attractiveness rises exponentially as the installed base grows relative to the Threshold for Compatibility Effects. The parameter Sensitivity of Attractiveness to Installed Base controls the strength of the effect. The threshold is a scaling factor that represents the size of the installed base above which network effects become important.[16] The exponential curve for attractiveness is plausible: When there were only two telephones in the United States, the utility of the phone was not very great to the third potential buyer, but when there were 100 million, the utility of the telephone to the next buyer was much, much greater. The exponential function means attractiveness rises at an increasing rate as the installed base grows.[17] The larger the threshold for compatibility effects, the larger the installed base must be before its effect on attractiveness begins to outweigh the effects of other factors of attractiveness.

For example, Betamax, as the first home VCR format to reach the market, had a large relative advantage in installed base in the early years. But even though there were many more Betamax machines than VHS machines early on, the effect of this relative advantage was slight: so few people had machines that

---

[16]Mathematically, only the ratio of the sensitivity to the threshold matters. Nevertheless, they are conceptually distinct. Applying the sensitivity to the normalized ratio of installed base makes it much easier to interpret the model and parameters.

[17]The exponential function is simple and convenient analytically but is not robust. With the exponential function for attractiveness the increase in attractiveness from adding another unit to the installed base is always greater than that of the unit before. A more realistic function would saturate for high levels of the installed base, representing the eventual dominance of diminishing returns as the installed base becomes very large. Chapter 14 discusses the construction of such nonlinear functions.

compatibility was not yet an issue for most potential purchasers. As the installed base grew, however, compatibility began to loom large in people's assessments of product attractiveness.

In this simple model the other factors of attractiveness are exogenous and assumed to vary randomly around the neutral value of one:

$$\begin{matrix} \text{Effect of Other Factors} \\ \text{on Attractiveness} \\ \text{of Product i} \end{matrix} = \text{NORMAL}\left(1, \begin{matrix} \text{Standard Deviation} \\ \text{of Random Effects,} \\ \text{on Attractivenes} \end{matrix} \begin{matrix} \text{Noise Seed for} \\ \text{Random Effects on} \\ \text{Attractiveness of Product i} \end{matrix}\right) \quad (10\text{-}7)$$

where the NORMAL(mean, standard deviation, noise seed) function samples from a normal distribution with a mean and standard deviation set by the modeler. The noise seed is different for each product to ensure that the random effects for each product are independent.[18]

The formulation for market share meets all three criteria for a good formulation. The greater the attractiveness of firm i, the greater its market share will be. Market share is zero if the attractiveness of the firm's products is zero and 100% if the competitors' products are completely unattractive. The sum of the market shares for all firms will always equal 100% for any number of firms. These properties hold for any functions relating product attributes to attractiveness. Many shapes for the individual attractiveness functions are plausible. The exponential function used here is especially convenient because it can be transformed into a form in which market shares can be expressed as a linear function of the attributes of product attractiveness, allowing the attractiveness functions to be estimated by standard regression techniques. When product attractiveness is specified as the product of exponential functions of each attribute, the formulation for market share is known as a logit function, because market share as a function of product attributes follows a logistic curve.[19]

Figure 10-24 illustrates the logit model for various values of the parameters. The graph shows the market share of firm 1 in a two-firm market as its installed base varies. The installed base of firm 2 is assumed to be constant and equal to the threshold for compatibility effects. The graph shows the resulting market share of firm 1 for different values of the sensitivity of attractiveness to installed base. In all cases, when the installed bases of the two products are equal (along with all other factors of attractiveness), each firm receives half the market. Market share follows the logistic curve as installed base varies. Note that the marginal impact of an increase in installed base on market share diminishes as installed base becomes very large: once market share approaches 100%, further increases in attractiveness

---

[18]The formulation for the random effects on attractiveness used here selects a new random draw every time step in the simulation. This is technically not correct, since changing the time step for updating the states of the model will dramatically alter the random shocks affecting the system. "Random" shocks in real systems are correlated, especially over short time frames, since real systems have inertia that prevents very large changes in the values of variables from one moment to the next. A more appropriate model of the noise process would be so-called pink noise, that is, noise that is serially correlated. See appendix B for models of pink noise suitable for use in continuous time simulations.

[19]The properties and estimation issues for logit models and other models of choice are discussed in many statistics texts, e.g., Aldrich and Nelson (1984).

FIGURE 10-24
Behavior of the
logit model for
market share

Two firms are
assumed. The
graph shows mar-
ket share of firm 1
as a function of
its installed base
relative to the
threshold for com-
patibility effects,
for various values
of the sensitivity of
attractiveness to
installed base s.
The installed base
of firm 2 is as-
sumed to be
constant and
equal to the
threshold in
all cases.

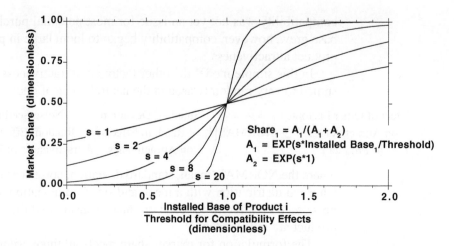

have a smaller and smaller effect since there is simply less additional market share to gain. The greater the sensitivity of attractiveness to the installed base, the sharper and steeper the logistic curve, and the more rapidly share approaches its extreme values as installed base varies.

10.8.2   Model Behavior

To simulate the model the parameters were set as shown in Table 10-2. In particular, the sensitivity of attractiveness to installed base is set to 2, representing a modest network effect. If, early in the history of the market, the installed base of product 1 is 20% of the threshold while that of the competitor is 10%, the market share of firm 1 will be only 55%, even though it enjoys a 2:1 advantage in installed base. If the competitor had 100% of the threshold while firm 1 had 200% as much (still a 2:1 advantage), the market share of firm 1 would then be 88%, reflecting the greater impact of a large installed base on attractiveness.

The simulation begins with a level playing field: the parameters for both firms are identical. The only difference between the firms arises through the random variations in the attractiveness of each product from other factors. These random effects are assumed to have a very small standard deviation, just 1%.

Figure 10-25 shows 20 simulations of the model. Prior to the introduction of any random variations in product attractiveness the two firms have the same overall attractiveness, and market share remains at the initial equilibrium of 50%. When the random effects begin, at time zero, the network effect is weak, so market share fluctuates randomly in the neighborhood of 50%. As the installed base of each firm grows, however, the positive network feedback gains in strength and amplifies any small advantage in installed base created by the random shocks in product attractiveness. As the installed base advantage of one firm grows, the positive network feedback gains even more strength, further boosting the market share of the leader until share approaches 100%. There are only two stable equilibria: complete market dominance or extinction. Given the parameters in the simulation, the system locks in to one of these equilibria quite rapidly.

Figure 10-26 shows the distribution of market shares for firm 1 at various times in a sample of 5000 simulations. Prior to year 0, there are no random effects

TABLE 10-2

Parameters for simulation of installed base model

Total Demand	1 million units/year
Sensitivity of Attractiveness from Installed Base	2 (dimensionless)
Threshold for Compatibility Effects	1 million units
Standard Deviation of Random Effects on Attractiveness	0.01 (dimensionless)
Initial Installed Base Product i	1 unit
Initial Time	−1 years
Time Step for Simulation	0.25 years

FIGURE 10-25

Simulations of the installed base model

Twenty simulations are shown. At time zero the standard deviation of the random effects on product attractiveness rises from 0 to 0.01.

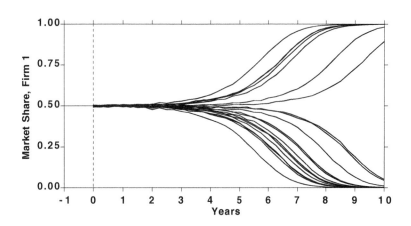

and the system is balanced on the unstable equilibrium of 50% market share. At time zero, the first random shocks begin to perturb the system, but the positive feedbacks have not yet begun to operate. Market share is tightly clustered between about 49% and 51%, and the distribution of market shares is normal (bell shaped). The distribution changes only slightly for the first few years, even after the feedbacks in the system begin to operate. By year 4 the variance of the distribution of market shares has grown substantially, but the distribution still appears to be roughly normal, with a single peak at 50% market share. By year 6, the distribution has spread still further and has begun to bifurcate into two modes. The positive network feedback now rapidly differentiates the two firms from one another, until one gains 100% of the market and the other is wiped out. By year 10, the market share of the winning firm in nearly all simulations is greater than 95%.

The behavior of the model is similar to the nonlinear Polya process in section 10.2. However, the model relaxes the restrictive assumptions of the Polya model. First, the model is formulated in continuous time. Second, where the Polya process selects only one stone per period, either black or white, here total sales are divided into simultaneous and continuous flows of sales for each product. Where the Polya process chooses which color to add based on a single random event, the model here includes multiple sources of random variation in consumer choices.

Most importantly, the attractiveness of each product depends not on the size of the installed base relative to that of other products but on the absolute size of each product's installed base. In the Polya process, the probability of selecting a given color depends only on the proportion of stones with that color already in the jar.

FIGURE 10-26   Evolution of the distribution of market share

The distribution of market share for Firm 1 in 5000 simulations, shown every 2 years. Vertical axis is the proportion of simulations falling within each 5% increment of market share.

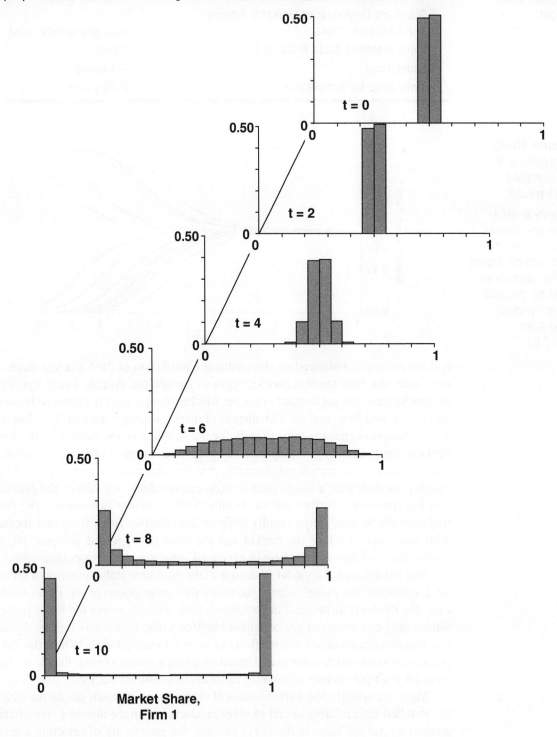

This assumption is not realistic for products with compatibility and network effects. First, consumers are not likely to know the installed base of each product, and the decision rules in models should not use information the real decision makers do not have. Second, the Polya assumption means the effect of compatibility on market share is the same for a given ratio of the installed bases of the different products, no matter how large the installed base. A 2:1 installed base advantage for VHS would yield the same market share advantage whether the installed base was 20 VHS to 10 Betamax machines or 20 million to 10 million.

People's decisions are influenced by compatibility with the machines owned by others in their social network. The larger the installed base of each product, the greater the chance that any potential buyer will have friends and family who already own that format. Clearly, when the installed base of products is very low, compatibility is not yet a factor for prospective purchasers. As the total installed base grows and more of the people a potential buyer interacts with have the product, compatibility becomes progressively more important. The formulation for product attractiveness meets this criterion because it depends on the size of the installed base of each product (scaled by the Threshold for Compatibility Effects). The exponential function for attractiveness reduces the effect of differences in installed base when the total installed base is very small and amplifies the difference as the total installed base grows.

As a result, the strength of the positive network feedback increases as the market grows. These shifts in loop dominance can be illustrated by constructing the phase plot for the model. The phase plot shows how market share for a given product depends on that product's share of the total installed base. The phase plot is analogous to the phase plot for the nonlinear Polya process shown in Figure 10-6. The fraction of the installed base of a given product is analogous to the proportion of stones of a given color already in the jar. Market share is analogous to the probability of adding a stone of a given color to the jar.

As in the prior phase plots, the fixed points (points where the phase plot crosses the 45° line) are equilibria for market share (Figure 10-27). Whenever the curve defining market share lies above the 45° line, market share for firm 1 exceeds firm 1's share of the installed base, causing firm 1's share of the installed base to rise. The trajectory of the system flows along the market share curve to the right, toward a higher share of the installed base, until share reaches equilibrium at a fixed point where it meets the 45° line. Conversely, when the phase plot lies below the 45° line, firm 1's market share is less than its current share of the installed base, so its share of the installed base will fall. The trajectory of the system flows along the phase plot to the left until it comes to another equilibrium where it meets the 45° line.

Because the share of installed base rises whenever market share is above the 45° line and falls whenever market share is below it, the stability of any equilibrium point is easily determined from the phase plot. If the slope of the phase plot at an equilibrium point is greater than 1, that equilibrium point is unstable. A slight increase in the product's share of installed base causes an even greater increase in market share, further boosting the product's share of the installed base and progressively moving the system away from the equilibrium. A slight decrease in the product's share of installed base causes a larger drop in market share, further reducing the share of installed base and moving the system farther to the left, away

FIGURE 10-27

Hypothetical phase plot showing location and stability of equilibria

Fixed points (where the phase plot crosses the 45° line) are the equilibria of the system. Fixed points where the phase plot has a slope greater than 1 are unstable; those with slope less than 1 are stable. Arrows indicate the flow along the phase plot.

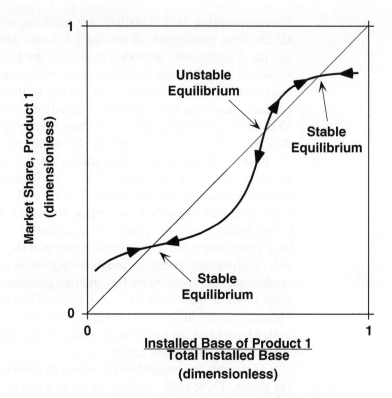

from the equilibrium point. When the slope of the phase plot is greater than unity, the system's dynamics are dominated by the positive feedbacks. When, however, the slope of the phase plot at an equilibrium point is less than 1, then a slight drop in product 1's share of the installed base causes a smaller drop in market share. Since market share exceeds the current share of the installed base, the share of the installed base will increase, raising market share and moving the system back toward the equilibrium point. An increase in installed base has a similar compensatory effect because the market share rises by less than the installed base, diluting the installed base until the system returns to the original equilibrium.

When the slope of the phase plot is less than unity, the system's dynamics are dominated by negative feedback. Because in general the phase plot is nonlinear, its slope varies, and as it does, so too does the relative importance of the positive and negative loops in the system. Points where the slope of the phase plot shifts from less than 1 to greater than 1 mark shifts in loop dominance from net negative to net positive feedback.

Figure 10-28 shows the phase plot for the market share model. The phase plot shows the market share of firm 1 as a function of the proportion of product 1 in the total installed base. However, unlike the nonlinear Polya process (Figure 10-6), the strength of the positive network effect loop grows as the total installed base grows. Therefore the shape of the phase plot relating firm 1's market share to its fraction of the total installed base changes as the total installed base grows. The figure shows four of these curves, for situations where the competitor's installed base is 0.10, 0.50, 1, and 2 times the size of the threshold for compatibility effects. The system always has an equilibrium where the market share and share of the total

FIGURE 10-28

Phase plot for network effects model

The phase plot shows the market share of firm 1 as a function of its share of the total installed base. The function depends on the size of the installed base of the competitor and is shown for four values of the competitor's installed base relative to the threshold for compatibility effects (B_2 = Installed Base Product 2/Threshold for Compatibility Effects). The arrows show the direction of flow for each curve.

To derive the phase plot, note that market share for firm 1 is given by the logit model

$$MS_1 = A_1/(A_1 + A_2)$$

where MS is market share and A is the attractiveness of each product. Assuming the other effects on attractiveness have a neutral effect, attractiveness is determined only by the network effect:

$$A_i = \exp(sB_i)$$

where s = Sensitivity of Attractiveness from Compatibility and B_i is the installed base of product i relative to the threshold for compatibility effects. The ratio of the installed base of product 1 to the total installed base, R, is

$$R = B_1/(B_1 + B_2).$$

Expressing B_1 as $B_2R/(1 - R)$ and substituting into the equation for attractiveness yields market share for product 1 as a function of product 1's share of the total installed base:

$$MS_1 = \exp[s(R/(1 - R))B_2]/$$
$$\{\exp[s(R/(1 - R))B_2] + \exp[sB_2]\}.$$

The four curves in the figure assume B_2 = 0.1, 0.5, 1, and 2.

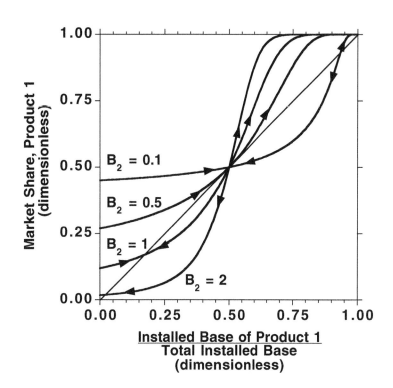

installed base are 50%. However, the shape of the curves, and the number and stability of equilibria, change dramatically as the market grows.

When the total installed base of the industry is small, the network effect is weak. The curve in Figure 10-28 labeled $B_2 = 0.1$ shows how market share evolves when the competitor's installed base is just 10% of the threshold for compatibility effects. When the installed base is very small, the network effect is so weak that the equilibrium at 50% of the installed base is stable (the phase plot crosses the 45° line at 50% share with a slope less than 1). Over a wide range, random shocks affecting market share are self-correcting: to the extent a shock moves the system away from 50%, market share adjusts to compensate, gradually returning the installed base to a ratio of 1:1. Note that there are two additional equilibria: an unstable point when the share of installed base is about 90% and a stable point when the share of installed base is 100%. To dominate the market when the total installed base is small, firm 1 would have to have at least 90% of the installed base.

As the total installed base rises, the positive network effect loop grows stronger. The slope of the phase plot at the 50% point rises, and the unstable equilibrium point at 90% share moves to the left. When the competitor's installed base is half the threshold (the curve labeled $B_2 = 0.5$), the slope of the phase plot at the 50% equilibrium is just about equal to 1. At this point, the initial

50% equilibrium is bistable: market share now always lies above the 45° line. If the share of installed base for firm 1 drops, market share rises, compensating for the disturbance and returning the share of installed base to 50%, but an increase in installed base causes an even greater rise in share, moving the system away from the 50% equilibrium. If random shocks initially give firm 1 a small advantage in installed base, market share will tend to rise further until firm 1 dominates the market and reaches the stable equilibrium at 100% of the installed base.

Further growth in the total installed base continues to increase the strength of the positive network effect loop until it dominates the dynamics of the system. When the competitor's installed base is equal to the threshold (the curve labeled $B_2 = 1$), the slope of the phase plot at the 50% equilibrium is greater than 1, and the equilibrium at 50% is unstable. There are now two stable equilibria: one at 100% of the installed base and one at about 20%. The positive loops dominate the system. The firm that gains the largest share of the installed base wins an even larger share of the market and begins to consolidate its dominance of the industry while those finding themselves with the smallest shares of the installed base fall farther and farther behind.

As growth continues, the strength of the positive network loop rises still more, further accelerating the leader's rise to dominance. By the time the competitor's installed base has reached twice the threshold (the curve labeled $B_2 = 2$), the phase plot is quite steep around the 50% equilibrium and the two stable equilibria have moved closer to 0 and 100%. The positive loops are now so strong that lock in to a single standard is quite rapid and the chance that any random shocks or policies might reverse the outcome is vanishingly small.

10.8.3   Policy Implications

The model results have clear implications for firms seeking to use positive feedbacks such as network effects to gain a decisive market share advantage and eliminate their competitors. When a new product is first introduced to a market where no prior standards have been established, the network effect is likely to be quite weak. Market share will be determined primarily by other product attributes such as quality, price, features, and so on. During this period, a late entrant might, by offering a superior product, aggressive pricing, joint ventures with providers of complementary assets, and other means, overcome the first mover's advantage in installed base and take leadership of the industry. The window of opportunity for such action is limited, however. As the market grows, network effects and the availability of complementary products (e.g., compatible prerecorded tapes for VCRs, compatible software for computers) grow in importance. A firm that establishes a lead in installed base, in the availability of complementary assets, and in the perception that it is the market leader is likely to gain an edge in market share that leads to further gains in a self-fulfilling prophecy. As the installed base grows and the network effects become even stronger, the chance that a late entrant can overcome the advantage of the first mover declines rapidly, both because the total installed base is growing (requiring the upstart to sell more units) and because compatibility becomes a more and more important determinant of customer purchase decisions (giving the current leader more of an edge).

These dynamics describe what happened in the VCR industry and help explain why Sony, as the first mover, was unable to convert its early lead into market dominance despite the large number of positive feedbacks conferring cumulative advantage to the leader. When VHS was introduced, the installed base of VCRs was so small that compatibility was not yet an issue for most customers. Other attributes of product attractiveness dominated in the purchase decision. Whereas Sony, hoping to monopolize the format they believed would become the industry standard, kept tight control of the technology, thus restricting its availability and keeping the price relatively high, Matsushita decided to license VHS widely and cheaply. The VHS consortium, though the later entrant to the market, was able to gain the largest share of the market just at the point where total sales growth exploded and rapidly overcame the initial installed base advantage of Betamax. VHS became the leader around the time film studios began to issue films for the home video market. Once the film studios decided to produce tapes for the home market, compatibility became the dominant attribute of attractiveness in the purchase decision of most customers, and film studios chose to issue tapes in the most prevalent format. Matsushita's strategy gave them the lead in share of VHS tapes just at the time compatibility became critical. Though Sony tried to fight back by lowering prices and encouraging production of Betamax format tapes, the window of opportunity had shut. The growth of the installed base had strengthened the network effects so much that VHS's lead could not be overcome. The fate of Betamax was sealed.

CHALLENGE

Policy Analysis

Use the model developed in section 10.8 to explore the policies suggested below. In these tests, start your simulations at time zero, with the parameters described in Table 10-2. However, you should eliminate the random shocks by setting the standard deviation of random effects on attractiveness to zero.

1. Suppose firm 1 attempts to gain initial advantage by seeding the marketplace with some free units, so that at the start of the simulation the installed base of firm 1 is 10,000 units, while firm 2's initial installed base remains 1 unit. Run the model. What is the initial market share of firm 1? What happens to market share over time, and why?

2. Suppose firm 2 attempts to counter firm 1's effort to win the market by doling out 10,000 free units of its own product. However, it takes time for firm 2 to react, so the free units of firm 2's product don't begin to reach the market until 6 months have passed. Suppose further that it takes 1 year to distribute all 10,000 units.

   To implement this policy, modify the equation for Sales of Product 2 as follows:

   Sales of Product 2 = Total Demand * Market Share Product 2 + Extra Sales of
       Product 2 * PULSE(Extra Sales Start Time, Duration of Extra Sales)

   Extra Sales Start Time = 0.5

   Duration of Extra Sales = 1   (10-2a) where

$$\text{PULSE}\binom{\text{Start Time,}}{\text{Duration}} = \begin{cases} 1 \text{ if Start Time} \leq \text{Time} \leq \text{Start Time} + \text{Duration} \\ 0 \text{ otherwise} \end{cases} \quad (10\text{-}2a)$$

The PULSE function is zero until the Start Time, then takes a value of 1 for Duration time units, and returns to zero thereafter.

The modified equation therefore increases sales of product 2 at a rate of 10,000 units per year for 1 year starting at time 0.5 years, increasing the installed base of product 2 exactly 10,000 units, all else equal.

Does firm 2's policy of seeding the market with 10,000 extra units to counter firm 1's initial 10,000 unit advantage work? Why/why not?

3. How many units must firm 2 add to its sales rate over the course of a year starting at time 0.5 to overcome firm 1's initial advantage and win the market? Estimating this quantity to the nearest 1000 units/year is sufficient precision.

4. Suppose firm 2 waits until year 5 to counter firm 1's advantage (again, firm 1 starts with an initial installed base of 10,000 units and firm 2 starts with 1 unit). How many units must firm 2 now add to its installed base over the course of 1 year to overcome the lead of firm 1 and capture the market? Why? Estimating this quantity to the nearest 10,000 units per year is sufficient precision.

5. What do you conclude about the optimal strategy for a firm in markets characterized by strong positive network effects? How would you implement the winning strategy? What considerations might temper or reverse this conclusion?

6. What other strategies besides free distribution of product might a firm use to counter the initial advantage of a rival? Give examples.

CHALLENGE   Extending the Model

This challenge invites you to relax some of the model's simplifying assumptions to explore the sensitivity of the results to alternative representations of industry and firm structure.

1. Turnover of the installed base: In the simple model there is no outflow from the installed base of product. In reality, products such as VCRs and computers wear out or are replaced by improved products. Revise the model to include product discards and turnover of the installed base. Assume the average lifetime of both products is the same and equal to 5 years. Also assume the discard process is first-order, that is, that the discard rate equals the installed base of each product divided by the average lifetime.

Assume every person or household discarding the product purchases a replacement. You will therefore need to modify the equation for total demand to include the replacement demand, consisting of the sum of the individual discard rates.

Explore the behavior of the revised model for different values of the product lifetime (setting the average lifetime of the product to a very large number [such as one trillion] gives you the base case of the original model). What is the effect of discards on the rate at which the system locks in to a standard? Explain in terms of the feedback structure. Hint: Plot the market share and share of installed base for firm 1. How does their relationship change as the average lifetime of the product changes?

2. The simple model aggregates many positive feedbacks into a single effect of installed base on product attractiveness. However, the network effect is only one of many important positive loops. The availability of complementary resources is often even more important. VCRs without compatible tapes and computers without compatible software are useless; the Dvorak typewriter keyboard is faster than the QWERTY keyboard but is useless without Dvorak-trained typists. Aggregating the effect of complementary products into the network effect is not generally appropriate because these two loops operate with different time delays and involve decisions made by different groups (complementary products can be produced by third parties).

Modify the model to include the availability of complementary products explicitly. To do so, make the following assumptions:

a. The total production of complementary products is divided into production of goods compatible with product 1 and production of goods compatible with product 2.

b. The total production of complementary goods should be proportional to the total installed base of product 1 and product 2. The bigger the size of the market, the greater the output of complementary products (e.g., videotapes, software, typists) will be.

c. Use the logit formulation to determine the share of total complementary good production going to each product. The share of complementary goods produced for each format is given by the attractiveness of that format relative to the attractiveness of all format options. The attractiveness of a given format to a producer of complementary goods depends on the size of the installed base of products using that format. Aggregate the effects of all other considerations into an exogenous term, "attractiveness of product i to third parties from other factors."

d. Production of each type of complementary good accumulates in a stock. Assume complementary goods have an average useful life of 5 years (assume a first-order discard process). Unlike part 1 above, discards of complementary goods are not automatically replaced (that is, the total production of complementary goods does not include the total discard rate). Assume the initial installed base of each type of complementary good is zero (you may vary this as a policy later).

e. Modify the formulation for the attractiveness of each product (equation (10-5)) to include an effect of the availability of complementary goods. The effect should be formulated analogously to the network effect. Select parameters you think are reasonable (use the VCR case as a guide, but don't try to replicate the history of the VCR industry exactly—you are trying to build a general model). In particular, set parameters so that both the network and complementary goods effects are important and so the relative importance of the network effect and availability of complementary goods are reasonable in your judgment. Document your model (see chapter 21); include brief justification for your selection of parameters.

f.   Test your model, refining the parameters if necessary. What is the impact of an explicit representation of complementary goods on the dynamics of standard formation? Explain in terms of the feedback structure. Explore the sensitivity of the system to parameters. Explore the response of the system to policies, including

   i.   Seeding the market with free units, as in the previous Challenge.

   ii.   Seeding the market for complementary goods by ensuring there is an installed base of complementary goods compatible with your format when your product is launched.

   iii.   Entering into joint ventures or other agreements that increase the attractiveness of your format to producers of complementary goods.

   iv.   Other policies you might entertain.

10.9   SUMMARY

Path dependence is a common phenomenon in natural and human systems. Path dependence arises in systems dominated by positive feedback. Even when all paths are initially equally attractive, the symmetry is broken by microscopic noise and external perturbations. The positive feedbacks then amplify these small initial differences to macroscopic significance. Once a dominant design or standard has emerged, the costs of switching become prohibitive, so the equilibrium is self-enforcing: the system has locked in. Lock in persists until an architectural shift or large external shock renders the dominant design obsolete. A wide range of positive feedbacks drives the growth of businesses. The evidence suggests that the profitability of individual firms and the evolution of the economy as a whole is strongly influenced by these positive loops and exhibits path-dependent behavior. Successful firms are able to strengthen several of the positive loops that can drive growth to create synergies that leads to cumulative success.

Path dependence in the economy is common because the growth of business enterprises is driven by a host of positive feedbacks. These feedbacks involve scale economies, learning, network effects, market power, and many other processes. The most successful firms are able to create synergy by using ensembles of these feedbacks to create a mutually consistent strategy. However, success with one set of these positive loops can lead to inertia and rigidity that prevent a firm that dominates in one regime from maintaining its dominance as the technical, economic, political, or social environment changes.

Part IV

Tools for Modeling Dynamic Systems

This section develops the tools needed to build realistic and robust models of dynamic systems, especially models of human behavior. The section covers tools for representing the physical structure of systems such as the stock and flow structure, delays, and demographics, and also techniques for modeling the decision-making processes of the actors in the system. Chapter 11 shows how delays can be modeled, covering both delays in material flows and information delays. Chapter 12 covers demographics, showing how the age structure of populations can be modeled (whether human or any other type, such as a population of machines in a factory). Chapter 12 also develops structures to model the attributes of a stock, such as the average experience of a workforce or the average productivity of a firm's equipment. Chapter 13 develops guidelines for representing human behavior in simulation models and presents generic formulations for decision rules you can use in your models. Chapter 14 examines nonlinear functions including specification, estimation from qualitative and quantitative data, methods for eliciting expert knowledge from clients, and sensitivity analysis. Examples include manufacturing, service delivery, and product development. Chapter 15 discusses the representation of bounded rationality, and shows how the formulations in models can be tested for intended rationality, a measure of their internal logic and consistency with principles of behavioral decision making. Chapter 15 also develops the "Market Growth Model," a model of a high-tech growth company, to illustrate how an entire organization can experience dysfunctional behavior even when the decision rules used by the individual actors are intendedly rational. Since forecasts and expectations are central to decision making in many fields, Chapter 16 shows how expectation formation can be modeled in a behaviorally realistic fashion, with forecasts of energy demand, inflation, and other domains as examples.

11

Delays

Delay always breeds danger.
— Miguel de Cervantes (*Don Quixote,* Book iv, Chap. ii.)

Never do today what you can put off till tomorrow. Delay may give clearer light as to what is best to be done.
— Aaron Burr

Delays are a critical source of dynamics in nearly all systems. Some delays breed danger by creating instability and oscillation. Others provide a clearer light by filtering out unwanted variability and enabling managers to separate signals from noise. In this chapter you will explore the structure and behavior of delays, develop various models of delays, and test their response to a range of inputs. The chapter will help you understand the dynamics of delays so that you can use them appropriately in more complex models. The chapter also presents case studies highlighting the use of delays in various contexts, including capital investment in the macroeconomy and forecasting demand at a successful semiconductor manufacturer.

11.1 DELAYS: AN INTRODUCTION

CHALLENGE **Duration and Dynamics of Delays**

Before considering how to model delays, reflect on some delays in common processes. Answer the following questions without using outside references or any computer simulations; give your best intuitive estimate. Don't spend more than a few minutes on this challenge.

1. Manufacturing firms determine the amount of plant and equipment they need based on the demand they expect for their products as well as the expected profitability of the new equipment. Suppose there is a sudden, unanticipated 10% increase in orders for the firm's product. How long does it take, on average, before the firm's production capacity increases to the new level? Assume investments in new capacity are expected to yield the firm's required return on investment.

2. Suppose there is a sudden, unanticipated increase of 10% in the total demand for manufactured goods throughout the economy. How long does it take for the economy as a whole to increase total manufacturing capacity to the new rate of aggregate orders?

3. Consider the market for agricultural commodities such as pork. What is the average delay between a rise in the price of pork and the resulting increase in pork supply?

4. How long does it take economic forecasters to revise their estimates of inflation? That is, if there is an unanticipated increase in the inflation rate, how long will it take for the forecasts of the experts to adjust to the new rate?

5. How long does it take a nation like the United States to respond to an environmental challenge such as air or water pollution? That is, what is the time required to recognize high levels of pollutants, such as carbon monoxide emitted by automobiles, and reduce them within safe limits?

6. Consider the post office. Suppose you deposit a mass mailing of 1000 letters—all sent first class—to various destinations around the country. Sketch the pattern of deliveries you expect, assuming no letters get lost.

7. Consider a firm's forecast of the order rate for its product. Suppose the actual order rate and the forecast have been equal for a long time. Now suppose the actual order rate suddenly and unexpectedly increases by 50% and remains at the new rate. Sketch the response of the forecast.

8. Suppose it takes 5 days for a manufacturer to receive parts from a supplier. If the firm orders 10,000 units per day, how many units are in the stock of parts on order? Suppose the parts order rate suddenly and unexpectedly increases to 20,000 per day and remains at the higher rate. Sketch the response of the delivery rate and of the stock of parts on order.

9. Suppose the part order rate for the firm in question 8 remains constant at 10,000 units/day. Suddenly the time required to deliver the parts permanently increases from 5 to 10 days. Sketch the response of the delivery rate and the stock of parts on order.

11.1.1   Defining Delays

Delays are pervasive. It takes time to measure and report information. It takes time to make decisions. And it takes time for decisions to affect the state of a system. Modelers need to understand how delays behave, how to represent them, how to choose among various types of delays in any modeling situation, and how to estimate their duration.

A delay is a process whose output lags behind its input in some fashion (see the top panel in Figure 11-1). Consider what's inside the box marked Delay: A little reflection shows there must be at least one stock within every delay. Since the output generally differs from the input (it lags behind), there must be a stock inside the process to accumulate the difference between input and output. Consider the process of mailing letters. The input to the delay is the rate at which you mail letters. The output is the rate at which your letters are delivered. Where are the letters between the time you mail them and the time they are delivered? They reside in a stock of Letters in Transit within the post office system (Figure 11-1 shows the structure for the post office and the general structure for material delays).

The type of delay shown in Figure 11-1 is known as a *material delay,* since it captures the physical flow of material (in this case letters) through a delay process. Other examples of material delays include the flow of product through a supply chain, the construction of buildings, or the progression of design tasks through a product development process. In each there are physical units (cases of beer, square feet of space, or engineering drawings) moving through the process. Notice that the only outflow from the stock of letters in transit in the diagram is the delivery rate; in the model, letters are never lost or misdirected (unlike in the real post office). The flow of letters through the delay is conserved.

FIGURE 11-1
Delays always contain stocks.

The output of a delay lags behind the input:

General structure of a material delay:

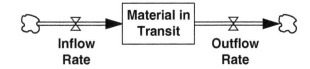

The post office as a delay:

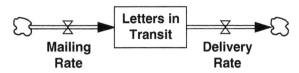

Many delays represent the gradual adjustment of perceptions or beliefs; these are *information delays*. The delay between a change in the order rate for your company's products and your belief about the likely future order rate is an example of an information delay. Suppose orders for your product have been steady at 1000 units per day, and you expect them to continue at that rate. Suddenly orders jump to 2000 units/day. You are unlikely to immediately increase your belief about tomorrow's orders to 2000 units. But if the order rate remains at 2000 units/day, day after day, you will gradually increase your expectation of future orders until it eventually reaches the new rate. There is a delay between the receipt of new information and the updating of your beliefs. Though there is no physical flow of material, information delays still involve stocks. In the example, the stock in the delay is your belief about future orders, a psychological state residing in your mental model. In general, any belief or perception involves an information delay because we cannot instantaneously update our mental models as new information is received. Other examples of information delays include averages such as the average production rate of a product. As shown below, information delays do not involve conserved flows and cannot be modeled with the same structures used for material delays.

11.2 MATERIAL DELAYS: STRUCTURE AND BEHAVIOR

Having defined the stock and flow structure for a material delay (Figure 11-1), it is necessary to formulate a decision rule (equation) for the outflow rate. In many situations the outflows from stocks are constrained by various resources and you must explicitly model the way these resources determine the outflow (see chapters 13 and 14). Production cannot occur without labor, materials, capital, and other resources. The capacity of the delay is sometimes high enough relative to the inflow rates that you can assume the outflow depends only on the past inflows. In modeling the commercial real estate market of a city you might conclude that the capacity of the construction industry in the region is ample, or sufficiently flexible, and model the construction delay for new buildings as a constant. You might model the diffusion of dioxin through a town's groundwater supply as a pure delay with a constant delay time based on the characteristics of the soil and subsurface morphology. In such pure delays the process governing the outflow from the stock of material in transit depends only on how much material is in transit and how long it's been there, not on any resources. The delay time is independent of the input or stock in transit, and the process is linear. Such pure delays are modeled as uncapacitated queuing processes.

The assumption that a delay is not capacity constrained is always an approximation and holds only over a certain range of inputs. If the real estate market in the city booms, orders for new buildings may outstrip the capacity of the construction industry, and the average delay between commissioning a new building and its completion will increase. In these cases the resources constraining the capacity of the process must be modeled explicitly.

You must answer two principal questions for every delay. First, what is the average length of the delay? Second, what is the distribution of the output around the average delay time?

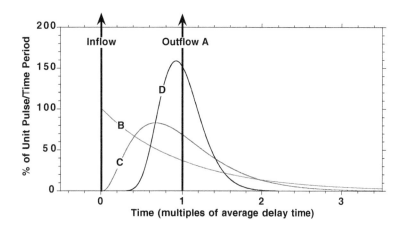

Some distributions of the outflow from a delay

The input in all cases is a unit pulse at time zero. Outflow A is a pipeline delay in which all items arrive together exactly 1 delay time after they enter. Outflow distributions B-D exhibit different degrees of variation in processing times for individual items so some arrive before and some after the average delay time. In all cases the average delay time is the same and the areas under each distribution are equal (100% of the quantity added by the pulse input). Each curve represents the probability distribution describing the chance that any particular item will exit the delay at a particular time.

11.2.1   What Is the Average Length of the Delay?

How long, on average, does it take items to flow through the delay? Equivalently, what is the *average residence time* for a unit in the delay (how long on average does a unit stay in the stock of material in transit)?

For the US post office, the average delay for domestic first class mail might be on the order of 2 days. For email, the average delay between sending and receiving messages via the internet might be on the order of a few seconds. (In what stock(s) do your emails reside between the time you send them and the time they are received?) In any application, the length of the delay is an empirical issue to be investigated by data collection and field study (see section 11.5).

11.2.2   What Is the Distribution of the Output around the Average Delay Time?

What happens once items enter the delay? Are they processed first-come, first-served or is there some mixing and reshuffling? Do all units spend the same time in the delay, or is there some variation around the average, with some units flowing through the delay faster and some slower than average? Figure 11-2 shows some possibilities for the outflow from a delay.

The figure shows the response of several different delays to a *pulse input.* A pulse input is analogous to a mass mailing of a large number of letters: a certain quantity of material is injected into the delay at a single instant.[1] The figure shows

---

[1]The pulse function, also known as the Dirac delta function $\delta(t)$, is the limit of a rectangular pulse starting at time T, with duration (width) W and height 1/W, as the duration of the pulse goes to zero:

$$\delta(t, T) = \lim_{W \to 0} \delta(t, T, W) = \begin{cases} 0 \text{ for } t \leq T \\ 1/W \text{ for } T < t \leq T + W \\ 0 \text{ for } t > T + W \end{cases}$$

The pulse function has an area of unity; thus an arbitrary pulse input of Q units at time T is given by $Q\delta(t, T)$. In simulation models, $Q\delta(t, T)$ is approximated by a rectangular pulse with a duration equal to the simulation time step DT and a height of Q/DT.

the output of the delay as a percent per time period of the total quantity input to the delay at time zero. In all four cases the average processing time is the same. One possibility (Outflow A) is that the items entering the delay all proceed through the delay in exactly the same order and exit after exactly the same time. In this case, the output of the delay is also a pulse exiting the delay exactly 1 delay time after the pulse input. An automobile assembly line approximates a pipeline delay. The cars move down the line in sequence, each exiting in the same order they entered. When the line is running smoothly the delay time or residence time in the delay is the same for all and the order of entry determines the order of exit. In the language of queuing theory, the service discipline of the assembly line is FIFO (first in, first out).

The term *service discipline* refers to the decision rule for choosing which of the units in the stock of material in transit will be processed and exit first. Other types of service discipline include LIFO (last in, first out), a common situation in my kitchen pantry, where the most recently purchased items are often placed at the front of the shelves and are then used first because they block the older items behind them. When you rotate your stock to reduce spoilage you are shifting from LIFO to FIFO discipline. Many other rules are possible, including random selection or selection based on some other attribute, as when candidates for organ transplants are selected based on how sick they are or the chances of success rather than on how long they've been on the waiting list.[2]

When large numbers of items or multiple servers are aggregated together, service discipline is often neither strictly FIFO nor LIFO. If you mail a large number of letters all at once, they will not all be delivered at once. There will be a distribution around the average delivery time, with some letters arriving sooner than average and some arriving later. The variation arises because the letters are destined for different recipients, and the travel times to each destination differ. More important, unlike car bodies on the assembly line, letters are not processed in the same order they are mailed. During the various stages of processing, the letters are mixed with others. Sorting the letters by destination so they can be routed properly causes some of the mixing. Some is inadvertent as when the contents of a corner mailbox are dumped into a bin for transport to the local branch.

The consequence of mixing is some randomization of the processing order. Another source of dispersion in the outflow distribution is caused by random variations in the processing time itself. Consider the checkout delay at a supermarket. You might choose to model the checkout process as a single material delay where the inflow rate is the rate at which shoppers join a checkout line and the outflow rate is the rate at which they leave the market. Variations in the amount of food in each shopper's basket and in the speed of the clerks mean the processing time for each customer and each checkout lane can differ. Customers joining the checkout line next to yours after you do sometimes leave before you do, so the order of exit is not the same as the order in which people queue (as everyone knows, the line you are in is always the slowest).

---

[2]Zenios, Chertow, and Wein (forthcoming) develop a dynamic model to evaluate various policies for allocating kidneys to transplant candidates.

These sources of dispersion mean that in general, when many items are introduced into a delay at one time, some items will exit earlier than others, spreading
out the distribution of the delivery rate. The response of a delay to a pulse input
such as shown in Figure 11-2 can be thought of as the probability distribution describing the likelihood that any given item is delivered at a particular time. Distribution A has no variability in delivery times. Distributions B–D have different
degrees of mixing; of these, distribution B has the most variability in delivery
times, while distribution D has the least. All four distributions A–D have the same
average delay time, and all conserve the inflow, so the area under each distribution
is the same (100% of the inflow eventually exits from the stock of material in transit, or, equivalently, the probability that any given letter is eventually delivered
is 100%).

In specifying delays, you must consider not only the average length of the delay but also the distribution of deliveries around the mean delay. Sometimes you
can estimate the output distribution from the data. Other times you must estimate
it by direct inspection of the delay process to see whether there is mixing or strict
FIFO discipline and whether the processing time of individual items is constant or
varies randomly from item to item.

11.2.3   Pipeline Delay

As in the example of the auto assembly line, you sometimes need to model a delay
in which the delay time is constant and in which the order of exit from the delay is
precisely the same as the order of entry. To do so requires a *pipeline delay,* also
known as transportation lag (the metaphor is an assembly line in which items are
transported in order and at a constant rate; Figure 11-3).

In the presentation below the inflow to the delays will be exogenous. Exploring the response of different delays to idealized exogenous inputs such as a pulse,
step, ramp, and fluctuation helps develop your intuition for their behavior so
you can select the appropriate type in any modeling situation. Of course, in your
models the inputs to delays will in general be an endogenous part of the feedback
structure.

The stock of material in transit for any material delay is given by

$$\text{Material in Transit} = \text{INTEGRAL}(\text{Inflow}(t) - \text{Outflow}(t), \text{Material in Transit}(0))$$

$$(11\text{-}1)$$

For the pipeline delay, the outflow is simply the inflow lagged by the average delay time D:

$$\text{Outflow}(t) = \text{Inflow}(t - D) \hspace{3cm} (11\text{-}2)$$

Distribution A in Figure 11-2 is a pipeline delay: When the inflow is a pulse, the
outflow is a pulse exactly D time units later. There is no mixing in the processing
order, nor any variation in individual processing times; the delay time for each item
equals the average delay time.

11.2.4   First-Order Material Delay

Many delays do not approximate a pipeline delay; there is mixing and variation
in the individual processing times, causing some variance in the distribution of

FIGURE 11-3   Pipeline delay: structure

In a pipeline delay individual items exit the delay in the same order and after exactly the same time, like widgets moving down an assembly line at a constant speed.

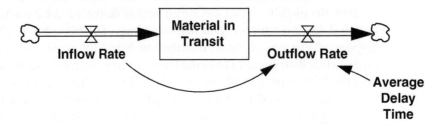

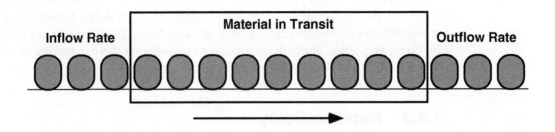

Material in Transit(t) = INTEGRAL(Inflow(t) – Outflow(t), Material in Transit(0))
Outflow(t) = Inflow(t – Average Delay Time)

deliveries. Consider an example at the opposite extreme from a pipeline delay, say, water draining from a sink. Further imagine that the water in the sink is thoroughly mixed at all times (Figure 11-4).

In the case of perfect mixing, the probability that any particular water molecule is the next to flow out of the sink is the same for all the molecules in the sink, independent of how long that molecule has been in the sink. Perfect mixing means the order of entry is irrelevant to the order of exit. Put another way, perfect mixing destroys all information about the order of entry.

The outflow from a first-order material delay is always proportional to the stock of material in transit:

$$\text{Outflow} = \text{Material in Transit}/D \qquad\qquad (11\text{-}3)$$

where D is again the average delay time. Note that the only inputs to the outflow rate are the stock of material in transit and the delay time; information about the order of entry of individual items to the stock is not used to determine the outflow rate.

Equation (11-3) is the familiar linear first-order negative feedback system (chapter 8). The outflow rate forms a negative feedback loop since the greater the stock of material in transit, the greater the outflow, lowering the stock. Distribution B in Figure 11-2 shows the response of a first-order material delay to a pulse input. The response is the familiar pattern of exponential decay (Figure 11-5):

FIGURE 11-4
First-order
material delay:
structure

FIGURE 11-4

First-order material delay: structure

The outflow is proportional to the stock of material in transit. The contents of the stock are perfectly mixed at all times, so all items in the stock have the same probability of exit, independent of their arrival time.

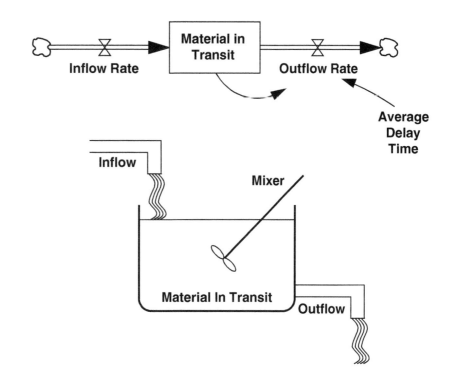

Outflow = Material in Transit/Average Delay Time

Immediately after the pulse, the stock of material in transit jumps up to 100% of the quantity added by the pulse input. The outflow rate immediately rises to 100%/D units per time period. Since the outflow now exceeds the inflow, the stock of material in transit starts to fall. As it falls, so too does the outflow rate, so the stock of material in transit and outflow rate fall at diminishing rates. The *initial* outflow rate would deplete the stock in transit in 1 delay time, but as the stock in transit falls, so does the outflow rate. After 1 delay time has passed the stock in transit has fallen by 63%; after 2D periods, 86% of the items have been delivered; and after 3D periods, 95% have been delivered.[3]

11.2.5 Higher-Order Material Delays

Pipeline delays, with their rigid FIFO service discipline, are good models for some processes such as assembly lines. First-order delays, with their assumption of perfect mixing, are reasonable models of other delay processes, such as chemical and heat diffusion in physical and biological systems, and some analogous diffusion processes in social systems. Between these extremes lie many intermediate cases where there is some mixing in the processing order. In these cases the outflow

---

[3]Recall that exponential decay is given by $S = S_0 \exp(-t/D)$ so when $t = D$, the stock S has fallen to $\exp(-1) \approx 0.37$ of its initial level. See chapter 8.

FIGURE 11-5

Pulse response of first-order material delay

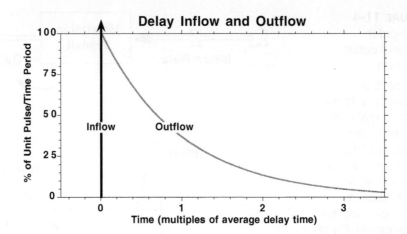

The input to the delay is a unit pulse at time zero. The stock of material in transit instantly jumps to 100%, then decays exponentially with a time constant equal to the average delay time. The initial rate of outflow would deplete the stock in transit in 1 delay time (note the tangent to the trajectory of the stock in transit at time zero), but as the stock in transit falls, so does the outflow rate, yielding the familiar pattern of exponential decay.

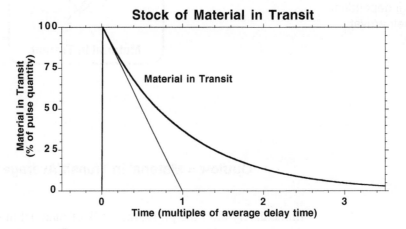

gradually rises, reaches a peak, and then tails off to zero, similar to distributions C and D in Figure 11-2. Consider again the post office. Letters do not all arrive at one time, as in a pipeline delay, but neither is the delivery rate greatest immediately after your letters are mailed. Though letters are not processed in lockstep, neither is the order of delivery independent of the order of mailing. There is partial mixing. Partial mixing can arise when a delay consists of multiple stages of processing in which items flow sequentially from one stage to the next, but where each stage introduces some mixing.

For the case of the post office, you can easily identify many stages of processing. Letters first go into the corner mailbox; then onto the truck that collects the mail; then into bins at the local post office; then, after sorting, onto trucks for delivery to the central post office; then through more stages of sorting and processing; then onto trucks, trains, or planes for transport to the destination cities; then to the local post offices in the destination communities; and so on until they arrive at the mailboxes of the recipients. Each stage introduces some mixing and variability in individual processing times. If the purpose of your model was to reengineer the post office workflow system you might have to represent all these stages separately and explicitly account for the different delay times and capacities of each stage.

FIGURE 11-6 Higher-order delays are formed by cascading first-order delays together.

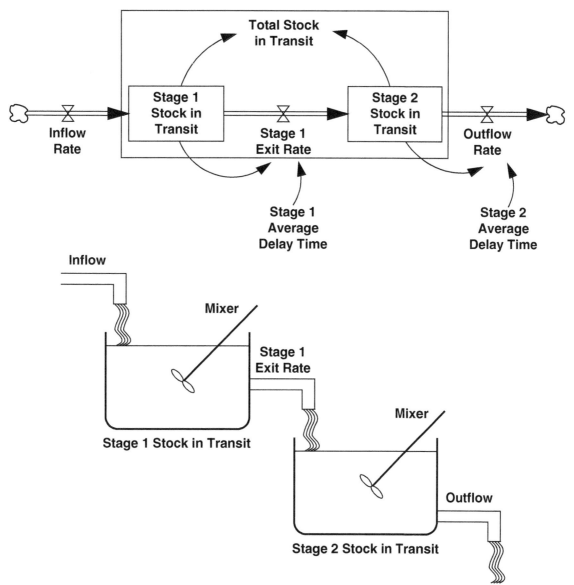

Stage 1 Exit Rate = Stage 1 Stock in Transit/Stage 1 Average Delay Time
Outflow Rate = Stage 2 Stock in Transit/Stage 2 Average Delay Time

You would have a very detailed model indeed. For other purposes, such detail would not be necessary and a pure delay might be appropriate.

In many settings the stages of processing in such a system can be approximated well by cascading several first-order material delays together in series. For example, a second-order material delay consists of two first-order delays in which the input to the second stage is the output of the first stage (Figure 11-6).

The total stock in transit is the sum of the stock in transit at each stage. The average total delay from inflow to outflow is the sum of the average delays of the individual stages. In this fashion you can construct delays with an arbitrary number of stages. Delay times for the individual stages can differ, if the data and model purpose warrant it, though often it is fine to assume each stage has the same delay time. A delay with n stages, each with 1/n of the total delay time, is known as an nth-order material delay. The equations for the nth-order material delay, denoted by the function DELAYn, are

Outflow = DELAYn(Inflow, D):

$$\text{Total Material in Transit} = \sum_{i=1}^{n} \text{Material in Transit}_i$$

Material in Transit$_i$ = INTEGRAL(Net Inflow$_i$, Material in Transit$_i$(0))

Material in Transit$_i$(0) = Inflow * D/n

$$\text{Net Inflow rate}_i = \begin{cases} \text{Inflow} - \text{Exit Rate Stage}_1 & \text{for } i = 1 \\ \text{Exit Rate Stage}_{i-1} - \text{Exit Rate Stage}_i & \text{for } i \in (2, \ldots, n-1) \\ \text{Exit Rate Stage}_{n-1} - \text{Outflow} & \text{for } i = n \end{cases}$$

Exit Rate Stage$_i$ = Material in Transit$_i$/(D/n) for i $\in$ (1, . . . , n − 1)

Outflow = Material in Transit$_n$/(D/n)

$$(11\text{-}4)$$

The initial condition Material in Transit$_i$ = Inflow * D/n initializes the delay in equilibrium so that the initial outflow equals the initial inflow.

Distributions C and D in Figure 11-2 show the response to a unit pulse for a third- and twelfth-order delay, respectively. The higher the order of the delay, the less mixing and the smaller the variance of the output. In the limit, an infinite-order delay consists of an infinite number of stages each with an infinitesimal delay time. Such a delay provides one bin or stock of material in transit for all items entering at a given instant and moves them from one stage to the next before the next set of items, entering in the next instant, are added. Thus an infinite-order delay preserves the order of entry and permits no mixing: it is equivalent to a pipeline delay.

Figure 11-7 shows the pulse response of a third-order delay; Figure 11-8 shows the stocks and flows for the intermediate stages of processing. Immediately after the pulse, the stock of material in stage 1 jumps to 100% of the quantity added. Each stage of the delay is a first-order delay; in a third-order delay the average delay for each stage is one-third of the total delay. Thus the stage 1 exit rate is exponential decay with a time constant of D/3. The exit rate from stage 1 is the input to stage 2. The stock of material in transit in stage 2 rises as long as its input exceeds its output. At about time = 0.34D, the stock in stage 2 has risen enough for the exit rate of stage 2 to equal its inflow from stage 1. The stock in stage 2 peaks. From then on the stage 2 exit rate exceeds the inflow to stage 2, so the stage 2 stock in transit falls and with it, the stage 2 exit rate. Similarly, the stage 2 exit rate is the input to stage 3. The stage 3 stock in transit rises until its outflow equals the inflow,

FIGURE 11-7
Pulse response of
a third-order delay

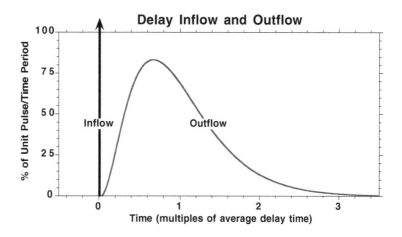

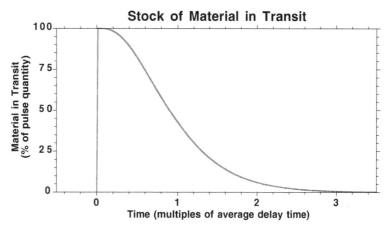

which occurs at about $t = 0.67D$, then gradually falls off as the outflow from the delay exceeds the inflow to stage 3.

Similar dynamics apply to delays with order higher than 3. Referring back to Figure 11-2, note that, except for the pipeline delay, the peak response of material delays of order n precedes the mean delay and there is a long tail in the distribution of deliveries: many items are delivered earlier than average, but some are delivered much later. Note also that as the order of the delay increases, and hence as the degree of mixing decreases, the delivery distribution tightens up: fewer items are delivered earlier than average, more are delivered near the average delay time, and fewer are delivered much later than average. The higher the order of the delay, the smaller the variance in the delivery distribution.

11.2.6 How Much Is in the Delay? Little's Law

The stock of material in transit accumulates the difference between the inflow and outflow to the delay. It's important to know how big the stock in transit will be for

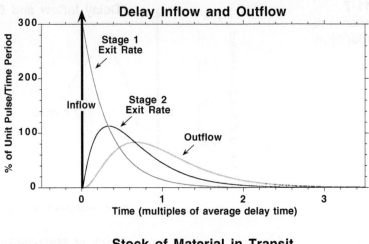

Delay Inflow and Outflow

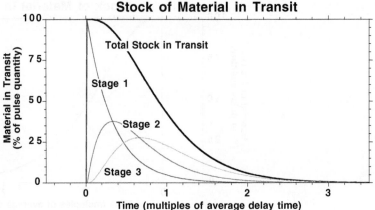

Stock of Material in Transit

any given delay and inflow. Suppose the inflow has been constant long enough for the delay to reach equilibrium. How big is the stock in transit? Consider the pipeline delay with input I, output O, and delay time D: $O(t) = I(t - D)$. Suppose the inflow and stock in transit are initially zero. At time zero the inflow suddenly increases to a constant level I. The outflow will continue to be zero until D periods have passed. During this time, the stock in transit S is increased by I units each period. After D periods, $O = I$ and the stock of material in transit reaches equilibrium. The equilibrium quantity in transit is therefore DI units.[4]

---

[4]The stock in transit for any delay with input I and output O is

$$S(t) = \int_0^t [I(s) - O(s)]ds + S(0)$$

For a pipeline delay with $S(0) = 0$ and a step increase in the input from 0 to I units/period at time zero, $O(t) = 0$ for $t < D$ and I for $t \geq D$, so the equilibrium value of the stock in transit S_∞ is

$$S_\infty = \int_0^D [I - 0]ds + \int_D^\infty [I - I]ds = DI$$

Now consider a first-order delay (equation (11-3)). The outflow of a first-order delay is O = S/D. Since in equilibrium the inflow and outflow are equal, the equilibrium stock in transit is DI units, the same as that for the pipeline delay. In fact, the equilibrium stock in transit for a delay is always DI units, *regardless of the probability distribution of the outflow.* This remarkable property is known as Little's Law, after John Little, an MIT professor of operations research who first proved it. Little's Law means that in equilibrium, the stock in transit is fully characterized by the average delay time and inflow rate. By Little's Law, a firm ordering 10,000 widgets per day from a supplier requiring 5 days to deliver will, in equilibrium, have 50,000 widgets on order, independent of the delivery distribution.

Little's Law helps explain how delays give systems inertia. If business goes sour and the company cuts part orders to zero, its widget inventory will still swell by an additional 50,000 units before deliveries from the supplier can be cut off (assuming no order cancellations are possible).

Little's Law can also be used to estimate the average length of a delay from knowledge of the stock in transit and flows through the delay. In equilibrium, the average residence time of items in the delay is given by the ratio of the stock in transit to the outflow rate, D = S/O = S/I. Thus if an insurance company has a pending pool of 50,000 unresolved claims and settles an average of 25,000 per month, the average time claimants wait to receive payment is 2 months. Again, this measure of delivery time holds strictly only in equilibrium.

Example: Construction Delays in the Electric Utility Industry

Little's Law has dramatic implications for the cash flow and financing requirements of a business. Consider the electric power industry. Up through the early 1970s typical lead times for new plants were about 5 years and the average service life of plants was about 20 years. If the demand for power was constant, an investor-owned utility with 10 gigawatts (gw, billion watts) of capacity would therefore need to add an average of 0.5 gw of capacity per year to replace retirements of old plants. With a 5-year construction delay, the utility would have to have—and finance—2.5 gw of capacity under construction at all times, one-quarter of its existing capacity. In the 1970s, lead times for large plants increased as utilities built larger and larger plants in a search for returns to scale and as environmental and regulatory constraints lengthened permitting delays. Lead times rose to about 10 years for large coal plants and even longer for nuclear plants. To offset the retirement of old plants when the lead time is 10 years, construction work in progress must double to 5 gw, half of capacity.

In reality, the situation was far worse, since the demand for power was growing at about 7%/year through the early 1970s. To offset the retirement of old plants and increase capacity 7%/year, a 10 gw utility would need to complete construction of 1.2 gw that year. With a 5-year construction delay, the utility would need to start construction of 1.8 gw of capacity and would have to finance the construction of about 7.2 gw of capacity under construction.

When the construction time doubles to 10 years, the required completion rate of 1.2 gw forces the utility to start construction of 2.4 gw of new capacity and finance more than 17.4 gw of capacity under construction—a 240% increase and an investment greatly exceeding the book value of existing capacity.[5] Orders for power plants surged in the mid 1970s, as utilities tried to respond to the rising lead times. Huge debts were taken on to finance the ever-greater stock of construction work in progress. In many cases, electric power rates were raised to enable utilities to service these debts. However, as higher rates (and lower than expected economic growth) caused power demand to fall, the utilities suddenly found themselves carrying debt for power plants they didn't need. Orders for new plants plummeted, and many were canceled, but as the huge stock of plants under construction continued to come on line, the industry found itself with excess capacity. Profits fell and rates rose still more. In some regions, the higher rates led to even lower growth in power demand, forcing rates even higher, in what many analysts called the "spiral of impossibility." A number of major utilities went bankrupt during this period, especially those building large, long lead-time plants. The excess capacity lasted through most of the 1980s. Many forward-thinking utilities realized that power plants with short planning, permitting, and construction times were a better investment even though their costs per kilowatt of capacity were higher: In an environment of uncertain demand growth, the value of improved cash flow and lower risks of having the wrong capacity exceed the generation cost savings offered by larger, long lead time plants (Ford 1997).

---

[5]This example is adapted from Ford (1997). Note that Little's Law holds only in equilibrium. When the inflow to a delay is growing the steady state size of the stock in transit is not independent of the outflow distribution. The calculations in the text assume the construction process for power plants is characterized by a pipeline delay. In this case, the construction completion rate $C(t) = S(t - D)$, where S is the construction start rate and D is the construction delay. In the steady state of exponential growth at fractional rate g/year, the start rate must therefore be $C\exp(gD)$. Given a 5-year construction delay and 7%/year demand growth rate, completion of 1.2 gw/year requires the start rate to be $1.2\exp(0.07 * 5) = 1.70$ gw/year; and a 10-year completion time yields $S = 1.2\exp(0.07 * 10) = 2.42$ gw/year. At any time t the stock of capacity under construction CUC is

$$CUC = \int_{-\infty}^{t} [S(s) - C(s)]ds$$

Without loss of generality, assume the construction completion rate is C_0 gw/year at time zero. In the steady state of exponential growth, the stock of capacity under construction at time zero is then

$$CUC(0) = \int_{-\infty}^{0} [C(t)\exp(gD) - C(t)]dt = [\exp(gD) - 1]\int_{-\infty}^{0} C(t)dt = [\exp(gD) - 1]\int_{-\infty}^{0} C_0\exp(gt)dt = \frac{C_0[\exp(gD) - 1]}{g}$$

With $C_0 = 1.2$ gw/year and $g = 0.07$, a 5-year construction delay requires construction work in progress to be $1.2[\exp(0.07 * 5) - 1]/0.07 = 7.18$ gw; with a 10-year delay construction in progress rises to $1.2[\exp(0.07 * 10) - 1]/0.07 = 17.38$ gw. To test the sensitivity of this calculation to the assumed distribution of power plant deliveries, consider the extreme assumption that the construction delay for power plants is first-order (the actual distribution of the delay outflow must be much closer to a pipeline delay). Then a construction completion rate of C_0 gw/year requires C_0D gw under construction, or 6 gw for a 5-year delay and 12 gw for a 10-year delay. For the stock of capacity under construction to grow at fractional rate g requires

$$\frac{dCUC}{dt} = S - C_0 = gCUC \Rightarrow S - C_0 = gC_0D \Rightarrow S = C_0(1 + gD)$$

implying $S = 1.62$ gw/year for a 5-year delay and $S = 2.04$ gw/year for a 10-year delay.

Example: Accumulation of Toxic Compounds in the Food Chain

Little's Law also helps explain why toxins such as dioxin accumulate in the food chain and in humans and may cause significant health problems even though their concentration in the environment is very low. The dioxin family (including some furans and PCBs [polychlorinated biphenyls]) are widely considered to be among the most potent carcinogens known. They are also estrogen mimics that may disrupt endocrine and reproductive function and have been associated with learning disabilities. Dioxins and other chlorinated hydrocarbons commonly used in pesticides and herbicides are soluble in fat and persist in the body for years. The half-life of dioxin and related toxins in fatty tissue has been estimated to be 7 to 11 years, corresponding to average residence times of 10 to 16 years.[6] By Little's Law, the equilibrium concentration of dioxin in any level of the food chain would be 10 to 16 years' worth of average intake. Predators consuming those organisms would then ingest much higher concentrations than their prey. At each level of the food chain, the accumulation of toxins caused by the long degradation delay amplifies the concentration of toxins. Some species of fish have dioxin concentrations 100,000 times that of the surrounding water.

While typical human intake rates of dioxin are very small, concentrations can build up to higher levels over a lifetime. Average daily exposure is estimated at 3 to 6 picograms of dioxin toxic equivalent per kilogram of body weight per day ($3 - 6$ pg TEQ/kg/day), most of which we ingest in our diet.[7] How can such small intake rates have any effect on human health? Besides the extreme toxicity of dioxin, the answer is the long residence time for dioxin in the body. Assuming a 16-year half-life, the equilibrium concentration of dioxin in humans ingesting 6 pg TEQ/kg/day would be 35,000 pg TEQ per kilogram of body mass. This value is roughly consistent with, though somewhat smaller than, estimates of average loads of 40,000 to 100,000 pg TEQ/kg body mass, suggesting either the half-lives are longer or the intake rates are higher than currently thought. Note that Little's Law applies only in equilibrium. In the dioxin example, it would take 40 to 64 years to reach the equilibrium level assuming a constant intake rate (a first-order delay adjusts 98% of the way to equilibrium after 4 time constants), further suggesting that estimates of dioxin ingestion rates or its half-life in the human body are too low.

CHALLENGE   # Response of Material Delays to Steps, Ramps, and Cycles

The discussion so far described the response of material delays to a pulse input, analogous to a single mass mailing of letters. Other common inputs used to test systems are the step (a sudden, permanent increase in the input from one rate to

---

[6]Recall from chapter 8 that the half-life of an exponential decay process with time constant D is $\ln(2)D \approx 0.7D$.

[7]A picogram is a trillionth of a gram (one part in 10^{12}). A toxic equivalent converts the toxicity of different dioxin-like compounds into the equivalent quantity of the parent compound in the dioxin family, 2,3,7,8-tetrachlorinated dibenzo-p-dioxin (2,3,7,8-TCDD). Sources for dioxin information: US EPA (1994); see also <www.epa.gov/futures/risk/nccr/dioxin.txt.html>.

another), the ramp (a sudden transition from a constant level to linear growth), exponential growth, and cycles. To test your understanding of delays, do the following challenge before proceeding.

1.   *Without using computer simulation,* sketch the response of a first-order material delay with an average delay time of 5 days to the inputs shown in Figure 11-9. In all cases assume that prior to time zero the delay is in equilibrium with the outflow and inflow both equal to 100 units/day.

     a.   **Step input.** At time zero the inflow steps up to 200 units/day and remains at the higher rate.

     b.   **Ramp input.** At time zero the inflow starts to rise linearly at a rate of 5 units/day.

     c.   **Exponential growth.** At time zero the input starts to grow exponentially at 5%/day.

     d.   **Oscillation.** At time zero the input begins to fluctuate with an amplitude of ± 100 units/day and a period of 10 days.

2.   *After* you have sketched your intuitive estimate of the response of the delay to these inputs, test your understanding by building a model of a first-order delay and simulating its response to these inputs. Were you correct?

3.   Repeat steps 1 and 2 for a third-order delay and for a pipeline delay. How does the order of the delay affect the response to the different types of inputs? Does the steady state response of the different delays differ? The steady state response is the behavior after a long time has passed and the relationship of input and output is no longer changing. How does the transient (short run) response of the different delays vary?

4.   Explore how the response of the different delays to the different inputs is affected by changes in the delay time. In particular, explore the response of the different delays to the fluctuating input for different delay times.

11.3   INFORMATION DELAYS: STRUCTURE AND BEHAVIOR

The discussion so far examines material delays in which the input to the delay is a physical inflow of items to a stock of units in transit and the outflow is the physical flow of items exiting the stock. However, many delays exist in channels of information feedback, for example in the measurement or perception of a variable, or in the updating of beliefs and forecasts, such as the perceived order rate for a firm's product or management's belief about future inflation rates.

Why do perceptions and forecasts inevitably involve delays? All beliefs, expectations, forecasts, and projections are based on information available to the decision maker at the time, which means information about the past. It takes time to gather the information needed to form judgments, and people don't change their minds immediately on the receipt of new information. Reflection and deliberation often take considerable time. We often need still more time to adjust emotionally to a new situation before our beliefs and behavior can change.

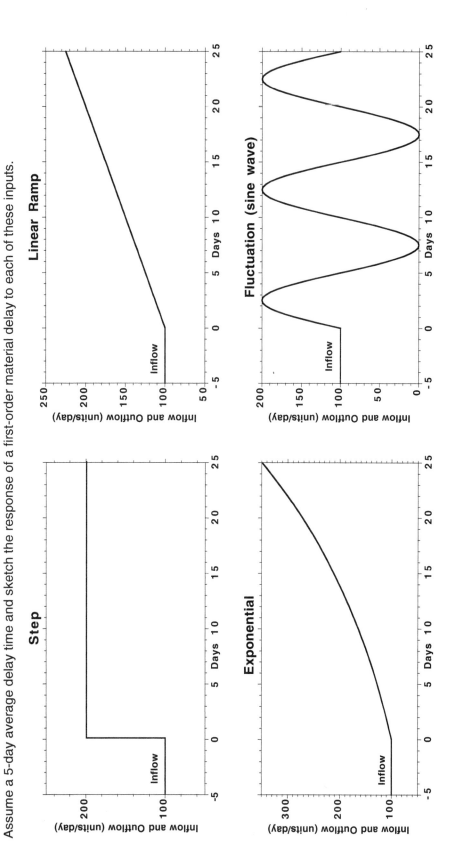

FIGURE 11-9 Four test inputs to a delay

Assume a 5-day average delay time and sketch the response of a first-order material delay to each of these inputs.

427

Information delays cannot be modeled with the same structure used for material delays because there is no physical inflow to a stock of material in transit. The inputs and outputs of material delays are conserved; for example, a strike at the post office lengthens the delay in delivering mail, reducing the delivery rate and causing the stock of mail in transit to build up. In contrast, information such as perceptions and beliefs is not conserved. Consider a firm's forecast of the order rate for its products. The expected order rate responds with a delay to changes in actual market conditions. The physical order rate does not flow into the delay; rather information about the order rate enters the delay. Because information, unlike material flows, is not conserved, a different structure is needed to capture information delays.

11.3.1 Modeling Perceptions: Adaptive Expectations and Exponential Smoothing

The simplest information delay and one of the most widely used models of belief adjustment and forecasting is called *exponential smoothing* or *adaptive expectations*. Adaptive expectations mean the belief gradually adjusts to the actual value of the variable. If your belief is persistently wrong, you are likely to revise it until the error is eliminated. Figure 11-10 shows the feedback structure of adaptive expectations.

In adaptive expectations the belief or perceived value of the input, $\hat{X}$, is a stock:

$$\hat{X} = \text{INTEGRAL(Change in Perceived Value, } \hat{X}(0)) \tag{11-5}$$

FIGURE 11-10
Feedback structure of adaptive expectations

The perceived value of the input adjusts to the actual input in proportion to the size of the error in your belief. The adjustment time determines how rapidly beliefs respond to error.

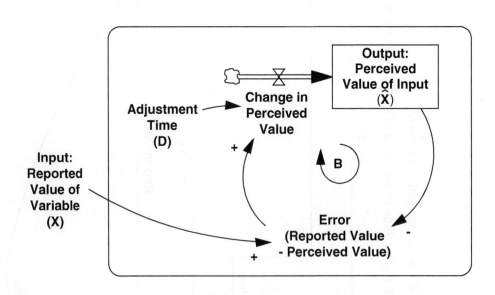

$$\hat{X} = \text{INTEGRAL(Change in Perceived Value, } \hat{X}(0))$$
$$\text{Change in Perceived Value} = \text{Error/D} = (X - \hat{X})/D$$

The rate of change in the belief is proportional to the gap between the current value of the input, X, and the perceived value:

Change in Perceived Value $= (X - \hat{X})/D$ (11-6)

In a material delay the stock is the quantity of material in transit and the output of the delay is a flow. In information delays the belief itself, $\hat{X}$, is a stock. Why? A perception or belief is a state of the system, in this case a state of mind. Your belief about the value of some quantity tends to remain at its current value until there is some reason to change it. In adaptive expectations, a belief changes when it is in error, that is, when the actual state of affairs differs from the perceived state of affairs. The larger the error, the greater the rate of adjustment in your belief. You should recognize this structure as another example of the familiar first-order linear negative feedback system (chapter 8). The state of the system adjusts in response to the gap between your current belief and the actual value of the variable. This structure is known as a *first-order information delay,* or as *first-order exponential smoothing.*

Figure 11-11 shows the response of first-order smoothing to a permanent change in the input, starting from an initial equilibrium in which the perceived and actual values of the variable are equal. The response is classic exponential goal-seeking behavior. The rate of belief updating is greatest immediately after the

FIGURE 11-11
Response of adaptive expectations to a step change in the input

The response to a permanent change in the input variable is exponential adjustment to the new level.

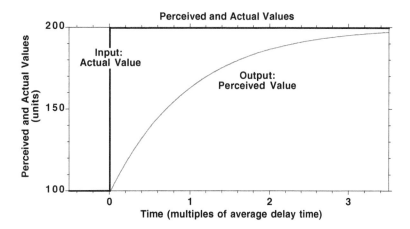

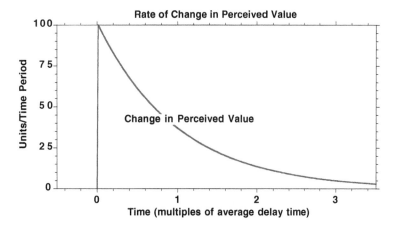

change in the actual value of the variable, when the error in the belief is greatest. As the belief is updated, the error falls, and subsequent adjustments diminish, until, after about four time constants have passed, the belief is once again correct.

A firm's forecasts of incoming orders illustrate. Firms must forecast demand because it is costly and time consuming to alter production rates. Inventories and backlogs should buffer short-term differences between orders and production. A good forecasting procedure should filter out short-term random changes in incoming orders to avoid costly changes in output (setups, changeovers, hiring and firing, overtime, etc.) while still responding quickly to changes in trends to avoid costly stockouts or excess inventories. The challenge is to be responsive without overreacting to noise, that is, to tell which change in demand is the beginning of a new trend and which is a mere random blip.

Exponential smoothing is widely used in forecasting due to its simplicity and low cost of computation. Additionally, exponential smoothing has the desirable property that it automatically attempts to eliminate forecast errors. Figure 11-12 shows the response of adaptive expectations to a simulated order stream for a product. The simulated order rate in this example follows a random walk, varying widely from day to day, week to week, and month to month. The expected order rate is formed by adaptive expectations with a 7-day time constant. Exponential smoothing does a good job of smoothing out the short-term, high-frequency noise while still following the slower movements in orders such as the rise from about 600 units/day around day 50 to about 1300 units/day around day 120. Note that the peaks and troughs in the expected order rate lag the turning points in the actual order rate: the process of smoothing inevitably introduces a delay.

To see why exponential smoothing introduces a delay, notice the role of the adjustment time constant D in the negative feedback structure of adaptive expectations. The negative loop functions to eliminate the error in the forecast but does so gradually, so as not to overreact to temporary changes in the input. Your belief is a weighted average of the current value of the variable and your past belief, which in turn reflects the prior history of the variable.[8]

The analogy with a weighted average can be made exact. Consider again the problem of forecasting a firm's order rate. A common way to filter out high-frequency noise is with a moving average. For example, a 7-day moving average of daily sales would be 1/7 of the sum of the daily sales for the past week. Every day, the average would be updated. In general a moving average, $\hat{X}$, can be represented as a weighted sum of all past values of the variable X:

$$\hat{X}(t) = \sum_{i=0}^{\infty} w_i X(t - i) \qquad (11\text{-}7)$$

---

[8]Recall the analytic solution of the first-order linear negative feedback loop system (chapter 8). When the input is a constant X^*, the current value of the state of the system, here $\hat{X}$, is given by

$$\hat{X}(t) = X^* - (X^* - \hat{X}(0))\exp(-t/D) = w\hat{X}(0) + (1 - w)X^*$$

where the weight $w = \exp(-t/D)$. That is, the current value of the perception is a weighted average of the initial value of the belief $\hat{X}(0)$ and the actual value of the variable X^*. The weight on the initial value of the belief declines exponentially at a rate determined by the time constant D.

FIGURE 11-12

Adaptive expectations smooth out short-term noise.

Response of exponential smoothing to hypothetical order rate for a product. The expected order rate is formed by exponential smoothing with a 7-day adjustment time. The order rate follows a random walk (the change in daily orders is normally distributed with a standard deviation of 50 units/day).

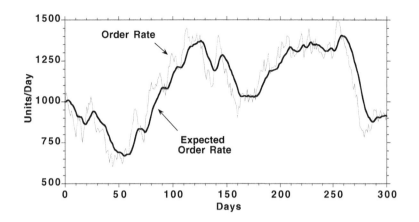

where the weights w_i must sum to 1. In the case of a 7-day moving average of daily values, the weights are 1/7 for the seven most recent values and zero for all prior values. Suppose sales had been constant for at least a week at a rate of X^* units/day. The sales forecast would equal the actual sales rate: $\hat{X} = X^*$. Now suppose sales suddenly doubled and remained at the higher level. On the next day the moving average forecast would only rise by 14%: $\hat{X} = (X^* + X^* + X^* + X^* + X^* + X^* + 2X^*)/7 = (8/7) X^*$. Each day the average would increase by another 1/7 until after a week the forecast $\hat{X}$ would finally equal the new sales rate $2X^*$. The process of averaging necessarily introduces a delay because new values are weighted in with the old values.

The weights in a moving average indicate the relative importance of each past observation in forming the current perception or belief. In the case of a 7-day moving average, yesterday's sales are given just as much weight as the week-old sales rate, while all sales data prior to last week are ignored. There is usually no strong reason to assume a sudden discontinuity in the importance of the past. A more reasonable model is to assume the importance of the data decline with age. First-order smoothing is a moving average where the weights w_i decline exponentially. The most recent value gets the most weight, with older values getting progressively less.

Adaptive expectations are a very simple model of expectation formation. Smoothing uses just a single input, rather than drawing on many sources of data. That single cue is then processed in a simple fashion. Can such a simple procedure actually be used to model the way firms form forecasts or the way people adjust their beliefs and expectations? Surprisingly, the answer is often yes. Surveys of forecasting methods show exponential smoothing is one of the most common forecasting tools used. Smoothing is especially popular when a firm must forecast the demand for thousands of distinct items. In these cases the simplicity, low cost, and error-correcting properties of smoothing make it an excellent choice.

Many studies show that first-order adaptive expectations are often an excellent model of the way people forecast and update beliefs. In a justly famous study, Makridakis et al. (1982, 1984) ran a competition to identify the best time-series forecasting methods. They compared the forecasting performance of 21 forecasting techniques, from naive forecasts (tomorrow will be like today) to sophisticated methods such as ARIMA models. The methods were compared across 1001 data series, encompassing a wide range of systems, time horizons, sampling frequencies, and patterns of behavior. In general, first-order exponential smoothing performed extremely well. A second competition (Makridakis et al. 1993) examined judgmental forecasting methods, finding many judgmental forecasts are well approximated by simple smoothing. Armstrong (1985) provides a comprehensive review of forecasting methods and documents the extensive literature showing the wide use and comparative accuracy of exponential smoothing in many contexts (see also chapter 16).

11.3.2 Higher-Order Information Delays

Just as there are cases where first-order material delays are not appropriate, so too there are situations where exponential smoothing is not the best model of an information delay. In a first-order information delay, like the first-order material delay, the output responds immediately to a change in the input. In many cases, however, beliefs begin to respond only after some time has passed.

In these cases, the weights on past information are initially low, then build up to a peak before declining. Recent values of the input might receive low weight for several reasons. Often the delay intervening between the actual state of a system and the decisions that alter it involves multiple stages. The current values of the input may simply be unavailable due to measurement and reporting delays. Once data are reported there may be administrative delays (reported information may not be taken up for consideration immediately). Finally, there may be cognitive and decision-making delays—it takes time for decision makers to revise their beliefs and further time to finalize a judgment and act on it. Information delays in which there are multiple stages are analogous to the multiple stages in material delays and require analogous higher-order delays.

One way to model a higher-order information delay is with the pipeline delay structure in which the output is simply the input lagged by a constant time period. Such a delay might be used to model the measurement and reporting processes, where the reported value available to decision makers is the actual value some period of time in the past:

$$\text{Reported Value}(t) = \text{Actual Value}\,(t - D) \qquad (11\text{-}8)$$

where D is the reporting delay. Such a delay is analogous to the infinite-order material delay or pipeline delay discussed above. The output of the delay tracks the input exactly but is shifted D units in time.

More often, the measurement and reporting of information involves multiple stages, and each stage involves some averaging or smoothing. Firms cannot report the instantaneous value of flows, such as the rate at which orders are being placed this instant, but must average (sum up, or accumulate) sales over some finite time period to filter out short-term variations and provide a meaningful estimate. Generating a forecast might actually involve several stages of information processing. First, order rates for a recent period such as a day or week are reported by individual sales representatives, introducing a reporting delay. Then the weekly sales figures are aggregated and reported to management, introducing another delay.

Management periodically reviews the sales figures and then applies a forecasting procedure such as smoothing (either formally or judgmentally). These estimates can then be used to set production schedules. Further delays are introduced as the information is processed for use in other decisions, such as budgets or earnings estimates prepared by market analysts.

In some cases the purpose of the model might require you to portray each of these steps explicitly. Usually it is sufficient to aggregate them together into a single information delay. Just as first-order material delays can be cascaded in series to generate higher-order delays with more realistic response rates, so too you can cascade first-order smoothing structures to generate a family of higher-order information delays (Figure 11-13).

An nth-order information delay, denoted by the SMOOTHn function, consists of n first-order information delays cascaded in series. The perceived value of each stage is the input to the next stage, and the output of the delay is the perceived value of the final stage. Each stage has the same delay time, equal to 1/n of the total delay D:

Output = SMOOTHn(Input, D):

$\quad$ Output = S_n

$\quad$ S_i = INTEGRAL(Change in Stage$_i$, $S_i(0)$) $\hfill$ (11-9)

$\quad$ $S_i(0)$ = Input

$\quad$ Change in Stage$_i$ = $\begin{cases} (\text{Input} - S_1)/(D/n) & \text{for i} = 1 \\ (S_{i-1} - S_i)/(D/n) & \text{for i} \in (2, \ldots, n) \end{cases}$

FIGURE 11-13 Structure of the third-order information delay

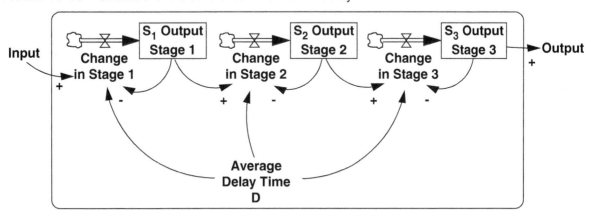

$\quad$ Output = SMOOTH3(Input, D)
$\quad\quad$ Output = S_3
$\quad\quad$ S_3 = INTEGRAL(Change in Stage 3, $S_3(0)$)
$\quad\quad$ Change in Stage 3 = $(S_2 - S_3)/(D/3)$
$\quad\quad$ S_2 = INTEGRAL(Change in Stage 2, $S_2(0)$)
$\quad\quad$ Change in Stage 2 = $(S_1 - S_2)/(D/3)$
$\quad\quad$ S_1 = INTEGRAL(Change in Stage 1, $S_1(0)$)
$\quad\quad$ Change in Stage 1 = $(\text{Input} - S_1)/(D/3)$

Figure 11-14 compares the response of the first-, third-, and twelfth-order information delays to a step increase in the input. As with the material delays, the higher the order, the smaller the initial response and the steeper and faster the eventual rise to the final value. In the limit of an infinite-order delay, the output would exactly track the input t − D periods in the past: a pipeline delay.

11.4   RESPONSE TO VARIABLE DELAY TIMES

Another important issue in modeling delays is whether the delay time is constant or changing. Relative to the purpose of your model, can you consider the duration of the delay to be constant, or might it vary? If it varies, does it vary exogenously or endogenously? What happens when the delay time changes?

The delay times for both material and information delays can change. Raising the speed limit on US interstate highways from 55 to 65 reduced the delay in the transport of raw materials from supplier to customer (assuming any truckers were actually obeying the 55 mph speed limit in the first place). Replacing a mainframe-based accounting system and manual data entry with a globally integrated, real time client–server network and point-of-sale scanner data can reduce the delay in the measurement and reporting of the sales rate for a firm's products.

Delay times can vary both exogenously and endogenously. For example, a critical parameter in a model of a firm's supply chain is the average delay between placing and receiving orders for parts and materials. Can you consider this time to be fixed? In many industries the resupply time is a variable, and both exogenous and endogenous factors influence it. For example, the resupply time often depends on the season of the year (an exogenous factor). The time required to deliver fresh strawberries to market in Boston is shorter in summer when local berries are in season and longer in winter when the supply line stretches to California and Mexico.

The length of a delay often depends on the state of the system itself. How long will you wait to withdraw cash from an ATM? If there are no people ahead of you in line, the delay is the minimum time required for you to insert your card, enter your code, collect your cash, and get your card back—about a minute. However,

FIGURE 11-14

Response of higher-order delays to a step input

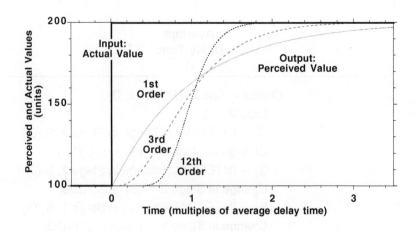

the length of time you must wait increases if there are people ahead of you in line. In turn, the rate at which people join the line depends on how many people are already in line: when the line is long, people will walk by and wait until the crowd isn't as big (a behavior known as balking). The average waiting time (the delay in getting served) therefore depends endogenously on the number of people in the delay (the length of the queue of people awaiting service).

Similarly, the delay in receiving parts from suppliers depends on both the normal order processing time and on the suppliers' backlog of orders relative to their capacity. When suppliers have ample capacity, they can deliver rapidly. When capacity is fully utilized, backorders accumulate, and customers are put on allocation (they receive a fraction of their order and are forced to wait longer than expected). In the long run, customers will seek alternative suppliers, forming a negative loop that reduces the delivery delay. But in the short run, before new suppliers can be found and qualified, customers may actually order more in an attempt to get what they really desire. If your supplier tells you it can only ship part of your order this week, you may order more than needed in the hope of receiving what you actually require. Placing such phantom orders creates a positive feedback that further increases the supplier's backlog and lengthens the delivery delay still more, often leading to instability in orders, production, and inventory (see chapter 18).

CHALLENGE | ## Response of Delays to Changing Delay Times

To develop your understanding of how the different types of delays respond to variations in the delay time, answer the following questions.

1.   Consider a model of the post office as a third-order material delay (equation (11-4)). Assume that the mailing rate is constant and that the system is in equilibrium—the mailing rate and delivery rate are equal. Without using simulation, sketch the behavior you expect if the delay time suddenly and permanently increases from 5 days to 10 days on day 5. Make two graphs—one showing the mailing rate and delivery rate and the other showing what you expect to happen to the stock of letters in transit. Sketch the response you would expect if the delay time suddenly dropped from 5 to 2.5 days.

2.   Now consider a firm's forecast of orders. Assume the firm uses adaptive expectations to forecast orders, equation (11-6). Assume that the order rate is constant and that the expected order rate is equal to the order rate (the system is in equilibrium). Without using simulation, sketch the behavior you expect if the time to adjust the forecast suddenly and permanently decreases from 6 months to 3 months.

3.   After you've sketched your intuitive estimates, build the models and simulate their response to changes in the delay time. Was your intuition correct? If there are differences in the response of the material and information delays to changes in the delay times, explain why.

11.4.1 Nonlinear Adjustment Times: Modeling Ratchet Effects

Often the time constant for an information delay depends nonlinearly on the input. The delay in adapting ourselves to a new situation may be longer than the delay in reacting to further instances of the stimulus once we have come to expect it. People get used to higher income faster than they adapt to a drop in their income. We sometimes learn more rapidly than we forget. Because first-order smoothing (and all the delays discussed up to now) is linear, it responds symmetrically to inputs of any magnitude and to increases as well as decreases. One way to model asymmetrical adjustments is with a nonlinear delay in which the time constant for the delay depends on the state of the system.

In the 1940s, the economist James Duesenberry noticed that aggregate consumption expenditures seemed to rise faster than they fell as income fluctuated over the business cycle. He hypothesized that people rapidly raised their expectations of future income when income increased, boosting their consumption quickly, but were slow to give up their desired standard of living in the face of hard luck, leading them to spend near the old rates even though income had fallen.

Such "ratchet effects" can be modeled by assuming the time constant D takes on one value when the input to the delay X exceeds the output $\hat{X}$ and another when the input falls below the output:

$$D = \begin{cases} D_I \text{ if } X \geq \hat{X} \\ D_D \text{ if } X < \hat{X} \end{cases} \qquad (11\text{-}10)$$

where D_I is the time constant that characterizes the adjustment when the output is increasing (when $X \geq \hat{X}$) and D_D is the time constant governing the adjustment when the output is decreasing (when $X < \hat{X}$). In the case of income expectations, the hypothesis suggests downward rigidity of expectations, that is, $D_I < D_D$.[9]

Sterman, Repenning, and Kofman (1997) used the nonlinear smoothing structure to capture the response of workers to news of layoffs in a model of process improvement. Improvement programs have the potential to create excess labor if productivity rises faster than the demand for the product. The willingness of workers to participate in improvement programs was hypothesized to depend on perceived job security. Perceived job security depended on workers' memory of past layoffs (along with other factors such as excess capacity): perceived job security is likely to be higher in a firm that hasn't laid off any workers for years than in one where layoffs are common. The memory of past layoffs was modeled using the nonlinear delay in equation (11-10). The input was the fraction of the workforce laid off in the recent past and the output was the memory of layoffs. Setting $D_I \ll D_D$ captured the results of our field studies showing that perceptions of job security fall swiftly on news of a layoff and take years to recover, even if there is no subsequent downsizing (Figure 11-15). The nonlinear smoothing structure also works with higher-order information delays.

---

[9]Though economists dating back to Keynes have suggested that wages and prices might also exhibit ratchet effects, rising more rapidly than they fall, empirical studies are scarce; some do not support the hypothesis (e.g., Rassekh and Wilbratte 1990).

FIGURE 11-15

Nonlinear time constants: structure and behavior

Simulation of response of perceived job security to pulse in layoffs. The time constant for increasing the memory of layoffs D_I = 1 week; for forgetting the history of past layoffs D_D = 50 weeks.

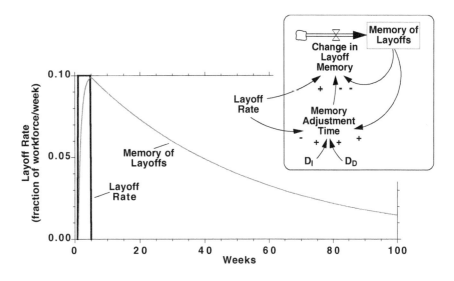

11.5   ESTIMATING THE DURATION AND DISTRIBUTION OF DELAYS

The average length of a delay and the shape of the response distribution can be estimated by two principal methods: statistical techniques and firsthand investigation of the process in the field.

11.5.1   Estimating Delays When Numerical Data Are Available

A wide range of econometric and statistical tools can help you estimate the duration and distribution of lags from time series data, when such data are available (see Hamilton 1980 for a review; further details are provided in any good econometrics text).

Though you can write the output of a lag as the weighted sum of past values of the input (see equation (11-7)), it is usually infeasible to estimate the weights directly due to multicollinearity and lack of data. The main econometric techniques available for estimating lags from time series data include the Koyck or geometric lag, polynomial distributed lags, rational distributed lags, and ARIMA models (see section 11.7). Many econometric and time series statistical packages are available to estimate these models from time series data.

In choosing an estimation method you must trade off the flexibility of the formulation against the number of parameters to be estimated. Some methods assume the shape of the response (equivalent to assuming the order of the delay) and estimate the mean delay time. The Koyck or geometric lag, for example, is easily estimated but assumes the delay is first-order (see section 11.7). Other techniques, such as the polynomial lag method, impose fewer a priori restrictions on the shape of the lag distribution but require more data. You should not constrain the shape of the delay in advance unless there is strong independent evidence to support a particular lag shape or if sensitivity analysis suggests the results of interest are not contingent on the shape of the delay distribution.

While you may estimate the length and distribution of a delay using econometric techniques, you should not use the estimated regression equation in your simulation model. Instead, you should replace the estimated distributed lag with the material or information delay that best matches the estimated lag. There are several reasons. First, econometric techniques are designed for discrete time since most economic and business data are reported at regular, discrete intervals such as a month, quarter, or year. System dynamics models are usually developed for continuous time. The time step for updating the state variables is often different from and usually shorter than the data reporting period used to estimate a delay. Using the continuous time delay that best matches the estimated discrete delay ensures that your model will be robust to changes in the simulation time step. Second, regression equations for lags have fixed lag weights, implying a fixed delay time. In many situations, however, the length of a delay is actually a variable. Even if the delay time is thought to be constant in the current version of your model, further work may reveal that the delay time must be incorporated as an endogenous variable. The material and information delay structures used in system dynamics respond appropriately to changes in the delay times, while a regression equation for a distributed lag does not enable delay times to vary. Regression equations for distributed lags also do not distinguish between material and information delays. Material and information delays respond differently to changes in delay times. Your model must properly distinguish between the two types of delay to respond appropriately to changes in delay times and to ensure conservation of material flows.

Example: The Lagged Response of Energy Supply to Price

Delays played an important role in Roger Naill's (1973) model of the natural gas industry. Exploration effort responds to changes in price, but only after a considerable delay. Fortunately, Khazzoom (1971) had carefully estimated the distributed lag response of gas supply to changes in price. Rather than using the discrete time formulation, however, Naill found that the estimated delay was approximated well by a third-order delay with a 4.5-year delay time (Figure 11-16). Whereas Khazzoom treated the delay between price and supply as a single, aggregate process, Naill's model explicitly portrayed the exploration and discovery process. Explicitly modeling investment in exploration capital with a material delay meant Naill could simulate the response of natural gas supply to changes in the delay between the initiation of exploration activity and its results, changes that might arise from changes in exploration technology, government regulations, the location and depth of gas resources, or the capacity of the industry supplying drill rigs.

Example: Capital Investment in the Macroeconomy I

Capital investment is a major decision for any business, and understanding the response of investment to changes in economic conditions is critical in the formation of fiscal and monetary policy. Since investment takes time, policy makers such as central bankers and governments must understand the length and distribution of the lags in the response of investment to changes in policy levers such as interest rates,

FIGURE 11-16

Approximating a discrete time distributed lag with a continuous delay

Khazzoom (1971) estimated the lagged response of natural gas supply to changes in price. The graph shows his estimates of the response to a 1¢/MCF (thousand cubic feet) impulse in the price of gas. Naill (1973) found a 4.5-year, third-order delay matched the estimated lag well.

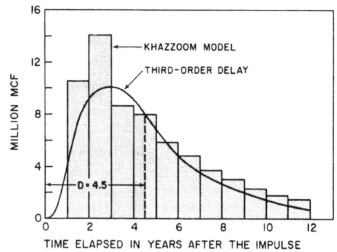

Source: Naill (1973, p. 229). Reproduced with permission.

taxes, and the level of demand in the economy. How long does it take to build new capital plant?

Figure 11-17 shows data for one part of the capital investment process: the construction delay. The figure shows the distribution of construction completions for private nonresidential investment projects derived by Montgomery (1995) from US Department of Commerce survey data. The surveys cover 52,000 construction projects from all sectors of the economy. The mean delay between the start of construction and completion is 16.7 months (1.4 years). The data describe only the physical construction process and do not include planning and administrative delays in the investment process.

The construction delay distribution is approximated extremely well by a second-order material delay with a 16.7-month average delay time, the same mean delay as the data. The low order of the delay, consistent with the large variance in completion rates, is due to the aggregation of many types of capital plant in the survey data, data spanning all sectors of the economy. Delay distributions for capital plant at the level of particular industries or types of structures (e.g., semiconductor wafer fabs, power plants, office buildings) would have lower variance and would require higher-order delays.

Interestingly, Montgomery found only small variations in the average delay across the decades, and his estimate of 16.7 months is very close to the 15-month mean construction time estimated by Mayer (1960) from a 1954 survey of US construction projects. The mean and distribution of construction times appears to be quite stable over the past 40 years despite significant technical change and shifts in the composition of the economy. The relatively small range of variation suggests that the construction delay and distribution can be modeled with the same structure and parameters over long time horizons.

Example: Capital Investment in the Macroeconomy II

The roughly 17-month average construction delay is only part of the total lag in the response of capital investment to changes in business conditions. Estimates of

FIGURE 11-17

The construction lag for capital plant: data vs. model

Data: Distribution of construction completion times for US private nonresidential structures, 1961–1991, as estimated by Montgomery (1995) from US Dept. of Commerce survey data. The mean lag is 16.7 months. *Model:* Second-order material delay with average delay time of 16.7 months.

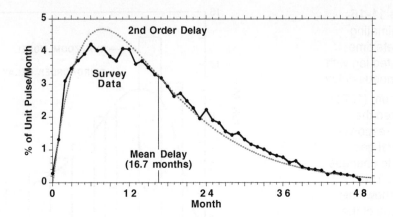

the total delay between a change in, say, demand for a firm's products and the completion of new capacity are much longer, typically 2 to 3 years, as they include the administrative, decision making, appropriations, permitting, design, and other delays as well as the physical construction process. Businesses and organizations such as the Federal Reserve must account for the entire delay when setting policy.

The lags in capital investment have been intensively explored in macroeconomics for more than 50 years. A common formulation known as the neoclassical investment function (see, e.g., Jorgenson, Hunter, and Nadiri 1970) presumes firms first calculate the optimal level of capital stock they desire, K^*, based on traditional static profit maximization considerations, then adjust the actual stock K toward the desired level:

$$K(t) = L(K^*, D) \tag{11-11}$$

The lag operator L denotes a distributed lag with mean delay time D. The optimal capital stock K^* is calculated by assuming firms set the desired capital stock at the level that maximizes profits, which in turn is a function of industry demand, interest rates, taxes, the marginal productivity of the capital stock, and possibly other variables. The distributed lag L is estimated from data on gross investment or capital expenditures by noting that the rate of change of the capital stock K is net investment, that net investment is gross investment less capital discards, and by assuming that discards depend on the current capital stock. Discards are usually assumed to be a first-order decay process with a constant average life of capital. The resulting lag estimates subsume the construction delay to yield a mean and distribution for the total delay between changes in business conditions and the response of capital investment.

A major problem with the neoclassical investment function is that the mean delay and lag distribution are assumed to be fixed. The time between placing an order for new plant and equipment and receiving that capital from the supplier is assumed to be independent of the supplier's capacity utilization. Yet when suppliers have excess capacity, the delivery time will be short, while during booms, when supplier capacity is fully utilized, the delivery delay will increase. Senge (1978) found that delivery delays for capital goods varied by ±50–75% over the business cycle.[10] Models where the lag distribution is fixed are misspecified because they implicitly assume suppliers of plant and equipment have unlimited or perfectly flexible production capacity, a physical impossibility. In general, models in which delays are specified as distributed lags rather than conserved stock and flow structures are not robust and frequently violate basic laws of physics.

The system dynamics national model (SDNM), a macroeconomic model developed by the MIT system dynamics group (Forrester 1977, 1979; Forrester et al. 1976; Mass 1975), addressed this and other defects of the neoclassical function by explicitly representing the investment process at the operational level. The model distinguishes between perception delays and material delays and captures the conserved flows of orders, acquisitions, and discards of plant and equipment. The acquisition delay varies with the capacity utilization of the capital producing industries. Figure 11-18 shows a simplified representation of the investment function. Instead of representing investment as a single distributed lag, the model represents the stages of investment separately, distinguishing between the planning process and the capital ordering and construction process. Capital stock is increased by acquisitions and decreased by discards. Discards are assumed, as in the neoclassical model, to be a first-order exponential decay process. The acquisition rate depends on the backlog of orders for capital and the current delivery delay for capital. The backlog of capital on order is increased by orders. Orders lag the rate of order starts, capturing appropriation and administrative delays in investment. The order start rate responds to four factors: (1) replacement of capital discards; (2) adjustment for the expected growth in demand, based on past growth in shipments; (3) the gap between the desired and actual stock of capital, and (4) the gap between the desired and actual supply line of capital on order (see chapter 17).

The desired supply line depends on the perceived delivery delay for capital and the required replacement of discarded capital. The desired stock of capital is proportional to desired production but is modified by the perceived marginal return on new capital. Firms are assumed to respond to the profitability of a new investment, but with a delay caused by the difficulty of assessing changes in the marginal productivity and marginal cost of capital. Desired production depends on expected demand, and is then adjusted to correct discrepancies between the desired and actual levels of inventory and backlog. Expected demand is modeled as an information delay of shipment data. The model provides an operational description of the capital investment process, allowing the delays in the different parts of the process to be separately specified and estimated.

Senge (1978, 1980) showed that the disequilibrium investment function used in the SDNM includes the neoclassical investment function as a special case. The SDNM investment function reduces to the neoclassical function when a number of equilibrium and perfect information assumptions are made. These include the assumptions that inventories, backlogs, and the stock of capital on order always

---

[10]The large variation in capital delivery delays Senge found does not conflict with the relatively stable distribution of construction times Montgomery (1995) documented. The total delivery delay includes the construction time plus any additional time an order spends in queue awaiting the start of construction. During boom periods, this preconstruction waiting period increases as the backlog of projects waiting for construction crews and equipment to become available builds up.

FIGURE 11-18 Simplified causal structure of the investment function in the system dynamics national model

Rectangles with rounded corners denote information delays. Delays requiring estimation shown in italics. Inputs to the investment function shown in small caps. Link polarities not shown for clarity.

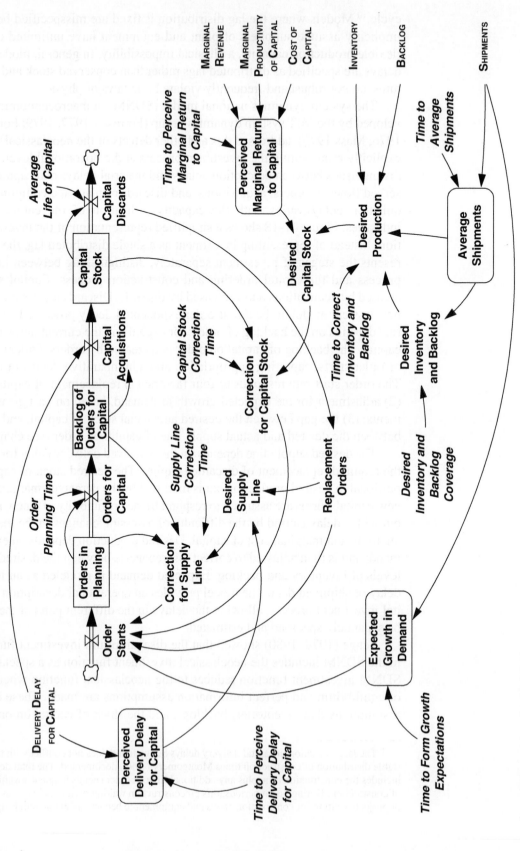

Source: Adapted from Senge (1978).

equal their desired levels; that firms instantly and perfectly perceive demand and the marginal productivity of capital; that the delivery delay for capital is constant; and that capacity utilization is always constant at the desired level. Senge used econometric techniques to estimate the parameters of the SDNM investment function. While the system dynamics model relaxed the unrealistic assumptions of the neoclassical theory, the added complexity of the model made econometric estimation of the various delays much more difficult, both statistically and in the creation of consistent data sets. To ensure the robustness of the results, Senge tested eight different specifications, each progressively relaxing more of the restrictive assumptions of the neoclassical formulation.

Senge tested the model with quarterly data for four industries: durable and nondurable manufacturing, electrical machinery, and textile products. These industries spanned two major levels of aggregation: durable and nondurable manufacturing together account for the entire manufacturing sector of the economy, while the other two industries tested the model's ability to explain investment at a more disaggregate level.

The regression results supported the disequilibrium system dynamics function. For all four industry groups, the SDNM investment function explains more of the variance in the data, with less autocorrelation in the residuals than the neoclassical function, while yielding statistically significant, plausible estimates for the model parameters. The model also generates more realistic behavior when simulated than the neoclassical function. Table 11-1 reports the estimation results for nondurable manufacturing. The estimated distributions for three key lags are shown in Figure 11-19. These delays were estimated by the polynomial distributed lag method, allowing the lag shape, as well as the mean delay, to be estimated rather than assumed.

The lag in averaging shipments to form demand forecasts was hypothesized to be first-order, and indeed, the estimated distribution of lag weights for average shipments is approximated well by first-order exponential smoothing with a delay time of about two quarters. The response of investment to changes in the perceived delivery delay for capital was also expected to be first-order, and the estimated weights are well approximated by first-order smoothing, though with a much longer average delay of about 1.3 years. A longer delay in the response to changes in capital availability is expected. Delivery quotes for plant and equipment are uncertain and unreliable; managers must wait a substantial fraction of the normal delivery delay before they can glean reliable information on the progress of equipment orders or the rate of construction of new plant. More time is required to determine how to alter investment plans to compensate for changes in lead time. Finally, the response of growth expectations to changes in the growth rate of shipments was hypothesized to be a higher-order delay. The regressions support this hypothesis. The estimated lag distribution is bell shaped: Growth expectations do not respond significantly to short-term changes in actual demand growth rates. The estimated distribution is approximated reasonably well by a third-order delay of the rate of change in average shipments (average shipments are given by first-order smoothing of actual shipments with the estimated 2.13 quarter delay).

Senge also compared the estimated delays to the a priori judgmental estimates developed by the modeling team (Table 11-1). In some cases the a priori estimates

FIGURE 11-19

Estimated lag
distributions
for investment
compared to
continuous
time lags

Estimated
lags found
by polynomial
distributed lag
method with
third degree
polynomial;
consumer
nondurables.
Error bars show
±1 estimated
standard error.

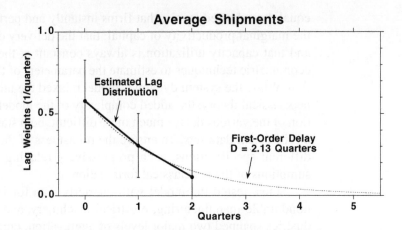

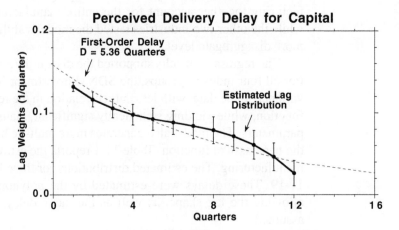

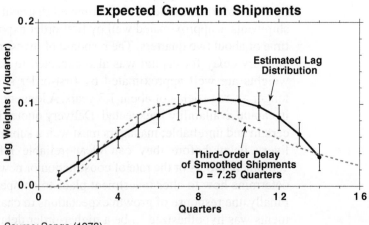

Source: Senge (1978).

are not statistically different from the estimated values. For other parameters there
is a large difference between the two. These discrepancies led to reconsideration of
the logic behind the judgmental estimates and the appropriateness of the data
sources and estimation methods. In some cases the judgmental estimates were
revised in light of the estimation results or improved model formulations were

TABLE 11-1   Comparison of estimated and judgmental estimates of investment delays

Parameter	Estimated Value (quarters)	A Priori Estimate (quarters)	Estimated Standard Deviation of Estimate (quarters)
Time to Average Shipments	2.13	2.00	1.88
Time to Perceive Marginal Return to Capital	4.12	8.00*	0.32
Time to Perceive the Delivery Delay for Capital	5.36	8.00*	0.96
Time to Form Growth Expectations	7.25	6.10	1.17
Supply Line Correction Time	3.02	10.00*	0.86
Capital Stock Correction Time	12.10	10.00	2.18
Time to Correct Inventory and Backlog	1.73	3.00*	0.37
Desired Inventory Coverage	0.47	1.33*	0.033
Desired Backlog Coverage	1.65	1.33	0.34
Fractional Discard Rate (Average Life of Capital)	0.0384/quarter (6.5 years)	0.0156/quarter* (16 years)	0.00043/quarter

Estimates for the consumer nondurables sector.

* indicates estimated and judgmental values differ by more than 2 estimated standard deviations, indicating a significant difference between the two estimates.

Source: Senge (1978, pp. 110).

developed. In other cases, the discrepancy was traced to limitations of the estimation protocol or an imperfect match between the concept in the investment function and the data series used to proxy it, and the a priori estimate was retained for simulation purposes.

11.5.2   Estimating Delays When Numerical Data Are Not Available

In many situations, data from which to estimate the duration and shape of delays are not available. In these cases you must estimate these parameters from direct inspection of the delay process, experience with analogous delays in related systems, or judgment.

Judgmental estimates of aggregate delays can be quite unreliable and usually underestimate their duration. Recall the challenges at the start of this chapter. What was your estimate of the investment delay for the manufacturing economy? How about the time required for pork supplies to respond to price changes or for economists to update their inflation forecasts? Most people dramatically underestimate these and other delays. The actual delays are roughly 3 years, 2 years, and 1 year, respectively (Senge 1978; Meadows 1970; Sterman 1987). The longer the delay, the greater the degree of underestimation. What was your estimate of the delay in recognizing and reacting to air pollution? As shown in Table 11-2, more than 50 years have passed from the first undeniable evidence that air pollution causes significant health problems, such as death, yet most major metropolitan areas in the US are still not in compliance with the provisions of the Clean Air Act.

Decomposition is a useful strategy to minimize the underestimation of delays. Instead of estimating the total length of the delay, decompose the process into its various stages, then estimate the length of time required for each. Senge's capital investment model decomposed the total response lag into a disaggregate, operational model whose individual lags could be estimated judgmentally from direct

TABLE 11-2 Delays in societal response to air pollution in the United States	• **1800s:** Widespread use of coal for industry and heating leads to growing air pollution in urban areas of Europe and the United States. • **1948:** Smog in Donora, Pennsylvania kills 20 people and sickens 6000. Soon after, coal fumes kill nearly 800 in London. • **1955:** First US Federal Air Pollution Control Act laid primary responsibility for limiting air pollution upon states and cities, but allocated $5 million for research. • **1963:** Federal Clean Air Act recognizes air pollution does not respect state boundaries; sets up regulations for control of interstate abatement; provides more assistance for state and local governments. • **1970:** Clean Air Act strengthened by defining "safe" standards for SO_2, CO, particulates, VOCs (Volatile Organic Compounds), NO_x, ozone, and lead. State plans to meet standards required by 1975. • **1977:** Deadline postponed until 1982 as 78 cities were in violation of the ozone standard. • **1988:** Ninety urban areas with 150 million inhabitants exceed ozone standard; 40 violate CO standard. • **1990:** Comprehensive amendments to Clean Air Act require all cities to meet ozone standard by 2007 (except Los Angeles which has until 2010). Stricter regulations for auto emissions, gasoline, SO_2, and many newly regulated pollutants. • **1997:** Ambient concentrations of all seven regulated pollutants dropping very slowly (except lead, which plummeted as soon as leaded gasoline was banned, though much lead from prior emissions remains in soils). Medical evidence shows health problems and deaths from air pollution growing. 122 million in US live in areas violating the ozone standard. EPA seeks to stiffen ozone and particulate standards. Industry allocates millions to fight the strengthening of standards. **Time from clear signal of problem to first meaningful law:** 22 years. **Time from first law to measurable, steady improvements in air quality:** 20 years. **Time from first law to full compliance with law:** 27 years and counting. **Total delay from first clear signal to full compliance:** > 50 years.

Source: Paraphrased and condensed with permission from D. Meadows and A. AtKisson, *The Balaton Bulletin,* 1997, pp. 16–17.

observation of business decision making; subsequent statistical estimation showed the judgmental estimates were often reasonable.

To decompose a delay for the purposes of judgmental estimation, map the stock and flow structure of the process at the operational level. For example, consider the delay in the response of aggregate pork supply to price changes (Figure 11-20).

Decomposition reveals the following sequence. First, hog farmers must decide that a rise in price is likely to persist long enough to justify investing in increasing production. Then they must increase their breeding stock (by withholding some mature sows from market), then breed the sows. After the gestation delay, the litters are born. The piglets require further time to mature, then spend additional time in a feedlot until they reach the optimal weight where the gain in market value from greater weight is balanced by the cost of additional feed. Only then are they sent to slaughter, increasing the supply of pork. Most of these delays are biologically determined, easily estimated, and quite stable. The gestation, maturation, and feedlot delays are about 3.8, 5, and 2 months, respectively, a total material delay of about 11 months (Meadows 1970). How long is the delay in adjusting producers' expectations about the future price and in building up the breeding stock? Because it takes about a year between breeding and the resulting increase in hog supply, producers cannot afford to react too quickly to price changes but must wait long enough to be confident higher prices will persist. Studies show forecasts of future hog prices are strongly influenced by recent prices, with little weight on prices more than a year in the past (Bessler and Brandt 1992). Meadows (1970) estimated the expectation formation delay to be about 6 months and the breeding stock adjustment delay at about 5 months. Thus the total delay between a change in the price of hogs and the resulting change in hog production is about 22 months. Not surprisingly, such a long delay in the market feedback regulating prices leads to instability: hog prices tend to oscillate with an average periodicity of about 4 years (see chapter 20).

Decomposition also gives insight into the shape of the outflow distribution for each delay. The more stages in a delay, the tighter the output distribution will be and the smaller the initial response. The variance in the gestation process is small; Meadows (1970) reports 90% of farrowings take place 111 to 119 days after breeding, indicating a very high-order delay. The variance in the maturation and feedlot delays is greater than that of the gestation delay, but the short run response to a pulse input is small. These delays could probably be modeled adequately with a third- or sixth-order delay. Price expectations and the delay in adjusting the breeding stock, however, can probably be modeled as first-order processes: Both price expectations and the breeding stock are likely to respond quickest when the gap between the desired and actual states is greatest. Because the total delay cascades many distinct stages, many of which have low variance, the short-run response of hog production to higher prices is negligible.[11]

---

[11]Actually, the short-run effect of price increases on supply is negative. For the aggregate industry, the breeding stock can only be increased by withholding some sows from slaughter. The first response of the slaughter rate to a rise in expected price is therefore a *reduction* in supply, creating a positive feedback loop: Higher prices lead to lower short-run supply and still higher prices as producers send fewer sows to slaughter to increase their breeding stock. A good model of the hog production system must include this destabilizing loop, a process that cannot be captured in models, such as cobweb models, that treat the supply response as an aggregate delay. See chapter 20.

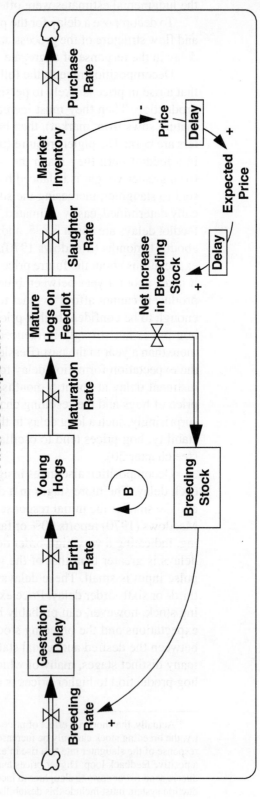

FIGURE 11-20 Estimating a delay by decomposition

How long is the delay in the response of hog production to price changes? Mapping the stock and flow structure of the process identifies the delays of the individual activities creating the delay. The individual stage delays are more reliably estimated than the aggregate total delay.

11.5.3 Process Point: Walk the Line

Even when numerical data are available, direct inspection is important. You should be suspicious of data in a firm's information systems, and take the time to investigate the process firsthand. In modeling a manufacturing process you should go to the actual plant and walk the line. Follow a few parts through the entire process, from the time they arrive at the receiving dock until they are shipped to a customer. In a service operation, follow the customer and paperwork from start to finish.

Finan (1993) studied the cycle times for fabrication of various parts at a major commercial aircraft manufacturer. The firm's order planning system was supposed to track parts and subassemblies as they flowed through the manufacturing process. Downloading the data for a representative sample of parts revealed that the recorded cycle times for each lot were always exactly equal to the time allotted. To take a typical example, the scheduled completion time for a particular part was 10 days. Data in the information system showed every lot was delivered exactly 10 days after the order was received. However, cross-checking other records, walking the line, and interviewing the workers showed the actual delay averaged 22 days, with a standard deviation of 9 days. Only 2 of 20 lots examined were completed in 10 days or less. Obviously the start times recorded in the information system had been back-calculated by subtracting the scheduled cycle time from the completion date of the lots.

Firsthand investigation of the process on the factory floor not only yielded a better estimate of the delay but revealed significant errors and wasted effort in the information and control systems governing the operation. Not surprisingly, the poor quality of systems and procedures kept the company from increasing production smoothly and rapidly when orders surged. The resulting production bottlenecks, extra costs, and delays in deliveries to customers led to more than $1 billion in extraordinary charges and a significant decline in profits just as demand reached an all-time high.

11.6 System Dynamics in Action: Forecasting Semiconductor Demand[12]

Understanding and modeling delays can often yield significant value, even without the complexity of a full simulation model of the feedback structure of the business. Chipmaker Symbios Inc. used simple models of delays to dramatically improve its ability to forecast demand for its integrated circuits, stabilizing production schedules, improving capacity utilization, and lowering production and capacity acquisition costs.

Symbios Inc. is a successful semiconductor and component manufacturer with headquarters in Fort Collins, Colorado. Symbios makes a full spectrum of hardware and software for storage management and peripherals including standard and

[12]I am indebted to Symbios and to Lyle Wallis, Karl Braitberg, Kevin Gearhardt, Michael Haynes, and Mark Paich for permission to present this case, their willingness to share their data and experiences, and their assistance in its preparation. In 1998 Symbios was sold to LSI Logic Corp, a chipmaker in Milpitas, California.

application specific integrated circuits (ASICs), host adapters, I/O technologies, and storage hardware for high-performance workstations and servers. Their customers are original equipment manufacturers (OEMs) in the computer and electronics industry. Throughout the 1990s Symbios enjoyed revenue growth of about 20%/year, reaching about $600 million in revenue in 1996 with 2300 employees worldwide.

Like all chipmakers, Symbios is caught between the rapid growth, technical change, and volatility of the semiconductor market on the one hand and the high costs and long delays of adjusting manufacturing capacity on the other. Semiconductor wafer fabs are among the most technically sophisticated and expensive factories ever built. Typical fabs for ASICs cost about $1 billion; fabs for high performance microprocessors cost a billion dollars more. Given the high fixed costs of semiconductor manufacturing, consistently high utilization of a chipmaker's fabs is essential for profitability. However, capacity can only be adjusted with long delays. The delay between the decision to build a fab and the first useable output is several years. Long capacity adjustment delays mean chipmakers must be able to forecast demand reliably over quite long horizons.[13]

As Director of Business Planning and Modeling for Symbios, Lyle Wallis struggled with this dilemma. There is little room for error. The integrated circuit market is very competitive. Many of Symbios' customers are very large and wield considerable market power over suppliers. Rapid technical change puts a premium on the quality and responsiveness of the firm's design and engineering staff. The quality standards OEMs require their suppliers to meet are among the most stringent in any industry. Price competition is intense. And, perhaps most important, delivery time is a critical competitive battleground. Because the life cycle of the products using these chips is often very short, chipmakers must deliver on time. As Wallis commented,

> When you underestimate demand your delivery time can stretch out from 12 weeks to 24 weeks—which seems like infinity to your customers. But at the same time you can't afford to hold excess capacity that is likely to go unutilized.

Symbios, like most chipmakers, continuously developed and revised bottoms-up forecasts of production requirements and revenues. These customer demand forecasts (CDFs) were developed by collecting the customers' own projections of delivery requirements by line item for the next four quarters. A Symbios manager described the process:

> The [CDF] process begins with a Symbios sales representative visiting . . . a customer to obtain the customer's demand projections. After obtaining the customer's forecast, the sales representative reviews the forecast with a Symbios sales manager. Together, the sales manager and sales representative determine the likelihood

---

[13]Symbios makes about 80% of its chips in its own fab. Like many firms in the industry, Symbios uses outside foundries to handle demand peaks and to produce some small volume, older products. While outsourcing to external foundries provides some flexibility, there are still substantial delays between the decision to outsource and the delivery of product, and the less predictable the need for outsourcing, the more expensive it is to locate, qualify, and contract with external foundries.

Figure 11-21

Actual billings compared to 6- and 12-month customer demand forecasts

The graph shows the CDFs prepared in month t − h plotted against actual billings for month t (where h is the forecast horizon of 6 or 12 months). If the forecasts were accurate they would correspond exactly to actual billings. All three series are 3-month centered moving averages to filter out monthly fluctuations.

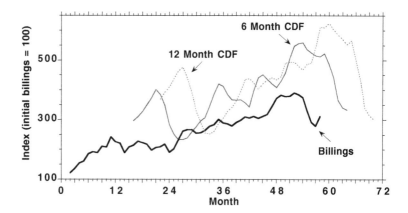

that the customer will hit their projections. If they have concerns that the customer may be over- or underforecasting, they enter a confidence factor into the forecast or adjust the projection. The forecast is then submitted to Symbios marketing managers and product marketing engineers. After reviewing the forecasts, the marketing managers and engineers also have the opportunity to adjust the confidence factor and alter the customer's forecast . . . Once reviewed by marketing, the forecast becomes available for use company-wide.

The rationale for the bottoms-up forecasts was for many years unquestioned throughout the organization. The demand forecast information came directly from the customers, who should know their own requirements best. Using customer requirements forecasts creates a strong channel of communication between the OEMs and chipmakers and demonstrates to the customers that the suppliers are listening and responding to their needs. Yet the more Wallis examined the accuracy of the bottoms-up CDFs, the more concerned he became.

Figure 11-21 shows the 6- and 12-month revenue forecasts based on the customer demand forecasts against actual billings. The forecasts of future sales prepared in month t − h are plotted at time t against actual billings for month t (h is the forecast horizon of 6 or 12 months; the data are 3-month centered moving averages to filter out high-frequency noise). If the forecasts were accurate the forecast and actual billings curves would be identical. Wallis immediately noticed several features of the forecasts. First, the bottoms-up forecasts are not very accurate. The mean absolute percent error is 40% for the 6-month forecasts and 46% for the 12-month forecasts.[14] Second, the forecasts correlate poorly with actual billings. The forecasts tend to move out of phase with actual billings; that is, they tend to be high when billings are low and vice versa. Third, the forecasts are consistently too high. Some of the bias reflects overoptimistic forecasts of consumer demand by the OEMs. Some reflects each OEM's effort to ensure receipt of sufficient output by padding orders to the supplier (and then canceling later if necessary). Fourth, the forecasts are extremely volatile. The forecasts fluctuate significantly around the

[14]The mean absolute percent error (MAPE) is defined as

$$\text{MAPE} = 100 * \frac{1}{n} \sum_{i=1}^{n} (|\text{CDF}_i - \text{Billings}_i|/\text{Billings}_i)$$

FIGURE 11-22

Six and 12-month
customer demand
forecasts
compared to
actual bookings

FIGURE 11-22

Six and 12-month
customer demand
forecasts
compared to
actual bookings

The forecasts are
plotted at the time
they were made.
Forecasts of future
demand are highly
correlated with
current orders.
All three series are
3-month centered
moving averages
to filter out
monthly
fluctuations.

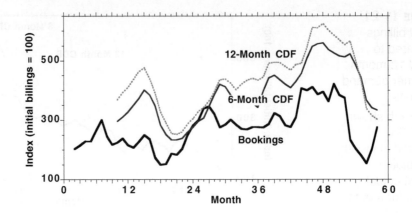

growth trend, with much greater variance than actual production. Chasing the fluctuations in forecasts caused costly errors in production planning and capacity
acquisition.

Figure 11-22 compares the 6- and 12-month forecasts against current bookings
(the order rate). Here, the forecasts of future sales have been plotted at the date the
forecasts were made to show the relationship between current bookings and the
current beliefs of customers about future demand. Both the 6- and 12-month customer forecasts are highly correlated with current customer orders (the correlation
between bookings and the customer demand forecasts is about 0.70 for both forecast horizons; the correlation between the two forecasts is 0.96). Looking closely,
you can see a lag of several months between the peak in actual bookings and the
peaks in the forecast. Customers appear to project their future requirements by extrapolating their recent actual orders. The lag arises from short-term smoothing of
recent orders and administrative delays in preparing the forecasts.

Wallis concluded that the customer demand forecasts responded strongly to recent events, particularly the current demand requirements of the customers, and
contained little useful information on future requirements. When customers need
more product right now, their 6- and 12-month forecasts increase sharply; when
they need less right now, their forecasts of future needs drop. Consequently, short-
term inventory and supply line adjustments find their way into forecasts of future
demand even though these temporary influences on orders usually have little bearing on demand 6 or 12 months out. The errors and volatility of the bottoms-up
forecasts caused Symbios to make frequent and costly changes in production
schedules and capacity, eating up profits and crimping the competitiveness of the
business.

Further, because the customers' MRP and production planning systems reacted
to the availability of the products from suppliers, forecast volatility was self-
reinforcing. Fluctuating demand meant products would sometimes be placed on
allocation, stretching out delivery schedules. During periods of allocation, customers' MRP systems and production planners responded by seeking to hold
greater safety stocks and ordering farther ahead, forecasting still greater future requirements and leading Symbios to add capacity. Once adequate capacity came on-
line and the product went off allocation, orders fell as customers responded to the

ready availability of the product by canceling their defensive orders, leading to excess capacity. As orders fell, so too did forecasts of future requirements, causing Symbios to cut production plans and capacity acquisition and setting up the next cycle of inadequate capacity, allocations, and surging orders.

Finally, producing and updating the bottoms-up forecasts took too long and cost too much. It took too long to get the data from the customers and ate up a lot of Symbios' sales and management time. The data frequently contained errors and inconsistencies that took further time to work out. Wallis ruefully concluded, "Using a 'bottoms-up' forecast is worse than nothing for sizing the business."

The poor performance of the bottoms-up forecasts was well known throughout the organization. Wallis noted the past reaction to each forecasting failure:

> In each case we would find something to blame. Usually, we blamed the sales force for not being able to forecast, so we would have the marketing groups do the work. Then we would switch back to sales after some time. Or, we blamed the software system and changed that.

He concluded that there were deeper structural reasons for the repeated failure of the bottoms-up forecasts:

> My position is that structurally each of these systems was similar and that each produced similar results. They always take the current situation and project it into the forecast horizon. In such a situation even normal seasonal fluctuation causes real problems. We have looked at the data produced by sales versus marketing versus different business units and can find no real difference in behavior.

And he recognized that he had not been immune to these problems himself:

> In fact, I went back and looked at my [forecasting] data for when I was a sales manager and when I was a business unit director—same behavior.

Despite the strong evidence of the failures of the bottoms-up forecasts, many in the organization—not to mention the customers—were strongly committed to the current forecasting process and didn't believe the analysis.

> As a very customer-oriented company, the customers' forecast is a very compelling input, even if intellectually one knows that the customers' forecasting process is flawed. First, it makes some sense that the customers should know their business. Second, they are IN YOUR FACE demanding whatever it is that they think they want, whether it makes sense or not. And, selective memory is pervasive. If they fall short of their forecast, it is forgotten. But miss their forecast just once and there is hell to pay. Customers appear to believe that their forecasts are pretty good in spite of evidence to the contrary.

Wallis knew that you can't beat something with nothing; pointing out the problems caused by the current system without proposing a better alternative would only create anger and frustration.

But what were the alternatives? One possibility was to use simple trend projection based on actual aggregate billings. Simple extrapolation is fast and cheap and yielded reasonable results at the aggregate level. However, extrapolative methods didn't provide enough detail to plan production or capacity at the level of particular production lines or product families, and many in the company didn't believe trend projections could be trusted because they didn't take the customers' own requirements forecasts into account.

Another possibility was to use econometric forecasts of semiconductor industry demand by segment. Many market research and consulting organizations sell such forecasts. However, the industry forecasts often, even usually, miss the turning points in the industry. Further, the turning points in the demand for Symbios' products didn't always coincide with the segment turning points. Finally, econometric models had poor forecasting accuracy at the longer time horizons needed to plan capacity.

Having played the Beer Distribution Game (Sterman 1989b, chap. 17), Wallis recognized that much of the volatility in orders and customer demand forecasts Symbios experienced was endogenously generated by feedbacks among the members of the semiconductor industry supply chain (Figure 11-23). Each firm in the chain, following its own self-interest, orders to meet anticipated customer demand and adjusts its inventories and backlogs of parts on order to ensure a steady supply of deliveries from suppliers. The result is powerful amplification of demand fluctuations from one level of the distribution chain to the next, causing instability for all players in the industry. As a chipmaker, Symbios held the tail position in the supply chain and experienced more volatility in demand than those downstream. For Symbios to temper the wild swings in orders caused by the amplification of inventory and supply line adjustments up the supply chain, it could no longer base capacity plans on forecasts derived from past actual order rates.

With the help of Mark Paich, an experienced modeler, Wallis began to develop a system dynamics model. Wallis also recruited two Symbios managers, Karl Braitberg and Kevin Gearhardt, from line positions into the team. They began by mapping the stock and flow structure that generated demand and quickly determined that the key to improved forecasts was the link between *design wins* and customer orders. A design win occurs when a customer commits to using a specific Symbios chip in a specific product. Design wins are the focus of the sales force's

FIGURE 11-23   Semiconductor industry supply chain

As in the Beer Distribution Game, each layer in the distribution chain amplifies fluctuations in final demand until orders for and production of semiconductors fluctuate significantly.

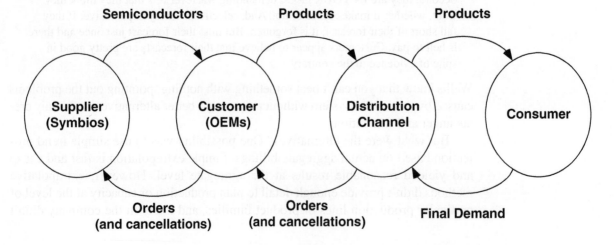

efforts. To generate business, sales people must persuade OEMs to use a Symbios chip in their products.

The progression of ASIC design wins from customer commitment to production is shown in Figure 11-24. An application-specific chip cannot go into production until the detailed design is developed, prototypes are tested, and the chip-specific tooling in the fab is developed and tested. Hence new design wins accumulate in a stock of Designs in Development. As designs are completed and reviewed, prototyping starts. After successful test (and concurrent development and test of the fabrication process), production begins. Production volume and revenue depend on the number of product designs in production and average selling prices. The stock of designs in production decreases as the designs reach the end of their useful life and are discontinued.

The conceptual model shown in Figure 11-24 was developed very rapidly. It was readily apparent that there were long delays in the design and prototyping process. The long delays meant today's revenue derived from past design wins, so knowledge of the recent wins in the development and prototyping pipeline should provide a better forecast of future build requirements and revenue.

The next step was to convert the conceptual model shown in Figure 11-24 into an operational, calibrated model. The team quickly realized that an aggregate model tracking the total number of design wins was not sufficient, since different design wins generated very different production volumes and prices. However, previous attempts to forecast demand based on individual design wins had not been successful. The delay between any particular design win and volume production is quite variable, as the product development time depends on the complexity

FIGURE 11-24   The stock and flow structure of design wins determines volume and revenue.

Current volume and revenue depend on past design wins due to development and prototyping delays. The delays in each stage are high-order processes.

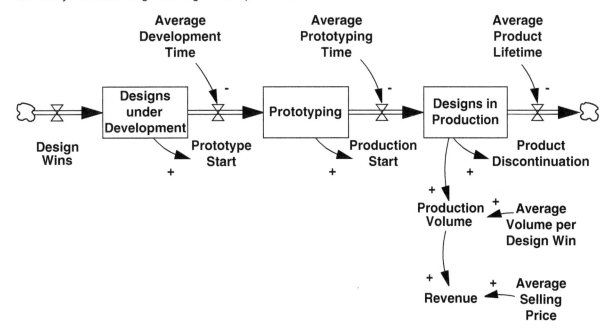

of the particular chip, the stability of customer specifications, and other attributes of the product development process. The sales organization routinely estimated the volume predicted to flow from each design win, but the manufacturing and marketing groups considered these projections unreliable. Indeed, some design wins never resulted in volume production, for example when the OEM canceled the product before production began; others became wild successes beyond the hopes of the customer.

The modeling team settled on an intermediate level of aggregation. Knowledge of the volumes generated by individual design wins was not necessary. Production planners needed to know how many wafers to start and how many units to build at the level of each production technology such as a line producing 8-inch wafers with a 0.35 micron line width and a certain number of layers. Sales and marketing needed to know likely future sales at the level of product families so they could allocate resources and set sales goals and sales force compensation. The modeling team disaggregated the model at the level of each product family and process technology. The delays, volumes, and revenues for ASICs are radically different from those for standard products, and there are differences among the different standard product families. Disaggregation allowed the model to generate information needed by key organizational constituencies in a form they could use by providing forecasts of volume and revenue at the product family and process technology level.

The simple stock and flow structure in Figure 11-24 is appropriate if the volume and average price associated with each design win are the same. In reality, volume and prices change over time with changes in the product mix, technology, and market conditions. The volume and revenue generated by design wins currently in production could be quite different from the volume and revenue anticipated from design wins farther upstream in the process. To model this variability, they disaggregated the model further by adding parallel stock and flow structures, known as coflows, to track the projected volumes and revenues associated with each design win (Figure 11-25). Coflow structures keep track of various attributes of the units in a stock and flow network (see chapter 12).

Each design win adds one design to the stock of designs under development and adds a certain expected volume to the stock of anticipated production volume from designs under development. The ratio of the anticipated volume from designs under development to the total number of designs under development is the average volume expected from each chip currently in the design phase. When the design moves from development to prototyping, the average expected volume associated with the designs under development also moves into the parallel stock for the expected production volume of designs in prototyping. When the design moves into production, the production volume expected from the designs in prototyping also moves into the stock of anticipated volume from designs in production. The operational model included an additional coflow structure to track the revenue expected from each design win. Production and capacity planners could use the volume projection to plan wafer starts by applying the expected yield and wafer size to volume requirements, and senior management could use the revenue projections to set budgets and generate pro forma financial statements.

FIGURE 11-25 Example of parallel coflow structure to track the attributes of design wins

The parallel stock and flow structure keeps track of the anticipated production volumes associated with new design wins as they flow through the development process. An additional coflow structure, not shown, tracks the anticipated revenue associated with each design win. The entire structure was disaggregated by product type and production technology. The diagram is simplified and does not show the flows representing the transfer of design wins and associated coflow contents from one product family to another or from one process technology to another resulting from changes in the wafer fabs or product line.

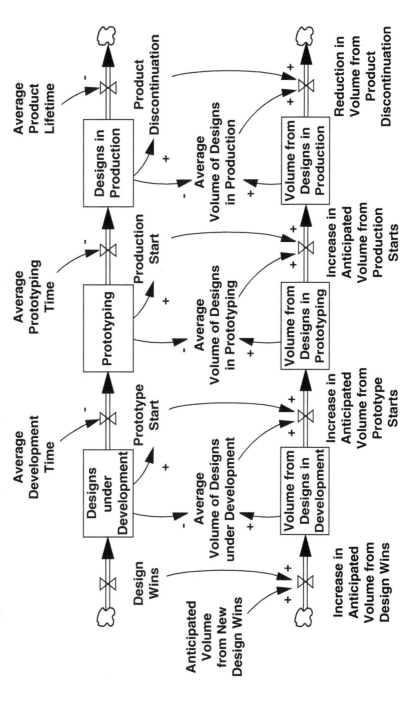

Calibrating the model required (1) estimating the length and distribution of the development and prototyping delays for each process technology and (2) estimating the expected volume, wafer requirements, and price for design wins in each product category.

Generating and collecting the data was a major challenge. The team needed current data on design wins and their attributes. Fortunately, in 1990 the sales organization had launched a new program in which sales representatives recorded the characteristics of each win at the time of the sale. The database tracked the product, customer, anticipated volumes, average selling prices, and other attributes for the next 3 years. These data were used by the sales organization to determine sales goals and compensation but were considered unreliable and unstable by the manufacturing and marketing organizations.

The estimates of price and volume recorded in the sales force design win database could not be used in raw form because they didn't account for subsequent order cancellations, changes in requirements, and changes in prices. But the modeling team realized that the sales force database didn't have to be accurate as long as the relationships between projected and realized volume and revenue were stable. The team then assembled the production histories of each product from data collected by the manufacturing organization. Cross-tabulating the sales organization's design win database against the actual production histories enabled the team to assess the accuracy of the sales database. Regressions showed fairly stable relationships between the volume and revenue projections recorded at the time a contract was won and the actual, realized volumes and revenues when the chips were actually made. These relationships were used to calibrate the model. Combining the sales force's design win data with the design and production histories for each product also allowed the modelers to estimate the length and distribution of the delays by product and process category. Since the design and prototyping processes are themselves composed of multiple stages (product definition, design, layout, masking, wafer fabrication, sorting, prototype assembly, testing, etc.), the team expected the delays to be very high-order (but not pipeline delays as there is considerable variation in processing times for each step). While the delays for any particular design win were unpredictable, the modeling team found that the distribution of the delay outflows in each category were approximated quite well by various high-order material delays (generally between ninth- and twentieth-order, a reflection of the many stages subsumed in the design and prototyping processes and the disaggregation of the model by process technology). Figure 11-26 shows the overall response of the estimated model for ASICs to a single design win (a unit pulse). Because custom chips have a long design time, there is no response at all for roughly a year. Production volumes then build rapidly to a peak roughly 3 years after the design win before gradually tailing off as product demand falls.

The calibrated design win model generated more accurate forecasts than the bottoms-up procedure. Figure 11-27 compares the revenue projection of the design win model to actual billings for product line A. The model tracks actual billings more accurately than the bottoms-up forecasts. The model also captures key shifts in revenue growth, such as the decline in sales between months 50 and 64 and the recovery in sales beginning around month 78.

FIGURE 11-26

FIGURE 11-26

Estimated revenue impact of a design win for ASICs

The curve shows the distribution of revenue over time given a unit pulse from a single design win.

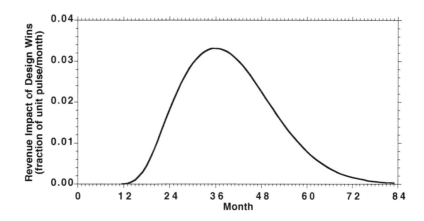

FIGURE 11-27

Actual and projected revenue from design win model for product line A

The projection is divided into revenue derived from prior year, current year, and assumed future design wins.

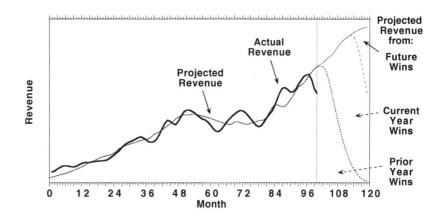

Note that the model is far from perfect. Actual revenues fluctuate around the projection. These errors caused intense discussion within the modeling team. They found that some of the errors arose from variations in volume and prices generated by the occasional very large or very small design win or other unpredictable events. However, after careful review of the data and some additional modeling, the modeling team ultimately concluded that much of the unexplained variation in production and billings was caused by fluctuations in overall industry demand around the long-term growth trend. Most of these excursions are themselves caused by industrywide supply chain volatility—situations where customers over-react to short-term inventory and lead time variations. Wallis commented, "We do not attempt to capture these effects with the design win model. Instead, we think of the model results as representing the longer-term growth trends for the business." Forecasts based on design wins help Symbios damp out temporary over-reactions in customer orders, tempering expensive swings in production and capacity acquisition.

The design win approach also provided insight into the drivers of growth for the business. Figure 11-27 breaks the projected revenue stream into revenues from projected design wins, from current year design wins, and from earlier design wins. Products in line A have short win-to-production and lifetimes. Design wins already in the pipeline will support sales for only about 2 years. After just

18 months, about a third of projected revenues are assumed to derive from design wins yet to be won. The long-term revenue forecast for line A is therefore highly sensitive to the assumed rate of future design wins. For product line A the boundary of the model might usefully be extended so design wins can be related to the size and experience of the sales force, their compensation incentives, and the relative attractiveness of the products.

More importantly, the drivers of design wins emerge as a key leverage point for growth, as Wallis pointed out:

> Understanding these product design win and life cycle characteristics allows our top management team to balance the required investments in technology, production capacity, and sales effectiveness against the likely timing and magnitude of the returns on those investments. Prior to development of the design win model, evaluations of proposed investments generally underestimated the delays between investment and results. Without a model, estimates of the total life of investment returns are generally too short, causing total investment return to be underestimated.

The calibrated, disaggregate design win model gained broad, though not universal, acceptance in the company. It is used to generate a rolling estimate of future volume requirements and revenue to manage production and plan inventories. The model is also used as a key input to the annual planning process, to long-term capital planning, and as part of the product development planning cycle.

Consistent with the experience of others, the modeling team found that abstract description and conceptual models did not change the thinking or behavior of key decision makers in the organization. Rather, the mental models and behavior of the managers responsible for production planning and capacity acquisition changed only when they actively worked with the model to address important issues. The modeling team worked hard to involve current and future line managers in the development and testing of the model. Some members of the modeling team were subsequently promoted into line positions where they used the model to help them in production planning and inventory management.

Karl Braitberg, who became manager for standard products, commented on the business impact of the model:

> We used to manage inventory by gut feel. For example, people would say, "This is a hot product so we better build a hundred thousand of them now." They'd base this on sample requests or other unreliable information coming from customers. Now we make better production scheduling decisions and time inventory builds better by taking the delays between design wins and volume demand into account. Customer service has improved: our ability to meet customer requested delivery dates has improved from about 60% to about 80%, and on time delivery to our commit date is 97%, while inventory days on hand are at a 3-year low. All the inventory metrics have improved. We have a better mix of product in stock and in WIP [Work in Process inventory]. Now we build the right inventory at the right time.

It is important to recognize that the model does not replace other considerations in the production planning and capacity decision. Managers do not slavishly follow the model's output, nor should they. Rather, the model informs the viewpoint of key participants in discussions about production and capacity planning, providing a sanity check on the customers' claimed requirements. Short-term, event-oriented thinking still exists, as Wallis commented: "For some people, when a customer calls and screams at them, they don't care what your model says." But the model helps temper the reaction to such pressure, helping to stabilize the operation, raise average utilization, and increase delivery reliability, all of which generate benefits for the customers as well as for Symbios. Wallis recalled that in the old days

> during revenue shortfalls we'd beat up the marketing and sales groups to go out and get some more design wins to fill the revenue hole next quarter. Of course, this never worked because of the long delays, and probably caused more instability. The model helps people understand these dynamics, stabilizing the business, increasing the efficiency of the organization, and boosting our growth.

While the model provides better forecasts of production volumes and revenues than the bottoms-up approach, modeling team members are careful to note its limitations and monitor its accuracy as the firm and industry continue to evolve.

The model treats design wins as a continuous flow. Most of the time, the continuous flow assumption works well. However, occasional extremely large individual design wins violate the continuous flow assumption and must be handled separately (they are added exogenously). Similarly, some customer products fail, leading to cancellation of orders at various points in the process. Finally, as some customers are bought by others the resulting consolidation of OEM product lines can affect the volume and revenue generated by design wins already in the pipeline. These issues are growing in importance: The computer industry in the 1990s became significantly more concentrated through mergers and acquisitions. As the industry consolidates, the number of design wins per year falls while their average size grows and forecasting becomes more difficult (for all methods, not just the design win model). Internal changes at Symbios also mean the model must be continually updated: the processes underlying the delay distributions estimated from the data change as the product mix and process technology change and as improvement programs shorten product development times.

For these reasons, the model (and all models) can never be considered finished. Models are always works in progress, and the model users must constantly ask whether the assumptions of the model are still reasonable as conditions change. Sustained implementation success depends on creating an ongoing process of modeling rather than a single model, no matter how accurate or comprehensive (Forrester 1985). Team members now continuously track their forecasting record and compare it to the accuracy of the other forecasts. Analysis of their errors generates important insight into model limitations and helps them to calibrate and improve the model. They continue to develop the model in concert with the needs and participation of the people responsible for production planning, capacity acquisition, and strategy to help ensure that the model continues to be understood and used.

Modeling efforts underway at the time this is written explicitly address the uncertainty caused by lumpy design wins through the development of a Monte Carlo version of the model which will generate the range of uncertainty as well as the expected trajectory of volume and billings. The modeling team is working with key customers to develop models to reduce further the volatility of orders and improve delivery performance. As one customer said, "We give you the worst information we have and then wonder why we have a problem."

As often found in modeling projects, the greatest insight into the structure and behavior of the business came when the model results were wrong. Yet because many organizations punish those who make mistakes, mistakes are often hidden, denying the organization the opportunity to learn from experience. The modeling process has helped Symbios overcome the natural tendency to find the people responsible for errors and blame them. Senior management is now more likely to interpret a forecasting failure as an opportunity to deepen their understanding of the business and less as an occasion to blame a bad outcome on sales, marketing, or customers.

11.7   MATHEMATICS OF DELAYS: KOYCK LAGS AND ERLANG DISTRIBUTIONS

This section presents the mathematics of the basic delay types in continuous and discrete time. System dynamics models typically treat time as continuous. However, the discrete time formulations are useful because the data from which delays are estimated are usually reported at discrete intervals. In the following I assume the delay time is constant, so the analysis applies equally to material and information delays. The assumption of constant delay times also allows delays to be treated as linear operators. Note that if the delay time is endogenous, for example when the delay process is capacitated, the delay time will in general be a nonlinear function of the history of the input.

11.7.1   General Formulation for Delays

The shape of the response of a delay to a unit pulse can be interpreted as the probability distribution of the outflow rate, analogous to the delivery distribution of letters following a mass mailing.

In discrete time, the output of a delay at time t is a weighted sum of all past values of the input up to the present time:

$$\text{Output(t)} = w_0 I_t + w_1 I_{t-1} + w_2 I_{t-3} + \cdots$$

or

$$\text{Output(t)} = \sum_{i=0}^{\infty} w_i \text{Input}_{t-i} \tag{11-12}$$

where the lag weights w are the probabilities of exiting the delay in any time period i and must sum to unity, that is,

$$\sum_{i=0}^{\infty} w_i = 1 \tag{11-13}$$

The constraint that the weights sum to unity ensures the conservation of material through the delay. If the weights summed to less than one, the quantity exiting the delay would be less than the quantity added to it; if the weights totaled more than one, more would leave the delay than entered, violating the conservation principle. In information delays, weights summing to one ensure the equilibrium output equals the input, giving an unbiased perception of the input.

Taking the limit of the discrete time formulation as the time interval between periods shrinks to zero yields the continuous time formulation. The output is the integral of past values of the input weighted by the probability of delivery at time $t - s$, where the probability of delivery s time units after entering the delay, $p(s)$, is given by a continuous distribution:

$$\text{Output(t)} = \int_0^\infty p(s)\text{Input}(t - s)ds \qquad (11\text{-}14)$$

$$\int_0^\infty p(s)ds = 1 \qquad (11\text{-}15)^{15}$$

In principle the pattern of weights—the probability distribution of exiting the delay—is arbitrary, subject to the constraint that the input to the delay is conserved (that the weights are nonnegative and sum to unity). However, in practice, only a few patterns are reasonable and realistic. At the instant a quantity of material is injected into a delay the output has not yet had any time to respond, so the probability of exit at time $p(0) = 0$ (in discrete time, the weight on the current value of the input $w_0 = 0$). The output of all delays must approach zero after a sufficiently long time has passed; that is, once the items are delivered the exit rate must fall to zero. Therefore $p(\infty) = w_\infty = 0$. Thus the probability of exiting a delay—its response to a unit pulse—must start at zero, rise to a maximum, then fall to zero.

It is reasonable to assume the exit distribution is smooth and that the distribution has a single maximum. If the data suggest the output distribution of a delay has more than one peak, it is almost certain the total output is the result of two different delays operating in parallel and you should model each delay separately. Within these constraints, there are two main types of responses: a delay in which the output responds immediately after a pulse input, then gradually declines; and a delay in which there is no response for some period of time, followed by a gradual increase, peak, and decline. The first-order delay models the former case and the higher-order delays provide a flexible family of distributions to model the latter case.

---

[15]Equation (11-14) can also be derived by applying the *convolution theorem* of linear systems theory. In general, the response of any linear system to an arbitrary input can be expressed as the *convolution* of the input with the pulse response of the system, that is, the product of the input with the lagged pulse response of the system:

$$\text{Output(t)} = \int_{-\infty}^t \text{Input}(s)h(t - s)ds$$

where $h()$ is the response of the system to a unit impulse.

In general, the pulse response of a linear system can take on negative as well as positive values, and its integral need not be unity, or even finite. In the case of delays, the pulse response must be nonnegative, and conservation of material requires the integral of the response to equal unity, so we may treat $h()$ as a probability distribution $p()$. The convolution integral can be derived by rewriting equation (11-12) as

$$\text{Output(t)} = \sum_{i=0}^\infty w_i\text{Input}_{t-i} = \sum_{i=-\infty}^t w_{t-i}\text{Input}_i$$

and taking the limit as the interval between time periods becomes infinitely small. Further details can be found in control theory texts such as Ogata (1997) or Rowell and Wormley (1997).

11.7.2   First-Order Delay

The first-order delay assumes the contents of the stock of material in transit are perfectly mixed at all times. Perfect mixing randomizes the order of exit from the delay, implying some items stay in the stock of material in transit longer than the average delay time and some stay for a shorter period. Since the first-order delay is equivalent to the first-order linear negative feedback system, its characteristic response to a pulse input is exponential decay. That is, the probability of exiting the first-order material delay is given by the exponential distribution

$$p(t) = (1/D)\exp(-t/D) \tag{11-16}$$

where the mean of the distribution is the average delay D.

What is the average delay or mean residence time for items in the delay? Is it in fact the delay time parameter D? By the mean value theorem of calculus, the average residence time T_r for any delay process is the time-weighted average of the outflow rate, given a unit pulse input at time zero:

$$T_r = \int_0^\infty t \cdot \text{Outflow}(t)dt = \int_0^\infty t \cdot p(t)dt \tag{11-17}$$

Note that the time-weighted average of the outflow from a unit pulse is the same as the time-weighted mean of the outflow probability distribution p(t). For the case of a first-order material delay, the outflow is the stock of material in transit, S, divided by the average delay time D:

$$\text{Outflow}(t) = S(t)/D \tag{11-18}$$

Immediately after a unit pulse input, the initial value of the stock of material in transit is unity. Since the first-order material delay is the linear first-order negative feedback system, the stock in transit then decays exponentially with time constant D:

$$S(t) = \exp(-t/D) \tag{11-19}$$

Therefore, the mean residence time is given by

$$T_r = \int_0^\infty t \cdot [S(t)/D]dt = \int_0^\infty t(1/D)\exp(-t/D)dt \tag{11-20}$$

Note that $(1/D)\exp(-t/D)$ in the latter expression is precisely the exponential probability distribution. Integrating by parts,

$$T_r = -t \cdot \exp(-t/D)\Big|_0^\infty + \int_0^\infty \exp(-t/D)dt = 0 - D\exp(-t/D)\Big|_0^\infty = D \tag{11-21}$$

which confirms that the mean residence time is in fact given by the delay time parameter D.

In discrete time, the weights w_i for a first-order delay decline geometrically (by a fixed proportion) over time:

$$w_i = (1 - L)L^i \tag{11-22}$$

where the lag weight parameter L, $0 \leq L < 1$, is related to the average delay time D by

$$D = L/(1 - L) \tag{11-23}$$

The discrete time geometric lag formulation is quite common in econometric modeling where it is also known as a Koyck lag, after Koyck (1954) who showed how the lag parameter L can be estimated (see any good econometrics text for details).

11.7.3 Higher-Order Delays

Cascading n first-order delays together in series creates the higher-order delays discussed above. Mathematically, the output of the nth-order delay is the convolution of the sequence of first-order delays, each with identical delay times equal to the total delay time D divided by the number of stages in the delay. In continuous time the higher-order delays are equivalent to the Erlang family of distributions, named after the Danish telephone pioneer known as the father of queuing theory. The Erlang distribution of order n is given by

$$p(t) = \frac{(n/D)^n}{(n - 1)!} t^{n-1} \exp[-(n/D)t]; t > 0 \tag{11-24}$$

You can use the mean value theorem to check that the mean residence time of the nth-order delay is in fact given by D. The Erlang distribution reduces to the first-order exponential distribution for $n = 1$.

In discrete time the higher-order delays are also known as Pascal lags, given by the distribution

$$w_i = \binom{i + n - 1}{i}(1 - L)^n L^i = \frac{(i + n - 1)!}{i!(n - i)!}(1 - L)^n L^i; i \in \{0, \infty\} \tag{11-25}$$

where again the mean delay is $L/(1 - L)$. Just as the first-order Erlang lag is equivalent to the exponential distribution, the Pascal lag reduces to the geometric lag for $n = 1$.

If sufficient data are available, the outflow distribution can be plotted and directly compared to the Erlang family to see if it is a good model of the delay process and to select the appropriate order of the delay (see section 11.5.1). Sometimes, however, only summary statistics such as the sample mean and variance are available, while the data for the full distribution are not. In this case the order of the delay can still be estimated, subject only to the assumption that the lag is well approximated by a member of the Erlang family. The variance of the nth-order Erlang lag is given by $\sigma^2 = D^2/n$. Consistent with intuition and the simulation results above, the smaller the variance relative to the mean delay the higher the order of the delay. Approximating the mean delay and variance of the outflow from their sample values, denoted $\hat{D}$ and s^2, respectively, yields a simple estimator for the order of the delay:

$$\hat{n} = \text{INT}\left(\frac{\hat{D}}{s^2}\right) \tag{11-26}$$

where INT() is the integer function. Of course, the ratio $\hat{D}/s^2$ won't in general be an integer, but rounding to the nearest integer generally introduces little error compared to the likely sampling errors in the data. Remember, however, that this estimator presumes the delay distribution is a member of the Erlang family; departures from the Erlang distribution will yield poor estimates. Information about the order of a delay gleaned from fieldwork should be used to check estimates derived from equation (11-26).

11.7.4   Relation of Material and Information Delays

As seen above, the outputs of material and information delays with equal delay times are identical *provided* the delay time remains fixed. To see why, consider the equation for the first-order information delay with input I and output O:

$$\frac{dO}{dt} = (I - O)/D \tag{11-27}$$

The output of the delay, the stock O, has a single net rate determined by the gap between the input and output. The net rate can be disaggregated into explicit increase and decrease rates:

$$\frac{dO}{dt} = \frac{I}{D} - \frac{O}{D} \tag{11-28}$$

Equation (11-28) is equivalent to a first-order material delay with inflow I/D, outflow O/D, and stock in transit O. As long as the delay time remains fixed, the behavior of the two delays is identical. However, in a material delay the output is the exit rate from the stock, while in the information delay the output is the stock O. Changing the delay time causes the behavior of the two delays to differ. Even though their response under constant delay times is the same, modelers must be careful to use the proper type of delays: A delay time currently thought of as fixed may become variable as a model is developed.

11.8   SUMMARY

This chapter discussed delays and showed how they can be modeled. First, all delays include at least one stock. Second, delays in material flow networks must be distinguished from delays in information feedback channels: material flows are conserved, while information is not. The difference affects how the two types of delays respond to changes in the delay time.

Every delay has two main characteristics: the mean delay time and the distribution of the output of the delay around that average. The chapter developed a family of formulations for material and information delays enabling modelers to capture a wide range of plausible delivery distributions. First-order delays are characterized by an exponentially declining output in response to a pulse input. The largest response occurs immediately after the pulse input. The response of higher-order delays, formed by cascading first-order delays in series, is initially zero, builds to a maximum, and then dies away. Pipeline delays preserve the order of entry to a delay so the output is exactly the same as the input, but shifted by the time delay. The first-order delay assumes the contents of the stock of material in transit are perfectly mixed at all times, so the outflow is independent of the order of entry. The higher the order of the delay, the less mixing is assumed; pipeline delays assume no mixing of the contents of the stock in transit at all. The higher the order of the delay, the lower the variance in the distribution of the output.

Finally, the chapter discussed how the length and output distribution of delays can be estimated. When numerical data are available, econometric tools can help estimate delay durations and distributions. When numerical data are not available, estimation by direct inspection of the relevant process can yield good estimates. Judgmental estimates are more accurate when you decompose the delay into its constituent steps and estimate the delays of each separately. You should use multiple sources of information to help you specify delays (and other model parameters) and inspect the process firsthand whenever possible.

12

Coflows and Aging Chains

[Mathematical demography] is concerned with commonsense questions about, for instance, the effect of a lowered death rate on the proportion of old people or the effect of abortions on the birth rate. The answers that it reaches are not always commonsense, and we will meet instances in which intuition has to be adjusted to accord with what the mathematics shows to be the case. Even when the intuitive answer gives the right direction of an effect, technical analysis is still needed to estimate its amount. We may see intuitively that the drop from an increasing to a stationary population will slow the promotion for the average person in a factory or office, but nothing short of an integral equation can show that each drop of 1 percent in the rate of increase will delay promotion to middle-level positions by 2.3 years.
—Nathan Keyfitz (1977/1985), *Applied Mathematical Demography,* p. viii.

The stock and flow structures described in previous chapters keep track of the quantities flowing through various stages of a system. Often, however, modelers must not only capture the total quantity of material in a stock and flow network but also various attributes of the items in the network. These attributes might include the average skill or experience of a workforce, the quality of materials, or the energy and labor requirements of a firm's machines. Coflows are used to account for the attributes of items flowing through a stock and flow network. The outflow rates of items from a stock often depend strongly on the age of the items. Human mortality rates depend on age, the rate at which people discard and replace their automobiles depends on the age of their cars, machine breakdowns in a plant depend on the time since the machines were last overhauled, and the probability exconvicts are re-arrested depends on the time since their release. Aging chains are used to represent situations where the mortality rates of items in a stock and flow structure are age-dependent and allow you to model changes in the age structure of any stock. This chapter shows how such situations can be modeled and provides examples including global population growth, organizational aging, on-the-job learning, and technical change.

12.1 AGING CHAINS

The stock and flow structure of systems is a critical determinant of their dynamics, and often there are significant delays between the inflow of material to a process and the outflow. In material delays (described in section 11.2) the flow of material through the delay is conserved. Material enters the delay, progresses through a number of intermediate stages, and finally exits. There are neither additions to nor losses from the intermediate stages: every item that enters eventually exits, and no new items can enter other than at the start of the delay. In many situations there are additional inflows and outflows to the intermediate stages. In these cases an *aging chain* is used to model the stock and flow structure of the system. Imagine the skilled labor force at a firm. Since it takes time for new hires to become fully experienced and productive, the modeler may choose to disaggregate the total stock of employees into two categories, rookie employees and experienced employees. An important aspect of the structure is the delay in the assimilation of rookies. However, this situation cannot be modeled with a second-order material delay because the firm can hire both rookies and experienced people, and both rookies and experienced employees can quit (or be fired). There are inflows and outflows to each of the stocks in the chain (Figure 12-1).

12.1.1 General Structure of Aging Chains

An aging chain can have any number of stocks (called cohorts), and each cohort can have any number of inflows or outflows. Figure 12-2 shows the general structure for an aging chain. The total stock is divided into n cohorts, C(i), each with an

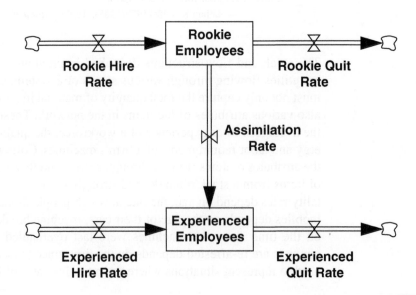

FIGURE 12-1
Example of an aging chain

inflow, I(i), and outflow, O(i). Material in cohort i moves to cohort i + 1 through the transition rate T(i, i + 1):

$$C(i) = INTEGRAL(I(i) + T(i - 1, i) - O(i) - T(i, i + 1), C(i)_{t_0}) \qquad (12\text{-}1)$$

FIGURE 12-2
General structure
of an aging chain

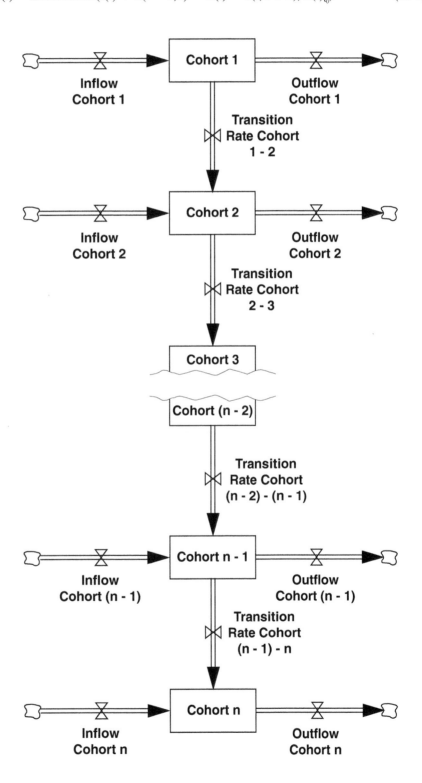

There is no transition rate into the first cohort and no transition rate out of the last cohort: T(0, 1) = 0 and T(n, n + 1) = 0. In general, the transition rates can be either positive or negative (a negative transition rate means items flow from cohort i + 1 to cohort i). Usually, however, the transition rates are formulated as a delay and most often as a first-order process:

$$T(i, i + 1) = C(i)/YPC(i) \tag{12-2}$$

where YPC(i) is the number of years per cohort (the average residence time before exiting via maturation). The average residence time for items in each cohort YPC(i) can differ from cohort to cohort. Recall from chapter 11 that a first-order outflow from a stock implies that the contents of the stock are perfectly mixed so that the probability a particular item exits is independent of when it entered the stock. Just as in higher-order material delays, the overall behavior of an aging chain with n cohorts will be similar to the nth-order material delay. The number of cohorts can be increased until the assumption of perfect mixing within each cohort becomes a reasonable approximation (see section 12.1.3 for a formulation that preserves the exact order of entry to each cohort).

The outflow rates can be formulated in a variety of ways. Often, however, the outflow represents the death rate (that is, the exit rate from the stock) and is formulated as

$$O(i) = C(i) * FDR(i) \tag{12-3}$$

where FDR is the fractional death rate for cohort i.

Aging chains can be applied to any population in which the probability of exiting the population depends on the age of the items in the population. Besides the aging and mortality of a population, examples include the failure of machines in a factory as a function of the time since the last maintenance activity, default and repayment rates for loans of different ages, the rate of divorce as a function of marriage duration, or the likelihood of re-arrest following parole.

12.1.2   Example: Population and Infrastructure in *Urban Dynamics*

Forrester's (1969) *Urban Dynamics* model includes aging chains for three key components of a city: the stock of commercial structures, the housing stock, and the population (Figure 12-3). Forrester divided the total stock of commercial structures into three categories: New Enterprise, Mature Business, and Declining Industry. The stock of New Enterprise is increased by New Enterprise Construction. The transition rate of New Enterprise to Mature Business is the New Enterprise Decline rate. Mature businesses age into the stock of declining industry through the Mature Business Decline rate. Finally, the stock of buildings in the Declining Industry cohort falls through the Declining Industry Demolition rate. Forrester chose to assume that all new construction adds to the New Enterprise cohort (there are no inflows to the mature or declining industry stocks other than the aging rates from the prior cohort). He also assumed that the demolition rate for new and mature businesses was small enough to ignore, so the only outflow from the aging chain is the declining industry demolition rate. The aging chain for commercial

FIGURE 12-3 Aging chains for businesses, housing, and labor in *Urban Dynamics*

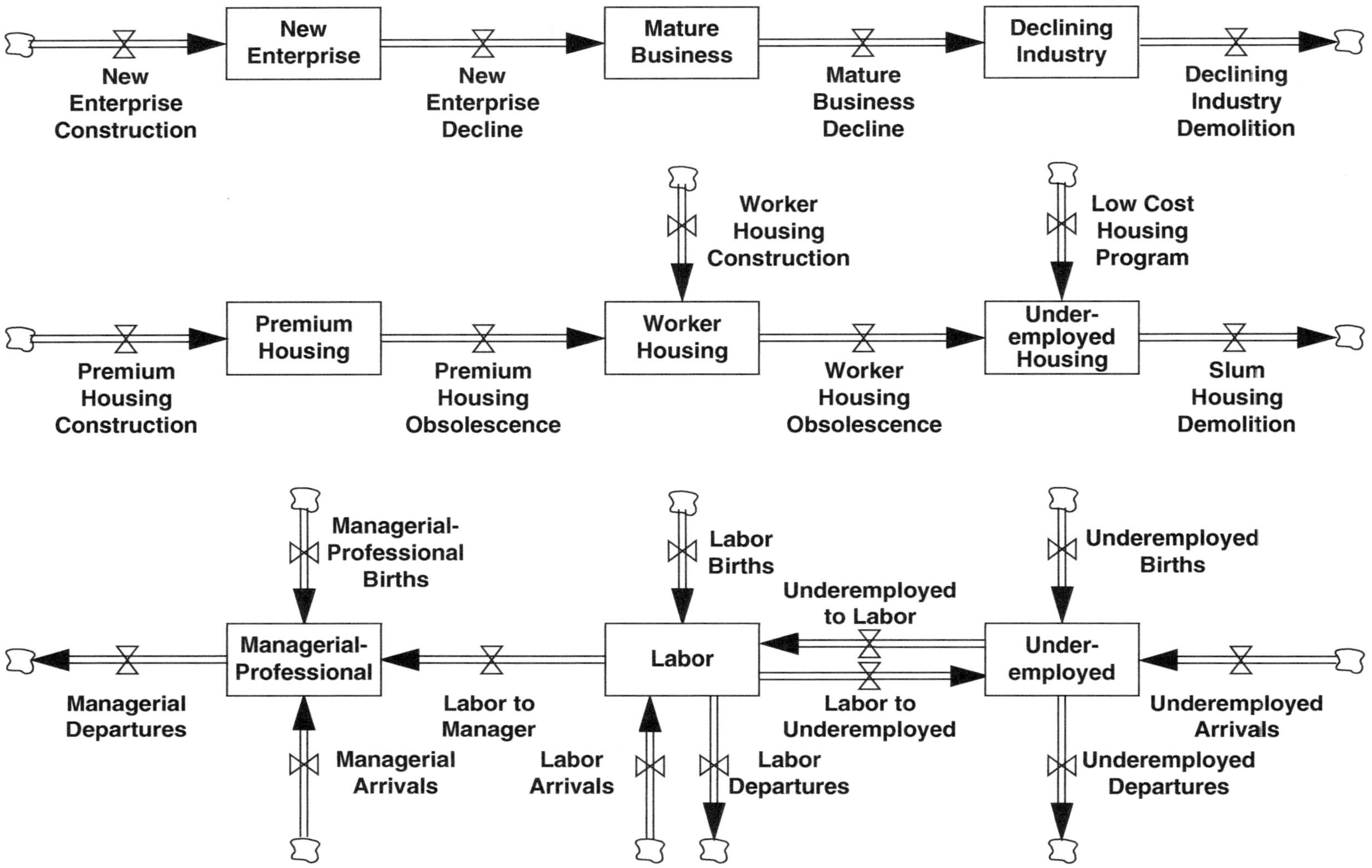

Source: Adapted from Forrester (1969, p. 16).

473

structures is therefore equivalent to a third-order material delay (though the life-times of each cohort are not equal and vary with changes in economic and social conditions in the simulated city).

The housing stock chain is more complex. Forrester divided the total housing stock into three categories—Premium Housing, Worker Housing, and Underemployed Housing—that correspond to the three types of people represented in the model: Managerial–Professional workers, skilled Labor, and the Underemployed. New housing of each type can be built. As each type of housing ages it is gradually converted into housing for the next type of worker. For example, in many cities large Victorian houses once occupied by the professional class were later divided into two- or three-family apartments occupied by the working class; as middle-class apartment blocks in the Bronx aged and deteriorated many became tenements primarily occupied by the underemployed.

Each of the three population classes included a net birth rate (births less deaths), an inmigration rate, and an outmigration rate. The underemployed could, by gaining jobs and experience, move into the worker class, and workers could advance into the managerial–professional class. Workers could also sink into underemployment.

As an initial model of urban problems and policies, Forrester deliberately kept the model as simple as possible. Not all possible flows in the aging chains are represented, and the model is no more disaggregated than necessary for the purpose. For example, Forrester ignored possible downward mobility of the professional class and did not explicitly represent the age structure of the population within each class of worker. In representing the infrastructure of the city, Forrester assumed that structures built for businesses could not be converted to housing, and vice versa, and that old, decayed housing could not be rehabilitated into premium housing. The experience of the past 30 years shows that some of the excluded flows did become important in many cities. A great deal of old industrial space was converted to housing (e.g., lofts in Soho and Brooklyn), gentrification rehabilitated much of the older housing stock, and many new businesses were created in people's garages and spare bedrooms. These flows could easily be added to the aging chains in the model. For example, Homer (1979a, 1979b) adapted the *Urban Dynamics* model to study insurance redlining. The modified model explicitly accounts for gentrification and rehabilitation of older housing, along with arson for profit. Mass (1974) and Schroeder, Sweeney, and Alfeld (1975) present a number of extensions and elaborations of the original model, generally showing that the policy recommendations of the original model were robust to major changes in the model boundary and level of aggregation; see also Alfeld and Graham (1976).

12.1.3 Example: The Population Pyramid and the Demographic Transition

A common use for aging chains is capturing the age structure of populations. Especially for long-lived species like humans, young and old behave differently and for many purposes cannot be aggregated into a single stock. Chapter 8 described the simplest demographic model where the number of people are aggregated into a single stock, with birth and death rates proportional to the total population:

$$\text{Population} = \text{INTEGRAL}(\text{Births} - \text{Deaths}, \text{Population}_{t_0}) \tag{12-4}$$

$$\text{Births} = \text{Fractional Birth Rate} * \text{Population} \tag{12-5}$$

$$\text{Deaths} = \text{Fractional Death Rate} * \text{Population} \tag{12-6}$$

In this first-order structure those just born can immediately reproduce and are just as likely to die as the oldest members of the population. For most real populations these are poor assumptions. For humans, mortality rates (the fractional death rate) are strongly age-dependent: mortality is high in the first years, low from childhood through the end of middle age, then rises with age. The childbearing years are roughly between 15 and 50, and fertility is not uniform during this interval. Variations in the population growth rate alter the age structure and affect its overall behavior. For example, a nation with high life expectancy can have a higher fractional death rate than one with a lower life expectancy. If population in the nation with low life expectancy is growing rapidly, then a much larger proportion of the population will be young, reducing the total number of deaths per year per person despite lower average life expectancy. The lag between birth and reproduction can induce fluctuations in the age structure. Modeling the effects of phenomena such as the baby boom of the 1950s—including the extra demand placed on schools, the job market, and, in coming decades the retirement system—requires a model that distinguishes between age groups.

Demographers often represent the age structure of a population by the *population pyramid,* a graph showing the number of people in each age group, by sex (Figure 12-4). The age structures for the world as a whole and for many developing nations such as Nigeria resemble pyramids because rapid population growth means there are many more young people than old. The age structures of the developed nations, where growth rates have been low for a generation or more, are more uniform, though it is still quite easy to see the variations in cohort size caused by phenomena such as the Great Depression, World War II, and the postwar baby boom. In the US, for example, the depression and war cut birth rates, so the cohorts born between 1930 and 1945 are much smaller than the baby boom cohorts born in the 1950s (even after accounting for normal mortality). The echo of the baby boom generation (the large cohorts of 5-19 year olds in the figure, representing the children of the baby boomers) is also clearly visible in the US age structure. For a number of developed nations (including Japan), fertility has been below replacement rates for some time, so the youngest cohorts are smaller than those in the prime childbearing years.

To model these issues, the total population can be represented by an aging chain in which the population is divided into n cohorts, each representing a certain age range, such as those age 5–10, 11–15, etc. The final cohort represents all people over a certain age. The following equations also disaggregate the population by sex:

$$P_S(0) = \text{INTEGRAL}(B_S + I_S(0) - D_S(0) - M_S(0), P_S(0)_{t_0}) \tag{12-7}$$

FIGURE 12-4   Age structures of world and selected national populations in 1998

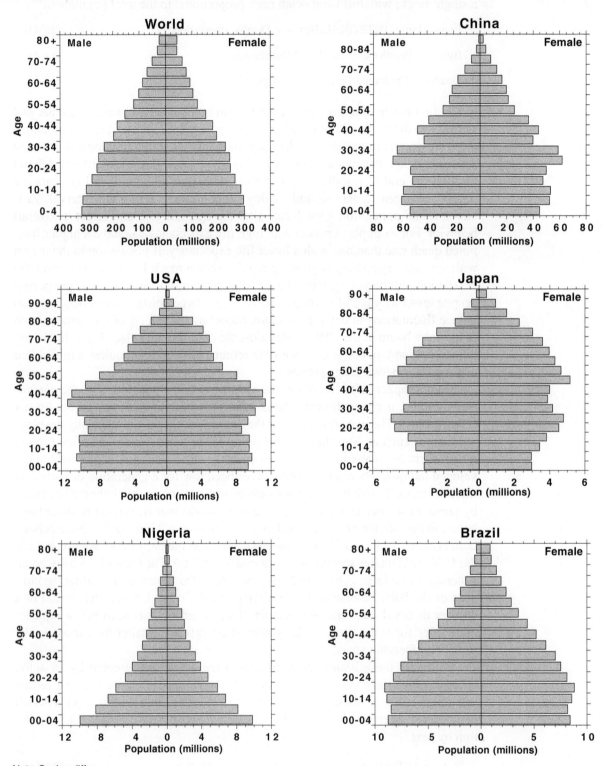

Note: Scales differ.

Source: US Census Bureau.

$$P_S(i) = \text{INTEGRAL}(M_S(i-1) + I_S(i) - D_S(i) - M_S(i), P_S(i)_{t_0})$$
$$\text{for } i \in (1, \ldots, n-1) \tag{12-8}$$

$$P_S(n) = \text{INTEGRAL}(M_S(n-1) + I_S(n) - D_S(n), P_S(n)_{t_0}) \tag{12-9}$$

where $P_S(i)$ is the population in cohort i, B is the birth rate, I(i) is net immigration to each cohort, D(i) is the cohort-specific death rate, and M(i) is the maturation rate from cohort i to i + 1. The subscript S denotes the sex (M or F). Each cohort represents YPC(i) years per cohort.

The birth rate is the sum of the children born to all women in the childbearing years:

$$B_S = S_S\left(\frac{TF}{(CY_F - CY_I + 1)}\right) \sum_{a=CY_I}^{CY_F} w(a)P_F(a), \text{ where } \sum_{a=CY_I}^{CY_F} w(a) = 1 \tag{12-10}$$

In this formulation, $P_F(a)$ is the female population in cohort a and TF is total fertility—the total number of children born to each woman during the childbearing years, where CY_I is the first and CY_F is the last childbearing year considered. The ratio $TF/(CY_F - CY_I + 1)$ is therefore the average number of births per woman per year during the childbearing years, inclusive, usually assumed to be ages 15 to 49. The age-specific weights $w(a)$ represent the fraction of lifetime births occurring in each of the childbearing years (Figure 12-5) and depend on both biological factors, such as nutrition, and socioeconomic factors, such as the role of women in the society, marriage age, and education. The sex ratio S_S is the fraction of births of each sex. These fractions are usually close to but not equal to 0.5. The sex ratio is also not constant over time: In societies where there is a preference for male offspring, technology now enables people to selectively abort female fetuses, reducing S_F. Female infanticide, which also occurs in a number of traditional societies, would be captured in the model by higher mortality rates for the youngest female cohort.

FIGURE 12-5
World average distribution of births by mothers' age, 1990–1995

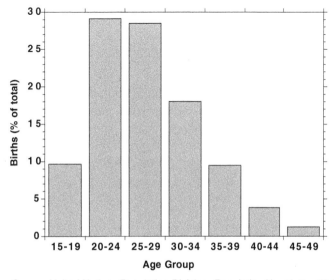

Source: United Nations Population Division, *Population Newsletter,* 59 (June 1995).

Over time people move through the aging chain. The process can be modeled with equations (12-1)–(12-3). Most standard demographic models, however, use a slightly different formulation. Many of these models use discrete time intervals equal in duration to the number of years per cohort, YPC(i). They further assume that the death rate within the cohort is constant and deduct the total number of deaths from the cohort population before moving the population from one cohort to the next:

$$M_S(i) = \text{Exit Rate}_S(i) * (SF_S(i)) \tag{12-11}$$

$$D_S(i) = \text{Exit Rate}_S(i) * (1 - SF_S(i)) \tag{12-12}$$

The total rate at which people leave each cohort (the exit rate) is divided into two flows: those who mature into the next cohort and those who die. The Survival Fraction, $SF_S(i)$, is the fraction maturing into the next cohort and $(1 - SF)$ is the fraction that died while in the cohort. The survival fractions are easily derived from life tables or survival distributions for the population.[1] The age-specific mortality rate (the probability of death per year or fractional death rate FDR) for a cohort with survival fraction SF is given by the rate of exponential decay that would leave the fraction SF remaining after YPC years, or $FDR_S(i) = -\ln(SF_S(i))/YPC(i)$. If the age-specific mortality rates FDR are known, then the survival fraction is given by

$$SF_S(i) = \exp(-FDR_S(i) * YPC(i)). \tag{12-13}$$

If the age-specific mortality rate for a 10-year cohort in a population were FDR = 0.01/year, then after 10 years the expected survival fraction would be 90.5%. The fraction surviving is greater than 90% because the number of deaths during each of the 10 years falls as the number surviving falls.

There are two common formulations for the exit rate. Standard demographic models assume discrete time intervals and constant death rates within them. This formulation can be modeled using a pipeline delay where the exit rate from each cohort is the total rate at which people enter the cohort (the sum of those maturing into the cohort plus any inmigration), delayed exactly YPC years:

$$\text{Exit Rate}_S(i) = \text{DELAYP}(M_S(i - 1) + I_S(i), YPC(i)) \tag{12-14}$$

where the DELAYP function represents a pipeline delay with a delay time here equal to the number of years per cohort YPC(i).[2]

The pipeline delay is appropriate for situations where the population resides in each cohort for exactly the same period. Often, however, the residence times for individuals are not identical and the death rate varies continuously. At the other end of the spectrum, such situations can be modeled by a first-order delay:

$$\text{Exit Rate}_S(i) = P_S(i)/YPC(i) \tag{12-15}$$

---

[1]Keyfitz (1977/1985), Lee (1992), and Rosner (1995) describe the mathematics of life tables and survival analysis in discrete and continuous time.

[2]The DELAYP function is defined as follows: Outflow = DELAYP(Inflow, Delay Time) implies Outflow(t) = Inflow(t − Delay Time). See section 11.2.3.

The first-order exit rate implies that while the *average* residence time in each cohort is YPC(i) years, some people leave earlier and some leave later. The formulation in equation (12-15) is appropriate in situations where the cohorts are defined not by age but by membership in a category such as the level in an organization where some are promoted to the next level faster than others (see the model in section 12.1.6). As the number of cohorts increases and the number of years per cohort falls, the behavior of an aging chain consisting of n first-order cohorts converges to the pipeline formulation.

Two Formulations for Mortality

The formulation for the transition (maturation) rate in equations (12-2) and (12-3) differs from the formulation in equations (12-11)–(12-15). In the former case, the maturation rate is given by the size of the cohort divided by the average residence time, while at the same time, deaths occur at a rate proportional to the size of the cohort. In the latter case, deaths are considered to occur at the time members exit the cohort. The two formulations are similar but not identical. Consider first equations (12-11)–(12-15), and for simplicity assume the exit rate is given by the first-order formulation in (12-15). The total outflow from each cohort P(i) is M(i) + D(i) = Exit Rate(i) = P(i)/YPC(i). The interpretation is that each member of the cohort P(i) resides in the cohort for an average of YPC(i) periods. On exiting the cohort, the total outflow is divided into those maturing into the next cohort and those exiting the aging chain. This formulation is common in discrete time demographic models based on the pipeline delay where each cohort represents a particular age range and by definition individuals remain in the cohort for a fixed period of time. It is also a reasonable behavioral model for some organizational structures, such as consulting firms, law practices, or universities where there is an up-or-out promotion policy. In these settings, the stocks in the aging chain represent categories such as associate, senior associate and partner. At every rank, each professional is reviewed after a certain number of years and is either promoted or terminated (section 12.1.6).

In the case of equations (12-2) and (12-3), the total outflow from each cohort is M(i) + D(i) = P(i)/YPC + P(i) * FDR(i). This situation represents a case where deaths continuously remove people from each cohort. The average residence time is less than YPC periods. This formulation is appropriate, for example, in the *Urban Dynamics* model where the population is divided into different socioeconomic categories: workers move from one category to another with a certain probability but also continuously face a chance of death.[3]

Which formulation is better? Returning to the case of a law firm or university with an up-or-out promotion policy, both processes clearly play a role. After an average period of, say, 8 years, all faculty are reviewed and either given tenure or terminated, as in equation (12-11), but there is also a certain rate at which untenured faculty leave the university prior to their mandatory review date, as in equation (12-2). If necessary for the purpose of the model both formulations can be combined. Usually, however, the data are not good enough to allow these processes to

---

[3]Statistically, the distribution of the population in each cohort is exponential in the case of equation (12-11); in the case of equation (12-2), the distribution is hyperexponential.

be estimated separately, and the differences between the two formulations are small enough that it is not necessary to include both.

12.1.4   Aging Chains and Population Inertia

An important consequence of the age structure of the human population is the enormous momentum of population growth. World population crossed the 6 billion mark in 1999 with a growth rate of about 78 million people per year (1.3%/year). If fertility around the world *instantly* fell to replacement rates, meaning that on average people have just enough children to replace themselves, the world population would *not* immediately stabilize. Instead, population would continue to grow. In the United Nations' 1998 instant replacement scenario, world population would reach 8.4 billion in 2050 and 9.5 billion in 2150, a rise of more than a third. As long as total births exceed total deaths, the population continues to grow. Though each cohort just replaces itself, those now in the childbearing years are much greater in number than those in the older cohorts. Because world population has been growing, more and more people will reach the prime childbearing years for the next 30 years or so, increasing total births still more. Long human lifetimes and the long delay between birth and reproduction mean population is very slow to adjust to changes in fertility and mortality.

The tremendous inertia caused by the age structure of a population is further illustrated by the experience of China. Fertility in China fell *below* the replacement level beginning in the late 1970s as the result of the government's one-child policy and other changes in social and economic circumstances (see Figure 12-4). Nevertheless, the population of China grew from 985 million in 1980 to 1.237 billion in 1998, more than 25% in less than 20 years. And although total fertility is expected to remain below replacement, the population is projected to grow to a peak of more than 1.4 billion by 2030 before gradually declining. Figure 12-6 compares China's

FIGURE 12-6
Projected age
structure of China
compared to
current distribution

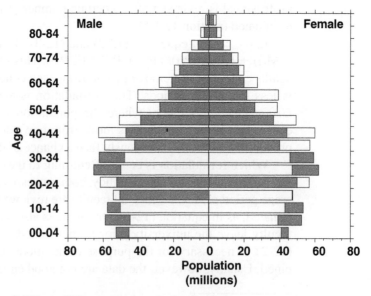

Solid bars, 1998; open bars, projection for 2010.

Source: US Census Bureau.

age structure in 1998 to the age structure the US Census Bureau projects for 2010. While the population under age 35 remains about the same or even falls, the population over age 35 increases dramatically, simply because those aging into each cohort over age 35 are much more numerous than those aging out.

These examples show that a population can continue to grow even though total fertility rates are below replacement and can shrink even when fertility is greater than replacement. Variations in fertility (more generally, in the rate of addition or removal from the cohorts) can induce variations in the age structure of a population that can cause its behavior to differ significantly from a model in which all ages are lumped into a single stock.

12.1.5   System Dynamics in Action: World Population and Economic Development

Most demographic models, such as the projections of the US Census Bureau and United Nations, assume total fertility, births, mortality, and migration are exogenous and calculate the resulting age distributions and total populations. These models are essential tools for businesses and government agencies seeking to understand demographic trends over the short term, for purposes such as forecasting school age populations or the number of people entering the workforce or becoming eligible for Social Security.

Over longer time horizons births and life expectancy should not be treated as exogenous inputs. Factors such as nutrition, access to health care, the material standard of living, pollution, and crowding all depend on the size and wealth of the population, creating a huge number of feedbacks. Nevertheless, virtually all demographic models including those of the UN cut all these loops. Official projections assume recent trends toward lower fertility will continue, until total fertility falls enough to bring world population to eventual equilibrium. The UN's 1998 medium fertility scenario, for example, assumes replacement fertility is achieved worldwide in 2055, leading to an equilibrium population of about 11 billion.

Forrester, in *World Dynamics* (1971b), and then Meadows et al. (1972, 1974) developed the first integrated models of world population, the global economy, natural resources, and the physical environment. These models were designed to investigate the effects of population and economic growth as human activity approaches the carrying capacity of the earth. Forrester's model represented world population as a single stock. Meadows et al. elaborated and expanded Forrester's model, disaggregating world population into four cohorts (ages 0–14, 15–44, 45–64, and 65 and over). Meadows showed the four-level aging chain behaved quite well and provided sufficient precision when applied to world population where many different populations are aggregated together and there is considerable measurement error and uncertainty about parameters. Wang and Sterman (1985), applying the Meadows population sector to the population of China, used a 66 cohort model (one per year up to age 65 and one for those over 65).

Meadows et al. sought to model the *demographic transition*. The demographic transition describes the pattern of change in population growth rates as nations industrialize. In traditional societies prior to economic development, both crude birth and death rates (births and deaths per thousand people) tended to be high and variable. Average life expectancy was comparatively low, and women bore many children to ensure that a few would survive to adulthood and support their parents in their old age. Population growth was slow.

According to the theory of the demographic transition, life expectancy rises sharply with the arrival of industrialization and the introduction of modern sanitation, public health systems, and medical care. Death rates fall. Birth rates eventually fall as well. Higher life expectancy and lower infant mortality mean more children survive to adulthood, so women do not need to bear as many to achieve their desired family size. Further, desired family size tends to fall as the cost of child rearing rises and as the contribution of children to the economic welfare of the family declines. Costs of child rearing rise and contributions fall in industrial societies because children enter the labor force much later than in traditional agricultural societies and must be supported by their parents for much longer and at higher cost. The decline in birth rates, however, is very slow, since norms for family size, marriage age, and other determinants of fertility are strongly embedded in traditional culture, religious norms, and other social structures; fertility is not the result of economic utility maximization by couples.

Consequently, during the demographic transition population growth accelerates sharply, since death rates fall while birth rates remain high. Eventually, according to the theory, fertility falls into rough balance with mortality, and population approaches equilibrium. Figure 12-7 shows crude birth and death rates (births or deaths per thousand people per year) for Sweden and Egypt. In Sweden, where industrialization began early, death rates fell slowly, so population growth was modest during the transition, taking 120 years to double (1875 to 1995). In Egypt, however, as in many later-developing nations, the death rate fell sharply after World War II. The birth rate, while starting to fall, remains high, so population growth is very rapid; population doubled in just 30 years (1966–1996). By the late 1990s the transition was far from over.

The Meadows et al. global model included a fully endogenous theory of the demographic transition. To do so, they not only had to represent the age structure of the world population but also had to model total fertility and changes in life expectancy. After testing 1-, 4-, and 15- cohort models, they determined that the 4-cohort model provided precision consistent with the state of the data at that time while preserving model parsimony and helping to keep the model within the capacity of the computers available in the early 1970s. In general, mortality rates for each cohort in the model should be specified as a separate function of food, health care, material standard of living, and other factors. In practice, the data were not available to do so. Meadows et al. (1974) showed that the distribution of mortality by age is reasonably stable as life expectancy varies. Mortality follows a U-shaped curve: mortality rates are highest for the very young, lowest for people between about age 10 and 30, and gradually rise as people age.[4] As average life expectancy

---

[4]Mortality rates change with age and with social and economic conditions. Debate continues about the maximum human life span and the effects of industrialization and economic development on life expectancy. For an overview, see Vaupel et al. (1998).

FIGURE 12-7
The demographic
transition

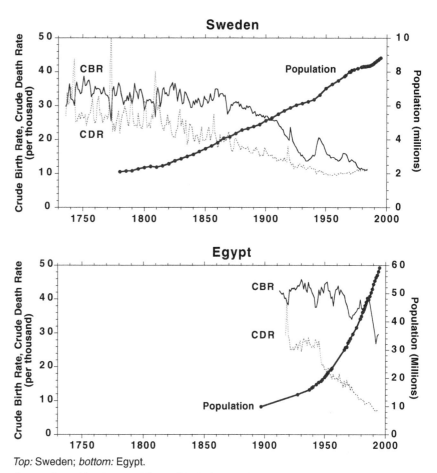

Top: Sweden; *bottom:* Egypt.

Source: Dana Meadows and Diana Wright (personal communication).

rises and falls, the distribution is shifted downward or upward, respectively, but retains roughly the same shape. Assuming the shape of the distribution remains stable, age-specific mortality can then be modeled as

$$\text{FDR}_S(i) = \text{RFDR}_S(i) f_{S,i}(\text{LE}) \tag{12-16}$$

where RFDR(i) is the reference fractional death rate for each cohort and LE is average life expectancy at birth. The reference death rate is the fractional death rate in a reference year, corresponding to the year in which life expectancy takes the value that yields $f_{S,i}(\text{LE}) = 1$. The downward-sloping age-specific functions $f_{S,i}$ relate mortality to average life expectancy and can be estimated from actuarial or demographic data.

Meadows et al. modeled aggregate life expectancy as depending on four factors: food per capita, health care services per capita, exposure to persistent pollution, and crowding. These factors interacted multiplicatively to capture important interdependencies and to ensure robustness under extreme conditions (e.g., life expectancy must approach zero as food per capita approaches zero; life expectancy remains finite even if all conditions are extremely favorable). The determinants of life expectancy were endogenously generated by other sectors of the model, closing the feedback loops in the model.

Total fertility TF depends on both a biological maximum and desired family size of each woman in the population. The effectiveness of fertility control determines whether total fertility is closer to the biological maximum or the desired level. A variety of socioeconomic factors determined desired family size and fertility control effectiveness in the model. The model also represented delays in the adjustment of cultural norms for desired family size to new social and economic conditions. The model did an excellent job replicating the aggregate historical data and provided the first fully endogenous model of the demographic transition, a model that, after more than 25 years, can still be fruitfully used to explore different policies relating to population growth.

By treating interactions of population, economic growth, and the environment in a fully endogenous fashion, Forrester and Meadows et al. provided the first integrated global models to study the dynamics of growth in a finite world. In the Meadows et al. model the demographic transition is not automatic, as assumed in models with exogenous fertility and mortality. If resources and environmental capacity are sufficient and if economic growth and development are distributed fairly so even the poorest people have sufficient food, clean water, access to health care, and decent jobs, then the world as a whole moves through the demographic transition and population eventually stabilizes with high life expectancy and low fertility. But if global economic development passes the have-nots by or if pollution, resource shortages, crowding, insufficient food, or other problems caused by growth limit development, then the economic and social conditions that eventually lead to low birth rates will not arise and the demographic transition will not occur. Population and economic growth continue, overshooting the earth's carrying capacity. Environmental degradation reduces the carrying capacity and mortality rises. Within a hundred years, population and economic output fall.

Meadows et al. (1972, pp. 23-24) summarized the conclusions of the study as follows:

1. If the present growth trends in world population, industrialization, pollution, food production, and resource depletion continue unchanged, the limits to growth on this planet will be reached sometime within the next one hundred years. The most probable result will be a rather sudden and uncontrollable decline in both population and industrial capacity.

2. It is possible to alter these growth trends and to establish a condition of ecological and economic stability that is sustainable far into the future. The state of global equilibrium could be designed so that the basic material needs of each person on earth are satisfied and each person has an equal opportunity to realize his [or her] individual human potential.

3. If the world's people decide to strive for this second outcome rather than the first, the sooner they begin working to attain it, the greater will be their chances of success.

Both Forrester and the Meadows team sought to encourage conversation and debate about growth and stimulate further scientific research leading to improved models, improved understanding, and, ultimately, actions and policies to prevent overshoot and collapse and encourage what is now known as sustainable development. Toward that end, the authors took pains to point out the limitations of their models. Meadows et al. (1972, p. 21) wrote "The model we have constructed is, like every other model, imperfect, oversimplified, and unfinished." They published complete documentation for both world models so anyone with access to a computer could replicate, revise, and modify the models. Many did so, and dozens of critiques and extensions were published.

The model triggered a vigorous and sometimes acrimonious public debate over growth, a debate still reverberating today. It also stimulated many other global modeling efforts, spanning a wide range of methods, model boundaries, time horizons, and ideological perspectives. Global models with narrow model boundaries, where many of the feedbacks are cut, tend to reach more optimistic conclusions. Models that capture the many feedbacks between human activity and the environment tend to reach conclusions consistent with the original study.[5]

12.1.6   Case Study: Growth and the Age Structure of Organizations

Variations in birth rates have dramatic effects on the age structure of the world population. But growth also has profound implications on the age structure and maturation of organizations. Most organizations contain various *promotion chains* that represent the different levels in the hierarchy within each department or function. Consulting firms, for example, typically include levels such as associate, senior associate, partner, and director.

The growth rate of the organization has a dramatic impact on the balance among the levels in a promotion chain hierarchy and on opportunities for advancement. Figure 12-8 shows the promotion chain for a typical American university. There are three faculty ranks: assistant professors, associate professors, and full professors. Most US universities operate an up-or-out promotion system: faculty are reviewed after a certain period and those not promoted are terminated. Faculty reaching full professor are granted life tenure and remain active until they choose to retire (mandatory retirement in the US was abolished in the 1980s). While occasionally senior faculty are hired from other institutions, the vast majority of hiring is at the new assistant professor level.

The up-or-out policy means the transition and departure rates are formulated as follows (the assistant professor flows are shown; flows for associates are analogous):

Assistant Promotion Rate = Assistant Review Rate * Assistant Promotion Fraction

(12-17)

---

[5]Forrester (1971b) provides the first global model with fully endogenous population and carrying capacity. Meadows et al. (1974) provides full documentation for the model, called WORLD3. Meadows et al. (1972) provides a nontechnical discussion of the assumptions and results of the study. Meadows, Meadows, and Randers (1992) updates the study and model and is the best starting point for those wishing to dig more deeply into these issues. Other global models and the science of global modeling itself are critiqued in Meadows, Richardson, and Bruckmann (1982).

FIGURE 12-8   Promotion chain for a typical American university

Hiring of associate and senior faculty is omitted. The Review Rate for the assistant and associate ranks is first-order; the Full Professor Retirement Rate is formulated as a third-order delay of the Associate Promotion Rate. Adapted from a model developed by David Peterson and used with permission.

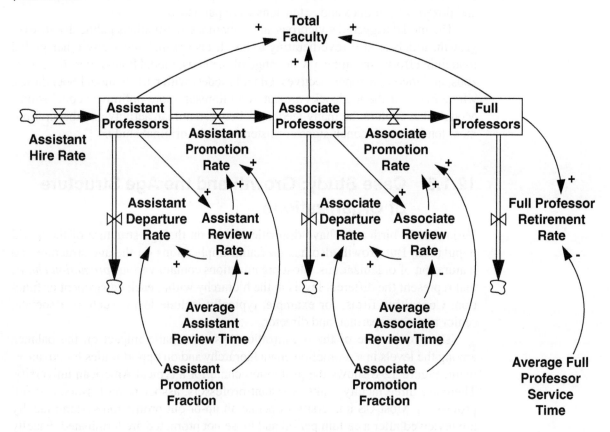

$$\text{Assistant Departure Rate} = \text{Assistant Review Rate} * (1 - \text{Assistant Promotion Fraction}) \tag{12-18}$$

$$\text{Assistant Review Rate} = \frac{\text{Assistant Professors}}{\text{Average Assistant Review Time}} \tag{12-19[6]}$$

Note that the assistant and associate ranks are formulated as first-order processes even though contracts are nominally all for the same specified duration, suggesting a pipeline delay. In practice some faculty are promoted earlier than others due to the varying incidence of personal and professional leaves of absence and to

---

[6]The formulation assumes all faculty remain at the institution until they come up for review. In fact, there is some probability faculty leave prior to their promotion reviews. A more realistic model would incorporate both effects, combining the two formulations for mortality. In practice the data to estimate the parameters are not available, and the error introduced by aggregating those who leave prior to mandatory review with those who leave after a negative promotion review is negligible.

differing market pressures (a hot young professor may be promoted early to re-spond to outside offers from competing universities). These sources of variation imply that the formulation for the exit rate should allow some mixing. The first-order formulation assumes perfect mixing, certainly an overestimate of the variance in promotion times. However, given the relatively short residence times in each junior rank, the first-order formulation is not likely to introduce significant error.

In contrast, the long tenure of full professors means a first-order formulation, with its assumption that the youngest full professors are just as likely to retire as the oldest, is clearly inappropriate. In the model analyzed here, a third-order for-mulation for the retirement rate is used.

Given these assumptions, what is the distribution of faculty across the three ranks? The distribution depends on the average residence times of faculty in each rank and the average promotion fractions, as well as the growth rate of the faculty. In most universities, faculty remain assistant professors for an average of 3 years before promotion to associate; associate professors are typically reviewed for pro-motion to full professor after an average of 5 years. Full professors typically serve about 35 years before retiring at an average age of about 70. Though promotion fractions vary over time, typical values might be roughly 50% at each rank. The equilibrium distribution given these parameters is readily calculated (by Little's Law) to be about 21% assistant, 18% associate, and 61% full professors, a distri-bution top-heavy with senior faculty. Where the total size of the faculty is fixed, junior faculty can only be granted tenure when a full professor retires or dies.

However, few universities are in equilibrium. Most US universities went through a period of rapid growth from the end of World War II through the early 1970s, when the baby boom generation graduated from college. Since then, due to declining college age populations and stagnating federal support for higher educa-tion, growth slowed or even became negative. Figure 12-9 shows the distribution of faculty ranks at MIT since 1930 (the pattern of behavior at other leading uni-versities is similar, though the timing and magnitudes differ). Until 1970 total fac-ulty grew rapidly, averaging 3.7%/year. The age distribution was skewed toward the younger ranks, with full professors averaging only about 36% of the faculty from 1930 through 1969. In the 1970s growth essentially ceased, and the total fac-ulty remained roughly constant through the mid 1990s. Hiring of new assistant professors fell, and the age distribution began to approach equilibrium. By 1993 assistant professors made up less than 18% of the faculty while more than 63% were full professors—very close to the equilibrium distribution.

The consequences of this transition were profound. During the era of rapid growth, the high proportion of young, untenured faculty gave the institution tremendous flexibility and brought large numbers of talented people into the orga-nization. Because there were relatively few senior faculty, the chances of promo-tion to tenure were good. Relatively young professors soon found themselves promoted to senior positions such as department chair or dean. After growth stopped and most departments began to fill with tenured faculty, flexibility de-clined. It became more difficult to get tenure. In some particularly top-heavy de-partments (those that had grown the fastest during the boom years), there was almost no turnover, little hiring, and few junior faculty. As similar dynamics played out at universities throughout the country, many doctoral candidates found they

FIGURE 12-9
Distribution of
faculty ranks, MIT

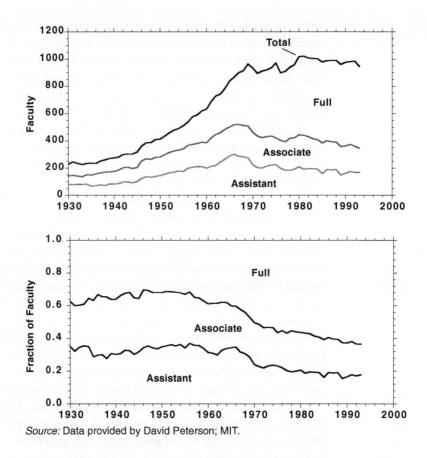

Source: Data provided by David Peterson; MIT.

could not get tenure-track positions after graduation; as a result, many were forced to accept low-paying postdoctoral positions or leave academia altogether.

The aging of the faculty also had important financial implications. Because senior faculty are generally paid more than junior faculty, the aging of the faculty increased the total cost of the faculty faster than the rise in salaries for each rank. For individual faculty salaries to keep pace with inflation, the total payroll had to grow even faster. The resulting cost escalation helped push tuition up much faster than inflation during the 1970s and 80s. Ultimately, in part to relieve budget pressure and in part to make room for fresh blood, MIT, along with other top research universities where the same dynamics had played out, implemented an early retirement incentive program to speed the outflow from the ranks of the full professors.

The discussion above suggests that the hiring rate and promotion fractions are not constant; they change as conditions in the university evolve. The data on faculty at each rank can be used to estimate what the hiring and promotion fractions must have been and therefore test these hypotheses, given the average time spent in each rank. Figure 12-10 shows the results. No attempt has been made to specify the hiring and promotion fractions every year; instead, these parameters are set to round numbers at widely spaced intervals. Despite the low resolution with which the inputs are estimated, the model closely tracks the actual data. The excellent fit shows that the assumption of first-order exit rates from each junior cohort (and

FIGURE 12-10

Simulated faculty age structure, MIT

Top: Simulated vs. actual faculty by rank using imputed hiring rate and promotion fractions. *Middle:* Imputed assistant professor hiring rate. *Bottom:* Imputed promotion fractions.

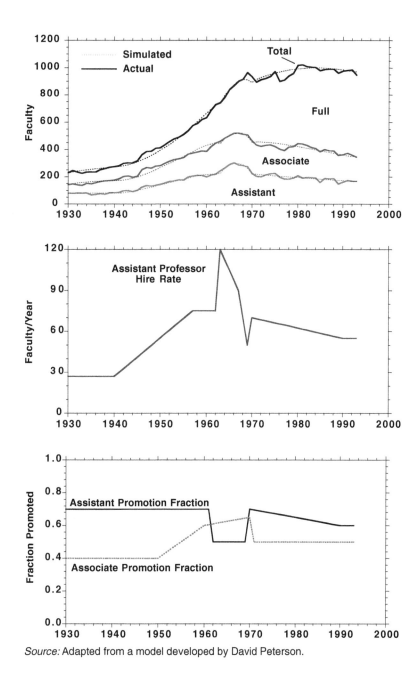

Source: Adapted from a model developed by David Peterson.

a third-order retirement rate) is acceptable and there is little need for further disaggregation of the age structure within each faculty rank. Consistent with the discussion above, promotion fractions and hiring were high during the years of rapid growth and fell when growth stopped. Note also the large burst of hiring in the 1960s, which dramatically increased the ranks of the assistant professors. As intuition would suggest, the hiring surge was followed by several years of depressed hiring. More interestingly, the increasing number of faculty in the upper ranks compared to the number of slots available meant that the probability of promotion from assistant to associate after the hiring boom in the 1960s fell significantly.

In reality, the size and composition of the faculty, and more generally any workforce, feeds back through the market and other channels to affect the hiring rate, promotion fractions, and other parameters. While important insights can be gleaned from the promotion chain model with exogenous hiring, promotion, and departure parameters, these structures are most useful when embedded in a full model of the organization. The promotion fraction, for example, can be modeled endogenously as depending on the normal span of control and the balance of senior to junior personnel. It is also affected by the financial health of the organization. The rate at which employees voluntarily quit to take better opportunities elsewhere depends on their perceptions of the chances for promotion. These chances, in turn, depend on the age structure and hence the growth rate of the organization. Since the most talented employees will have the most attractive outside opportunities, a slowdown in growth, by reducing promotion opportunities, can systematically drain an organization of its best talent. Loss of talent can then feed back to worsen performance in the marketplace, further eroding growth in a vicious cycle (see section 10.4.9).

The faculty example shows how an aging chain can be used to model the demographic structure of organizations and illustrates the dramatic impact of growth on the distribution of personnel among the different ranks. The steady state age structure of any population depends on its growth rate. Changes in population growth rates at the community, national, or global levels change the ratios of children to people of childbearing age and of the working age population to retirees, significantly changing the social, economic, and political pressures faced by the population. Similarly, as the growth rate of a business or other organization changes, it necessarily goes through large changes in the ratio of senior to junior employees, in promotion opportunities, and in the average cost of the workforce. These changes arise solely as a function of changes in the growth rate of the organization. Since the growth of all organizations must slow as they become larger, the age distribution tends to become top heavy, posing great challenges to organizations seeking to renew themselves while preserving attractive career paths for those already in the hierarchy. The larger and faster the decline in growth rates, the worse this problem becomes. The fastest-growing, most successful organizations always face the greatest challenge when their growth inevitably slows.

12.1.7   Promotion Chains and the Learning Curve

Consider again the two-level promotion chain for rookie and experienced workers (shown in Figure 12-11). This structure is very useful in modeling the effect of training and assimilation delays on the productivity of a workforce as the growth rate varies.[7] The promotion chain provides a simple and effective way to model the learning curve for new employees. To keep the model simple, assume it is not

---

[7] Oliva (1996) applies the promotion chain structure to service quality in a major UK bank; Abdel-Hamid and Madnick (1991) apply it to software product development; Packer (1964) applies it to a model of high-tech growth firms.

FIGURE 12-11 A two-level promotion chain to explore worker training

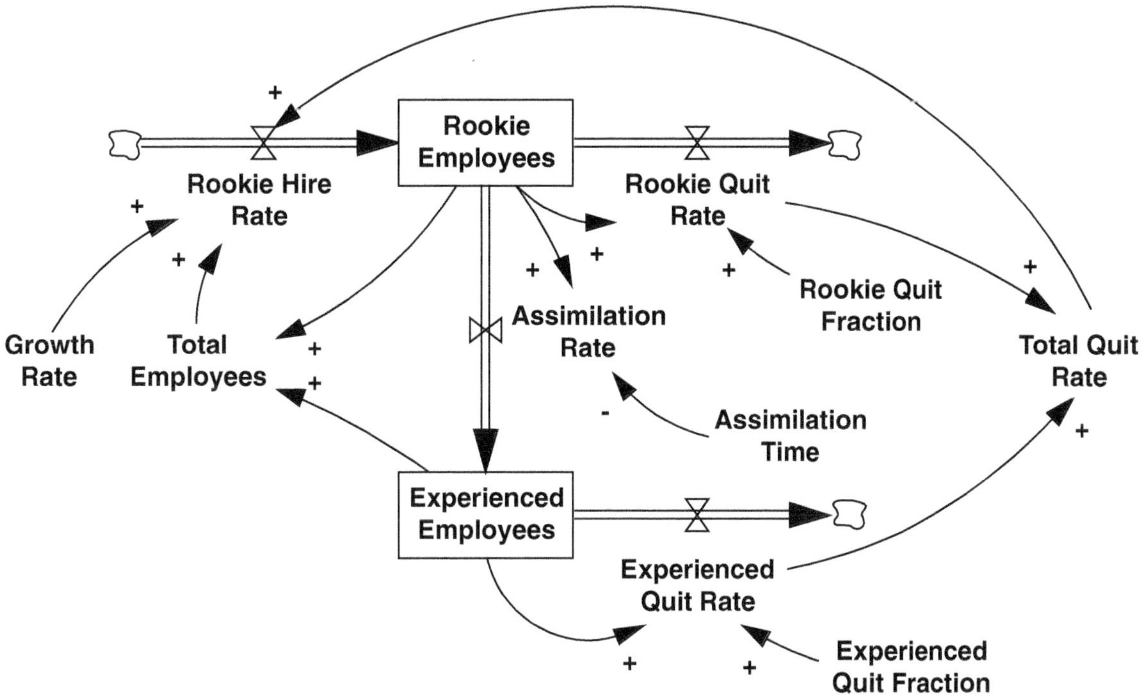

possible to hire experienced people. In some industries, experienced hires are unavailable or too expensive. More commonly, becoming fully productive depends on the accumulation of situation-specific knowledge, so prior experience is of limited benefit.

The productivity of rookie employees is typically a fraction of that for fully experienced employees. The total potential output of the workforce is then given by

$$\frac{\text{Potential}}{\text{Output}} = \frac{\text{Experienced}}{\text{Productivity}} * \left(\frac{\text{Rookie Productivity}}{\text{Fraction}} * \frac{\text{Rookie}}{\text{Employees}} + \frac{\text{Experienced}}{\text{Employees}} \right) \quad (12\text{-}20)$$

Average productivity is

Average Productivity = Potential Output/Total Employees (12-21)

Formulating the flows as first-order processes yields

Rookie Quit Rate = Rookie Employees * Rookie Quit Fraction (12-22)

Experienced Quit Rate
   = Experienced Employees * Experienced Quit Fraction (12-23)

Assimilation Rate = Rookie Employees/Assimilation Time (12-24)

For purposes of testing, assume the workforce grows at a constant exponential rate. To do so, the firm must replace all those who quit and continuously add a fraction of the current total workforce:

Rookie Hire Rate = Total Quit Rate + Growth Rate * Total Employees (12-25)

Total Quit Rate = Rookie Quit Rate + Experienced Quit Rate (12-26)

What is the equilibrium distribution of employees between the rookie and experienced categories? The equilibrium conditions, when the growth rate is zero, are

Rookie Hire Rate = Rookie Quit Rate + Assimilation Rate   (12-27)

Assimilation Rate = Experienced Quit Rate   (12-28)

Given the definitions of the flows, the equilibrium number of rookies is easily shown to be:

$$\text{Rookie Employees}_{eq} = \frac{\text{Experienced}}{\text{Employees}} * \left(\frac{\text{Experienced}}{\text{Quit Fraction}} * \frac{\text{Assimilation}}{\text{Time}} \right) \quad (12\text{-}29)$$

which means the equilibrium Rookie Fraction is

$$\text{Rookie Fraction}_{eq} = \frac{\dfrac{\text{Experienced}}{\text{Quit Fraction}} * \dfrac{\text{Assimilation}}{\text{Time}}}{\left(1 + \dfrac{\text{Experienced}}{\text{Quit Fraction}} * \dfrac{\text{Assimilation}}{\text{Time}} \right)} \quad (12\text{-}30)$$

Equilibrium average productivity, as a fraction of the productivity of experienced employees, is

$$\frac{\substack{\text{Average} \\ \text{Productivity}_{eq}}}{\substack{\text{Experienced} \\ \text{Productivity}}} = \frac{\left(1 + \dfrac{\text{Rookie Productivity}}{\text{Fraction}} * \dfrac{\text{Experienced}}{\text{Quit Fraction}} * \dfrac{\text{Assimilation}}{\text{Time}} \right)}{\left(1 + \dfrac{\text{Experienced}}{\text{Quit Fraction}} * \dfrac{\text{Assimilation}}{\text{Time}} \right)} \quad (12\text{-}31)$$

As intuition would suggest, the lower the relative productivity of rookies, the lower the equilibrium productivity of the workforce will be, unless rookies are assimilated instantly. Longer assimilation times mean there must be more rookies in training, and higher experienced quit rates mean more rookies must be hired to offset those experienced workers who leave. Both effects lower equilibrium productivity.

Note that the rookie quit fraction has no impact (in this model). Because rookies are represented as a single cohort, those who quit are immediately replaced, so rookie quits cancel out in the net rate of change of rookies. Of course, higher rookie quit rates would increase the load on and cost of the firm's human resource organization. In a more realistic model where the rookie population is disaggregated into more than one cohort, or where filling vacancies takes time, the equilibrium would depend on the quit rates of the intermediate stocks.

As an example, suppose the assimilation delay is 100 weeks (about 2 years) and experienced employees remain with the firm for an average of 10 years (the experienced quit fraction is 0.002/week). Assume rookie employees quit at a higher rate of 0.01/week as some of the rookies wash out or decide the job doesn't suit them. Assume the average rookie is only 25% as productive as experienced workers. The equilibrium rookie fraction is then ⅙, and equilibrium productivity is 0.875 of the experienced level.[8]

---

[8]Without loss of generality, the productivity of experienced employees can be defined as 1, allowing potential output to be measured in full-time equivalent (FTE) experienced personnel.

The assimilation delay and rookie productivity fraction jointly determine the learning curve for new employees. Imagine hiring a group of rookie employees when there are no experienced employees. Productivity initially will be the rookie productivity fraction and ultimately will be 100% of the experienced level. Because the assimilation process is first-order, productivity must approach 100% exponentially with a time constant equal to the assimilation delay. If the evidence suggested the learning curve for new employees was not first-order, the promotion chain could be disaggregated further to yield the appropriate pattern of productivity adjustment.

What happens if the firm is growing? Figure 12-12 shows a simulation in which the workforce grows at an exponential rate of 50%/year (0.01/week), starting in week 5. The initial number of experienced workers is 1000; therefore, the initial hiring rate is 100 per year. The hiring rate immediately rises above the total quit rate, and the workforce begins to grow at 50%/year. Because all new hires are inexperienced, the rookie fraction immediately begins to rise and average productivity immediately begins to fall. In the steady state, the rookie fraction rises to 54% and productivity falls to just 59% of the experienced level. Though every employee goes through a learning process that boosts individual productivity from 0.25 to 1, the shift in the age distribution caused by growth lowers average productivity. Consequently, given the parameters in the example, potential output (shown on the graph in FTE experienced employees) barely changes for the first 6 months even though the total workforce and payroll begin to rise immediately. After a year, potential output has risen by only 36% compared to the 50% growth in total employees.[9]

12.1.8   Mentoring and On-the-Job Training

In the model so far rookie employees gain experience automatically and without cost. In reality, on-the-job (OTJ) training often requires the help and mentoring of experienced employees. Inexperienced workers reduce the time experienced people can devote to their own jobs by asking questions and by causing experienced people to work at a slower rate. Modifying the model to account for the impact of mentoring requires reformulating potential output as depending on the number of Effective Experienced Employees:

$$\frac{\text{Potential}}{\text{Output}} = \frac{\text{Experienced}}{\text{Productivity}} * \left(\frac{\text{Rookie}}{\text{Productivity}} * \frac{\text{Rookie}}{\text{Employees}} + \frac{\text{Effective}}{\text{Experienced}} \right) \quad (12\text{-}32)$$

where the effective number of experienced employees is the total number less the time devoted to training the inexperienced employees. That is,

$$\frac{\text{Effective Experienced}}{\text{Employees}} = \text{MAX}\left(0, \frac{\text{Experienced}}{\text{Employees}} - \frac{\text{Time Spent}}{\text{Training Rookies}} \right) \quad (12\text{-}33)$$

---

[9]Note that the pattern of adjustment of productivity and the rookie fraction is exponential, a direct consequence of the first-order assimilation rate. A more realistic model disaggregating the rookie population into more cohorts would show an even slower increase in potential output.

FIGURE 12-12

Response of two-level promotion chain to growth

The total work-force grows at 50%/year starting in week 5. The Rookie Productivity Fraction = 0.25, The Assimilation Delay = 100 weeks, the Experienced Quit Fraction = 0.002/week, and the Rookie Quit Fraction = 0.01/week.

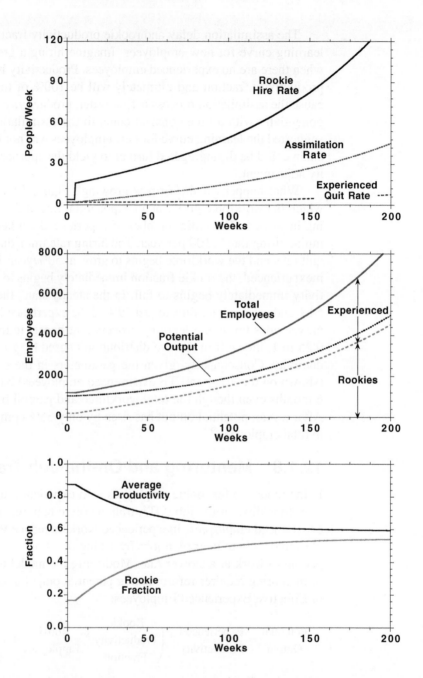

$$\frac{\text{Time Spent}}{\text{Training Rookies}} = \text{Rookies} * \frac{\text{Fraction of Experienced Time}}{\text{Required for Training}} \qquad (12\text{-}34)$$

Each rookie consumes an amount of experienced worker time equal to the Fraction of Experienced Time Required for Training. Under extreme circumstances, the number of rookies might be so high, or their training demands might be so great, that the time remaining for experienced workers to actually do their jobs may fall to zero.[10]

Mentoring has only a small impact on the equilibrium productivity of the workforce. Equilibrium productivity for the case of mentoring by experienced workers is easily found to be

$$
\frac{\text{Average Productivity}_{eq}}{\text{Experienced Productivity}} = \frac{\left[1 + \left(\begin{array}{c} \text{Rookie} \\ \text{Productivity} \\ \text{Fraction} \end{array} - \begin{array}{c} \text{Fraction of} \\ \text{Experienced} \\ \text{Time Required} \\ \text{for Training} \end{array} \right) * \begin{array}{c} \text{Experienced} \\ \text{Quit} \\ \text{Fraction} \end{array} * \begin{array}{c} \text{Assimilation} \\ \text{Time} \end{array} \right]}{\left(1 + \begin{array}{c} \text{Experienced} \\ \text{Quit Fraction} \end{array} * \begin{array}{c} \text{Assimilation} \\ \text{Time} \end{array} \right)}
$$

(12-35)

With the parameters in the example above and assuming a rather high value of 0.5 for the fraction of an experienced employee's time consumed in training each rookie, productivity in equilibrium falls to 79% of the experienced level, compared to 87.5% in the case with no mentoring by experienced workers.

While mentoring has only a modest effect on equilibrium productivity, the impact on productivity and potential output when the workforce is growing is dramatic. Figure 12-13 shows the effect of mentoring in the same scenario as Figure 12-12. In the simulation, each rookie requires mentoring by the equivalent of 0.5 experienced people. The rookie and experienced employee stocks follow the same trajectory, but now, as the rookie fraction rises, the total time spent training rookies grows, and the time experienced workers can contribute to production drops. Given the parameters, productivity falls to a steady state value of 0.32, compared to 0.59 in the case with no mentoring, a drop of 46%. In the short run, growth actually causes potential output to fall. Potential output drops to a minimum 9% below the initial equilibrium and only reaches the initial level after 67 weeks.

CHALLENGE

The Interactions of Training Delays and Growth

The training model in section 12.1.8 shows that the higher the growth rate of the labor force, the lower the steady state experience level and productivity will be.

1.   Using the model with OTJ training, derive an algebraic expression for steady state productivity as a function of the growth rate and other parameters, including the fractional quit rate of experienced employees, the assimilation time, the relative productivity of rookies, and the fraction of experienced time required for training.

---

[10]More realistically, production pressures will slash the time devoted to training rookies below what is required long before the number of effective experienced employees falls to zero. Therefore to be fully robust, the assimilation time should be reformulated as a variable, rising when total mentoring time is less than required.

FIGURE 12-13

Adding mentoring by experienced employees

Conditions are the same as in Figure 12-12, with each rookie requiring 0.5 FTE experienced workers for OTJ training.

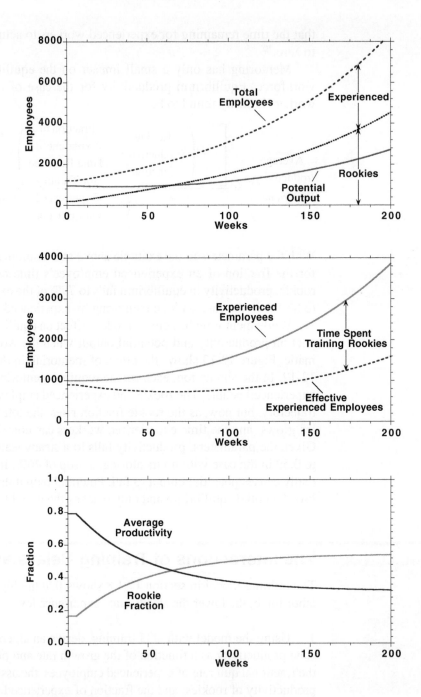

How do these parameters affect the loss of productivity in the steady state as growth rates increase?

2.   The current model assumes the learning and assimilation process is first-order. In many high-skill settings this is unrealistic. Modify the model to include a third-order training and assimilation process (with the same fractional rookie quit rate and average assimilation time). Assume rookie employees are equally likely to quit in each of the three trainee categories you create. Be sure you modify the total hiring rate to replace all employees who quit. Each category of rookies still requires

the same time from experienced employees through OTJ training and mentoring. Initially, assume the productivity of all rookies is still 0.25 that of experienced workers. Repeat the test shown in Figure 12-13 (in which growth at a constant fractional rate begins from an initial equilibrium). Next, assume more realistically that rookie productivity is 0, 0.25, and 0.50 that of experienced workers for rookies in stages 1, 2, and 3 of their training, respectively. What is the impact of a higher-order training process on the transition from stability to growth?

3.   In many organizations, such as consulting firms, law firms, and other professional service organizations, experienced employees not only mentor junior employees on the job but also participate in recruiting new employees. Modify the model to capture the loss of productive time due to recruiting effort. Assume recruiting each new employee requires a certain fraction of an experienced person's time (rookies do not participate in recruiting). Pay careful attention to the units of measure. Select parameters to represent the case of consulting firms recruiting MBA students. The leading consulting firms invest heavily in the recruiting process. Besides on-campus recruiting events and interviews, promising candidates face second, third, and often fourth rounds of interviews at company sites during which they meet many senior members of the firm. Senior people must then devote further time to discussion and selection of the finalists. Further, many candidates must be interviewed for each one ultimately hired. Make the selectivity of the firm an explicit parameter in your model, measured as a dimensionless ratio of the number of offers made per candidate considered. Also introduce a parameter reflecting the fraction of offers accepted (the yield). Using your estimate of these parameters and the time senior employees invest in recruiting each candidate, run the model for various growth rates. What is the impact of recruiting effort on average productivity and effective production capacity? What is the impact of growth on the time senior people have available for revenue-generating activities? What would happen if the firm tried to cut back on the time senior people invest in recruiting? What would happen if the firm became less selective? If the reputation of the firm declined, eroding their yield? Develop a causal diagram showing how potential output and average productivity might feed back to affect the firm's ability to deliver high-quality results to their clients and to recruit and retain the best candidates. What are the implications for the growth strategy of a firm?

12.2   COFLOWS: MODELING THE ATTRIBUTES OF A STOCK

The stock and flow networks developed thus far keep track of the number of items in a stock and flow chain. The size of a stock indicates how much material is in the stock but does not indicate anything about other attributes of the items. A model of a firm might include stocks for different kinds of employees, but these stocks only indicate how many employees there are and do not reveal how productive they are, their average age, their training level, or other characteristics that might be important for the model purpose. Often it is necessary to keep track of attributes such as the skill and experience of workers, the productivity of machine tools, the defects embodied in designs moving through a product development process, or the book value of a firm's inventory. Coflow structures are used to keep track of the attributes of various items as they travel through the stock and flow structure of a system.

As an example, consider a model designed to help a company understand how fast new technology can be deployed and how it changes the number of workers it needs. Each machine the company buys from equipment suppliers requires a certain number of workers to operate it. Over time, as technology improves, the production process grows more automated and fewer workers are required. The company is interested in knowing how quickly the new, labor-saving machines will be deployed and how fast their total labor requirements will change.

A simple model of the situation begins with the firm's stock of capital plant and equipment, such as machine tools. The capital stock is augmented by capital acquisitions and reduced by capital discards. For simplicity, assume the discard process is first-order:

Capital Stock   (12-36)
    = INTEGRAL(Capital Acquisition – Capital Discards, Capital Stock(t_0))

Capital Acquisition = Exogenous   (12-37)

Capital Discards = Capital Stock/Average Life of Capital   (12-38)

The total labor requirements of the firm are equal to the product of the number of machines in the firm's plants and the average labor requirements of each machine:

Total Labor Requirements = Capital Stock * Average Labor Requirements   (12-39)

How should average labor requirements be modeled? Obviously, if a new type of machine requiring only half as many workers suddenly became available, the average labor requirements would change only slowly as the new machines gradually replaced the existing, labor intensive machines. There is a delay between a change in the labor requirements available in new machines and the adjustment of average labor requirements. Similar considerations apply to other factor inputs to the production process such as the energy requirements of the machines, their total productivity, and so on. It is tempting to model the adjustment of these factor requirements as a simple delay where the adjustment time is equal to the average life of capital:

Average Labor Requirements   (12-40)
    = SMOOTH(Labor Requirements of New Capital, Average Life of Capital)

However, the delay formulation is fundamentally flawed and will lead to significant errors if the capital stock is not in equilibrium. An extreme conditions test exposes the defect in the proposed formulation. Suppose the firm's equipment suppliers introduce a new type of machine that requires only half as many workers. Now suppose that at the same time, the firm stops buying new equipment altogether (say, because of a recession). The firm then must continue to use the existing, inefficient machines, and there is no change in the average labor required per machine. However, the delay in equation (12-40) will continue to adjust average labor requirements to the new, low level of the new machines even though the firm isn't buying any. The firm's required labor force falls as the delay magically converts the old machines to the productivity of new ones without the need for any investment or expenditure. The rate of change in average labor requirements depends

FIGURE 12-14   Coflow to track the labor requirements embodied in a firm's capital stock

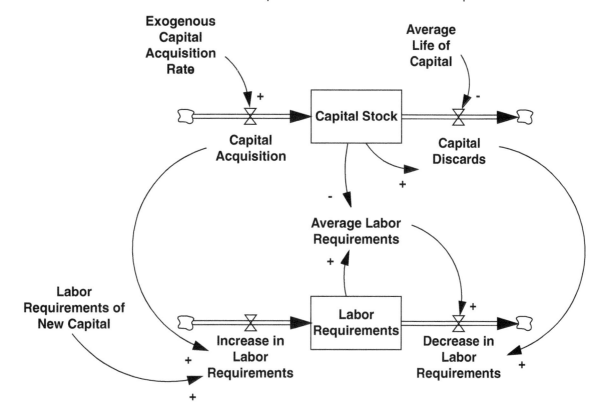

on the rates at which new machines are added to and old machines are discarded from the capital stock. The labor requirements of the firm's equipment are embodied in the machines themselves. Modeling the adjustment as a delay divorces changes in this attribute of the stock of machines from changes in the stock itself. To model such a situation requires the modeler to keep track of the labor requirements of every machine added and every machine discarded. Coflow structures allow you to do this.[11]

Figure 12-14 shows the structure for the capital stock model described above. The coflow is a stock and flow structure exactly mirroring the main stock and flow structure. The coflow tracks the labor requirements embodied in the capital stock as new machines are acquired and old ones are discarded.

The stock of capital is augmented by acquisitions and reduced by discards. For now, the capital stock is treated as a first-order process. The capital acquisition rate is exogenous.

---

[11]Some try to save the delay formulation in equation (12-40) by making the average life of capital a variable or representing the adjustment process with a higher-order delay, but the critique remains valid. In fact, there are many models in the literature where the adjustment of input requirements is modeled as a delay, including a wide range of econometric models of energy demand in which the energy intensity of the economy (BTU/$ of output or BTU/year per $ of capital stock) are assumed to adjust to changes in price with some form of distributed lag, independent of the characteristics, size, or turnover of the capital stocks consuming that energy.

The total labor required to operate the company's existing machines is given by the Labor Requirements stock. Every time a new machine is added to the capital stock, the total labor requirements of the firm rise by the labor required for that machine. Every time a machine is discarded, the total labor requirements decrease by the average labor requirements of the discarded machine:

$$\text{Increase in Labor Requirements} = \text{Capital Acquisition} * \text{Labor Requirements of New Capital} \tag{12-41}$$

For example, if each machine requires, say, 100 workers, then a purchase of 10 machines increases total labor requirements by 1000 people. Since the discard process is assumed to be first-order, the probability of discard is independent of acquisition time and of any other attributes of the capital stock. Therefore the average labor requirements of the discarded machines equal the average for the entire existing stock. That average is given by the total labor requirements divided by the total capital stock. Thus

$$\text{Decrease in Labor Requirements} = \text{Capital Discards} * \text{Average Labor Requirements} \tag{12-42}$$

$$\text{Average Labor Requirements} = \text{Labor Requirements/Capital Stock} \tag{12-43}$$

$$\begin{array}{l} \text{Labor} \\ \text{Requirements} \end{array} = \text{INTEGRAL}\left(\begin{array}{c} \text{Increase in} \\ \text{Labor} \\ \text{Requirements} \end{array} - \begin{array}{c} \text{Decrease in} \\ \text{Labor} \\ \text{Requirements,} \end{array} \begin{array}{c} \text{Labor} \\ \text{Requirements}(t_0) \end{array} \right)$$
$$\tag{12-44}$$

If each existing machine required 200 workers, then the discard of 10 machines would reduce labor requirements by 2000 people. The replacement of these machines with new ones requiring 100 instead of 200 people reduces total labor requirements by 1000 people.

The coflow structure has some obvious and desirable properties. In equilibrium, capital acquisitions and discards are equal, and, if the labor requirements of new capital are constant, the labor requirements of the firm will also be constant, since the loss of jobs associated with discarded machines just offsets the increase in labor required to operate new ones. The equilibrium labor requirements of the firm will be Labor Requirements of New Capital * Capital Stock.

Changes in capital acquisition or discards have no effect on average labor requirements as long as the labor requirements of new capital remain constant. Now imagine that a new labor-saving technology suddenly becomes available so that all new machines require only half as much labor. Figure 12-15 shows the response of labor requirements over time. As expected given the first-order structure for the capital discard rate, the labor requirements of the firm approach the new equilibrium exponentially, with a time constant given by the average life of capital.

If the response of the system is simple exponential decay, why is a coflow formulation needed? The behavior shown in Figure 12-15 is exactly what would be generated by the delay formulation in equation (12-40). Why not simply model the adjustment of average labor requirements with the simple and easy to explain delay? The answer is that the response of average labor requirements depends on the

FIGURE 12-15

Response of labor requirements to a sudden 50% reduction in the labor required to operate new machines

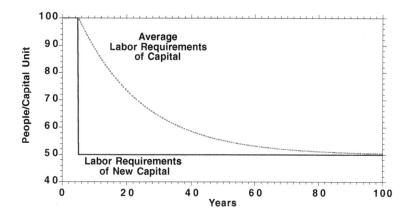

FIGURE 12-16

Changes in the growth rate of the stock alter the adjustment of its attributes

In all cases the labor requirements of new capital drop by 50% in year 5. The responses in situations of 10%/year growth in capital acquisitions, equilibrium, and 10%/year decline in acquisitions are shown.

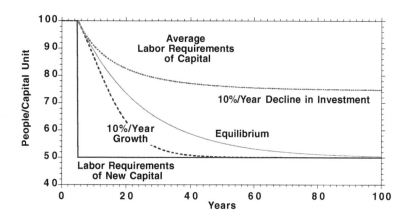

behavior of the acquisition and discard rates. In equilibrium, with constant acquisitions, discards, and capital stock, the coflow behaves exactly like a first-order delay with a time constant equal to the average life of capital. But now suppose the firm is growing, so the acquisition rate rises exponentially at some rate. New machines will be added ever faster, quickly diluting the contribution of old machines to average requirements. Or suppose the discard rate varies with the utilization of the firm's capital stock. In these cases the rate at which old machines are replaced varies over time and so too will the evolution of average labor requirements. Figure 12-16 compares the behavior of labor requirements in stationary equilibrium to the cases where the acquisition rate grows at 10%/year and where it shrinks at 10%/year.

When the capital stock is growing, new machines are added at an ever-greater rate, so new machines with low labor requirements quickly dominate the stock of capital. Average labor requirements fall to the new level after only about 35 years, compared to more than 90 years in the equilibrium case. Even more interesting, in the case where the firm is shrinking at 10%/year, new investment quickly becomes so small that average labor requirements never reach the new level. After about 20 years, new investment is negligible and the firm is stuck with a capital stock consisting primarily of old, inefficient machines. By explicitly modeling the attributes of the items flowing into and out of the stock of machines, the coflow model correctly tracks changes in the total and average labor requirements of the firm.

The labor requirements example can be generalized to any attribute of any stock. Figure 12-17 shows the generic structure for a coflow for the case where there is a single inflow and single outflow to the stock.

In general, the main stock may have any number of inflows and outflows, say m inflows and n outflows:

$$\text{Stock} = \text{INTEGRAL}(\text{Total Inflow} - \text{Total Outflow}, \text{Stock}(t_0)) \tag{12-45}$$

$$\text{Total Inflow} = \sum_{i=1}^{m} \text{Inflow}(i) \tag{12-46}$$

$$\text{Total Outflow} = \sum_{j=1}^{n} \text{Outflow}(j) \tag{12-47}$$

$$\text{Outflow}(j) = \text{Stock/Average Residence Time for Outflow}(j) \tag{12-48}$$

Each outflow is modeled as a first-order process with an outflow-specific time constant. The time constants can be variables.

The coflow structure tracking the attribute of the stock exactly mirrors the structure of the main stock. Each unit flowing into the stock adds a certain number of attribute units to the total attribute stock. In the example, each new machine adds a certain number of workers to the total number required to operate all the machines. The number of attribute units added per stock unit, denoted the marginal attribute per unit, can differ for each inflow. For example, the firm might buy different types of machines, each requiring a different number of workers to operate it. Thus,

$$\begin{matrix} \text{Total} \\ \text{Attribute} \end{matrix} = \text{INTEGRAL}\left(\begin{matrix} \text{Total} & & \text{Total} \\ \text{Increase in} & - & \text{Decrease in} \\ \text{Attribute} & & \text{Attribute,} \end{matrix} \quad \begin{matrix} \text{Total} \\ \text{Attribute}(t_0) \end{matrix} \right) \tag{12-49}$$

$$\text{Total Increase in Attribute} = \sum_{i=1}^{m} \text{Marginal Attribute per Unit}(i) * \text{Inflow}(i) \tag{12-50}$$

Similarly, for each outflow from the main stock there is a corresponding drain from the total attribute stock. Each unit leaving the stock removes the average attribute per unit. The average attribute per unit is simply the total attribute level divided by the total number of units in the stock:

$$\text{Total Decrease in Attribute} = \sum_{j=1}^{n} \text{Average Attribute per Unit} * \text{Outflow}(j) \tag{12-51}$$

$$\text{Average Attribute per Unit} = \text{Total Attribute/Stock} \tag{12-52}$$

You can model as many different attributes as you desire, each captured by a separate coflow structure. For example, one coflow might represent the labor requirements of the firm's capital stock, another might represent the energy requirements, a third might represent the productivity of the machines, a fourth might represent the defect rate in the output of the machines, and so on.

FIGURE 12-17   Generic coflow structure

Each unit flowing into the stock adds the marginal attribute to the total attribute. Each unit flowing out removes the average attribute. In general, there can be any number of inflows and outflows to the main stock, each with a corresponding flow into the total attribute stock.

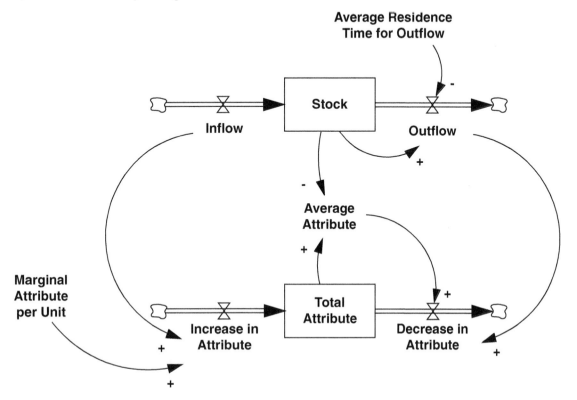

CHALLENGE

Coflows

Build and test coflows for the following situations:

1. A firm maintains a make-to-order system for its products. The order backlog is increased by the order rate; it is decreased as orders are fulfilled and by order cancellations. Assume the average delivery delay (the order fulfillment time) is constant and equal to 4 weeks. Assume also that on average 1% of orders are cancelled per week. Customers pay on delivery but pay the price in effect at the time their order was placed, even if price has changed in the meantime. Create a coflow that tracks the average value of the orders in the backlog and determines the average price associated with the orders filled. Also formulate the equation for the firm's revenues (assume revenue is recorded when orders are fulfilled).

2. Consider the national debt of the United States. The debt is increased by borrowing and decreased by repayment. The repayment rate depends on the average maturity of the outstanding debt. The mix of Treasury notes, bills, and bonds determines average maturity. Assume the average maturity is 5 years. The Treasury rolls over maturing debt and must issue new debt to finance any fiscal deficit. The

deficit is expenditure less revenue. Assume revenue is constant at $900 billion (900e9) per year. Expenditures consist of interest on the debt and spending on government programs. Assume program spending is also constant at $900 billion/year. These values are approximately correct for 1988; in 1988 the outstanding debt was about $2.5 trillion (2.5e12). Interest payments are equal to the product of the outstanding debt and the average interest rate. First, formulate the average interest rate as an exogenous constant initially equal to 7%/year. Next, replicate the model and formulate the average interest rate by using a coflow. The coflow formulation accounts for the fact that the average interest rate depends on the interest rates at which each bill, bond, or note was issued, even if interest rates on new debt have changed.

Verify that when the interest rates in both formulations are constant and equal, the behavior of the two formulations is identical. Next, compare the behavior of the two formulations for the case where the interest rate falls from 7%/year to 3%/year in 1992. What difference does the coflow structure make, and why? To approximate a continuous compounding situation, use a small time step, such as $\frac{1}{16}$ year, for the simulations.

3.   It is often important to model the average age of items in a stock or the average date at which the items entered the stock. As an example, consider a model of a firm's labor force. Assume a single stock of labor, increased by a hiring rate and decreased by an attrition rate. Assume that the attrition rate is first-order and that employees stay with the firm an average of 10 years. Formulate a coflow that keeps track of the average age of the people in the labor force and also the average date at which they joined the firm. Hint: You only need one coflow stock to calculate both the average date at which each person was hired and the average age of the workers. Formulate the model so it begins in equilibrium. Demonstrate that in equilibrium the average age of the workers is equal to the average tenure in the job plus their average age at the time of hiring. Explore the response of the average age of the employees to various test inputs such as changes in the average time people stay with the firm, step and pulse changes in the hiring and attrition rate, and exponential growth or decline in the hiring rate. Note: This challenge requires that you introduce a flow that alters the attribute stock for which there is no corresponding flow into or out of the stock of labor. Such a structure is called a nonconserved coflow because the attribute stock can change even when there is no inflow to or outflow from the main stock.

4.   The capital stock of a firm is increased by acquisitions and decreased by discards. The average lifetime of each unit of capital is 20 years. Given the cost of each unit of capital create a coflow that models the book value of the firm's capital stock. Assume the value of each unit of capital is reduced by depreciation with an average depreciation life of capital that can differ from the actual lifetime.

12.2.1   Coflows with Nonconserved Flows

The coflow structures described so far represent the attributes of the stock as conserved quantities: the only way the total attribute stock can change is through the inflow or outflow of a unit from the main stock. Often, however, the attributes associated with a stock can change without any change in the main stock. Retrofits can change the labor or energy requirements of a firm's capital stock even though the firm doesn't buy or discard any new equipment. The value of a firm's inventory can be written down to reflect changes in its market value though the physical inventory itself doesn't change. In these cases, the total attribute associated with a stock is not conserved and the coflow structure includes additional flows into or out of the total attribute stock, flows for which there are no corresponding flows affecting the main stock.

Suppose as in Figure 12-18 you are modeling a firm's labor force, which is increased by hiring and decreased by attrition. For the purposes of this example, the hiring rate and fractional attrition rate are assumed to be exogenous, though in

FIGURE 12-18   Example of a nonconserved coflow: tracking the experience of a labor force

New employees bring a certain amount of experience with them; departing employees take their experience with them. In addition, experience increases with tenure in the job and declines as workers forget or as changes in the process make existing experience obsolete.

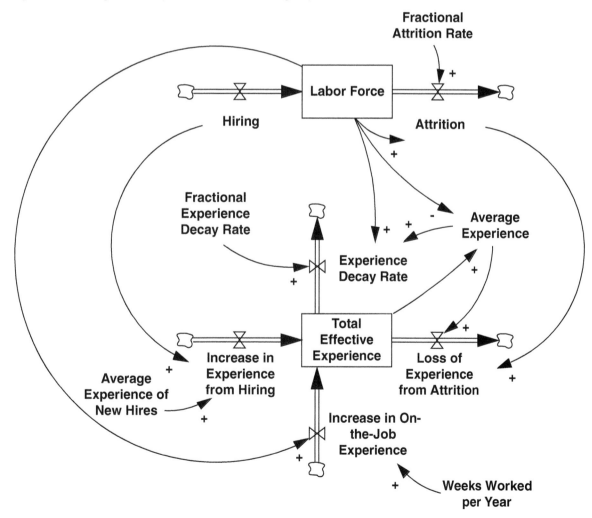

general they will be modeled as endogenous variables. The coflow measures the average and total effective experience of the workforce. The stock Total Effective Experience (measured in person-weeks) is the effective number of weeks of service each employee has, summed over all employees. Each employee hired brings a certain amount of effective experience. Employees leaving the labor force take the average experience with them:

$$\text{Average Experience} = \text{Total Effective Experience/Labor Force} \qquad (12\text{-}53)$$

$$\begin{aligned} \text{Total Effective Experience} = \text{INTEGRAL}(&\text{Increase in Experience from Hiring} \\ &+ \text{Increase in On-the-Job Experience} - \text{Loss of Experience from Attrition} \\ &- \text{Experience Decay Rate, Total Effective Experience}(t_0)) \qquad (12\text{-}54) \end{aligned}$$

$$\begin{aligned} &\text{Increase in Experience from Hiring} \\ &\quad = \text{Average Experience of New Hires} * \text{Hiring} \qquad (12\text{-}55) \end{aligned}$$

$$\text{Loss of Experience from Attrition} = \text{Average Experience} * \text{Attrition} \qquad (12\text{-}56)$$

Each employee accrues additional experience at the rate of 1 week per week worked. In this example, the unit of time for the simulation is the year, while average experience is measured in weeks. The increase in total effective experience is the number of weeks each person works per year summed over the entire labor force:[12]

$$\begin{aligned} &\text{Increase in On-the-Job Experience} \\ &\quad = \text{Labor Force} * \text{Weeks Worked per Year} \qquad (12\text{-}57) \end{aligned}$$

Finally, effective experience also decays as people forget relevant knowledge and as changes in the production process render experience obsolete. The fractional decay rate is assumed constant here but might vary with changes in organizational structure or process technology. The total loss of experience is the average loss of experience summed over the entire workforce:

$$\begin{aligned} &\text{Experience Decay Rate} \\ &\quad = \text{Labor Force} * \text{Average Experience} * \text{Fractional Experience Decay Rate} \qquad (12\text{-}58) \end{aligned}$$

Because the stock of effective experience is modified by the nonconserved flows of experience accrual and decay, the equilibrium experience of the average worker will not, in general, equal the average experience of new hires, as it would in a conserved coflow. In equilibrium the sum of the four rates affecting total effective experience must be zero. When hiring and attrition are also equal so the labor force is in equilibrium with Hiring = Attrition = Labor * Fractional Attrition Rate, a little algebra reveals equilibrium average experience to be:

---

[12]Time in the simulation of this example is measured in years, while experience is measured in weeks. There is no contradiction. Consider the units of equation (12-57). The increase in OTJ experience is measured in person-weeks/year, determined by the labor force and the average number of weeks worked each year. If time was measured in months, the Increase in On-the-Job Experience would be the labor force multiplied by the number of weeks worked per month. Note that the number of weeks worked per year will not in general equal 52. Vacation time, sick leave, strikes, or promotion to management all reduce the rate at which employees accumulate experience.

$$\text{Average} \atop \text{Experience}_{eq} = \frac{\left({\text{Fractional} \atop \text{Attrition Rate}} * {\text{Average Experience} \atop \text{of New Hires}} + {\text{Weeks Worked} \atop \text{per Year}} \right)}{\left({\text{Fractional} \atop \text{Attrition Rate}} + {\text{Fractional Experience} \atop \text{Decay Rate}} \right)} \quad (12\text{-}59)$$

Equilibrium total effective experience is simply the equilibrium average experience multiplied by the labor force. As expected, the greater the experience of new hires or the number of weeks worked per year, the greater the equilibrium average experience will be; the faster experience decays or people leave the organization, the lower the equilibrium experience level will be.

Greater average experience should translate into greater productivity, higher quality, and lower cost. Learning curve theory provides a variety of models to relate experience with a process to attributes such as productivity, quality, or cost. One common formulation for the learning curve posits that productivity rises by a given percentage with each doubling of relevant experience:

$$\text{Productivity} = \text{Reference Productivity} * \left(\frac{\text{Average Experience}}{\text{Reference Experience}} \right)^c \quad (12\text{-}60)$$

where Reference Productivity is the productivity attained at the Reference Experience level. The exponent c determines the strength of the learning curve and is equal to

$$c = \log_2(1 + f_p) = \ln(1 + f_p)/\ln(2) \quad (12\text{-}61)$$

where f_p is the fractional change in productivity per doubling of effective experience (see the challenge in section 9.3.4; see also Zangwill and Kantor (1998) for a derivation of this and other forms of learning curves).[13] Similar equations could be used to model other attributes such as defect rates, mean time between failure for equipment, or unit costs as they depend on average experience.

Most learning curve models measure experience by cumulative production, a stock that can never decline, so productivity can only rise over time. The model developed here represents productivity as dependent on the average effective experience of each worker. Modeling learning as a process embedded in the human capital of the firm means that, in contrast to standard learning curve models, it is possible for the productivity of the firm to fall. Productivity can fall if there is a sudden exodus of experienced workers or if there is a large change in technology that makes past experience obsolete.

Clearly, while worker-specific knowledge is important, learning is also embedded in longer-lived stocks such as plant and equipment, organizational routines, and other infrastructure. Cumulative experience with these infrastructures could be modeled in the same way as effective labor experience, though these other elements of firm infrastructure would have smaller attrition rates than labor. Modeling productivity as dependent on experience embedded in a firm's resources and infrastructure, rather than as a function of some disembodied notion of cumulative

---

[13]The fractional change in productivity f_p will be positive because greater experience boosts productivity. If the learning curve is used to represent unit costs, f_p will be negative since increasing experience reduces costs.

experience, allows productivity, cost, or quality to decay should experience decline, while standard learning curves cannot exhibit such behavior.

There is some evidence for such "forgetting curves." Sturm (1993) estimated learning curve models for the nuclear power industry in Europe, the former Soviet Union, and the USA. Surprisingly, the number and duration of unplanned outages actually increased with cumulative operating experience in about half the countries, primarily in the nations of the former Soviet bloc. Sturm hypothesized that knowledge of safe operations fell in the wake of the political and economic turmoil caused by the fall of the command economies. Henderson and Clark (1990) found that dominant firms in the semiconductor equipment industry often lost their leadership position when there was a change in product architecture that rendered the cumulative experience of the firm obsolete, eroding their competitive advantage and allowing younger and less experienced firms to overtake them. Accurately modeling such situations requires nonconserved coflows.

CHALLENGE

The Dynamics of Experience and Learning

Explore the behavior of the workforce experience model in Figure 12-18. Assume the hiring rate equals the attrition rate (plus exogenous test inputs) so that those leaving are instantly replaced. Assume the initial labor force is 1000 people. Consider the following parameters:

Fractional Attrition Rate = 0.20/year.

Average Experience of New Hires = 10 weeks.

Average Weeks Worked per Year = 50 weeks/year.

Fractional Experience Decay Rate = 0.10 /year.

Fractional Improvement in Productivity per Doubling of Experience (f_p) = 0.30.

Reference Productivity = 100 (widgets/week)/person.

Reference Experience = 10 weeks.

1. What is the equilibrium average experience per worker? Explore how the equilibrium varies with the values of the different parameters.

2. What happens to average experience and productivity if no one ever leaves the firm? Generate the learning curve for a cohort of new employees by setting the initial labor force to a very small number (one), setting the Fractional Attrition Rate to zero, and then adding a large pulse of new employees (1000) at the start of the simulation. Without attrition, experienced employees never leave. Does effective experience rise indefinitely? Why/why not? What is the equilibrium (if it exists) for average experience and productivity?

3. Consider the response of average experience and productivity to changes in the various parameters (from an initial equilibrium). Assume employee turnover doubles. What is the impact on average experience and productivity and why?

4. From the original equilibrium, assume changes in the production process accelerate, so effective experience suddenly begins to decay at twice its original rate. What is the impact on average experience and productivity and why?

5. What is the behavior of average experience if the firm begins to grow? From the initial equilibrium described above, assume the hiring rate starts to grow exponentially at 30%/year. What is average experience in the steady state? How long does it take to reach the steady state? What is the impact on productivity? How does the behavior of the model compare to that of the rookie/experienced worker model in section 12.1.7?

12.2.2   Integrating Coflows and Aging Chains

The assumption that each unit leaving the main stock removes the average attribute per unit is clearly an approximation. In particular, the first-order structure for the decrease in the total attribute implicitly assumes that all items in the stock are perfectly mixed. As seen in chapter 11, the assumption of perfect mixing is often not appropriate: A better model requires higher-order delays or a high-order aging chain. The coflow structure for these cases will exactly mirror the stocks and flows in the higher-order delay or aging chain.

For example, Sterman (1980) developed a general model to capture the production function of a firm or economic system. Production depends on inputs of capital, labor, energy, and materials. These input requirements are embodied in the firm's capital stocks (as in the labor requirements example). However, econometric evidence and field study show that the distribution of discards from capital stocks is not first-order; for example, new machines and facilities are not nearly as likely to be scrapped as older units. The distribution is clearly higher-order. I therefore disaggregated the capital stock into an aging chain, with corresponding coflows. I further assumed that the labor, energy, and materials requirements of capital equipment were determined at the time construction starts (the energy requirements of a new office building can't be changed significantly after groundbreaking except by costly retrofit). The resulting vintaging structure and corresponding coflows for the embodied input requirements are shown in Figure 12-19. The number of vintages can be increased as needed to fit the data for the survival distribution of items in the main aging chain. In the simplified representation of the model shown in the figure, the construction delay is assumed to be first-order, while a third-order delay, with a corresponding third-order coflow structure for the factor requirements of capital under construction, would be more realistic. Likewise, capital is discarded only from the oldest vintage. If the data warrant it, it is easy to include a discard rate from each vintage. In that case the modeler must also include the reduction in the factor requirements of each vintage from discards, equal to the product of the factor intensity of each vintage and the discard rate from each vintage.

Finally, note that the model shown in the figure does not permit changes to the factor requirements of capital. This is known as a *putty-clay* model because factor requirements can be varied prior to investment, like putty, but once the firm

FIGURE 12-19 Vintaging structure for capital stock with coflow for embodied factor requirements

The coflow structure exactly mirrors the aging chain of the capital stock. One coflow structure is used for each factor input (Labor, Energy, Materials, etc.). In this model, retrofits are not allowed. For a more detailed model with retrofits, see Sterman (1980).

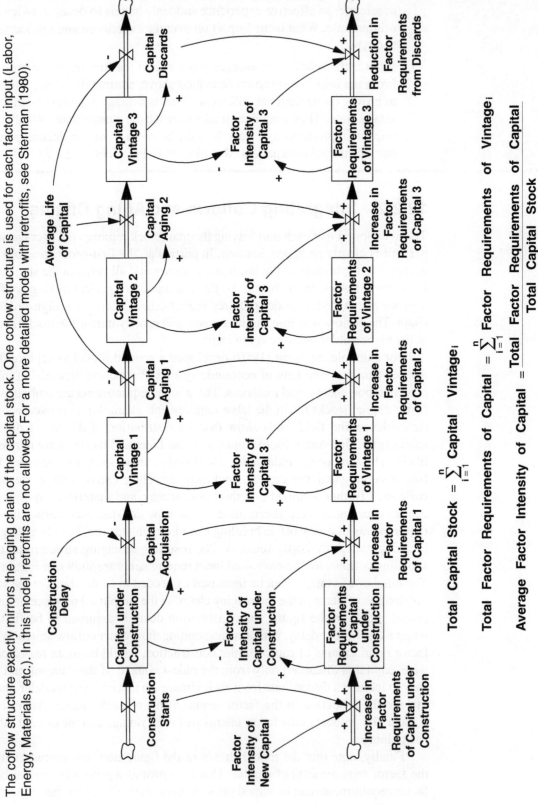

$$\text{Total Capital Stock} = \sum_{i=1}^{n} \text{Capital Vintage}_i$$

$$\text{Total Factor Requirements of Capital} = \sum_{i=1}^{n} \text{Factor Requirements of Vintage}_i$$

$$\text{Average Factor Intensity of Capital} = \frac{\text{Total Factor Requirements of Capital}}{\text{Total Capital Stock}}$$

commits to an investment, the embodied factor requirements are fixed until that capital is discarded (the factor proportions harden like clay fired in a kiln). In reality, retrofits, maintenance activity, and wear and tear can alter the factor requirements of existing capital. The model is easily modified to incorporate such changes in factor requirements (Sterman 1980 develops a general model of production including a variable retrofit potential which allows the modeler to specify any degree of variability in the factor requirements of existing capital, from pure putty-clay to full putty-putty).

CHALLENGE

Modeling Design Wins in the Semiconductor Industry

Section 11.6 describes the design win model that Symbios uses to forecast its revenues. The model consists of an aging chain that tracks the number of design wins for Symbios products as they move from the initial commitment of the customer to purchase a Symbios chip through design, prototyping, and production, finally generating a flow of revenues. At each stage there is some probability the project will be canceled by the customer. As shown in Figure 11-25, the model includes a coflow structure to keep track of the anticipated production volumes associated with each design win.

Build a model corresponding to the aging chain with coflow structure for design wins shown in Figure 11-25. Though the actual model represents each stage (designs under development, prototyping, and designs in production) as a high-order delay, for this challenge assume each transition rate is first-order. Include in your model a cancellation rate for each of the three stages (these flows are not shown in the figure). Ensure that your model is initialized in equilibrium. Select reasonable parameters.

Symbios, like the semiconductor industry in general, experiences large amplitude cycles in demand. Simulate these conditions by testing your model with a fluctuation in design wins and in the anticipated volume of new design wins. Assume a sine wave with an average period of about 4 years, and assume the anticipated volumes associated with each win are at a peak at the same time the design win rate peaks.

12.3 SUMMARY

Aging chains are widely used to capture the demographic structure of a population. The population need not be a living population but can be the stock of machines in a plant, the number of cars on the road, or the accounts receivable of a firm. Any time the rate at which items exit a stock and flow network depends on their age, that is, any time the mortality rates of individuals in the stock are age-dependent, an aging chain may be required to model the situation with sufficient accuracy for the purpose of the model.

Coflows are used to keep track of the attributes of the items in a stock and flow network. Attributes can include the age of the items, the productivity and experience of labor, the energy requirements or level of technology embedded in plant and equipment, the level of defects in product designs, or any property that is associated with the items in the stock and flow network. Coflows are useful in situations where the qualities of the items in a system's stocks, as well as their quantity, affect the decision making of the agents in the system.

13

Modeling Decision Making

A model for simulating dynamic system behavior requires formal policy descriptions to specify how individual decisions are to be made. Flows of information are continuously converted into decisions and actions. No plea about the inadequacy of our understanding of the decision-making processes can excuse us from estimating decision-making criteria. To omit a decision point is to deny its presence—a mistake of far greater magnitude than any errors in our best estimate of the process.

—Jay W. Forrester (1992, pp. 51–52)

Prior chapters discussed how to represent the physical and institutional structure of systems, for example, how to represent stock and flow networks and select the level of aggregation. This chapter explores the formulation of the decision rules representing the behavior of the agents. The decision rules in models must be formulated so that they are appropriate for the purpose of the model. They must be consistent with all available knowledge about the system, including numerical and qualitative data. The information used in the model of a decision process must be available to the actual decision makers. And all formulations must be robust so that no matter how extreme the inputs, the output behaves appropriately.

The chapter also presents common and important formulations that conform to these principles, the structure and behavior of each formulation, and examples. These formulations constitute a library of frequently used components from which you can assemble a larger model.

13.1 PRINCIPLES FOR MODELING DECISION MAKING

The structure of all models consists of two parts: assumptions about the physical and institutional environment on the one hand and assumptions about the decision processes of the agents who operate in those structures on the other. The physical and institutional structure of a model includes the model boundary and stock and flow structures of people, material, money, information, and so forth that characterize the system. For example, Forrester's (1969) *Urban Dynamics* sought to understand why America's large cities continued to decay despite massive amounts of aid and numerous renewal programs. To do so the model represented key physical components of a typical city including the size and quality of the housing stock, commercial structures, and other infrastructure; the size, skill mix, income, and other attributes of the population; the flows of people and capital into and out of the city; and other factors describing the physical and institutional setting.

The decision processes of the agents refer to the decision rules that determine the behavior of the actors in the system. The behavioral assumptions of a simulation model describe the way in which people respond to different situations. In the *Urban Dynamics* model, these included decision rules governing migration and construction. In another pioneering simulation study, Cyert and March (1963) found that department stores used a very simple decision rule to determine the floor price of goods. In essence, the rule was to mark up the wholesale cost of the items by a fixed percentage. If excess inventory piled up on the shelves, a sale was held and the markup was gradually reduced until the goods were sold. If sales goals were exceeded, then prices were raised. Prices were also adjusted toward those of competitors. The normal markup was determined by tradition—it adjusted very slowly toward the actual markup on the goods sold (taking account of any sales or other price changes). Cyert and March found that these rules for pricing reproduced the pricing decisions of the store managers quite well.[1]

Accurately portraying the physical and institutional structure of a system is relatively straightforward. In contrast, discovering and representing the decision rules of the actors is subtle and challenging. To be useful, simulation models must mimic the behavior of the real decision makers so that they respond appropriately, not only for conditions observed in the past but also for circumstances never yet encountered. You must specify a robust, realistic decision rule at every decision point in the model.

13.1.1   Decisions and Decision Rules

Modelers must make a sharp distinction between *decision rules* and the *decisions* they generate. Decision rules are the policies and protocols specifying how the decision maker processes available information. Decisions are the outcome of this process. In the department store example, the decision rule is the procedure for marking up wholesale costs and adjusting the markup based on inventory turnover,

---

[1]The agents in models need not be human decision makers. They might be other types of organisms (such as wolves and moose in a predator–prey model) or physical objects (such as the sun and planets in a model of the solar system). In these cases, the decision rules of the agents represent the ways in which the moose, wolves, and planets respond to the state of the systems in which they operate. In the solar system simulation, the modeler would specify the forces acting on each mass according to either Newtonian gravitation or general relativity; in the predator–prey case, the decision rules specifying the behavior of the moose and wolves (fertility, mortality, foraging and hunting behavior, migration, etc.) would be grounded in field and perhaps laboratory study.

FIGURE 13-1
Decision rules
govern the rates
of flow in
systems.

Decisions are the
result of applying
a decision rule
to the available
information cues.
The cues are
generated by the
physical and
institutional
structure of the
system, including
measurement
and reporting
processes.
The output of a
decision process
is the rate of
flow that alters
the state of the
system.

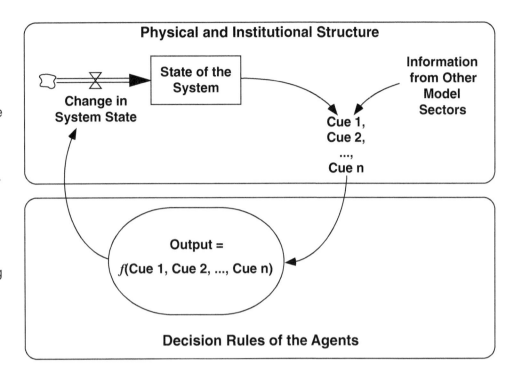

competitor prices, and so on. The decision rule leads to decisions such as pricing a particular item at, say, $9.95.

It is not sufficient to model a particular decision. Modelers must detect and represent "the guiding policy" that yields the stream of decisions (Forrester 1961). Every rate of flow in the stock and flow structure constitutes a decision point, and the modeler must specify precisely the decision rule determining the rate.

Every decision rule can be thought of as an information processing procedure (Figure 13-1). The inputs to the decision process are various types of information, or *cues*. The cues are then interpreted by the decision maker to yield the decision. The cues used to revise prices in the department store case include wholesale costs, inventory turnover, and competitor prices. Decision rules do not necessarily utilize all available or potentially relevant information. The mental models of the decision makers, along with organizational, political, personal, and other factors, influence the selection of cues from the set of available information. Those cues actually used in decision making are also not necessarily processed optimally. Cyert and March found that department store pricing decisions did not depend on interest rates or required rates of return, store overhead, trade-offs of holding costs against the risk of stockouts, estimates of the elasticity of demand, or any sophisticated strategic reasoning.

The decision rules in a model embody, explicitly or implicitly, assumptions about the degree of rationality of the decision makers and decision-making process. The spectrum of possibilities is broad. At one extreme, some models represent decision makers as simple automata, making decisions by rote from a small, fixed repertoire of choices, without any possibility of learning or adaptation. At the other extreme lies the theory of *rational expectations* which holds that decision makers understand the structure of the system perfectly, never make systematic errors in their inferences about its future behavior, and therefore always make optimal decisions (Muth 1961; Miller 1994; Lucas 1996). Nobel laureate Gary Becker (1976, p. 14) summarized the view of many economists when he said, "All human behavior can be viewed as involving participants who maximize their utility from a stable set of preferences and accumulate an optimal amount of information [to do so]." In this view, not only do people make optimal decisions given the information they have, but they also invest exactly the optimal time and effort in the decision process, ceasing their deliberations when the expected gain to further effort equals the cost.

13.1.2   Five Formulation Fundamentals

The nature of a decision process and its rationality are empirical questions that must be addressed by primary field study, experimental tests, and other means. Chapters 15 and 16 discuss different views on the rationality of decision making and its implications for models of human behavior. But whatever your view about the sophistication and rationality of decision making, your models must conform to certain basic principles (Table 13-1).

The Baker Criterion: The inputs to all decision rules in models must be restricted to information actually available to the real decision makers.   In 1973, during the US senate's hearings on the Watergate burglary, rumors flew about the possible involvement of President Nixon. Senator Howard Baker, a moderate Republican, kept asking the witnesses before the committee, "What did the President know, and when did he know it?" His point was that the president could not be implicated in the scandal if he was unaware of the actions of his staff and subordinates. When it later became clear from the White House tapes that Nixon had known early on and had participated in the cover up, Baker had the answer to his question and called for Nixon to resign.

You must also apply the Baker Criterion when formulating the decision rules in your models. You must ask, What do the decision makers know, and when do they know it? To properly mimic the behavior of a system, a model can use as an input to a decision only those sources of information actually available to and used by the decision makers in the real system. If managers of an oil company do not know the true size of the undiscovered resource in a basin, this information cannot be used in modeling their decision to drill. If ship owners do not know how many ships are under construction around the world, information about this supply line cannot be used as an input to their forecasts of future rates nor their decision to expand their fleets. If production planners do not know the current order rate, they cannot use that information to set the production schedule. The true size of the basin, the actual supply line of ships on order, and the actual order rate *will* be present in the model, but information about them *cannot* be used as inputs to the assumed decision rules if these data are not known by the actual decision makers.

The principle that decisions in models must be based on available information has three important corollaries.

First, no one knows with certainty what the future will bring. All beliefs and expectations about the future are based on experience. Modelers must represent the

TABLE 13-1
Principles for
modeling human
behavior

1.   **The Baker Criterion: The inputs to all decision rules in models must be restricted to information actually available to the real decision makers.**
• The future is not known to anyone. All expectations and beliefs about the future are based on historical information. Expectations and beliefs may therefore be incorrect.
• Actual conditions and perceived conditions differ due to measurement and reporting delays, and beliefs are not updated immediately on receipt of new information. Perceptions often differ from the actual situation.
• The outcomes of untried contingencies are not known. Expectations about "what if" situations that have never been experienced are based on situations that are known and may be wrong.
2.   **The decision rules of a model should conform to managerial practice.**
• All variables and relationships should have real world counterparts and meaning.
• The units of measure in all equations must balance without the use of arbitrary scaling factors.
• Decision making should not be assumed to conform to any prior theory but should be investigated firsthand.
3.   **Desired and actual conditions should be distinguished. Physical constraints to the realization of desired outcomes must be represented.**
• Desired and actual states should be distinguished.
• Desired and actual rates of change should be distinguished.
4.   **Decision rules should be robust under extreme conditions.**
5.   **Equilibrium should not be assumed. Equilibrium and stability may (or may not) emerge from the interaction of the elements of the system.**

way in which people form and update their beliefs from information about the current and past states of the system. You cannot assume that decision makers have perfect knowledge of future outcomes or that forecasts are correct, even on average.

Second, perceived and actual conditions often differ. Information about the current state of a system is generally not known; instead decisions are based on delayed, sampled, or averaged information. Plant managers may have some data about the order rate, but their information may differ from the actual order rate. Models must account for the delays and other imperfections in the measurement and reporting of information. Measurement and reporting not only introduce delays, but can also create bias, noise, error, and other distortions. Models should represent the processes by which information is generated, and decisions should be represented as depending on the reported information, not the true state of affairs.

Third, modelers cannot assume decision makers know with certainty the outcomes of contingencies they have never experienced. Decisions involve choosing from various alternatives. The choices lead to consequences. People usually (but not always) choose the alternative they believe will yield the best outcome (however they define it). Some of the alternatives may have been chosen in the past, and the decision maker may have a good idea of their likely consequences. But others, probably most, have never been tried, either by the decision maker or by anyone else from whom the decision maker might learn.

Economic theory requires firms to allocate their resources to those activities that yield the highest return, for example, to choose the mix of capital, labor, and other inputs to the production process that maximizes profit. But managers in a firm don't have any direct knowledge about the productivity of most of the possible combinations of these activities and factor inputs. Would a new fax machine in accounting increase productivity more than one in purchasing? Should the firm buy a new automated machine tool to reduce the number of workers required? No one knows with certainty because there is no experience of these situations. Instead, impressions about which investments and combinations of inputs might be most productive are sketchy, incomplete, and conjectural. These impressions are gleaned over time from anecdotes, observations of other organizations, experiments the firm might conduct, and so on. Information about the true consequences of contingencies and choices that have never been realized cannot be used in models. Instead, models must represent the way in which people form expectations about the likely consequences of trying new things. These beliefs are often incorrect and slow to adjust to new information.

The decision rules of a model should conform to managerial practice.
Every variable and parameter in a model must have a real world counterpart and should be meaningful to the actors in the real system. Equations must be dimensionally consistent without the addition of fudge factors or arbitrary parameters. Managers and model users are justly suspicious of models with variables such as "technical adjustment factor" or parameters with units of measure such as widgets^2/person-mile/leap year, suspecting, often correctly, that they are fudge factors used only to get the model to work and lack any empirical or theoretical justification.

Many models, especially in operations research and economics, assume decision making is optimal. Simulation models, in contrast, must mimic the way people actually make their decisions, warts and all. Modelers must study the decision processes of the actors in the field, through laboratory experiments, or other means. You should not assume people will behave according to any a priori theory, such as the assumptions in economic models that people are motivated by narrow self-interest and are perfectly rational, or that they are naïve automatons and unresponsive to new information.

Desired and actual conditions should be distinguished. Physical constraints to the realization of desired outcomes must be represented.
We live in a world of disequilibrium. Change arises from the gaps between the desired and actual states of affairs. Models should separate desired states—the goals of the decision makers—from the actual states of the system. The decision rules in models should explain how the actors would respond to problems, shortfalls,

pressures, and other indications that things aren't where they think they should be. Goals are themselves dynamic, and modelers often need to represent the way the actors in the system form and update their aspirations.

Modelers should separate the desired rates of change in system states from the actual rates of change. Decision makers determine the *desired* rates of change in system states, but the *actual* rates of change often differ due to time delays, resource shortages, and other physical constraints. A plant manager may determine the desired rate of production from cues such as inventory and order backlogs, but the actual rate of production cannot immediately respond to changes in the desired rate. Actual production depends on stocks of labor, capital equipment, and materials, along with less tangible system states including the workweek, workforce effort and skill, and process quality. Decision makers cannot instantly change these states but can only affect the decision to hire, the acquisition of new equipment, the rate of worker training, and so on. Actually, managerial decisions only determine the authorization of vacancies and the ordering of new equipment. The actual rate of hiring and installation of new equipment depend on the availability of workers and the ability of toolmakers to produce and deliver.

Decision rules should be robust under extreme conditions.   Complex systems often generate behavior far from the range of historical experience. Indeed, one purpose of modeling is to design policies that move the system into an entirely new regime of behavior. To be useful, the decision rules in models must behave plausibly in all circumstances, not only those for which there are historical records. Robustness means decision rules must generate outcomes that are physically possible and operationally meaningful even when the inputs to those decisions take on extreme values. Production can never be negative. Shipments from a warehouse must fall to zero when the inventory of product is zero, no matter how many orders there are. Robustness necessarily means models will include many nonlinear relationships. Under normal situations, a firm's liquidity has no impact on employment. But if cash on hand approaches zero, a firm may be forced to lay off its workers even though the backlog of work is high and the firm is profitable. The impact of liquidity on net hiring is highly nonlinear.

Equilibrium should not be assumed. Equilibrium and stability may (or may not) emerge from the interaction of the elements of the system. The existence and stability of any equilibria in a system emerge from the interactions of the decision rules of the agents with the physical and institutional structure of the system. They are characteristics of system behavior. Modelers should not build into their models the presumption that the system has a particular equilibrium or equilibria, or that any equilibria are stable. Instead, modelers should represent the processes by which decision makers respond to situations in which the state of the system differs from their goals. Model analysis then reveals whether these decision rules, interacting with one another and with the physical structure, result in stable or unstable behavior.

These principles may seem to be nothing more than common sense. It seems obvious that people can't base their decisions on information they don't have, that desires are not instantly and perfectly realized, and that physical impossibilities are, well, impossible. Yet many models routinely violate these principles. In particular, many economic and optimization models assume the agents have complete and perfect information about the preferences of customers, the production function governing output, and other information that real managers perceive through a fog, if at all. Many others give decision makers perfect foresight, endowing people with crystal balls that give them perfect knowledge of the future and the ability to predict how other people would behave in hypothetical situations. Decision makers are assumed to be concerned solely with the maximization of their personal utility (or profits in the case of a firm). These assumptions are used to derive the equilibrium of the system, and either no dynamics are considered or the system is assumed to be stable, returning swiftly and smoothly to equilibrium after a shock.[2]

At the other end of the spectrum, some models assume decisions are made by rote from a limited repertoire of options. These models often show that very complex behavior can arise from extremely simple decision rules. Epstein and Axtell's (1996) Sugarscape model develops an artificial society in which agents with very simple rules compete for resources (sugar). Complex behavior they interpret as coalition formation, trade, and war arises from the interaction of the agents. The results are fascinating and can help build understanding of the behavior of complex systems. However, unless the decision rules are grounded in firsthand study of actual decision making, such models have limited utility to decision makers, and the correspondence between their dynamics and the behavior of real systems remains conjectural.[3]

CHALLENGE   # Finding Formulation Flaws

The formulations below all appeared in actual models (some simplifications have been made for clarity). Using the formulation principles above, critique each formulation. If you identify a flaw or flaws, propose a revised formulation that corrects the problem.

---

[2]There are of course exceptions. Many economic models are dynamic. Others, such as many game-theoretic models, restrict the information available to the agents. A few explore alternatives to the assumption that people are motivated by selfish utility maximization. Still fewer are grounded in firsthand study of decision making. Fully dynamic, disequilibrium behavioral models grounded in primary fieldwork remain rare in economics. Psychologists, in contrast, often utilize fieldwork and experiment to study decision making and have developed models that accommodate motives for action other than utility maximization such as fairness, altruism, revenge, and others. However, many of these models explain single decisions at the level of the individual in static, one-shot decision contexts and cannot capture the dynamics of a system or organization.

[3]There are exceptions. Since discovering and understanding the decision processes of people in complex systems is often difficult, it is often useful to develop models that assume different degrees of rationality to test the robustness of results to a wide range of assumptions about human behavior. Models of fully rational behavior can also be used to establish upper bounds for the performance of a system and help measure the value of potential improvements in decision making. Models such as Sugarscape can generate useful ideas for further research and illustrate the well-known property of complex systems that their behavior arises more from the interaction of the elements and agents with one another than from the complexity of the individual components themselves (see, e.g., Forrester 1961 and Simon 1969).

1. In a model of a firm's supply chain and inventory management policies, the inventory of finished product was increased by the production rate and decreased by the shipment rate. The following formulation for production was proposed:

    Production = Shipments + Inventory Shortfall   (13-1)

    Inventory Shortfall = Desired Inventory − Inventory   (13-2)

    where

    Production = Rate at which products are completed and enter inventory,

    Shipments = Rate at which products are shipped to customers from inventory,

    Inventory Shortfall = Shortage or surplus of inventory relative to the desired level,

    Desired Inventory = Inventory level the firm considers appropriate,

    Inventory = Actual stock of product available for shipment to customers.

2. In the same model, the modeler initially proposed

    Shipments = Orders   (13-3)

    but then realized that inventory could become negative if orders were large enough for a long enough period. The modeler then proposed the following formulation to correct the flaw:

    Shipments = MIN(Orders, Inventory)   (13-4)

3. A model of a firm's investment in capital plant assumed investment was determined by the gap between the desired level of capital stock and the current level, plus replacement of worn-out capital (the discard rate):

    Investment = Capital Discard Rate
    $\quad$ + DELAY3[(K^* − K), Construction Delay]   (13-5)

    where

    K^* = Desired capital stock,

    K = Capital stock,

    DELAY3 = Third-order material delay,

    Construction Delay = Average construction delay for capital.

4. In the same model, the desired stocks of capital and other factors of production such as labor were determined by the solution to the profit maximization problem for a firm under perfect competition. In equilibrium, the marginal revenue derived from use of an additional unit of any factor of production F_i is just balanced by its marginal cost P_i:

    $$P \frac{\partial Q}{\partial F_i} = P_i \qquad\qquad (13\text{-}6)$$

    where

    P = Price of output (marginal revenue),

P_i = Price of a unit of factor i (marginal cost of factor),

$Q = Q(F_1, F_2, \ldots, F_n)$ = Production, given by the firm's production function,

$\partial Q/\partial F_i$ = Marginal productivity of factor i (additional output generated by one additional unit of factor i).

5. A model of the US dairy industry specified the equilibrium consumption and production of milk as depending on gross domestic product (GDP)—a measure of the income of the nation—and the price of milk P_m:

$$\text{Consumption(t)} = \text{Production(t)} = a + b\text{GDP(t)} + cP_m(t) + e(t) \qquad (13\text{-}7)$$

where a, b, and c are parameters estimated from historical data and e is a random error.

13.2   FORMULATING RATE EQUATIONS

This section presents a library of common formulations with examples for each. Each conforms to the guidelines above. These generic structures are the building blocks from which more complex and realistic models can be built. In any real project you will often have to customize and elaborate them. In particular, every constant in a formulation can be modeled as a variable, with its own decision rules governing its evolution. Whether a concept can be assumed constant, exogenous, or must be modeled as an endogenous part of the system structure depends on the purpose and time horizon of the model.

13.2.1   Fractional Increase Rate

Consider a stock S with inflow rate R_I. Often the inflow is proportional to the size of the stock. The stock grows at a fractional increase rate g, which may be constant or variable:

$$R_I = gS \qquad (13\text{-}8)$$

Examples

Birth Rate = Fractional Birth Rate * Population $\qquad (13\text{-}9)$

Interest Due = Interest Rate * Debt Outstanding $\qquad (13\text{-}10)$

When the fractional growth rate g is a constant, the formulation reduces to the linear first-order positive feedback system described in chapter 8 and generates exponential growth.

The growth rate can be less than zero, in which case R_I becomes the net inflow rate and g becomes the net fractional growth rate. However, as shown in section 13.3.3, it is generally preferable to separate the inflows and outflows instead of lumping them into a single net rate. Different decision processes and physical constraints often govern inflows and outflows, and it is difficult to formulate a single net rate that is transparent and robust. The net rate of change of any stock can always be calculated as an auxiliary variable from the individual inflows and outflows.

13.2.2   Fractional Decrease Rate

Consider the outflow rate R_O from a stock S. The outflow is often proportional to the size of the stock. The outflow can be formulated either as depending on the fractional decrease rate d or equivalently as the stock divided by the average lifetime L for the items in the stock:

$$R_O = dS = S/L \qquad \qquad (13\text{-}11)$$

Examples

Death Rate = Fractional Death Rate * Population
$$= \text{Population/Average Lifetime} \qquad (13\text{-}12)$$

Defaults on Accounts Receivable = Fractional Default Rate * Accounts Receivable
$$= \text{Accounts Receivable/Average Time to Default} \qquad (13\text{-}13)$$

These examples all form linear, first-order negative loops and generate exponential decay with a time constant of L = 1/d. They are equivalent to a first-order material delay. The fractional rates or average residence times can be variables.

13.2.3   Adjustment to a Goal

Managers often seek to adjust the state of the system until it equals a goal or desired state. The simplest formulation for this negative feedback is

$$R_I = \text{Discrepancy/AT} = (S^* - S)/\text{AT} \qquad (13\text{-}14)$$

where Discrepancy is the gap between the desired state of the system S^* and the actual state S. The adjustment time AT is the average time required to close the gap.

Examples

Change in Price = (Competitor Price − Price)/Price Adjustment Time   (13-15)

Net Hiring Rate = (Desired Labor − Labor)/Hiring Delay   (13-16)

Heat Loss from Building = Temperature Gap/Temperature Adjustment Time

Temperature Gap = Outside Temperature − Inside Temperature   (13-17)

Production Rate = Perceived Inventory Discrepancy/Inventory Adjustment Time

Perceived Inventory Discrepancy = Desired Inventory − Perceived Inventory
(13-18)

"Desired minus actual over adjustment time" is the classic linear negative feedback system, and, in the absence of other rates, generates exponential adjustment to the goal (see chapters 4 and 8). In equation (13-15) a firm adjusts its price to match the competition. In (13-16) the modeler has chosen not to represent hiring, firing, and quits separately but to aggregate them into a single net hiring rate. The hiring delay represents the average time required to adjust the actual workforce to the desired level. When net hiring is negative the firm is implicitly laying off its workers. In (13-17) the rate of heat loss from a building depends on the temperature difference between the building and the air outside and the thermal resistance or R-factor of the structure. Often the actual state of the system is not known to the decision makers, who rely instead on perceptions or beliefs about the state of the system (see the Baker Criterion). In these cases the discrepancy is given by the difference between the desired and *perceived* state of the system, as in (13-18). Note that to be robust (13-18) should be modified so production never becomes negative.

13.2.4   The Stock Management Structure: Rate = Normal Rate + Adjustments

When there is an outflow from a stock, the adjustment rate formulation $R_I = (S^* - S)/AT$ will produce a steady state error. If there is an outflow R_O, the stock S will be in equilibrium when $S = S^* - R_O * AT$. The larger the outflow or the longer the adjustment time, the greater the equilibrium shortfall will be. The stock management structure adds the expected outflow to the stock adjustment to prevent steady state error:

Inflow = Expected Outflow + Adjustment for Stock   (13-19)

Adjustment for Stock = $(S^* - S)/AT$ (13-20)

Since the instantaneous value of rates cannot be measured the expected outflow is usually formed by averaging past outflows.

Example

A manufacturing firm may set production to replace the shipments it expects to make, adjusted to bring inventory in line with the desired level. Expected shipments are often estimated by smoothing past shipments.

Production = Expected Shipments + Adjustment for Inventory   (13-21)

Adjustment for Inventory
    = (Desired Inventory – Inventory)/Inventory Adjustment Time   (13-22)

Expected Shipments
    = SMOOTH(Shipment Rate, Shipment Averaging Time)   (13-23)

To be fully robust, the production rate must be constrained to be nonnegative even when there is far too much inventory. Additional adjustments can be included, for example, to adjust for stocks of work in process inventory, backlogs of unfilled orders, and so on.

The stock management structure is one of the most important and useful formulations and is discussed in detail in chapter 17.

13.2.5   Flow = Resource * Productivity

The flows affecting a stock frequently depend on resources other than the stock itself. The rate is determined by a resource and the productivity of that resource:

Rate = Resource * Productivity   (13-24)

Or equivalently,

Rate = Resource/Resources Required per Unit Produced   (13-25)

Examples:

$$\underset{\text{(Units/Period)}}{\text{Production}} = \underset{\text{(People)}}{\text{Labor Force}} * \underset{\text{((Units/Period)/Person)}}{\text{Average Productivity}} \qquad (13\text{-}26)$$

$$\underset{\text{(Customers/Hour)}}{\text{Customers Served}} = \underset{\text{(People)}}{\text{Service Personnel}} \Big/ \underset{\text{(Person-Hours/Customer)}}{\text{Average Time per Customer}} \qquad (13\text{-}27)$$

$$\underset{\text{(Bugs/Day)}}{\text{Bug Generation Rate}} = \underset{\text{(Lines of Code/Day)}}{\text{Code Production Rate}} * \underset{\text{(Bugs/Lines of Code)}}{\text{Error Density}} \qquad (13\text{-}28)$$

In (13-26) production depends on the labor force and average productivity. The labor force will typically be another stock in the model, varying with hiring and attrition. Average productivity could be constant or a variable dependent on factors such as skill and experience, motivation, fatigue, and the adequacy of other factors of production such as equipment. In (13-27) the number of service personnel and the average number of person-hours required to serve each customer determine the rate at which customers are served. If a call center has 20 service representatives and each call requires an average of 10 person-minutes, then the rate at which customers are processed is 2 per minute. Note that productivity is the inverse of average time per customer. In (13-28) the rate at which bugs are introduced into a software product is the product of the number of lines of code the programmers write each day and the bug density.

13.2.6 $Y = Y^* *$ Effect of X_1 on Y $*$ Effect of X_2 on $Y * \cdots *$ Effect of X_n on Y

In all the formulations above, parameters such as the fractional change rates, time constants, and productivities can be variables. They often depend nonlinearly on one or more other variables. A common formulation sets a variable Y to its normal, or reference value Y^*, multiplied by the product of various effects, each a (possibly nonlinear) function of a variable X_i.

$$Y = Y^* * \text{Effect of } X_1 \text{ on } Y * \text{Effect of } X_2 \text{ on } Y * \cdots * \text{Effect of } X_n \text{ on } Y \quad (13\text{-}29)$$

The variable Y can be a rate or an auxiliary that feeds into a rate. The nonlinear functions are often normalized by the normal or reference value of the inputs X_i:

$$\text{Effect of } X_i \text{ on } Y = f(X_i/X_i^*) \qquad (13\text{-}30)$$

Normalization ensures that when the inputs X_i equal their reference levels, the output Y equals its reference level. Normalizing means the input and output of the Effect of X_i on Y are both dimensionless, allowing the modeler to separate the normal values from the effect of deviations from normal. The reference levels Y^* and X_i^* can be constants or variables representing equilibrium levels, the desired state of the system, or the values of the variables at some time in the past. A common variant is

$$\begin{aligned} \text{Rate} = {}& \text{Normal Fractional Rate} * \text{Stock} \\ & * \text{Effect of } X_1 \text{ on Rate} * \cdots * \text{Effect of } X_n \text{ on Rate} \end{aligned} \qquad (13\text{-}31)$$

Examples

Workweek = Standard Workweek * Effect of Schedule Pressure on Workweek

$$(13\text{-}32)$$

Effect of Schedule Pressure on Workweek
 = f(Schedule Pressure); $f(1) = 1, f' \geq 0$ (13-33)

Schedule Pressure = Desired Production/Standard Production   (13-34)

The workweek for an individual or group can be modeled as a standard value, such as 40 hours/week, adjusted by a nonlinear function of the workload, measured by Schedule Pressure, a dimensionless ratio of desired to standard production. Standard Production is the rate of output achieved given the size and productivity of the workforce at the standard workweek. The function f(Schedule Pressure) is upward sloping and passes through the point (1, 1). It also must saturate at a maximum workweek when workload is high. Chapter 14 discusses the formulation of nonlinear functions in general and the workweek function in particular.

Reference levels can also be defined as arbitrary constants chosen by the modeler, so long as they are consistent. Consider the following formulation for labor productivity:

Productivity = Reference Productivity * Effect of Experience on Productivity

$$(13\text{-}35)$$

Effect of Experience on Productivity $= f\left(\dfrac{\text{Average Experience}}{\text{Reference Experience}}\right);$ (13-36)
    $f(1) = 1, f' \geq 0$

Reference productivity could be defined as the productivity of the average new employee with a month of experience, in which case reference experience is 1 person-month. Reference productivity could equally be defined as that of a 10-year veteran, in which case the reference experience level is 10 person-years. Section 12.2.1 applies this formulation to the learning curve.

Reference values can also be defined as the values the variables take on in a reference year. In the WORLD2 model, Forrester (1971b) formulated the birth rate as

Birth Rate = Normal Fractional Birth Rate
    * Population * Effect of Food on Births
    * Effect of Material Standard of Living on Births   (13-37)
    * Effect of Crowding on Births * Effect of Pollution on Births

Forrester defined the normal fractional birth rate as the world average in the reference year 1970. The inputs to the effects modifying births were all normalized by their 1970 values. For example, the input to the Effect of Food on Births was a dimensionless index given by the level of food per capita normalized by the world average in 1970.

A common form of the multiplicative formulation in (13-29) is the power law or log-linear model where the effects are specified as power functions of the (normalized) inputs:

Effect of X_i on $Y = \left(\dfrac{X_i}{X_i^*}\right)^{a_i}$ (13-38)

where the exponents a_i are the elasticities of Y with respect to the normalized inputs (if $a_i = 0.5$, a 1% increase in X_i boosts Y by 0.5%). Substituting the effects into the equation for Y and taking logs of both sides gives the log-linear formulation

$$\ln(Y) = \ln(Y^*) + a_1\ln(X_1/X_1^*) + a_2\ln(X_2/X_2^*) + \cdots + a_n\ln(X_n/X_n^*). \qquad (13\text{-}39)$$

The log-linear model is common because it can be estimated by linear regression.

Process Point: Variable Names for Nonlinear Effects.   In keeping with the formulation principle that every variable should have a real-life meaning, you should avoid technical jargon for the names of the nonlinear effects in formulations such as equation (13-29). The nonlinear function in a formulation such as $Y = Y^* * f(X/X^*)$ should be given a name that reflects what it does or the effect it captures. A common convention is to denote such functions by the "Effect of X on Y," yielding Y = Normal Y * Effect of X on Y. The Effect of X on Y is then defined separately as a nonlinear function, either analytically or as a table function (chapter 14). Though this convention sometimes leads to long variable names, the gain in clarity is worthwhile.

13.2.7 $Y = Y^* +$ Effect of X_1 on Y + Effect of X_2 on Y $+ \cdots +$ Effect of X_n on Y

The additive formulation

$$\begin{aligned} Y = Y^* &+ \text{Effect of } X_1 \text{ on } Y + \text{Effect of } X_2 \text{ on } Y \\ &+ \cdots + \text{Effect of } X_n \text{ on } Y \end{aligned} \qquad (13\text{-}40)$$

is sometimes seen. The effects of the X_i can still be nonlinear, and the reference values X^* can be constants or variables. Often, however, the linear form is used:

$$Y = a_0 + a_1(X_1/X_1^*) + a_2(X_2/X_2^*) + \cdots + a_n(X_n/X_n^*) \qquad (13\text{-}41)$$

Example

Consider a model of the wage rate paid by a firm or industry. The average wage rate is a stock that responds to a variety of pressures including the demand and supply of workers, the expected inflation rate, the firm's expectation for productivity growth, firm profitability, and comparisons to wages paid for comparable work in other firms or industries. The fractional change in wages per year can be modeled as the sum of the fractional change in wage arising from each pressure.

$$\text{Wage} = \text{INTEGRAL}(\text{Change in Wage, Wage}_{t_0}) \qquad (13\text{-}42)$$

$$\text{Change in Wage} = \text{Fractional Change in Wage} * \text{Wage} \qquad (13\text{-}43)$$

$$\begin{aligned} \text{Fractional Change in Wage} = &\text{ Change in Wage from Labor Availability} \\ &+ \text{Change in Wage from Inflation} + \text{Change in Wage from Productivity} \\ &+ \text{Change in Wage from Profitability} + \text{Change in Wage from Equity} \end{aligned} \qquad (13\text{-}44)$$

$$\begin{aligned} \text{Change in Wage from Labor Availability} \\ = f(\text{Labor Supply Demand Balance}); f(1) = 0, f' \le 0 \end{aligned} \qquad (13\text{-}45)$$

$$\text{Change in Wage from Inflation} = f(\text{Expected Inflation}); f(0) = 0; f' \ge 0 \qquad (13\text{-}46)$$

Change in Wage from Productivity
$$= f(\text{Expected Productivity Growth}); f(0) = 0; f' \geq 0 \qquad (13\text{-}47)$$

Change in Wage from Profitability
$$= f(\text{Perceived ROI} - \text{Reference ROI}); f(0) = 0, f' \geq 0 \qquad (13\text{-}48)$$

$$\text{Change in Wage from Equity} = f(\text{Relative Wage}); f(0) = 0, f' \geq 0 \qquad (13\text{-}49)$$

$$\text{Relative Wage} = (\text{Perceived Industry Average Wage} - \text{Wage})/\text{Wage} \qquad (13\text{-}50)$$

Presumably, lower labor availability, higher expected inflation or productivity growth, higher profitability, and higher wages in other firms all increase the rate of wage growth. The labor supply/demand balance could be measured different ways, possibly including factors such as the average time to fill vacancies, the number of unfilled positions, and the unemployment rate in the industry or region. Expectations for future inflation and productivity growth could depend on the history of inflation and productivity (see chapter 16). Profitability could be measured by return on investment (ROI) normalized by a reference reflecting industry or economy-wide norms. Finally, the fractional gap between wages at comparable firms and the firm in question provides a measure of wage equity. Adjusting the shapes and strengths of the different nonlinear functions can capture different labor market institutions, from collective bargaining to the market for day laborers. The shapes and values of the functions for each contribution to the total fractional change in wages must be carefully chosen so that the overall response of wages is appropriate even when the inputs take on extreme values.

Multiplicative or Additive Effects?

When should you choose a linear formulation such as equation (13-40) and when is the multiplicative formulation in (13-29) better? Linear formulations are common because linear models are simple, can be solved analytically, and facilitate parameter estimation by linear regression.[4] However, the multiplicative formulation is generally preferable and sometimes required.

The actual relationship between a variable and its inputs, such as between births and food, health care, crowding, and pollution, is typically complex and nonlinear. Both the multiplicative and additive formulations are approximations to the underlying, true nonlinear function $Y = f(X_1, X_2, \ldots, X_n)$. Each approximation is centered on a particular operating point given by the reference point $Y^* = f(X_1^*, X_2^*, \ldots, X_n^*)$. Both the additive and multiplicative approximations will be reasonable in the neighborhood of the operating point but increasingly diverge from the true, underlying function as the system moves away from it.

The additive formulation assumes the effects of each input are strongly separable: The impact of a change in any one input is the same no matter what values the other inputs have. Strong separability is clearly incorrect in extreme conditions. In the birth rate example, the birth rate must be zero when food per capita is zero no matter how favorable other conditions are. The additive formulation can never

---

[4]The growth in computer power and widespread availability of nonlinear estimation routines means there is now little reason to enforce linearity for estimation purposes. You should capture the nonlinearities the data suggest and robustness requires, then estimate them with an appropriate statistical technique.

capture that nonlinear effect. The multiplicative formulation should be used whenever an extreme value of any input dominates all other effects.[5]

CHALLENGE   ## Multiple Nonlinear Effects

In a model of urban growth an analyst finds that the migration rate to the city is proportional to the current population and that the fractional inmigration rate depends on the (perceived) availability of jobs and housing and the crime rate. The analyst proposes the following formulation:

Inmigration = Inmigration Fraction * Population   (13-51)

Inmigration Fraction = Normal Inmigration Fraction
    + Effect of Jobs on Inmigration + Effect of Housing on Inmigration   (13-52)
    + Effect of Crime on Inmigration

Job availability is measured by the ratio of jobs available to the labor force. Housing availability is measured by the ratio of housing to households. The crime rate is measured by crimes/year per thousand people.

1. Is the proposed formulation reasonable? Why/why not? Sketch the likely shapes of the functions for each effect on migration so that the individual functions take on appropriate extreme values if, for example, there were no jobs, no housing, or high crime.

2. Is the proposed formulation robust in extreme conditions? If not, give an example of a situation in which the formulation would generate unrealistic results.

3. Reformulate the inmigration rate so it is robust to any combination of inputs.

13.2.8   Fuzzy MIN Function

Often a rate or variable is determined by the most scarce of several resources. For example, capacity or insufficient demand can limit production:

Production = MIN(Desired Production, Capacity)   (13-53)

or more generally, $Y = MIN(X, Y^*)$, where Y^* is the capacity of the process.

However, the sharp discontinuity created by the MIN function is often unrealistic. Many times the capacity constraint is approached gradually due to physical characteristics of the system at the micro level. Consider a single worker and workstation in a job shop. As the required rate of production increases from the normal rate, the worker at first can keep pace by speeding up and reducing idle time. These responses gradually experience diminishing returns, until the maximum rate of

---

[5]The linear formulation in (13-40) corresponds to the first terms of the Taylor series for the true underlying formulation, thus assuming strong separability of the individual effects. The power law formulation in (13-39) corresponds to the first terms of the Taylor series of the log of the true function and assumes multiplicative separability. It is possible to include higher-order terms to capture interactions, but care must be used to ensure that the resulting formulation is globally robust to extreme combinations of inputs.

FIGURE 13-2
The fuzzy
minimum
function

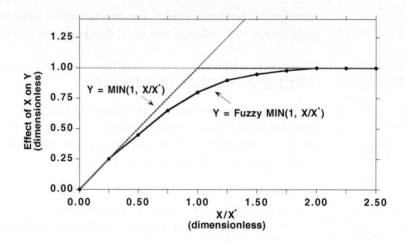

output is reached. Even when a capacity constraint is sharply discontinuous at the level of the individual unit, the response of the aggregate system is likely to be smooth, since there will typically be a distribution of individuals around the average capacity level. The following formulation captures a "soft" or "fuzzy" minimum function for use in situations where the effect of a constraint is gradually felt.

$$Y = Y^* * \text{Effect of X on Y} \tag{13-54}$$

$$\text{Effect of X on Y} = f(X/X^*); f(0) = 0, f(\infty) = 1, f' \geq 0, f'' \leq 0 \tag{13-55}$$

Figure 13-2 illustrates the function. The 45° reference line represents $Y = X/X^*$. In the case of production and capacity utilization, the 45° line implies Utilization = Desired Production/Capacity, which means Production = Desired Production. The function labeled Fuzzy MIN in the figure captures a gradual approach to the constraint as the input rises. See chapter 14 for examples and discussion.[6]

The formulation can also be expressed equivalently as

$$\text{Rate} = \text{Desired Rate} * \text{Fraction of Desired Rate Satisfied} \tag{13-56}$$

$$\text{Fraction of Desired Rate Satisfied} = f(\text{Capacity/Desired Rate}); \\ f(0) = 0, f(\infty) = 1, f' \geq 0, f'' \leq 0 \tag{13-57}$$

Here the actual rate is expressed as a fraction of the desired throughput achieved given the capacity of the process. The construction and interpretation of the function is the same. The order fulfillment ratio defined in the manufacturing supply chain models of chapter 18 provides an example.

13.2.9 Fuzzy MAX Function

The fuzzy MAX function is analogous to the fuzzy MIN function. In many situations a variable must remain nonnegative. For example,

$$\text{Hiring Rate} = \text{MAX}(0, \text{Desired Hiring Rate}) \tag{13-58}$$

---

[6]A common alternative formulates the utilization function so that $f(1) = 1$ and $f(\infty) = f_{max} \geq 1$. In this case the function passes through the normal point (1,1) and capacity represents normal output; the actual maximum rate of output for the process is given by $Y^* * f_{max}$.

FIGURE 13-3
The fuzzy
maximum
function

The effect can lie
along the 45° line
when X/X* > 1
or eventually
saturate, combin-
ing the fuzzy max
and fuzzy min
functions.

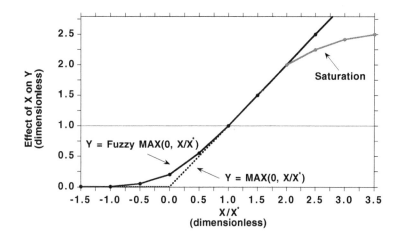

The desired hiring rate may be negative if the firm has far too many workers, but the hiring rate can fall at most to zero (net hiring can still be negative since workers quit and can be laid off; see chapter 19). The fuzzy maximum function is

$$Y = Y^* * \text{Effect of X on Y} \tag{13-59}$$

$$\text{Effect of X on Y} = f(X/X^*); f(-\infty) = 0, f(1) = 1 \tag{13-60}$$

The fuzzy maximum function is useful in situations where individual decision makers are reluctant to cut the output Y to zero as X falls. For example, a firm may choose to keep a chemical plant running above the desired rate when demand is low to avoid shutdown expenses. The function is also useful when the model aggregates a population with a distribution of desired and normal rates around the averages. When the average desired rate is zero, some members of the population will have desired rates less than zero and will be shut down while others have desired rates greater than zero, so average output is greater than zero. You can combine the fuzzy minimum and fuzzy maximum into a single effect by including a saturation nonlinearity $f(X/X^*) = f^{\text{max}}$ for large values of X/X*, as shown in Figure 13-3.

Example

Applying the fuzzy maximum function to the hiring rate,

$$\text{Hiring Rate} = \text{Normal Hiring Rate} * \text{Effect of Desired Hiring on Hiring} \tag{13-61}$$

$$\text{Effect of Desired Hiring on Hiring} = f\left(\frac{\text{Desired Hiring Rate}}{\text{Normal Hiring Rate}}\right);$$
$$f(-\infty) = 0, f(1) = 1, f(\infty) = f^{\text{max}} \tag{13-62}$$

The desired hiring rate would include replacement of those employees who quit or retire modified by an adjustment to close any gap between the desired and actual labor force (as in the stock management structure). The normal hiring rate represents the capacity of the firm's human resource organization and can be modeled most simply as a normal fraction of the labor force. Actual hiring gradually approaches zero as desired hiring falls below normal because labor requirements by facility and skill are imperfectly correlated: Some hiring will be needed to fill vacancies for particular skills in particular departments or firms even when the average desired hiring rate for the firm or industry as a whole is zero. At the other extreme, the human resources organization cannot hire faster than a certain rate; in the example shown in Figure 13-3, hiring gradually saturates at 2.5 times the normal rate when labor demand is high.

13.2.10   Floating Goals

Many formulations respond to some measure of the discrepancy between the desired and actual state of the system. Where do the goals come from? In some cases, goals are exogenous to the decision. In the manufacturing example in section 13.2.4, desired inventory might depend on the firm's forecast of demand and a target for inventory coverage. Often, however, there are no obvious external reference points to determine goals. In these cases, the desired state of the system is, at least partially, affected by the state of the system itself. The goals float with the ebb and flow of the system itself.

Consider the classical linear negative feedback system:

$$S = \text{INTEGRAL(Net Change in Stock, } S_{t_0}) \tag{13-63}$$

$$\text{Net Change in Stock} = (S^* - S)/\text{SAT} \tag{13-64}$$

where S^* and S are the desired and actual states of the system and SAT is the stock adjustment time. The formulation for the net change in the stock assumes decision makers initiate corrective actions in response to any discrepancy between desired and actual. In a pure floating goal structure the desired state of the system is itself a variable:

$$S^* = \text{INTEGRAL(Net Change in Goal, } S^*_{t_0}) \tag{13-65}$$

$$\text{Net Change in Goal} = (S - S^*)/\text{GAT} \tag{13-66}$$

where GAT is the goal adjustment time. The goal adjustment rate forms a first-order linear negative feedback loop that acts to eliminate any discrepancy between the desired and actual states of the system—but by eroding the goal rather than changing the world. There is ample empirical support for such adaptive aspirations. Habituation, the tendency to get accustomed to your present circumstances, is a form of goal adaptation. People find the tension created by unfulfilled goals uncomfortable and often erode their goals to reduce cognitive dissonance (Festinger 1957; see also Lant 1992).

Figure 13-4 shows a causal diagram for the pure floating goal structure. The mutual dependence of the state of the system and goal form a positive feedback loop. The mutual adaptation of goals and outcomes causes such systems to be path dependent. A random shock that lowers the state of the system will generate corrective actions that raise the state of the system back up, but while the actual state is low the goal will be adjusted downward. The system will return to equilibrium, but not the original equilibrium. The degree of goal erosion will depend on how fast the goal adjusts relative to the state of the system.

FIGURE 13-4   Feedback structure created by floating goals

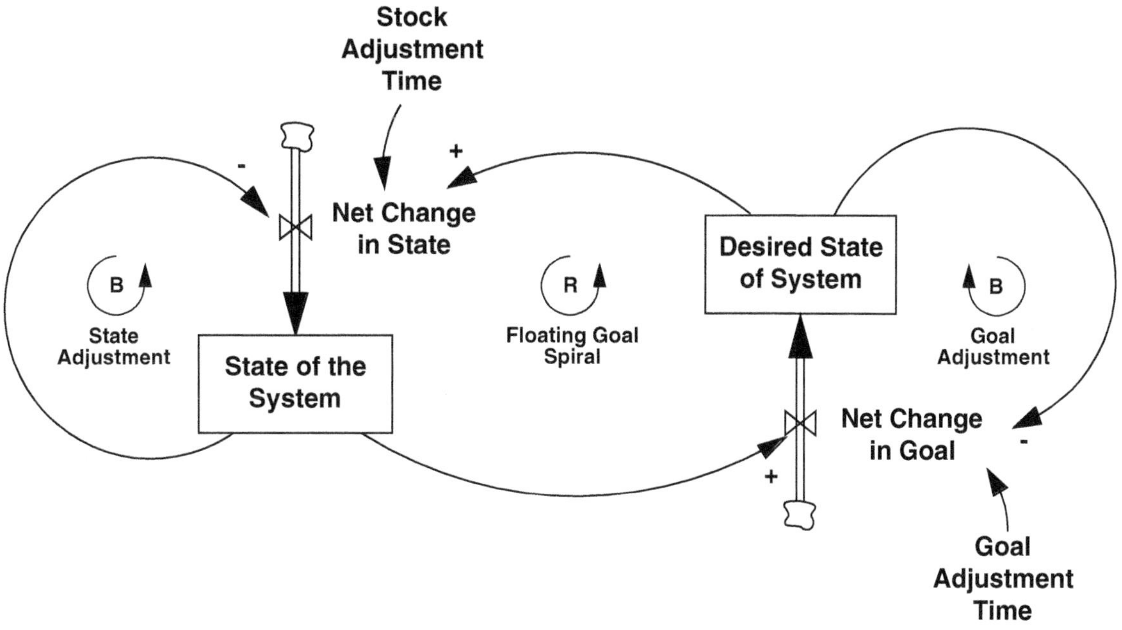

Example

Recall the student workload management model in section 5.4. Figure 5-25 suggests the student's desired grade point average (GPA) adjusts to the actual GPA:[7]

$$\text{Desired GPA} = \text{INTEGRAL(Change in Desired GPA, Desired GPA}_{t_0}) \qquad (13\text{-}67)$$

$$\begin{aligned}&\text{Change in Desired GPA}\\&\quad = (\text{GPA} - \text{Desired GPA})/\text{Grade Goal Adjustment Time}\end{aligned} \qquad (13\text{-}68)$$

CHALLENGE   ## Floating Goals

Consider the floating goal structure in equations (13-63) through (13-66). For illustration, assume the state of the system is a student's actual GPA and the goal is the student's desired GPA. Without using simulation, sketch the behavior you expect for the following situations.

1. The state of the system begins at zero and the desired state, at 100. Assume the adjustment time for the state of the system SAT is 8 weeks. What is the behavior of the system and equilibrium GPA when the goal adjustment time GAT = ∞ (the goal remains fixed)?

---

[7]Actual achievement is more complex, depending on student aptitude compared to the difficulty of the material; the student's motivation, preparation, and effort; and the support, encouragement, and expectations of teachers, parents, and peers. Nancy Roberts (1978) develops a model of student-teacher-parent interactions in which the dynamics depend strongly on the goal formation process for each of these actors.

2. What is the behavior of the system when goals are flexible? What is the equilibrium GPA when GAT is 32, 16, 8, 4, and 2 weeks?

3. After sketching your intuitive estimates of the behavior, simulate the system for the conditions above. Were your mental simulations correct?

4. Discuss the implications of flexible goals. Under what circumstances should goals remain absolute? When should goals be adaptive? Give examples of floating goals from your own experience.

Goals are often partially affected by past performance and partly by various external factors. In these cases the goal can be formulated as a weighted average of the various external factors S^E and the traditional performance of the system S^T. Traditional performance adjusts over time to actual performance.

$$S^* = W^T * S^T + (1 - W^T) * S^E \tag{13-69}$$

$$S^T = \text{SMOOTHn}(S, AT^T) \tag{13-70}$$

where AT^T is the adjustment time for the tradition and SMOOTHn is the nth-order information delay (chapter 11.3).

Modeling a goal as a weighted average of past performance and external pressures is consistent with the common judgmental heuristic known as *anchoring and adjustment*.

People often estimate a quantity or make a judgment by anchoring or beginning with a known reference point, then adjusting their judgment to account for factors specific to the case at hand. Often the adjustments are insufficient, leading to bias toward the anchor.

Judgments are often strongly anchored to information people know to be irrelevant. Northcraft and Neale (1987) had professional real estate agents appraise the value of various houses. Agents received 10-page packets describing each house, identical except for one piece of information—the asking price, which should be irrelevant in appraising the true market value of a house. Nevertheless, the appraisals were significantly anchored to the asking price. Appraisers told the house was listed at $119,900 gave an average appraised value of $114,200; appraisers told the very same house was listed for $149,900 gave a mean appraised value of $128,800. Most of the agents denied considering the asking price in their judgment.

Russo and Schoemaker (1989) asked MBA students for the last three digits of their phone number, say XYZ, then added 400 to the answer. Students were then asked, "Do you think Attila the Hun was defeated in Europe before or after [the year XYZ + 400]?" After responding, the students were then asked, "In what year would you guess Attila the Hun was actually defeated?" The students know their phone number has nothing to do with the date of Attila's defeat, yet this irrelevant anchor significantly biased their answers. Those for whom XYZ + 400 was between 400 and 599 gave average estimates of the year 629; those for whom XYZ + 400 was between 1200 and 1399 gave average estimates of the year 988. Attila was actually defeated in the year 451.

CHALLENGE	## Goal Formation with Internal and External Inputs

Modify the formulation for desired GPA to include an external aspiration for grades, for example, the grades needed to get into graduate school or the grades your teachers and parents expect you to earn. Assume traditional grades adjust by first-order smoothing to actual grades. Set the external grade goal to 90, while maintaining the other assumptions from the challenge above. Sketch your intuitive estimate of the behavior of the system for various combinations of the weight on traditional grades and the time constant for modifying the tradition. Then simulate these cases and compare the results to your intuitive estimates. Comment on the role of external reference points in the formation of goals.

Floating goals are pervasive. Examples include company goals for quality, delivery time and delivery reliability, customer satisfaction, and so on. Organizational norms of all types tend to adjust to past experience, including norms such as dress codes, the length of the workweek, and the degree of civility in the organization. Your personal goal for your weight may be affected by the official target for your stature calculated by nutritionists, but is probably strongly conditioned by your past weight and by the size of the clothes in your closet. Since those clothes probably fit you when you bought them, your current weight goal is largely determined by how much you actually weighed when you bought the clothes you are wearing now. Similarly, goals that appear to be exogenous are actually often endogenous. A firm may set its goals for service quality, delivery time, and reliability by benchmarking its competitors. From the point of view of the individual firm, these goals are exogenous. But when all firms benchmark performance against one another, goals are actually endogenous and determined by past performance. An entire industry can suffer from goal erosion even as each firm seeks external reference points for its aspirations.

13.2.11   Nonlinear Weighted Average

A variable is often a compromise or weighted average of several cues near a certain operating point but restricted by maximum or minimum limits in extreme conditions, thus requiring a nonlinear weighted average. For example, the weighting of internal and external factors in goal formation is often nonlinear. When the external inputs to a goal are very different from the current situation, people sometimes discount them as unrealistic, suggesting that the goal is anchored nonlinearly to traditional performance:

$$S^* = S^T * \text{Effect of External Factors on Goal} \tag{13-71}$$

$$\text{Effect of External Factors on Goal} = f(S^E/S^T); f(1) = 1, f' \geq 0 \tag{13-72}$$

Figure 13-5 shows a typical form for the function $f(S^E/S^T)$. The 45° reference line represents the case $S^* = S^E$: External factors fully determine the goal. The line $f(S^E/S^T) = 1$ implies $S^* = S^T$: The external factors have no role in goal formation. The slope of the function is the weight on the external factors. The maximum and

FIGURE 13-5

Function for a nonlinear weighted average

The effect is a weighted average of S^E and S^T when $S^E \approx S^T$ but limited to $\pm 50\%$ of S^T. As shown the weight on S^E around the operating point is 2/3.

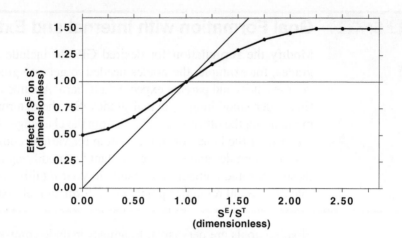

minimum values capture the idea that decision makers are unwilling or unable to set goals too far from traditional norms for performance.

Example

Jones and Repenning (1997) studied the dynamics of quality improvement at a major motorcycle producer. Fieldwork revealed that the workers' quality goals were strongly affected by their own experience with the product, both as employees and customers. Many owned one or more of the firm's bikes and put many miles on them each year. In the 1980s the loyalty and knowledge of the employees was a major asset as the company dramatically improved the quality, reliability, and styling of its bikes. The quality improvement contributed to a dramatic surge in demand and renewed popularity for the firm's products. By the early 1990s a new type of customer became important. Known as "rubbies" (rich urban bikers), these new customers tended to buy the company's bikes more for status value than transportation. The rubbies didn't actually ride much and were far more sensitive to minor cosmetic issues related to the paint and finish than the company's traditional blue-collar customers, including their own workers. As customer standards and warranty claims increased, management aggressively boosted goals for finish quality. Some workers initially resisted these new, higher standards. One manufacturing manager said, "Sometimes [customer] standards are too high. He's an artist or a banker and expects everything to be 100% perfect." An engineer commented,

> I'd kind of like to drop cosmetics as a quality problem. That is more of a subjective kind of quality problem—what the customer expects versus what we are producing. I don't even want to talk about them, because half of the cosmetic defects that will turn up in paint or chrome you won't see.

Another commented, "We don't build motorcycles, we build jewelry."

The engineers viewed external data such as market research or warranty claims as unreliable or irrelevant: "Data from the customers is too subjective. We don't use it to learn about quality improvement." Instead, employee quality goals were strongly anchored on their own experience. When asked how he learned about the quality of the product, one engineer said, "By buying them. By hanging around in the field. I use our product extensively."

The tendency to discount evidence significantly different from their own standards suggests the employees' quality goals were flexible only up to a point, consistent with the nonlinear anchoring and adjustment formulation:

Employee Quality Goal
$\quad$ = Traditional Quality * Effect of Customer Feedback on Quality Goal $\qquad$ (13-73)

Effect of Customer Feedback on Quality Goal
$\quad$ = f(Customer Quality Goal/Traditional Quality) $\qquad$ (13-74)

The traditional quality goal responded to past quality and emphasized mechanical functionality rather than cosmetics. Customer goals for quality, once similar to the employees' goals, had risen, and now emphasized cosmetic concerns. The interview data suggested the Effect of Customer Feedback on Quality Goal had a slope much less than 1 near the neutral point and saturated for high values of the input. Boosting the operational goal for quality required changing employees' perceptions of what quality should be, not merely applying additional pressure for higher quality. Management used the results of the Jones and Repenning study, along with other work, to make significant changes in product development and the PD-manufacturing relationship, helping to lift quality goals—and quality—throughout the organization. By the end of the 1990s quality was trending up while sales continued at record rates.

13.2.12   Modeling Search: Hill-Climbing Optimization

In many situations decision makers strive to optimize a system but lack knowledge of the system structure that might help them identify the optimal operating point. For example, a firm may seek the price that maximizes profit or the mix of labor and capital that minimizes the cost of production. A variant of floating goals enables the agents in models to find the optimum point in such cases in a behaviorally realistic way. Since firms, for example, do not know what the optimal mix of labor and capital is, they must find it by sensing whether there is too much labor or too much capital, then adjusting the mix in the right direction. Such a procedure is called hill climbing.

Imagine yourself trying to climb a mountain in a complete whiteout. Visibility is zero. You have no idea which way will lead you to the summit. You carefully take one step in each direction to see which way the ground around you slopes, then strike out in the direction that leads most steeply uphill. Every few steps, you stop and take a step in each direction to reassess which way is uphill. You continue in this fashion, stopping only when every direction you can move takes you downhill. If the mountain is smooth, has only a single peak, and you reassess the gradient often enough, you are guaranteed to make the summit even though you have no idea where the summit lies.[8]

---

[8]Nelson and Winter (1982) develop a search heuristic similar in spirit to the hill-climbing procedure assumed here, show how boundedly rational firms can use it to search for best-practice combinations of inputs and technology, and demonstrate how such search can lead to economic growth.

Hill climbing sounds simple and is widely used as an optimization technique, but there are important subtleties. Hill climbing can lead to suboptimization. If there are multiple peaks (known as local optima), you can end up stuck at a peak lower than the main summit. If the mountain is not smooth (the landscape is rugged), you can't reliably tell which way is uphill and might wander aimlessly forever. If you are too aggressive and walk a long way before reassessing the gradient, you can overshoot and oscillate around the peak. Sophisticated hill-climbing methods solve the overshoot problem by adjusting the step size as the gradient changes. If the mountain is smooth enough, the slope must diminish as you approach the summit. Therefore, a steep slope means you can go a long way before reassessing the gradient without much risk of missing the mark, thus saving time. As the slope flattens, you take smaller steps so as not to overshoot the summit.

Hill climbing is a very common and often effective heuristic for optimization and learning. To model hill climbing, the desired state of the system is anchored on the current state, then adjusted by various external pressures representing the gradient of the hill and indicating the way uphill. The general structure for such a hill-climbing process is

$$S = INTEGRAL(\text{Change in State of System}, S_{t_0}) \tag{13-75}$$

$$\text{Change in State of System} = (S^* - S)/SAT \tag{13-76}$$

$$S^* = S * \text{Effect of } X_1 \text{ on } S^* * \text{Effect of } X_2 \text{ on } S^* * \cdots * \text{Effect of } X_n \text{ on } S^* \tag{13-77}$$

$$\text{Effect of } X_i \text{ on } S^* = f(X_i/X_i^*) \tag{13-78}$$

The effects of the external pressure are formulated here as multiplicative and are normalized to their reference values, though other formulations are possible. Figure 13-6 shows the feedback structure. There are two loops. The negative State Adjustment loop closes any gap between the desired state of the system S^* and the actual state S. The goal itself depends on the state of the system, creating the positive Goal Revision loop.

As long as the net effect of the pressures on the goal causes S^* to exceed S, the state of the system will grow exponentially. When the net pressures push the goal below the current state, the system will decay exponentially. To see why, suppose the net effects of the external pressures $f(X_i/X_i^*)$ equal some constant k, so $S^* = kS$. Substituting in (13-76) yields

$$\text{Change in State of System} = (kS - S)/SAT = (k-1)S/SAT \tag{13-79}$$

which is the formulation for a first-order linear feedback system. If $k > 1$, the positive Goal Revision loop dominates, and the system grows exponentially at the fractional rate $(k-1)/SAT$. If $k < 1$, the system decays exponentially. In reality, and in a full model, the variables X_i driving the goal would be part of the feedback structure and affected by the state of the system. Usually, the state of the system will change until the external pressures cause S^* to equal S, at which point S reaches equilibrium—the optimal point where there is no further pressure to change the state of the system. The equilibrium is not predetermined. Instead, the system settles at whatever value of S causes the pressures on the goal to net out. Chapters 15 and 20 provide examples and tests of the hill-climbing formulation. Of

FIGURE 13-6   Structure for hill-climbing search

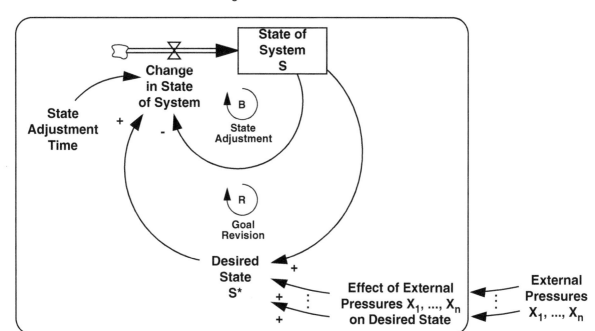

course, whether an equilibrium or optimal value of S exists, and whether the approach to it is stable or unstable, depends on the parameters of the goal revision and stock adjustment process, as well as those governing the reactions of the other variables X_i. As in the real world there is no guarantee that the hill-climbing process will converge.

Example

Consider the price setting process in a market such as a commodity or stock market. The demand for the good falls as prices rise; supply rises as price rises. In equilibrium price is just high enough to balance demand with supply. But how do the market makers (the people who set prices by calling out bids and offers in the trading pit) find the equilibrium price? And how do prices change when there is an imbalance between demand and supply? Price P adjusts to an indicated price over an interval given by the price adjustment time PAT:

$$P = INTEGRAL(Change\ in\ Price,\ P_{t_0}) \tag{13-80}$$

$$Change\ in\ Price = (P^* - P)/PAT \tag{13-81}$$

In a trading pit such as a stock exchange PAT may be a matter of minutes; for large industrial products PAT may be months. Since the true equilibrium price that will clear the market is unknown, market makers form P^* by anchoring on the current price and then adjusting in response to the perceived balance between demand and supply:

$$P^* = P * Effect\ of\ Demand\ Supply\ Balance\ on\ Price \tag{13-82}$$

$$\text{Effect of Demand Supply Balance on Price} = f(\text{Demand/Supply});$$
$$f(1) = 1, f' \geq 0 \tag{13-83}$$

If demand exceeds supply, indicated price will rise. As it does, so too will the actual price. The price will therefore grow exponentially as long as demand exceeds supply. Price will fall as long as supply exceeds demand. The Effect of Demand Supply Balance on Price can be approximated simply by

$$\text{Effect of Demand Supply Balance on Price} = (\text{Demand/Supply})^s \tag{13-84}$$

where $s > 0$ is the sensitivity of price to the demand/supply balance. The values of s could be estimated from data relating price changes to the relative size of buy and sell orders in a stock market or order rates and capacity in a firm.

To test the ability of the hill-climbing formulation to find the market-clearing price, assume demand and supply respond to price with constant elasticities:

$$\text{Demand} = \text{Reference Demand} * \text{Effect of Price on Demand} \tag{13-85}$$

$$\text{Effect of Price on Demand} = (\text{Price/Reference Price})^{e_d} \tag{13-86}$$

$$\text{Supply} = \text{Reference Supply} * \text{Effect of Price on Supply} \tag{13-87}$$

$$\text{Effect of Price on Supply} = (\text{Price/Reference Price})^{e_s} \tag{13-88}$$

where $e_d < 0$ and $e_s > 0$ are the elasticities of demand and supply, respectively. The equilibrium price P_{eq} is found by equating demand D and supply S and solving for price:

$$P_{eq} = P_R * \left(\frac{D_R}{S_R}\right)^{1/(e_s - e_d)} \tag{13-89}$$

where P_R, D_R, and S_R are the reference values of price, demand, and supply, respectively. Equilibrium price depends only on the demand and supply curves. The price adjustment time and sensitivity of price to the demand/supply balance characterize the disequilibrium behavior of market makers and do not affect the equilibrium price. Figure 13-7 shows the feedback structure of the price discovery process.

The price formation process forms two loops. Price adjusts to the indicated level, forming the negative Price Adjustment loop, but the indicated price is based on the current price, forming the positive Price Discovery loop. The responses of demand and supply to price form two additional negative loops (see chapter 5.5 for discussion). Figure 13-8 shows a simulation beginning from an initial equilibrium with Price = Reference Price = \$100/unit and Demand = Supply = Reference Demand = Reference Supply = 100 units/period. The price adjustment time is set to 1 period. The elasticities e_d and e_s are set to -0.25 and 0.50, respectively. The sensitivity of indicated price to the demand/supply balance is one. At time zero the demand curve shifts upward by 20%.

Given the parameters, the market clears at a new equilibrium price of \$127.52/unit, with demand and supply equal to about 113 units/period. However, market makers, ignorant of the true demand and supply curves, do not know the equilibrium price and must hunt for it through a gradual process of price adjustment. Faced with excess demand, market makers immediately increase P^* above P, so price starts to rise. After a short time, the higher price begins to suppress demand

FIGURE 13-7   Price discovery by hill climbing: structure

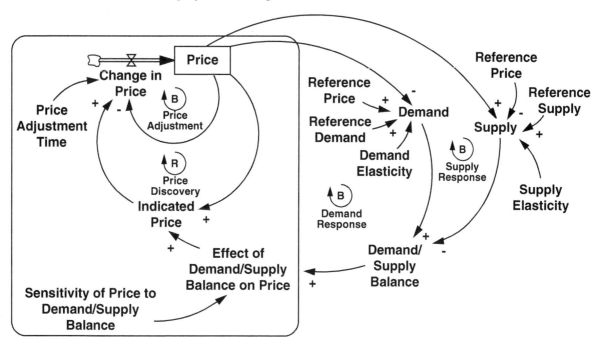

and stimulate supply. However, there is still an imbalance, so indicated price remains above price. Price continues to rise until demand and supply come into balance, at which point $P^* = P$ and price change ceases.

The adjustment in this simple example is first-order, without overshoot and oscillation, because demand and supply are assumed to respond to price immediately, and the model ignores changes in inventories or backlogs. A proper treatment of the stocks and delays in these feedbacks could cause instability. Further, the only external pressure on price arises from the demand/supply balance. Section 20.2.6 presents a richer model of price discovery that can be applied to a variety of markets.

A more realistic and subtle use of the hill-climbing structure arises in modeling the problem of selecting the optimal mix of inputs to a production process. Factor inputs typically include capital and labor, or capital, labor, energy, and materials (K, L, E, M). As all introductory economics students learn, in equilibrium, assuming competitive factor and output markets, firms should choose the mix of production factors so that the revenue generated by an additional unit of each factor is just balanced by the cost of the additional unit. That is,

$$\text{Marginal Revenue} * \text{Marginal Productivity of } F_i = \text{Marginal Cost of } F_i \qquad (13\text{-}90)$$

where F_i denotes a factor of production $i \in \{K, L, E, M\}$. The marginal productivity of each factor is given by

$$\text{Marginal Productivity of } F_i = \partial Q / \partial F_i \qquad (13\text{-}91)$$

where output Q is given by the production function

$$Q = f(K, L, E, M) \qquad (13\text{-}92)$$

FIGURE 13-8

Price discovery by hill climbing: behavior

At time zero, Reference Demand increases 20%. Demand Elasticity = −0.25; Supply Elasticity = 0.50; Sensitivity of Price to Demand/Supply Balance = 1; Price Adjustment time = 1 period.

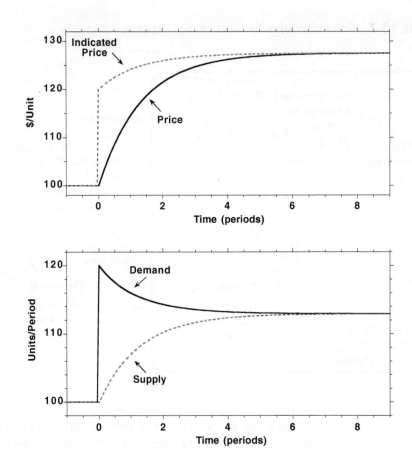

Equilibrium models solve these equations and then set the factor stocks to the optimal levels or adjust factor stocks gradually to the optimal levels. In reality managers do not know the true production function for the firm and cannot solve for the optimal input mix. Instead, they make gradual adjustments based on their sense of which direction to move to improve the efficiency of operations (for an explicit model of this process see Nelson and Winter 1982). Out of equilibrium, the marginal benefit of an additional unit of any input may yield more or less than its marginal cost. As these pressures are perceived, the firm gradually increases or decreases the use of that factor. The following formulation captures the local search for a better mix of inputs:

$$\text{Desired Factor}_i = \text{Factor}_i * \text{Effect of Relative Demand on Desired Factor} \\ * \text{Effect of Relative Return on Desired Factor}_i \quad (13\text{-}93)$$

The desired stock of each input factor is anchored to the current stock, then adjusted in response to relative demand and relative return. Relative demand is the ratio of desired production to capacity and affects all factors equally; relative return is the perceived marginal return generated by each factor relative to its cost.

$$\text{Effect of Relative Demand on Desired Factor} \\ = f(\text{Relative Demand}); f(1) = 1, f' \geq 0. \quad (13\text{-}94)$$

$$\text{Relative Demand} = \text{Desired Production/Production Capacity} \quad (13\text{-}95)$$

A typical formulation for the effect of relative demand on desired factor stocks lies along the 45° reference line near the operating point where relative demand = 1 but saturates for very low and very high values.

The effect of relative return captures pressures to rebalance the mix of inputs as their relative return varies. The effect depends on the perceived and not the actual relative return. Perceived relative return is modeled with an information delay.

Effect of Relative Return on Factor$_i$
$\quad = f$(Perceived Relative Return to Factor$_i$) $; f(1) = 1, f' \geq 0.$ (13-96)

Perceived Relative Return to Factor$_i$
$\quad$ = SMOOTH(Relative Return to Factor$_i$, (13-97)
Time to Perceive Relative Return to Factor$_i$)

The Time to Perceive Relative Return to Factor captures the time required to form reliable estimates of the marginal return of each factor. Like the effect of relative demand, the effect of relative return on desired factor stocks lies along the 45° line near the operating point and saturates for very high and very low values.

Relative return is the ratio of the marginal revenue generated by another unit of the factor to the marginal cost of the factor. When the ratio is greater than one, the firm should increase its use of that factor; when it is less than one the factor costs more than it yields and should be cut back. Marginal revenue (price net of returns and taxes) and marginal cost (the unit cost of each input) are perceived rapidly and are relatively unambiguous. However, information about the marginal productivity of each factor is difficult to get and hard to interpret. Beliefs about marginal productivity are therefore likely to change only slowly, so relative return depends on the perceived marginal productivity of each factor, which adjusts with a delay to the actual value.

$$\frac{\text{Relative Return}}{\text{to Factor}_i} = \frac{\begin{matrix}\text{Marginal} \\ \text{Revenue}\end{matrix} * \begin{matrix}\text{Perceived Marginal Productivity} \\ \text{of Factor}_i\end{matrix}}{\text{Marginal Cost of Factor}_i} \quad (13\text{-}98)$$

Perceived Marginal Productivity of Factor$_i$
$\quad$ = SMOOTH(Marginal Productivity of Factor$_i$, (13-99)
Time to Perceive Marginal Productivity$_i$)

Marginal Productivity of Factor$_i$ = ∂Production Capacity$/\partial$Factor$_i$ (13-100)

The marginal productivity of each factor can be modeled using the analytic expression for the true marginal productivity given the particular production function used or estimated by comparing the output generated by different combinations of inputs (e.g., in different business units or at different times).

CHALLENGE

Finding the Optimal Mix of Capital and Labor

Recognizing that the actual factor stocks will adjust to the desired levels (with some delay), sketch the feedback structure of the formulation for desired factor stocks developed above. Remember that individual factors experience diminishing returns as they increase relative to fixed factors. Given the feedback structure you identify, what is the likely response of the system to a change in the relative prices of factor inputs?

Consider a model of an aggregate industry or sector of the economy such as manufacturing or transportation. Assume for simplicity that capital and labor are the only factors of production considered in the model. Further, assume production capacity Q is given by the Cobb-Douglas production function:

$$Q = P_R * (K/K_R)^{a_k} * (L/L_R)^{a_l} \tag{13-101}$$

where P_R, K_R, and L_R are reference production, capital, and labor, respectively. The exponents a_k and a_l capture the response of production to each factor. Assume constant returns to scale, so $a_k + a_l = 1$. The marginal productivity of a factor in the Cobb-Douglas production function $\partial Q/\partial F_i = a_i Q/F_i$.

Assume for simplicity that each factor adjusts to the desired level in a first-order fashion:

$$\text{Factor}_i = \text{INTEGRAL}(\text{Change in Factor}_i, \text{Factor}_{i, t_0}) \tag{13-102}$$

$$\text{Change in Factor}_i = (\text{Factor}_i^* - \text{Factor}_i)/AT_i \tag{13-103}$$

The adjustment time AT is longer for capital than for labor.[9] Finally, assume demand and the prices of each factor P_i (the cost of capital and the wage) are exogenous.

Build the model, selecting parameters you believe are appropriate given the adjustment times and other considerations. Section 11.5 provides guidance on parameters for capital investment.

Simulate the model under the following conditions:

1. Unanticipated changes in demand (both increases and decreases)
2. Unanticipated changes in the price of each factor.

In each case, does the model end up at the appropriate equilibrium? Since the managers represented in the model do not know the equilibrium factor stocks they should be using, how do their responses to imbalances enable them to respond to changes in factor prices or productivity? What are the adjustment dynamics, and why? What defects do you see in the model, and how might you correct them?

13.2.13   Resource Allocation

It is often necessary to allocate resources among multiple uses. The total demand for automobiles is divided among each producer. The capacity of a firm is divided among different products. A worker's time is allocated to production, training, maintenance, process improvement, and other tasks. Formulations for resource allocation must ensure that the share of the resource going to each use remains between zero and one and that the sum of the resources going to each use equals the total resource available. A useful formulation for resource allocation give each use a share of the resource proportional to its contribution to the total attractiveness of all uses and is known as SHARE = US/(US + THEM).

---

[9]A more realistic model uses the stock management structure to represent the capital and labor supply chains (chapters 17 and 19), and might model labor requirements as embodied in the capital stock, as in section 12.2.

Assume there are n possible uses for a resource. For concreteness, consider the problem of determining the market share of n competitors in an industry with total demand D_T. The share of demand going to each firm is given by its attractiveness, A_i, relative to the sum of the attractiveness levels of all competitors:

$$D_i = S_i * D_T \qquad (13\text{-}104)$$

$$S_i = A_i \Big/ \sum_{k=1}^{n} A_k \qquad (13\text{-}105)$$

$$A_i = f(a_{i1}, a_{i2}, \ldots, a_{im}) \qquad (13\text{-}106)$$

where attractiveness is a function of various attributes a_{ij}. There may be $j = 1, \ldots, m$ attributes, such as price, delivery delay, quality, functionality, warranty terms, service capability, and so on. No matter how attractiveness is formulated, the share going to any firm is bounded between zero and one, and the sum of the shares always equals one (as long as $A_i \geq 0$).

Many formulations for attractiveness are possible. Usually the true underlying attractiveness function is approximated by a multiplicatively separable formulation:

$$A_i = f_1(a_{i1}) * f_2(a_{i2}) * \cdots * f_m(a_{im}) \qquad (13\text{-}107)$$

The product of individual effects is usually better than the sum for the same robustness reasons discussed in section 13.2.7. The individual effects can in principle be any nonlinear function. A common choice is the exponential function

$$f_j(a_{ij}) = \exp(k_j * a_{ij}/a_j^*) \qquad (13\text{-}108)$$

where k_j is the sensitivity of attractiveness to attribute j and a_j^* is the reference value of attribute j. With the exponential function for the individual attributes of attractiveness, the US/(US + THEM) formulation is known as the *logit* model because the share going to any option follows a logistic curve as the attractiveness of that option is increased relative to the others. Section 10.8 uses the logit model to model market share.

The logit model is convenient because it can be estimated by linear regression. However, the formulations for attractiveness need not be exponential, and indeed, the exponential is generally not robust in extreme conditions. You should specify the effects of the individual attributes on attractiveness to capture appropriate nonlinearities and not simply assume they follow any particular analytic function such as the exponential.

13.3 COMMON PITFALLS

The formulations above provide templates you can use to create meaningful, robust formulations for the decision rules in models. This section discusses several common pitfalls to be avoided.

13.3.1 All Outflows Require First-Order Control

Real stocks such as inventories, personnel, cash, and other resources cannot become negative. You must formulate the rates in your models so that these stocks remain nonnegative even under extreme conditions. Doing so requires all outflows to have *first-order control*. First-order control means the outflows are governed by a first-order negative feedback loop that shuts down the flow as the stock drops to zero. For example, shipments of finished goods from inventory must be zero when inventory is zero no matter how great the demand for the product. These loops must be first-order because any time delay could allow the flow to continue even after the stock falls to zero. As discussed above, these outflow-limiting loops are often highly nonlinear, having no effect under normal conditions but sharply constricting the flow when the stock becomes small relative to normal.

A useful generic formulation to prevent nonnegativity of a stock sets the outflow to the lesser of the desired rate or the maximum rate:

$$\text{Outflow} = \text{MIN(Desired Outflow, Maximum Outflow)} \qquad (13\text{-}109)$$

The maximum outflow rate depends on the quantity in the stock and the minimum time required to drain it:

$$\text{Maximum Outflow} = \text{Stock/Minimum Residence Time} \qquad (13\text{-}110)$$

In many situations the constraint imposed by the maximum outflow rate gradually becomes binding. In these cases, you should use the fuzzy minimum function (section 13.2.8):

$$\text{Outflow} = \text{Desired Outflow} * \text{Effect of Availability on Outflow} \qquad (13\text{-}111)$$

$$\begin{aligned}&\text{Effect of Availability on Outflow}\\&\quad = f(\text{Maximum Outflow/Desired Outflow}); f(0) = 0, f' \geq 0\end{aligned} \qquad (13\text{-}112)$$

Under normal conditions when the stock is in ample supply, the outflow equals the desired rate. If the stock falls far enough, however, the outflow will be constrained and the stock will fall exponentially to zero. You should check to make sure every outflow from every real stock in your model has first-order control.

Example

The shipment rate from a firm's inventory can be formulated as the lesser of the desired shipment rate (based on demand) or the maximum shipment rate (based on inventory availability). The maximum shipment rate is given by inventory and the minimum time required to process and fill an order.

$$\text{Inventory} = \text{INTEGRAL(Production} - \text{Shipments, Inventory}_{t_0}) \qquad (13\text{-}113)$$

$$\text{Shipments} = \text{MIN(Desired Shipments, Maximum Shipments)} \qquad (13\text{-}114)$$

$$\text{Maximum Shipments} = \text{Inventory/Minimum Order Fulfillment Time} \qquad (13\text{-}115)$$

Under normal conditions when inventory is ample, shipments equal desired shipments and the availability loop is not active. Only when inventory drops far enough will availability constrain shipments. The use of a MIN function is appropriate for the case where all inventory is identical (no aggregation of different products or warehouse locations). When the model aggregates different product types and sites together, there is some probability of local stock outs for particular items even when aggregate inventory is sufficient. In these cases, the fuzzy minimum function should be used, as in chapter 18.

CHALLENGE	### Preventing Negative Stocks

Preventing Negative Stocks

The cash balance of a business is increased by receipts and decreased by payments. Cash cannot become negative. To ensure this is so, a modeler proposes the following formulation for payments:

$$\text{Payments} = \text{IF (Cash} > 0) \text{ THEN (Required Payments) ELSE (0)} \qquad (13\text{-}116)$$

where the IF (P) THEN (Q) ELSE (R) function returns Q if P is true and R otherwise.

Identify at least two flaws in this formulation. Hint: What is the minimum payment time (analogous to the minimum order fulfillment time in the shipment rate example)?

Reformulate the payment rate to be robust, dimensionally consistent, and behaviorally plausible.

13.3.2 Avoid IF . . . THEN . . . ELSE Formulations

Many modelers, especially those with strong computer programming backgrounds, are tempted to make extensive use of logical statements such as IF . . . THEN . . . ELSE. Resist the temptation. Conditional statements such as IF . . . THEN . . . ELSE introduce sharp discontinuities into your models, discontinuities that are often inappropriate. Individual decisions are rarely entirely either/or. In many situations the decision is a compromise or (possibly nonlinearly) weighted average of competing pressures. In the cash balance example from the challenge above, the firm is not likely to continue to pay all its bills fully and on time until its cash is completely exhausted but will gradually cut back and defer payments as its cash on hand dwindles. Even when individual decisions are sharply discontinuous, most models aggregate a population of individual agents with heterogeneous characteristics, smoothing out the relationships. Even if each firm in an industry followed the policy of paying in full until cash is completely exhausted, the distribution of liquidity among firms in the industry means payments would vary smoothly as the average cash balance changes.

On a practical note, conditional statements such as IF . . . THEN . . . ELSE are often difficult to understand, especially when the conditions are complex or nested with others (see 13-122) for an example).[10]

13.3.3 Disaggregate Net Flows

In general you should model inflows and outflows from a stock explicitly rather than as a single net flow. Instead of a single net hiring rate, for example, it is usually better to model the hiring, layoff, and voluntary quit rates separately. Instead of net migration, model inmigration and outmigration separately.

---

[10]While you should generally avoid conditionals in modeling decision making, there are occasional exceptions (e.g., the nonlinear smoothing structure in section 11.4.1). Conditionals can also be useful in representing switches to select among different policies or scenarios for model testing.

There are several reasons for this practice. First, the decision processes governing the various flows often differ. These differences can include differences in the information inputs used in the decision and the decision rule for processing the cues. Time delays can differ as well. Second, it is often difficult to create robust and transparent formulations for net flows.

Consider a firm's labor force. A simple model assumes the labor force adjusts to the desired labor force through a net hiring rate:

Net Hiring = (Desired Labor − Labor)/Labor Adjustment Time   (13-117)

This formulation assumes labor rises as fast as it falls. In the real world, these adjustments are governed by different delays and different constraints. It can take substantially longer to find, recruit, and train new workers than it can to lay them off, so the symmetrical adjustment time for increases and decreases is often not appropriate. The net hiring rate is gross hiring less voluntary quits and any layoffs. These decisions are made by different groups of people using different cues and are limited by different constraints. Hiring depends on the firm's desired hiring rate but is constrained by the availability of workers with the skills the firm seeks. Potential new hires judge the desirability of taking the firm's offer on the basis of indirect information: The firm's reputation, word of mouth about what it's like to work there, and so on. It takes time to form and revise these perceptions. Current workers, however, know what it's actually like to work there, so the quit rate is affected by different information than the hire rate.

Aggregating inflows and outflows into a single net rate also makes it hard to capture costs accurately. A firm with a net hiring rate of zero could have employee turnover of 10%/year or 1000%/year. In the former case, the costs of hiring, training, and recruiting are low and the average experience of the workers will be high; in the latter case human resources costs are high and average experience is low. Because the net rate does not distinguish between the two cases, it cannot properly model the costs or consequences of employee turnover.

Finally, it is often difficult to formulate robust net rates. Consider the labor force model in section 12.1.7. The labor force is represented with a two-cohort aging chain consisting of rookie (new) employees and experienced employees. Rookies become experienced after an average assimilation time. Both rookies and experienced workers quit at certain fractional rates. Suppose the modeler attempted to aggregate hiring and layoffs into a single Net Hiring Rate (the net change in the labor force is then Net Hiring – Total Quit Rate). Net hiring can be formulated simply using the classic Inflow = Replacement + Stock Adjustment form:

Net Hiring Rate = Total Quit Rate + Adjustment for Labor   (13-118)

Adjustment for Labor = (Desired Labor – Labor)/Labor Adjustment Time (13-119)

If desired labor is much less than actual labor, the adjustment for labor could easily exceed turnover, causing the net hiring rate to become negative. That is not a problem per se—after all, rookies can be fired. However, the net hiring rate could still be negative even after all new employees have been fired, causing the absurd result of negative rookie employees.

The modeler might correctly recognize that when net hiring is negative there must be first-order control on the outflow rate so that layoffs go to zero when rookies are zero. However, the number of rookies only constrains net hiring when net hiring is negative. After some trial and error, the modeler defines two new variables:

$$\text{Indicated Net Hiring} = \text{Total Quits} + \text{Adjustment for Labor} \qquad (13\text{-}120)$$

$$\text{Maximum Layoff Rate} = \text{Rookies/Layoff Time} \qquad (13\text{-}121)$$

Indicated net hiring is the net rate the firm would like to have before any constraints are applied. The maximum layoff rate will limit layoffs so that the stock of rookies never becomes negative. The layoff time represents the amount of notice management must give terminated employees. The net hiring rate then becomes

$$\text{Net Hiring Rate} = \text{IF (Indicated Net Hiring} > 0) \text{ THEN (Indicated Net Hiring)}$$
$$\text{ELSE } (-\text{MIN}(-\text{Indicated Net Hiring, Maximum Layoff Rate})) \qquad (13\text{-}122)$$

This formulation works in the sense that the rookie population will never become negative, but it is poor modeling practice because other formulation principles are violated to ensure the formulation is robust. The equation involves nested logical statements and embodies several different ideas. How long did it take you to parse (13-122) and understand that it will work? Few clients will find this formulation intuitive and may lose confidence in the model. A better formulation would represent the hiring rate separately from the layoff rate:

$$\text{Hiring Rate} = \text{MAX}(0, \text{Indicated Net Hiring}) \qquad (13\text{-}123)$$

$$\text{Layoff Rate} = \text{MIN}(\text{Indicated Layoff Rate, Maximum Layoff Rate}) \qquad (13\text{-}124)$$

$$\text{Indicated Layoff Rate} = \text{MAX}(0, -\text{Indicated Hiring Rate}) \qquad (13\text{-}125)$$

This formulation is fully robust (rookies can never become negative) and much easier to understand. Each equation contains only one idea. The individual formulations can be modified as needed to enhance model realism; in particular, layoffs and hiring need not be based on the same information. The MAX and MIN functions in the formulation are easily replaced by their fuzzy equivalents to eliminate unrealistic discontinuities. The structure and principles in this section apply to any resource, not only labor.

13.4   SUMMARY

Discovering the decision rules of the actors in a system and representing them in models is challenging and requires skillful combination of theory, experiment, and observation. While there are many theories about the degree of sophistication and rationality of human decision making, all models must conform to basic principles of formulation. Decision rules and models must be robust in extreme conditions so that physical impossibilities cannot occur, no matter how extreme the inputs to the decision rules may be. All equations must be dimensionally consistent without the use of arbitrary fudge factors with no real world meaning. The decision rules in models cannot utilize information the real decision makers do not have, such as information about the future, about hypothetical contingencies, and about the current value of variables whose values are only known with a delay.

This chapter developed a number of standard formulations for robust rate equations. These canonical formulations provide templates for use in your own models. You should use the simplest formulation you can that conforms to the principles outlined here and suits the purpose of the model.

14

Formulating Nonlinear Relationships

Up until now most economists have concerned themselves with linear systems, not because of any belief that the facts were so simple, but rather because of the mathematical difficulties involved in nonlinear systems ... [Linear systems are] mathematically simple, and exact solutions are known. But a high price is paid for this simplicity in terms of special assumptions which must be made.
—Paul A. Samuelson (1947, p. 288)

Nonlinear relationships are fundamental in the dynamics of systems of all types. A company regularly ships at the desired rate—unless inventory is inadequate. Improvements in nutrition and health care boost life expectancy—up to a point. The demand for a product must tend to zero as availability or quality fall to zero, no matter how cheap it is. The importance of nonlinearities has been recognized for centuries (e.g., the straw that broke the camel's back, you can't push on a rope), but it is only since the advent of computer simulation that nonlinearity has become important in dynamic modeling. This chapter describes the formulation of realistic and robust nonlinear relationships for use in dynamic models. The focus is specifying the appropriate shapes and values for nonlinear functions, drawing on all available information, both qualitative and quantitative. The chapter also presents a practical method for eliciting information about nonlinear relationships from experts. Examples from manufacturing, the service industry, product development, and other contexts illustrate the principles.

14.1   TABLE FUNCTIONS

Many of the formulations in system dynamics models involve nonlinear functions $Y = f(X)$. Sometimes these functions are specified analytically, for example, $f(X) = X^a$. More often, nonlinear relationships are captured using lookup or *table functions*, where the relationship is specified as a table of values for the independent and dependent variables. Linear interpolation is used for values between the specified points. The function $Y = f(X)$ is represented as

$$Y = \text{Effect of X on Y} \tag{14-1}$$

$$\text{Effect of X on Y} = \text{Table for Effect of X on Y}(X) \tag{14-2}$$

$$\text{Table for Effect of X on Y} = (x_1, y_1), (x_2, y_2), \ldots, (x_n, y_n) \tag{14-3}$$

where (x_i, y_i) represents each pair of points defining the relationship. Figure 13-2 provides an example. All system dynamics software packages support table functions. In most, the extreme values are used if the independent variable exceeds the specified domain (some support linear extrapolation using the slope defined by the last two points).[1]

14.1.1   Specifying Table Functions

The information you need to specify the shape and values for nonlinear relationships can be gleaned from various sources, including statistical studies, fieldwork, interviews, considerations of extreme conditions, and physical laws. Some table functions represent physical constraints, others represent purely behavioral influences, and some capture both types of effect. Table 14-1 gives guidelines for specifying the shapes and estimating the values of table functions.

14.1.2   Example: Building a Nonlinear Function

To illustrate the steps in formulating a nonlinear function, consider a firm operating a make-to-order system. Orders accumulate in the backlog until completed and shipped. Shipments are determined by the size of the backlog but are limited by the firm's production capacity. This structure, known as a capacitated delay, is very common. It arises any time the outflow from a stock depends on the quantity in the stock and normal residence time but is also constrained by a maximum capacity. Besides the make-to-order case, examples include work in process inventory and the production rate, the rate at which customers and paperwork are processed in any service delivery supply chain, and the completion rate of tasks in any project. Figure 14-1 shows the structure of the system.

The average residence time for orders in the backlog (the delivery delay) is the ratio of the backlog to the current shipment rate:

$$\text{Delivery Delay} = \text{Backlog/Shipments} \tag{14-4}$$

$$\text{Backlog} = \text{INTEGRAL}(\text{Orders} - \text{Shipments}, \text{Backlog}_{t_0}) \tag{14-5}$$

---

[1]Most system dynamics software packages issue a warning whenever an input to a table function moves outside the range of specified values. These warnings are helpful diagnostics to ensure that the system is operating where you believe it should.

TABLE 14-1
Guidelines for formulating table functions

1. Normalize the input and output, if appropriate. Instead of $Y = f(X)$, normalize the function so that the input is the dimensionless ratio of the input to a reference value X^* and the output is a dimensionless effect modifying the reference value Y^*, $Y = Y^*f(X/X^*)$.

2. Identify the reference points where the values of the function are determined by definition. For example, in normalized functions of the form $Y = Y^*f(X/X^*)$, the function usually must pass through the point $(1, 1)$ so that $Y = Y^*$ when $X = X^*$.

3. Identify reference policies. Reference policies are lines or curves corresponding to standard or extreme policies. The reference policy $f(X/X^*) = 1$ represents the policy that X has no effect on Y. The 45° line represents the policy that Y varies 1% for every 1% change in X and is often a meaningful reference policy. Use the reference policy curves to rule out infeasible regions.

4. Consider extreme conditions. What values must the function take at extremes such as $-\infty$, 0, and $+\infty$? If there are multiple nonlinear effects in the formulation, check that the formulation makes sense for all combinations of extreme values and that the slopes of the effects at the normal operating points conform to any reference policies and constraints on the overall response of the output.

5. Specify the domain for the independent variable so that it includes the full range of possible values, including extreme conditions, not only the normal operating region.

6. Identify the plausible shapes for the function within the feasible region defined by the extreme conditions, reference points, and reference policy lines. Select the shape you believe best corresponds to the data (numerical and qualitative). Justify any inflection points. Interpret the shapes in terms of the physical constraints and policies of the decision maker.

7. Specify the values for your best estimate of the function. Use increments small enough to get the smoothness you require. Examine the increments between values to make sure there are no kinks you cannot justify. If numerical data are available you can often estimate the values statistically. If numerical data are not available, make a judgmental estimate using the best information you have. Often, judgmental estimates provide sufficient accuracy, particularly early in a project, and help focus subsequent modeling and data collection efforts (see item 9 below).

8. Run the model and test to make sure the behavior of the formulation and nonlinear function is reasonable. Check that the input varies over the appropriate range (e.g., that the input is not operating off the ends of the function at all times).

9. Test the sensitivity of your results to plausible variations in the values of the function. If sensitivity analysis shows that the results change significantly over the range of uncertainty in the relationship, you need to gather more data to reduce the uncertainty. If the results are not sensitive to the assumed values, then you do not need to spend additional resources to estimate the function more accurately.

FIGURE 14-1
Structure for a
capacitated delay

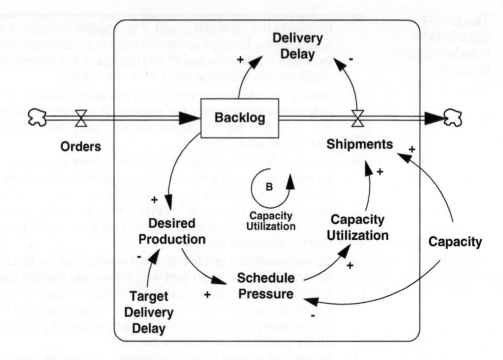

Desired Production depends on the backlog and the target delivery delay:

Desired Production = Backlog/Target Delivery Delay   (14-6)

A simple formulation would specify shipments as a nonlinear function of desired production, saturating at high levels as capacity is reached:

Shipments = f(Desired Production)   (14-7)

Data on shipments and backlog might be used to estimate the function for the shipment rate in (14-7).

1. Normalization.

Equation (14-7) is not robust as it only applies given the firm's current capacity. If capacity changes, through productivity improvements or the acquisition of new equipment, the relationship would change. Even if you believe capacity won't change over the current time horizon of the model, it is better to normalize the relationship so that the model will work properly in case capacity were to change or in case the client wanted to explore policies where capacity changed. Normalize the relationship by defining shipments as the product of capacity and capacity utilization:

Shipments = Capacity * Capacity Utilization   (14-8)

Utilization becomes a function of schedule pressure, the ratio of desired production to capacity:

Capacity Utilization = f(Schedule Pressure)   (14-9)

Schedule Pressure = Desired Production/Capacity   (14-10)

Schedule pressure measures the pressure to produce above or below the normal rate. Normalizing means both the input and output of the function are dimensionless ratios.

2. Reference points.

Capacity can be defined as the normal rate of output achievable given the firm's resources. Given that definition, the capacity utilization function must pass through the reference point (1, 1): When Schedule Pressure = 1, Shipments = Desired Production = Capacity and the actual delivery delay equals the target.

The normalization chosen here defines capacity as the normal rate of output, not the maximum possible rate when heroic efforts are made. If you preferred to define capacity as the maximum possible output, implying utilization is less than one under normal conditions, then Schedule Pressure would be defined as Desired Production/(Normal Capacity Utilization * Capacity). The utilization function would pass through the reference point (1, Normal Capacity Utilization) and saturate at one. The normalization and reference point are arbitrary as long as you are consistent.

3. Reference policies.

There are three reference policy lines for the relationship. First, the line Capacity Utilization CU = 1 corresponds to a policy where Shipments always equal Capacity. Second, the 45° line CU = SP (Schedule Pressure) corresponds to a policy where utilization is varied just enough so the firm always produces at the desired rate. Third, the line CU = s_{max} * SP, where s_{max} is the maximum slope of the function, corresponds to the policy of producing and delivering as fast as possible, that is, with the minimum delivery delay. To see why, substitute the reference policy CU = s_{max} * SP into the equation for Shipments:

$$
\begin{aligned}
\text{Shipments} &= \text{Capacity} * \text{Capacity Utilization} \\
&= C * s_{max} * SP \\
&= C * s_{max} * DP/C \\
&= s_{max} * DP \\
&= s_{max} * B/DD^*
\end{aligned}
\tag{14-11}
$$

where DP is Desired Production, C is Capacity, and DD^* is the Target Delivery Delay. Substituting into the equation for delivery delay yields the minimum delivery delay DD_{min}:

$$
DD_{min} = B/(s_{max} * B/DD^*) = DD^*/s_{max}
\tag{14-12}
$$

Solving for s_{max},

$$
s_{max} = DD^*/DD_{min}
\tag{14-13}
$$

The minimum delivery delay thus determines the value of s_{max} and further limits the feasible region for the utilization function.

4. Extreme conditions.

Turning to the extreme conditions, the utilization function must pass through the point (0, 0) because shipments must be zero when schedule pressure is zero or else the backlog could become negative, an impossibility. At the other extreme, high schedule pressure eventually causes utilization to saturate at the maximum feasible rate, CU_{max}.

5. Specifying the domain for the independent variable.

The domain for the input to a table should be wide enough to capture the full range of possible values, not only the range observed in the data. Schedule Pressure cannot be less than zero, but could in principle rise to infinity. However, since Capacity Utilization saturates at a maximum value for large values of Schedule Pressure, the function need only be specified for values large enough to ensure that it has reached its saturation point. The data might suggest that maximum output is reached by the point SP = 2. To be safe and allow for sensitivity analysis, you specify the function over the interval [0, 2.5].

6. Plausible shapes for the function.

The reference policies and extreme conditions define a rather narrow region in which the true utilization function must lie. The function must lie below the line $CU = s_{max} * SP$ because orders cannot be delivered faster than the minimum delivery delay. It must also lie below the reference policy $CU = CU_{max}$ since utilization cannot be greater than its maximum. When Schedule Pressure is greater than one, the firm would not produce at less than the normal rate nor would it produce more than desired. Similarly, when schedule pressure is below one, the firm would not cut production back more than needed to meet the low level of desired production, nor would it produce at utilization rates greater than one. The resulting feasible region is rather small.

To bound the relationship further, you turn to the data. Numerical data on desired production, capacity, and shipments may be available so you can estimate the relationship statistically. However, most often such data are difficult to get and only span a limited range, providing no information about the extreme values. Qualitative data gained from fieldwork and interviews are extremely helpful in these circumstances. Your discussions might show that management prefers to utilize capacity fully and avoid layoffs if it can. When schedule pressure is low, management cuts utilization back less than proportionately, allowing the backlog to run down instead. Therefore the slope of the function is less than one at the normal point where SP = 1. When schedule pressure is very low there is a lot of excess capacity and the firm can produce at close to the minimum delivery delay. Therefore utilization rises close to the reference policy defining the minimum delivery delay. As it rises, it becomes more and more difficult to deliver in the minimum time. Utilization rises steadily, but at ever-diminishing rates. When schedule pressure exceeds one, utilization rises less than the amount required to produce at the desired rate, until it saturates at maximum output.

7. Specifying the values of the function.

The principal uncertainties are the maximum of the function and the minimum delivery delay. Review of the data and discussions with management might reveal normal capacity utilization to be about 80%, implying the maximum value of the Effect of Schedule Pressure on Shipments to be 1/0.80 = 1.25. Suppose also that delivery delay can never be less than about 75% of normal. These two data points tightly circumscribe the plausible values for the function. Thus even if numerical data to estimate the relationship statistically are not available, you can have confidence that judgmental estimates of the function are reasonable. If numerical data are available, you can use them to refine the estimated values of the function further. Figure 14-2 shows the selected function and values, along with the increments between values. The slope diminishes monotonically: There are no kinks or inflections in the table. Values are specified in increments of 0.25, giving a reasonably smooth function. If necessary for the purpose, you can specify more points until you achieve the smoothness you require.

8.   Testing the formulation.

Many industries experience cyclical patterns in demand. A good starting point for testing is to assume orders vary cyclically with an amplitude A and period P around an average equal to capacity:

$$\text{Orders} = \text{Capacity} * [1 + A\sin(2\pi t/P)] \tag{14-14}$$

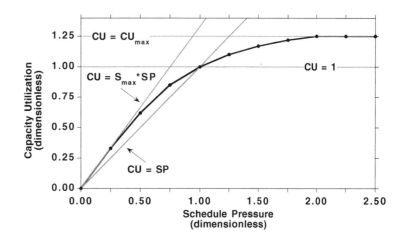

FIGURE 14-2

Formulating a table function for capacity utilization

By calculating the increments between points you can check that there are no inappropriate kinks or changes in slope for the function.

Schedule Pressure	Capacity Utilization	Increment
0.00	0.00	
0.25	0.33	0.33
0.50	0.62	0.29
0.75	0.85	0.23
1.00	1.00	0.15
1.25	1.10	0.10
1.50	1.17	0.07
1.75	1.22	0.05
2.00	1.25	0.03
2.25	1.25	0.00
2.50	1.25	0.00

For illustrative purposes, assume the Target Delivery Delay = 1 month and Capacity = 100 units/month. Many industries experience peak-to-trough swings in utilization of 15% or more over their characteristic cycles (see chapters 17 and 20 for examples), implying a larger swing in orders, so set A = 0.20 and P = 12 months.

Figure 14-3 shows the resulting behavior. In steady state the 20% peak-to-trough swing in orders causes schedule pressure to vary from 0.76 to 1.33. Capacity utilization varies less, from 0.86 to 1.12, because the slope of the utilization function is less than one near the operating point. Average schedule pressure is 1.05. The saturation nonlinearity means shipments respond less to high schedule pressure than low. The backlog therefore builds up until schedule pressure is just high enough for shipments to equal orders on average over the full cycle. For the same reason, the average delivery delay is 1.04, greater than normal. Note also the phase lag between orders and shipments. The relative amplitudes and phase relationships among orders, shipments, utilization, and delivery delay are all reasonable and consistent with the dynamics observed in a wide range of industries.

9. Sensitivity analysis.
The feasible region for capacity utilization defined by the reference policies and extreme conditions tightly constrains the plausible values of the function.

FIGURE 14-3
Behavior of the capacitated delay with cyclical orders

Orders fluctuate ±20% with a 1-year period. Note the amplification of desired production and the phase lag between orders and shipments.

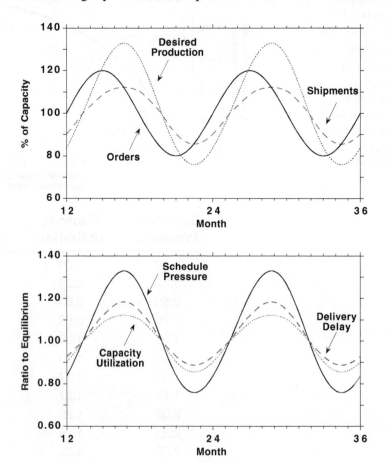

Nevertheless, it is important to test the sensitivity of the results to uncertainty in the assumed shape and values of all nonlinear functions. Suppose the numerical data and client expert opinion suggest the following: The slope around the operating point might vary by $\pm 25\%$ from your best estimate; maximum utilization might vary between 1.20 and 1.30; and the minimum delivery delay might be as small as 60% of normal, or as high as 85% of normal. Remembering the overconfidence bias (section 8.2.5), you suspect these confidence limits are too narrow. You decide to test the sensitivity of the system to much wider variations in the assumed capacity utilization function. You vary the slope at the operating point by a factor of ± 2, allow maximum utilization to vary between 1.12 and 1.5, and vary the minimum delivery delay from twice as large as normal to the other extreme where it equals the target value (Figure 14-4).

Many people expect that a factor of two variation in the responsiveness of the relationship will induce a factor of two variation in capacity utilization. If there were no feedback processes in the system, this intuition would be correct. In the base case the peak-to-trough variation in schedule pressure is 1.33 to 0.76, causing utilization to vary from 1.12 to 0.86, a range of 0.26. If there were no

FIGURE 14-4

Alternative capacity utilization functions for sensitivity analysis

The flat and steep cases vary the responsiveness of utilization to schedule pressure by a factor of two relative to the base case.

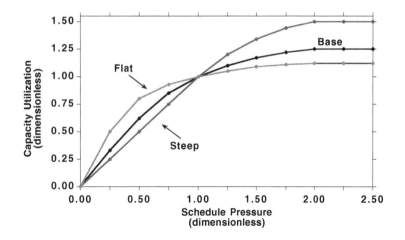

Schedule Pressure	Flat Case	Base Case	Steep Case
0.00	0.00	0.00	0.00
0.25	0.50	0.33	0.25
0.50	0.80	0.62	0.50
0.75	0.93	0.85	0.75
1.00	1.00	1.00	1.00
1.25	1.05	1.10	1.20
1.50	1.09	1.17	1.34
1.75	1.11	1.22	1.44
2.00	1.12	1.25	1.50
2.25	1.12	1.25	1.50
2.50	1.12	1.25	1.50

feedback between utilization and schedule pressure, then the steep case should induce swings in utilization from 1.24 to 0.76, a range 85% greater than the base case.[2] Instead, utilization in the steep case varies from 1.17 to 0.82, only 35% more than the base case. Similarly, under the flat case, the base case variation in schedule pressure should cause utilization to vary from 1.06 to 0.93, a range 50% as large as the base case. Utilization actually varies from 1.07 to 0.90, some 65% as much as the base case.

The intuition that a function twice as steep will cause variations in the output of the function twice as large assumes no feedback. It reflects an open-loop mental model. With utilization more responsive to schedule pressure, output rises more than the base case, draining the backlog faster and reducing schedule pressure. As shown in Figure 14-5, schedule pressure in the steep case varies only from 0.82 to 1.21, a range 32% less than the base case. In the flat case, less responsive utilization forces the backlog to higher peak levels during order upswings and lower troughs during downswings. Schedule pressure ranges from 1.40 to 0.70, 23% more than the base case. Overall, open-loop considerations predict the peak-to-trough range of utilization would vary from 0.48 to 0.13 between the steep and flat cases. Because the negative feedback regulating backlog compensates for changes in the values of the utilization function, the actual change in the range of utilization is only 0.35 to 0.17, only half as much.

The sensitivity results demonstrate a general principle. The behavior of complex feedback systems is often insensitive to large variations in many parameters. In this case there is only a single negative feedback loop, yet a factor of two change in the strength of the relationship causes the range of utilization to change by only ± 35%. A more complete model might include additional negative feedbacks that would further reduce the sensitivity of the behavior to variations in the responsiveness of utilization to schedule pressure. For example, high schedule pressure also means high delivery delays, which typically depress new orders and lead to cancellations, reducing schedule pressure and utilization. Many systems contain so many interacting negative feedbacks that their behavior is quite insensitive to large variations in parameters. Indeed, the function of most negative feedbacks is to reduce the sensitivity of a system to unpredictable disturbances including changes in parameters. Most systems contain a great many negative feedbacks for precisely this reason. The negative loops constitute control processes that were designed, or evolved, to compensate for changes in the environment or in the characteristics of system actors and components.

There are three important caveats to the principle that many systems are relatively insensitive to variations in parameters. First, there are exceptions. Not all systems are dominated by negative feedback. In path-dependent systems and others dominated by positive feedback, small changes in parameters can cumulate to large effects. Further, most systems contain a few influential parameters that do greatly affect their behavior. These high leverage points must

---

[2]The open-loop variation in utilization is less than ± 2 because utilization depends nonlinearly on schedule pressure, in particular, because utilization saturates for high values of schedule pressure (calculate the sensitivities for a smaller or larger amplitude cycle in orders to see the effect).

FIGURE 14-5

Sensitivity analysis illustrates compensating feedback.

The negative feedback loop regulating utilization through schedule pressure compensates for the assumed change in the utilization function. Utilization is about half as sensitive to changes in the utilization function than open-loop considerations suggest.

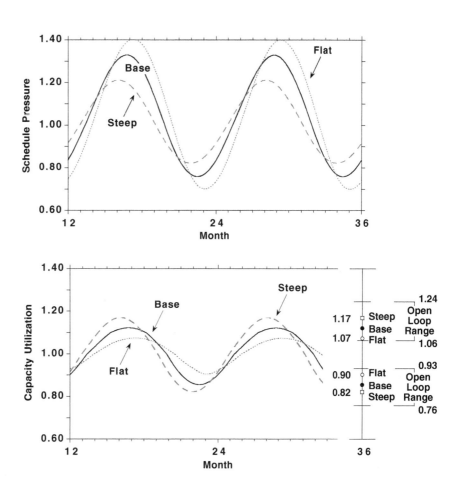

Base Case	Flat Case		Steep Case	
Range of CU	Open Loop	Closed Loop	Open Loop	Closed Loop
0.26	0.13	0.17	0.48	0.35
Change from Base	−50%	−35%	85%	35%

be identified and modeled carefully. They are also the best intervention points for effective policies; identifying them is a major goal of sensitivity analysis.

Second, real systems are highly nonlinear, so the sensitivity of behavior to assumptions can differ as the system moves from one operating regime to another. In nonlinear systems the sensitivity of a system to variations in multiple parameters is not a simple combination of the response to the parameters varied alone. System behavior can be quite insensitive to a relationship in one operating regime but highly sensitive to that same parameter under different conditions. For example, the behavior of an innovation diffusion system depends strongly on the strength of the positive word of mouth feedback during the growth phase, but is totally insensitive to that same loop after the market has saturated. In nonlinear systems sensitivity analysis requires multiple tests for multiple operating points and conditions.

Finally, the criteria for deciding what constitutes a significant impact on your results depend on the purpose of the model. The numerical values of the variables do change between the flat, base, and steep utilization cases; the model exhibits *numerical sensitivity* (though less than open-loop thinking predicts). If the purpose of the model required very small tolerances, these changes might matter, in which case you must attempt to reduce the uncertainty by additional empirical study or by designing policies that further reduce the sensitivity of the system to parameter variations. In many cases, however, the purpose of the modeling process is to understand the patterns of behavior generated by the system or to design policies that lead to greater success. A model whose basic modes of behavior change as assumptions are varied over the plausible range of uncertainty is said to exhibit *behavior mode sensitivity*. Changes in the desirability of policies indicate *policy sensitivity* (see chapter 21 for further discussion).

Though the sensitivity tests conducted here are not comprehensive, variations in the capacity utilization function far greater than the likely uncertainty in its values are unlikely to alter significant model results such as the modes of behavior it generates or the relative desirability of policies. If that result holds up after further testing, it means the judgmental estimate of the utilization function derived above provides sufficient accuracy. It would be an inefficient use of time and resources to gather additional data in an attempt to refine the estimated relationship further. Limited resources can best be used for other purposes such as estimating those parameters and relationships that do matter to the results.

14.1.3   Process Point: Table Functions versus Analytic Functions

Why use table functions at all? Why not use an appropriate analytic function to capture any nonlinear relationships? Diminishing returns can be captured by $y = \log(x)$ or $y = x^a$ for $a < 1$. Saturation nonlinearities can be captured by $y = \arctan(x)$ or $y = ax/(k + x)$. S-shaped curves can be captured by the logistic curve $y = y_{max}/[1 + \exp(-a(x - b))]$. And so on. Why not use these analytic functions rather than the cumbersome tables?

As always, the answer depends on the purpose of the model and the expectations and criteria of your client. Analytic functions do have some advantages. They are generally smooth and differentiable, while table functions are only piecewise continuous (the slopes of the tables jump at each point). Table functions sometimes lead to small kinks in the behavior of model variables (see Figure 14-16). Analytic functions are often defined over the entire domain of real numbers, or at least the positive real numbers, so you don't have to worry about what happens outside the specified values for the input in a table.

Analytic functions also pose problems. First, analytic functions are not as flexible as table functions. Simple analytic functions often do not allow you to control the shape, slopes, and saturation points of the function while ensuring the function always remains in the feasible region defined by the reference policies. For example, you might approximate the capacity utilization function in Figure 14-2 with the function

$$CU = CU_{max} * SP/[(CU_{max} - 1) + SP] \qquad (14\text{-}15)$$

The function always passes through the reference point $(1, 1)$ and saturates at the maximum capacity utilization CU_{max}, but you cannot separately specify the slope at the origin so that it conforms to the reference policy defined by the minimum delivery delay. In fact, for realistic values of CU_{max} the implied minimum delivery delay is implausibly short. More complicated functions with more parameters can increase flexibility and overcome these problems but reduce transparency and ease of use.

Second, many clients find it difficult to interpret the meaning and visualize the shape of functions such as $y = y_{max}/[1 + \exp(-a(x - b))]$. Anything that slows client understanding reduces their confidence in the model and ultimately cuts the chances the modeling process will change client beliefs or behavior. Finally, analytic functions follow a particular shape or a small number of possible shapes. Suppose you used $CU = CU_{max} * SP/[(CU_{max} - 1) + SP]$ for capacity utilization, but your clients then asserted that actually the function was s-shaped. You could not test the clients' hypothesis without coming up with an entirely different function. At the least, the process would grind to a halt while you selected an appropriate s-shaped function and estimated its parameters; at worst, you might become defensive and resist the clients' request, destroying their confidence in the model and in you. With a table function, the clients can take the mouse and draw any shape they want in less than a minute, then run the model themselves, involving them more deeply in the modeling process and freeing up valuable time to focus on the issues of concern instead of technical details.

14.2 CASE STUDY: CUTTING CORNERS VERSUS OVERTIME

A structure closely related to the capacity utilization formulation above arises often in models where labor is the primary determinant of capacity. These situations arise in service delivery settings, in project management, in back-office operations, in manufacturing—in any situation where workers must process a stock of tasks. There are only four options available to an organization when the backlog of tasks rises: (1) reduce the arrival rate of new tasks (or cancel some pending tasks); (2) add service capacity; (3) increase the workweek; or (4) spend less time on each task. The first option, slashing the backlog by limiting task arrivals or canceling pending tasks, is often difficult or impossible. In many processes the task arrival rate is exogenous or responds to quality and delivery time only with long lags. In an insurance claims operation, for example, the rate at which claims are filed is determined by the number and risk levels of the policies in force and by random events. The claims operation cannot tell customers that new claims are no longer being accepted. The remaining three options all involve increasing the processing rate of tasks in the backlog. Each involves different delays, costs, and consequences. Adding service capacity is expensive and time-consuming. In many organizations it is a last resort, and in any case new capacity cannot come on-line quickly. In the short-run, output can increase only if the labor force works longer hours or spends less time on each task. Figure 14-6 shows the structure of such a system. The task arrival rate and labor force are exogenous. The two principal feedbacks affecting the completion rate are the balancing Midnight Oil loop

FIGURE 14-6 Generic structure for a labor capacitated process

A high backlog causes workers to use overtime (the Midnight Oil loop) or to reduce the time spent on each task (the Corner Cutting loop). The Completion Rate is also limited by the minimum time required to process and deliver a task (the Work Availability loop).

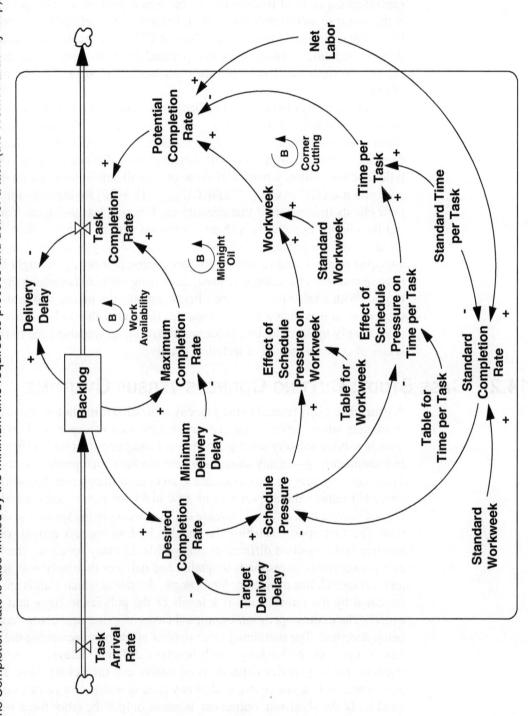

formed by the use of overtime and the balancing Corner Cutting loop created by the willingness of workers to spend less time on each task to cut down a high backlog. Both responses are nonlinear (section 5.4 presents a simple causal diagram for these feedbacks). The overall structure is a variant of the capacitated delay discussed in section 14.1.2.

Tasks accumulate in a backlog until they are processed and delivered to the customer. The tasks could be loan requests in a bank, claims awaiting settlement in an insurance company, tasks in a product development project, or paperwork in any administrative process. The arrival rate is exogenous to the process (though it may be endogenous in a full model). The average delivery delay is the ratio of the backlog to the completion rate:

Delivery Delay = Backlog/Task Completion Rate   (14-16)

Backlog
    = INTEGRAL(Task Arrival Rate − Task Completion Rate, Backlog_{t_0})   (14-17)

The task completion rate is determined by the lesser of the potential completion rate based on the size and productivity of the workforce and the maximum completion rate based on the number of tasks in the backlog and the minimum time required per task.

Task Completion Rate
    = MIN(Maximum Completion Rate, Potential Completion Rate)   (14-18)

Maximum Completion Rate = Backlog/Minimum Delivery Delay   (14-19)

The minimum delivery delay represents the minimum time required to process and deliver a task. The maximum completion rate forms the Work Availability loop, a first-order negative feedback that ensures the backlog remains nonnegative.

The potential completion rate represents the rate at which tasks could be completed given the labor force, the workweek, and the time allocated to each task:

Potential Completion Rate = Net Labor * Workweek/Time per Task   (14-20)

Net Labor is the number of FTE employees net of absenteeism and the amount of time lost due to meetings, training, and so on. For now net labor is exogenous, though in a full model these factors should be modeled endogenously.

The workweek is a standard workweek modified by an effect of schedule pressure, a measure of the pressure to work at a greater or lesser rate than normal.

Workweek
    = Standard Workweek * Effect of Schedule Pressure on Workweek   (14-21)

Effect of Schedule Pressure on Workweek = f(Schedule Pressure)   (14-22)

Schedule Pressure = Desired Completion Rate/Standard Completion Rate   (14-23)

The Desired Completion Rate is determined by the Backlog and the organization's goal for delivery time:

Desired Completion Rate = Backlog/Target Delivery Delay   (14-24)

The Standard Completion Rate represents the throughput the organization could achieve with the current labor force working normal hours and allocating the standard time to each task. Standard Time per Task represents the organizational norm for the level of effort the average task requires.

Standard Completion Rate
= Net Labor * Standard Workweek/Standard Time per Task

(14-25)

The average time devoted to each task, in person-hours/task, is determined by Standard Time per Task and Schedule Pressure. Standard Time per Task represents the current norm for how long each customer interaction or task should take and is exogenous for the purposes of this example. In a more complex model it may respond endogenously to worker experience and training, task complexity, management norms, experience, task quality, and other factors.

Time per Task = Standard Time per Task
    * Effect of Schedule Pressure on Time per Task

(14-26)

Effect of Schedule Pressure on Time per Task = *f*(Schedule Pressure)   (14-27)

The response of the organization to schedule pressure depends on the relative strength of the Midnight Oil and Corner Cutting loops. The strength of these loops, in turn, depends on the two nonlinear functions governing the response of the workweek and time per task to schedule pressure.

CHALLENGE

Formulating Nonlinear Functions

1. Formulate the relationship between schedule pressure and workweek. Figure 14-7 provides the axes and shows two reference policy lines to help you formulate the function. What is the policy represented by the line *f*(Schedule Pressure) = 1? What policy for workweek does the 45° line represent?

Using your interpretation of the reference policies, sketch the range of plausible shapes for the Effect of Schedule Pressure on Workweek. Assume the standard workweek is 40 hours/week. Pay special attention to the extreme values. What is

FIGURE 14-7
Specifying a function for the workweek

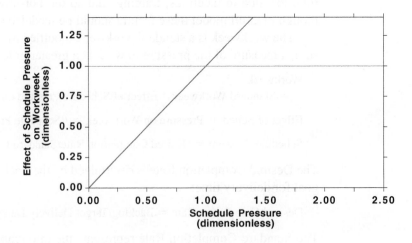

the effect when schedule pressure is very high? When it is zero? Briefly explain the rationale for your relationship.

2.   Formulate the relationship for the Effect of Schedule Pressure on Time per Task. First, draw any reference policies that help bound the feasible region for the relationship. Then draw the range of plausible shapes for the function. Justify your choice.

14.2.1   Working Overtime: The Effect of Schedule Pressure on Workweek

Even without data for a particular case a great deal can be said about the plausible shape and values of the workweek and time per task functions. First consider the reference policies for the workweek function. In the following, denote the effects of schedule pressure on workweek and time per task as $f_{ww}(SP)$ and $f_{tpt}(SP)$, respectively. The reference policy $f_{ww}(SP) = 1$ means the workweek never varies: The workers put in their 8 hours no matter how much there is to do; when the whistle blows, it's quittin' time, period. To derive the reference policy corresponding to the 45° line, assume that the backlog is large enough that the Work Availability loop is not a binding constraint (that is, that the Completion Rate CR is determined by the Potential Completion Rate PCR). Then, substituting the equations for the workweek and time per task into (14-20),

$$PCR = \text{Net Labor} * WW^* * f_{ww}(SP)/[TPT^* * f_{tpt}(SP)] \qquad (14\text{-}28)$$

where WW^* and TPT^* are the standard workweek and standard time per task, respectively. Noting that the Standard Completion Rate SCR = Net Labor * WW^*/TPT^*,

$$PCR = SCR * f_{ww}(SP)/f_{tpt}(SP) \qquad (14\text{-}29)$$

To derive the reference workweek policy corresponding to the 45° line, assume time per task equals the standard and note that the 45° line implies $f_{ww}(SP) = SP$:

$$PCR = SCR * f_{ww}(SP) = SCR * SP = SPR * DCR/SCR = DCR \qquad (14\text{-}30)$$

The 45° reference line therefore means workers vary the workweek exactly enough to complete tasks at the desired rate.

These considerations mean the workweek function must lie in the area between the two reference lines in Figure 14-7. In the region SP > 1, indicating insufficient capacity, it is not reasonable to assume that the workweek would rise more than needed to lift task completion beyond the desired rate. Likewise, in the region SP < 1, it is not reasonable for the workweek to be cut back so much that completions fall below the desired rate. Similarly, excess capacity should never cause a firm to schedule overtime, and insufficient capacity should never lead to undertime.

The workweek must saturate at a maximum value. A reasonable maximum workweek for the entire workforce might be 50 hours per week, or 25% more than normal. Some workers would be putting in longer hours and some, shorter.[3] Many firms are unwilling to reduce the workweek below normal when there is excess capacity (especially when they are contractually obligated to pay for a full week), instead using the excess labor to work off the backlog while waiting for attrition or layoffs to reduce the labor force. Firms may also choose to maintain throughput in the face of low schedule pressure to keep worker skills from eroding.[4]

14.2.2   Cutting Corners: The Effect of Schedule Pressure on Time per Task

Turning to the Corner Cutting loop, there are two reference policy curves for the Effect of Schedule Pressure on Time per Task. At one extreme, workers may be completely insensitive to schedule pressure, devoting the standard time to each task no matter how great the pressure to increase throughput may be. This policy means $f_{tpt}(SP)$ is always unity. At the other extreme, workers may adjust the time per task just enough so that the delivery delay always equals the target, implying the completion rate always equals the desired rate. To derive this reference policy, assume again that the availability loop is not binding (so that the Task Completion Rate = Potential Completion Rate = Desired Completion Rate). Then assume the workweek equals the standard. From (14-29),

$$DCR = PCR = SCR/f_{tpt}(SP) \tag{14-31}$$

Solving for the effect of schedule pressure on time per task,

$$f_{tpt}(SP) = SCR/DCR = 1/SP \tag{14-32}$$

Thus the policy of cutting corners to get the work done in the desired time yields a reference policy defined by the hyperbola $y = 1/x$. When schedule pressure is less than one, this extreme policy requires the workers to take longer and longer on each task.[5]

The feasible region for the true Effect of Schedule Pressure on Time per Task must lie between the two reference policies. Further, time per task cannot fall

---

[3]Note that the maximum effect of schedule pressure on workweek and standard workweek are not independent. Given a maximum workweek of 50 hours, the effect saturates at a value of 1.25 when the standard workweek is 40 hours but at 1.43 when the standard workweek is 35 hours.

[4]The workweek function need not be zero when schedule pressure is zero because (14-18) ensures that the actual completion rate falls to zero even when the potential completion rate remains high. If the workweek remains high when schedule pressure is low, the workers may easily deplete the backlog so far that the availability loop becomes active. In this case, the workers may sit at their desks but much of the time have no tasks to process. If the availability effect were not modeled explicitly as a separate feedback, the constraint that work cannot be completed faster than the minimum delivery delay would have to be embedded in the workweek function, as in the formulation for capacity utilization in section 14.1.2.

[5]The hyperbolic reference policy is often confusing. Defining Productivity P as the inverse of time per task, the potential completion rate can be reformulated as $PCR = SCR * f_{ww}(SP) * f_p(SP)$, where the effect of schedule pressure on productivity $f_p(SP)$ is simply $1/f_{tpt}(SP)$. The reference policy $DD = DD^*$ then becomes the 45° line, as in the workweek effect. The two formulations are equivalent; the choice is governed by ease of explanation and robustness under extreme conditions. It is very difficult to specify table values that conform to the reference policy $y = 1/x$ as the input goes to zero.

below some minimum even when schedule pressure is very high: It takes some minimum time to complete a task even when most of the steps are skipped or done in a shoddy fashion. Similarly, workers will not spend more than a certain maximum time on each task even when schedule pressure is very low.

14.3 CASE STUDY: ESTIMATING NONLINEAR FUNCTIONS WITH QUALITATIVE AND NUMERICAL DATA

Oliva (1996) used the structure above in his model of service quality delivery (see also Senge and Sterman 1992). The model relates service quality to the balance between the demand for service and the number, skill, motivation, and quality norms of the service workers. The full model included many additional feedbacks besides the Midnight Oil and Corner Cutting loops, including service quality acquisition, the effect of fatigue on service quality and employee turnover, and feedbacks governing the adjustment of quality norms by employees, management, and customers. Oliva tested his model through a detailed field study of retail lending operations in a major UK bank. Through interviews, archival data collection, and participant observation, he gathered extensive data on the operations of the bank's major retail lending center.

In the context of the task management structure, the tasks to be done were loan requests to be approved or denied. Loan officers, working in cubicles in a large call center, received customer requests from local branches by computer network, telephone, and mail. They processed the loan requests using their workstations and might also phone or write the branch, customer, and credit references to verify information or sell additional products and services to the customer. The loan officers were salaried employees and did not receive payment for any overtime they put in. Oliva observed some variation in the workweek including break and lunch times as schedule pressure varied. The employees also faced strong pressure to clear the backlog every day—management did not tolerate long delivery delays. Interviews and observation also suggested that the employees were more willing to cut corners than to work overtime or cut back on breaks to meet the delivery delay target and clear the backlog each day. The organization's policies and procedures and other data suggested that the fastest each task could possibly be done was about 60% of the standard. At the other extreme, the time spent on each task could not rise too high since an employee could do only so many phone calls, credit checks, and so on for each loan application.

CHALLENGE Refining Table Functions with Qualitative Data

While the reference policies and extreme conditions sharply limit the feasible shape and values for the effects of schedule pressure on workweek and time per task, there is still some uncertainty over their values. What are the slopes of the functions near the normal point? How do the workers trade off the pressure to work to the standards and the pressure to meet delivery targets? Imagine your client is

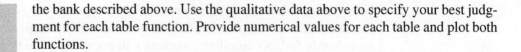

the bank described above. Use the qualitative data above to specify your best judgment for each table function. Provide numerical values for each table and plot both functions.

From the time series data he collected Oliva was able to estimate many of the nonlinear relationships in the model econometrically, including both the dependence of workweek and time per task on schedule pressure. During the year for which Oliva collected data, schedule pressure varied from about 0.88 to 1.14. This range does not reveal any information about the saturation limits for the two relationships but does permit the slopes of the curves near the normal operating point to be estimated. Around the normal point the true functions are well approximated by the power functions

$$f_{ww}(SP) = SP^{s_{ww}} \quad \text{and} \quad f_{tpt}(SP) = SP^{s_{tpt}} \tag{14-33}$$

Estimating the exponents s_{ww} and s_{tpt} for the workweek and time per task effects by log-linear regression gives highly significant results. For the workweek, the estimated exponent (with 95% confidence bounds) is $0.56 \leq s_{ww} = 0.63 \leq 0.69$, $R^2 = 0.86$. The estimated exponent for time per task is $-0.43 \leq s_{tpt} = -0.36 \leq -0.30$, $R^2 = 0.70$.[6]

Figures 14-8 and 14-9 show the resulting effects of schedule pressure on workweek and time per task. The values of the table functions lie along the estimated slopes in the neighborhood of the data. The saturation limits for workweek are $\pm 25\%$. For time per task, the saturation limits are $\pm 40\%$. These limits are consistent with interviews, observation, and other archival data Oliva collected at the bank. The figures also show a close-up of each function around the operating point including the data, estimated slope, and 95% confidence bounds. How close to the estimated functions did your judgmental estimates lie?

The considerations above help specify the shape and values of the individual tables. However, when a formulation involves several nonlinear effects it is important to check that the formulation is robust and consistent with the data when all the effects interact. The extreme conditions and sensitivities at the normal operating point should be established. First, consider the total impact of a change in schedule pressure near the normal operating point. Each individual relationship must satisfy the constraint defined by the reference policy defined by $DD = DD^*$. That is, the delivery delay should not fall below normal when there is excess demand nor rise above normal when there is excess capacity.

In addition, the joint effect of schedule pressure on both workweek and time per task should satisfy the same constraint. In general, workers are unlikely to do more than required to process tasks in the target delivery time when workload is high nor cut back so much that delivery delay rises above normal when there is too little work. In the case of the UK bank, Oliva's qualitative data suggest that the workers cleared the backlog each day. The combined effect of overtime and corner

---

[6]Oliva used a more sophisticated partial model estimation procedure but the results were essentially identical to the log-linear regression estimates reported here.

FIGURE 14-8   Effect of schedule pressure on workweek

Lower graph shows data points. Dashed lines indicate the 95% confidence bounds for the estimated relationship.

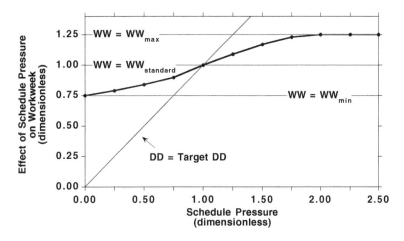

Schedule Pressure	Effect of SP on WW	Increment
0.00	0.75	
0.25	0.79	0.04
0.50	0.84	0.05
0.75	0.90	0.06
1.00	1.00	0.10
1.25	1.09	0.09
1.50	1.17	0.08
1.75	1.23	0.06
2.00	1.25	0.02
2.25	1.25	0.00
2.50	1.25	0.00

SP = Schedule Pressure; WW = Workweek; DD = Delivery Delay.

Source: Data from Oliva (1996).

cutting should therefore just enable the lending center to meet the target delivery delay.

To check that the two relationships conform to this constraint, substitute the estimated power law functions into (14-29):

$$PCR = SCR * f_{ww}(SP)/f_{tpt}(SP) \approx SCR * SP^{s_{ww}}/SP^{s_{tpt}} = SCR * SP^{(s_{ww} - s_{tpt})} \qquad (14\text{-}34)$$

The estimated values give $s_{ww} - s_{tpt} = 0.63 - (-0.36) \approx 1$, which means

$$PCR \approx SCR * SP = SCR * DCR/SCR = DCR \qquad (14\text{-}35)$$

The independently estimated relationships indicate that the loan officers cut corners and used overtime just enough to process the backlog at the target delivery delay and are consistent with the qualitative data derived from interviews and

FIGURE 14-9   Effect of schedule pressure on time per task

Lower graph shows data points. Dashed lines indicate the 95% confidence bounds for the estimated relationship.

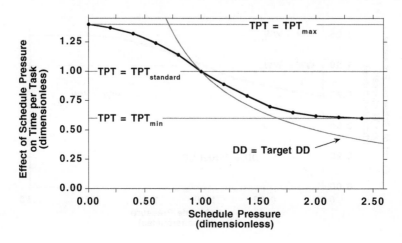

Schedule Pressure	Effect of SP on TPT	Increment
0.00	1.40	
0.20	1.37	−0.03
0.40	1.32	−0.05
0.60	1.24	−0.06
0.80	1.14	−0.10
1.00	1.00	−0.14
1.20	0.89	−0.11
1.40	0.79	−0.10
1.60	0.70	−0.09
1.80	0.65	−0.05
2.00	0.62	−0.03
2.20	0.61	−0.01
2.40	0.60	−0.01
2.60	0.60	0.00

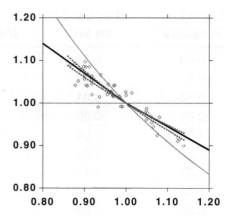

TPT = Time per Task; DD = Delivery Delay.

Source: Data from Oliva (1996).

direct observation of the process, providing an important check on the estimated table values.

Turning to extreme conditions, high schedule pressure boosts the total processing rate to 1.25/0.60 = 2.08 * SCR while low schedule pressure reduces the potential completion rate to 0.75/1.40 = 0.54 * SCR, roughly a factor of two around the standard processing rate. These bounds are plausible.

The estimated functions reveal that workers at the bank were much more willing to cut corners than to work overtime when schedule pressure rose above normal. This result has important implications for the quality of service the bank was able to deliver. Within broad limits, a rise in workload was quickly accommodated by spending less time with each customer and, to a lesser extent, cutting back on lunch and breaks. Management therefore perceived little pressure to add service capacity. Indeed, management may interpret the rise in throughput per person as productivity growth and may cut service personnel to reduce expenses, further increasing schedule pressure and perpetuating high workloads in a positive loop. Indeed, Oliva found strong evidence for just this loop, leading to persistent erosion of service quality (see chapter 21 and Appendix B for further discussion).

14.4   COMMON PITFALLS

This section discusses some common pitfalls in the specification and use of nonlinear functions.

14.4.1   Using the Wrong Input

Care must be taken to ensure that the inputs to nonlinear functions are properly specified, that the reference policies are easily interpreted, and that the resulting relationship is robust, without any inappropriate kinks. Consider the standard formulation $Y = Y^* *$ Effect of X on Y where the Effect of X on Y $= f(X/X^*)$. A common problem arises when the reference policy curve for the formulation is the hyperbola $f(X/X^*) = 1/(X/X^*)$ instead of the 45° line $f(X/X^*) = X/X^*$. The hyperbola becomes very steep for small values, becomes infinite when $X = 0$, and is difficult to approximate with piecewise linear segments. One solution is to invert the input to the table, so the reference policy becomes $f(X^*/X) = X^*/X$. Another solution is to invert the Effect of X on Y in the equation where it is used. Reformulating the equation for Y as $Y = Y^*/$Effect of X on Y, the reference policy becomes $f(X/X^*) = X/X^*$, which is easier to specify and interpret.

Example

Shantzis and Behrens (1973) developed a model of an indigenous tribe in Papua New Guinea and their slash-and-burn agricultural system (see section 21.4.6 for further description). The model examined the relationship between the size of the population, food production, land fertility, and the incidence of ritual war with neighboring clans. They modeled food production as the product of the available land, land fertility, and the intensity of cultivation:

$$\frac{\text{Food Production}}{\text{(Calories/Year)}} = \frac{\text{Arable Land}}{\text{(Acres)}} * \frac{\text{Yield per Acre}}{\text{(Calories/Year/Acre)}} * \frac{\text{Intensity of Cultivation}}{\text{(Dimensionless)}} \tag{14-36}$$

The intensity of cultivation was formulated as a dimensionless function of potential food output relative to the food needed:

Intensity of Cultivation
    $= f(\text{Potential Food/Food Needed}); f(0) = 1, f(\infty) = 0$ (14-37)

Food Needed = Human Population * Desired Food per Capita (14-38)

Potential Food = Arable Land * Perceived Yield per Acre (14-39)

FIGURE 14-10

Intensity of
cultivation in
the original
Tsembaga model

The reference
policy curve y =
1/x represents the
policy that food
production equals
food needed.

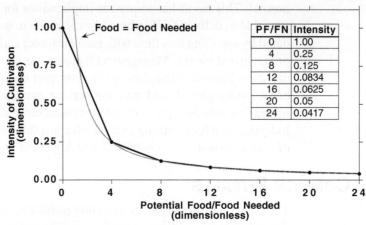

PF/FN	Intensity
0	1.00
4	0.25
8	0.125
12	0.0834
16	0.0625
20	0.05
24	0.0417

Source: Shantzis and Behrens (1973).

The perceived yield per acre was formed by first-order smoothing of the actual
yield to represent the time required for the Tsembaga to revise their beliefs about
the fertility of their land.

Figure 14-10 shows the function Shantzis and Behrens selected for cultivation
intensity with the reference curve y = 1/x, which represents the policy that food
production is just equal to the food needed (when perceived and actual yield per
acre are equal). The table captures the idea that food production adjusts to meet demand but is constrained by the maximum intensity of cultivation, defined as one.

Figure 14-10 reveals several problems. While the values of the table fit the reference policy closely for ratios of Potential Food/Food Needed (PF/FN) greater
than eight, the piecewise linear approximation is poor for values of PF/FN less
than eight. In particular, the table function values lie above the reference policy
curve when PF/FN ≥ 1.33, meaning food production exceeds food requirements.
Since important dynamics arise in the model from degradation of land fertility due
to excessive cultivation, this error might matter. The function also fails a basic extreme condition test: When the population is zero, so no food is needed, somehow
food is still produced at about 4% of capacity. Finally, the important dynamics in
the model arise in the region where PF/FN is less than one, but the table specifies
values only every 4 units, providing very low resolution for the relationship in the
active region.

The problem is solved by formulating intensity as a function of the ratio Food
Needed/Potential Food, the inverse of the input Shantzis and Behrens used. The ratio FN/PF is more intuitive (the fraction of maximum production needed to meet
demand). By using FN/PF, the reference policy Food Production = Food Needed
becomes the easily interpreted 45° line. Figure 14-11 plots the original function
against the inverted input FN/PF. For FN/PF ≤ 0.75 the original function lies
above the reference line and contains many inappropriate kinks. Kampmann
(1991) proposed a revised formulation for the table that corrects all the flaws of the
original: Production smoothly saturates at maximum intensity and never exceeds
requirements. And when there are no people there is no cultivation.

FIGURE 14-11

Revised function for intensity of cultivation

The 45° line represents the policy that food production equals food needed. Note the kinks in the original function for FN/PF ≤ 0.75.

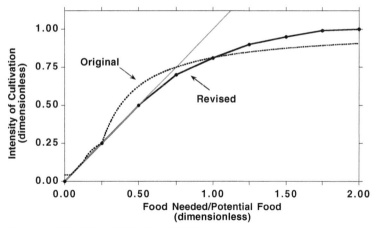

Source: Adapted from Kampmann (1991).

CHALLENGE

Critiquing Nonlinear Functions

Naill (1973) modeled the life cycle of natural gas. The stock of undiscovered gas resources is reduced by the discovery rate, which makes gas deposits available for development and production. Naill formulated the discovery rate as depending on exploration effort (the number of drill rigs and other equipment deployed in the search for new deposits) and the cost of discovery:

$$\frac{\text{Discovery Rate}}{\text{(Cubic Feet/Year)}} = \frac{\text{Exploration Effort}}{\text{(\$/Year)}} \Big/ \frac{\text{Cost of Exploration}}{\text{(\$/Cubic Foot)}} \qquad (14\text{-}40)$$

Exploration Effort was a (delayed) function of the expected profitability of new deposits (see section 11.5). The cost of exploration captures the difficulty of finding new deposits, and depends on the size, location, and depth of the remaining undiscovered deposits. Naill (pp. 221–222) explains:

> Initially . . . industry will explore . . . in the most accessible places and exploit the largest fields available, making the cost of exploration relatively low. As most of the larger deposits are discovered, producers must look in less accessible places, such as the sea bottom or Alaska, causing the cost of exploration to rise. In addition, both the size of the reserves found and the success ratio of wildcat wells drilled decrease, further increasing costs as the fraction of unproven reserves diminishes. Finally, as the fraction of unproven reserves remaining . . . approaches zero, the cost of exploration approaches infinity as no more gas can be found at any cost.[7]

Naill captures this logic with the following formulation:

Cost of Exploration
   = Normal Cost of Exploration * Effect of Resource Remaining on Costs   (14-41)

---

[7]This passage describes the effect of depletion alone; other forces such as technological progress can reduce the costs of exploration, but these are omitted for the purposes of this challenge. Davidsen, Sterman, and Richardson (1990) present a nonrenewable resource model with endogenous technological progress as well as depletion.

Effect of Resource Remaining on Costs
    $= f$(Fraction of Undiscovered Resource Remaining)

(14-42)

$$\text{Fraction of Undiscovered Resource Remaining} = \frac{\text{Undiscovered Resources}}{\text{Undiscovered Resources}(t_0)}$$

(14-43)

The values Naill used for the Effect of Resource Remaining on Costs as a function of the fraction of undiscovered resource remaining FURR are

FURR	f(FURR)
0.0	10,000
0.1	9.97
0.2	5.00
0.3	3.32
0.4	2.48
0.5	1.99
0.6	1.67
0.7	1.42
0.8	1.25
0.9	1.10
1.0	1.00

Critique Naill's formulation, then reformulate it to correct any problems you identify.

14.4.2   Improper Normalization

Normalizing nonlinear functions by the reference values of the input and output is often useful. Normalizing converts the raw input and output of a function $Y = f(X)$ into a dimensionless effect as in $Y = Y^* * f(X/X^*)$. Care must be taken, however, that the normal or reference values are properly chosen.

Example

An analyst extends the service delivery model in section 14.3 to include the quality of service as experienced by the customers. Fieldwork showed that quality of service was judged largely by the care, concern, and willingness to answer questions evidenced by the employee during the service encounter. Employees in a hurry or who limited the duration of the interaction caused customer dissatisfaction. The analyst proposes to model quality as a function of time per task. The shorter the time per task relative to a reference, the fewer chances the customer had to ask questions, the more peremptory and impersonal the service, and the lower the quality of the experience. Thus

Quality of Service
    = Reference Quality * Effect of Time per Task on Quality

(14-44)

Effect of Time per Task on Quality
    = *f*(Time per Task/Standard Time per Task)   (14-45)

Time per task is normalized by Standard Time per Task (see (14-25)). The function is upward sloping and passes through the points (0, 0) and (1, 1). The function probably has an S-shape: Only after a certain minimum time is devoted to the customer's needs will the customer feel even partially satisfied. The effect also saturates at a maximum: Once the employee takes all the time the customer feels is required, additional time does not add to the customer's feeling of satisfaction.

The problem here is the normalization by the standard time per task. Standard time per task represents management's current goal for the appropriate amount of time employees should spend on each customer interaction. Suppose management decided to reduce standard time per task to boost productivity, and suppose actual time per task fell accordingly. Equation (14-45) implies there would be no change in customer satisfaction. Indeed, the proposed normalization implies that cutting standard and actual time per task nearly to zero has no impact on service quality. In reality, of course, satisfaction would drop since the work will be less thorough and the customers will be treated in an increasingly abrupt manner.

Standard time per task represents a management goal. In (14-45) it is used inappropriately to represent a customer goal. The proper formulation normalizes by a new concept, the Customer Standard for Time per Task, representing how much effort the customers believe employees should put into the service encounter. The customer standard may be constant or variable and likely differs from management's norm. Research indicates customer standards are conditioned by past experience and by the service received from competitors and in other similar settings, suggesting the customer standard could be modeled as a floating goal with past experience and competitive benchmarks as inputs (see section 13.2.10).

14.4.3   Avoid Hump-Shaped Functions

In chapter 5 I argued that all causal links in your models should have unambiguous polarity. The same principle applies to the nonlinear functions you specify in your models. Your functions should be either nondecreasing (flat or rising) or nonincreasing (flat or falling). Nonlinear functions with rising and falling sections, with peaks or valleys, imply the polarity of the causal link between the input and output depends on the value of the input. A hump- or U-shaped relationship indicates the presence of multiple causal pathways between the input and output. You should represent each separately so the individual effects have a unique, unambiguous polarity.

The famous Yerkes–Dodson Law in psychology provides an example. Yerkes and Dodson (1908) explored how performance in various tasks depended on the level of arousal or stress imposed. Low levels of arousal yield low performance. As stress or stimulation increases, performance increases, but at diminishing rates. As stress continues to rise, performance peaks and falls, forming an inverted U or hump-shaped function. The Yerkes–Dodson Law has been applied to a wide range of tasks, both physical and cognitive (see Fisher 1986 for a review). In the context of the backlog management model of section 14.3, schedule pressure measures the stress in the workers' environment and output (the task completion rate) corresponds to performance. Consistent with the Yerkes–Dodson Law, many people argue that the impact of stress (measured by schedule pressure) on output is hump shaped, as illustrated in Figure 14-12. At low workloads, increasing schedule pressure boosts output as workers speed up, cut breaks, and work longer hours. However, these effects encounter diminishing returns, while the negative effects of fatigue and stress gain strength, eventually causing productivity per hour to decline more than hours increase.

Even if the applicability of the Yerkes–Dodson Law to the model was established, it would be a mistake to specify a table function corresponding to Figure 14-12. First, the conflation of the different effects makes it hard to specify meaningful reference policies or rule out infeasible regions. Second, the output gains from working faster and overtime should be separated from each other and from the productivity-destroying effects of fatigue because each has different costs and benefits and each is affected differently by organizational policies and incentives. An increase in schedule pressure may boost overall throughput, but it makes a big difference whether that increase is gained by working longer hours or cutting the quality of work. Finally, the different effects may involve different time delays. Lumping them into a single function requires equal time delays in the causal links. A rise in schedule pressure will increase throughput quickly through overtime and corner cutting; only later, as sustained long work hours take their toll, will fatigue begin to erode productivity.

Extended overtime and the fatigue it leads to have many harmful effects. These include decreased alertness and performance on cognitive and other tasks, higher stress, lower job satisfaction, increased injury and accident rates on and off the job, increased illness, decreased psychological health, increased incidence of substance abuse, higher suicide rates, and higher overall mortality (Rosa 1995 provides a survey).

FIGURE 14-12
Hypothesized hump-shaped relationship between schedule pressure and output: the Yerkes–Dodson Law

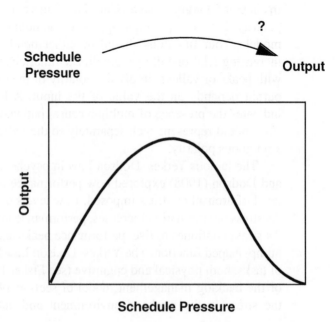

Figure 14-13 adds a properly formulated fatigue effect to the model in section 14.3. The effect of fatigue on productivity is separated from the effect of schedule pressure on the workweek and from the effect of schedule pressure on time per task (not shown). The fatigue effect creates the Burnout loop, a positive loop in which long hours cut productivity, reducing the task completion rate. As the backlog builds up, schedule pressure rises, leading to still longer work hours and even more fatigue (see section 5.4).

The formulation for the potential completion rate is modified by the Effect of Fatigue on Productivity. Fatigue does not set in immediately but builds up gradually as workers consistently find themselves unable to get the rest or breaks they need. The fatigue effect is therefore a nonlinear function of the Recent Workweek, a measure of the average hours workers have sustained over an interval given by the Fatigue Onset Time.

$$\frac{\text{Potential}}{\text{Completion Rate}} = \frac{\text{Net Labor * Workweek * Effect of Fatigue on Productivity}}{\text{Time per Task}}$$

$$(14\text{-}46)$$

$$\text{Effect of Fatigue on Productivity} = f(\text{Recent Workweek}) \qquad (14\text{-}47)$$

FIGURE 14-13   The burnout loop formed by the effect of fatigue on productivity

The box around the Recent Workweek indicates that it is an information delay of the actual Workweek, with a time constant given by the Fatigue Onset Time. The order of the delay is not indicated. The diagram does not show the availability and corner cutting feedbacks in Figure 14-6.

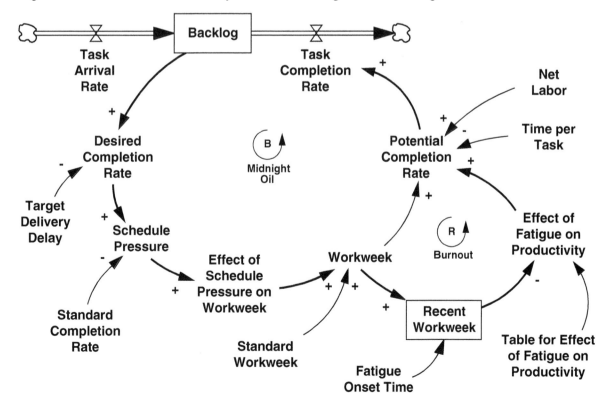

$$\text{Recent Workweek} = \text{SMOOTHn(Workweek, Fatigue Onset Time)} \qquad (14\text{-}48)$$

where the SMOOTHn function represents an nth-order information delay.

Studies of the construction industry and other manual labor contexts indicate that long work hours begin to reduce productivity after a week or two, with the full effect requiring somewhat longer (Oliva 1996). Experience suggests the time constant for white collar work is similar, indicating the fatigue onset time constant should be several weeks. In the absence of strong evidence to the contrary, first-order smoothing is probably adequate to capture the recent workweek.[8] The fatigue effect captures not only the physiological and psychological effects of long work hours but also logistical considerations. In a crisis, people can work very long hours for short periods. Other important activities in their lives, from exercise to food shopping to laundry to spending time with their friends and family, can be deferred. As time passes, however, these activities can no longer be put off. People must again devote time to them, draining time from work and reducing productivity. If these activities are deferred too long, the consequences grow increasingly dire, including declining health from lack of exercise and poor diet, loss of friends due to lack of a social life and of clean clothes, and, all too common, family problems and divorce. The formulation here is a simple approximation to this more complex underlying structure.

Figure 14-14 shows a plausible function for the effect of fatigue on productivity. The input to the function is the recent workweek. A common error is to normalize the fatigue effect by the standard workweek (section 14.4.2). The standard workweek represents the organization's norm for the workweek. Increasing it does not endow people with greater resistance to fatigue. If the function were normalized by the standard workweek, boosting the normal workweek from 40 to, say, 75 hours would have no impact on fatigue, an absurdity.

The function is normalized so the effect on productivity is one when the workweek is 40 hours. Reducing the workweek below 40 hours increases productivity only slightly. Longer hours, however, have a progressively greater effect; eventually, of course, the function must gradually approach zero. People need an irreducible minimum amount of sleep, roughly 6 hours/night over the long term. Allowing just 3 hours/day for all other activities (eating, bathing, exercise, social life, etc.) implies productivity must fall quite low when the sustained workweek rises above 100 hours.

The rate at which long hours cut into productivity will depend on the characteristics of the job and the training, expectations, and lifestyles of the workforce. The degree to which the job requires physical labor obviously has an effect. More subtly, the less pleasant and varied the work, the less important people perceive it to be, the less the work is suited to worker skills and interests, or the weaker people's social support networks, the steeper the drop off will be.

---

[8]Homer (1985) develops a model of worker burnout in which the individual's energy level is represented as an explicit stock with recovery and depletion rates based on the workweek and stress levels. The formulation here is an approximation to a host of more complex psychological and physiological processes.

FIGURE 14-14

Effect of fatigue on productivity

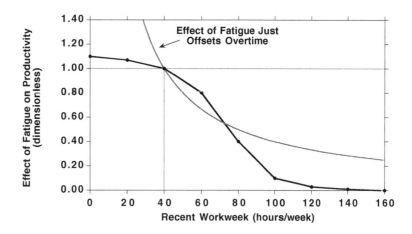

Recent Workweek	f(RWW)	Increment
0	1.10	
20	1.07	−0.03
40	1.00	−0.07
60	0.80	−0.20
80	0.40	−0.40
100	0.10	−0.30
120	0.03	−0.07
140	0.01	−0.02
160	0.00	−0.01

RWW = Recent workweek.

At what point will the negative effects of fatigue dominate the increase in work hours caused by schedule pressure? If the fatigue effect fell along the reference policy shown in Figure 14-14 the rise in work hours would eventually be exactly offset by the decline in productivity per hour. The hypothesized fatigue effect shown in the figure falls below the reference policy when the recent workweek rises above about 72 hours. Beyond that point, sustained long workweeks actually reduce output (in equilibrium) below the level achieved at the reference 40 hour workweek.

Figure 14-15 shows the equilibrium relationship between output per person and workweek taking both the overtime and fatigue effects into account (but assuming no variation in time per task). In equilibrium, the recent workweek equals the actual workweek, so the net effect is given by the product WW * f(WW). When the workweek is less than 40 hours, output rises nearly linearly since the fatigue effect is nearly flat. Beyond 40 hours, net output rises, but at diminishing rates as fatigue begins to cut productivity. Given the values in the table, output reaches a maximum when the workweek is 60 hours, then falls. At about 72 hours/week output falls below the level achieved at the reference workweek of 40 hours/week. Further increases in workweek rapidly drop equilibrium output to zero. In equilibrium, fatigue interacts with overtime to generate the hypothesized hump-shaped curve consistent with the Yerkes–Dodson Law.[9]

The curve in Figure 14-15 represents equilibrium productivity. The actual profile of output will depend on the magnitude and duration of overtime. Figure 14-16 shows simulations of the workweek and fatigue structure for various exogenously specified periods of overtime. A first-order delay with a Fatigue Onset Time of 2 weeks is assumed for the Recent Workweek.

Simulated workweek rises at time zero from 40 to 50, 60, 80, or 100 hours/week, remains high for 10 weeks, then falls back to normal. In each case, output relative to the reference 40 hour/week level immediately jumps by the fractional increase in work hours. However, as the recent workweek rises and fatigue sets in,

FIGURE 14-15

Net effect of overtime and fatigue on output

The graph shows equilibrium output relative to the reference value when the workweek is 40 hours/week.

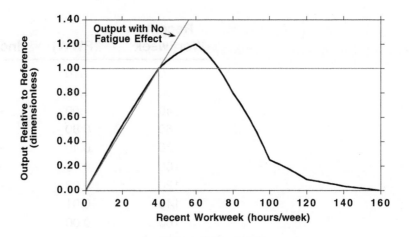

FIGURE 14-16

Dynamics of overtime and fatigue

Response of output relative to the 40 hour/week reference level during various periods of extended hours. The workweek rises from 40 to the value indicated for 10 weeks, then falls back to the normal level. Assumes the recent workweek adjusts with a first-order delay and 2-week fatigue onset time.

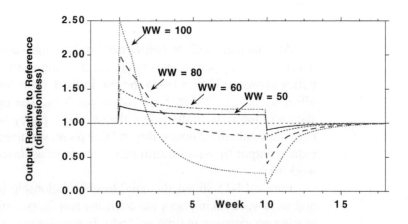

---

[9]The kinks in the net output curve shown in Figure 14-15 arise because the table function approximates the smooth relationship between workweek and productivity by linear interpolation between a small number of points. If the kinks mattered, more points could be specified or an appropriate analytical function could be used for the effect of fatigue on productivity (e.g., the logistic function). In practice, the kinks caused by the piecewise linear approximation used in the table are small relative to the uncertainty in the true values and unlikely to matter to policy results.

productivity falls, cutting output. For workweeks less than 72 hours/week, equilibrium output remains higher than the 40 hour/week rate. For workweeks greater than 72 hours/week, output soon falls below the reference level. In the case of a jump to 100 hours/week, output actually falls below normal after a little over 2 weeks. In all cases, output falls below normal after the workweek returns to normal: The workers are still fatigued and require several weeks to recover.

CHALLENGE

Formulating the Error Rate

The positive burnout loop is a side effect of excessive overtime. Additional side effects arise from the corner cutting loop. Cutting corners by reducing the time devoted to each task increases errors, reduces the amount and effectiveness of quality assurance, and lowers customer satisfaction. Tasks done incorrectly must be reworked, which boosts schedule pressure and leads to still more corner cutting and errors. The resulting positive feedback, the Haste Makes Waste loop, might cause schedule pressure and errors to spiral out of control (see Figure 5-9).

There are several ways to model errors. To keep the example simple, assume tasks done erroneously are detected rapidly and therefore remain in the backlog until they are reworked.[10] Modify the formulation for the task completion rate to account for the fraction of tasks done erroneously:

Task Completion Rate = Gross Completion Rate * (1 − Error Fraction)   (14-49)

Gross Completion Rate
    = MIN(Maximum Completion Rate, Potential Completion Rate)   (14-50)

The error fraction in any process depends both on the capability of the process and on how well the people operating it do their jobs. A poor process will generate a high error fraction even if the workers do the best they can; a great process operated by careless, rushed people will also yield many mistakes. To capture these effects the error fraction can be modeled as a function of the time allocated to each task and a minimum error fraction:

Error Fraction = f(Minimum Error Fraction, Time per Task)   (14-51)

The minimum error fraction represents the best that can be done even when workers take as much time as they desire on each task. It is convenient to normalize the formulation for the error fraction by the minimum value since the actual error fraction must lie between the minimum and 100%.

Formulate the error fraction to capture the Haste Makes Waste loop. Be sure your equations conform to the formulation principles and guidelines for nonlinear functions above. Hint: The minimum error fraction can differ from process to process and in a more complete model may also change endogenously through process improvement efforts, learning, or changes in technology and organization. For the purposes of this challenge, assume the minimum error fraction is constant.

---

[10]In many situations, errors cannot be detected immediately, so the erroneous tasks exit the backlog on the belief that they have been completed. The flawed tasks accumulate in a stock of undiscovered rework or customer complaints (see section 2.3).

Your formulation, however, must ensure the error fraction remains between the minimum and one even if the minimum error fraction were to change.

The formulation for the standard completion rate must also be modified to account for the fact that not all tasks are completed correctly:

$$\begin{matrix} \text{Standard} \\ \text{Completion} \\ \text{Rate} \end{matrix} = \frac{\text{Net Labor * Standard Workweek}}{\text{Standard Time per Task}} * (1 - \text{Standard Error Fraction})$$

(14-52)

The standard error fraction is the estimate of quality management and workers use when assessing the normal rate at which work can be completed correctly. The larger the standard error fraction, the more workers are needed to ensure the task completion rate equals the task arrival rate. For now, assume that the standard error fraction is a constant. Select a value that initializes the model in a balanced equilibrium with Schedule Pressure = 1.[11]

Test your formulation to make sure it is robust under extreme conditions and lies within the feasible region defined by any reference policies you identify. Given your best estimates of any nonlinear relationships you specify, determine the overall response of the task completion rate to schedule pressure. Does the Haste Makes Waste effect ever dominate the Corner Cutting loop, and if so, at what point?

Errors do not depend on time per task alone. As the recent workweek rises, workers become so tired that the quality of their work falls. Errors increase even when the same time is allocated to each task. The effect of fatigue on errors forms the positive Too Tired to Think loop (section 5.4). Add this loop to your causal diagram.

Revise your formulation for the error fraction to include an additional effect of fatigue on errors. Be sure that your function is robust under extreme conditions and consider the joint extremes as well as the extremes of the individual functions.

Given your best estimates for the effects of time per task and fatigue on errors, what is the overall response of the completion rate to schedule pressure? Make a graph showing how the completion rate (relative to the standard) depends on schedule pressure, taking all the loops—Midnight Oil, Corner Cutting, Burnout, Haste Makes Waste, and Too Tired to Think—into account. Is the overall dependence of output on schedule pressure reasonable? What are the implications of the resulting function for the management of a service, project, or other task?

---

[11]Applying the Baker Criterion, management and workers do not know the true value of the equilibrium error fraction and must estimate it from experience. You can find the initial equilibrium value for the standard error fraction by trial and error or by solving the simultaneous initial value equations for schedule pressure and error fraction. In a more complete model the standard error fraction might adjust over time to the observed rate of errors and perhaps factors such as the quality achieved by other organizations. Observed errors, in turn, may not equal the true error fraction since quality assurance is never perfect: Some errors slip by undetected while some tasks that were in fact done properly are mistakenly reworked. However, for the purposes of this challenge it is acceptable to omit this more realistic structure.

CHALLENGE   # Testing the Full Model

Build the full model including the fatigue and error fraction structures and initialize it in equilibrium. Then simulate its response to various patterns for the task arrival rate. Explore the response of the system to one-time temporary increases in the backlog of work using pulse inputs of different sizes (both increases and decreases). Also consider the response to permanent changes in the task arrival rate using step inputs of various heights. Given a fixed labor force, a step in task arrivals means the system will not return to the initial balanced equilibrium with the delivery delay, workweek, and time per task all at their standard values and may not return to any equilibrium. What determines whether an equilibrium exists when there is a permanent increase in task arrivals?

In each case, explore the relative importance of the different feedbacks in determining the behavior of schedule pressure, the workweek, time per task, the completion rate, and delivery delay. Conduct sensitivity analysis in which you vary the strengths of the various feedbacks. How sensitive is the behavior to feasible variations in the values of the various nonlinear functions?

The model omits other important feedbacks. Identify the additional feedbacks that might operate in the structure described above. Add these additional loops to your causal diagram of the system. Identify the polarity of the new loops and comment on how they might affect the dynamics. Formulate and sketch any nonlinear functions in your new loops.

14.5   ELICITING MODEL RELATIONSHIPS INTERACTIVELY

Most of the time numerical data to estimate nonlinear functions statistically are not available. When numerical data do exist, they often do not cover a wide enough range to reveal extreme values or saturation points. Generating reliable estimates of the nonlinear functions in models requires methods to elicit qualitative information from clients and others with firsthand experience in the system. Most of this information is tacit, residing only in the mental models of the experts. This section describes a method for eliciting nonlinear functions from system experts. The method is applicable to any relationships but is particularly useful for behavioral relationships for which no numerical data are available. The elicitation method also increases the involvement of the clients in the modeling process, increasing their understanding of the model and the chances they will actually use it.[12]

The method can be used with individual experts or small groups. Working with small groups is efficient and also helps build shared understanding among the members of the client or expert team. Care should be taken, however, that the individuals are not pressured to arrive at a single, consistent set of results

---

[12]Section 14.5 is adapted from Ford and Sterman (1998a), which should be consulted for further details.

representing the group. Capturing the diverse views of a group is an important result of the elicitation process.

The elicitation process has three phases: positioning, description, and discussion. The positioning phase establishes the context and goals of the workshop. Though your model probably includes many nonlinear relationships, you should focus on one at a time. The facilitator describes the model purpose and structure and the relationship to be estimated. Describe the relationship operationally by defining the input and output variables with their units of measure, why the relationship is important, where the relationship is used in the model, and which other parts of the system it affects. Provide worksheets to help the experts articulate their knowledge. As illustrated below, these worksheets help the experts go through the steps described in Table 14-1 and include blank graphs of the function. Give each expert a set of worksheets that have been completed based on an example from an analogous setting, and use multiple examples to reduce suggestion bias. Explain the examples in detail to illustrate the process and reasoning the experts should use.

The description phase guides experts through four different descriptions of the relationship. Each helps transform their tacit knowledge into usable form. During the description phase the experts are directed to use their own images and not to interact with the other experts. (1) *Visualize the process:* Ask the experts to take a few minutes to visualize the process. Invite them to close their eyes or otherwise disengage from others during this step. (2) *Record a description:* Ask each expert to create a written "walk through" of the process. The completeness or accuracy of descriptions is not emphasized until the discussion phase of the method. (3) *Identify anchor points:* Have the experts record any reference points. The anchor or reference points are those values of the relationship required by system constraints (e.g., shipments must fall to zero when inventory is zero), defined by convention (e.g., the 1997 value = 1.0), or in which the expert has high confidence. A separate portion of the description worksheet should provide space to record anchor point coordinates and the reasoning or data justifying each. (4) *Graph the relationship:* Have the experts draw the relationship in two steps. First, plot the anchor points on a blank set of axes on the worksheet. The blank graph you provide should include reference policies that constrain the feasible region for the relationship. Next have them consider the shape of the relationship between anchor points and use their reasoning to sketch their estimate of the relationship. Emphasize that the second step is significantly more than connecting the anchor points with straight lines, and do not direct them to generate smooth graphs. However, ask them to explain and justify any inflections or discontinuities.

The discussion phase seeks to test, understand, and improve the descriptions of different experts. The discussion phase begins by displaying the different experts' graphs side by side. The experts share their verbal descriptions with the group to explain the anchor points and shape in their graphs of the function. Comparing multiple descriptions of each expert improves consistency and uncovers beliefs about important features of the relationship. Differences among descriptions are inevitable because of the complexity of the relationships being described and the partial and particular knowledge of different experts. These differences naturally lead the experts to discuss their mental models and assumptions used to describe the relationship. The facilitator helps the experts to identify and investigate the causes of differences based on their roles in the process, relationships among functional groups, and organizational structures. No attempt is made to resolve differences or reach consensus.

14.5.1 Case Study: Estimating Precedence Relationships in Product Development

Ford and Sterman (1998a) used the knowledge elicitation method described above to estimate important nonlinear functions for a product development model (see Ford and Sterman 1998b for model details). The model is designed to understand the sources of cost and schedule overruns so common in development projects (see sections 2.3 and 6.3.4) and to evaluate policies such as increased use of concurrent engineering to speed development, lower costs, and boost quality. To test the model, we calibrated it for the case of a moderately complex ASIC (application specific integrated circuit) developed by a major player in the semiconductor industry.

The model disaggregated the overall development project, here code-named Python, into a number of phases: product definition, design, prototype development and testing, and manufacturing process development. Each phase was represented by an identical generic structure calibrated with parameters specific to that phase. The generic module can be configured to represent any number of phases in any arbitrary network of interdependencies and contains five subsectors. The Scope subsystem defines phase sizes and tracks changes in customer or project requirements. The Targets subsystem describes project objectives for delivery time, quality, and cost. The Resources sector allocates personnel and other resources to each activity based on the pressure to meet deadlines as perceived by developers and management. The Process Structure sector captures the degree to which tasks can be done concurrently within a phase and between phases. Finally, the Performance sector tracks the completion and release of work, the number of defects and errors the work contains, and costs.

The phases are mutually dependent on one another for information needed to complete the work. Design cannot proceed without product specifications from the definition phase; prototype builds cannot begin without at least some design information, and so on. In project and product development models *precedence relationships* describe the constraint imposed on one activity by another by characterizing the degree to which activities can be carried out in parallel or must be done sequentially. *External precedence relationships* describe the dependency of the development tasks in one phase on the release of tasks from another, such as the constraint imposed on testing by the release of design work. *Internal precedence relationships* describe the interdependency of the development tasks within a single development phase. Internal precedence relationships are necessary because each phase in a development project aggregates a number of different activities. The activities in a given phase cannot always be done independently. The

FIGURE 14-17   External precedence relationships

Left: Reference policies for fully concurrent and fully sequential precedence constraints. *Right:* Typical nonlinear external precedence constraints.

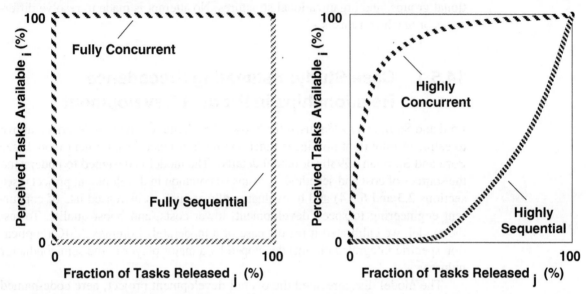

Source: Adapted from Ford and Sterman (1998a).

second floor of a building cannot be erected before the structural members for the first floor are placed no matter how many workers and cranes are available.[13]

External precedence relationships limit the work that can be done in phase i as a function of the work released to it by another phase j. The precedence constraints are formulated as fractions of the tasks in phase i that can be done as a function of the fraction of the tasks of phase j released:

Perceived Fraction of Tasks Available$_{i,j}$ = $f_{i,j}$(Fraction of Tasks Released$_j$)   (14-53)

When there are many other phases, the work phase i can do is constrained by the most limiting of the external precedence relationships. Two reference policies are useful in specifying the external constraints (Figure 14-17). If phase i is completely independent of phase j, the external precedence function is always unity. The work of the two phases can be completely concurrent. At the other extreme, if the work is completely sequential, so that phase i cannot begin its work until phase j has released all its tasks, the function is zero until phase j releases all its tasks. Any intermediate degrees of concurrency can be captured between these extremes. Nonlinear precedence functions imply that the degree of concurrency changes as the work of phase j proceeds. The highly sequential curve in Figure 14-17 implies phase i cannot complete any of its work until phase j releases about half its work. The highly concurrent curve indicates phase i can do about half its work when

---

[13]Internal and external precedence relationships are identical to the gate functions used in the pulp mill model described in section 6.3.4.

phase j releases only about 10% of its work and nearly all its work when phase j releases more than half its work.

The external precedence functions determine the *perceived* fraction of tasks available because the functions $f_{i,j}()$ represent the judgment of the workers in each phase about how much they can do based on the fraction of tasks released by other phases. That judgment could be wrong. A full project model must distinguish between the degree of concurrence the project attempts and the optimal degree of concurrence; differences between these feed back to the quality of work and the fraction of tasks done correctly. Design engineers, for example, might underestimate how much they can do based on the product specifications released to date. In this case, the project is more sequential than it needs to be and the completion rate falls below what might have been done. If they overestimate how much they can do relative to what is actually possible, the completion rate rises, but the error rate for tasks done sooner than they should have been rises as well. The result is the discovery of additional rework later, often after other phases have begun their work.

Internal precedence functions are analogous, except that the constraint depends on the fraction of tasks phase managers believe is complete:

Perceived Fraction of Tasks Available$_i$
$$= f_i(\text{Fraction of Tasks Perceived Complete}_i) \tag{14-54}$$

Internal precedence constraints must lie above the 45° line. A function below the 45° line implies the number of tasks that can be completed is less than the number actually done, an impossibility. To illustrate internal precedence functions, consider the construction of an office building. Not all tasks involved in erecting the steel skeleton for an office tower can be accomplished simultaneously. The internal precedence relationship for this phase captures the physical constraint that the building must be erected sequentially one floor at a time from the ground up. The work of placing the beams and girders for the next floor cannot be done until the members for the previous floor have been placed and secured. In a 10-story building, completing the first 10% of the work (one floor) makes it feasible for the crew to do the next 10% (the second floor), and so on. Figure 14-18 shows the worksheet for this example, with anchor points and comments, along with the resulting graph of the function. The linear progression reflects the sequential increase in the number of total floors available for steel erection as work proceeds up the building.

Seven precedence relationships were estimated by Python engineers and managers in a set of seven workshops. Each focused on estimating one function, with a different set of experts from the affected phases, and averaged 45 minutes in duration. The experts had an average of over 10 years of experience developing computer chips and a minimum of 5 years' experience in the company's product development organization. Most developers in the Python organization also had management roles. The experts were familiar with the system dynamics approach to modeling product development projects and several had received training in systems thinking. A few of the experts had heard an informal conceptual description of the model but none had knowledge of the formal model structure or descriptions of specific relationships used in it. The number of participants in each workshop varied from two to five.

FIGURE 14-18   Internal precedence relationship for building construction

Top: Worksheet showing anchor points with explanation for the erection of the steel skeleton of a 10-story building. *Bottom:* Graph of internal precedence relationship.

Tasks Perceived Complete (%)	Perceived Tasks Available (%)	Notes
0	10	Can do 1st floor at start
10	20	Completing 1st floor makes 2nd floor available
20	30	Completing 2nd floor makes 3rd floor available
. . .	. . .	. . .
90	100	Completing 9th floor makes entire structure available
100	100	Building structure erection complete

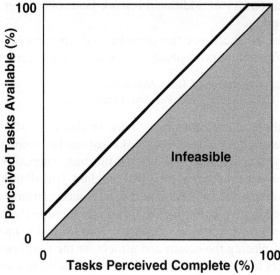

Source: Adapted from Ford and Sterman (1998a).

The workshops began with the positioning phase. The facilitator described the purpose of the work and overall architecture of the project management model. The construction example was used to illustrate the concept of internal and external precedence relationships and demonstrate the process of filling out the worksheets.

Figure 14-19 illustrates the worksheet. The worksheet describes the dependence of the Design phase on Product Definition and was completed by a product architect working in the Product Definition phase. The written notes show that the product architect believes Product Definition and Design are highly concurrent. He asserts that designers can do about 40% of their work with only about 10% of the product specifications in hand, noting that designers can begin high-level layout as soon as a concept straw man is available. In his image of the process designers can do nearly all their work when the specifications are only 80% complete. He argued

FIGURE 14-19

Sample worksheet for elicitation of nonlinear relationships

Handwritten responses typed for clarity.

EXTERNAL PRECEDENCE WORKSHEET

Upstream Development Activity: _____ Product Definition _____

Downstream Development Activity: _____ Design _____

Position held by author: _____ Product Architect _____

PROCESS STORY NOTES:

1. Product "straw man" complete—can begin high-level design & acquisition of needed design info [information] (e.g., cells, tools).

2. Feedback incorporated into straw man, producing 1st-cut product def'n [definition].

3. Incremental product def'n [definition] refinement.

4. Handoff complete.

ANCHOR POINTS IN TABLE:

Upstream Tasks Released (%)	Downstream Tasks Available (%)	Notes	
10	40	1.	[see above]
35	65	2.	[see above]
60	85	3.	[see above]
80	100		

Source: Ford and Sterman (1998a).

that the Python project was a line extension product similar to other ASICs the company had designed in the past.

The elicitation protocol described above proved highly effective. Besides a graph of the relationship (e.g., Figure 14-20), nearly all participants provided a written description of the process and justification of their anchor points, improving internal consistency and the experts' ability to explain their thinking.

During the discussion phase the experts explained the reasoning underlying their estimates of the relationship. The following captures the verbal descriptions given by the process experts of the internal precedence relationship for the design phase, which produces the software used to lay out the physical features of the chip on the silicon wafers: The code to be produced is organized into 17 blocks (code modules). A few of these blocks must be designed and written before the others can be started. Therefore only these initial blocks (estimated to be 20% of the code) can be done at the beginning of the design phase. It's not feasible to begin work on the other blocks of code until the initial blocks are nearly complete. When the initial blocks are complete, most of the remaining code can be developed. When most of the blocks have been written the work of integrating them into a single operational program begins. Integration is fundamentally less parallel, producing a flat tail on the right side of the graph. The dashed lines in Figure 14-21 show the relationships developed by three experts.

EXTERNAL PRECEDENCE WORKSHEET

Upstream Development Activity: _Product Definition_   [Product Definition]

Downstream Development Activity: _Design_   [Design]

Position held by Author: _Product Architect_   [Product Architect]

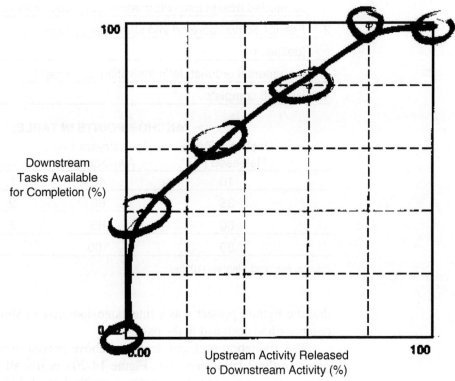

Source: Ford and Sterman (1998a).

Differences among the experts provided the opportunity for testing and improvement in the discussion phase. The three experts were in general agreement with the verbal description of the relationship above despite the differences in their graphic descriptions. After discussion the experts decided that the relationship should be horizontal at the beginning of the phase because most of the code blocks could not be started until the first 20% were nearly complete. The discussion led to an improved graphic description for use in the model (the solid line in Figure 14-21). Note that the revised relationship is not simply the average of the three estimates but is shaped by discussion of the underlying process as described in the written notes and supplemented by the conversation in the discussion phase.

Differences among descriptions also identified conflicts and inconsistencies in the views of the experts. Consider the external concurrence relationship between product definition and design (Figure 14-22). Product architects and marketing representatives gradually define the requirements for the new product. As these are

FIGURE 14-21
Four estimates
of the internal
precedence
relationship
for design

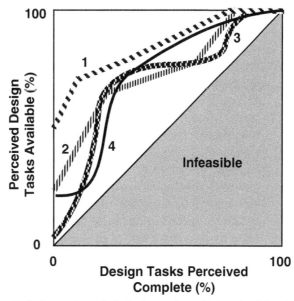

1, Design manager; 2, design engineer A; 3, design engineer B; 4, revised description after discussion phase.

Source: Ford and Sterman (1998a).

FIGURE 14-22
Estimates of the
precedence
relationship
between product
definition and
design

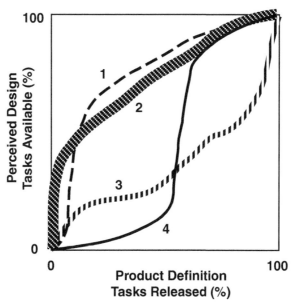

1, Strategic marketing representative; 2, product architect; 3, design manager; 4, design engineer.
Source: Ford and Sterman (1998a).

released the designers can begin to write the software that generates the chip layout so that it provides the specified functionality. Four experts, two from the product definition phase (one from strategic marketing and one product architect) and two from the design phase (a designer and a design manager) participated in the workshop. The strategic marketing representative was the participant farthest upstream in the product definition/design portion of the Python project. His estimate suggested the most concurrence, implying little product definition work needed to be completed and released before designers could usefully do most of their work. The product architect, whose work is also upstream of design, similarly suggested that design can begin after only a small fraction of the product specifications are released (see his worksheet in Figure 14-19). In contrast the designers believe the degree of potential concurrence is much lower and estimated that roughly half the product specifications must be released before any significant design work can begin.

The workshop revealed a huge gap between the mental models of the two groups. Marketers believe design work can begin very early, when product attributes are still vague and evolving, while designers believe they must have detailed and stable specifications to do their work. The perceptions of these two groups differed by more than half of the design phase scope. Also note that the design engineer, who actually does the design work, believes the process is most sequential, while the person farthest upstream (from strategic marketing) believes the two processes are highly concurrent. The gap caused conflict and delay since marketers felt little pressure to stabilize requirements before releasing them, which leads to excessive iteration, delays, and higher costs. The passionate discussion in this workshop helped the different parties come to a better understanding of the source of prior conflicts between their groups and how to improve specification handoff in the future.

The method described here can be used in any situation where expert knowledge is an important source of data for the specification of parameters or nonlinear relationships for use in models. In many cases numerical data to estimate important parameters and relationships are unavailable or cannot be developed in time or at reasonable costs. In these cases modelers must rely on judgmental estimates, and a reliable method to elicit the largely tacit knowledge of experts is essential. The method is also valuable even when numerical data are available, both to triangulate and check them and because numerical data often do not span a wide enough range to reveal extreme conditions.

Generating the relationship through a succession of smaller steps (image to words to anchor points to graph) rather than asking people to simply "draw the relationship" improves knowledge elicitation by reducing the cognitive processing required at each step. Multiple formats and steps also slow the elicitation process, providing more time for reflection and revision. Explaining and providing complete documentation of the steps to be performed by the experts using an example from a familiar but different context improves the quality of the descriptions and the experience of the experts. Differences among the experts' assessments help specify the ranges of variation in parameters and relationships for sensitivity testing.

Though the primary purpose of these workshops was to elicit the information needed to specify important relationships in the model, they also provided immediate benefits to the organization by allowing experts and clients to share and compare their mental models. By documenting the data and assumptions underlying each person's perspective the workshops helped begin a process of learning to replace distrust and finger pointing.

The workshops also boosted the credibility of the work by involving those responsible for the system in the modeling process, acknowledging and honoring participant expertise, and making special efforts to incorporate that expertise into the model. Developing such understanding is essential to successful transfer of insight, the development of systems thinking skills among the client team, and ultimately, successful implementation of model-based policy recommendations.

14.6 SUMMARY

Table or lookup functions provide a flexible tool to specify nonlinear relationships. This chapter presented guidelines for the construction of table functions, estimation of their shape and values from qualitative and quantitative data, methods to test the sensitivity of results to uncertainty in their values, and a practical process for eliciting their shapes and values from experts.

Using all available data to specify nonlinear functions, including extreme conditions, reference policies, and other qualitative data often sharply restricts their feasible shape and values and limits the plausible range they can take. Sensitivity analysis often shows that the modes of behavior and response to policies of the system are often unaffected by wide ranges of variation in the assumed values of nonlinear relationships. When systems include many negative feedbacks around a particular parameter or nonlinear relationship, the system compensates for variations in parameter values so that the numerical sensitivity of results is low as well. Those functions and parameters shown to be insensitive need not be investigated further. Judgmental estimates for these parameters often provide sufficient accuracy, releasing time and resources that can be devoted to deeper empirical and theoretical study of those parameters and relationships that do matter.

15

Modeling Human Behavior: Bounded Rationality or Rational Expectations?

> *There can no longer be any doubt that the micro assumptions of [economic] theory—the assumptions of perfect rationality—are contrary to fact. It is not a question of approximation; they do not even remotely describe the processes that human beings use for making decisions in complex situations.*
>
> —Herbert A. Simon (1979, p. 510).

To mimic the behavior of real systems models must capture decision making as it is, not as it should be, nor how it would be if people were perfectly rational. Experimental and field studies show that the rationality of human decision making is *bounded*. People use a variety of heuristics—rules of thumb—to form judgments and make decisions, and while these heuristics often work well in simple settings, they lead to persistent, systematic departures from rational behavior in many realistic situations, including systems with even modest levels of dynamic complexity. Previous chapters presented useful formulations and techniques to capture decision making in dynamic models. This chapter presents principles for formulating the decision rules in models so they are consistent with the actual decision-making capabilities of real people. A model of a high-tech firm is used to illustrate how bounded rationality can be incorporated in model formulations and how the intended rationality of the decision rules for the individual agents in the model can be tested. Challenges give you a chance to design and implement policies for improved performance.

15.1 HUMAN DECISION MAKING: BOUNDED RATIONALITY OR RATIONAL EXPECTATIONS?

Chapters 13 and 14 provide a wide range of robust formulations for use in models of human behavior. But these formulations still leave considerable room for different assumptions about the degree of rationality in the decision-making process. Given the information available to them, do people make rational, optimal decisions or is their behavior naive and mindless? Do people make systematic errors? How and how quickly do learning and adaptation occur?

An extensive body of experimental and field studies document human decision-making behavior in diverse contexts. As you might expect, the way people make decisions depends somewhat on the situation. Some decisions are made automatically (which pair of socks should I wear this morning?). Others involve considerable time, resources, and deliberative effort, along with emotions and feelings (what kind of car should I buy?). Human decision making generally falls in between the extremes of mindless rote behavior and the perfect rationality of economic theory. The evidence suggests that the rationality of human decision making is *bounded* (see, e.g., Simon 1957, 1982; Cyert and March 1963; and Nelson and Winter 1982; Conlisk 1996 surveys the evidence and discusses theoretical issues in the context of economics).

Bounded rationality arises because human cognitive capabilities, as wonderful as they are, are overwhelmed by the complexity of the systems we are called upon to manage. Chapter 1 discussed bounded rationality; here I repeat Herbert Simon's (1957, p. 198) principle of bounded rationality:

> The capacity of the human mind for formulating and solving complex problems is very small compared with the size of the problem whose solution is required for objectively rational behavior in the real world or even for a reasonable approximation to such objective rationality.

Bounded rationality results from limitations on our knowledge, cognitive capabilities, and time. Our perceptions are selective, our knowledge of the real world is incomplete, our mental models are grossly simplified and imperfect, and our powers of deduction and inference are weak and fallible. Emotional, subconscious, and other nonrational factors affect our behavior. Deliberation takes time and we must often make decisions before we are ready.

As an example, consider a basic problem facing the managers of any business: capital investment. Managers must decide when and how to invest in capacity and only desire to invest when they believe the investment will be profitable. To do so optimally, they must choose the rate of investment that maximizes the net present value of the firm's expected profits, for all future time, as the competitive environment, input costs, demand, interest rates, and other factors affecting profits change. They must take into account all possible contingencies including the ways in which other actors in the environment (suppliers, competitors, workers, customers, government, etc.) might react to any decision the firm makes. In general, these inputs are linked in a complex network of feedback relationships and may also be influenced by random shocks.

Choosing investment optimally requires the firm's managers to formulate and solve an exceedingly complex stochastic, dynamic optimization problem. To do so the managers must have (1) knowledge of the cost and demand functions facing the firm; (2) knowledge of the future behavior of all variables and other actors in the system, or, equivalently, a perfect model of the system from which the future behavior of these variables and actors may be deduced (the rational expectations hypothesis, see Muth 1961); (3) the cognitive capability to solve the resulting optimization problem; and (4) the time do so.

None of these conditions is met in reality. In practice, the complexity of the problem is so overwhelming that no one can solve it or even agree on what the relevant variables and policy options are. Economists working with investment models must make severe simplifying assumptions to render the problem tractable, for example, assuming input and product markets are perfectly competitive, discount rates are constant, and adjustment costs are quadratic. Even then, as Pindyck and Rotemberg (1983) comment with dry understatement,

> Stochastic control problems of this sort are generally difficult, if not impossible to solve. This, of course, raises the question of whether rational expectations provides a realistic behavioral foundation for studying investment behavior.

Optimal decision making is impossible even for problems much simpler than capital investment, such as choosing which job candidate to hire or which students to admit to a university. To do so requires assessing all relevant candidate characteristics and predicting the likely success and failure of the candidates given the attributes and performance history of all similar applicants, including those who were not selected. Many studies show that simple decision rules based on a small number of inputs often significantly outperform the experts in a wide range of tasks, from predicting the performance of students and the life expectancy of cancer patients to predicting business failures and stock market performance (Dawes 1979; Camerer 1981).

This chapter began with Herbert Simon's blunt assessment, in his Nobel Prize address, that the theory of rational choice underlying economics does not "even remotely describe the processes that human beings use for making decisions in complex situations." Such a bold statement suggests three questions: First, what is the evidence that people don't behave according to the principles of rational choice and economic theory? Second, how then *do* people make decisions? Finally, how can the ways people make decisions be modeled?

15.2 COGNITIVE LIMITATIONS

Humans have a limited ability to process information. As a consequence, "perception of information is not comprehensive but *selective*" (Hogarth 1987, p. 4; original emphasis). For both physiological and psychological reasons, we perceive and attend to only a small fraction of the information available in the environment. Instead, people take very few cues into account when making decisions. Attention is a scarce resource and must be allocated among competing demands. We focus our attention on some cues and ignore or remain unaware of other, potentially important cues. Under normal circumstances, our attention moves from one cue to another as their salience and perceived importance change and as we become distracted by events. In stressful situations the flood of information can overwhelm our processing capabilities and we fail to perceive new information, regardless of its importance. Studies of pilots in crises, for example, show how easily information overload can arise. In some cases, the pilots are doing so many things at once and are bombarded by so many different types of information (visuals, instruments, radio instructions, auditory cues, and others) that they are literally unable to notice critical cues such as the copilot shouting emergency instructions. Crashes have resulted from such information overload.

Our cognitive capabilities are similarly bounded. Miller (1956) famously showed that short-term working memory is limited to "7 ± 2" chunks of information; constraints on the storage and recall of information in long-term memory and on intuitive computational power have also been identified. Ideally attention and cognitive effort should be allocated optimally according to the importance and utility of the different cues available to the decision maker, but people do not have the time or cognitive capability to decide what that optimal allocation is. Indeed, the attempt to do so complicates the decision problem, aggravates information overload, and can lead to even worse decision making. Rather, people tend to focus their attention and effort on cues that are readily available, salient, and concrete. We focus on cues we believe to be relatively certain, systematically underweighting uncertain or remote information even when it has diagnostic value (Hogarth 1987; Kahneman, Slovic, and Tversky 1982, chap. 4). Our mental models affect which of the many cues in an environment we think are important and useful, directing attention to those cues at the expense of others. However, as discussed in chapter 1, people are notoriously poor judges of causality and correlation, and systematically create mental models at variance with the known situation, so that our expectations sometimes lead us to notice cues that have low diagnostic power and prevent us from attending to more useful cues.

Because our cognitive and decision-making capabilities are limited, we cannot make decisions according to the prescriptions of optimization theory. Instead, we use, consciously and unconsciously, a wide range of heuristics to make decisions. A large and diverse body of empirical and experimental research, generally known as behavioral decision theory (BDT), documents the heuristics people use in judgment and decision making.[1]

While some heuristics work well under some situations, the research shows that many yield systematic, significant, and persistent errors. While training can moderate some of the errors, many are robust in the face of experience and are difficult to overcome.

---

[1]The literature is large. For good overviews, see Hogarth (1987); Kahneman et al. (1982); Plous (1993); Russo and Schoemaker (1989); and Thaler (1991, 1992).

15.3 INDIVIDUAL AND ORGANIZATIONAL RESPONSES TO BOUNDED RATIONALITY

Since optimal decision making with perfect models is impossible, people and organizations have developed a number of ways to simplify the task of decision making.

15.3.1 Habit, Routines, and Rules of Thumb

Habits and routines are procedures followed repetitively and without significant deliberative effort. Instead of deciding what to do each morning by considering the costs and benefits of all our options, most of us follow a routine: Exercise, shower, get dressed, and so on. We don't think about it, we just do it.

Routines are nearly automatic procedures triggered by particular conditions. They are the organization's standard operating procedures. Routines may be informal or highly codified protocols. They may be rigid or permit some flexibility in response to local conditions. They often evolve with experience. Organizational routines are simultaneously embedded in, justified by, and reinforce the organization's traditions, culture, and folklore.

Another common method to reduce the complexity of decision making is through rules of thumb. A rule of thumb is a procedure designed to yield a pretty good decision quickly and easily. Rules of thumb, or decision-making heuristics, are based on simplified, incomplete models of the problem situation. They tend to rely on relatively certain information readily available to the decision maker. In the department store pricing example cited in section 13.1, managers do not have the information, cognitive capability, or time to set the prices of each item to optimize store profits. Setting floor prices by multiplying wholesale costs by a traditional markup ratio is a rule of thumb that allows store managers to set prices quickly. The rule is not optimal but performs well enough in most situations. When prices prove to be too high or too low, other rules of thumb such as "hold a sale for slow moving products" allow managers to correct errors.

15.3.2 Managing Attention

Since attention is a scarce resource, controlling the information people have access and attend to is an important source of power. Organizations have developed many structures and routines to control access to information, directing the attention of its members toward some cues and away from others. These devices include formal reporting relationships, agenda setting, the geographical structure of the organization and physical layout of its facilities, and accounting and information systems. Informal networks of communication also critically influence the allocation of attention. Some of the most powerful people in any large organization are the executive secretaries—the people you must persuade to give you access to busy senior executives.

15.3.3 Goal Formation and Satisficing

Another strategy to reduce the complexity of the decision task is goal setting. Instead of making decisions by explicitly solving optimization problems, people instead tend to set goals and adjust their behavior in an attempt to meet them. Once the goals are met, problem solving efforts often stop so the attention and cognitive resources they consume can be used elsewhere. Herbert Simon coined the term "satisficing" to describe behavior in which effort is reduced once a satisfactory solution to a problem is found or a satisfactory level of performance is attained. Students often reduce their study effort once they achieve the grades they desire; consumers stop searching for bargains once a low enough price is found for the item they desire; employers often hire the first candidate meeting the requirements for the job rather than searching for the best one.

Setting specific goals provides decision makers with a concrete target against which they can compare the actual performance of the system and initiate corrective action when there is a discrepancy. The more concrete and specific the goal, the easier it is for people to determine which information cues are important and which can be ignored and to decide which actions to take to reach the goal.

Aspirations and goals themselves are adaptive and respond to experience. In the department store pricing example, the standard markup over wholesale costs adapted to experience. Store managers gradually adjusted target markups to the actual markups realized by the store after responding to competitor prices and holding sales to move surplus inventory. The quota for a sales force is often based on an average of recent sales plus a certain margin to encourage greater effort, and a student's desired grade point average tends to adjust to the actual grades received, again perhaps biased by a margin to encourage greater achievement (Cyert and March 1963; Lant 1992; Morecroft 1985).

15.3.4   Problem Decomposition and Decentralized Decision Making

Limited information processing capability forces people to divide the total task of making a decision into smaller units. By establishing subgoals the complexity of the total problem is vastly reduced.

Decomposition of decision problems into subgoals is also an important motivation for organizational specialization. Each organizational subunit is charged with achieving a small number of subgoals: The sales organization is charged with meeting sales goals; the manufacturing organization must deliver on time and below certain cost targets. Within each of these functions, further decomposition takes place: Inside the manufacturing organization, individual machine operators must hit their daily quotas and maintenance technicians strive to clear the backlog of work orders. Typically, the goals of each organizational subunit are broken down into still smaller subgoals until the connections between the decisions the agent can make and the agent's goals are clear and unambiguous.

In deciding how to achieve a goal, decision makers tend to ignore, or treat as exogenous, those aspects of the situation they believe are not directly related to it (Simon 1957, p. 79):

> Individual choice takes place in an environment of "givens"—premises that are accepted by the subject as bases for his choice; and behavior is adaptive only within the limits set by these "givens."

For example, a firm may lower prices to increase market share on the assumption that competitor prices will remain at current levels; a real estate developer may begin construction of a new property on the assumption that low vacancy rates and high rents will persist until the building is ready for occupancy; a machine operator striving to hit the daily quota may choose to defer scheduled maintenance, ignoring the effect of this action on future yield and quality. The implicit assumption of problem decomposition and decentralized decision making is that achieving each subgoal will enable the decision maker or organization to achieve their overall goals. This assumption is often incorrect.

15.4 INTENDED RATIONALITY

Cognitive limitations and the other bounds on rationality mean decisions are often made as if there were no time delays, side effects, feedbacks, or nonlinearities. Since real systems often involve considerable dynamic complexity, decisions made in this fashion often cause policy resistance, instability, and dysfunction. Does this mean decision makers are irrational or just plain stupid? Not at all. Human behavior is usually purposeful. Most decisions are motivated by a certain logic. The modeler must uncover and represent the mental models of the decision makers and represent the rationale for their decision rules. What are the implicit assumptions that make their behavior sensible, from their point of view and given their goals? That is, is the decision rule *intendedly rational?*

A decision rule is locally or intendedly rational if it would produce reasonable and sensible results if the actual environment were as simple as the decision maker presumes it to be, that is, if the premises accepted by the subject were true. For example, it is sensible for a firm to cut prices to stimulate market share when capacity utilization is low *if* the mangers believe that competitors won't or can't respond by cutting their own prices. Figure 15-1 shows a causal diagram of the situation. The company cuts prices when capacity utilization falls below some normal or target level, forming a negative feedback as managers attempt to Fill the Line (loop B1). If the system were as simple as the managers presume it to be, that is, if the price of competing products were in fact exogenous, then cutting prices to stimulate demand and boost profits would make sense. But the managers' mental model is like the proverbial tip of the iceberg: It includes only a small fraction of the feedback structure in the system. Competitors are likely to set prices using the same fill the line logic. Cutting prices when utilization drops creates a reinforcing feedback (R1) in which a drop in price causes the market share and hence utilization of competing firms to fall, leading them to cut their prices. The company finds its market share and utilization do not improve as expected and cuts price again, closing the positive loop. When the presumption of exogenous competitor prices is false, locally rational attempts to fill the line lead to an unintended price war that destroys profitability for all.[2]

---

[2]Not all price wars are unanticipated or irrational. Firms may start a price war in an attempt to bankrupt rivals they believe are weaker or to punish defectors from a cartel (e.g., Green and Porter 1984).

FIGURE 15-1   An intendedly rational pricing policy can lead to an inadvertent price war.

Top: Mental model of a firm in which competitor prices are believed to be exogenous. Cutting prices to Fill the Line (B1) when capacity utilization falls is locally rational if the boundary of management's mental model cuts the feedbacks to competitor prices.

Bottom: When competitor firms behave the same way and also cut prices to boost their own capacity utilization (B2), then the intendedly rational decision to lower prices in the hope of stimulating demand creates the reinforcing feedback R1 (shown by the thick lines) and a price war ensues whenever industry demand drops below capacity. For clarity, additional feedbacks from prices to industry demand and from demand to capacity are not shown.

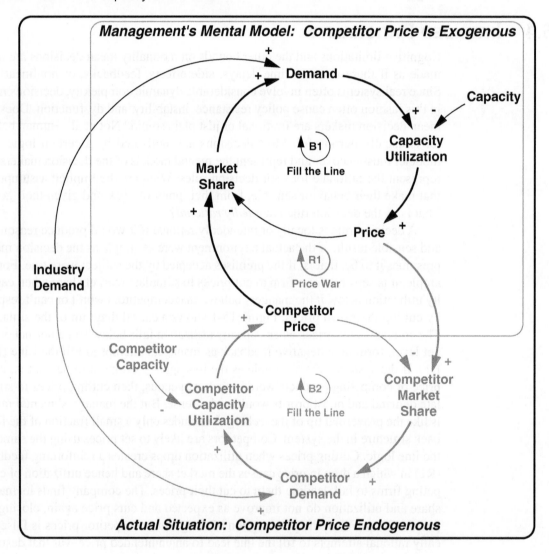

The account above does assume the managers explicitly consider competitor prices but decide that the competitors won't respond to a price cut with a price cut of their own. Alternatively, the managers may never consider competitor prices at all, assuming implicitly and without reflection that lower prices stimulate demand and will help fill the line.

15.4.1   Testing for Intended Rationality: Partial Model Tests

Partial model tests help you determine whether the decision rules in your model are intendedly rational. In a partial model test each organizational function or decision point is isolated from its environment until the environment is consistent with the mental model that underlies the decision rule. The subsystem can then be challenged with various exogenous patterns in its inputs. Does a firm's inventory management policy behave appropriately when demand suddenly increases? Does the capital investment process adjust capacity to appropriate levels without excessive instability? How does the firm's price respond to a change in unit labor costs? In the price war example above, the managers cut prices to fill the line when utilization is low because they believe competitor prices will not respond. A partial model test of this pricing rule would be implemented by making the competitor price exogenous, then challenging the model with a decline in demand. Lower prices would boost demand and fill the line, demonstrating that the decision rule is sensible in a world where the feedback to the market is cut, as the managers believe.

15.5   CASE STUDY: MODELING HIGH-TECH GROWTH FIRMS

Forrester's (1968) "market growth" model illustrates how bounded rationality can be represented in models and how the intended rationality of a model can be tested.[3] The market growth model grew out of Forrester's experience advising entrepreneurs and companies in the high-tech industry. It is one of several models of high-tech growth firms Forrester built during the 1960s (Forrester 1975a; see also Packer 1964 and Nord 1963). These models addressed a puzzle that is still an issue today. Most new companies fail. Some grow for a while but then stagnate. Still fewer manage to grow but experience periodic crises, often inducing turnover of top management. Only a very small number seem able to grow rapidly and steadily for extended periods of time (see Figure 3-6).

Forrester could discern no obvious differences between the successes and failures in the quality of the products, the creativity of their engineers, or other fundamentals. He became convinced that the explanation for the differing outcomes lay in the different decision rules used to manage the enterprise and the unanticipated side effects of policies that appeared to be rational and well-intentioned when viewed in isolation.

In the market growth model, Forrester set out to create the simplest possible model that could still capture the key decision rules of the entrepreneurs and chief executives he knew. Though based on the case of a particular firm, the model is

---

[3]The analysis of intended rationality in the market growth model was inspired by and draws on Morecroft (1983). Morecroft pioneered the development of the concepts of intended rationality in system dynamics (see also Morecroft 1985) for which he won the Jay Forrester prize in 1990. The version of the market growth model developed here differs from both Forrester's original and Morecroft's 1983 version in some details, but the essence of key formulations is the same, as are the behavior and implications of the model.

quite general and its lessons apply to growing organizations in any industry. The parameters are therefore chosen to be representative of typical high-tech products and not to replicate the experience of any one company.

To illustrate how interactions of intendedly rational policies could produce failure, Forrester deliberately made the strong simplifying assumption that the market for the firm's product was unlimited. The potential of the computer and high-tech industry in the 1960s seemed to him to be so great that this was a reasonable assumption.

15.5.1   Model Structure: Overview

The model represents a single firm competing in a potentially unlimited market. To keep the model as simple as possible, Forrester deliberately omitted many organizational functions and structures. For example, there is no income statement or balance sheet, and competitors are included implicitly in a simple market sector. The representation of the firm itself consists of three sectors, each representing a different organizational subunit (Figure 15-2): sales, order fulfillment, and capacity acquisition.

FIGURE 15-2   Sectors of the market growth model

The model divides the firm into distinct organizational subunits. Each function operates on the basis of different information.

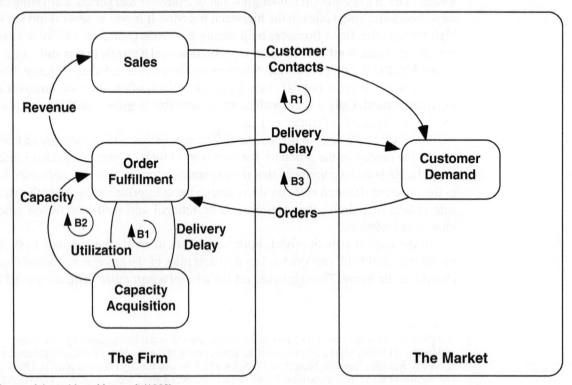

Source: Adapted from Morecroft (1983).

Interactions of organizational functions create important feedback loops, such as the balancing loop B3, which couples the firm to the market through product availability. An increase in orders boosts the backlog and delivery delay, causing some delivery-sensitive customers to take their business to the firm's competitors. The model represents the firm and its market as an ecology of interacting agents—the individual organizational functions—each with their own goals and decision rules.

Consistent with the principles of bounded rationality, managers operating in the individual subunits are not assumed to understand the overall feedback structure. Each subunit is assumed to have access to and use a small number of informational cues, not the full set of information potentially available. For example, the capacity expansion decision is based on product availability as measured by the delivery delay and does not depend on forecasts of future sales generated by the marketing organization, which were generally distrusted and ignored by senior management.

15.5.2   Order Fulfillment

Figure 15-3 shows the structure of the order fulfillment function.

FIGURE 15-3   Order fulfillment

The rectangle with rounded corners denotes the boundary of a subsystem or organizational subunit in the model (Morecroft 1982). Variables outside the boundary are determined in other subsystems. Often the members of the subunit view these inputs as exogenous givens. Here, production capacity is taken to be outside the control of the order fulfillment organization.

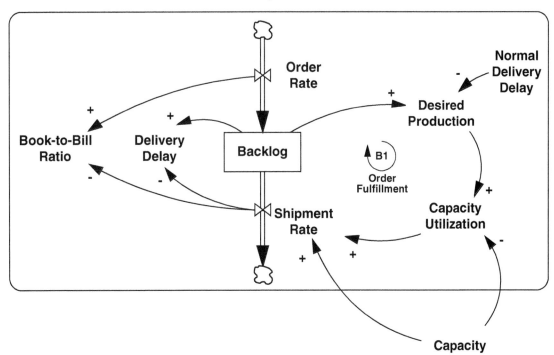

Forrester assumed the firm manufactured a complex high-tech product and operated a build-to-order system. Orders accumulated in a backlog until they could be produced and shipped. The actual average delay in delivering orders (the mean residence time of orders in the backlog) is given by the ratio of the backlog to the current shipment rate (see section 11.2.6). The book-to-bill ratio is a common measure of the health of high-tech companies. Book-to-bill ratios greater than one indicate the order book is growing.

Backlog = INTEGRAL(Order Rate – Shipment Rate, Backlog$_{t_0}$)   (15-1)

Delivery Delay = Backlog/Shipment Rate   (15-2)

Book-to-Bill Ratio = Order Rate/Shipment Rate   (15-3)

The desired production rate depends on the backlog and the normal delivery delay—the normal time required to process, build, and ship an order:

Desired Production = Backlog/Normal Delivery Delay   (15-4)

Production capacity and capacity utilization determine shipments:

Shipment Rate = Capacity * Capacity Utilization   (15-5)

Capacity Utilization = f(Desired Production/Capacity)   (15-6)

From the point of view of the managers responsible for order fulfillment, capacity is a given, one of the premises people accept as a basis for their choices. Capacity is not under their direct control and responds only slowly to senior management's decisions to invest. Operations managers must accommodate variations in demand through changes in the level of capacity utilization. The higher the backlog, the higher the utilization rate, though of course, utilization saturates when the firm's plants are operating at their maximum rate. Figure 15-4 shows the assumed capacity utilization function. By definition, when desired production equals capacity, utilization is unity. When desired production is less than capacity, plant managers cut utilization back gradually, preferring to run the backlog down rather than idling their plants and laying off employees. Therefore the assumed utilization curve lies above the 45° reference policy. However, when the backlog is zero, utilization and

FIGURE 15-4
Capacity
utilization

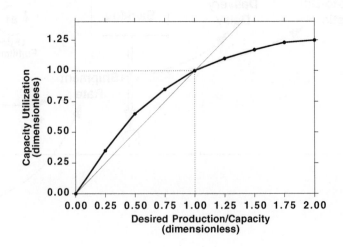

shipments must also be zero: If there are no orders in the backlog, there are no customers to whom a product can be shipped, and the firm never accumulates inventory. Utilization rises above one when desired production exceeds capacity but at sharply diminishing rates until it reaches a maximum assumed to be 25% above normal.[4]

The intended rationality of the order fulfillment decision rule can be examined through two partial model tests. First, the formulation for shipments should allow the firm to meet its delivery goals when capacity is not a constraint. If there were no capacity constraint on shipments so capacity utilization was perfectly flexible, utilization would lie along the 45° line in Figure 15-4. The formulation for the shipment rate would then reduce to

$$\begin{aligned}
\text{Shipment Rate} &= \text{Capacity} * \text{Capacity Utilization} \\
&= \text{Capacity} * (\text{Desired Production/Capacity}) \\
&= \text{Desired Production} \\
&= \text{Backlog/Normal Delivery Delay} \quad\quad\quad\quad (15\text{-}5a)
\end{aligned}$$

which is the formulation for a first-order material delay. If capacity were never a constraint on shipments, the production scheduling decision rule would always enable the firm to fulfill orders within the normal delivery delay.

The second partial model test examines the intended rationality of the entire order fulfillment process. Now capacity is taken as exogenous and constant, and the shipment formulation is challenged with a step increase in orders (Figure 15-5). Capacity is 500 units/month. The initial backlog is 1000 units. Since the normal delivery delay is 2 months, desired production is 500 units/month and initial utilization is 100%. In month 0 orders increase to 600 units/month. The backlog begins to rise and managers increase utilization. Since capacity is fixed, the delivery delay rises above the normal level. Shipments smoothly approach the new equilibrium rate of 600 units/month. In the new equilibrium, utilization has reached 120% of normal and the delivery delay rises to 2.7 months.

These tests demonstrate the intended rationality of the formulation for order fulfillment. In isolation, the order fulfillment decision rule tracks changes in orders in a smooth and stable manner and maintains the delivery delay as low as possible given the capacity constraint. Note, however, that if orders were sustained at a rate greater than 125% of capacity (the maximum rate of output), the shipment rate would always be less than orders and the backlog would increase indefinitely. Such behavior would still be intendedly rational: The best the managers could do is produce at the maximum rate.

15.5.3   Capacity Acquisition

Figure 15-6 shows the structure of the capacity acquisition sector.

---

[4]The backlog–shipment structure is an example of a capacitated delay, discussed in chapter 14, along with the construction of the nonlinear utilization function. The model defines utilization of 100% to be the normal rate achieved when desired production equals capacity. Many firms define utilization as the fraction of maximum output achieved. Since the maximum utilization is 25% above normal, the formulation is equivalent to assuming the firm normally operates at 80% of maximum capacity.

FIGURE 15-5

Response of order fulfillment sector to a step in demand

Capacity is fixed at 500 units/month. Orders increase from 500 to 600 units/month at time zero.

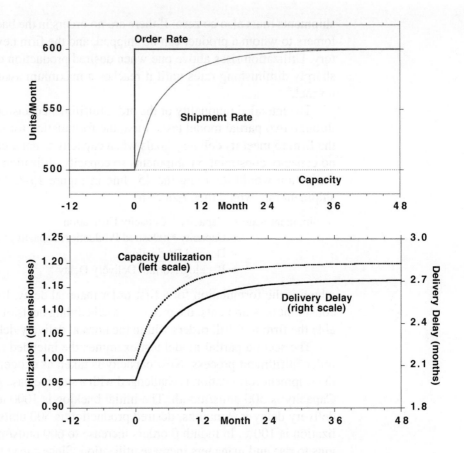

Rather than model the capacity ordering and acquisition process in detail, capacity is assumed to adjust to the desired level of capacity with a third-order delay. The capacity acquisition time is set to 18 months, a typical value (section 11.5.1).[5]

$$\text{Capacity} = \text{SMOOTH3}(\text{Desired Capacity, Capacity Acquisition Delay}) \qquad (15\text{-}7)$$

The formulation for desired capacity captures several important aspects of bounded rationality. Forrester observed that senior managers in the company upon which his model was based, as in many firms, were very conservative about capital investment. Investments in capacity are expensive and largely irreversible. Senior managers, in particular the founder and CEO, were reluctant to invest until there was clear evidence of need and until they could be sure that any new capacity would not go unutilized. Though the sales and marketing organizations produced sales forecasts, senior management didn't trust them. Senior management's view was that "marketing can forecast the moon, and plant managers are always complaining about capacity shortages. The only reliable evidence that we need more capacity comes when we start missing delivery dates."

---

[5]Note that because the model does not represent the physical flows of capacity orders, arrivals, and discards, the information delay (SMOOTH3) is used rather than a material delay (section 11.3; chapter 17 develops formulations to model capacity acquisition explicitly).

FIGURE 15-6   Capacity acquisition

The rectangles around Delivery Delay Perceived by Company and Capacity represent delays without showing their full stock and flow structure.

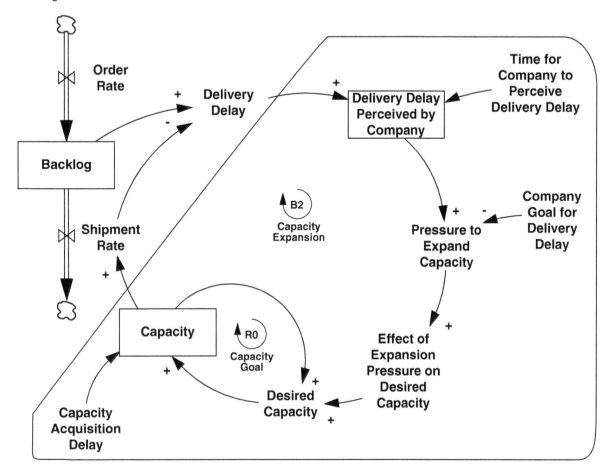

The desired capacity decision is modeled as an anchoring and adjustment process (section 13.2.10). Management forms desired capacity by anchoring on current capacity, then adjusting it up or down based on various pressures. Because cues such as sales forecasts are noisy, unreliable, and untrustworthy, the pressure to expand capacity derives from the firm's perceived ability to deliver compared to its goal.

Desired Capacity
= Capacity * Effect of Expansion Pressure on Desired Capacity   (15-8)

Effect of Expansion Pressure on Desired Capacity
= f(Pressure to Expand Capacity)   (15-9)

$$\text{Pressure to Expand Capacity} = \frac{\text{Delivery Delay Perceived by Company}}{\text{Company Goal for Delivery Delay}} \quad (15\text{-}10)$$

$$\begin{array}{l}\text{Delivery Delay} \\ \text{Perceived by Company}\end{array} = \text{SMOOTH}\left(\text{Delivery Delay,} \begin{array}{l}\text{Time for Company} \\ \text{to Perceive Delivery Delay}\end{array}\right)$$
(15-11)

FIGURE 15-7

Effect of product
availability on
capacity
expansion

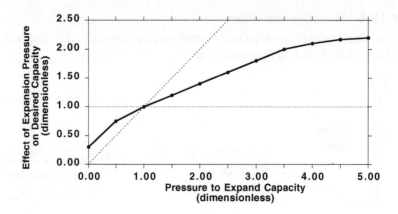

Pressure to expand capacity is the ratio of the delivery delay senior management
perceives compared to their goal for delivery delay. Managers' beliefs about product availability are assumed to lag the true delivery delay due to the difficulty of
measuring availability and delays in updating their beliefs once data become available. First-order exponential smoothing is assumed, with a perception delay of
3 months. For now, the company goal for delivery delay is constant and equal to
the normal delivery delay. In Forrester's original model the goal was itself a variable (see the challenge below).

The pressure to expand capacity has a nonlinear effect on desired capacity, as
shown in Figure 15-7. When perceived delivery delay is very low compared to the
goal, management concludes there is substantial excess capacity and cuts desired
capacity below the current level. When the perceived delivery delay exceeds the
goal, desired capacity rises above the current level. To capture management's conservative approach to capacity expansion the adjustment is weak: A 10% increase
in expansion pressure causes a less than 10% increase in desired capacity, and the
effect saturates at a maximum value.

Management's capacity expansion behavior is consistent with the principles of
bounded rationality. Management had little confidence in sales forecasts, market
research, and other possible signals of future demand and instead based its decision
on delivery delay—an important, direct measure of the firm's ability to meet demand. Perceptions of delivery delay lag behind the actual situation. A temporary
increase in delivery delay will therefore not result in much investment. Only when
delivery schedules are consistently missed does management become aware of and
deem the need for capacity sufficiently compelling to justify investment.

To test the intended rationality of the capacity decision, first consider a simulation in which the delivery delay perceived by the company is exogenous. This
partial model test cuts the balancing capacity expansion loop B2 and tests the response of the anchoring and adjustment formulation for desired capacity. In Figure
15-8 the pressure for expansion begins at the normal value of one. Management
believes product availability is at the desired level. The perceived delivery delay
then jumps by 25% for a period of 2 years before returning to normal. In month 60,
perceived delivery delay drops to 75% of normal before returning to normal after
another 2 years.

FIGURE 15-8
Response of
capacity to
changes in
expansion
pressure

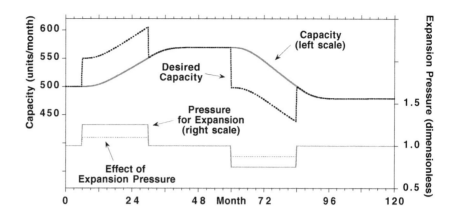

The increase in the perceived delivery delay creates pressure for capacity expansion. Management increases desired capacity above its current level. Capacity gradually begins to rise. Because the feedback from capacity to product availability is cut, the increase in capacity does not reduce delivery delay. Managers continue to experience pressure for expansion. Though capacity has increased, the continuing high delivery delay they perceive is evidence that capacity has not yet increased enough. Desired capacity remains higher than capacity, and capacity adjusts to the desired level, closing the positive Capacity Goal loop (R0). The formulation for desired capacity enables management to search for the right level of capacity, whatever it may turn out to be. When production pressure returns to normal in month 30, managers conclude that the current level of capacity is, finally, the right one. Desired capacity falls back to the level of actual capacity. Actual capacity rises for a few more months due to the delay in capacity acquisition but the effect is modest. The response to evidence of excess capacity is similar. As long as the pressure for expansion is less than one, indicating the presence of excess capacity, management gradually reduces capacity. Note that the final level of capacity is not equal to the initial level. The assumed change in availability is symmetric, but the nonlinear formulation for capacity acquisition means the response is not. In equilibrium the managers are content with the capacity they have because there is no pressure to change it.

Having established the intended rationality of the formulation for desired capacity and capacity acquisition, the next test considers the overall performance of the capacity subsystem by closing the balancing Capacity Expansion loop (B2). In Figure 15-9 the capacity subsystem begins in an initial equilibrium with orders, capacity, and shipments all equal to 500, capacity utilization at 100%, and delivery delay at the normal value. The order rate is exogenous. At time zero orders increase to 600 units/month and remain at that level.

As in the test of the order fulfillment sector, the first response is an increase in the backlog and capacity utilization. As utilization begins to saturate, delivery delay rises. Eventually, senior managers become convinced that high delivery delays are significant and persistent enough to warrant capacity expansion. Capacity gradually rises. In a little over a year, capacity has risen enough that utilization peaks and begins to drop. Delivery delay falls back toward the desired level. The pressure to increase capacity gradually diminishes. Capacity smoothly approaches the new

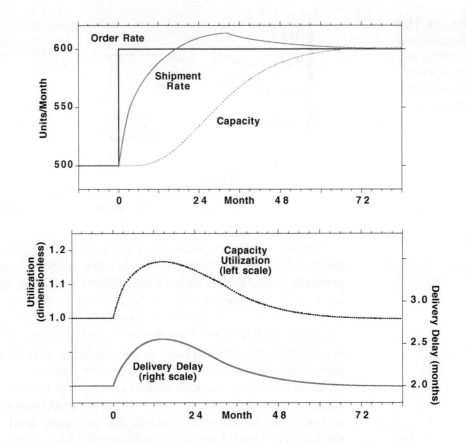

equilibrium of 600 units/month, and both utilization and delivery delay return to normal values.

The response is intendedly rational. Capacity increases in a smooth, stable fashion, without significant overshoot or instability. Consistent with the 18-month capacity acquisition delay and management's cautious approach to investment, the full adjustment takes several years.

Shipments do overshoot orders before returning to equilibrium. The overshoot is an inevitable consequence of the physical structure of the system and not a flaw in the decision rules. The capacity acquisition lag means shipments fall behind the desired rate after the step increase in orders. The backlog and delivery delay rise above their equilibrium values. The only way backlog and delivery delay can fall back to normal is for shipments to exceed orders. In the test, the required increase in shipments is accomplished through utilization. A large enough increase in orders would saturate the utilization loop, forcing capacity to rise above orders long enough to clear the excess backlog.

Notice that the simulated managers increase capacity by exactly the required amount even though they do not know the optimal level of capacity. The formulation for desired capacity is an example of the hill-climbing structure developed in section 13.2.12. Hill-climbing optimization uses local knowledge—the slope of the terrain around you—to decide which way leads most steeply uphill. If the terrain is smooth enough and the mountain has only a single peak, you will always end up at the summit.

In the context of capacity acquisition, moving uphill means managers adjust capacity in the direction they believe will improve performance by eliminating the pressure for capacity expansion. Capacity increases when delivery delay is perceived to be high and falls when low delivery delay signals excess capacity. Because they always anchor the desired capacity decision on the current level of capacity, they continue to move uphill until the slope of the hill (production pressure) is zero. Note from Figure 15-7 that the fractional expansion in capacity falls as the pressure to expand capacity drops. The cautious investment policy means expansion slows as the summit is approached, reducing the chance of overshoot.[6]

CHALLENGE	## Hill Climbing

You propose the capacity acquisition formulation in Figure 15-6 in a model and demonstrate its intended rationality to your client by showing the tests in Figure 15-8 and Figure 15-9. Your client objects that the response of capacity to changes in orders in Figure 15-9 is too slow, pointing to the conservative capacity expansion fraction as the problem. Explore the impact of more aggressive responses to expansion pressure by repeating the partial model tests with a steeper expansion policy.

Test a policy in which the expansion fraction rises by the same proportion as the pressure to expand capacity. If the pressure to expand capacity were 1.5, indicating delivery delay was perceived to be 50% above normal, the firm would set desired capacity 50% above its current level. The reference line in Figure 15-7 shows the capacity expansion fraction for this policy. What is the behavior of the capacity subsystem with this aggressive policy? Is the response still intendedly rational? What happens when the capacity expansion policy is twice as aggressive as the reference line (the slope of the relationship is 2)? Under what circumstances could you justify the use of such aggressive policies in your model?

15.5.4   The Sales Force

Figure 15-10 shows the policy structure for the sales force.

---

[6]Hill climbing is not the most efficient or reliable optimization heuristic. More sophisticated methods such as simulated annealing, taboo search, and genetic algorithms have been developed to solve the local optimum, rugged landscape, and overshoot problems. In different ways, they each strike out at random from time to time as a way to get off a local peak and increase the chance that you eventually make your way to the main summit (the global optimum). For details see, for example, Aarts and Lenstra (1997); Rayward-Smith et al. (1996); and Barhen et al. (1997). These methods have proven to be effective in many optimization contexts, including np-hard tasks such as the travelling salesperson problem. Some modelers find it tempting to replace the simple hill-climbing heuristic embedded in the capacity acquisition decision rule with one of these more sophisticated methods. However, few firms are willing to conduct such experiments. The conservative managers in the firm Forrester studied, and in most firms, were unwilling to invest in expensive capacity just to see if by chance it would improve performance. While these heuristics are often excellent optimization methods, they are usually poor models of actual human behavior. To justify the use of one of these methods would require evidence from field study of the decision makers that they behaved in a fashion consistent with the more sophisticated procedure.

FIGURE 15-10   Structure of the sales organization
The gray link from Backlog to Shipment Rate represents the order fulfillment process (Figure 15-3) and closes the Sales Growth loop R1.

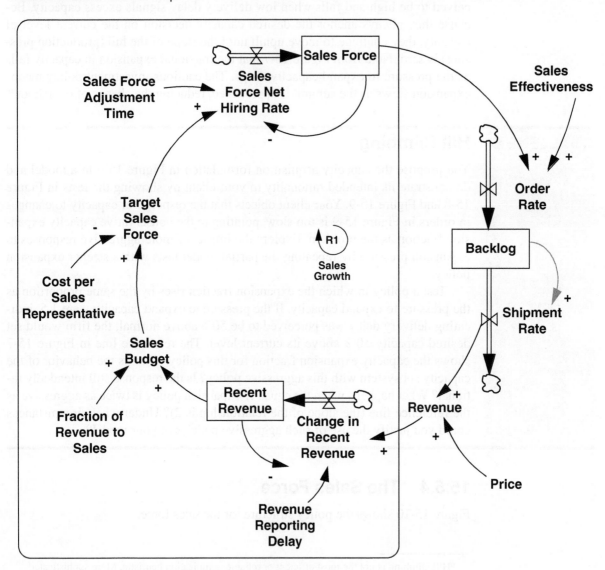

The order rate depends on the number of sales representatives and their effectiveness as measured by orders booked per person per month:

Order Rate = Sales Force * Sales Effectiveness   (15-12)

Sales effectiveness depends on the number of customer calls each sales person can make per month (assumed to be constant) and the fraction of calls resulting in a sale (the closing rate), which depends on the attractiveness of the product in the marketplace (see the market subsystem).

The actual sales force adjusts to the target sales force through the net hiring rate. The adjustment time for the sales force represents the time required to recognize and fill a vacancy and for new sales people to become fully effective.[7]

$$\text{Sales Force} = \text{INTEGRAL}(\text{Sales Force Net Hiring Rate, Sales Force}_{t_0}) \qquad (15\text{-}13)$$

$$\text{Sales Force Net Hiring Rate} = \frac{(\text{Target Sales Force} - \text{Sales Force})}{\text{Sales Force Adjustment Time}} \qquad (15\text{-}14)$$

The number of sales representatives the sales organization can support is determined by the sales budget and the average cost of a sales representative, including benefits and overhead.

$$\text{Target Sales Force} = \frac{\text{Sales Budget}}{\text{Cost per Sales Representative}} \qquad (15\text{-}15)$$

Budgeting, as in many organizations, is based on expected revenue. Expected revenues are regularly updated and are modeled by smoothing actual revenue with a 3-month revenue reporting delay. The fraction of expected revenue allocated to the sales organization is assumed to be constant. Shipments and price determine revenue.

$$\text{Sales Budget} = \text{Fraction of Revenue to Sales} * \text{Recent Revenue} \qquad (15\text{-}16)$$

$$\begin{aligned}&\text{Recent Revenue}\\&\quad = \text{INTEGRAL}(\text{Change in Recent Revenue, Recent Revenue}_{t_0})\end{aligned} \qquad (15\text{-}17)$$

$$\begin{aligned}&\text{Change in Recent Revenue}\\&\quad = (\text{Revenue} - \text{Recent Revenue})/\text{Revenue Reporting Delay}\end{aligned} \qquad (15\text{-}18)$$

$$\text{Revenue} = \text{Price} * \text{Shipment Rate} \qquad (15\text{-}19)$$

Consistent with the principles of bounded rationality, the formulations for the sales budget and for the target sales force do not involve any attempt to determine the optimal number of sales representatives. Instead, as in many organizations, each major organizational function receives a traditional fraction of the budget, perhaps adjusted slightly as other factors vary. Budgets are based on recent actual revenue and do not involve complicated forecasting.

Isolating the sales organization from the rest of the system tests the intended rationality of the sales organization's decision rules. The average cost is set to $8000 per person per month. The fraction of revenue to sales is set to 20%, and the product price is $10,000/unit. In the simulation in Figure 15-11, capacity is assumed to be perfectly flexible, so orders can always be filled in the normal delivery delay, and sales effectiveness is assumed to be exogenous.

For the first 60 months, sales effectiveness is high—10 units/person/month. As a result, the sales force generates more money for the sales organization than it costs. As revenue grows, and with it the sales budget, the sales force rises. The additional sales people book even more orders, leading to still more revenue growth

---

[7]A more realistic model would separate net hiring into separate hiring, quit, and layoff rates since the decision processes and time delays affecting each of these flows are different (section 13.3.3). However, Forrester's net hiring formulation provides a reasonable first approximation for the present purpose.

FIGURE 15-11

Partial model test
of the sales
organization

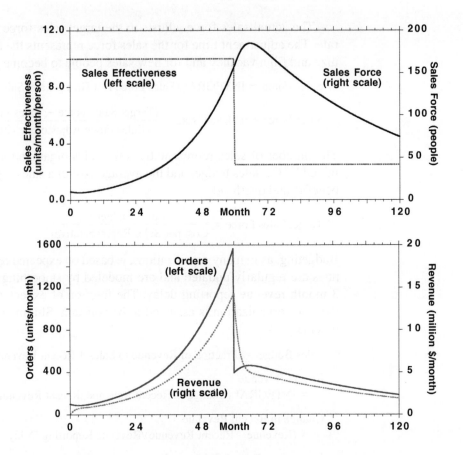

and even more hiring. The positive Sales Growth loop (R1) dominates, and the firm enjoys rapid exponential growth. In month 60 sales effectiveness suddenly drops to 25% of its original value. Orders immediately fall. The sales force continues to grow for a few months due to revenues generated by orders already in the backlog and the delay in revising the sales budget. Soon, however, the sales organization is forced to downsize. With sales effectiveness so low, the sales force now costs more than it generates in sales budget. The sales force declines exponentially and would eventually reach zero.[8]

As in the case of capacity expansion, the decision rules for budgeting and for investing funds in the sales organization involve no optimization. The firm is not

---

[8]The company will grow whenever the open-loop steady state gain (OLSSG) of loop R1 is greater than one. For a loop consisting of n variables, $x_1, \ldots, x_n$, the OLSSG is defined by first breaking the loop at any point, say x_1, defining an input variable x_1^I and an output variable x_1^O. The OLSSG is then given by the steady state change in the output in response to a presumed change in the input:

$$\text{OLSSG} = \lim_{t \to \infty} \frac{\partial x_1^O}{\partial x_1^I} = \left(\frac{\partial x_1^O}{\partial x_n}\right)\left(\frac{\partial x_n}{\partial x_{n-1}}\right)\cdots\left(\frac{\partial x_2}{\partial x_1^I}\right)$$

To calculate the OLSSG for the Sales Growth loop, recall that in equilibrium the output of a first-order negative feedback process such as exponential smoothing equals its input. Thus in steady state, Sales Force = Target Sales Force, Shipments = Orders, and Recent Revenue = Revenue.

able to calculate the optimal allocation of its resources among different activities and does not know the optimal sales force. The decision rules the firm uses for budgeting and sales force management embody a significant degree of bounded rationality.

Yet these decision rules enable the sales organization to behave rationally. Whenever each dollar of revenue generates more than a dollar in new bookings, the company grows. When each dollar of revenue returns less than a dollar in new bookings, the sales organization and company shrink. The rules of thumb for budgeting and sales force management enable the firm to grow until it reaches the equilibrium predicted by standard economic theory, even though the agents in the model do not have the information or capability to solve the profit maximization problem (see the challenge below).

15.5.5   The Market

In the full system sales effectiveness is not constant. Figure 15-12 shows the structure of the market sector.

Sales effectiveness depends on the attractiveness of the product in the marketplace. For simplicity, Forrester assumed attractiveness depended only on the availability of the product, measured by delivery delay. In reality, the attractiveness of the product depends on a host of attributes besides availability, including price and financing terms, quality, support and service, and so on. Forrester's full "corporate growth model" (Forrester 1964, 1975a; Packer 1964), as well as many models since, represents market share and demand as depending on a wide range of attributes (see Figure 3-7).

$$\text{Sales Effectiveness} = \text{Normal Sales Effectiveness} * \frac{\text{Effect of Availability}}{\text{on Sales Effectiveness}} \quad (15\text{-}20)$$

$$\frac{\text{Effect of Availability}}{\text{on Sales Effectiveness}} = f\left(\frac{\text{Delivery Delay Perceived by Market}}{\text{Market Target Delivery Delay}}\right) \quad (15\text{-}21)$$

$$\begin{array}{l}\text{Delivery} \\ \text{Delay} \\ \text{Perceived} \\ \text{by Market}\end{array} = \text{SMOOTH}\left(\begin{array}{cc}\text{Delivery Delay} & \text{Time for Market to} \\ \text{Perceived by Company,} & \text{Perceive Delivery Delay}\end{array}\right) \quad (15\text{-}22)$$

A one-unit change in the Sales Force therefore produces a steady state change in the Target Sales Force of

$$\text{OLSSG} = \frac{\text{Sales Effectiveness} * \text{Price} * \text{Fraction of Revenue to Sales}}{\text{Cost per Sales Representative}}$$

Loops with OLSSG > 1 exhibit exponential growth, those with OLSSG < 1 exhibit exponential decline, and those with OLSSG = 1 have neutral stability. With the parameters of the base case growth requires

$$\text{Sales Effectiveness} > \frac{8000 \ \$/\text{person/month}}{10,000 \ \$/\text{unit} * 0.20} = 4 \ \text{units/person/month}$$

While the OLSSG determines whether the firm grows or declines, the rate of growth depends on the time constants of the delays in the loop: The shorter the delays, the faster the growth rate.

FIGURE 15-12   Structure of the market subsystem

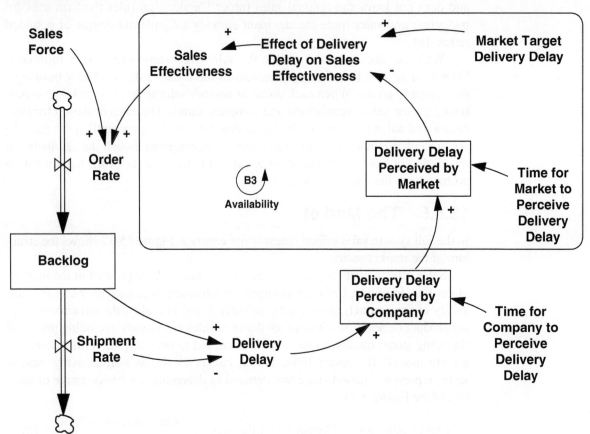

Applying the Baker Criterion (what do customers know about availability, and when do they know it?), it is clear that customers are not aware of the actual delivery delay but must estimate it from delivery quotes provided by the company (and their own experience). The market's perception of availability therefore lags the company's own perception of the delivery delay used to provide delivery quotes. The market's reaction to availability is further delayed because it takes time for customers to update their perceptions of delivery delay and still more time to shift their business to or away from the company. The perception and reaction delay for the market response to delivery delay is assumed to be 12 months, long enough to capture both the perception time and the time required to respond. A large increase in lead times induces some customers to drop the company and go with a competitor, but it takes time for them to select and qualify a new supplier and to reconfigure their own products and operations accordingly. Figure 15-13 shows the assumed effect of perceived product availability on sales effectiveness.

When the market perceives that delivery lead times equal their target, sales effectiveness equals its normal value. As delivery lead times increase relative to the acceptable level, sales effectiveness falls. The decline in sales effectiveness accelerates as delivery delay rises above the acceptable level, until the only customers left are those who are willing to wait for the product due to its unique suitability to

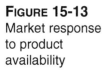

FIGURE 15-13
Market response
to product
availability

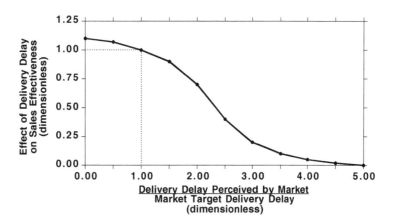

their needs. Long enough delivery delays, however, eventually drive even these loyal customers away.

The market's response to availability creates the balancing Availability feedback (B3). An increase in lead times causes the market to shift to other suppliers, reducing orders and eventually halting further increases in lead time. The delay in the market response ensures that customers don't overreact to short-term fluctuations in lead times.

15.5.6   Behavior of the Full System

The partial model tests above show that each organizational function and decision-making center in the model firm is intendedly rational. Each unit can respond in an appropriate, stable fashion to changes in its environment. Operations managers can meet demand as long as they have sufficient capacity. Senior management increases capacity smoothly and by the right amount when demand increases. The sales organization grows when it is profitable and shrinks when it is not.

Each function in the organization behaves in a sensible fashion from the local perspective of its managers. If each subsystem is intendedly rational and smoothly adjusts to meet its goals, shouldn't the organization as a whole reach its objectives as well?

Figure 15-14 shows the behavior of the whole model. Now the individual functions interact with one another and with the market.

The behavior of the firm as a whole is far from optimal or even desirable. Sales do grow, but unanticipated interactions of the different organizational functions create severe problems. First, growth is much slower than potential. (Compare sales to the curve labeled Potential Revenue, which shows how fast sales would grow if the firm were always able to deliver on time.) Second, growth is far from smooth. The firm goes through repeated boom and bust cycles, as seen in the fluctuation of the book-to-bill ratio. During sales slumps orders fall by as much as 50%. Revenue also drops during the slumps, though less than orders as the firm draws down its backlog. With the parameters of the base case, the sales slumps are so severe it is likely senior managers would be fired and quite possible the company would be taken over during one of the downturns.

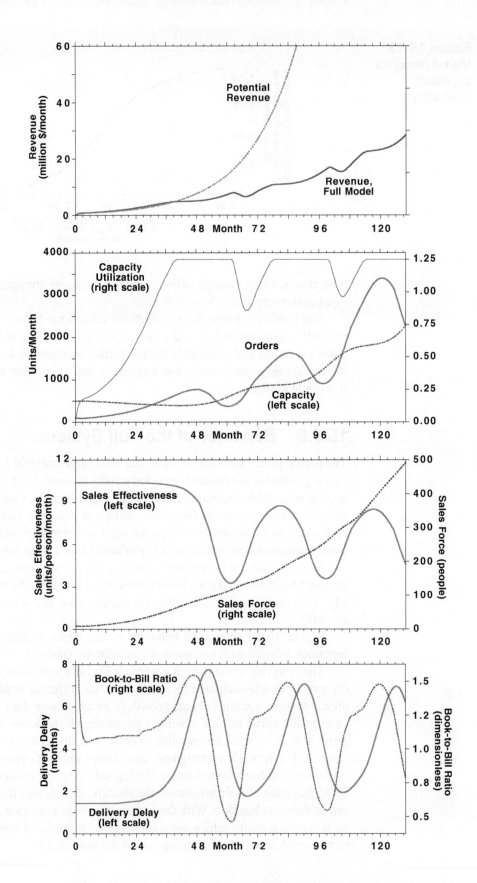

FIGURE 15-14
Behavior of the full
market growth
model
The potential
revenue curve
shows what
revenue would be
if the firm always
had enough
capacity to fill
orders on time.

The slow growth and boom–bust cycles are entirely self-inflicted. They arise through the interaction of the feedback loops coupling the different organizational functions of the firm to one another and to the market. Specifically, the locally rational capacity acquisition and sales force expansion policies interact with the market's response to availability to create a persistent mismatch between orders and capacity. At first, capacity is ample, and the firm experiences healthy growth in sales as the Sales Growth loop dominates the behavior of the system. Growing revenue leads to expansion of the sales force and still more revenue. After about 3 years, capacity begins to constrain shipments, utilization rises above normal, and delivery delay starts to rise. After waiting to ensure the rise in lead times isn't temporary, senior management begins to expand capacity. Due to their conservative investment policy and the long capacity acquisition delay, however, capacity continues to lag behind orders, allowing delivery delay to build up even higher.

While the firm struggles to expand capacity, customers learn that lead times for the firm's products are very high and begin to design the firm out of their own products while they seek other sources of supply. Sales effectiveness drops. Orders fall just as capacity starts to increase. The book-to-bill ratio soon drops below one and the backlog declines. Delivery delay now improves, but it takes time for the market to respond. Capacity ordered during the earlier shortage continues to arrive. Utilization and delivery delay soon fall below normal. Management, responding to the excess capacity, scales back its investment plans and soon capacity growth slows. At the same time, sales effectiveness begins to rise as customers respond to the ready availability of product. Sales representatives find it much easier to close, and a new spurt of order growth begins just as capacity growth slows. Orders and capacity fluctuate out of phase, with capacity growth lagging well behind orders.

Managers in each organizational function believe they are making sensible and rational decisions. Their mental models treat variables outside their function as exogenous inputs—the givens of their situation. The order fulfillment organization takes orders and capacity as given and outside its control and does its best to ship product under these constraints. The sales organization does the best it can to generate orders given the sales budget. But because each function is linked with the others in a network of feedback loops, these inputs are actually not exogenous givens but are strongly influenced by their own behavior. Because the managers of the individual functions do not account for these loops their decisions generate unanticipated side effects, in this case, effects counter to their goals. Because they don't understand the systemic origin of these dynamics, the individual managers are likely to blame their problems on the incompetence of their colleagues in other functions, the fickle decisions of the customers, or just plain bad luck.

Imagine how management might react to the first crisis, which begins around month 48. The principal symptom of difficulty is a precipitous decline in orders. Examining the monthly numbers, senior managers immediately see that the sales force has continued to grow and that the cause of the slump is therefore a sharp drop in sales effectiveness. How might they interpret this information? Often, as Forrester observed, they blamed the sales slump on the weak leadership and mismanagement of the vice president for sales, a poorly motivated or unskilled sales force, increasing competition, or other external factors. These attributions are consistent with behavioral decision theory. People tend to view cause and effect as closely related in time and space: Orders depend on the number and effectiveness of sales representatives; if orders fall, the sales force must be at fault.

The tendency to blame outcomes on individuals or individual characteristics instead of situational, systemic factors—the fundamental attribution error—reinforces the problem (chapter 1). In the context of the simulated company, managers are likely to reason that poor sales force performance must indicate the sales force is burned out, poorly managed, or just plain lazy. Senior management responds by attacking these apparent causes, firing the sales VP, sending the sales force to a motivational workshop to boost sales effort, starting a new ad campaign, or cutting prices. From the perspective of the firm's managers, with their open-loop mental models, these policies make sense. The policies directly attack what they have concluded are the causes of the problem.

In fact, the actual cause of the problem is senior management's conservative capacity acquisition policy and the unintended interactions of that policy with the delays in capacity acquisition, the policies of the sales organization, and the response of the market to availability. However, these systemic causes are distant in time and space from the symptoms of difficulty. Insidiously, policies designed to attack the symptoms appear to work in the short term. After replacing the sales VP, sales rebound, reinforcing the managers' erroneous beliefs about the causes of difficulty and preventing them from discovering the high leverage points for improvement (Repenning and Sterman 1999 show how a major automaker was able to overcome these self-reinforcing attribution errors).

| CHALLENGE | **Policy Design in the Market Growth Model** |

This challenge asks you to extend and deepen your analysis of the market growth model to build confidence in the realism and intended rationality of the proposed decision rules. You also are asked to design and implement various policies to improve the performance of the firm.

1. **Policy analysis: sales force productivity**

    Consider the base case behavior of the full model. Suppose senior management responds to the first sales slump by firing the vice president for sales, improving sales force training, and bringing in an expensive motivational speaker to pump up the troops. Assume these policies are in fact successful in *permanently* increasing the energy, skill, and effort of the sales force, boosting normal sales effectiveness by 25%. Further, ignore any costs associated with the new policy (specifically, assume there is no change in the cost per sales representative or any other parameters). Also, ignore any implementation delays. Implement the policies in month 60. Obviously, replacing the VP for sales and the other policies are unlikely to yield such a large, permanent increase in sales productivity and will have significant costs. Examining the costless, permanently effective policy may provide insight into the dynamics of the business.

a. *Before* simulating the model, write down what you expect. Sketch the behavior you expect for the variables in Figure 15-14 under the new policy. Briefly explain the rationale for your judgment.

b. Simulate the policy. What is the short-run effect of the policy? What is the long-run effect? Why? Does the intervention solve the problems facing the firm? Why/why not? How did the actual behavior differ from your expectations, and why?

c. How do you think senior managers might interpret the outcome of the policy intervention? What might they do next?

2. **Flexible goals for availability**

The capacity acquisition formulation assumes senior management's goal for delivery delay is constant and equal to the normal delay of 2 months. Because production technology and product designs are constantly changing the normal time required to fill orders could vary. Forrester found that management's goal for delivery delay—the delivery delay senior executives considered to be acceptable—adjusted over time to the delivery delay perceived by the company (a floating goal, see section 13.2.10). He also found that senior management tended to think that delivery delays were lower than they actually were. Management's perceptions tended to be based on the firm's own lead time quotes, not on the actual delivery experience of customers. Forrester found, in turn, that lead time quotes, especially those provided to senior management, tended to be overoptimistic. Consequently, management's perception of delivery delay was biased and was actually lower than the data indicated.

Figure 15-15 shows one way to model the goal-setting process. The formulation for the pressure to expand capacity subtracts the bias from the delivery delay perceived by the company. The company goal for delivery delay becomes a weighted average of a fixed goal and the traditional delivery delay. The traditional delay adjusts via first-order smoothing to the delivery delay perceived by the company.

a. Add the goal setting structure in Figure 15-15 to your model. Assume the fixed goal for delivery delay is 2 months, as in the original model, and the time to adjust the traditional delivery delay is 24 months. Setting the delivery delay bias to zero and the weight on the traditional delivery delay to zero is then equivalent to the original model in which the target delivery delay is constant. Make sure your formulation is dimensionally consistent.

b. Next, design and implement partial model tests to examine the intended rationality of the goal-setting process. Assume the weight on the traditional delivery delay is one and the delivery delay bias is zero. Is the formulation intendedly rational? How might the formulation be justified in terms of the principles of bounded rationality and the empirical findings of behavioral decision theory? Repeat the tests, setting the bias to, for example, 0.5 months. Are the results still intendedly rational? Why/why not? How might the delivery delay bias be justified in terms

FIGURE 15-15   Revised structure for the delivery delay goal

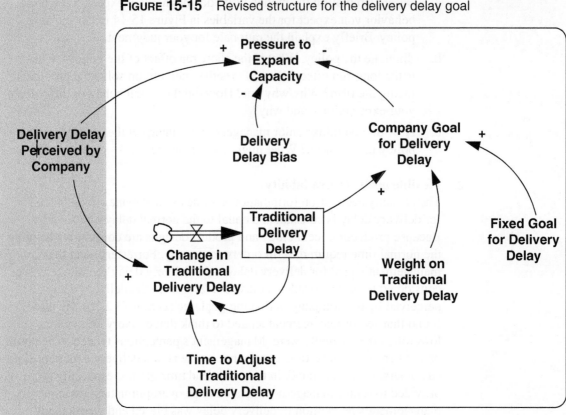

of the theory of bounded rationality and the results of behavioral decision theory?

c.   After you have tested the goal setting formulation in isolation, run the full model under the following conditions:

i.   Set the weight for the traditional delivery delay to one; keep delivery delay bias set at zero.

ii. Set the weight for the traditional delivery delay to one and delivery delay bias to 0.5 month.

How does the goal-setting process affect the dynamics of the firm as a whole?

3. **Designing a high leverage policy**

a.   Design a revised capacity acquisition policy for the firm to overcome the limitations of the original policy. Your policy should enable the firm to avoid the boom and bust and slow growth of the original model. Keep your policy simple. Your policy must be consistent with the formulation principles discussed in chapter 13 and with the principles of bounded rationality and behavioral decision theory. If your policy utilizes different information cues than the original policy, be sure to consider possible delays in the acquisition and interpretation of these cues.

b. Test your revised policy for intended rationality. When orders are considered to be exogenous, will your revised decision rule adjust capacity in an appropriate and reasonable fashion when demand changes?

c. Finally, test the behavior of your revised formulation in the full system. Discuss the results. Consider the reasons for the differences and improvements in the behavior of the model, the feasibility of implementing such a policy in real organizations, and the robustness of your policy in the real world. For example, will your policy work in a world where market potential is not unlimited and the market might saturate, decline, or fluctuate?

4. **Effectiveness of search for profit-maximizing equilibrium**
   Return to the partial model test of the sales organization in the original model. In the discussion of the sales organization's behavior, I asserted that the rules of thumb for budgeting and sales force management enable the firm to grow until it reaches the equilibrium predicted by economic theory even though the agents in the model do not have the information or capability to solve the profit maximization problem. However, in the test shown in Figure 15-11 there is no equilibrium because the market potential is assumed to be unlimited. The test shows only that the company grows whenever sales effort yields more revenue than it costs, and vice versa. A more realistic assumption is that market potential is finite and that the effectiveness of sales effort falls as that limit is approached. In that situation the sales force should grow until sales effectiveness has fallen enough so that the cost of additional sales representatives just equals the additional sales budget they generate.

   a. Evaluate the ability of the formulation for the sales organization to reach the profit-maximizing equilibrium predicted by economic theory. Assume sales effectiveness declines as the company grows. Specifically, assume sales effectiveness declines linearly as the sales force grows relative to some market potential:

$$\text{Sales Effectiveness} = f(\text{Sales Force}) = \text{Normal Sales Effectiveness}$$
$$* \text{MAX}\left(0, 1 - \frac{\text{Sales Force} * \text{Normal Sales Effectiveness}}{\text{Market Potential}}\right) \quad (15\text{-}23)$$

   where Market Potential is a constant. Using this formulation for sales effectiveness, replicate the partial model test of the sales organization by assuming the shipment rate is always equal to the desired shipment rate. Assume Market Potential = 2000 units/month and Normal Sales Effectiveness = 10 units/person/month.

   b. Does the sales force reach an equilibrium? If there is an equilibrium, is the approach to that equilibrium smooth and stable or does the model fluctuate around it? If there is an equilibrium, is it the profit-maximizing equilibrium predicted by economic theory? To answer this last question, treat the sales organization as a profit center. The net profit of the sales department π is defined as its revenue (the sales budget it receives) less its expenditures (the cost of the sales operation):

$$\pi = \text{Sales Budget} - \text{Sales Expenditures} \tag{15-24}$$

Revenue and the fraction of recent revenue allocated to sales determine the sales organization's budget (15-16); the sales force and cost per sales representative determine expenditures:

$$\pi = \frac{\text{Fraction of}}{\text{Revenue to Sales}} * \frac{\text{Recent}}{\text{Revenue}} - \frac{\text{Sales}}{\text{Force}} * \frac{\text{Cost per}}{\text{Sales Representative}} \tag{15-25}$$

In equilibrium, Recent Revenue = Revenue = Price * Shipments = Price * Order Rate. The sales force and sales effectiveness yield the order rate (15-12)). Therefore, equilibrium profits are

$$\pi = \frac{\text{Fraction of}}{\text{Revenue to Sales}} * \text{Price} * \frac{\text{Sales}}{\text{Effectiveness}} * \frac{\text{Sales}}{\text{Force}} - \frac{\text{Sales}}{\text{Force}} * \frac{\text{Cost per}}{\text{Sales Representative}} \tag{15-26}$$

From (15-26) you can derive an expression for the profit of the sales organization as a function of the size of the sales force. The maximum profit occurs where the rate of change of profits as a function of sales force is zero, that is, when

$$0 = \frac{d\pi}{d(\text{Sales Force})} = \frac{\text{Fraction of}}{\text{Revenue to Sales}} * \text{Price} * \frac{\text{Sales}}{\text{Effectiveness}} - \frac{\text{Cost per}}{\text{Sales Representative}} \tag{15-27}$$

Derive the equilibrium sales force from the expression for equilibrium profits, assuming sales effectiveness is specified according to (15-23).[9] Compare the economic equilibrium to the behavior in your partial model test. Does the boundedly rational formulation for sales management enable the organization to reach the profit-maximizing equilibrium even though the organization does not know what that equilibrium is? What circumstances might prevent the sales organization from converging to the profit-maximizing equilibrium?

5. **Generalizing the hill-climbing heuristic**

   Give other examples where locally rational decision rules enable people or organizations to search for the optimal state of a system without global knowledge of the terrain.

---

[9]Technically, (15-27) is the first-order condition for profit maximization. To be sure any value of sales force satisfying (15-27) maximizes profits instead of minimizing them requires satisfying the second-order condition that the second derivative of profits with respect to sales force be negative. Confirm that this is so for your solution.

15.6   SUMMARY

Simulation models are descriptive. The decision rules in models must conform to actual practice, warts and all. The modeler can then design policies to improve performance. An extensive body of evidence shows that the rationality of human decision making is bounded. Bounded rationality arises because the complexity of the systems in which we live and the decisions we must make overwhelm our cognitive capabilities. Consequently, we use various heuristics—rules of thumb—to enable us to make reasonable decisions in the time available. However, sometimes these heuristics produce systematic errors and cause the quality of decision making to fall far short of rational behavior. Research in behavioral decision theory has documented a wide range of these heuristics and identified many errors and biases to which they frequently lead.

The chapter showed how models consistent with bounded rationality and behavioral decision theory can be formulated and how the intended rationality of the decision rules can be tested. Partial model tests enable you to assess whether the simulated agents and organizational subunits are locally rational given their mental models, local incentives, and knowledge of the system. Partial model tests help uncover flaws in model formulations and help build confidence that your representation of the decision rules of the people in the system are sensible and consistent with your knowledge of how they think and behave. Partial model tests help you to identify situations where sensible people operating with intendedly rational decision rules can interact to create dysfunctional dynamics for the system as a whole.

16

Forecasts and Fudge Factors: Modeling Expectation Formation

Stocks have reached what looks like a permanently high plateau.
—Irving Fisher, Professor of Economics,
Yale University, October 1929

The trend will continue until it ends.

—James Dines, stock market analyst
(*The Wall Street Journal,* 21 May 1992)

Expectations are fundamental to decision making. Modelers must portray the way the agents represented in their models form forecasts and update expectations. These models must be consistent with the principles of model formulation developed in earlier chapters and must be grounded in empirical study in the field. This chapter develops a boundedly rational formulation for modeling forecasting and expectation formation, particularly for situations where the variable of interest is growing. Examples used to test the model include forecasts of inflation, commodity prices, and energy consumption.

16.1 MODELING EXPECTATION FORMATION

All decisions depend on our mental models of the situation. Expectations about the future behavior of the system form a critical component of these mental models. We constantly form expectations about what is likely to happen, and these expectations guide our actions. Businesses and governments spend enormous sums on forecasts, from predictions of economic growth, inflation, and exchange rates to the chance of a revolution or terrorist attack.

Models of the forecasting process must capture the way people form expectations. Are forecasts prepared judgmentally or with formal techniques? Are the formal tools simple (e.g., exponential smoothing) or complex (e.g., large-scale econometric modeling)? The model must capture the cues used in the forecasting process and the way in which the cues are combined to yield the forecast. How is this possible? After all, different organizations forecast in different ways. Some use complex models to prepare forecasts; in that case, do modelers have to include the actual model used by the decision maker in their simulations of the organization? There are cases where simulation models do incorporate the other models used by the organization. In practice, however, such complexity is rarely needed. In a survey of forecasting practices at about 100 US corporations Sanders and Manrodt (1994) found that

> Although managers are more familiar with quantitative forecasting methods than in the past, the level of usage has not increased. Practitioners continue to rely largely on judgmental forecasting methods... Further, when quantitative forecasting methods are used, they frequently are judgmentally adjusted.

Realistic models must also capture the social and political forces that influence an organization's forecasts and decision making. An organization may use a large econometric model with hundreds of variables to forecast the economic environment, but if senior managers ignore the model's output and go with their gut feelings, then your model of the forecasting process can't assume the sophistication of the large-scale model. Instead you must capture the ways in which the managers' intuitive judgments are formed, that is, how the information they consume and the way they digest it lead to that certain feeling in their gut.

Though many organizations spend considerable resources generating and purchasing forecasts, forecasting is a social, political, and bureaucratic activity, not a scientific one. Galbraith and Merrill (1992) studied the forecasting practices of large companies and found that management frequently adjusted, tweaked, and ignored the forecasts generated by corporate forecasting staff (Table 16-1).

The social and political nature of forecasting means many judgmental heuristics and other manifestations of bounded rationality may have considerable influence on the forecasting process and can lead to persistent, systematic forecasting errors.

Expectations are usually modeled in system dynamics as adaptive learning processes such as exponential smoothing. Adaptive expectations are common in economic models as well.[1] Adaptive expectations (single exponential smoothing) outperform many other forecasting methods over longer time horizons (Makridakis et al. 1982; Makridakis et al. 1984; Carbone and Makridakis 1986).

---

[1]For example, Irving Fisher's (1930) theory of interest rates, Nerlove's (1958) cobweb model, Friedman's (1957) permanent income hypothesis, Holt et al.'s (1960) production scheduling models, the behavioral models of Cyert and March (1963), Ando and Modigliani's (1963) life cycle hypothesis of saving, and Eckstein's (1981) theory of "core inflation."

TABLE 16-1
Forecasting is a
social and political
activity, not a
purely scientific
one.

Results of a
survey of
corporate
forecasting staff
in a sample of
New York and
American Stock
Exchange
listed firms
and comparable
privately held
firms.

Management requests staff revisions to show more favorable outcomes	45%
Management makes own revisions to show more favorable outcomes	26%
Management requests backcasts (model used to justify preselected outcome)	38%
Incorrect techniques or assumptions used:	
Accidentally	19%
Deliberately	13%
Management ignores models/forecasts	11%*
Departments withhold information from others	26%
Departments supply misleading information to others	13%
Models are deliberately misspecified	17%

Source: Galbraith and Merrill 1992.

*Probably an underestimate since the surveys were reported by the forecasting staff, who have an incentive to believe their work is useful, are likely to be told their work is important by superiors, and are not always (or even usually) privy to the actual decision-making process.

However, sometimes expectations respond not just to the history of the variable but to its past growth rate as well. For example, the past values *and* past trend in orders may be used to estimate the likely future order rate. Exponential smoothing doesn't work well for trends. The output always lags behind the input, causing a steady state error whenever the input is steadily growing. Steady state error means the output never equals the input, even after sufficient time for transient adjustments has passed.[2]

All procedures for estimating a trend require comparing recent values to historical values in some fashion. For example, a company may estimate the future growth rate of revenue by comparing current year revenue to revenue from the prior year. Several issues arise in this seemingly simple task (Figure 16-1).

First, the forecaster must get up-to-date information on the variable of interest. Often there are significant measurement and reporting delays. A firm may have to wait until the close of the fiscal year to get an accurate estimate of annual revenue to compare against prior year sales.

Second, most variables are somewhat noisy—their values fluctuate in an unpredictable fashion around the trend. Short-term noise must be filtered out so the expected trend does not bounce around with temporary variations in the current value. A company can shorten the delay in getting revenue data by using unaudited quarterly or monthly estimates rather than waiting for the close of the fiscal year. However, quarterly or monthly data are more likely to vary with seasonal and other temporary factors that diverge from the underlying trend and are more likely to be revised. Shortening reporting delays reduces the reliability of the data.

---

[2]Recall that in adaptive expectations the rate of change in the expectation X^* is given by $dX^*/dt = (X - X^*)/D$, where X is the input variable and D is the time constant. Suppose X grows linearly at rate r units/time period. In the steady state X^* must also be growing linearly at rate r, requiring $(X^* - X)/D = r$, yielding a steady state error given by $X^* - X = rD$. Section 16.6 derives the steady state error when the input grows exponentially.

FIGURE 16-1
The forecasting challenge

Hypothetical forecasts of a variable. Measurement and reporting delays mean the actual current value of the variable to be projected is unknown, introducing error. The length of the historical time horizon used to estimate the trend in the input dramatically affects the forecast.

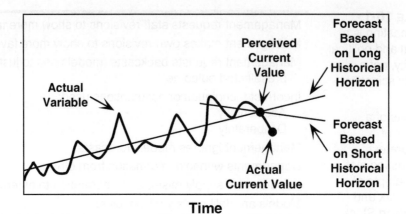

Third, the forecaster must decide how far back in history to consider. In estimating future revenue growth, should the firm compare recent sales to prior year sales or to sales over a longer horizon such as 5 years? A short historical time horizon will lead to an earlier response to changes in trends but also amplifies the reaction to temporary fluctuations. The answers to these questions depend on the purpose for which the forecast is used, the amount of noise in the data, and institutional features such as the frequency of data collection, along with the various judgmental heuristics people use—deliberately and inadvertently—to process the data.

16.1.1 Modeling Growth Expectations: The TREND Function

Growth expectations in system dynamics are often modeled with the TREND function (Sterman 1987). The input to the TREND function can be any variable. The output is an estimate of the fractional growth rate in the variable. But TREND is not just a clever way to calculate growth rates. As the input to decision rules in models, TREND represents a behavioral theory of how people form expectations and takes into account the time required for people to collect and analyze data, the historic time horizon they use, and the time required to react to changes in the growth rate. The causal structure of the TREND function is shown in Figure 16-2.

The TREND function generates the expected rate of change in the input variable, expressed as a fraction of the input variable per time unit. The TREND function involves three parameters, each the time constant of a first-order exponential smoothing process:

$$\text{Perceived Trend} = \text{TREND(INPUT; TPPC, THRC, TPT)}$$
$$\text{TREND} = \text{INTEGRAL(Change in TREND, TREND}_{t_0})$$
$$\text{TREND}_{t_0} = <\text{specified by user}>$$
$$\text{Change in TREND} = (\text{ITREND} - \text{TREND})/\text{TPT}$$
$$\text{ITREND} = [(\text{PPC} - \text{RC})/\text{RC}]/\text{THRC}$$
$$\text{RC} = \text{INTEGRAL(Change in RC, RC}_{t_0})$$
$$\text{RC}_{t_0} = \text{PPC}_{t_0}/(1 + \text{THRC} * \text{TREND}_{t_0})$$
$$\text{Change in RC} = (\text{PPC} - \text{RC})/\text{THRC}$$

FIGURE 16-2 Causal structure of the TREND function

The output is an estimate of the fractional growth rate in the input variable. The structure has three parameters: the time to perceive the present state of the input, TPPC; the historical time horizon against which the perceived condition is compared, THRC; and the time for beliefs about the trend to respond to changes in its indicated value, TPT.

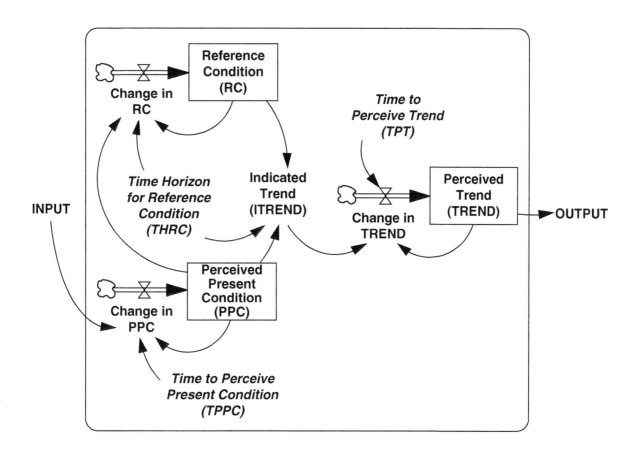

$$PPC = INTEGRAL(Change\ in\ PPC, PPC_{t_0})$$
$$PPC_{t_0} = INPUT_{t_0}/(1 + TPPC * TREND_{t_0})$$
$$Change\ in\ PPC = (INPUT - PPC)/TPPC \tag{16-1}$$

where

INPUT = Input variable (units),

TREND = Perceived fractional growth rate of the input variable (1/time units),

ITREND = Indicated Trend in the input (1/time units),

RC = Reference Condition of the input (units),

PPC = Perceived Present Condition of the input (units),

TPT = Time to Perceive the Trend (time units),

THRC = Time Horizon for the Reference Condition (time units),

TPPC = Time to Perceive the Present Condition of the input (time units).

How is the perceived growth rate determined from the input?[3] To begin, the instantaneous, raw value of the input variable is smoothed, generating the Perceived Present Condition. First-order smoothing is assumed. The time to perceive the present condition TPPC represents two factors. First, assessing the current status of any variable takes time; TPPC must therefore not be less than the measurement and reporting delays for the input variable. In the case of corporate and economic data, the data collection and reporting lag may range from several weeks to a year. In the case of demographic, environmental, and social indicators the delays may be even longer. Second, even if the raw data were available immediately, forecasters may smooth the reported values of the input to filter out high-frequency noise. Noise arises from the process itself, from measurement error, and from subsequent revisions in the reported data. The extent of noise in one important and widely predicted economic variable is shown in Figure 16-3, the rate of inflation in the US consumer price index (CPI). The CPI is reported monthly. Between 1947 and 1986 the standard deviation of inflation from month to month was 111% of its mean value, clearly showing the need to filter out short-term fluctuations.

Decision makers then compare the perceived present condition to its past values, measured by the Reference Condition RC, to determine whether the input is rising or falling. The reference condition of the input is formed by first-order exponential smoothing of the perceived present condition. The time horizon for the reference condition THRC determines the historical period decision makers consider to be relevant in the forecasting process. Equivalently, 1/THRC is the rate at which past values of the perceived input are discounted.[4]

The output of the TREND function is expressed as a fractional growth rate per time period. Hence the indicated trend ITREND is the difference between the perceived present condition of the input and the reference condition, expressed as a fraction of the reference condition and then divided by the time horizon for the reference condition.[5]

The indicated trend provides the most up-to-date information on the current fractional rate of change in the input. However, beliefs do not adjust instantly to

---

[3]The initial values of the reference and perceived present condition are set to initialize the TREND function in steady state at the initial perceived growth rate set by the modeler (section 16.6).

[4]Note that the RC is not the value of the input at some particular point in the past but an exponentially weighted average of all past values of the input. The longer the historic horizon THRC, the more weight is given to older values of the input.

[5]While the equation for the indicated trend appears to compute the linear and not compound growth rate the expression for the indicated trend actually yields the continuous compounding fractional growth rate in the input because the reference condition is formed by exponential smoothing of the input (section 16.6).

FIGURE 16-3

Consumer price inflation in the United States, 1947–1986

The graph shows the annualized fractional rate of change in the monthly values of the CPI.

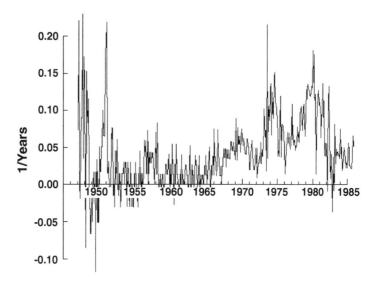

Source: Sterman (1987).

new information. The TREND function allows the decision maker's belief about the trend in the input variable to adjust gradually to the value indicated by the most recent data. First-order information smoothing is assumed with a delay given by the Time to Perceive the Trend TPT. The lag in the adjustment of the perceived trend represents the time required for a change in the indicated trend to be recognized and accepted by decision makers as a basis for their actions.

How should the parameters of the TREND function be interpreted and estimated? The time to perceive the present condition is at least as long as any measurement and reporting delays but may be longer if the input variable is highly noisy and decision makers apply additional averaging or smoothing. The time horizon for establishing the reference condition THRC represents the time frame over which the trend is assessed and will depend on the purpose of the forecast. In general, the longer the time horizon for the forecast, the longer the historical horizon should be. However, the time horizon for establishing the reference condition is a subjective judgment and is influenced by the memories and experiences of individual decision makers. During the 1970s the rate of economic growth in the industrialized world slowed significantly from the rates of the 1950s and 60s. However, economic forecasters whose professional experience was gained during the high-growth decades continued to forecast high growth for many years despite the lower actual growth rates of the 1970s and 80s. They believed the slow growth after 1973 was a temporary aberration and that the economy would soon resume the growth rate that characterized the past. The delay in the acceptance of a new trend as an operational input is often significant. The adjustment lag depends not only on the time required for individual decision makers to recognize the change but also on organizational inertia. A new trend may have to become part of the conventional wisdom before some are willing to act. In such cases, perceived trends may change only as fast as management turns over and is replaced.

The TREND function represents forecasting as a boundedly rational procedure in which forecasters smooth recent data and project recent trends. Is there any evidence that people form forecasts using smoothing and trend projection? Sanders and Manrodt's (1994) survey found judgmental methods such as "manager's opinion," a "jury of executive opinion," and "sales force composite" opinions were the most common methods used in sales forecasting in US corporations. Studies of judgmental forecasting (e.g., Makridakis et al. 1993) show that most judgmental forecasts are quite similar to simple smoothing with trend extrapolation. Among the formal techniques used by the surveyed firms, the most popular were moving averages, exponential smoothing, regression, straight-line projections, and naive models. All of these are forms of adaptive expectations. Naive models and moving averages are similar to exponential smoothing, differing only in the weights accorded to past data. Regression and straight-line projection likewise average out noise and fluctuations in the past data, though unlike simple smoothing they also account for growth trends.

16.1.2   Behavior of the TREND Function

The TREND function has the desirable property that it provides, in the steady state, an unbiased estimate of the fractional growth rate of the input. If the input grows exponentially at rate g, the steady state output of the TREND function is also g (see section 16.6 for a proof).

The parameters of the TREND function determine its transient response to changes in the growth rate. Figure 16-4 shows partial model tests illustrating, for a range of parameters, its response to a change in the growth rate of the input. In the simulations, a one-quarter-year measurement and reporting delay (TPPC) is assumed—a value typical of many corporate and macroeconomic data series. The input, initially constant, suddenly begins to grow at a constant exponential rate of 5%/year. The perceived trend in the variable generated by the TREND function at first does not change—though the input has started to grow, it takes time for the new values to be reported. The perceived trend then gradually rises to the true value of 5%/year. The longer the time horizon for establishing the reference condition or the longer the time required for decision makers to perceive the trend, the more gradual the response.

16.2   CASE STUDY: ENERGY CONSUMPTION

What will energy consumption be in the year 2020? How much electricity will utilities have to supply 10 years from now? Long-term forecasts of energy consumption, both at the aggregate national level and at the fuel- and region-specific level, are critical to both energy suppliers and to the government. Power plants, refineries, and oil fields involve some of the longest lead times of any construction projects, often a decade or more. Fortunately for utilities and oil companies, energy consumption in the industrialized world grew at fairly steady exponential rates for most of the postwar period, and forecasting was easy. But after the first oil shock in 1973 economic growth slowed. Energy consumption fell significantly, and even after the economy recovered from the recession of 1974–75, consumption growth was both slower and more variable. The break in historic energy consumption pat-

FIGURE 16-4

Behavior of the TREND function

The input, initially constant, begins to grow exponentially at 5%/year at time zero. The parameters are as indicated, with TPPC = 0.25 years in all cases.

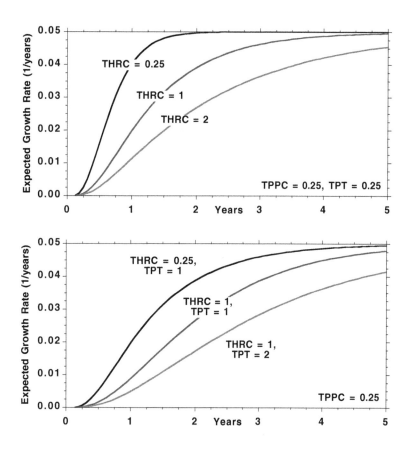

terns provides a natural experiment to examine the ability of forecasters to anticipate the crisis. In short, they didn't—the 1973 crisis came as a surprise to nearly all energy producers, governments, and forecasters. It may be unreasonable to expect forecasters to have foreseen such a dramatic shift in the global economics and politics of oil. How well, then, did forecasters do in adapting to the new world of volatile energy prices and slower economic growth?

The first oil shock in 1973 led to the growth of a huge energy modeling industry, which soon offered detailed models of every aspect of the energy system. Many of these models are among the most complex public policy models ever developed. Unfortunately, their forecasting record is poor.

Forecasts of energy consumption in the United States (and other nations) adjusted very slowly to the new realities of the energy system. Figure 16-5 shows forecasts of total US energy consumption for 1985 along with actual consumption. After 1973, as actual consumption fell, forecasts of energy consumption in the United States also began to drop. Forecasts made in the early 1970s projected US energy consumption in 1985 to be about 130 quadrillion BTUs or "quads" (1 quad/year = 10^{15} BTU/year). Actual energy consumption in 1985 was less than 74 quads, a 75% overestimation. Similar errors were observed in the forecasts for other nations and time horizons and for electricity and other fuels (Lynch 1994; Nelson and Peck 1985). The large errors and seemingly reactive nature of the forecasts suggest trend extrapolation may have been used by many of the forecasters.

FIGURE 16-5

Forecasts of US total energy consumption in 1985

Each point represents a forecast of consumption in the year 1985, plotted in the year the forecast was made.

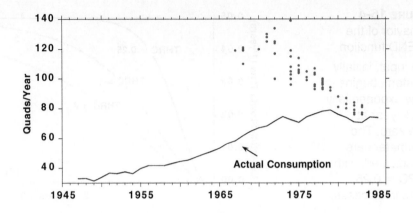

Many early forecasts, particularly prior to the oil shocks of the 1970s, were indeed made by extrapolation. But trend extrapolation seems naive to many observers, who point out—quite correctly—that energy demand forecasts are often the result of extensive studies involving detailed, multidisciplinary analysis and sophisticated models.

In Sterman (1987, 1988b) I tested the ability of the TREND function to model the evolution of forecasts of total US primary energy consumption in 1985 (Figure 16-5). The input to the forecasts was actual energy consumption. The expected fractional growth rate estimated by the TREND function was then projected to continue from the current time to the forecast horizon of 1985.

Specifically, the forecast made in year t of energy consumption in forecast year FY, denoted $FC_{FY}(t)$, was calculated by

$$FC_{FY}(t) = PPC(t) * (1 + TREND(t) * TPPC) * \exp(TREND(t) * (FY - t)) \quad (16\text{-}2)$$

where PPC is the perceived present condition of actual energy consumption and

$$TREND(t) = TREND(C(t); TPPC, THRC, TPT) \tag{16-3}$$

is the expected trend in actual consumption C estimated by the TREND function.

In equation (16-2) forecasters recognize that the most recent data are out of date due to measurement and reporting delays and adjust the perceived present condition by the growth expected to have occurred between the date represented by the most recent data and the present time. The growth correction is TREND(t) * TPPC. As shown in section 16.6, this correction ensures that the perceived present condition will equal the actual value of the input when the input is growing at a steady exponential rate. The forecast for some future year is then constructed from the estimate of current consumption given by PPC * (1 + TREND * TPPC) by assuming consumption will grow at the current perceived TREND between the present time and the forecast horizon FY. Equations (16-2) and (16-3) therefore yield an unbiased forecast in the steady state of exponential growth in the input.

I estimated the parameters of the TREND function econometrically for forecasts of energy consumption in 1985. The estimated parameters were TPPC = 1.2, THRC = 5.4, and TPT = 3.2 years, respectively. Data for annual energy consumption at any time were only available through the prior year, at best, due to measurement and reporting lags, so the estimated value of TPPC is reasonable. The

FIGURE 16-6
Response of
TREND function
with parameters
estimated for
energy forecasts

The input
begins growing
exponentially
at 5%/year at
time zero.

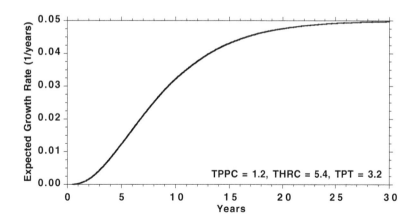

TPPC = 1.2, THRC = 5.4, TPT = 3.2

FIGURE 16-7
Simulated and
actual forecasts of
US primary energy
consumption in
1985

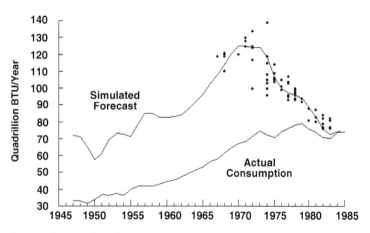

Source: Sterman (1987).

other parameters are also reasonable. Energy consumption is tied to the size of the capital stock in the economy, a stock that turns over only slowly, giving consumption significant inertia. Forecasts of long-term growth in energy consumption should be based on a correspondingly long-term historical view and are likely to react slowly; long-term forecasts should not rise and fall with short-term movements in energy consumption caused by business cycles and other temporary variations. Figure 16-6 shows the response of the TREND function with the estimated parameters to a step change in the growth rate of the input. The response is quite slow: After 5 years, the expected growth rate has adjusted only 25% of the way to a change in the growth rate of the input; two decades are required for the expected growth rate to adjust 95% of the way.

Figure 16-7 compares the simulated forecasts to the actual forecasts for 1985. As the growth rate of actual consumption rose during the postwar boom, the simulated forecasts rise from about 70 quads/year in the early 1950s to about 125 quads/year in 1973. The forecasts steadily fall after 1973 as actual consumption growth slowed in the wake of 1973 and 1979 oil shocks and the deep recessions of 1974–75 and 1979–82. The simulated forecasts pass quite close to the median of the

FIGURE 16-8

Forecast and
actual total
electricity
consumption
in the US

Forecasts of the
North American
Electricity
Reliability
Council (NERC),
1974–1990.

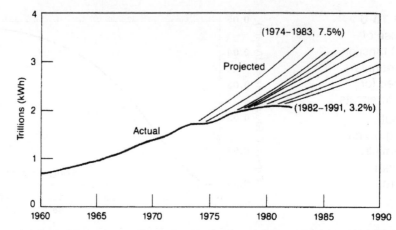

actual forecasts. The mean absolute error between the model and the forecasts as a percent of the median forecast exceeds the minimum possible error by just 1%.[6]

Similar behavior is also documented for other fuels. For example, 10-year forecasts of total US electricity demand produced by the North American Electric Reliability Council, an industry association of electric utilities, exhibit similar overshooting (Figure 16-8). Electricity growth before 1973 had been rather constant at about 7%/year. After 1973 the growth rate fell. The forecasts only slowly adapted to the change, leading to more than a decade of grossly overoptimistic forecasts. Nelson and Peck (1985) show that the NERC forecasts are modeled extremely well by exponential extrapolation of current consumption assuming the historic growth rate will continue. They modeled the historic growth rate with first-order smoothing of the year-to-year growth rate, a procedure similar to the TREND function. They found the smoothing time during the 1970s to be about 5 years, consistent with the estimated parameters for total energy consumption.

Forecasts of energy consumption have been made with a wide range of techniques and models. Many of these models are quite complex and do not appear to be simple univariate extrapolations. Yet no matter how sophisticated, each model relies upon exogenous variables or parameters. These might include GDP, population, energy prices, and technological progress. Theory provides no strong guidance in selecting the assumed future values of these inputs, all of which must be forecast judgmentally. Along with highly uncertain parameters such as the price elasticities of energy demand and the supply curves for different resources, the exogenous inputs serve as free parameters modelers use to manipulate the forecasts to be consistent with the conventional wisdom of the day. The correspondence of the simulated and actual forecasts suggests that the recent trend acts as a strong constraint upon choice of these fudge factors.

I frequently observed such behavior when I worked at the US Department of Energy in the late 1970s. Senior officials in the department were keenly aware of

---

[6]Since there are often multiple forecasts for a given year, the minimum possible error is greater than zero.

the forecasts their agency and other organizations had made the prior year; these forecasts constrained what they deemed to be politically acceptable for the current forecast. Some officials believed the department could not, for political reasons, forecast future consumption to be as low as projected by environmental groups. Forecasts in which the economy was assumed to grow at less than historical rates or in which conservation reduced energy consumption per capita were considered unacceptable. At the same time, they felt it would be unseemly for the government to project consumption exceeding the aggressive forecasts of oil companies and energy industry associations. The department's forecasts generally fell near the high end of the range.

A strong herd mentality among forecasters reinforced the dominance of trend extrapolation by ensuring that next year's forecasts were based on and not too different from last year's. In 1972 forecasts of US primary energy consumption in the year 2000 ranged from a high of nearly 200 quads/year, projected by the Department of the Interior and Federal Power Commission, to a low of 125 quads/year, projected by environmental activist Amory Lovins. By 1983, as the trend extrapolation model suggests, the forecasts had fallen by a factor of two. Government and industry groups projected consumption in 2000 to be about 100 quads/year, while Lovins projected that consumption could be less than 50 quads/year if the nation pursued a "soft energy path" emphasizing efficiency rather than production. Though the forecasts fell by a factor of two in just a decade, the rank order of forecasts within any year remained remarkably stable. Year after year the highest forecasts were those of the energy industry, followed closely by government agencies, with environmentalists projecting the lowest totals. The close attention each forecaster paid to the projections of others and the political constraints on departures from the range of prior forecasts slowed the adjustment of the forecasts to reality. The median forecast followed the path predicted by simple trend extrapolation of past growth in actual consumption, with the forecasts of individual groups and organizations adjusted above or below the median in accordance with their particular ideology and political agenda.

In such highly politicized environments it is small wonder that many modelers cherish the free parameters enabling them to adjust their forecasts to match the expectations of their clients.

16.3   CASE STUDY: COMMODITY PRICES

Smoothing and trend extrapolation also explain forecasts of the prices of many commodities. As an example, Figure 16-9 shows the cash price of cattle in the US from 1972 to 1986, a period of great price volatility.[7] Also shown are the one-quarter-ahead forecasts of Glenn Grimes, a professor of agricultural economics at the University of Missouri and a respected professional livestock market analyst. Grimes' forecasts are widely circulated through the agricultural extension system in cattle country. Grimes' forecasts are also interesting because, as Bessler and Brandt (1992) show, his 3-month-ahead forecasts are actually more accurate than

---

[7]Figure 20-2 shows a much longer history of the cattle market, illustrating the persistent cycles in prices, production, and stocks.

FIGURE 16-9

Cattle prices and forecasts

Actual and forecast cash price for cattle in Omaha, $/CWT (hundredweight). Forecasts are one-quarter-ahead forecasts of Glenn Grimes, plotted against the actual outcomes.

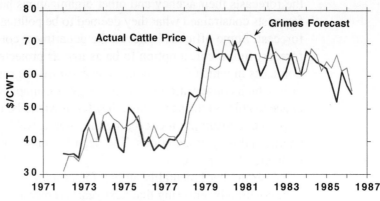

Source: Bessler and Brandt (1992).

the cattle futures market (specifically, Grimes' forecasts have lower mean square error than the 3-month-ahead futures price). Inspection of Grimes' forecasts, however, reveal a tendency to miss the turning points in the market and to overshoot after sustained price movements, for example, after the large rise in prices between 1977 and 1979.

The phase lag and overshoot in the predictions suggests Grimes may be forecasting by smoothing recent prices and then extrapolating the recent trend. The same formulation used to model the energy demand forecasts is specified to test this hypothesis. The one-quarter-ahead forecast of cattle prices, $P^*(t)$, is modeled by extrapolating the perceived present condition by the expected growth rate g^* over the one-quarter-year forecast horizon FH:

$$P^*(t) = PPC(t) * [1 + TPPC * g^*(t)] * \exp(FH * g^*(t)) \tag{16-4}$$

$$g^*(t) = TREND(P(t), TPPC, THRC, TPT) \tag{16-5}$$

As in the case of energy demand, the perceived present condition is adjusted for the change expected to occur over the time required to perceive the present condition TPPC. The formulation for the simulated forecast will therefore yield an unbiased estimate of price in the steady state of exponential growth.

The parameters were estimated econometrically and found to be TPPC = 0.60, THRC = 6.00, and TPT = 0.56 years, all reasonable values. Figure 16-10 shows the correspondence between the simulated and actual forecasts. The model replicates Grimes' forecasts well: The mean absolute percent error is about 4.5%, and the R^2 of the model is 0.95. Because smoothing introduces a delay, the simulated forecasts, like the actual forecasts, miss major turning points in price. Because it takes time for expectations about the trend to change, the model also captures the overshoot of the forecasts after the large price rise in the late 1970s when Grimes, like the TREND function, predicted price increases to continue for a while even though actual price fell.

Professor Grimes reported that he forecasts by closely monitoring fundamentals in the market. He stays in close touch with market participants including breeders, producers, and packers, and draws on extensive supply-side data including stocks of cattle on feedlots, breeding stocks, and slaughter rates. On the

FIGURE 16-10
Simulated and
actual cattle price
forecasts

Top: Simulated vs.
actual forecasts.
Bottom: The
simulated
expected growth
rate in cattle
prices.

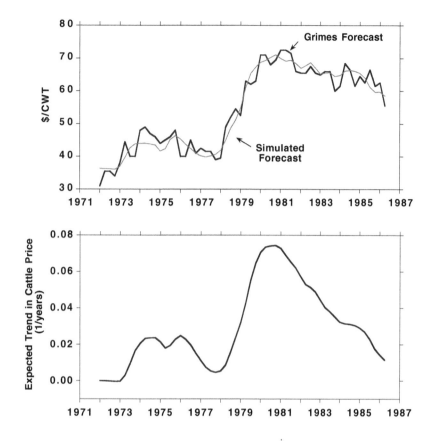

demand side, he tries to assess not only the impact of prices but also changes in people's lifestyles such as the trend in the past decades toward leaner diets with less red meat. His experience, contacts, and focus on fundamentals did allow him to forecast significantly better than participants in the futures market. Nevertheless, as observed in the case of energy consumption, univariate extrapolation explains the bulk of the variance in the forecasts, leaving only a small residual to be explained by the influence of other variables such as the number of cattle on feedlots, breeding and slaughter rates, the prices of other commodities, and so on. Past prices form a powerful anchor on judgments of future price. Subjective adjustments in response to other factors have only a weak effect due to their variability, uncertain connection to price movements, and lack of salience compared to prices themselves. No doubt these factors do have some impact on the forecasts. But subjective assessments of lifestyle changes causing people to eat less beef, and even reports that certain breeders want to increase their herds, are likely to have a weak effect indeed compared to a powerful trend in price itself.

16.4   CASE STUDY: INFLATION

Inflation expectations are critical to decisions throughout all sectors of the economy, including monetary policy, the pricing of stocks and bonds, capital investment, collective bargaining, projections of tax revenue and government expenditures, and your own investment decisions. The stakes are high and the task is daunting: Inflation is volatile (Figure 16-3) and is affected by a host of economic events and variables. Consequently, inflation is one of the most intensively studied economic indicators. A small army of professional economists in academia, private businesses, government agencies, and professional forecasting firms devote the better part of their careers to forecasting inflation. How well do they do?

For more than 50 years, beginning in 1946, the Philadelphia-based financial journalist Joseph Livingston conducted a survey of economic forecasters. The panel included a wide range of professional forecasters and economists from business, government, and academia. One of the survey questions solicited forecasts of the CPI, 6 and 12 months ahead. These inflation forecasts provide one of the longest continuous series directly measuring people's expectations and have been extensively analyzed in the economics literature.[8]

Figure 16-11 compares the Livingston panel's 6- and 12-month forecasts to the actual inflation rate through 1985. Actual inflation was quite volatile from the end of World War II through the Korean war. Inflation was low during the late 1950s and early 60s. Between the mid 60s and 1980, inflation generally accelerated and fluctuated substantially over the business cycle. After 1981 inflation fell sharply. Comparing the forecasts against the actual outcome highlights

1. **Bias:** The forecasters consistently underpredict inflation during the 1960s and 1970s, when inflation accelerated, and overestimate somewhat during the 1980s, when inflation fell.

2. **Phase shift:** The peak (trough) of the expected inflation rate lags the peak (trough) of the actual inflation rate. Forecasters consistently missed the turning points in inflation caused by the business cycle.

3. **Attenuation:** The actual rate of inflation fluctuates significantly over the business cycle, particularly in the 1970s and 1980s. The amplitude of the forecasts is substantially less than that of actual inflation.

The bias, phase lag, and attenuation are all suggestive of smoothing and trend extrapolation. How well can the TREND function replicate the forecasts of the panel?

In Sterman (1987) I examined the ability of the TREND function to model the 6-month Livingston forecasts. The output of the TREND function was compared against the panel's forecasts of the inflation rate over the next 6 months:[9]

Expected Inflation = TREND(CPI; TPPC, THRC, TPT)   (16-6)

In most modeling situations actual expectations data are unavailable and the modeler must estimate the parameters judgmentally. While the parameters for the

---

[8]E.g., Croushore (1997), Caskey (1985), Peek and Wilcox (1984), Bomberger and Frazer (1981), Jacobs and Jones (1980), Pearce (1979), Mullineaux (1978), and Pesando (1975).

[9]The panel actually forecast the level of the CPI. However, because the CPI has risen so much since 1946 it is difficult to assess forecast accuracy from the predicted levels of the CPI. Instead the rate of inflation implicit in the panel's forecasts is compared directly against the expected growth rate generated by the TREND function.

FIGURE 16-11
The Livingston
panel's inflation
forecasts
compared to
actual inflation

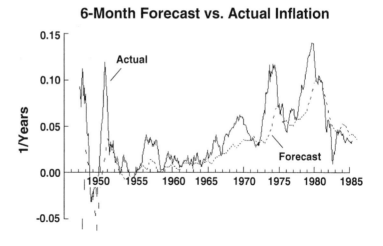

6-Month Forecast vs. Actual Inflation

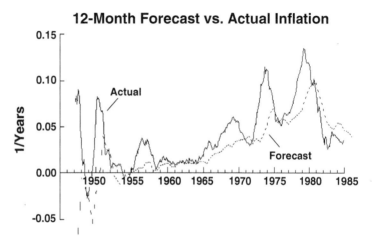

12-Month Forecast vs. Actual Inflation

energy and cattle forecasts were estimated econometrically, I used judgmental estimates of the parameters to model the inflation forecasts.

The values chosen to model the 6-month forecasts were TPPC = 2, THRC = 12, and TPT = 2 months. The Livingston forecasts were dated June and December of each year. Carlson (1977) shows that due to lags in reporting the CPI and in the time required to administer and tabulate the survey the Livingston panel made their forecasts knowing the CPI only through April and October, respectively. Thus the panel members were actually making 8- and 14-month forecasts and TPPC is set to 2 months to capture the delay in perceiving the current value of the CPI.[10]

The 1-year time horizon for the reference condition was selected as follows. First, 1 year is a common, convenient, and easily justified reference point. Second, comparing the most recent data against the year-ago value is a simple way to filter out any residual seasonal variations in inflation (the panel used the seasonally

---

[10]After the 1970s some forecasters probably knew the May and November CPI values, but Livingston's procedure does not definitively indicate which values the panel used.

FIGURE 16-12

TREND function compared to the Livingston panel's 6-month forecast

The parameters of the TREND function are TPPC = 2, THRC = 12, and TPT = 2 months.

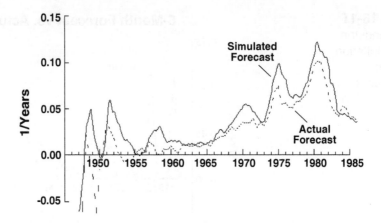

adjusted CPI but the adjustments are not perfect). Third, the raw inflation data (Figure 16-3) are dominated by high-frequency (monthly) noise. Six- and 12-month forecasts should not be overly sensitive to monthly changes in reported inflation that may be revised or reversed next month. For professional reasons (consistency) and cognitive reasons (minimizing dissonance) forecasters are unlikely to revise their expectations dramatically from month to month despite the volatility of the data. With a smoothing time of 12 months, the reference condition attenuates 97% of the month-to-month noise yet adjusts to 63% of a change in the perceived present condition (Forrester 1961, p. 417).

The trend perception time of 2 months implies respondents' beliefs adjust nearly completely to a change in the indicated trend within 6 months (three time constants), meaning the forecasters assimilate and respond to apparent changes in the trend since their last forecast. One would expect THRC and TPT to be slightly longer for the 12-month forecasts.[11]

Figure 16-12 shows the simulation results for the 6-month forecasts. The TREND function reproduces the bias, attenuation, and phase shift apparent in the actual forecasts, but the simulated forecasts are high on average compared to the Livingston data. In fact the TREND function yields a better forecast than the Livingston panel! The mean absolute error (MAE) between simulated and actual forecasts is 0.014 (Table 16-2). The Theil inequality statistics (Theil 1966; Sterman 1984) decompose the mean square error (MSE) into three components: bias, unequal variation, and unequal covariation so systematic error can be separated from unsystematic random differences between the simulated and actual data (see chapter 21). A full 40% of the MSE is caused by bias. The remainder is due to unequal covariation, meaning 60% of the MSE is unsystematic. The unequal variation term is virtually zero (the two series have equal variances).

There are two principal competing explanations for the bias. The actual forecasting process used by the Livingston panel may be more sophisticated than the univariate TREND function. Other economic variables may be considered, such as

---

[11]But only slightly. The 6-month forecast determines the inflation path for the first half of the annual forecasts. Forecasters are unlikely to project a radically different inflation rate for the second half of the forecast year. In fact, the 6- and 12-month forecasts are quite similar (Figure 16-11).

TABLE 16-2

Error analysis of simulated inflation forecasts

MAE = Mean Absolute Error; MSE = Mean Square Error; U^M = Fraction of MSE due to bias; U^S = Fraction of MSE due to unequal variation; U^C = Fraction of MSE due to unequal covariation; r = Correlation coefficient between simulated and actual forecasts. See text for explanation of the three models; see chapter 21 for explanation of the Theil statistics.

Model	MAE (1/years)	MSE (1/years)^2	U^M	U^S	U^C	r
			(dimensionless)			
No anchor	0.0140	4.0 E-4	0.40	0.00	0.60	0.88
Fixed anchor	0.0099	2.41E-4	0.08	0.15	0.77	0.88
Sea anchor	0.0088	1.92E-4	0.16	0.03	0.81	0.91

money supply growth, the government budget deficit, and the unemployment rate. In addition, different information processing routines may be used. Some researchers, such as Caskey (1985), assume that the Livingston forecasters draw on a wide range of macroeconomic indicators and use optimal Bayesian updating to predict inflation. This seems unlikely. Experimental evidence suggests people are much more conservative in belief updating than Bayes' Theorem predicts (Plous 1993). Further, any theory that people optimally combine a wide range of cues must explain why this more sophisticated process is decidedly inferior to univariate trend extrapolation. The fact that simple extrapolation of recent inflation rates outperforms the professional forecasters suggests accurate modeling of the inflation forecasting process requires even greater bounds on the rationality of the expectation formation process than the TREND function presumes.

The TREND function assumes forecasters track the actual rate of inflation, with a delay. Over time errors will be gradually corrected. However, behavioral decision theory suggests forecasters may be influenced by several heuristics known to cause systematic errors in judgment. In particular, past inflation itself is likely to act as a strong anchor on people's forecasts. Anchoring and adjustment, as described in section 13.2.10, is a common and powerful judgmental heuristic, one that often affects judgments inadvertently. The advantage of the anchoring and adjustment strategy is its simplicity and intuitive appeal. The disadvantage is the common tendency to underpredict, that is, to revise prior beliefs too little when faced with new data. Judgments are often unintentionally anchored to reference points that are implicit (such as even odds in a bet or the axis of a graph). People's judgments exhibit anchoring even when the irrelevance of the anchor to the task is made salient.

These considerations suggest the forecasters' judgments may be influenced by an anchor that biases the forecast downward from the values indicated by extrapolation of the recent inflation rate. The anchoring and adjustment strategy can be modeled as follows: Suppose the Livingston panel forms inflationary expectations as

Expected Inflation
$$= (1 - w) * \text{TREND(CPI; TPPC, THRC, TPT)} + w * \text{ANCHOR} \qquad (16\text{-}7)$$

In (16-7), the simulated Livingston forecast is a weighted average of the TREND function and an ANCHOR, with the anchor given a weight w. The parameters of the TREND function are the same as those used in (16-6). The anchor can be thought of as an underlying reference point that the panel uses, consciously or unconsciously, when forecasting.

The simplest assumption is the "fixed-anchor" model in which ANCHOR = 0. Zero price change is a natural choice for the anchor: Zero change is the simplest naive model ("tomorrow will be like today") and zero inflation is a commonly stated goal of policy makers. Equation (16-7) then reduces to

$$\text{Expected Inflation} = (1 - w) * \text{TREND(CPI; TPPC, THRC, TPT)} \qquad (16\text{-}8)$$

which implies forecasters will always underpredict the magnitude of inflation. Figure 16-13 shows the fit of the fixed-anchor model using $w = 0.20$. The fit is improved substantially compared to the "no-anchor" model: The MAE falls by 29%. The Theil statistics show the bias is reduced to 8% of the MSE and the bulk of the remaining error is unsystematic (unequal covariation).

The anchoring and adjustment model fits the forecasts better than the TREND function alone. However, the fixed-anchor model assumes forecasters always underpredict and would never learn to correct their optimistic bias even if the rate of inflation held steady indefinitely. The fact that the no-anchor model is generally high between 1947 and 1983 suggests that the panel felt the underlying inflation rate was lower than the actual rate of inflation, biasing their forecasts. However, the underestimation by the no-anchor model after 1983 suggests the anchor had risen during the high-inflation 70s, causing the panel to continue to forecast high inflation in the mid 80s despite much lower actual rates.

The idea that the anchor represents the panel members' long-term experience of inflation suggests a model in which the anchor itself adjusts very slowly to changes in the inflation rate—a "sea-anchor" model. A sea anchor is a large object, usually a cone of sailcloth, suspended by a cable in the calmer waters below a ship. Sea anchors stabilize a ship's position in waters too deep for conventional anchors to attach to the bottom. The ship still moves with the wind, waves, and currents, but the sea anchor slows its motion by creating extra drag. Similarly, panel members' life experience with inflation, their belief about the underlying inflation environment, may act as a sea anchor on their judgments of short-run inflation.

The anchor is now specified by the TREND function, but with much longer parameters:

$$\text{ANCHOR} = \text{TREND(CPI; TPPC}_A, \text{THRC}_A, \text{TPT}_A) \qquad (16\text{-}9)$$

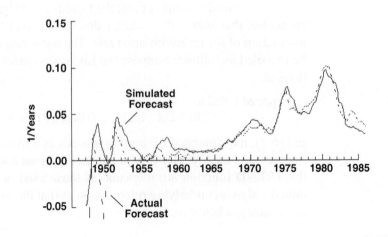

FIGURE 16-13

Simulated 6-month Livingston forecasts: fixed-anchor model

where the parameter $TPPC_A$ is the time to perceive the present condition for the anchor, and so on. The anchor should respond slowly to changes in the underlying inflation rate and should not respond significantly to temporary changes. The parameters were chosen to reflect the long-term nature of the anchor: $TPPC_A = 1$, $THRC_A = 10$, and $TPT_A = 3$ years. These values are long enough to attenuate changes in inflation more rapid than the short-term business cycle. The initial (1947) value of the anchor was set to $-3\%/year$, implying that the panel's judgments were initially biased toward mild deflation. Many economists, recalling the deflation of the Great Depression and the recession and falling prices that followed World War I, worried that the United States would return to depression after World War II. The weight on the anchor was set to 0.25. Figure 16-14 compares the sea-anchor and actual forecasts and shows the components of the sea-anchor forecast. The anchor reduces the forecasts until 1983, when inflation falls substantially. The anchor then keeps the simulated forecast high, improving the fit between 1983 and 1985.

The sea-anchor model is theoretically more satisfying and also more robust than the fixed-anchor model. It allows for learning: If inflation remains steady the model eventually produces unbiased forecasts (as seems to have occurred between

FIGURE 16-14
Simulated
Livingston
forecast: sea-
anchor model

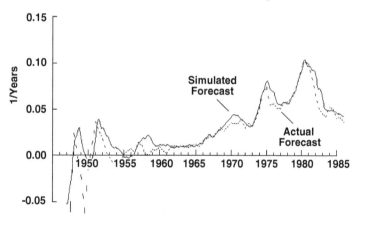

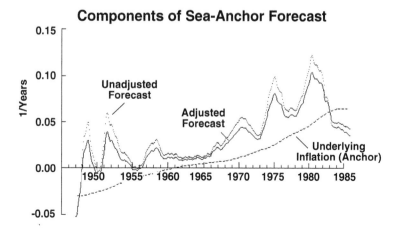

1958 and 1965). In a hyperinflation the fixed-anchor model would seriously under-predict inflation, while the sea-anchor model would learn to expect it. The sea-anchor model reduces the MAE by another 11%. The MSE is still primarily unsystematic, and the correlation between the simulated and actual forecasts improves slightly.

The analysis in Sterman (1987) reported here was done with data from 1947 through 1985. The sea-anchor model does quite well in explaining the behavior of inflation forecasts over this 40-year span. Since 1985, however, the dynamics of inflation have changed dramatically. Inflation continued to fall, and the economy attained virtual price stability by the mid 1990s. By 1997 many respected economists were, for the first time since the Great Depression, seriously discussing the dangers of deflation. How does the sea-anchor model hold up in tracking this turbulent period? Since Livingston's death in 1990 the Federal Reserve Bank of Philadelphia has continued the survey. Figure 16-15 shows the 6-month forecasts against actual inflation through 1997. Consistent with the sea-anchor hypothesis, forecasters generally continued to expect inflation to be somewhat higher than it turned out to be throughout the late 1980s and 1990s.

Figure 16-16 compares the performance of the sea-anchor model to the actual forecasts, using the judgmentally estimated parameters originally chosen in the 1987 analysis. The model suggests that the underlying long-term trend anchoring

FIGURE 16-15
Six-month
Livingston forecast
vs. actual inflation,
1947–1997

The plotted values
of actual inflation
differ slightly
compared to
Figure 16-11 due
to revisions in the
CPI since 1985.

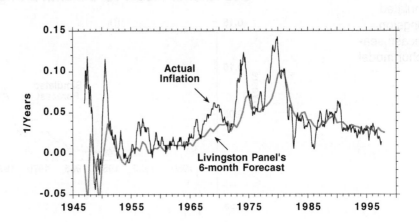

FIGURE 16-16
Livingston panel's
6-month forecast
compared to sea-
anchor model,
1947-1997

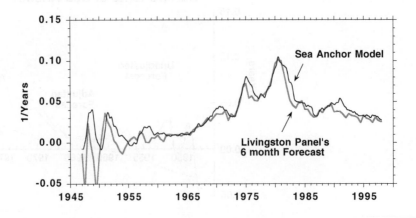

the inflation forecasts peaked around 1985 at about 6.5%/year and fell to around 4%/year by 1997. The simulated forecasts track the actual forecasts reasonably well, though the model forecasts are high by an average of about 0.3%/year between 1985 and 1997, a small fraction of the standard deviation of the individual forecasts comprising the panel mean.

Clearly, the fit between the data and model is not perfect. The fit could be improved by incorporating the influence of other economic variables and by estimating the parameters econometrically rather than using the original judgmental estimates selected in the 1987 paper.

The historical fit of the model could also be improved by allowing the parameters of the model to vary over time. Over the 50 years examined here the basis for and methods of computing the CPI have changed dramatically. These revisions in the CPI mean the historic rate of inflation is now different from what it was at the time the forecasts were made. The quality and availability of other potentially relevant economic data have improved markedly, and the tools available to forecasters were transformed from slide rules and graph paper to computers and sophisticated econometric models. And of course, the membership of the Livingston panel has changed completely. Forecasters, reacting to the greater volatility of inflation since the 1970s, may have become more sensitive to recent price changes.

Nevertheless, the ability of the sea-anchor model to track the forecasts as well as it does for half a century, though it relies on only a single cue and uses fixed, judgmentally estimated parameters, suggests that the underlying cognitive processes people use to forecast inflation are rather simple and stable.

The TREND function and the sea-anchor model portray inflation forecasting as a process that is highly bounded in its rationality. While there are dozens of economic variables people believe to be causally or statistically related to the likely future rate of price change, the sea-anchor model assumes forecasts are formed solely through consideration of the past trend in prices itself. While many forecasters use complex economic models and sophisticated forecasting methods, the sea-anchor model assumes people forecast that recent inflation rates will continue but adjust their estimates by their intuitive feeling about the underlying inflation environment. The close correspondence of the actual forecasts to the sea-anchor model suggests the impact of other potentially relevant economic variables on the panel's forecasts is weak.

The weak influence of other indicators in the panel's forecasts is consistent with behavioral decision theory. People are incapable of correctly deducing the consequences of intricate dynamic systems such as the economy and tend instead to process information with simple, incomplete, and erroneous mental models. In doing so people prefer relatively certain information to uncertain, noisy information. The future values of potentially relevant variables such as the money supply, interest rates, unemployment, economic growth, exchange rates, and budget deficits are themselves noisy, uncertain, variable, controversial, and difficult to forecast. There is substantial disagreement among economists about the nature of the relationships between these variables and the rate of inflation. Recent inflation itself, in contrast, provides a powerful, salient, and relevant cue, measured in the same units as the target variable, and is likely to form a strong anchor on people's forecasts.

As discussed for the case of energy demand, decision aids such as econometric models do not solve the problem since the modeler's judgment is always needed to specify the model structure and the future values of the exogenous variables. In fact, the forecasts of many econometric models are heavily "add-factored" by the modelers. An add factor is simply a quantity added to the output of an econometric model to bring the forecast in line with the modeler's intuition; it is a fudge factor. A model might predict inflation was going to be 2% over the next year, but if forecasters believed that was too low, they might add a fudge factor of, say, 1% to bring the forecast up to their intuitive judgment that inflation will be 3%/year (see chapter 21). Defenders of add factoring argue that it allows them to take the latest available data into account, overcomes limitations of the models, and enables them to bring their expert knowledge to bear. But experts are prone to many of the same judgmental biases observed in the public at large (Tversky and Kahneman, 1974; Kahneman, Slovic, and Tversky, 1982). Indeed, Caskey (1985) shows the Livingston panel's forecasts of inflation are virtually identical to those generated by DRI (Data Resources, Inc.), one of the largest and most successful econometric forecasting firms. In a world of great uncertainty, inflation forecasts are strongly influenced by recent trends in inflation itself despite the fact that forecasters claim to consider a wide range of variables and spend considerable resources on complex econometric models.

The close correspondence of the forecasts produced by different forecasters and different methods also reflects a herd mentality in the forecasting community. Professional forecasters pay careful attention to the projections of their rivals and colleagues. Herding behavior among forecasters arises in part from basic psychological factors and social pressures. Research shows people tend to revise their opinions toward those of others, even strangers. Asch (1951, 1956) had people select which of three lines was the same length as a reference line. Alone, people got it right more than 99% of the time. Then people were asked to judge the length of the lines after a group of others announced their opinions. The other people, secretly working with Asch, would deliberately give erroneous answers, saying that a line of, for example, 3 inches was the same length as another of 3.75 inches. Asch found that groups as small as three caused one-third of the people tested to agree that the 3-inch line was in fact equal in length to the 3.75-inch line. The tendency to revise opinions toward those of others in a group is stronger when the other group members are known to and respected by the subject and when the opinion concerns matters more ambiguous and uncertain than the length of a line—for example, the future rate of inflation.

The incentives forecasters face also reinforce herding. Many believe it is much worse to be the only one wrong than to be one of many making the same error. When misery loves company it is rational for individuals to shade their forecasts toward the consensus view even when market fundamentals or their private information indicate a different forecast. Forecasters herd together, adjusting their forecasts toward the views of and emphasizing the cues used by whomever among them has gotten lucky lately and produced an accurate forecast (Froot, Scharfstein, and Stein 1992 develop a related game-theoretic model of herding in investor behavior).

16.5   IMPLICATIONS FOR FORECAST CONSUMERS

The results suggest important lessons for forecasters and especially for managers and decision makers who must choose which forecasts and forecasting methods to buy.

First, most forecasts are not very good. Forecasts are most accurate when the underlying dynamics are stable, as when predicting the influence of regular phenomena such as seasonal variations. But forecasting methods are particularly poor when there are changes in trends, noise, and other sources of turbulence. These are precisely the times when people are most interested in forecasts.

Second, most forecasting methods frequently miss changes in trends and turning points in cycles, lagging behind rather than anticipating them. The systematic errors in forecasts of inflation, commodity prices, energy use, and other variables strongly suggest adaptive expectations and simple trend extrapolation often dominate professional forecasts. These methods do correct errors over time, but because they involve smoothing past data, they inevitably introduce delays that cause the forecasts to miss key turning points and shifts in growth rates.

Third, smoothing and extrapolation of the past trend in the variable itself seems to dominate other considerations in forecasting. Though forecasters often claim to (and indeed may) examine a wide range of variables in making their forecasts, past values and past trends strongly anchor their forecasts. The influence of other variables is weak because their connections to the target variable are poorly understood, unstable, noisy, and ambiguous. Forecasters often behave as if they were using simple smoothing and naive extrapolation even when they are using complicated formal models. They adjust the parameters and values of exogenous inputs until the output of the model is "reasonable," that is, until it matches their intuition. Intuition, however, is biased by a variety of judgmental heuristics and tends to be strongly anchored to recent trends.

Fourth, forecasters tend to underestimate uncertainty in their forecasts, often failing to provide a range, alternative scenarios, or a list of factors to which their forecasts are sensitive (see the overconfidence bias, section 8.2.5).

How then can managers improve the value they get from forecasts? Fight against the overconfidence bias by explicitly challenging assumptions and asking how your expectations might be wrong (for practical examples, see Russo and Schoemaker 1989). Require forecasters to document their assumptions, make their data sources explicit, and specify the methods they are using. Don't allow forecasters to use add factoring (chapter 21 discusses standards for replicability and rigor in modeling).

Even so, improving forecast accuracy is difficult. The best way to improve the benefit/cost ratio of forecasting is to reduce the cost. The projections of expensive forecasting services and models tend to be dominated by smoothing and trend extrapolation. Managers can save a great deal of money by smoothing and extrapolating the data themselves. Forecast accuracy may not improve, but the cost of acquiring the forecasts will fall.

Finally, focus on the development of decision rules and strategies that are robust to the inevitable forecast errors. The real value of modeling is not to anticipate and react to problems in the environment but to eliminate the problems by changing the underlying structure of the system. Modelers and their clients should be designers, not diviners. In the words of Antoine de Saint-Exupèry, "As for the future, your task is not to foresee, but to enable it."

CHALLENGE	## Extrapolation and Stability

The expectation formation process can dramatically affect the stability and performance of a system. To explore the impact of extrapolative expectations in dynamic models, consider the models of new-product growth developed in chapters 9 and 10. These models did not explicitly include expectations about future demand. Because it takes time to build capacity, however, managers in growth markets must forecast the demand for their products far in advance. Forecasting too little growth leads to capacity shortages, eroding market share (you can't sell more than you can make). Forecasting too much growth, on the other hand, leads to excess capacity, destroying profitability.

Consider the typical life cycle of a successful new durable product. Sales rise initially at rapid exponential rates. As the market grows, the fractional growth rate slows. Eventually, sales peak, then fall to a rate that covers replacement of discarded units and growth in the total customer base. The diffusion of VCRs in the US shown in Figure 10-8 provides an example.

Figure 9-22 in section 9.3.6 presents a simple model of the life cycle for durable products. Based on the Bass diffusion model, the model represents sales as the sum of initial and replacement purchases:

$$\text{Sales Rate} = \text{Initial Purchase Rate} + \text{Repeat Purchase Rate} \tag{16-10}$$

The model does not include production capacity at all, implicitly assuming capacity is always adequate and never constrains sales (orders always equal sales equal deliveries). The assumption that capacity is always adequate requires either that capacity can be adjusted instantly or that demand forecasts are always perfect. Both assumptions are false. Capacity acquisition delays in many industries are long, and forecasts are often erroneous.

Modify the model shown in Figure 9-22 to include demand forecasts and capacity adjustments. To begin, note that in the original model there are no distinctions among orders, sales, and deliveries. All are implicitly assumed to be equal. When capacity adjustment lags are introduced, you must distinguish between these concepts. Let the sales rate in equation (16-10) represent the order rate (demand) for the product. The firm can only deliver product if capacity exceeds sales:[12]

$$\text{Delivery Rate} = \text{MIN}(\text{Sales Rate, Capacity}) \tag{16-11}$$

---

[12]The formulation for the delivery rate assumes that any sales (orders) that can't be delivered due to capacity constraints are lost forever. Implicitly, customers are highly delivery sensitive and forego adoption when the product is unavailable. More realistically, any unfilled orders accumulate in a backlog, and the desired delivery rate depends on the size of the backlog, not the current order rate. For the purposes of this challenge ignore the backlog (and possible inventories). You might add backlogs to test the robustness of your results in this challenge to this important assumption about market structure. You can also replace the MIN function with its fuzzy counterpart (section 13.2.8).

It is not necessary to model the stock and flow structure for capacity acquisition in detail (chapter 17 develops this structure). Instead, it is sufficient to assume capacity adjusts to the desired level with a delay (as assumed in the market growth model developed in chapter 15). For simplicity, assume the lag in capacity is the same for increases and decreases. A third-order delay provides a realistic representation of the capacity adjustment process (chapter 11):

$$\text{Capacity} = \text{SMOOTH3(Desired Capacity, Capacity Acquisition Lag)} \qquad (16\text{-}12)$$

Desired capacity represents demand projected into the future by the capacity lead time and then adjusted by the normal capacity utilization level:

$$\text{Desired Capacity} = \text{Projected Sales/Normal Capacity Utilization} \qquad (16\text{-}13)$$

1. **Adaptive expectations**

   First, assume the firm has myopic expectations and sets projected sales to its belief about the recent sales rate.

   $$\text{Projected Sales Rate} = \text{Recent Sales Rate} \qquad (16\text{-}14)$$

   As explained in chapter 11, it takes time to measure and report sales and additional time to filter out short-term noise in sales. Hence the recent sales rate is modeled with adaptive expectations (assume first-order exponential smoothing):

   $$\text{Recent Sales Rate} = \text{SMOOTH(Sales Rate, Sales Perception Time)} \qquad (16\text{-}15)$$

   To measure the firm's ability to match capacity to demand, define the adequacy of capacity as the gap between normal production and sales. Normal production is the production rate given by capacity at normal utilization.

   $$\text{Adequacy of Capacity} = \frac{(\text{Normal Production} - \text{Sales Rate})}{\text{Sales Rate}} \qquad (16\text{-}16)$$

   $$\text{Normal Production} = \text{Capacity/Normal Capacity Utilization} \qquad (16\text{-}17)$$

   Begin with the parameters for the model shown in Figure 9-23. Assume a half-year capacity acquisition delay, a one-quarter-year delay in perceiving sales, and normal capacity utilization of 90%. Compare the behavior of capacity, projected sales, and sales. How well does capacity match demand? Do the forecast errors and adequacy of capacity vary systematically over the product life cycle? Explain. Explore how the forecast and capacity errors vary with the parameters (both the lags in capacity adjustment and the parameters governing the product life cycle).

2. **Extrapolative expectations**

   Forecasting by adaptive expectations will always cause capacity to be inadequate when demand is growing. Modify projected sales to include the expected growth in sales. Assume managers believe recent sales growth will continue over the forecast horizon:

   $$\begin{aligned}\text{Projected Sales Rate} = &\ \text{Recent Sales} \\ &* (1 + \text{Expected Growth in Sales} * \text{Forecast Horizon})\end{aligned} \qquad (16\text{-}14a)$$

The forecast horizon is the capacity acquisition lag. Assume the firm forecasts sales growth using the TREND function:

$$\text{Expected Growth in Sales} = \text{TREND(Sales Rate, Sales Perception Time, Historical Horizon for Sales, Time to Perceive Sales Growth)} \quad (16\text{-}18)$$

Assume the firm looks back over the past year to estimate the trend in sales (Historical Horizon for Sales = 1 year) and that the Time to Perceive Sales Growth is one-quarter year. By setting TPPC to the Sales Perception Time, the perceived present condition equals the Recent Sales Rate.

Compare the behavior of the revised forecast to the myopic case of simple smoothing. Does incorporating the growth in demand improve the ability of capacity to track demand during the growth phase of the product life cycle? What happens when the market saturates? Is there a trade-off between the ability to match demand growth during the growth phase and the saturation phase? Explain.

Comment on the effectiveness of extrapolative expectations as a forecasting method in product life cycle settings. What are its advantages and disadvantages? Do you think real firms forecast by extrapolation of recent sales growth? What alternative methods might work better?[13]

16.6   INITIALIZATION AND STEADY STATE RESPONSE OF THE TREND FUNCTION

To be a reasonable model of growth expectation formation, TREND should produce, in the steady state, an accurate (unbiased) estimate of the growth rate in the input variable. That is, if

$$\text{Input} = I_0 \exp(gt) \quad (16\text{-}19)$$

then

$$\lim_{t \to \infty} \text{TREND(Input)} = g \quad (16\text{-}20)$$

The proof relies on the fact that the steady state response of first-order exponential smoothing to exponential growth is exponential growth at the same rate as the input but with a steady state error: When the input is growing exponentially, the

---

[13]Note that the formulation for Projected Sales Rate does not correct for the lag in the perception of sales (the recent sales rate). By equation (16-22), recent sales will lag actual sales by g * Sales Perception Time. Further, since capacity is modeled as a third-order delay, the proper growth correction for the capacity lag is $[1 + g * (\text{Capacity Acquisition Lag}/3)]^3$ (you can derive this expression from the analysis in section 16.6). However, there is no reason to expect real firms to make such precise corrections or to avoid steady state error under growth. Doing so requires them to understand the length and distribution of the sales perception delay and capacity acquisition delay. In experimental product life cycle markets (Paich and Sterman 1993), subjects, including many with business experience, generally did not forecast aggressively enough to correct for steady state error. Most subjects found themselves short of capacity during the initial growth phase, failed to anticipate the saturation of the market, and experienced a significant capacity overshoot as boom turned to bust.

smoothed variable lags behind the input by a constant fraction of the smoothed value.

The equation for first-order smoothing of an input is

$$\frac{dOutput}{dt} = (Input - Output)/D \tag{16-21}$$

where D is the adjustment time. The steady state solution of equation (16-21) for the case of an exponentially growing input can be found in many differential equations texts:

$$Output = Input/(1 + gD) \tag{16-22}$$

That is, the smoothed variable lags the input with a steady state error depending on the product of the growth rate of the input and the average lag between input and output. The solution can be verified by substitution in the differential equation. Intuitively, the gap between input and output must be just great enough to cause the fractional rate of change of the output to equal the fractional growth rate of the input, that is, in steady state, $d(Output)/dt = (Input - Output)/D = gOutput$.

In the TREND function, PPC is a smooth of the Input, so in the steady state of exponential growth at rate g/period, PPC will also be growing exponentially at rate g. Since the reference condition RC is a smooth of PPC, it will also be growing at fractional rate g:

$$\frac{dRC}{dt} \bigg/ RC = g \tag{16-23}$$

But by equation (16-21)

$$\frac{dRC}{dt} = \frac{(PPC - RC)}{THRC} \tag{16-24}$$

so

$$g = \frac{dRC}{dt} \bigg/ RC = \frac{(PPC - RC)}{THRC} \bigg/ RC \tag{16-25}$$

which is precisely the expression for the indicated trend, ITREND, equation (16-1). Since TREND is a smooth of ITREND, TREND = ITREND = g in the steady state. Thus, in the steady state, TREND yields an unbiased estimate of the exponential growth rate in the input. During transients, of course, TREND will differ from the true growth rate of the input.

When using the TREND function, the modeler must specify the initial condition for each state variable. The modeler sets the initial value of the perceived trend at some value, denoted $TREND(t_0)$. Usually, the initial values of the perceived present condition and reference condition should be set so that the TREND function is initialized in steady state at the assumed initial growth rate. From equation (16-25), the steady state initial conditions are readily found to be

$$PPC(t_0) = \frac{INPUT(t_0)}{(1 + TREND(t_0) * TPPC)} \tag{16-26}$$

$$RC(t_0) = \frac{PPC(t_0)}{(1 + TREND(t_0) * THRC)} \tag{16-27}$$

These initial conditions avoid unwanted transients in the adjustment of TREND to the actual growth of the input.

16.7   SUMMARY

Forecasts and expectations are fundamental to decision making. Theories of forecasting range from rational expectations, in which people are assumed to have a nearly perfect understanding of complex systems and never make systematic errors, to theories in which behavior is simple and people never learn. Experimental and field studies support an intermediate theory in which rationality is bounded. Behavior and expectations do adapt, but slowly. We often learn the wrong lessons from experience and frequently make systematic errors in forecasting and controlling complex systems.

The chapter introduced and tested a boundedly rational formulation for modeling the formation of growth expectations, the TREND function. The TREND function models the way in which people form expectations about the rate of growth in a variable based on the history of the variable itself.

The TREND function was tested with several examples, including forecasts of inflation, commodity prices, and energy consumption. In all cases (and many more discussed in the forecasting literature) the forecasts can be modeled well by adaptive learning processes such as exponential smoothing and trend extrapolation. Forecasters frequently miss turning points, overreact to trends, and generate other systematic errors. Learning is often quite slow relative to the dynamics of the variables people seek to forecast.

Forecasts are often dominated by simple adaptation to past events even though forecasters claim to consider a wide range of variables and use complicated models to generate their forecasts. The past history and trend in a variable act as a strong anchor on people's judgments and constrain the range of values they consider reasonable. In situations where the relationships among variables in the system are noisy, unstable, or obscure, the trend in the target variable will loom large in the forecasting process and dominate the effect of other predictors. Similarly, forecasters often adjust the inputs to their models until the outputs conform to their intuition and to social and political pressures.

Part V

Instability and Oscillation

Oscillation and instability are among the most common dynamic behaviors. This section examines the origins of oscillations in a wide range of systems. Chapter 17 develops the stock management structure, a fundamental and widely used structure to model the management of any quantity in a supply chain. Chapter 18 uses the stock management structure to develop models of manufacturing supply chains, showing how intendedly rational policies at each decision point can lead to costly and undesirable oscillations for all. Chapter 19 examines the management of human resources and shows how interactions of production scheduling with workforce management can cause oscillations and instability for firms. Chapter 20 examines commodity cycles in price-mediated markets, from pulp and paper to livestock. Important formulations are developed along the way, including models of capital investment, inventory and supply line management, human resources, pricing, and production.

17

Supply Chains and the Origin of Oscillations

> *The distinction between stocks and flows is well known . . . Yet economic theories still revolve primarily around flow concepts of supply and demand . . . [S]tock-variable concepts of supply and demand must be incorporated explicitly in economic models in order to capture the rich disequilibrium behavior characteristics of real socioeconomic systems.*
> —Nathaniel J. Mass (1980, p. 97)

A supply chain is the set of structures and processes an organization uses to deliver an output to a customer. The output can be a physical product such as an automobile, the provision of a key resource such as skilled labor, or an intangible output such as a service or product design. A supply chain consists of (1) the stock and flow structures for the acquisition of the inputs to the process and (2) the management policies governing the various flows. The next several chapters consider the structure and behavior of supply chains in various settings. Supply chains often exhibit persistent and costly instability. This chapter lays the foundation by illustrating the behavior of supply chains in important contexts and developing a fundamental formulation—the stock management structure—useful in modeling supply chains in all types of systems, not only business systems, but also physical, biological, and other systems.

The stock management structure is used to explain the origin of oscillations. Oscillation requires *both* that there be time delays in the negative feedbacks regulating the state of a system *and* that decision makers fail to account for these delays—ignoring the supply line of corrective actions that have been initiated but have not yet had their effect. Though it is foolish to ignore time delays, experimental evidence shows people often do just that. Case studies of various industries suggest these misperceptions of feedback lie at the root of the persistent cycles in real estate, shipping, and related industries.

17.1   SUPPLY CHAINS IN BUSINESS AND BEYOND

A firm can be viewed as a set of processes: A process for order fulfillment, for manufacturing the product, for pricing, for advertising, for hiring, and so on. Each of these processes requires various inputs, which must be acquired from suppliers. A supply chain is the structure through which the inputs are acquired, transformed into an output, and then delivered to a customer. The customer can be external or internal. The inputs and outputs can be tangible, such as an automobile and its parts and raw materials, or intangible, as in product development where the output is a completed design and the inputs include customer specifications.

Supply chains consist of a stock and flow structure for the acquisition, storage, and conversion of inputs into outputs and the decision rules governing the flows. The automobile supply chain includes the stock and flow networks of materials such as steel. Steel moves from rolls of sheet metal through stamping into body parts to assembly and shipment to dealers. At each stage in the process there is a stock of parts buffering the different activities (an inventory of sheet steel between steel acquisition and usage, an inventory of stamped parts between stamping and assembly, an inventory of cars between dealer acquisition and sales). The decision structure governing the flows includes policies for ordering steel from suppliers, scheduling the stamping of body parts and assembly, shipping new cars to dealers, and the customers' purchase decision.

Supply chains often extend beyond the boundaries of a single organization. Effective models must represent different actors and organizations including suppliers, the firm, distribution channels, and customers. Because they involve multiple chains of stocks and flows, with the resulting time delays, and because the decision rules governing the flows often create important feedbacks among the partners in a supply chain, system dynamics is well suited for supply chain modeling and policy design. Several examples of supply chains have already been discussed (see chapter 2 and sections 6.3 and 11.6).

The concept of a supply chain need not be restricted to business settings or even to human systems. For example, the supply of glucose providing the energy required for metabolic activity in your body is the output of a supply chain beginning with the consumption of food and ending with the metabolism of glucose and excretion of wastes. There are important time delays in the process, including delays in the digestion and transport of sugars and in the synthesis and diffusion of insulin (see Sturis et al. 1991 for a system dynamics model of the human glucose-insulin system).

17.1.1   Oscillation, Amplification, and Phase Lag

The purpose of a supply chain is to provide the right output at the right time. As customer requirements change, the managers of the supply chain respond by adjusting the rate at which resources are ordered and used. Supply chains are thus governed primarily by negative feedback. Because supply chains typically involve substantial time delays, they are prone to oscillation—production and inventories chronically overshoot and undershoot the appropriate levels. Figure 17-1 shows industrial production in the US. The data exhibit several modes of behavior. First, the long-run growth rate of manufacturing output is about 3.4%/year. Second, as seen in the bottom panel of the figure, production fluctuates significantly around the growth trend. The dominant periodicity is the business cycle, a cycle of prosperity and recession of about 3–5 years in duration, but exhibiting considerable variability.

The amplitude of business cycle fluctuations in materials production is significantly greater than that in consumer goods production (Figure 17-2; again, the exponential growth trend has been removed). The peaks and troughs of the cycle in materials production also tend to lag behind those in production of consumer goods.

These three features, *oscillation, amplification,* and *phase lag,* are pervasive in supply chains. Typically, the amplitude of fluctuations increases as they propagate from the customer to the supplier, with each upstream stage in a supply chain tending to lag behind its immediate customer.

The amplification of fluctuations from consumption to production is even greater in specific industries. The top panel in Figure 17-3 shows the petroleum

FIGURE 17-1

Industrial production in the US

Top: US industrial production since 1947. *Bottom:* Detrended industrial production showing fluctuations in the US manufacturing sector.

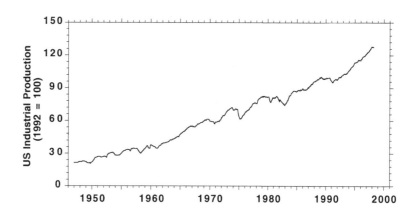

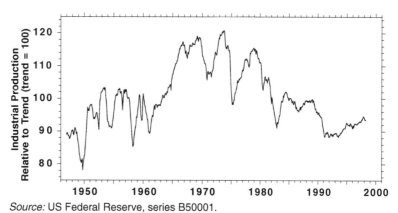

Source: US Federal Reserve, series B50001.

FIGURE 17-2
Oscillation,
amplification,
and phase lag in
the aggregate
supply chain

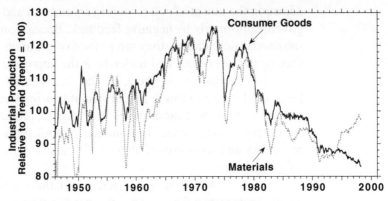

Source: US Federal Reserve, series B51000 and B53010.

supply chain (the figure shows the annualized growth rate; all monthly data are shown as 12-month centered moving averages to filter out the high-frequency month-to-month noise). The amplification is substantial. Production fluctuates more than consumption. In turn, drilling activity fluctuates about three times more than production, imposing large boom and bust cycles on the suppliers of drill rigs and equipment. The middle panel shows the machine tool industry. Fluctuations in economic growth lead to much larger swings in motor vehicle sales. During recessions, people keep their old cars going, leading to unanticipated inventory accumulation and forcing even larger production cutbacks. The automotive industry generates a large share of total machine tool orders. During a production downturn, the auto companies postpone or cancel their capital investment plans, causing even larger drops in the orders they place for machine tools. During the next upswing they scramble to build capacity and orders surge. The phase lag between vehicle production and the induced changes in machine tool orders is clearly visible. The bottom panel shows the semiconductor industry. Semiconductor production is at the upstream end of the supply chain for computers and electronic equipment and fluctuates much more than industrial production as a whole.

17.2   THE STOCK MANAGEMENT PROBLEM

Supply chains consist of cascades of firms, each receiving orders and adjusting production and production capacity to meet changes in demand. Each link in a supply chain maintains and controls inventories of materials and finished product. To understand the behavior of a supply chain and the causes of oscillation, amplification, and phase lag, it is first necessary to understand the structure and dynamics of a single link, that is, how an individual firm manages its inventories and resources as it attempts to balance production with orders. Such balancing processes always involve negative feedbacks.

All negative feedback processes involve comparing the state of the system to the desired state, then initiating a corrective action to eliminate any discrepancy. In such a *stock management* task, the manager seeks to maintain a stock (the state of the system) at a particular target level, or at least within an acceptable range. Stocks are altered only by changes in their inflow and outflow rates. Typically, the manager must set the inflow rate to compensate for losses and usage and to

FIGURE 17-3

Amplification in supply chains

Top: Oil and gas drilling fluctuates far more than production or consumption. The graph shows 12-month centered moving averages of the annualized fractional growth rate calculated from the monthly data.

Source: US Federal Reserve, series S13000 and A13800.

Middle: Orders for machine tools fluctuate far more than the production of their major customer (the auto industry). Graph shows annual growth rates.

Source: Anderson, Fine and Parker (1996).

Bottom: Semiconductor production fluctuates far more than industrial production as a whole. The graph shows 12-month centered moving averages of the annualized fractional growth rate calculated from the monthly data.

Source: Federal Reserve, series B50001 and I36790.

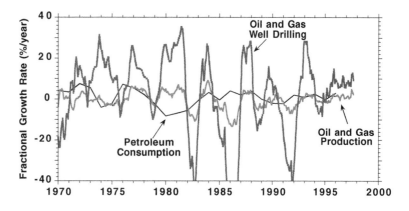

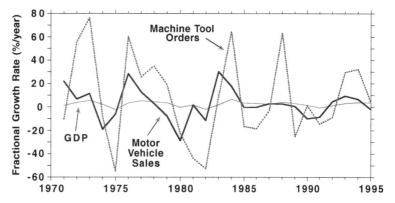

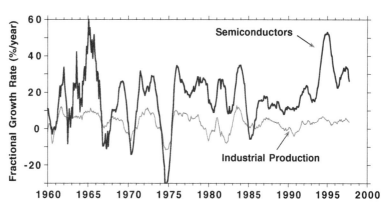

counteract disturbances that push the stock away from its desired value. Often there are lags between the initiation of a control action and its effect and lags between a change in the stock and the perception of that change by the decision maker. The duration of these lags may vary and may be influenced by the manager's own actions.

Stock management problems occur at many levels of aggregation. At the level of a firm, managers must order parts and raw materials to maintain inventories sufficient for production to proceed at the desired rate. They must adjust for variations in the usage of these materials and for changes in their delivery delays. At the individual level, you regulate the temperature of the water in your morning shower, guide your car down the highway, and manage your checking account balances. At the macroeconomic level, the US Federal Reserve seeks to manage the stock of money to stimulate economic growth and avoid inflation, while compensating for variations in credit demand, budget deficits, and international capital flows.

17.2.1   Managing a Stock: Structure

The stock management control problem can be divided into two parts: (1) the stock and flow structure of the system and (2) the decision rule used by the managers to control the acquisition of new units.

To begin, consider a situation in which the manager controls the inflow rate to the stock directly and there is no delay in acquiring units (Figure 17-4).[1] Filling a glass of water from a faucet provides an example: The delay between a change in the state of the system (the level of water in the glass) and the inflow to the stock (the rate at which water flows from the tap) is short enough relative to the flow that it can safely be ignored.

The stock to be controlled, S, is the accumulation of the acquisition rate AR less the loss rate LR:

$$S = \text{INTEGRAL}(AR - LR, S_{t_0}) \tag{17-1}$$

Losses include any outflow from the stock and may arise from usage (as in a raw material inventory) or decay (as in the depreciation of plant and equipment). The loss rate must depend on the stock itself—losses must approach zero as the stock is depleted—and may also depend on sets of other endogenous variables $\mathbf{X}$ and exogenous variables $\mathbf{U}$. Losses may be nonlinear and may depend on the age distribution of the stock:

$$LR = f(S, \mathbf{X}, \mathbf{U}) \tag{17-2}$$

How should the acquisition rate be modeled? In general, managers cannot add new units to a stock simply because they desire to do so. First, the acquisition of new units may involve time delays. Second, the acquisition of new units for a stock usually requires resources: Production requires labor and equipment; hiring requires recruiting effort. These resources may themselves be dynamic. The resources available at any moment impose capacity constraints. For now, assume the capacity of the process is ample and that there are no significant time delays in acquiring new units. Therefore the actual acquisition rate, AR, is determined by the desired acquisition rate, DAR:

$$AR = \text{MAX}(0, DAR) \tag{17-3}$$

The MAX function ensures that the acquisition rate remains nonnegative. In most situations, the acquisition rate cannot be negative (once concrete is delivered and

---

[1]The discussion assumes the manager controls the inflow to the stock and must compensate for changes in the outflow. There are many stock management situations in which the manager's task is to adjust the outflow from a stock to compensate for changes in the inflow. A firm must adjust shipments to keep its backlog under control as orders vary; managers of a hydroelectric plant must adjust the flow through the dam to manage the level of impounded water as the inflow varies. The principles for stock management in these situations are analogous to those for the case where the managers control the inflow alone.

FIGURE 17-4
Structure for
managing a stock
when there are no
acquisition delays

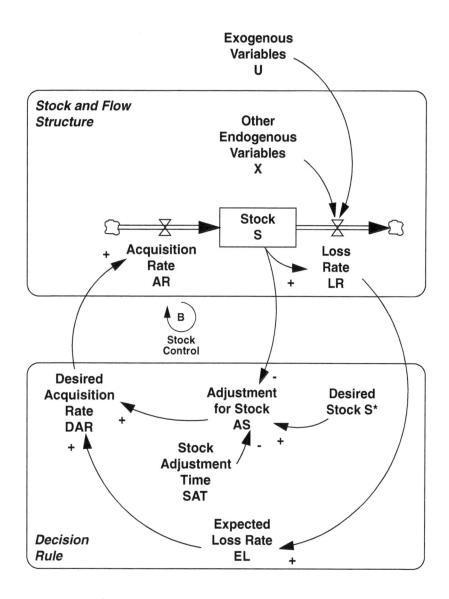

poured at a construction site it cannot be returned to the supplier). In those cases
where excess units can be returned or discarded, these processes are usually governed by different costs and criteria and should be modeled separately, not as a
negative acquisition rate.[2]

The formulation for the desired acquisition rate captures the decision-making
process of the managers. There are many possibilities. Following the principles
outlined in chapter 13, such formulations must be based only on information actually available to the decision makers, must be robust under extreme conditions, and
must be consistent with knowledge of the actual decision-making process, even if
the way people actually make decisions is less than optimal. In most stock management situations the complexity of the feedbacks among the variables makes it

---

[2]See section 13.3.3. All the MIN and MAX functions in the formulations in this chapter can be
replaced with their fuzzy counterparts if the purpose of the model requires it.

impossible to determine the optimal strategy. Instead, people use heuristics or rules of thumb to determine the order rate. The ordering decision rule proposed here assumes that managers, unable to optimize, instead exercise control through a locally rational heuristic. The model thus falls firmly in the tradition of bounded rationality as developed by Simon (1982), Cyert and March (1963), and others and as described in chapter 15.

The desired acquisition rate represents the rate at which managers would like to be adding units to the stock. Two considerations are fundamental to any decision rule for desired acquisitions. First, managers should replace expected losses from the stock. Second, managers should reduce the discrepancy between the desired and actual stock by acquiring more than expected losses when the stock is less than desired and less than expected losses when there is a surplus. Thus the desired acquisition rate is the expected loss rate EL plus an adjustment for the stock AS to bring the stock in line with its desired level:

$$DAR = EL + AS \tag{17-4}$$

The formulation can be interpreted as an example of the anchoring and adjustment heuristic (Tversky and Kahneman 1974; chapter 13). Here the anchor is the expected loss rate EL. Adjustments are then made to correct discrepancies between the desired and actual stock.

Why does the desired acquisition rate depend on expected losses rather than the actual loss rate? The current value of a flow represents the instantaneous rate of change. Actual instruments, however, cannot measure instantaneous rates of change but only average rates over some finite interval. The velocity of an object is calculated by measuring how far it moves over some period of time and taking the ratio of the distance covered to the time interval. The result is the average speed over the interval. The actual speed throughout the interval can vary, and the velocity at the finish line may differ from average. Similarly, the sales rate of a company *right now* cannot be measured. Instead sales rates are estimated by accumulating total sales over some interval of time such as a week, month, or quarter. The reported sales rate is the average over the reporting interval, and sales at the end of the period may differ from the average over the interval. No matter how accurate the instruments, the rate of change measured and reported to an observer always differs from the instantaneous rate of change.

While in principle all flows are measured and reported with a delay, in practice the delay is sometimes so short relative to the dynamics of interest that it can safely be omitted from your models. In a stock management situation, the loss rate is sometimes directly observable by the decision maker with essentially no delay or measurement error so that it is acceptable to assume EL = LR. Most often, however, the loss rate is not directly observable and must be estimated, introducing measurement, reporting, and perception delays. The expected loss rate might then be modeled as an information delay of the actual loss rate (see chapter 11). Sometimes decision makers extrapolate recent trends in reported losses to compensate for expected growth. In these cases the TREND function can be used to model the process by which managers form the expected loss rate (see chapter 16).

The feedback structure of the heuristic is shown in the bottom part of Figure 17-4. The adjustment for the stock AS creates the negative Stock Control feedback loop. The simplest formulation is to assume the adjustment is linear in the discrepancy between the desired stock S* and the actual stock:

$$AS = (S^* - S)/SAT \qquad\qquad (17\text{-}5)$$

where S* is the desired stock and SAT is the stock adjustment time (measured in time units). The stock adjustment forms a linear negative feedback process. The desired stock may be a constant or a variable.

17.2.2   Steady State Error

The inclusion of the expected loss rate in the formulation for the desired acquisition rate is an important behavioral assumption. Expected losses are included for two reasons: First, omitting replacement of expected losses leads to a *steady state error* in which the stock differs from its desired value even in equilibrium. Steady state error means a gap between desired and actual states persists even after the system has had time to settle into its steady state (i.e., even after the relationships among the state variables stop changing). Steady state error can arise despite the existence of a negative feedback loop, such as the stock adjustment loop, which strives to eliminate discrepancies between the desired and actual state of the system.

Imagine a firm that sets its production target based only on the gap between its desired and actual inventory levels. The stock to be controlled is inventory, shipments determine the loss rate, and production is the acquisition rate. Suppose their decision rule is to eliminate any gaps between desired and actual stocks over a period of 1 week:

Production = (Desired Inventory − Inventory)/Inventory Adjustment Time   (17-6)

where the Inventory Adjustment Time = 7 days and the nonnegativity constraint on production is omitted.

The equilibrium condition for inventory is Production = Shipments. Therefore the stock of inventory will reach balance only when

$$\text{Production} = \frac{(\text{Desired Inventory} - \text{Inventory})}{\text{Inventory Adjustment Time}} = \text{Shipments} \qquad (17\text{-}7)$$

or when

Inventory = Desired Inventory − Shipments * Inventory Adjustment Time   (17-8)

Producing in response to the size of the inventory shortfall guarantees that the firm will, in equilibrium, be operating with less inventory than it desires. When inventory = desired inventory, production will be zero. But if there are shipments, inventory will decline, opening a gap between desired and actual inventory. The gap grows until it is just large enough to induce production equal to shipments. The bigger the loss rate or the weaker the stock adjustment, the bigger the steady state error.

The solution is to include the expected loss rate in the production decision. Expected losses might be based on the average order rate:

Production = Average Order Rate
+ (Desired Inventory − Inventory)/Inventory Adjustment Time   (17-6a)

In equilibrium, average orders now equal actual orders, orders will equal shipments, and inventory will equal its desired level. Average rather than actual orders are used because the instantaneous value of the order rate is not measurable and firms deliberately average incoming orders to smooth out high-frequency noise and avoid costly changes in production.

Automatic replacement of expected losses improves the performance of the decision rule for the desired acquisition rate. However, you may not include a formulation in your model just because it would make sense. You must also have evidence that people actually do make decisions that way. The second reason for including the expected loss rate in the model is that the evidence suggests people do in fact account for the losses they expect when managing stocks (see, e.g., Sterman 1989a, b)—provided loss rate information is available. In some situations, loss rate information is unavailable or unreliable. In these cases there is likely to be a steady state error. Close inspection of the decision process may reveal that the desired stock includes a safety margin that roughly compensates for the steady state error.

17.2.3   Managing a Stock: Behavior

The simple stock management structure, as basic as it is, yields important insight into the sources of amplification observed in supply chains. To illustrate, consider a firm managing its stock of plant and equipment. The loss rate represents the discard of old buildings and equipment. Assume losses follow a first-order process with an average lifetime of 8 years. Also assume the delays in reporting the discard of broken-down or obsolete equipment are short relative to the dynamics of interest, so the expected loss rate can be set equal to the actual loss rate. The stock adjustment time is set to 3 years. These parameters are consistent with the values estimated by Senge (1978) for capital investment in various sectors of the US economy (see section 11.5.1).

The desired capital stock depends on the demand for the firm's products. To explore the behavior of a single link in a supply chain, desired capital is exogenous. Figure 17-5 shows the response of the system to a step increase in desired capital. The system begins in equilibrium with a desired stock of 100 units and throughput of 12.5 units/year. At the start of year 1 the desired stock suddenly increases to 120 units. The step increase in desired capital immediately opens up a gap of 20 units between the desired and actual stock. The adjustment for the stock of capital jumps by 20 units/3 years = 6.67 units/year, increasing the desired acquisition rate to 19.17 units/year. Because there are no delays or capacity constraints on the acquisition rate, the stock begins to rise. As it does, the capital shortfall diminishes, reducing the stock adjustment. The acquisition rate gradually falls back to the loss rate. As the stock rises, so too does the loss rate. Because the expected loss rate is assumed to equal the actual loss rate, the net change in the capital stock is equal simply to the stock adjustment:

$$\text{Net Change in Capital Stock} = (S^* - S)/\text{SAT} \qquad (17\text{-}9)$$

which is the familiar first-order linear negative feedback system. Therefore, as seen in the figure, after three adjustment times (9 years), the capital stock has adjusted about 95% of the way to its new equilibrium.

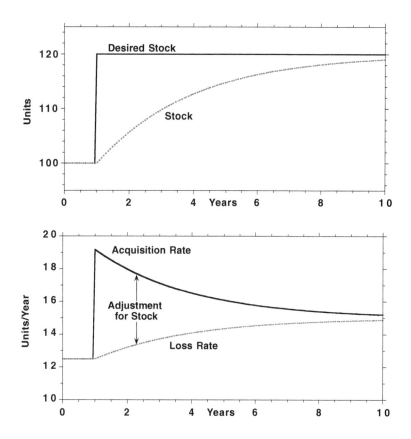

FIGURE 17-5

Response to a step increase in the desired stock

The consequences of the stock management structure for supply chain management are profound. First, the process of stock adjustment creates significant amplification. Though the desired stock increased by 20%, the acquisition rate increases by a maximum of more than 53% (the peak acquisition rate divided by the initial acquisition rate = 19.2/12.5). The *amplification ratio* (the ratio of the maximum change in the output to the maximum change in the input) is therefore 53%/20% = 2.65. A 1% increase in desired capacity causes a 2.65% surge in the demand for new capital. While the value of the amplification ratio depends on the stock adjustment time and capital lifetime, the existence of amplification does not. A longer adjustment time reduces the size of the adjustment for the stock for any given discrepancy between the desired and actual stocks and thus reduces amplification, but also lengthens the time required to close the gap and reach the new goal.

Second, amplification is temporary. In the long run, a 1% increase in desired capital leads to a 1% increase in the acquisition rate. But during the disequilibrium adjustment, the acquisition rate overshoots the new equilibrium. The overshoot is an inevitable consequence of the stock and flow structure. The only way a stock can increase is for the acquisition rate to exceed the loss rate. The acquisition rate must increase above the loss rate long enough to build up the stock to the new desired level. The firm's suppliers face much larger changes in demand than the firm itself and much of the surge in demand is temporary.

CHALLENGE

Exploring Amplification

Explore the behavior of the simple stock management model with the parameters in the example shown in Figure 17-5. Try the following tests:

1.   Explore the response of the acquisition rate to different magnitudes for the step increase in desired capital stock. How does the size of the step affect the rate of adjustment of the capital stock to the new equilibrium? Does the amplification ratio for the acquisition rate depend on the size of the step in desired capital? Why/why not?

2.   What is the response of the acquisition rate to a 20% step *decrease* in desired capital? What is the response to a 60% decrease? Are there any differences? Why/why not?

3.   How does the amplification of changes in demand depend on the stock adjustment time? With an adjustment time of 3 years it takes 9 years to reach 95% of the desired capital stock. Some managers in the firm argue this is too long. What is the amplification ratio generated by an adjustment time of 2 years? 1 year? What are the implications of a more aggressive stock adjustment policy for the firm and its equipment suppliers?

4.   Explore the dependence of the amplification ratio on the lifetime of capital. What happens to the amplification of demand changes as the lifetime of capital increases? Why? How does this help explain why the amplitude of business cycles in the construction industry is greater than that of the service sector?

5.   Can the simple stock management system oscillate? With the base case parameters the response to a step increase in desired capital is a single overshoot of the acquisition rate: The system amplifies demand changes but does not generate oscillation. Are there any parameters that can induce an oscillatory response? Why/why not?

6.   The step is a simple input that tests the response of a system to an unexpected change in the environment. In the real economy the demand for a firm's product (and hence its desired capital stock) exhibits more complex behavior, including fluctuations, random shocks, and growth. Test the response of the system to a fluctuation by assuming desired capital stock fluctuates sinusoidally (assume the system remains in equilibrium until the start of year 1):

$$S^* = 100 * [1 + A\sin(2\pi(t - 1)/P)] \text{ for } t > 1$$

where A is the amplitude of the fluctuation and P is the period. To begin, set $A = 0.10$ and $P = 1$ year. Calculate the steady state amplification ratio in the acquisition rate. The amplification ratio is the ratio of the amplitude of the fluctuation in the acquisition rate to the amplitude of the fluctuation in desired capital. Steady state means you should measure the amplitude of the variables after initial transients have died out (after about three time constants SAT have passed). How does the amplification ratio depend on the period of the cycle P? How does it depend on the stock adjustment time SAT? It is helpful to make a graph showing the amplification ratio as a function of the ratio P/SAT.

7.   Now explore the response of the system to growth in the desired capital stock. Consider two cases, and once again, assume desired capital stock is constant until the start of year 1:

a.   Linear growth (start with a slope of 20 units/year).

b.   Exponential growth (start with a growth rate of 10%/year).

Is there a steady state error for the case of growth in the desired stock? That is, does the actual stock eventually equal the desired stock? Why/why not? Find an algebraic expression for the steady state stock S in terms of the input S^* and the other parameters in the system.

8.   So far the loss rate has been assumed to be first-order, meaning the likelihood any unit in the stock is discarded does not depend on its age. In reality, the probability of discard usually rises sharply for older vintages. Disaggregate the capital stock into a third-order aging chain. Each vintage (stock of a given average age) should have a residence time equal to one-third the average lifetime. Assume there are no discards from the first two vintages (the loss rate will therefore be equivalent to a third-order delay of the acquisition rate). What is the impact of an explicit vintaging structure on the behavior of the model?

17.3   THE STOCK MANAGEMENT STRUCTURE

The simple model above yields important insights into the behavior of supply lines; however, the model invokes a number of unrealistic assumptions. Most serious is the assumption that there is no delay in the acquisition process. A firm seeking to increase its capital stock cannot acquire new units immediately but must await construction or delivery. New workers cannot be hired and trained instantly. It takes time for your car to stop after you step on the brakes, and it takes time for the economy to respond after the Federal Reserve changes interest rates.

Figure 17-6 modifies the structure of the stock management system to include a delay between orders and acquisition. As before, the stock is increased by acquisitions and decreased by the loss rate; these are formulated as in equations (17-2) and (17-3). The stock and flow structure now includes a *supply line* of unfilled orders—those orders that have been placed but not yet received:

$$SL = INTEGRAL(OR - AR, SL_{t_0}) \tag{17-10}$$

The order rate OR is now the managers' decision point. The acquisition rate depends on the supply line SL of units that have been ordered but not yet received and the average acquisition lag AL:

$$AR = L(SL, AL) \tag{17-11}$$

$$AL = f(SL, \mathbf{X}, \mathbf{U}) \tag{17-12}$$

where the lag function $L()$ denotes a material delay. The acquisition lag could be a pipeline delay, a first-order delay, or any other distribution of arrivals around the average acquisition lag. In general, the acquisition lag may depend on the supply line itself and on the other endogenous and exogenous variables. Often, the average acquisition lag is relatively constant up to the point where the required acquisition rate exceeds the capacity of the process, as for example when the desired

FIGURE 17-6   The generic stock management structure

The determinants of the desired supply line are not shown (see text).

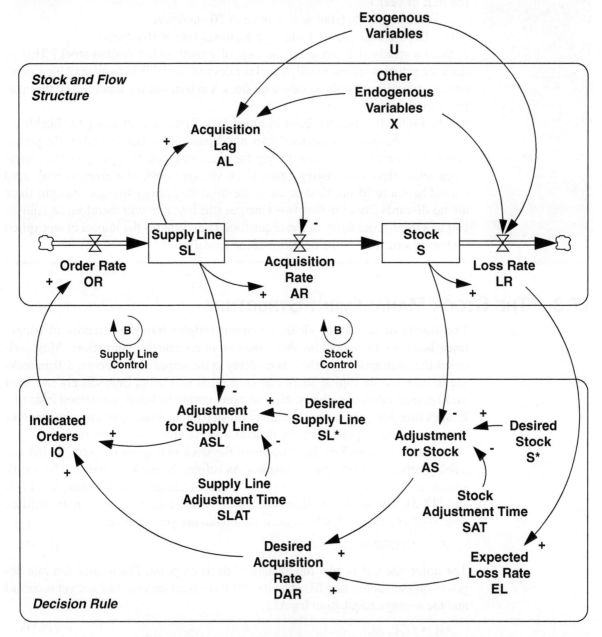

construction rate for capital plant exceeds the capacity of the construction industry. The acquisition lag can also be influenced by the manager's decisions, as when a firm chooses to expedite delivery of materials by paying premium freight.

The structure represented by Figure 17-6 is quite general. The system may be nonlinear. There may be arbitrarily complex feedbacks among the endogenous variables, and the system may be influenced by a number of exogenous forces, both systematic and stochastic. The delay in acquiring new units is often variable and may be constrained by the capacity of the supplier. Table 17-1 maps common

TABLE 17-1 Examples of the stock management structure

System	Stock	Supply Line	Loss Rate	Acquisition Rate	Order Rate	Typical Behavior
Inventory management	Inventory	Goods on order	Shipments to customers	Arrivals from supplier	Orders for goods	Business cycles
Capital investment	Capital plant	Plant under construction	Depreciation	Construction completion	New contracts	Construction cycles
Equipment	Equipment	Equipment on order	Depreciation	Equipment delivery	New equipment orders	Business cycles
Human resources	Employees	Vacancies & trainees	Layoffs and quits	Hiring rate	Vacancy creation	Business cycles
Cash management	Cash balance	Pending loan applications	Expenditures	Borrowing rate	Loan application rate	Cash flow cycles
Marketing	Customer base	Prospective customers	Defections to competitors	Recruitment of new customers	New customer contacts	Boom and bust in customer base
Hog farming	Hog stock	Immature and gestating hogs	Slaughter rate	Maturation rate	Breeding rate	Hog cycles
Agricultural commodities	Inventory	Crops in the field	Consumption	Harvest rate	Planting rate	Commodity cycles
Commercial real estate	Building stock	Buildings under development	Depreciation	Completion rate	Development rate	Real estate booms and busts
Cooking on electric range	Temperature of pot	Heat in coils of range	Diffusion to air	Diffusion from coils to pot	Setting of burner	Overcooked dinner
Driving	Distance to next car	Momentum of car	Friction	Velocity	Gas and brake pedals	Stop-and-go traffic
Showering	Water temperature	Water temp. in pipes	Drain rate	Flow from showerhead	Faucet settings	Burn then freeze
Personal energy level	Glucose in bloodstream	Sugar and starch in GI tract	Metabolism	Digestion	Food consumption	Cycles of energy level
Social drinking	Alcohol in blood	Alcohol in stomach	Metabolism of alcohol	Diffusion from stomach to blood	Alcohol consumption rate	Drunkenness

examples into the generic form. In each case, the manager must choose the order rate over time to keep the stock close to a target. Note that most of these systems tend to generate oscillation and instability.

Managers still order to replace expected losses from the stock and reduce any discrepancy between the desired and actual stock. In the presence of an acquisition delay managers must also maintain an adequate supply line of unfilled orders, adjusting it so that acquisitions are close to the desired rate. To formalize this heuristic, first note that the order rate in most real life situations must be nonnegative:

$$OR = MAX(0, IO) \qquad\qquad (17\text{-}13)$$

where IO is the indicated order rate, the rate indicated by other pressures. Order cancellations are sometimes possible and may sometimes exceed new orders (e.g., the US nuclear power industry since the 1970s). As before, the costs of and administrative procedures for cancellations are likely to differ from those for new orders. Cancellations should therefore be modeled as a distinct outflow from the supply line, governed by a separate decision rule, rather than as negative orders (see chapter 19 for a suitable formulation).

The indicated order rate is formulated as an anchoring and adjustment process. The desired acquisition rate DAR is the anchor, which is then adjusted by an amount designed to bring the supply line of unfilled orders in line with its goal (the adjustment for the supply line ASL):

$$IO = DAR + ASL \qquad\qquad (17\text{-}14)$$

The adjustment for the supply line is formulated analogously to the adjustment for the stock:

$$ASL = (SL^* - SL)/SLAT \qquad\qquad (17\text{-}15)$$

where SL^* is the desired supply line and SLAT is the supply line adjustment time. The supply line adjustment forms the negative Supply Line Control loop.

Figure 17-6 does not show the feedback structure for the desired supply line. In some cases the desired supply line is constant. More often, however, decision makers seek to maintain a sufficient number of units on order to achieve the acquisition rate they desire. By Little's Law (chapter 11) the supply line must contain AL period's worth of the throughput the decision maker desires to achieve. Several measures for desired throughput are common. The decision maker may set the supply line to yield the desired acquisition rate DAR:

$$SL^* = EAL * DAR \qquad\qquad (17\text{-}16)$$

where EAL, the expected acquisition lag, represents the decision maker's current belief about the length of the acquisition delay (which, in general, may differ from the actual acquisition delay).

Equation (17-16) assumes a rather high degree of rationality on the part of decision makers. They are assumed to adjust the supply line to achieve the desired acquisition rate, which includes replacement of expected losses and correction of temporary gaps between desired and actual inventory. As described in section 17.4, experimental evidence shows decision makers are often not so sophisticated. Managers frequently do not adjust the supply line in response to temporary imbalances in the stock but base the desired supply line on their estimate of long-run through-put requirements—the expected loss rate EL:

$$SL^* = EAL * EL \tag{17-16a}$$

The formulation for the desired supply line must depend on empirical investigation of the actual decision-making process.

Whichever formulation for the desired supply line is used, the longer the expected delay in acquiring goods or the larger the desired throughput rate, the larger the supply line must be. If a retailer wishes to receive 1,000 widgets per week from the supplier and delivery requires 6 weeks, the retailer must have 6000 widgets on order to ensure an uninterrupted flow of deliveries. The adjustment for the supply line creates a negative feedback loop that adjusts orders to maintain an acquisition rate consistent with desired throughput and the acquisition lag. Without the supply line feedback, orders would be placed even after the supply line contained sufficient units to correct stock shortfalls, producing overshoot and instability (section 17.4). The supply line adjustment also compensates for changes in the acquisition lag. If the acquisition lag doubled, for example, the supply line adjustment would induce sufficient additional orders to restore throughput to the desired rate.

There are many possible representations for the expected acquisition lag EAL, ranging from constants through sophisticated forecasts. It is sometimes acceptable to assume the expected acquisition lag equals the actual lag, EAL = AL. Usually, however, it takes time to detect changes in delivery times. Customers often do not know that goods they ordered will be late until after the promised delivery time has passed. The expected acquisition lag can then be modeled by a perception delay representing the time required to observe and respond to changes in the actual delay: EAL = L(AL, TPAL), where TPAL is the Time to Perceive the Acquisition Lag.

Finally, to ensure the formulation is robust, the equation for the desired acquisition rate must be modified so that DAR remains nonnegative even when there is a large surplus of inventory.

$$DAR = MAX(0, EL + AS) \tag{17-4a}$$

Every formulation should be evaluated in terms of its robustness, its underlying informational and computational requirements, and its consistency with the formulation principles described in chapter 13. The formulation for the order rate conforms to these principles. First, the formulation is robust: Orders remain nonnegative no matter how large a surplus stock there may be, and the supply line and stock therefore never fall below zero. Second, information not available to real decision makers is not utilized (such as the solution to the nonlinear optimization problem determining the optimal order rate or the instantaneous value of the loss rate or acquisition delay). Finally, the ordering decision rule is grounded in well-established knowledge of decision-making behavior, in particular, the anchoring and adjustment heuristic. Expected losses form an easily anticipated and relatively stable starting point for the determination of orders. Loss rate information will typically be locally available and highly salient to the decision maker. Replacing losses will keep the stock constant at its current level. Adjustments are then made in response to the adequacy of the stock and supply line. No assumption is made that these adjustments are optimal. Rather, pressures arising from the discrepancies between desired and actual quantities cause managers to adjust the order rate above or below the level that would maintain the status quo.

17.3.1   Behavior of the Stock Management Structure

To illustrate the behavior of the stock management structure, consider again a firm's capital investment decision. The stock is the total quantity of capital equipment and the supply line is the amount of plant and equipment on order or under construction. As before, the loss rate is a first-order process with an average lifetime of 8 years and the stock adjustment time is set to 3 years. In this simple version of the model, the acquisition process is assumed to be a first-order material delay (more realistic, higher-order delay distributions are considered below), and there are no capacity constraints. The average acquisition delay is therefore constant and is set to 1.5 years, consistent with the 17-month average found by Montgomery (1995). Assume the delay in observing and reacting to the discard of old equipment is short relative to the other time constants, so the expected loss rate can be set to the actual loss rate. Likewise, assume the acquisition delay can be perceived immediately, so that the expected acquisition lag equals the actual lag.

Following Senge's (1978) results, the supply line adjustment time is set to 0.75 years. The supply line adjustment time is shorter than the stock adjustment time. Adjusting the capital stock is difficult, expensive, and time consuming; the long lifetime of plant and equipment means mistakes are not easily undone. Hence for both managerial and administrative reasons, gaps between desired and actual capital are closed only slowly. In contrast the supply line of orders can be adjusted much more rapidly. The cost of adjusting orders is much lower than the cost of adjusting the capital stock, and the delay in acquiring new units is much shorter than the life of new capital. It still takes time to adjust the supply line. It takes time to renegotiate contracts, specify and execute change orders, and make other adjustments. Further, firms are often reluctant to make large changes in the quantities they order from their suppliers since many contracts specify expediting costs or cancellation fees. Figure 17-7 shows the stock management structure adapted to the capital investment example.

Figure 17-8 shows the response of the system to a 20% step increase in desired capital. Capital stock smoothly approaches the new goal, and the time required to reach the new equilibrium is little changed from the case without an acquisition delay. However, the acquisition delay dramatically increases the amplification generated by the system. The maximum change in the order rate is 160% greater than the initial level, an amplification ratio of 8.00 (compared to 2.65 without the acquisition delay).

When desired capital increases, the desired acquisition rate suddenly rises (through the stock adjustment loop). There are two effects on the order rate: First, the order rate rises with the desired acquisition rate; second, the desired supply line increases in proportion to the rise in the desired acquisition rate. As the desired supply line rises above the actual supply line, orders rise above the desired acquisition rate. Because the supply line adjustment time is relatively short, the adjustment for the supply line is initially large (in fact larger than the adjustment for the

FIGURE 17-7   Adapting the stock management structure to capital investment

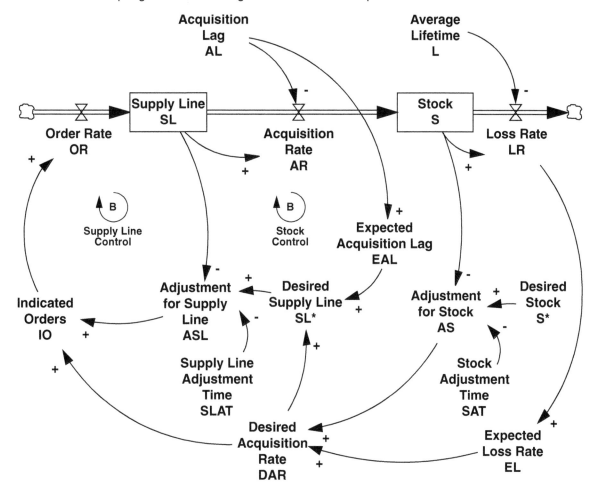

stock). After about 1 year, the supply line has increased enough to equal the desired supply line and the order rate falls back to the desired acquisition rate. As acquisitions raise the capital stock, the adjustment for the stock falls, and as it does, so too does the desired supply line. Because the actual supply line lags behind the desired level, the firm finds itself with slightly more capital on order than it requires, causing the supply line adjustment to be slightly negative. The order rate continues to exceed the loss rate, however, due to the stock adjustment, until capital reaches the new desired level.

The amplification created by the acquisition delay depends of course on the parameters, particularly the length of the delay and the supply line adjustment time. The longer the acquisition delay, or the shorter the supply line adjustment time, the greater the amplification. Given the realistic parameters in Figure 17-8, the amplification of orders with respect to desired capital is a factor of eight, a value roughly consistent with the amplification observed in the oil and machine tool industries (Figure 17-3).

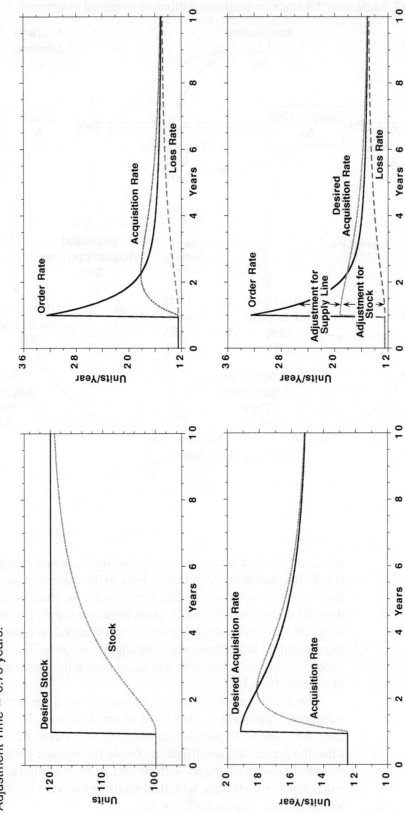

FIGURE 17-8 Response of the stock management structure to an increase in the desired stock

Parameters: Average Life of Capital = 8.0 years; Average Acquisition Lag = 1.5 years; Stock Adjustment Time = 3.0 years; Supply Line Adjustment Time = 0.75 years.

CHALLENGE

Exploring the Stock Management Structure

Explore the behavior of the stock management structure with the parameters used in Figure 17-8.

1. Repeat the tests in questions 1 and 2 of the challenge in section 17.2.3. How does the inclusion of the supply line affect the response of the system to increases and decreases in desired capital?

2. How does the amplification of demand depend on the stock adjustment time? With the parameters used in Figure 17-8, it takes about 8 years for capital to increase 95% of the way to desired capital. How much can the adjustment be accelerated by more aggressive stock and/or supply line adjustments? What is the effect of these changes on the amplification of orders?

3. Can the system oscillate? With the base case parameters the response to a step increase in desired capital is a single overshoot of the order and acquisition rate. Are there other parameters that can induce an oscillatory response? Why/why not? How does this compare to the case where there is no acquisition delay or supply line, and why? Contrast the behavior of the system with the two formulations for the desired supply line, equations (17-16) and (17-16a). Which is more responsive? Can the system oscillate with the formulation in (17-16a)? Explain.

4. Test the response of the system to a fluctuation in the demand for its product by assuming desired capital stock fluctuates sinusoidally as in section 17.2.3:

$$S^* = 100 * [1 + A\sin(2\pi(t - 1)/P)] \text{ for } t > 1$$

Calculate the steady state amplification ratio in the order rate, acquisition rate, and capital stock. How does the amplification ratio depend on the period of the cycle P? How does it depend on the stock adjustment time SAT and supply line adjustment time SLAT? How does it depend on the acquisition lag AL? Make graphs showing the amplification ratio as a function of the cycle period relative to these parameters.

5. Repeat the analysis in (4) with the amplitude of the sine wave in desired capital A = 0.50. How does the behavior of the system differ from the small amplitude case? Calculate the amplification ratios of orders, acquisitions, and the capital stock with respect to desired capital. What is the steady state average value of the capital stock, and why?

6. So far the acquisition delay has been assumed to be first-order. As shown in chapter 11, the actual capital acquisition process is actually a higher-order process. Replace the first-order acquisition delay with a third-order delay (with the same average delay time). What is the impact of a higher-order acquisition delay on the behavior of the stock management structure? Consider response time and shape, amplification, and stability, and consider the sensitivity to different values of the parameters including SAT and SLAT, not only the base case. Consider the impact of specifying the desired supply line SL^* by equation (17-16a).

17.4   THE ORIGIN OF OSCILLATIONS

Chapter 4 discussed the generic structure responsible for oscillations: negative feedbacks with time delays. In every negative loop the state of the system is compared to the desired state and any discrepancy induces a corrective action. When there are no time delays, the corrective actions respond immediately to the discrepancy and immediately alter the state of the system. The result is a smooth approach to equilibrium. As shown in chapter 4 and section 8.5.2, negative feedback systems without time delays cannot oscillate. Oscillations can arise only when there are time delays in at least one of the causal links in a negative feedback loop. But not all negative loops with delays oscillate. What are the causes of oscillations? Under what circumstances will a system oscillate?

Delays always involve stocks (chapter 11). When the input and output of a delay differ, the difference accumulates in a stock of material (or information) in transit. Time delays between corrective actions and their effects create a supply line of corrections that have been initiated but not yet had their impact. The mere existence of the time delay and supply line, however, does not lead to oscillations. In the stock management structure adapted for capital investment, for example (Figure 17-7), there is a 1.5-year delay between ordering and receiving new capital, yet the system does not oscillate (with the estimated parameters). Even though the acquisition delay means orders placed today do nothing to reduce the gap between the desired and actual stock, managers are assumed to recognize when the supply line fills enough to solve the problem—and reduce orders appropriately. To oscillate, the time delay must be (at least partially) ignored. The manager must continue to initiate corrective actions in response to the perceived gap between the desired and actual state of the system even after sufficient corrections to close the gap are in the pipeline.

17.4.1   Mismanaging the Supply Line: The Beer Distribution Game

The Beer Distribution Game illustrates how oscillations arise.[3] The game is a role-playing simulation of a supply chain originally developed by Jay Forrester in the late 1950s to introduce students of management to the concepts of system dynamics and computer simulation. Since then the game has been played all over the world by thousands of people ranging from high school students to chief executive officers and senior government officials.

The game is played on a board portraying a typical supply chain (Figure 17-9). Orders for and cases of beer are represented by markers and chips. Each brewery consists of four sectors: retailer, wholesaler, distributor, and factory (R, W, D, F). One person manages each sector. A deck of cards represents customer demand.

---

[3]The game is described in detail in Sterman (1989b, 1992) and Senge (1990). Information on the game and materials are available from the System Dynamics Society at <system.dynamics @albany.edu>. There is no real beer in the beer game and it does not promote drinking. When the game is used with, e.g., high school students, it is easily recast as the "apple juice game." Many firms have customized the game to represent their industry.

FIGURE 17-9 The Beer Distribution Game

The game is a role-play simulation. Each player manages one of the links in the distribution chain from Retailer to Factory. In the game, chips of various denominations represent cases of beer and move through the supply chain from Raw Materials to Customers. Customer Orders are written on a deck of cards. Each week players place orders with the supplier on their right and the factory sets the production schedule. The orders, written on slips of paper, move upstream (left to right). The initial configuration is shown.

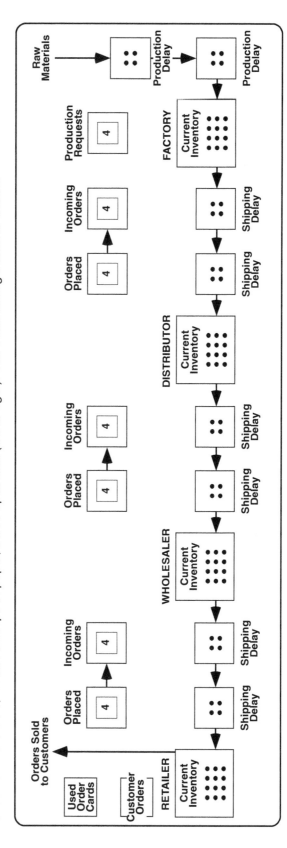

Each week, customers demand beer from the retailer, filling the order out of inventory. The retailer in turn orders beer from the wholesaler, who ships the beer requested from wholesale stocks. Likewise the wholesaler orders and receives beer from the distributor, who in turn orders and receives beer from the factory. The factory produces the beer. At each stage there are order processing and shipping delays. Each link in the supply chain has the same structure.

The players' objective is to minimize total costs for their company. Inventory holding costs are usually set to $0.50 per case per week, and stockout costs (costs for having a backlog of unfilled orders) are $1.00 per case per week. The task facing each player is a clear example of the stock management problem. Players must keep their inventories as low as possible while avoiding backlogs.[4] Incoming orders deplete inventory, so players must place replenishment orders and adjust their inventories to the desired level. There is a delay between placing and receiving orders, creating a supply line of unfilled orders.

The game is far simpler than any real supply chain. There are no random events—no machine breakdowns, transportation problems, or strikes. There are no capacity constraints or financial limitations. The structure of the game is visible to all. Players can readily inspect the board to see how much inventory is in transit or held by their teammates. The game is typically played with a very simple pattern for customer demand. Starting from equilibrium, there is a small, unannounced one-time increase in customer orders, from 4 to 8 cases per week.

Despite the apparent simplicity of the game, people do extremely poorly. Among first-time players average costs are typically an astonishing 10 times greater than optimal. Figure 17-10 shows typical results. In all cases customer orders are essentially constant (except for the small step increase near the start). In all cases, the response of the supply chain is unstable. The oscillation, amplification, and phase lag observed in real supply chains are clearly visible in the experimental results. The period of the cycle is 20–25 weeks. The average amplification ratio of factory production relative to customer orders is a factor of four, and factory production peaks some 15 weeks after the change in customer orders.

Most interesting, the patterns of behavior generated in the game are remarkably similar (there are, of course, individual differences in magnitude and timing). Starting with the retailer, inventories decline throughout the supply chain, and most players develop a backlog of unfilled orders (net inventory is negative). In response, a wave of orders moves through the chain, growing larger at each stage. Eventually, factory production surges, and inventories throughout the supply chain start to rise. But inventory does not stabilize at the cost-minimizing level near zero. Instead, inventory significantly overshoots. Players respond by slashing orders, often cutting them to zero for extended periods. Inventory eventually peaks and slowly declines. These behavioral regularities are all the more remarkable because there is no oscillation in customer demand. The oscillation arises as an endogenous consequence of the way the players manage their inventories. Though players are

---

[4]Minimum costs are obtained when inventory is zero, but since incoming orders are uncertain and backlogs are more costly than inventories, it is optimal to set desired inventory to a small positive number.

Figure 17-10 Typical results of the Beer Distribution Game

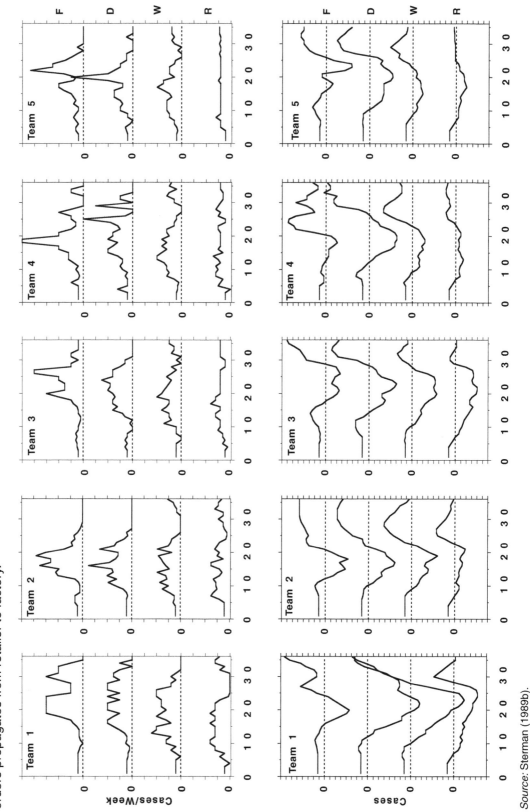

Top: Orders. *Bottom:* Net inventory (Inventory − Backlog). Graphs show, bottom to top, Retailer, Wholesaler, Distributor, and Factory. Vertical axes tick marks denote 10 units. Note the characteristic oscillation, amplification, and phase lag as the change in customer orders propagates from retailer to factory.

Source: Sterman (1989b).

free to place orders any way they wish, the vast majority behave in a remarkably uniform fashion.

To understand the origin of the oscillation, amplification, and phase lag, consider the structure and behavior of a typical link in the distribution chain. Figure 17-11 maps the structure of a single link into the stock management framework (chapter 18 develops more realistic supply chain models for manufacturing). Net inventory is the stock to be managed. The supply line is the stock of orders the player has placed but not yet received, including orders in transit to the supplier, the supplier's backlog (if any), and the goods in the shipping delays. Adapting the ordering decision rule to the production–distribution setting in the game is straightforward. The expected loss rate is the player's forecast of incoming orders. Analysis of the beer game and related stock management experiments (Sterman 1989a, b; Diehl and Sterman 1995) showed that most people form their forecasts by smoothing or averaging past orders. The data also show that people do not

FIGURE 17-11   Causal structure of the Beer Distribution Game

Shows the structure of a single link in the supply chain. Customer orders are exogenous. Managers must place orders with their suppliers to replace shipments to customers and restore inventories to the desired level.

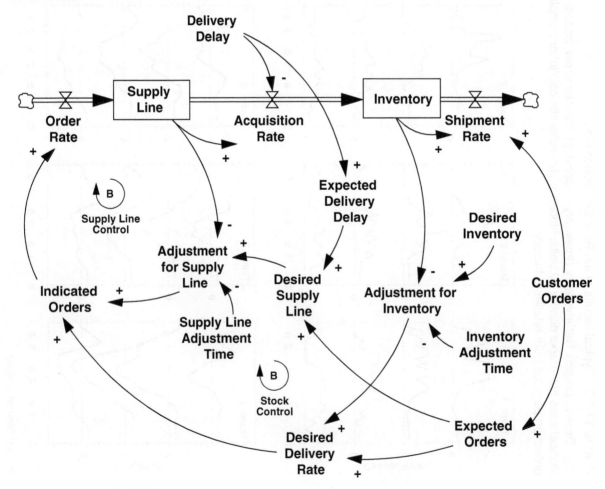

manage the supply line in the sophisticated manner assumed in equation (17-16). The desired supply line does not respond to the inventory adjustment but only the replacement of expected losses, as in equation (17-16a).

Table 17-2 shows what happens when managers completely ignore the supply line. The system is simulated in discrete time intervals of 1 week, just as in the actual experiment. For illustration, desired inventory is 400 units and the delivery delay is 3 weeks. Customer orders, and expected customer orders, are constant at 100 units/week. Assume the manager corrects the entire discrepancy between inventory and desired inventory each week (SAT = 1 week). To knock the system away from the initial equilibrium, 100 units of inventory are unexpectedly lost during week 1, reducing inventory at the start of week 2 to 300 cases. The manager responds by ordering 200: 100 to replace customer orders and 100 to restore inventory to the desired level. The supply line rises to 400 units. Due to the delivery delay, inventory in week 3 is still only 200. The manager, ignoring the supply line, again responds to the inventory gap and orders 200. The supply line rises to 500 units. In week 4 the manager again finds inventory is 100 units short, again ignores the supply line, and again orders 200 units. The fifth week is the same.

By the end of the fifth week the first order of 200 finally arrives. Week 6 begins with inventory restored to its desired level. The manager cuts orders back to the equilibrium rate of 100 units/week. But the system is far from equilibrium: The supply line has swollen to 600 units. The next week, 200 more units are delivered, boosting inventory to 500. Facing a surplus of 100 units, the manager now cuts orders to zero. Too late: Over the next 3 weeks inventory soars to 700 units.

Since orders cannot be canceled and goods cannot be returned, inventory remains high until the supply line is completely drained and deliveries fall to zero (week 10). It takes 3 weeks to eliminate the excess inventory. In week 13 inventory again equals the desired level, so orders rise to the equilibrium rate of 100 units/week. But there is now nothing in the supply line. Nothing is delivered in week 14. Inventory falls to 300, forcing orders to rise 100 units above the order rate. Again, nothing is delivered in week 15. Inventory falls another 100 units, and the manager now must order 100 to replace customer demand plus 200 to restore inventory to the desired level. By the start of week 16 inventory has fallen to 100, forcing the manager to order 400 units. By the start of week 17 the first order of 100 arrives, stabilizing inventory at 100 units. The manager, responding only to the inventory shortfall, again orders 400. The supply line has now swollen to 1100 units. Over the next 3 weeks these orders are delivered, soon pushing inventory above the desired level. Though the manager slashes orders to zero, deliveries continue, swelling inventory to a peak of 1200 units. And so the cycle continues (Figure 17-12).[5]

---

[5]Given the chosen parameters, the no-supply-line control case generates a limit cycle: The equilibrium is unstable and cycle amplitude increases to a maximum determined by the nonlinearities in the system, specifically the nonnegativity of orders. You should experiment with different parameters (delivery delay, inventory, and supply line adjustment times) to explore how stability varies with the strengths of the inventory and supply line control loops and the length of the delay in the response of inventory to orders. See section 4.3.3.

TABLE 17-2 Behavior of distribution system when managers ignore the supply line

Discrete time simulation of system in Figure 17-11. Desired Inventory = 400 units. Delivery Delay = 3 weeks. Customer Orders = 100 units/week. Inventory Loss equals shipments of 100 units/week except in week 1 when an additional 100 units are unexpectedly removed from inventory. Managers place orders based on the starting inventory for each week (before inventory for week t + 1 is known). Managers completely ignore the supply line (SLAT = ∞).

Week	Starting Inventory	+ Delivery Rate	− Inventory Loss	= Inventory t + 1	Starting Supply Line	+ Order Rate	− Delivery Rate	= Supply Line t + 1
0	400	100	100	400	300	100	100	300
1	400	100	200	300	300	100	100	300
2	300	100	100	300	300	200	100	400
3	300	100	100	300	400	200	100	500
4	300	100	100	300	500	200	100	600
5	300	200	100	400	600	200	200	600
6	400	200	100	500	600	100	200	500
7	500	200	100	600	500	0	200	300
8	600	200	100	700	300	0	200	100
9	700	100	100	700	100	0	100	0
10	700	0	100	600	0	0	0	0
11	600	0	100	500	0	0	0	0
12	500	0	100	400	0	0	0	0
13	400	0	100	300	0	100	0	100
14	300	0	100	200	100	200	0	300
15	200	0	100	100	300	300	0	600
16	100	100	100	100	600	400	100	900
17	100	200	100	200	900	400	200	1100
18	200	300	100	400	1100	300	300	1100
19	400	400	100	700	1100	100	400	800
20	700	400	100	1000	800	0	400	400
21	1000	300	100	1200	400	0	300	100
22	1200	100	100	1200	100	0	100	0
23	1200	0	100	1100	0	0	0	0
24	1100	0	100	1000	0	0	0	0
25	1000	0	100	900	0	0	0	0

FIGURE 17-12
Oscillation caused
by failure to
consider the
supply line

The behavior of
the system in
Table 17-2:
Inventory
unexpectedly
falls by 100 units
in week 1.

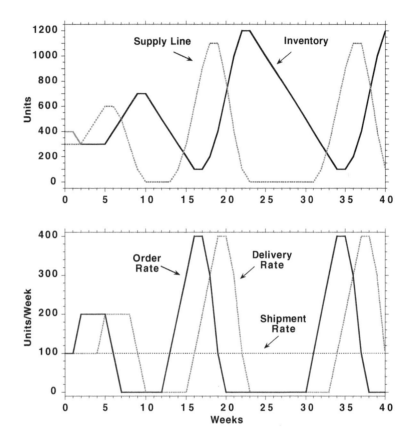

The oscillation in Figure 17-12 arises not from the time delay alone but because the manager places orders without regard to the supply line of unfilled orders. The only thing the manager cares about is whether there is enough inventory *right now.*

What happens when the manager fully accounts for the supply line? Table 17-3 shows a simulation of the system for the same situation except that now the supply line is given as much weight as inventory on hand, that is, SLAT = SAT = 1 week. As before, inventory unexpectedly drops by 100 units in week 1. Also as before, the manager orders 100 units to replace expected customer orders plus an additional 100 cases to restore inventory to the desired level, increasing the supply line of unfilled orders to 400 units. Due to the delivery delay, inventory remains at 300 in week 2. The adjustment for inventory is again 100 units. This time, even though inventory is still 100 units short, the manager realizes that the total amount of inventory on hand and on order is equal to the desired level, cuts orders back to the replacement rate, and waits patiently for the extra units in the supply line to be delivered. Over the next 2 weeks the extra 100 units make their way through the supply line. In week 5 deliveries are 200 units, inventory is restored to the desired level of 400, and the supply line drops from 400 back to its equilibrium level of 300. The inventory and supply line adjustments both return to zero. Equilibrium is restored after just 4 weeks, with no oscillation.

TABLE 17-3 Behavior of distribution system when managers account for the supply line

Conditions are the same as in Table 17-2 except the manager fully accounts for the supply line of unfilled orders (SLAT = SAT = 1 week).

Week	Starting Inventory	+	Delivery Rate	−	Inventory Loss	=	Inventory t + 1	Starting Supply Line	+	Order Rate	−	Delivery Rate	=	Supply Line t + 1
0	400		100		100		400	300		100		100		300
1	400		100		200		300	300		100		100		300
2	300		100		100		300	300		200		100		400
3	300		100		100		300	400		100		100		400
4	300		100		100		300	400		100		100		400
5	300		200		100		400	400		100		200		300
6	400		100		100		400	300		100		100		300
7	400		100		100		400	300		100		100		300
8	400		100		100		400	300		100		100		300

To understand the role of the supply line adjustment in the origin of oscillations more formally, substitute the definitions of the adjustment for the stock and adjustment for the supply line into the equation for the order rate:

$$OR = MAX\{0, IO\} = MAX\{0, EL + AS + ASL\}$$
$$= MAX\{0, EL + (S^* - S)/SAT + (SL^* - SL)/SLAT\} \qquad (17\text{-}13a)$$

Now define the Weight on the Supply Line as the ratio of the two adjustment times: WSL = SAT/SLAT. Substituting WSL into equation (17-13a) gives

$$OR = MAX\{0, EL + (S^* - S)/SAT + WSL * (SL^* - SL)/SAT\} \qquad (17\text{-}13b)$$

Combining terms,

$$OR = MAX\{0, EL + [S^* + WSL * SL^* - (S + WSL * SL)]/SAT\} \qquad (17\text{-}13c)$$

Now define the effective total stock, ETS, as the sum of current inventory and the fraction of the supply line the manager accounts for, ETS = S + WSL * SL. The desired effective total stock, ETS* = S* + WSL * SL*, represents the total stock on hand and on order the managers believe they need. Substituting ETS and ETS* into equation (17-13c) gives

$$OR = MAX\{0, EL + (ETS^* - ETS)/SAT\} \qquad (17\text{-}13d)$$

The interpretation is straightforward. Equation (17-13d) defines a first-order negative feedback system in the state variable ETS. If WSL = 1, managers give the supply line as much weight as inventory on hand and effective total stock equals the actual, true total inventory in the system. Fully accounting for the supply line converts the potentially oscillatory negative loop with a delay into an effectively first-order negative feedback system. Corrective actions (orders) immediately correct the discrepancy between the desired and actual total stock on hand and on order, and changes in the total stock immediately affect the order decision. Unanticipated shocks induce no oscillation in the total stock, despite the delay between placing and receiving orders. If WSL = 0, however, managers completely ignore the supply line. The failure to consider the delay in receiving goods then leads to oscillation. As WSL approaches 1, the greater the damping and the more stable the response of the system to shocks will be.

The analysis above shows why it is important to recognize the time delays in negative loops and supply lines of corrective actions already taken. Yet people often fail to do so. In Sterman (1989b) I estimated the decision rule shown in equation (17-13d) for a sample of 44 players.[6] Overall, the decision rule worked quite well, explaining 71% of the variance in the order decisions of the subjects. The estimated parameters showed that most were using grossly suboptimal cue weights. The average weight on the supply line was only 0.34. Only 25% of the subjects considered more than half the supply line and the estimated value of WSL was not significantly different from zero for fully one-third. Figure 17-13 compares simulated and actual behavior for the factory in an actual game. The estimated stock

---

[6]To estimate the decision rule the total desired stock ETS* was treated as a constant and the expected loss rate (demand forecast) was modeled by first-order exponential smoothing of incoming orders.

FIGURE 17-13

Estimated vs. actual behavior in the beer game

Factory orders for an actual player compared to estimated orders from equation (17-13c).

Parameters:
Smoothing time for forecast of customer orders, 1.82 weeks; desired total stock on hand and on order, 9 cases; stock adjustment time SAT, 1.25 weeks; weight on supply line WSL, 0.

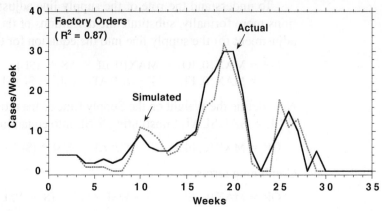

Source: Sterman (1989b).

adjustment time SAT is just 1.25 weeks—the player reacted aggressively to inventory shortfalls, ordering nearly the entire inventory shortfall each week. At the same time, the estimated weight on the supply line WSL is zero. As you would expect, aggressively reacting to current inventory shortfalls while completely ignoring the supply line leads to severe instability and high costs. Because it takes 3 weeks to receive production requested today, the player effectively ordered three times more than needed to correct any inventory shortfall.

Other experiments (Sterman 1989b; Diehl and Sterman 1995; Brehmer 1992) show that the tendency to ignore time delays and underweight the supply line is robust. In several of these experiments the supply line was prominently displayed to the subjects, yet they ignored it anyway. As discussed in chapter 1, the information you use in decision making is conditioned by your mental models. If you don't recognize the presence of a time delay or underestimate its length, you are unlikely to account for the supply line even if the information needed to do so is available.

Many players find these results disturbing. They argue that they took a wide range of information into account when placing orders and that their subtle and sophisticated reasoning cannot be captured by a model as simple as equation (17-13d). After all, the decision rule for orders only considers three cues (incoming orders, inventory, and the supply line)—how could it possibly capture the way people place orders? Actually, players' behavior is highly systematic and is explained well by the simple stock management heuristic. People are often surprised how well simple decision rules can mimic their behavior.

In fact, one of the games shown in Figure 17-10 is a simulation, not the actual play of real people. I simulated the beer game with the decision rule in equation (17-13d). The parameters of the rule, for all four players, were set to the average estimated values. A small amount of random noise was added to the order rate. Can you tell which is the simulation?[7]

---

[7]Simulated orders were generated by $OR_t = MAX\{0, EL_t + [ETS^* - (S_t + WSL * SL_t)]/SAT + e_t\}$ where ETS^* is the desired total stock and e_t is a normally distributed random variable with standard deviation equal to the mean of the standard errors of the estimated equation over the sample. The forecast EL_t was formed by first-order exponential smoothing of the actual incoming order rate, $EL_t = (COR_{t-1} - EL_{t-1})/TEO$, where TEO, the time to form expected orders, is the smoothing time constant. The mean of the estimated parameters is TEO = 1.82 weeks, ETS^* = 17 units, SAT = 3.85 weeks, and WSL = 0.34.

17.4.2   Why Do We Ignore the Supply Line?

The beer game clearly shows it is folly to ignore the time delays in complex systems. Consider the following situation. You are involved in an automobile accident. Thankfully, no one is hurt, but your car is a total loss. Insurance settlement in hand, you visit a dealer and select a new car. You agree on a price, but the model you want is not in stock—delivery will take 4 weeks. You pay your deposit and leave. The next morning, noticing that your driveway is empty—*Where's my car!*—you go down to the dealer and buy another one. Ridiculous, of course. No one would be so foolish as to ignore the supply line. Yet in many real life situations people do exactly that. Consider the following examples (Table 17-1 shows how they map into the stock management structure):

- You cook on an electric range. To get dinner going as soon as possible, you set the burner under your pan to "high." After a while you notice the pan is getting quite hot, so you turn the heat down. But the supply line of heat in the glowing coil continues to heat the pan even after the current is cut, and your dinner is burned anyway.

- You are surfing the worldwide web. Your computer did not respond to your last mouse click. You click again, then again. Growing impatient, you click on some other buttons—any buttons—to see if you can get a response. After a few seconds, the system executes all the clicks you stacked up in the supply line, and you end up far from the page you were seeking.

- You arrive late and tired to an unfamiliar hotel. You turn on the shower, but the water is freezing. You turn up the hot water. Still cold. You turn the hot up some more. Ahhh. Just right. You step in. A second later you jump out screaming, scalded by the now too-hot water. Cursing, you realize that once again, you've ignored the time delay for the hot water to heat the cold pipes and get to your shower.

- You are driving on a busy highway. The car in front of you slows slightly. You take your foot off the gas, but the distance to the car in front keeps shrinking. Your reaction time and the momentum of your car create a delay between a change in the speed of the car ahead and a change in your speed. To avoid a collision, you have to slam on the brakes. The car behind you is forced to brake even harder. You hear the screech of rubber and pray you won't be rear-ended.

- You are young, and experimenting with alcohol for the first time. Eager to show your friends you can hold your liquor, you quickly drain your glass. You feel fine. You drink another. Still feeling fine. You take another and another. As consciousness fades and you fall to the floor, you realize—too late—that you ignored the supply line of alcohol in your stomach and drank far too much.[8]

---

[8]Tragically, young people die every year from alcohol poisoning induced by aggressive drinking (a short stock adjustment time, SAT, and failure to account for the supply line of alcohol they've already ingested, WSL ≈ 0).

How often have you fallen victim to one of these behaviors? We may not buy another car when the first one isn't delivered immediately, but few of us can say we've never burned our dinner or been scalded in the shower, never drunk too much or been forced to brake hard to avoid a collision.

Recognizing and accounting for time delays is not innate. It is behavior we must learn. When we are born, our awareness is limited to our immediate surroundings. Everything we experience is *here* and *now*. All our early experiences reinforce the belief that cause and effect are closely related in time and space: When you cry, you get fed or changed. You keep crying until mother or father appears, even when you hear your parents say, "We're coming" (i.e., despite knowledge that your request for attention is in the supply line). As all parents know, it takes years for children to learn to account for such time delays. When my son was two he might ask for a cup of juice: "Juice please, Daddy." "Coming right up," I'd say, taking a cup from the shelf. Though he could see me getting the cup and filling it up, he'd continue to say, "Juice, Daddy!" many times—ever more insistently—until the cup was actually in his hand.

Learning to recognize and account for time delays goes hand in hand with learning to be patient, to defer gratification, and to trade short-run sacrifice for long-term reward. These abilities do not develop automatically. They are part of a slow process of maturation. The longer the time delays and the greater the uncertainty over how long it will take to see the results of your corrective actions, the harder it is to account for the supply line.[9]

You might argue that by the time we become adults we have developed the requisite patience and sensitivity to time delays. There may be no cost to saying "juice" a dozen times, but surely when the stakes are high we would quickly learn to consider delays. You don't burn yourself in your own shower at home—you've learned where to set the hot water faucet to get the temperature you like and to wait long enough for the water to warm up. Most people soon learn to pay attention to the supply line of alcohol in their system and moderate their drinking. The conditions for learning in these systems are excellent. Feedback is swift, and the consequences of error are highly salient (particularly the morning after). There is no doubt in either case that it was the way you made decisions—the way you set the faucet or drank too fast—that caused the problem. These conditions are frequently not met in business, economic, environmental, and other real world systems (see chapter 1 for discussion). Cause and effect are obscure, creating ambiguity and uncertainty. The dynamics are much slower, and the time required for learning often exceeds the tenure of individual decision makers. Ignoring time delays is also sometimes rational for the individual. In a world of short time horizons, of annual, quarterly, or even monthly performance reviews, the incentives people face often mean it is rational for them to be aggressive and ignore the delayed consequences of their actions.

---

[9]More subtly, our childhood experiences reinforce the idea that there is no cost to ignoring the supply line. Though my son may have said "Juice, Daddy" 10 times before I could fill his "order," I brought him only 1 cup. He didn't take the supply line into account, but I did. In that situation, there is no cost to overordering, while patience might not work (dad might get distracted and forget to bring the juice). In many real stock management situations, there is no central authority to account for the time delays and prevent overordering.

The French economist Albert Aftalion recognized in the early 1900s how failure to account for the time delays could cause business cycles. Using the familiar fireplace as an analogy, his description explicitly focuses on the failure of decision makers to pay attention to the supply line of fuel:

> If one rekindles the fire in the hearth in order to warm up a room, one has to wait a while before one has the desired temperature. As the cold continues, and the thermometer continues to record it, one might be led, if one had not the lessons of experience, to throw more coal on the fire. One would continue to throw coal, even though the quantity already in the grate is such as will give off an intolerable heat, when once it is all alight. To allow oneself to be guided by the present sense of cold and the indications of the thermometer to that effect is fatally to overheat the room.[10]

While Aftalion argued that "the lessons of experience" would soon teach people not to "continue to throw coal," he argued that business cycles in the economy arose because individual entrepreneurs focused only on current profitability and failed to account for the lags between the initiation of new investment and its realization, leading to collective overproduction.

Yet even if individuals can't learn effectively, shouldn't the discipline imposed by the market quickly weed out people who use suboptimal decision rules? Those who ignore the supply line or use poor decision rules should lose money and go out of business or be fired, while those who use superior decision rules, even by chance, should prosper. The selective pressures of the market should quickly lead to the evolution of optimal decision rules.

The persistent cycles in a wide range of supply chains presented at the start of this chapter suggest Aftalion was right. Learning and evolution in real markets appear to be slow, at best, despite decades of experience and the huge sums at stake. Part of the problem is lack of information. Individual firms usually do not ignore the supply lines of materials on order or capital under construction. The problem is one of aggregation. The individual firm tends to view itself as small relative to the market and treats the environment as exogenous, thereby ignoring all feedbacks from prices to supply and demand. The individual firm may not know or give sufficient weight to the supply lines of all firms in the industry or the total capacity of all plants under construction. Firms tend to continue to invest and expand as long as profits are high today, even after the supply line of new capacity under construction is more than sufficient to cause a glut and destroy profitability. Each investor takes market conditions as exogenous, ignoring the reactions of others. When all investors react similarly to current profit opportunities the result is overshoot and instability.

The financial markets, seen by many as the most efficient and farsighted, should rapidly evolve to near-optimality due to the huge stakes and enormous talent brought to bear. Yet even the highly sophisticated hedge funds bear the scars of self-inflicted wounds from open-loop thinking. These funds use complex models developed by PhDs in finance, mathematics, and physics to exploit small

---

[10]Quoted in Haberler, G. (1964) *Prosperity and Depression.* London: George Allen and Unwin, pp. 135–136.

departures from equilibrium in the markets. In the fall of 1998, Russia defaulted on its external debt, throwing stock and bond markets into a sharp correction. The hugely successful hedge fund Long Term Capital Management (LTCM) collapsed as its highly leveraged bets, based on models assuming certain historical regularities would continue, failed. Forced to sell many of their positions at a loss, the crisis rapidly cascaded beyond LTCM to shake the entire financial world, ultimately leading to a multi-billion dollar bailout orchestrated by the US Federal Reserve. Kestenbaum (1999, p. 1247) commented:

> Some competitors watched LTCM's fire sale with a certain glee. "It was hypnotic," one recalls, "then sickening." Sickening because it started to happen to everyone. "It wasn't supposed to be so hard to sell," one trader says. "What we missed was that other hedge funds were doing the same thing. That wasn't an input to anybody's model."

17.4.3   Case Study: Boom and Bust in Real Estate Markets

Real estate markets are among the most unstable and cyclic asset markets, exhibiting large amplitude cycles of 10–20 years. Real estate constitutes a large fraction of the total wealth in any economy, generates a significant fraction of banking activity and debt, and strongly affects the job market. Consequently, real estate booms are often accompanied by periods of intense speculation involving expansion of credit and banking activity, stimulating the local and even national economy. When the bubble bursts, the resulting bad loans, defaults, and unemployment can throw an entire region into recession or even depression.

Figure 17-14 shows a classic example, the real estate cycle in Chicago from 1830 to 1932 (Hoyt 1933). Over this period Chicago grew from a small town of a few hundred people with property valued at less than $100,000 to an economic powerhouse with more than 3 million inhabitants and real estate valued at more than $3 billion. Growth, however, was anything but smooth. Land values and development activity went through repeated cycles of boom and bust. Land valuations fluctuate roughly ±50% around the trend, while construction activity surges from a low some 60% below average during downturns to more than double the average during booms. These amplitudes are much larger and much longer than the business cycle—the real estate cycle cannot be blamed on some external variation in the pace of economic activity.

Real estate cycles are not limited to Chicago nor are they an artifact of mere archaeological interest. The cycle continues to have a large amplitude and long period. Most recently, North American and European property markets boomed in the late 1980s, only to crash resoundingly in the early 1990s. From the 1980s bubble economy of Japan to the building boom and bust in southeast Asia in the late 1990s, instability in property markets is alive and well.

How does the cycle arise? Figure 17-15 shows the causal structure of the market. The demand for commercial space depends on economic activity. The greater the employment in the region, the more space is needed, and vacancy rates fall. When vacancy rates are low, effective rents start to rise (effective rents are gross rents net of tenant concessions such as moving and remodeling expenses). Higher

FIGURE 17-14   Real estate cycles

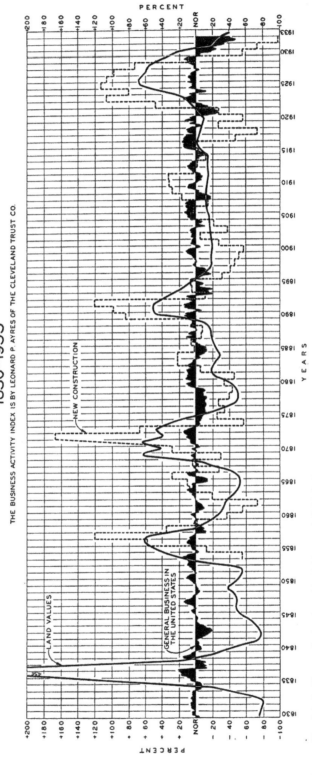

THE CHICAGO LAND VALUE AND BUILDING CYCLES COMPARED WITH
GENERAL BUSINESS ACTIVITY IN THE UNITED STATES
1830–1933

THE BUSINESS ACTIVITY INDEX IS BY LEONARD P. AYRES OF THE CLEVELAND TRUST CO.

Source: Reprinted with permission from Hoyt, Homer J. (1933) *One Hundred Years of Land Values in Chicago.* Chicago: University of Chicago Press.

FIGURE 17-15 Causal structure of commercial real estate markets

Additional feedbacks involving the availability of financing, credit standards, developer experience, and feedback from the pace of construction activity to economic growth are omitted.

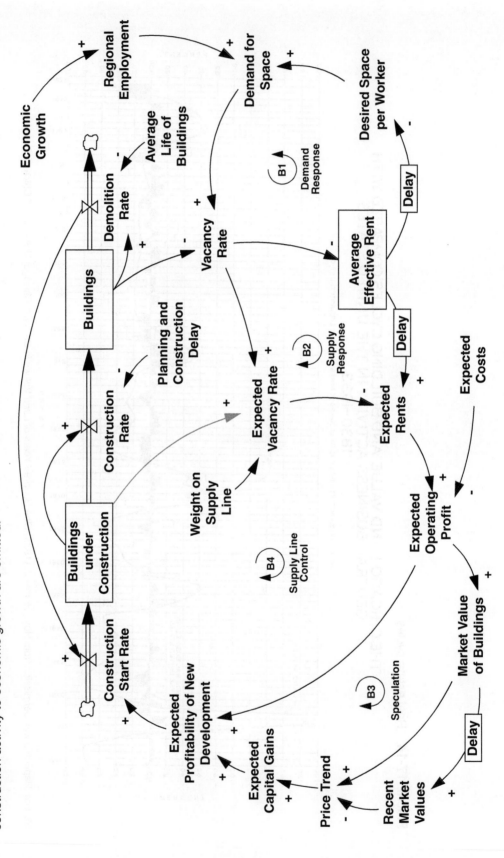

rents lead to some reduction in demand as businesses make do with less space per worker, but the elasticity of the negative Demand Response feedback (loop B1) is low and the response time is long. On the supply side, rising rents boost the profitability and market values of existing properties. When prices are high and rising, rents and operating profits are high and developers can realize substantial capital gains as well. High profits attract new developers, who find no shortage of financial backers eager to cash in on the boom. Many new projects are started, swelling the supply line of buildings under development. After a long delay (2–5 years), the stock of space rises, vacancy rates rise, and rents start to fall, dragging down market values. As profits fall, so does the development rate. The market creates negative loops that attempt to balance demand and supply through price (the negative Supply Response and Speculation loops B2 and B3).

In assessing the profitability of a potential new development, developers and their investors should forecast the future vacancy rate by projecting the growth of demand and supply. To do so they should take the feedback structure of the market into account (the Supply Line Control loop B4). In particular, developers should consider the supply line of buildings on order and under construction when estimating future supply. If they did, the rate at which new projects are initiated would fall well before prices peak. Developers would realize that there was enough space in the pipeline to balance demand and supply even though vacancies remain low and profits are high today. Note, however, in Figure 17-14 that construction reaches its peak at or after the peak in prices, that is, *after* the market has already developed excess supply, vacancy rates are rising, and rents are falling. Developers continue to start new projects as long as they perceive profits are high *right now*, even though it takes 2–5 years to complete a project. Failure to account for the supply line contributes to overbuilding during booms, and prevents investment from recovering early enough to prevent a tight market after the bust ends. The situation has not improved over the last hundred years. Reflecting on the real estate bust of the late 1980s, Downs (1991, p. 2) commented:

> Investors are not always swayed by objective evidence—even overwhelming evidence—if it leads to conclusions that contradict their immediate interests as perceived by the "herd." Evidence of overbuilding in office and other markets was overwhelming by 1987, and probably even earlier. By 1987, the national office-space vacancy rate—which was under 5% in 1981—had exceeded 19% for three years running. Yet banks *accelerated* their investments in new construction loans in 1988 and 1989. Even long-term investors continued to buy real estate at rather high prices, although effective rents were falling sharply.

How can it be that real estate developers ignore the supply line of buildings under development? After all, the financial stakes are huge. Buildings under construction are visible to all, and even the projects on the drawing board or awaiting approval are generally known in the development community.

In the late '80s and early '90s a group of students at the MIT system dynamics group investigated this question through a series of field studies and laboratory experiments. Hernandez (1990) and Thornton (1992) interviewed a range of developers. The interviewees were senior executives in leading national or regional real estate development or advisory firms, people with bottom-line responsibility for development and financing decisions. The goal was to identify the mental models they used to guide development decisions. In particular, we were interested in their understanding of market dynamics. Did they account for the feedback structure of the market? Did they view the market as cyclical, or did they expect trends in demand, supply, and prices to continue? Most important, did they account for the time delays and supply line of pending projects?

Eliciting the mental models of decision makers through interviews is difficult. There is a danger that the informants will tell you what they think you want to hear. The students initially asked neutral questions encouraging the developers to talk about how they made development decisions, how they arranged financing, and so on. If, without prompting, people mentioned cycles, the supply line, or delays it would provide strong evidence that they understood the feedback structure in Figure 17-15 and took the time delays into account. The developers were asked explicitly about cycles and the supply line only if they made no mention of these concepts on their own.

Amazingly, almost none spontaneously mentioned cycles, time lags, the supply line, or any related dynamic concepts. Instead, their descriptions focused heavily on the detail complexity of the development system—how to select a promising site, how to sell a project and win financial backing, how to navigate the permitting process, and so on:

> Location is a bigger factor than the macro market. I know it's cliché but really the key to real estate is location, location, location . . . We . . . try to stay within San Francisco because we know it. We know the politics. We know the architects, engineers, consultants, and subcontractors. (Developer A)

> We did our market analysis kind of haphazard[ly]. [The CEO] had his own feelings about markets and submarkets. He did it by gut feel. His ability was amazing. He could walk along a street and point to a retail center [in the city]. He'd say, "See that center? It's never in the sun, nobody will walk on that side of the street, it will never work"—little things like that . . . most of our market analysis was micro, mainly locational. (Developer B)

> Our biggest strength is our knowledge of the political approval process. (Developer D)

There is no doubt that successful developers must master the detail complexity of the process. But the interviews revealed little appreciation for the dynamic complexity of the market. When asked at the end of the interviews about cycles, most were skeptical:

> We don't consciously pay attention to cycles; more intuitively. We look at the more micro aspects of the market. (Developer A)

> We never looked at cycles. Our analysis figured stable, positive economic growth. (Developer B)

> I'd say we looked at cycles in a qualitative, subjective kind of way. We did not do any empirical analysis of cycles or try to measure the length of the real estate cycles. (Developer C)

> We really have no sense for cycles. (Developer D)

> Quite frankly, I am lousy when it comes to cycles. I think they exist but don't pay a lot of attention to them. There are too many other factors that affect supply

and demand. External factors make it difficult to look at cycles. In fact, I think they probably negate them. (Developer E)

> Real estate cycles? C'mon. No, we don't really analyze them; it's outside our area of expertise… I'll go to these industry forums where people will pull out newspaper articles that are talking gloom and doom, and then they'll tell you these articles are from 1929, 1974, and 1981. But even with this supposed evidence of real estate cycles in history, [they] won't change [people's] minds! The pressure of the system is very strong and they can't resist it either way. (Advisor A)

Like Developer B, many explicitly acknowledged that they focused on current market conditions, extrapolated recent trends, and made minor adjustments to take other factors into account:

> In analyzing market information we would make trend line projections to determine if growth would continue and the space that we were contemplating building would be absorbed. The same as last year's benchmark, greater or less. And the way you would determine that, is to say most people are bearish, rents are coming down, so we won't do as much. Or the conclusion would be that most people are bullish, rents are firm, so we will do a little more. (Developer F)
>
> What problems do we have in tracking the supply side effects? Estimating a correlation between vacancy rates and rental rates is tough. You just kind of wag your finger in the air to determine what it might be. (Advisor A)
>
> We used to use a flat 5% vacancy rate in our pro formas. (Developer E)

Most confessed that they didn't consider the supply line of projects under development in their investment decisions. Many projected that rents and prices would rise at constant rates, independent of the volume of construction activity. They did not recognize the feedbacks among vacancies, rents, profits, construction, and the supply of space—an open-loop mental model:

> It's difficult to assess the supply side. We don't have a formal way of doing it. Word of mouth is usually the best. (Developer A)
>
> We do nothing formal about analyzing projects that are in the pipeline, nothing structured. We just talk to people in the industry, learn our markets. (Developer B)
>
> Tracking the supply in the pipeline is a real difficult task. Nothing is done formally. Will the office building down the street go? I don't know. It is a total guess and there is a lot of broker lip service that you have to sift through. (Advisor A)
>
> There wasn't any real sophisticated analysis of the supply side. (Developer C)
>
> We never did a formal or thorough analysis of what supply may be in [the] works in competition with one of our developments. In analyzing future supply and demand, I think it's too unpredictable to put a lot of emphasis and time in trying to figure it out. (Developer G)

Even when developers claimed to account for the supply line, they failed to close the feedbacks to the market:

> We paid strong attention to the supply side. But we didn't consider that added supply would affect rental rates, we figured it would just affect the amount of time it took to lease up the property. (Developer C)

But when the entire market is overbuilt, even the best projects in the most desirable locations suffer:

Problem was, even if you were a smart developer you had other guys adding space and therefore affecting the rents of your proposed projects. It would even affect existing projects fully leased up. Lease renewals became difficult negotiations and many tenants would want to renegotiate their leases even before they expired. (Developer D)

When evidence of overbuilding eventually became undeniable developers often thought other, less desirable projects than theirs would be the ones to suffer, slowing the reaction to excess capacity:

Developers are promoters and must motivate people. It's difficult to be realistic. You're always selling and after a while you start believing your own delusions of grandeur. (Developer G)

Of course developers' egos had something to do with it. All developers believe that their building is better than their neighbor's. (Developer E)

The sunk cost fallacy, in which people are reluctant to abandon losing strategies, further slowed developers' response to evidence of overbuilding:

At this point, I am not about to walk away from this project given the time and money I have already invested in it… I will be a developer no matter how tough it may get. It's a big ego thing. It's not like you're producing a homogeneous, mass-merchandised product. Development is a more personal thing, like creating a work of art. Being a developer I identify with developer groups and it's like being in a fraternity. It's the majority of my identity that I just can't walk away from. (Developer G)

Nearly all built spreadsheet models to do cost/benefit or discounted cash flow (DCF) analysis. However, financial analysis was used primarily to help sell projects, not as a tool of inquiry to aid the developers' understanding. Many developers believed making good decisions was primarily a matter of intuition:

You can tailor the numbers to say anything you want them to say, but I'm going to trust my gut. My gut has been rarely wrong. (Developer A)

All pro forma financial models require assumptions about future rents, expenses, market values, and interest rates. These inputs are generally based on extrapolation of recent trends. No feedbacks are considered. The inputs are then manipulated to make a project appear to be more profitable:

In-depth market analysis was not done for decision making, it was done to obtain financing . . . Frankly, during that period of time [the boom of the late 1980s] you were concerned about getting the deal done and didn't really care about cycles—it was all ego and pressure to do the deal. (Developer B)

Instead of capping today's income they [developers] trend rents upward period by period. For example, the pro forma would show 4% annual revenue increase and a 3% annual expense increase. Think about it—those lines never intersect! That pro forma and a couple of glossy pictures and the bank gives them the loan! (Developer A)

We would use fifteen page spreadsheets—large sheets with small print—which would compute net present values and internal rates of return of projects by using costs of the project in great detail . . . Rents were assumed to increase yearly by five percent or the inflation rate. At the time I thought that was a conservative estimate and it wasn't really questioned by lenders . . . I spent much time and human resources in tweaking the numbers on these spreadsheets to get the internal rate of return which the bank wanted to be willing to finance the project. (Developer G)

Developers assumed market values would keep on rising, leading to capital gains (the Speculation loop B3 in Figure 17-15). Projects that couldn't make money from rental operations can still be made to seem profitable due to the reversion (capital gain) anticipated when the developer cashed out a few years later:

> In DCF analysis, one rule of thumb was that we never wanted to get in a position where the residual component was 50% of the valuation. Unfortunately, we broke this rule a few times. You know how it is—the market was the market at that time—you gotta have the building. (Advisor A)
>
> [During the boom in the 80s] there was so much competition to do deals you really began relying on the DCF model, and especially relying too much on the reversion component. Then we all started running into problems with cash flow because of rent concessions… It got to be so competitive…that you would be [showing] leveling operating expenses, use a [low] 10% IRR [internal rate of return], and push the income growth and reversion components of the DCF… We just relied on the marketplace. Mostly we believed that three years down the line we would benefit from appreciation. (Developer B)

As a boom gathers momentum, the capital gains dominate, leading to huge profits. For many developers, greed overwhelms reason and experience:

> The guys making the decisions should have been smart enough to know better. They should have seen it. It wasn't just the younger guys either, who hadn't been through a cycle. Everyone sitting on the committee had gray hair and was in their forties or fifties. But we all got greedy. When we should have sold we would hold out for just a little bit more. They weren't good sellers. They believed all their own [lies], all the [lies] they told the people financing the projects. (Developer B)

Though developers cook the numbers to make their projects look more attractive, they must still obtain financing. Most commercial developments rely heavily on OPM (other people's money). The financial markets are supposed to dampen the dreams and schemes of developers, weeding out the unprofitable projects. But when rents and market values are high and rising, developers can easily get financing on favorable terms as investors scramble to get in on the boom. Down payment and debt/equity standards fall, and nonrecourse financing rises as banks compete for the fees generated by the frantic rate of development.[11]

> [During the boom] it was too easy to get money. Look at it this way. You own a piece of property—you are the managing partner. All your equity is in that property. Who knows what you paid for it? You prepare a pro forma which includes your estimated land value, which is undoubtedly greater than what you paid for it. You can then sign an interim note based on that estimated land value. All of a sudden you have a check in your hand for the land value of the pro forma. I'm not kidding! (Developer D)
>
> In the glory days percentages are thrown away all together, and I've done projects in which I contributed practically no money. (Developer G)

---

[11]In nonrecourse financing the project itself is the only collateral. If the developer defaults on the loan, the bank cannot recover its loss from the developer's other assets.

Easy money and the erosion of credit standards during booms increase the development rate and contribute to overbuilding, but developers' reliance on OPM only begs the question, Why don't the investors take account of the supply line when evaluating whether to put their money at risk? One problem is the competition for up-front fees by lenders. Another is the lack of experience among banks, especially during a boom when their real estate operations grow rapidly. Many of the loan officers hired during booms are young and have never experienced a market downturn. Finally, without an appreciation for the structure and dynamics of the market, the financial community suffers from groupthink and the herd mentality:

> The banks are supposed to be the last line of checks and balances, but they were just the opposite. They were too easy . . . The banks had no concept of the market. But not only were the banks too easy, they actually helped to drive a lot of deals. I remember because I worked at a bank for some of that time. Loan officers were given goals that they were pressured to meet: Total amount of loans, total amount of fees, total amount of renewal fees. If you put a banker out in the middle of [nowhere] . . . and you tell him he is going to be compensated . . . by the amount of loans he makes, guess what? He will find a way to make loans! It got so competitive. Banks were not only making ill-advised loans, they were undercutting each other's fees to get the deal. (Developer A)

> The appraisers, who were supposedly independent, also got involved . . . and effectively rubber-stamped anything that the lender and developer agreed were reasonable . . . It was one big complicitous circle. No one wanted to say no or they would lose business. (Developer G)

> There is a tremendous pressure to follow the crowd. If you are standing on the sidelines and not making investments and your competitors are collecting fees for placing funds, what are you going to do? If the pressure is there to place the money, you will find a way to buy. (Advisor A)

> Will the banks or the developers learn? Well, a number of lenders are now saying that they will never again lend on real estate. I have an answer for that. All it takes is just one generation. A generation of bankers and developers to churn through. A generation that hasn't been through the cycles. (Developer A)

The interviews strongly suggest developers and investors do not understand the feedback structure of real estate markets and do not adequately account for the time delays or supply line of pending space. They are overwhelmingly influenced by current conditions and tend to extrapolate recent trends. But interviews can be misleading. To test the conclusions from the interviews, Bakken (1993) conducted an experiment with a management flight simulator representing the real estate market. Based on the structure shown in Figure 17-15, players had to manage a portfolio of properties and could develop new projects and buy or sell existing properties. Professional developers working for what was then one of the largest real estate development firms in the US did no better than MBA students at MIT. Average performance was a small fraction of that achieved by a simple investment rule that accounted for the supply line. Learning was slow and transfer of learning to different market conditions was weak. When the professionals went bankrupt in the simulation they often criticized the model, claiming that in the real world prices could never drop so far or so fast. A few years later, most had lost everything.

CHALLENGE   ## Expanding the Real Estate Model

The causal diagram in Figure 17-15 includes only a few of the feedbacks discussed in section 17.4.3 and suggested by the interviews with real estate developers. Expand the causal diagram to include these other feedbacks. In particular, consider

1. The impact of market conditions on credit standards, lending practices, and the availability of financing for new projects.

2. The impact of real estate market and construction activity on the pace of economic growth in the region.

3. The effect of development activity on the availability and cost of architectural and construction firms and how the availability of these resources affects planning and construction times and costs.

4. The effect of development booms and busts on tax rates, zoning and permitting regulations, and other factors that may affect the attractiveness of the region to developers and to business in general.

5. Other feedbacks and effects you think might be important in understanding the full impact of real estate cycles on a community.

For each new feedback process, assess its likely impact on the period, stability, and other characteristics of the market.

17.5 SUMMARY

Supply chains are fundamental to a wide range of systems and many exhibit persistent instability and oscillation. Every supply chain consists of stocks and the management policies used to manage them. These management policies are designed to keep the stocks at their target levels, compensating for usage or loss and for unanticipated disturbances in the environment. Often there are important delays between the initiation of a control action and the result, creating a supply line of unfilled orders.

This chapter developed a generic model of the stock management structure and showed how it can be customized to various situations. The model was used to explain the sources of oscillation, amplification, and phase lag observed in supply chains. These patterns of behavior are fundamental to the basic physical structure of stock management systems and supply chains. Oscillation arises from the combination of time delays in negative feedbacks and failure of the decision maker to take the time delays into account. Field and experimental studies show that people often ignore the time delays in a wide range of systems.

The beer game and real estate industry are but two examples of situations where cyclical instability arises from the failure of decision makers to account for time delays. There is no one single cause for the failure to account for time delays and the supply line. A range of factors, from information availability to individual incentives, all contribute. But behind these apparent causes lies a deeper problem. True, the supply line is often inadequately measured, but if people understood the importance of the supply line they would invest in data collection and measurement systems to provide the needed information. True, compensation incentives often encourage people to ignore the delayed consequences of today's actions, but if investors understood the structure and dynamics of the market they could redesign compensation incentives for their agents to focus on long-term performance. Our mental models affect the design of our institutions, information systems, and incentive schemes. These, in turn, feed back to our mental models. The failure to account for the supply line reflects deeper defects in our understanding of complex systems. Ignoring time delays is one of the fundamental misperceptions of feedback that leads to poor performance in systems with high dynamic complexity (chapter 1). Failure to understand the role of time delays worsens the instability we face and leads to more surprises—usually unpleasant—reinforcing the belief that the world is inherently capricious and unpredictable and strengthening the short-term focus still more.

What can be done? The next chapters take up the challenge of modeling supply chains and oscillations, with special consideration to policies firms can undertake to improve performance.

18

The Manufacturing Supply Chain

The central core of many industrial companies is the process of production and distribution. A recurring problem is to match the production rate to the rate of final consumer sales. It is well known that factory production rate often fluctuates more widely than does the actual consumer purchase rate. It has often been observed that a distribution system of cascaded inventories and ordering procedures seems to amplify small disturbances that occur at the retail level . . . How does the system create amplification of small retail sales changes? . . . [W]e shall see that typical manufacturing and distribution practices can generate the types of business disturbances which are often blamed on conditions outside the company.
—Jay W. Forrester (*Industrial Dynamics,* p. 22)

The stock management structure described in chapter 17 is quite general and can be used to model supply chains for a variety of resources. This chapter shows how the stock management structure can be adapted to represent the supply chain in manufacturing firms. Locally rational policies that create smooth and stable adjustment of individual organizational units may, through interactions with other functions and organizations, cause oscillation and instability. Instability can feed back to undermine trust among partners in a supply chain, leading to behavior that worsens the instability.

The model is developed in stages. Simplifying assumptions are relaxed one at a time and only after the behavior of each version is fully analyzed. This iterative process deepens your understanding of the underlying relationships between the structure and behavior of dynamic systems and in the long run speeds the development of useful, effective models.

18.1   THE POLICY STRUCTURE OF INVENTORY AND PRODUCTION

Figure 18-1 shows the *policy structure diagram* for a simple model of a manufacturing firm.[1] The firm maintains a stock of finished inventory and fills orders as they arrive. In this initial model, assume that customers are delivery sensitive—orders the company cannot fill immediately are lost as customers seek other sources of supply (section 18.1.7 adds an explicit backlog of unfilled orders). In this initial model, customer orders are exogenous. Production takes time. The stock of WIP (work in process) is increased by production starts and decreased by production. The key production control and inventory management decisions made by the firm include order fulfillment (determining the ability to fill customer orders based on the adequacy of inventory) and production scheduling (determining the rate of production starts based on the demand forecast and inventory position of the firm, including the WIP inventory). The model includes three important negative feedbacks. The Stockout loop regulates shipments as inventory varies: If inventory is inadequate, some items will be out of stock and shipments fall below orders. In the extreme, shipments must fall to zero when there is no inventory. The Inventory Control and WIP Control loops adjust production starts to move the levels of inventory and WIP toward their desired levels. In this initial model there are no stocks of materials and no capacity constraints (either from labor or capital). These extensions are treated below.

FIGURE 18-1   The policy structure of inventory management

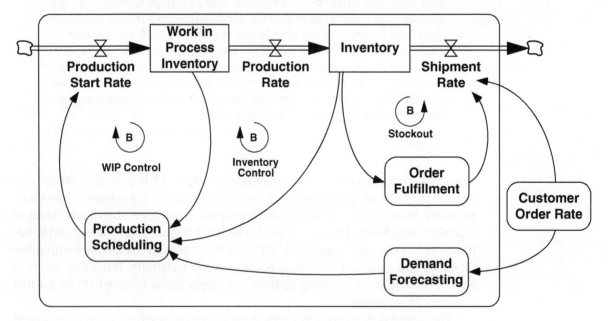

---

[1]A *policy structure diagram* shows the stock and flow and decision structure of a model at a high level (not at the level of the individual equations). The rounded rectangles denote organizational subunits, policies, or decision rules and show the boundary of organizational units. Policy structure diagrams provide an overview of a model highlighting the feedback structure without showing all the details found in the model diagram (Morecroft 1982).

18.1.1   Order Fulfillment

Figure 18-2 shows the structure of the order fulfillment process and shipment rate.

Inventory coverage is the number of weeks the firm could ship at the current rate given its inventory:

$$\text{Inventory Coverage} = \text{Inventory/Shipment Rate} \qquad (18\text{-}1)$$

$$\text{Inventory} = \text{INTEGRAL}(\text{Production Rate} - \text{Shipment Rate}, \text{Inventory}_{t_0}) \qquad (18\text{-}2)$$

The shipment rate normally equals the desired shipment rate, but if inventory is inadequate, some of the items customers request will be out of stock, reducing the order fulfillment ratio (the ratio of orders filled to the desired fulfillment rate):

$$\text{Shipment Rate} = \text{Desired Shipment Rate} * \text{Order Fulfillment Ratio} \qquad (18\text{-}3)$$

The order fulfillment ratio is a function of the ratio of the maximum shipment rate to the desired shipment rate; the values are specified by the Table for Order Fulfillment:

$$\frac{\text{Order}}{\text{Fulfillment Ratio}} = \frac{\text{Table for}}{\text{Order Fulfillment}}\left(\frac{\text{Maximum Shipment Rate}}{\text{Desired Shipment Rate}}\right) \qquad (18\text{-}4)$$

The maximum shipment rate depends on the firm's current inventory level and the minimum order fulfillment time:

$$\text{Maximum Shipment Rate} = \text{Inventory/Minimum Order Fulfillment Time} \qquad (18\text{-}5)$$

The minimum order fulfillment time is determined by the firm's order fulfillment process, the complexity of the product, and the proximity of customers to the

FIGURE 18-2   Structure of order fulfillment

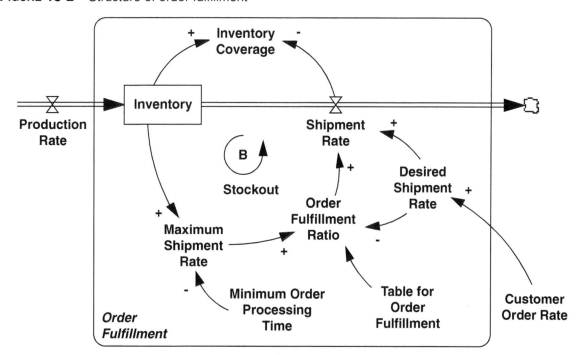

firm's distribution centers. It represents the minimum time required to process and ship an order.

In this simple model, there is no backlog of unfilled orders, and all orders not immediately filled are lost as customers seek alternate suppliers. Hence

$$\text{Desired Shipment Rate} = \text{Customer Order Rate} \tag{18-6}$$

where the customer order rate is exogenous from the point of view of the inventory and order fulfillment subsystem.

A much simpler formulation for shipments is

$$\text{Shipment Rate} = \text{MIN(Desired Shipment Rate, Maximum Shipment Rate)} \tag{18-3a}$$

Why use the fuzzy minimum function in equations (18-3) through (18-6)? Equation (18-3a) says the firm ships what it wants to ship or what it can ship, whichever is less. This simple logic is compelling for the case of a single product or stock-keeping unit (SKU). However, models often represent firms that carry many different SKUs, sometimes tens of thousands. Usually it is not necessary for the model's purpose to represent each SKU separately. The inventory level in such models represents the aggregate of all SKUs. The mix of SKUs requested by the customers varies unpredictably, as do the inventory levels of individual items. When many items are aggregated, some individual items are likely to be out of stock even when the aggregate desired shipment rate equals the maximum shipment rate. The order fulfillment ratio will then be less than 1. Figure 18-3 shows a typical shape for the order fulfillment ratio.

To interpret the figure, note the two reference lines. Combining equations (18-3) and (18-4),

$$\text{SR} = \text{DSR} * \text{OFR} = \text{DSR} * f(\text{MSR/DSR}) \tag{18-3b}$$

FIGURE 18-3
Order fulfillment as a function of inventory

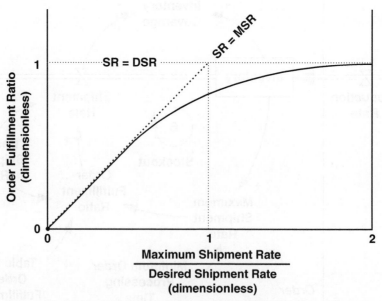

SR = shipment rate; DSR = desired shipment rate; MSR = maximum shipment rate.

where SR, DSR, and MSR are the shipment, desired shipment, and maximum shipment rates, respectively, and OFR is the order fulfillment ratio. The horizontal line Order Fulfillment Ratio = 1 represents the case where shipments always equal desired shipments. If the shipment rate SR fell along the 45° line passing through the origin, then SR = MSR: Shipments always equal the maximum level inventory supports. The actual relationship must therefore be restricted to the region to the right and below both reference lines. When the firm has ample inventories, so that the maximum aggregate shipment rate is much greater than the desired shipment rate, then the chance that any individual item will be out of stock is negligible and the order fulfillment ratio is 1—shipments equal desired shipments. As the aggregate maximum shipment rate falls, the chances that some items will be out of stock increase, reducing the order fulfillment ratio. The order fulfillment ratio will therefore be less than 1 at the point where the aggregate maximum shipment rate equals the desired shipment rate. Further reductions in availability force the order fulfillment ratio down until goods are being shipped at the maximum rate inventory permits. The greater the number of individual items aggregated together, or the greater the unpredictability of demand for individual items, the smaller the order fulfillment ratio will be for any ratio of the maximum to desired shipment rate. The case where the order fulfillment ratio equals the 45° line when MSR < DSR and 1 when MSR ≥ DSR corresponds to the formulation SR = MIN(DSR, MSR) and would represent a situation where either there is only one SKU or where the demand for each type of inventory is perfectly correlated and predictable.

The discussion so far assumes the firm will ship an item if it can. In practice firms with inadequate inventories may choose not to fill the orders of some smaller customers so as to maintain a reserve against the chance that a favored customer will place an order. Such strategic product withholding reduces the order fulfillment ratio further below the reference lines, particularly in the region where MSR < DSR.

18.1.2   Production

Figure 18-4 shows the policy structure of the production rate. Typically production involves multiple steps that create significant inventories of work in process

FIGURE 18-4   Production and WIP inventory

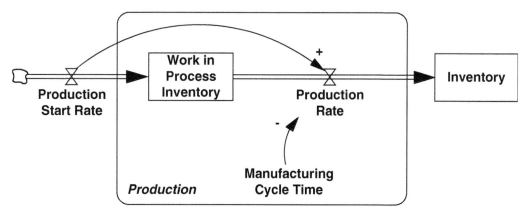

(WIP). Chapter 6 provides examples of the stock and flow networks for manufacturing processes, showing how the various stages of production can be represented. For the purpose of this model, all stages of the process are aggregated together into the WIP inventory.

A third-order delay is used to model the production process:

Work in Process Inventory
= INTEGRAL(Production Start Rate − Production Rate, WIP_{t_0}) (18-7)

Production Rate
= DELAY3(Production Start Rate, Manufacturing Cycle Time) (18-8)

The manufacturing cycle time represents the average transit time for all items aggregated together in the model. The fewer items aggregated together, the smaller the variance in individual cycle times and the higher the order of the delay that best characterizes production.

18.1.3   Production Starts

Figure 18-5 shows the structure of the production start decision. For now, no capacity constraints are considered: Production starts do not depend on materials availability, labor, or capital plant and equipment.

The production starts decision rule is formulated using the generic stock management structure. The Production Start Rate is constrained to be nonnegative but otherwise equals the Desired Production Start Rate (since no resource constraints are yet considered). Desired Production Starts are determined by the Desired Production rate and the Adjustment for WIP (the supply line of pending production):

Production Start Rate = MAX(0, Desired Production Start Rate)   (18-9)

Desired Production Start Rate = Desired Production + Adjustment for WIP (18-10)

The Adjustment for WIP modifies production starts to keep the WIP inventory in line with the desired level. Desired WIP is set to provide a level of work in process sufficient to yield the desired rate of production given the current manufacturing cycle time:

Adjustment for WIP
= (Desired WIP − Work in Process Inventory)/WIP Adjustment Time (18-11)

Desired WIP = Manufacturing Cycle Time * Desired Production   (18-12)

Desired production is determined by the Expected Order Rate, modified by the Adjustment for Inventory. Desired Production is constrained to be nonnegative:

Desired Production
= MAX(0, Expected Order Rate + Adjustment for Inventory) (18-13)

Adjustment for Inventory
= (Desired Inventory − Inventory)/Inventory Adjustment Time (18-14)

Desired Inventory Coverage
= Minimum Order Processing Time + Safety Stock Coverage (18-15)

To provide adequate inventory as a buffer against unexpected variations in demand or production, the firm seeks to maintain a certain coverage of expected demand.

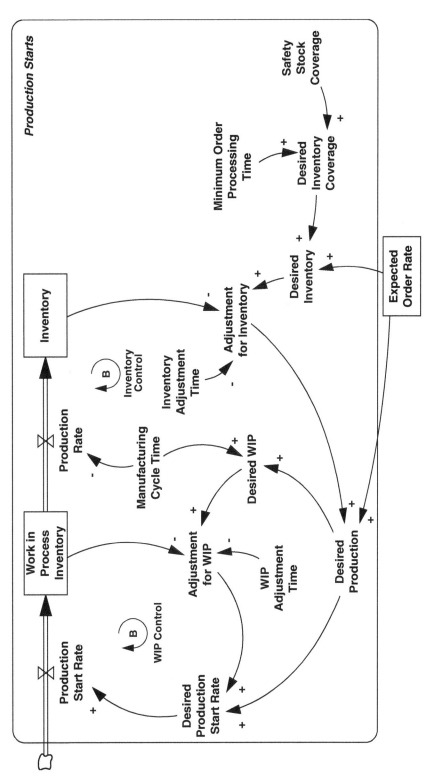

FIGURE 18-5 Structure of production starts

Desired inventory coverage includes two components. First, the firm must maintain enough coverage to ship at the expected rate, requiring a base coverage level equal to the minimum order processing time. Second, to ensure an adequate level of service, the firm maintains additional safety stocks. The higher the coverage provided by the safety stock, the greater the service level (fraction of orders filled on average) will be.

18.1.4   Demand Forecasting

The firm is assumed to forecast demand using first-order exponential smoothing of the actual order rate (Figure 18-6).

$$\text{Expected Order Rate} = \text{INTEGRAL}(\text{Change in Exp Orders, Expected Order Rate}_{t_0}) \qquad (18\text{-}16)$$

$$\text{Change in Exp Orders} = \frac{(\text{Customer Order Rate} - \text{Expected Order Rate})}{\text{Time to Average Order Rate}} \qquad (18\text{-}17)$$

As shown in chapters 11 and 16, smoothing provides a realistic model of the forecasting process used in many firms. The forecasting process could easily be augmented to include seasonal adjustments or an extrapolative component to anticipate demand growth.

18.1.5   Process Point: Initializing a Model in Equilibrium

Model testing should be a process of controlled experimentation. For this reason, you should strive to initialize your models in a *balanced equilibrium.* Equilibrium means that all stocks in the system are unchanging, requiring their inflows and outflows to be equal. A balanced equilibrium further implies that all stocks are equal to their desired values. In the present model, equilibrium requires production starts = production = shipments (the conditions for WIP and Inventory to be constant); the change in expected orders must also be zero. In addition, a balanced equilibrium requires that Inventory = Desired Inventory, WIP = Desired WIP, and that all flows equal their target rates as well: Shipments, desired shipments, expected orders, desired production, desired production starts, production starts, and production should all equal customer orders. (Note that the model does not include

FIGURE 18-6
Demand
forecasting

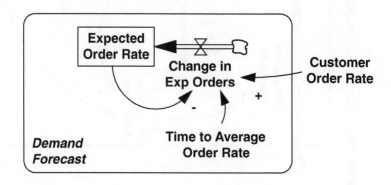

scrap rates; if it did, production would have to exceed shipments by the scrap rate to achieve a balanced equilibrium.)

Initializing your models in a balanced equilibrium facilitates the process of model testing because the system remains in equilibrium until disturbed by test inputs you choose to impose. If your model begins out of equilibrium its behavior will confound the response to any test input with the transient behavior induced by the initial disequilibrium.

In the present model, a balanced equilibrium is easily achieved with the following initial conditions:

$$\text{Inventory}_{t_0} = \text{Desired Inventory} \tag{18-18}$$

$$\text{WIP}_{t_0} = \text{Desired WIP} \tag{18-19}$$

$$\text{Expected Order Rate}_{t_0} = \text{Customer Order Rate} \tag{18-20}$$

Under these conditions, the adjustments for inventory and for WIP will be zero, so desired production starts = desired production = expected orders = customer orders; further, when inventory = desired inventory, shipments = desired shipments = customer orders—provided desired inventory coverage is sufficiently large that the order fulfillment ratio is 1.

Note that the initial conditions are specified in terms of other variables and parameters, not as numerical values. By specifying the initial conditions as expressions depending on other parameters in the model, the stocks will be initialized at their equilibrium values for any set of parameters and inputs. Specifying a numerical value will throw the model out of equilibrium if you change the parameters. You should strive to find an algebraic expression for each initial condition so that your models always begin in a balanced equilibrium.

Not all models possess a unique balanced equilibrium or any balanced equilibrium at all. In the present model, there is no balanced equilibrium if desired inventory coverage is set at a level that causes the order fulfillment ratio to be less than 100%. For some models there is no equilibrium, balanced or otherwise. Many of the models of growth and product diffusion developed in chapter 9, for example, have no nontrivial equilibrium consistent with the situation near the beginning of the diffusion process. The market growth model (chapter 15) has no equilibrium at all because the base case parameters cause growth in an unlimited market. In these cases it is still useful to initialize each subsystem so that it is in equilibrium relative to its inputs or to initialize the model in a steady state, if one exists, even if that steady state is one of growth.

Simultaneous Initial Condition Equations

Sometimes you will find that the algebraic expressions you select for initial conditions will create a simultaneous equation system. For example, suppose the initial value of inventory had been specified as

$$\text{Inventory}_{t_0} = \text{Desired Inventory Coverage} * \text{Shipment Rate} \tag{18-18a}$$

This formulation appears to be reasonable: The initial inventory should provide the desired coverage of initial shipments for the system to be in equilibrium. But specifying initial inventory in terms of the shipment rate creates a situation in which initial inventory depends on itself:

$$
\begin{aligned}
\text{Shipment Rate} &= \text{Desired Shipment Rate} * \text{Order Fulfillment Ratio} \\
&= \text{Desired Shipment Rate} * f(\text{Maximum Shipment Rate/Desired Shipment Rate}) \\
&= \text{Desired Shipment Rate} * f\left[\frac{(\text{Inventory/Minimum Order Fulfillment Time})}{\text{Desired Shipment Rate}}\right]
\end{aligned}
$$

$$(18\text{-}21)$$

There are several remedies for situations with simultaneous initial value equations. The best solution is to specify the initial value in terms of other parameters that do not participate in the loop creating the simultaneity. Initial inventory could be expressed as

$$\text{Inventory}_{t_0} = \text{Desired Inventory Coverage} * \text{Desired Shipment Rate} \qquad (18\text{-}22)$$

The simultaneity is resolved because the desired shipment rate does not depend on inventory. The two formulations will differ only to the extent that initial shipments fall short of the desired rate. Another approach is to solve the system of simultaneous equations and use the solution as the initial value. Sometimes simple algebra will suffice to solve the equations; in other cases the solution is more complex and requires linearization of the model's nonlinear functions. As a last resort, simultaneous initial value equations can be resolved by using a numerical value for one of the stocks in the loop.

CHALLENGE   Simultaneous Initial Conditions

Consider the simple macroeconomic model shown in Figure 18-7 (based on Samuelson 1939; see also Low 1980). The model provides a simple explanation of the consumption multiplier, an important concept in Keynesian analysis of the economy. In essence, the demand for goods and services depends on consumers' expectations of their future income. Income expectations, in turn, depend on the total income of all households, which, since the entire population is included, is the total output of the economy (gross domestic product [GDP]). The result is a positive feedback, the consumption multiplier, in which an increase in GDP boosts income and raises consumption, further increasing aggregate demand and GDP. In the simple model here, inventories and the supply chain in the actual economy are omitted, so production adjusts to aggregate demand with a short lag. Consumer expectations of future income also adjust to actual income (GDP) with a delay.

The total production of goods and services (GDP) adjusts with a short delay to the rate of aggregate demand in the economy. First-order smoothing is assumed, a common assumption in many macroeconomic models. The initial value of GDP is set to its equilibrium value, aggregate demand AD. When GDP = AD, the change in GDP is zero:

$$\text{GDP} = \text{INTEGRAL}(\text{Change in GDP, AD}) \qquad (18\text{-}23)$$

$$\text{Change in GDP} = (\text{AD} - \text{GDP})/\text{Time to Adjust Production} \qquad (18\text{-}24)$$

FIGURE 18-7   A simple macroeconomic model of the consumption multiplier

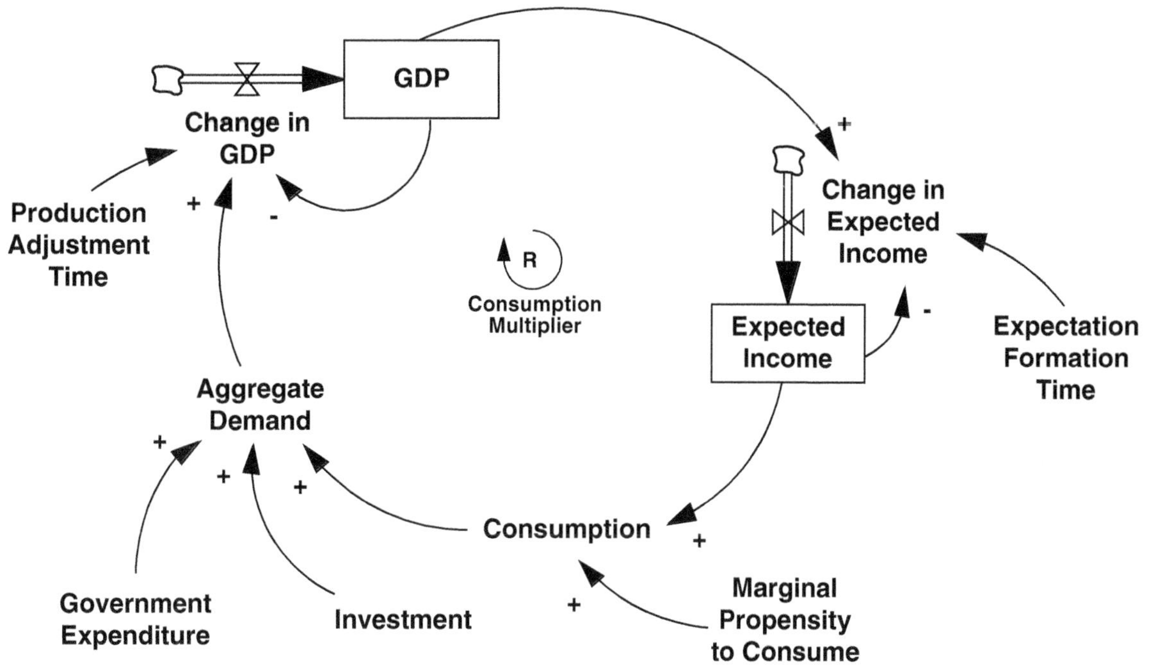

Aggregate demand is the sum of consumption C, government expenditure G, and investment I:

$$AD = C + I + G \qquad (18\text{-}25)$$

Consumers spend a fraction of their expected income, the Marginal Propensity to Consume MPC:

$$C = MPC * \text{Expected Income} \qquad (18\text{-}26)$$

Expected income adjusts to actual income, which in the aggregate is the GDP. Many models assume first-order exponential smoothing for the adjustment process. The initial value of Expected Income is set to GDP, its equilibrium value:

$$\text{Expected Income} = \text{INTEGRAL}(\text{Change in Expected Income}, \text{GDP}) \qquad (18\text{-}27)$$

Change in Expected Income
$$= (\text{GDP} - \text{Expected Income})/\text{Expectation Formation Time} \qquad (18\text{-}28)$$

In this simple model, both government expenditure and investment are exogenous.

The initial conditions are individually sensible: Each stock is set so that it is initially equal to its equilibrium value. But together they create a simultaneous initial value equation: The initial GDP depends on aggregate demand, which in turn depends on expected income, which equals GDP.

1.   Resolve the simultaneous initial value problem in the multiplier model. Be sure your initial values will start the model in equilibrium for any set of parameters. Which parameters determine the equilibrium? Does the equilibrium depend

on the time constants (the time to adjust production and the time to form expectations)? Why/why not?

2.   Simulate the model with your revised initial values and confirm that the system does begin in equilibrium. In this model it may be obvious from inspection of your equations that it will begin in equilibrium. You should still run the test. You may have made a typographical error in an equation. In more complex models, simulating to confirm that your model does indeed begin in a balanced equilibrium is an essential check on your calculated initial conditions.

3.   Typical parameters for the macroeconomy might be MPC = 0.8, Production Adjustment Time = 1 year, and Expectation Formation Time = 2 years. Set government expenditure to 90 and investment to 10. What is the equilibrium GDP? Now simulate the model assuming the government stimulates the economy by increasing government expenditures by 10 units (yielding a 10% increase in aggregate demand) at the start of year 1. What is the new equilibrium? How long does it take to reach it? What is the pattern of adjustment? Why?

18.1.6   Behavior of the Production Model

To begin testing of the model, Table 18-1 shows illustrative parameters for a manufacturing firm. Note that while the minimum order processing time is 2 weeks, the firm desires a safety stock of an additional 2 weeks of coverage. Given the assumed values for the order fulfillment function, inventory coverage equal to the minimum order processing time would result in a service level of only 85%. Adding a safety stock equal to an additional 2 weeks of expected demand means the maximum shipment rate would be twice the desired rate when inventory equals its desired value, enabling the firm to fill 100% of the incoming orders.

Figure 18-8 shows the response of the firm to an unanticipated 20% step increase in customer orders. The initial customer order rate is 10,000 widgets per week.

The desired shipment rate rises immediately after the step increase in demand. Inventory coverage immediately drops from its initial value of 4 weeks to 3.33 weeks. At the instant the customer order rate increases inventory has not yet changed, so the Maximum Shipment Rate remains the same (20,000 widgets/week). The 20% increase in orders reduces the ratio of maximum to desired shipments from 2.00 to 1.67. The order fulfillment ratio at that point is over 99%, so the firm is initially able to fill nearly all the incoming orders, despite the increase. However, because production continues at the initial rate of 10,000 widgets/week, inventory falls. As inventory falls, so too does the firm's ability to ship. The order fulfillment ratio drops to a minimum of roughly 95% about 7 weeks after the demand shock, causing the firm to lose business (and its reputation as a reliable supplier).

The growing gap between desired and actual inventory forces desired production to rise above expected orders. As it does the quantity of work in process

TABLE 18-1	Parameter	Base Case Value (Weeks)
Base case parameters for the production model	Minimum Order Processing Time	2
	Safety Stock Coverage	2
	Manufacturing Cycle Time	8
	Inventory Adjustment Time	8
	WIP Adjustment Time	2
	Time to Average Order Rate	8

Table for Order Fulfillment Ratio:

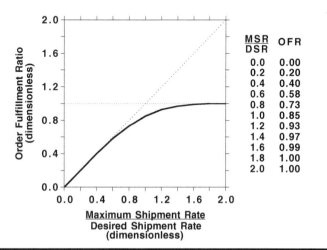

required to meet the higher production goal also grows, opening a gap between the desired and actual level of WIP. Thus the desired production start rate rises further above the desired production rate.

As time passes the firm recognizes that the initial increase in demand is not a mere random blip and its forecast of demand gradually rises. Given the 8-week smoothing time for the forecast, it takes about ½ year for the forecast to adjust 95% of the way to the new order rate. During this time, the system cannot achieve a balanced equilibrium: If inventory and WIP inventory were equal to their desired values, production would equal the demand forecast, which, since it is less than orders, would cause inventory to fall.

As expected orders rise, so too does desired inventory, adding to the gap between desired and actual inventory and boosting desired production still further. Production starts reach a peak more than 42% greater than the initial level about 4 weeks after the shock, an amplification ratio of 2.12.

The rapid increase in production starts soon fills the supply line of WIP, but production lags behind due to the 8-week delay. Production does not surpass shipments until more than 6 weeks have passed; throughout this period inventory continues to fall even as the desired inventory level rises. Inventory stops falling when production first equals shipments. The system is not yet in equilibrium, however,

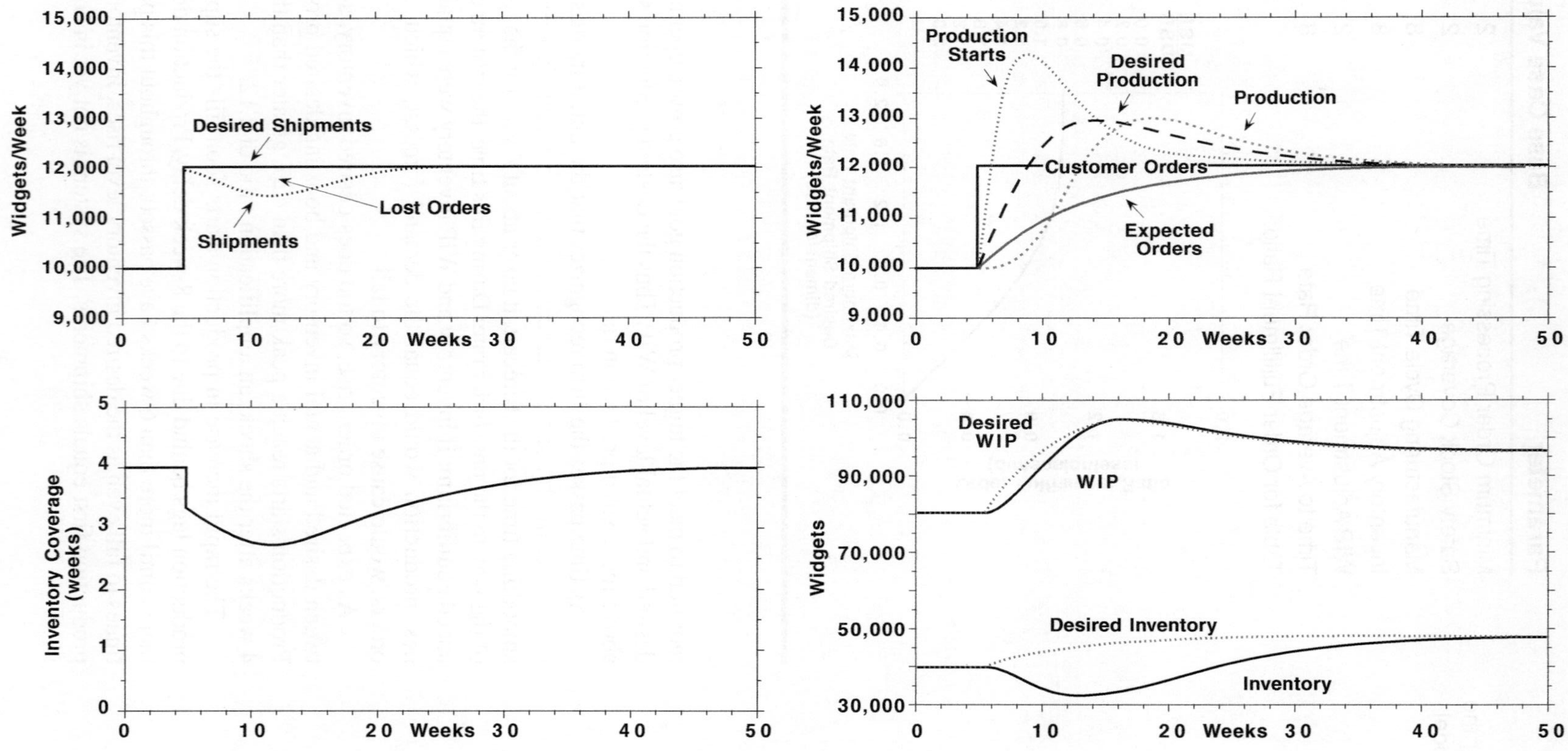

FIGURE **18-8** Response of manufacturing model to a 20% step increase in orders

because of the large gap between desired and actual inventory and between orders and expected orders. Production eventually rises above shipments, causing inventory to rise, until it eventually reaches the new, higher desired level. Note that the peak of production comes about ¼ year after the change in orders, much longer than the 8-week production delay suggests.

The simulation reveals several fundamental aspects of supply chain behavior. First, the initial response of the firm to an unanticipated increase in demand is a decline in inventory. The production delay means an initial drop in inventory is inevitable—it is a fundamental consequence of the physical structure of the system. The reduction in inventory contrasts sharply with the firm's desire to hold more inventory when demand increases.

Second, amplification of the demand shock is unavoidable. Because inventory must initially fall, the only way to increase it back to its initial level and then raise it to the new, higher desired level is for production to exceed shipments. Production must overshoot the shipment rate long enough and by a large enough margin to build inventory up to the new desired level. Production starts must overshoot orders even more so that the level of WIP can be built up to a level consistent with the higher throughput rate.

Third, the peak production start rate must lag the change in customer orders. The adjustment to production from the inventory gap reaches its maximum about when the inventory reaches its minimum. Inventory bottoms out only after production has finally risen enough to equal shipments, an event that must lag the change in orders. Like amplification, this phase lag, characteristic of many real supply chains, is a fundamental and inevitable consequence of the physical stock and flow structure.

The stock management structure thus explains why supply chains generate amplification and phase lag. Given the structure of the system (in particular, production delays and forecast adjustment delays), production and production starts must overshoot, amplify, and lag changes in demand, no matter how smart the managers of the firm may be.

Though amplification and phase lag are inevitable, oscillation is not. The response of the firm to the demand shock is intendedly rational in the sense defined in chapter 15. The response of the firm to the shock is smooth and stable (given the base case parameters). Explaining oscillation requires the expansion of the model to include additional structure.

18.1.7   Enriching the Model: Adding Order Backlogs

So far the model assumes that orders not immediately filled are lost forever. While this assumption is reasonable in some settings, such as retail sales and some delivery-sensitive industrial products, most manufacturing firms cannot deliver immediately and maintain a backlog of unfilled orders that accumulates the difference between orders and shipments. Backlogs arise whenever there is a delay between the receipt and delivery of an order. Such delays can be caused by administrative activities such as credit approval and order processing, by the need to customize or configure the product to the needs of particular customers, and by delays in shipping to the customer site, among others. When the value and carrying costs of

FIGURE 18-9   Structure for order backlog

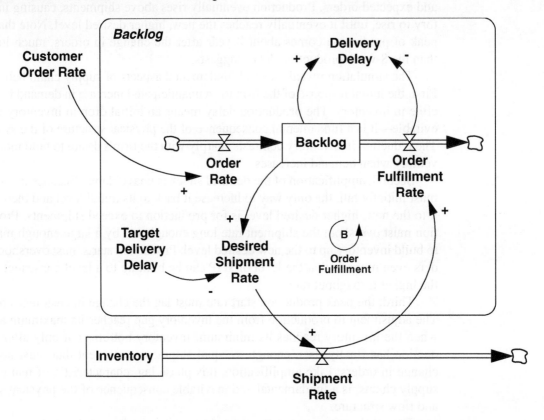

inventory are very high, firms prefer to maintain backlogs of unfilled orders and operate make-to-order systems even if they technically could stock finished product. Boeing does not make 777s to stock.[2] Figure 18-9 shows how the order fulfillment subsystem can be modified to include an explicit order backlog.

An order backlog implies that there is a delay between the placement and receipt of orders. By Little's Law the ratio of the backlog to the order fulfillment rate measures the average delivery delay at any moment:

$$\text{Delivery Delay} = \text{Backlog/Order Fulfillment Rate} \qquad (18\text{-}29)$$

$$\text{Backlog} = \text{INTEGRAL}(\text{Order Rate} - \text{Order Fulfillment Rate}, \text{Backlog}_{t_0}) \quad (18\text{-}30)$$

The order fulfillment rate is equal to the shipment rate. Every time a widget is shipped to a customer, the backlog is decremented by one unit as well. Note that while the shipment rate and order fulfillment rate are assumed to be numerically equal and both are measured in the same units (widgets/week), they are distinct

---

[2]More precisely, aircraft manufacturers do not intend to make jetliners for inventory. However, an unexpected downturn in the aircraft market leads to order cancellations and can cause unintended inventory accumulation. The excess aircraft must then be mothballed until customers can be found. Unsold or surplus jets are often flown to the Mojave desert where they can be stored cheaply and safely until they can be sold.

concepts. The shipment rate is the rate physical product leaves the firm, while the order fulfillment rate represents an information flow.

In the revised structure the desired shipment rate is now the rate of shipments that will ensure orders are filled within the target delivery delay. The target delivery delay is the firm's goal for the interval between placement and receipt of orders. The actual delivery delay will equal the target when the shipment rate equals the desired shipment rate.

$$\text{Desired Shipment Rate} = \text{Backlog/Target Delivery Delay} \qquad (18\text{-}6a)$$

Finally, the firm's order rate is now set to the customer order rate. In models with multiple customers, the order rate would be the sum of the individual customer order rates. To ensure that the model begins in a balanced equilibrium, the initial backlog must equal the target delivery delay's worth of incoming orders:

$$\text{Backlog}_{t_0} = \text{Target Delivery Delay} * \text{Order Rate} \qquad (18\text{-}31)$$

18.1.8   Behavior of the Firm with Order Backlogs

Figure 18-10 shows a simulation of the model with the target delivery delay set to 2 weeks and all other parameters as in Figure 18-8. As before, there is an unanticipated 20% increase in customer orders from an initial balanced equilibrium. Though quite similar to the model without backlog, there are some subtle differences. Immediately after the increase in orders, shipments continue at the initial rate. The backlog therefore builds up, and as it rises, so too does the desired shipment rate. Actual shipments keep pace initially, but as the firm's inventory level falls, the order fulfillment ratio drops below 100%, causing shipments to drop below desired shipments. The delivery delay then begins to rise.

A backlog has two effects. First, because the backlog buffers orders and shipments, desired shipments rise more gradually than in the case without backlog. As a result, the decline in inventory is more gradual, reducing the amplification in production starts slightly, to 1.97 compared to 2.12 in the no-backlog case. The peak in the production start rate also lags the change in orders slightly more than in the no-backlog case. Second, orders that cannot be shipped immediately are no longer lost but remain in the backlog until they can be shipped. The shipment rate therefore must rise above the order rate as the firm works off its excess backlog once sufficient inventory becomes available.

18.1.9   Adding Raw Materials Inventory

So far the production start rate always equals the desired production start rate, implying resources such as materials, labor, and capital are always ample. Figure 18-11 shows how the structure of the model can be revised to include an explicit stock of raw materials or components. The materials inventory is modeled as a stock management structure analogous to the inventory of finished goods. Production can only begin if there is a sufficient stock of materials, and the firm must order enough materials to keep the parts inventory at the appropriate level.

The Production Start Rate is reformulated to equal Feasible Production Starts from Materials, the rate at which production can be begun based on the Material

FIGURE 18-10 Response of model with backlog to step increase in orders

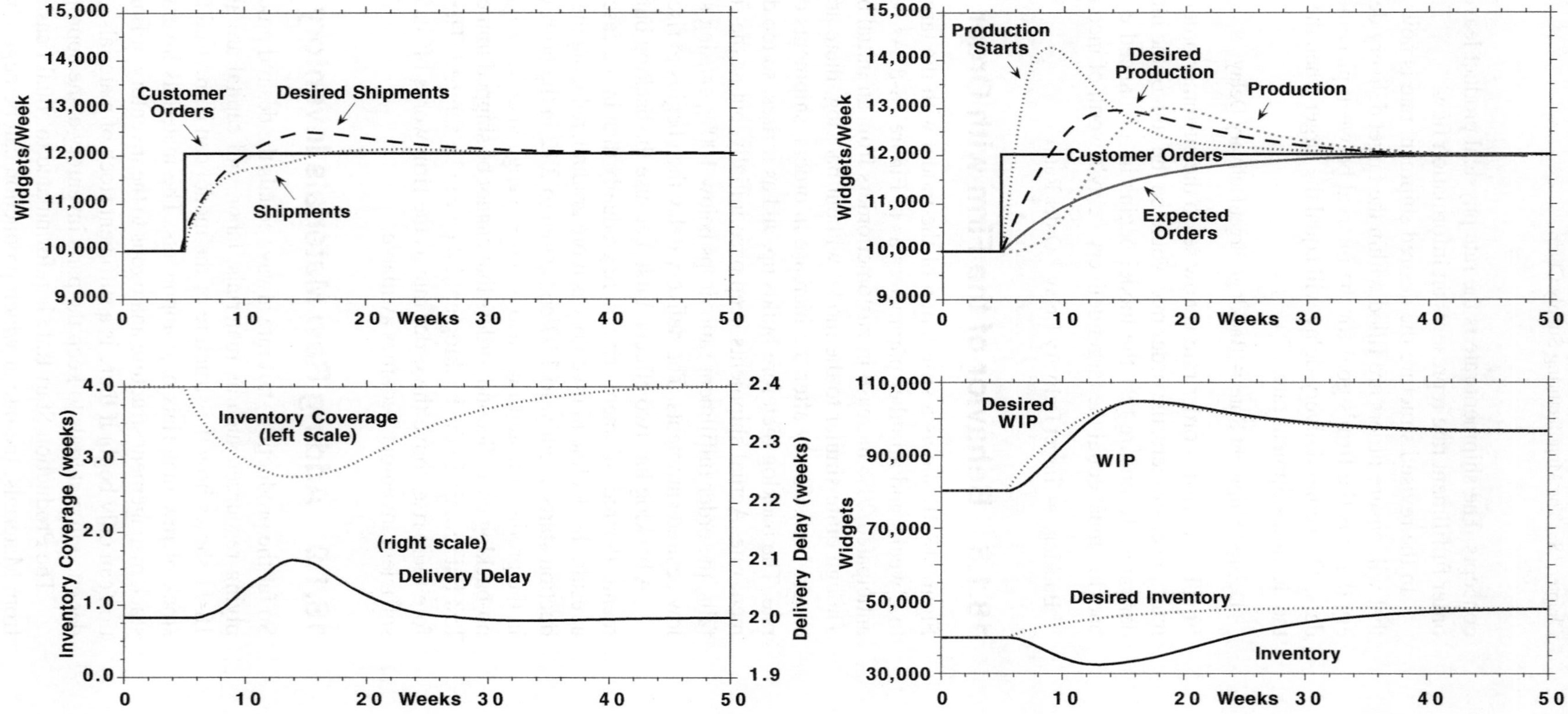

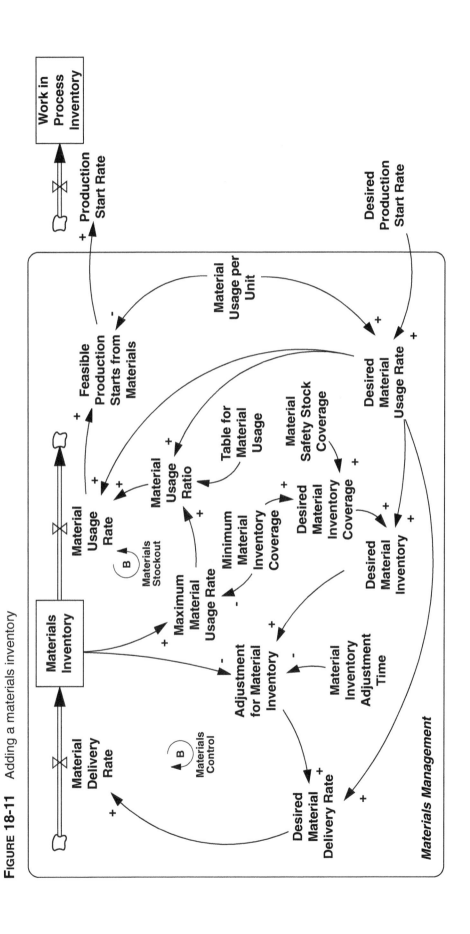

FIGURE 18-11 Adding a materials inventory

727

Usage Rate (materials/week) and Material Usage per Unit (materials/widget), the quantity of materials required per unit of output:

Production Start Rate = Feasible Production Starts from Materials   (18-32)

Feasible Production Starts from Materials
    = Material Usage Rate/Material Usage per Unit   (18-33)

The material usage rate is analogous to the shipment rate. The actual material usage rate is the desired material usage rate unless the stock of materials is inadequate, in which case usage falls below the desired rate. The Material Usage Ratio is the fraction of the desired rate achieved based on the adequacy of the materials inventories. Because the model aggregates many types of materials and components together, the usage ratio gradually drops below 100% as the maximum material usage rate falls below the desired usage rate:

Material Usage Rate
    = Desired Material Usage Rate * Material Usage Ratio   (18-34)

Material Usage Ratio
    = f(Maximum Material Usage Rate/Desired Material Usage Rate)   (18-35)

The function determining the Material Usage Ratio is analogous to the formulation for the Order Fulfillment Ratio (see Figure 18-3).

   The desired rate of material use is given by desired production starts and material usage per unit:

Desired Material Usage Rate
    = Desired Production Start Rate * Material Usage per Unit   (18-36)

The maximum rate at which materials can be used is determined by the current inventory and the minimum time required to prepare and deliver materials to the production line. This minimum material inventory coverage depends on the firm's materials handling systems and the transportation time between the materials stocks and the production line.

Maximum Material Usage Rate
    = Materials Inventory/Minimum Material Inventory Coverage   (18-37)

The stock of materials is increased by the material delivery rate and decreased by the material usage rate:

Materials Inventory
    = INTEGRAL(Material Delivery Rate − Material Usage Rate, Materials$_{t_0}$)
     (18-38)

For now, immediate delivery with no supply constraint is assumed:

Material Delivery Rate = MAX(0, Desired Material Delivery Rate)   (18-39)

The desired material delivery rate is formulated using the stock management structure, analogous to the management of finished goods inventory:

Desired Material Delivery Rate
    = Desired Material Usage Rate + Adjustment for Material Inventory   (18-40)

$$\frac{\text{Adjustment for}}{\text{Material Inventory}} = \frac{(\text{Desired Material Inventory} - \text{Materials Inventory})}{\text{Material Inventory Adjustment Time}} \quad (18\text{-}41)$$

The desired material inventory is determined by the desired usage rate and desired materials inventory coverage, which, like finished goods inventory, is set to the sum of the minimum coverage required and a safety stock coverage to ensure parts stocks do not constrain production starts under normal circumstances:

$$\begin{aligned}\text{Desired Material Inventory} \\ = \text{Desired Material Usage Rate * Desired Material Inventory Coverage}\end{aligned} \quad (18\text{-}42)$$

$$\begin{aligned}\text{Desired Material Inventory Coverage} \\ = \text{Minimum Material Inventory Coverage + Material Safety Stock Coverage}\end{aligned}$$
$$(18\text{-}43)$$

To facilitate analysis of the model, and without loss of generality, the simulations below assume Material Usage per Unit = 1 material unit/widget. Minimum Materials Inventory Coverage is 1 week, and a 1-week safety stock coverage is assumed. The materials inventory adjustment time is set to 2 weeks. The function determining the materials usage ratio is assumed to be the same as that used for shipments from final inventory. Figure 18-12 shows the response of the model to an unanticipated 20% step increase in customer orders. Given the parameters and the assumed increase in demand, the materials inventory never constrains production starts. Therefore production starts always equal the desired start rate and the behavior of all model variables is the same as shown in Figure 18-10 (this would not be true for a larger demand shock). The materials order rate exhibits additional amplification caused by the increase in the desired materials stock triggered by the surge in desired production starts. The amplification ratio of materials orders relative to customer orders is 2.52 (compared to 1.97 for production starts). Adding additional delays or stocks in a supply chain increases the amplification of demand shocks.

18.2   INTERACTIONS AMONG SUPPLY CHAIN PARTNERS

So far the stock management structure has been applied to a single firm. Real supply chains couple multiple organizations together, and the amplitude of fluctuations usually increases at every link. Producers at the upstream end of these supply chains experience much more instability in orders and production than those nearer the final customer.

The model developed so far constitutes a generic model of a firm's manufacturing process. An industry supply chain can be modeled by linking several of the single firm models together. Each member of the supply chain is then represented by the same structure, though of course the parameters can differ. The generic modules can be linked in an arbitrary network to capture the structure of an industry or economy, including multiple suppliers, competitors, and customers.

To illustrate, consider a supply chain consisting of two firms (or sectors, such as the automobile industry and its principal suppliers). As before, the customer order rate received by the downstream firm (the producer) will be considered exogenous. The order rate received by the upstream firm (the supplier) will now be

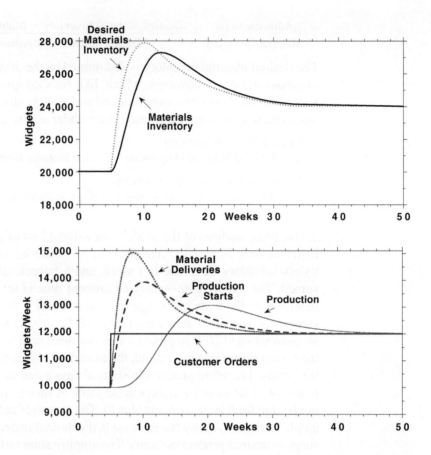

FIGURE 18-12
Response of materials inventory to an unanticipated 20% increase in demand

determined by the downstream firm. In the single firm model, actual material deliveries were equal to the desired delivery rate, implying materials orders were delivered instantly and fully. Linking the firm to a supplier means the delivery rate of materials to the producer will now depend on the supplier's ability to ship. Delays in the response of the supplier to changes in demand might now limit materials inventories and constrain the output of the producer firm.

The structure and equations for the upstream supplier are identical to those for the producer except that the order rate received by the supplier is now given by the producer's material order rate. Likewise, the supplier's forecasts are based on the orders it receives. Denoting the supplier by the subscript i and the producer by the subscript j;

Backlog i
$$= \text{INTEGRAL}(\text{Order Rate i} - \text{Order Fulfillment Rate i, Backlog i}_{t_0}) \qquad (18\text{-}44)$$

$$\text{Change in Exp Orders i} = \frac{(\text{Order Rate i} - \text{Expected Order Rate i})}{\text{Time to Average Order Rate i}} \qquad (18\text{-}45)$$

$$\text{Order Rate i} = \text{Material Order Rate j} \qquad (18\text{-}46)$$

Figure 18-13 shows the structure of the producer's materials supply line.

Because it takes time for materials to be received from the supplier, the producer keeps track of the supply line of materials on order. The stock of materials

FIGURE 18-13 Adding a supply line of materials to the model

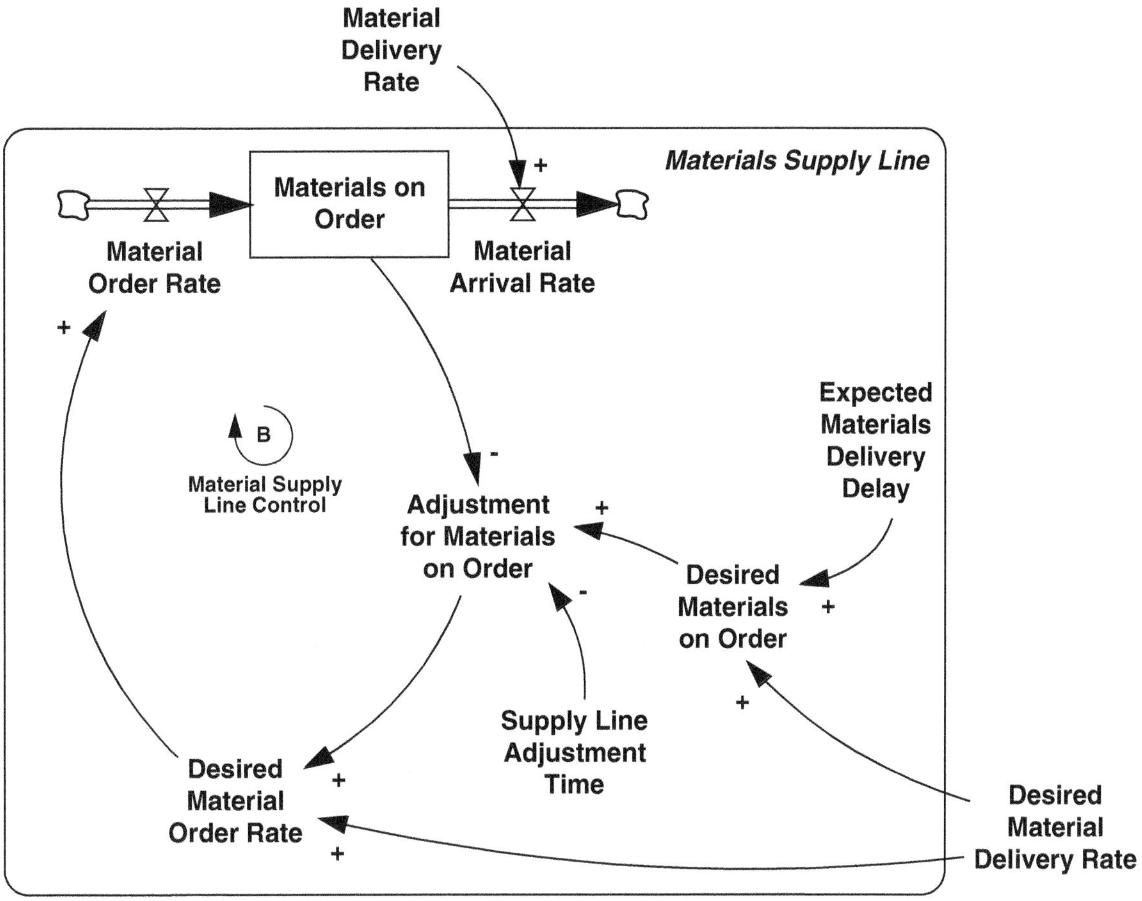

on order is increased by the material order rate and decreased by the material arrival rate:

Materials on Order j
$$= \text{INTEGRAL}(\text{Material Order Rate j} - \text{Material Arrival Rate j}, \quad (18\text{-}47)$$
Materials on Order j_{t_0})

Note that because Material Order Rate j = Order Rate i and Material Arrival Rate j = Material Delivery Rate j = Shipment Rate i, the stock of Material on Order j = Backlog i.[3] The order rate for materials is formulated using the stock management structure. Material orders are determined by the desired material delivery rate modified by an adjustment to maintain the supply line of materials on order at the appropriate level. The desired stock of materials on order is determined by the

---

[3]Provided Backlog i_{t_0} = Material on Order j_{t_0}, which should always be the case. The equilibrium Backlog i_{t_0} = Target Delivery Delay i * Order Rate i.

desired production start rate and the firm's belief about the delivery delay for receipt of materials (the expected delivery delay):

$$\frac{\text{Material}}{\text{Order Rate j}} = \text{MAX}\left(0, \frac{\text{Desired Material}}{\text{Delivery Rate j}} + \frac{\text{Adjustment for}}{\text{Materials on Order j}}\right) \qquad (18\text{-}48)$$

$$\frac{\text{Adjustment for}}{\text{Materials on Order j}} = \frac{\left(\frac{\text{Desired Materials}}{\text{on Order j}} - \frac{\text{Materials}}{\text{on Order j}}\right)}{\text{Supply Line Adjustment Time j}} \qquad (18\text{-}49)$$

$$\frac{\text{Desired Materials}}{\text{on Order j}} = \frac{\text{Expected Materials}}{\text{Delivery Delay j}} * \frac{\text{Desired Material}}{\text{Delivery Rate j}} \qquad (18\text{-}50)$$

The addition of a materials acquisition delay introduces a new feedback loop, the Materials Supply Line Control loop. This negative loop regulates the supply line of materials on order by adjusting the order rate so as to achieve the delivery rate the firm desires.

The linked model captures interactions between two firms in a supply chain. Customer demand is still exogenous, and the supplier is assumed to receive the materials it requires instantly and fully. Labor and capital are again implicitly assumed to be ample and never constrain production.

For now, assume the expected materials delivery delay is a constant, even though the actual delivery delay may vary if the supplier's inventory becomes inadequate. A constant expected delivery delay may arise if the customer does not monitor delivery delays or if the information system used to control purchasing is not updated frequently.

Figure 18-14 shows the response of the linked model to a 20% step increase in customer orders. For the purposes of exposition, the parameters of the two firms are assumed to be identical.

The two-stage supply chain performs much worse than the case where materials can be acquired fully and without delay. The producer's materials orders reach a peak of about 18,000 units/week, an amplification ratio of 4.08 (compared to 2.52 when materials are instantly available). The increase in amplification is caused by the inability of the supplier to deliver on time, causing a large drop in the producer's materials inventory and a consequent increase in producer orders (note the behavior of inventory coverage).

While the producer's response to the demand increase is still comparatively stable, the supplier is whipsawed through large amplitude fluctuations. The supplier material delivery rate reaches a peak of more than 28,000 units/week, an amplification ratio of 2.22 compared to the supplier's order rate (the material order rate of the producer). But because the order rate received by the supplier is itself already greatly amplified by the inventory, WIP, materials, and supply line adjustments of the producer, the amplification ratio of supplier material deliveries relative to customer orders is more than a factor of nine. The surge in orders received by the supplier causes a severe and prolonged shortage of inventory at the supplier, causing stockouts of some items and boosting the supplier lead time to a peak of 3.5 weeks, 75% greater than normal. Note the "double dip" behavior of the supplier shipment rate. As incoming orders surge, the supplier's delivery rate at first keeps pace, while production continues at the original rate. Supplier inventory falls

FIGURE 18-14   Response of two-stage supply chain to a 20% unanticipated demand increase

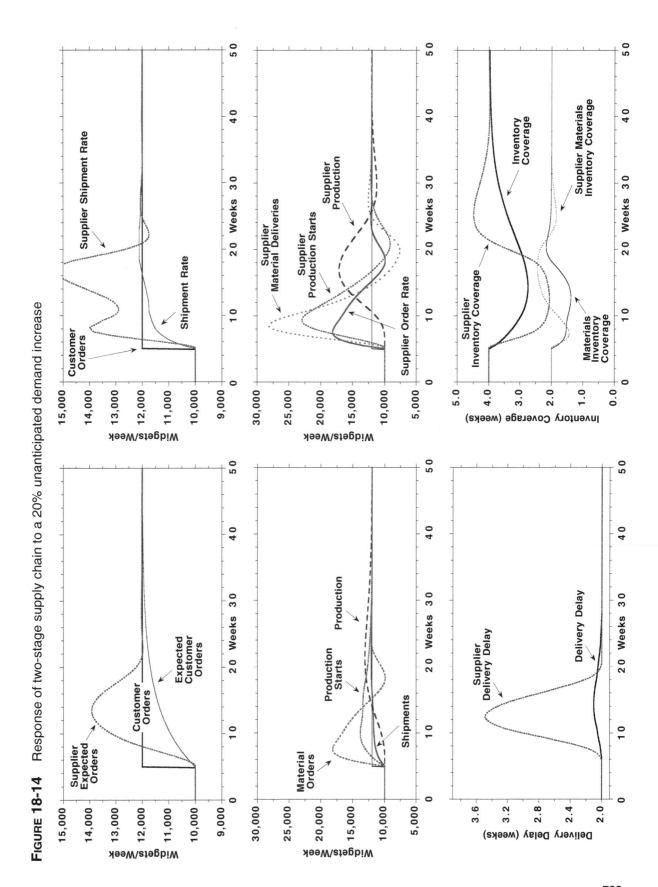

sharply, limiting shipments. The backlog swells and delivery delay rises. Eventually, new production begins to arrive, and supplier shipments rise to an even higher peak as the backlog of unfilled orders is worked off. Eventually, the shipment rate stabilizes at the new equilibrium of 12,000 units/week.[4]

The transient surge in producer orders compounds the supplier's problems. Though the supplier smooths incoming orders to filter out short-term fluctuations, the supplier's forecast of orders significantly overshoots the final equilibrium. The supplier does not know final sales and cannot tell which orders reflect an enduring change in consumer demand and which reflect temporary inventory and supply line adjustments. Consequently, the supplier first finds itself with far too little inventory and materials, leading to aggressive efforts to boost production. But just as the tap begins to flow, orders received from the producer fall, leaving the supplier with significant surplus inventory and forcing supplier production starts and production to fall far below producer orders. The delays and stock adjustments cause supplier production to be nearly completely out of phase with producer orders. Supplier output reaches its peak just about the time incoming orders fall to their low point.

The simulated supply chain, though it represents only two links, exhibits all three phenomena observed in real supply chains: oscillation, amplification, and phase lag. Most important, these attributes arise endogenously. The supplier experiences oscillation in output even though the external environment does not oscillate at all. The dynamics emerge from the interaction of the physical structure of the supply chain with the decision rules of the managers.

Of course, the step increase in customer demand is not realistic. The step is analogous to hitting a bell with a single tap of the clapper. A sudden, permanent change in demand suddenly knocks the system out of equilibrium, allowing the modeler to observe how the system responds to a single shock. Just as a single strike of the clapper causes a bell to ring for many seconds, so too a single change in customer demand causes the supply chain to oscillate, in this case, for nearly a year.

In the real world, of course, supply chains are not struck once but are continuously perturbed by changes in customer orders (and random variations in other key rates, including production, materials orders, and so on). As discussed in chapter 4, these random shocks constantly knock systems out of equilibrium, eliciting a characteristic response determined by their feedback structure. A stream of random changes in, for example, customer orders, can be thought of as a continuous succession of small pulses in demand, each with a random magnitude. Figure 18-15 shows the response of the two-firm model to a random customer order rate. For realism, the random shocks are correlated. Successive values of customer orders depend to some extent on recent orders. Such persistence is realistic because all

---

[4]The double-dip behavior of supplier shipments illustrates how a dynamic system can generate harmonics (oscillations at various multiples of a system's fundamental frequency). The production of such harmonics is fundamentally a nonlinear phenomenon and could not arise if the equations governing the supply chain were linear. In this case, the nonlinear function governing stockouts, coupled with the delay in production of new units, causes a harmonic in shipments roughly double the frequency of the underlying cycle in orders and production.

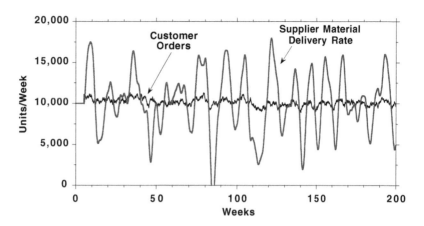

real systems have a certain degree of inertia and cannot change infinitely fast (the weather 1 hour from now is quite likely to be similar to the weather right now).[5] In the simulation the correlation time constant is 4 weeks, meaning that most of the variance in customer orders arises from rapid, week-to-week variations.

As expected, random shocks in customer orders cause the supply chain to ring like a bell. The supplier's material delivery rate fluctuates with much larger amplitude and for a much longer period than the changes in customer orders. The standard deviation of customer orders is less than 5%, but the standard deviation of the supplier's materials delivery rate is more than seven times greater (37% of the average order rate). And while most of the random fluctuation in customer orders consists of day-to-day or week-to-week variations, the response of the supply chain is a cycle with a period of about ¼ year in duration.

The purpose of inventories and backlogs in a supply chain is to buffer the system against unforeseen fluctuations in demand. The supply chain does a good job of absorbing the very rapid random fluctuations in customer orders. However, typical management policies can significantly amplify the slower variations in demand, leading to persistent, costly fluctuations. These fluctuations are progressively amplified by each stage. The system selectively attenuates high-frequency variations in demand while amplifying low frequencies. Small perturbations in demand can result in huge swings in production of raw materials.

18.2.1   Instability and Trust in Supply Chains

It is worth pausing to consider the effect of such supply chain instability on the beliefs and behaviors of managers in the different firms. In the unstable world illustrated by the simulations and the industry data shown in chapter 17, trust among partners in a supply chain can rapidly break down. Downstream firms find their suppliers to be unreliable. Delivery quotes will often not be met, and producers too often find the suppliers place their products on allocation (where each customer receives less than their full order due to a shortage of supply). In turn, suppliers find the ordering patterns of their customers to be volatile and capricious. Inside

---

[5]Technically, the random disturbance is first-order pink noise (see appendix B).

each firm, managers find their forecasts of incoming orders are rarely correct and always changing. As shown in Figure 18-14, the supplier's forecast of incoming orders (the expected order rate) reaches its peak just as actual incoming orders fall below their equilibrium level and begin to approach their minimum. Before long, the forecasts, which are typically produced by the sales and marketing organization, lose all credibility with the production and operations people. The marketing organization, in turn, complains that unreliable production makes forecasting, not to mention selling, difficult. The endogenous instability caused by the structure of a supply chain—in particular, management's own policies—can breed blame and mistrust within and between firms in a supply chain. The example of semiconductor maker Symbios, presented in chapter 11, illustrates this phenomenon. The forecasts Symbios prepared, based on the customers' own projections of their future requirements, were systematically out of step with the actual situation, degrading stability, raising costs, and slowing growth.

The conflict and mistrust created by supply chain instability feed back to worsen the instability in a vicious cycle. In the model so far, the producer manages its supply line of materials orders on the assumption that the materials delivery delay is constant. As shown in Figure 18-14, however, fluctuations in materials orders can cause large swings in supplier lead time. In many supply chains, downstream firms have learned to monitor supplier delivery quotes and lead times closely and adjust their ordering accordingly. For example, when supplier lead times increase and customers are placed on allocation, the customers often respond by increasing their desired inventory levels and ordering farther ahead, further swelling their supply line and stretching delivery delays out still more.

Figure 18-16 shows the structure of the modified model. Now the expected materials delivery delay the producer uses to manage its materials supply line is a variable, responding to changes in the actual supplier lead time.

The expected delivery delay is now a nonlinear function of the firm's belief about supplier lead times (the perceived materials delivery delay). The function is also normalized by the firm's Reference Delivery Delay, which allows the formulation to be used in situations with different normal delivery delays:

$$\begin{array}{l}\text{Expected Materials} \\ \text{Delivery Delay}\end{array} = \begin{array}{l}\text{Reference} \\ \text{Delivery Delay}\end{array} * f\left(\frac{\text{Perceived Materials Delivery Delay}}{\text{Reference Delivery Delay}}\right)$$

$$(18\text{-}51)$$

The perceived delivery delay adjusts with a delay to changes in the actual supplier lead time due to the time required to receive and check the accuracy of supplier delivery quotes, the time required to revise beliefs, and the lag in the response of the purchasing and procurement systems. First-order smoothing is assumed, with an average lag given by the Materials Delivery Delay Perception Time:

$$\begin{array}{l}\text{Perceived Materials} \\ \text{Delivery Delay}\end{array} = \text{SMOOTH}\left(\begin{array}{cc}\text{Supplier} & \text{Materials Delivery Delay} \\ \text{Delivery Delay,} & \text{Perception Time}\end{array}\right)$$

$$(18\text{-}52)$$

Figure 18-17 shows a typical nonlinear function relating the perceived delivery delay to the expected delay.

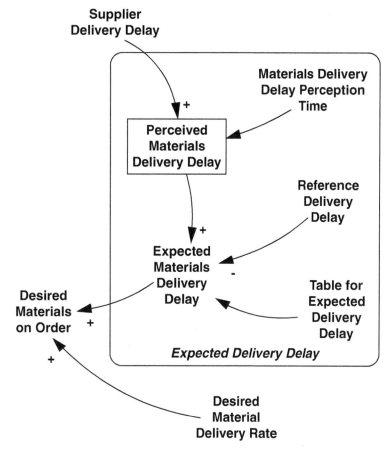

FIGURE 18-16
Structure for dynamic lead time expectations

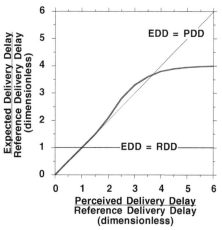

FIGURE 18-17
Relationship between the perceived and expected delivery delay

The function is normalized by the Reference Delivery Delay. The line EDD/RDD = 1 represents the base case in which the firm uses a constant delivery delay to manage the supply line of materials orders. The 45° line represents a policy in which the expected delivery delay always equals the firm's current belief about supplier lead times. The assumed relationship saturates at a maximum for very high delivery delays: The purchasing managers of the firm believe very high delivery delays will not persist and do not increase the materials supply line without limit. The region where the relationship rises above the 45° line indicates a situation in which the purchasing managers don't trust the delivery delay quotes they receive from the supplier and hedge even further by increasing their estimate of lead times beyond what recent experience would indicate. Such hedging is particularly likely in situations where the supplier serves multiple customers. Suppose the supplier runs short of product and places the customers on allocation: Each will only receive 80% of its order. Customers are likely to respond by ordering 125% or even more of what they actually require. Each inflates its order to seek a larger share of the pie at the expense of its competitors. Firms that fail to play this allocation game will likely lose market share to more aggressive competitors. Customers faced with long delivery delays from their suppliers also frequently place orders with multiple suppliers, then cancel them when the lead time falls and products become available.

The response of the modified model to an unanticipated 20% step increase in customer orders is shown in Figure 18-18. The delay in perceiving supplier lead times is assumed to be 4 weeks. To determine that a delivery quote will not be met requires waiting at least until the promised delivery date, and further time is required to react to changes in availability by altering purchase orders.

Active monitoring and revision of supplier lead times, while intended to improve the flow of materials to the producer, actually destabilize the system further. Supplier lead times rise to a peak value about 23% greater than the case where the expected delivery delay is constant. As producer materials orders surge and the supplier lead time begins to rise, the producer reacts by gradually boosting its estimate of the delivery delay, leading to a large increase in the desired supply line of materials. Orders increase still more, pushing the delivery delay up still higher, in a positive feedback. The supplier is forced to expand output even more. As the surge of new production becomes available and the supplier's delivery delay begins to fall, the producer responds by cutting the desired supply line of materials, and producer materials orders plummet. Due to the lag in perceiving and responding to the supplier lead time, however, the drop in orders comes too late to prevent the producer from accumulating a much larger surplus of unneeded materials. The supplier is hurt much more. When producer orders collapse, the supplier finds itself with so much excess inventory, WIP, and materials that it cuts its own materials procurement to zero for nearly a month. Supplier inventory coverage rises to a peak of more than 6 weeks, 50% more than the desired level and much more than the base case.

On the surface, it appears that the supplier bears most of the excess costs created by the positive lead time feedback. However, these costs must eventually be passed on to the downstream firms in the form of higher prices, poor customer service, and unreliable delivery. Producer firms have a strong incentive to improve the stability of their suppliers. Nevertheless, the parochial, local incentives facing individual functions and firms often lead to actions that degrade the stability of the entire supply chain.

Why would customers revise their delivery delay estimates when the effect is harmful to both their suppliers and themselves? Flexible expectations for supplier lead times are locally rational. To ensure an appropriate delivery rate of materials,

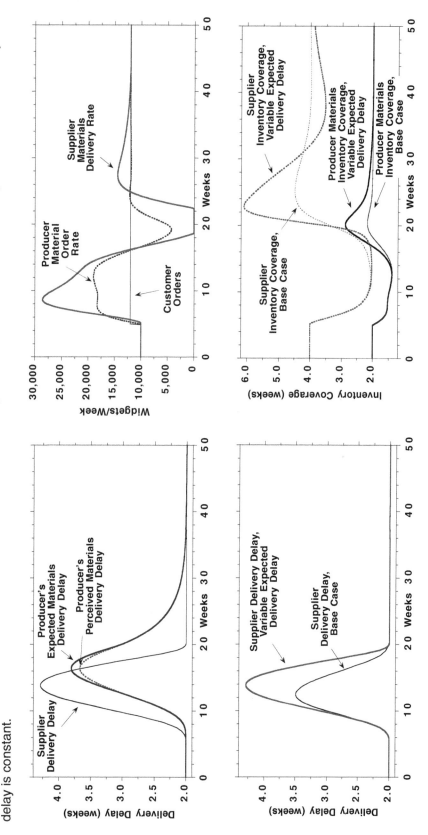

FIGURE 18-18 Behavior of the supply chain with forward purchasing by customers

The top panels show the behavior of the model when the producer's expected delivery delay for materials is variable, as specified in equations (18-51)–(18-52). The bottom panels compare the behavior against the base case in which the expected materials delivery delay is constant.

the purchasing department must maintain a supply line proportional to the delivery delay. From the point of view of the purchasing managers in a firm, it is critical that they monitor and respond to changes in supplier lead times, either manually or by revising the assumed lead times in their procurement system software. Failure to respond to changes in lead times could result in costly accumulation of excess parts inventories, or, worse, shortages that could shut down production.

The mental models of the purchasing managers in downstream firms typically treat the supplier lead time as exogenous and outside their control. In some cases each firm reasons that it is responsible for only a small part of the supplier's total demand, so changes in its orders won't affect supplier lead times. Organizational routines such as updating the supplier lead time assumptions of the materials requirement planning (MRP) system based on recent delivery experience implicitly presume that the resulting changes in materials orders won't affect supplier lead times. But when all customers act in a similar fashion, the positive loop is closed. The mismatch between the mental models of the supplier, in which lead times are exogenous, and the actual situation, in which lead times are strongly affected by the ordering behavior of the downstream firms, further degrades supply chain performance and reinforces the view of the different organizations that their partners are unpredictable and untrustworthy.

18.2.2   From Functional Silos to Integrated Supply Chain Management

The supply chain model developed so far treats each firm as a separate entity. The information passed between customer and supplier is limited to orders, delivery delays, and shipments. Other information is kept private. Indeed, downstream firms are quite reluctant to share other information, such as their actual sales rate. If their suppliers knew the actual customer sales rate it would be more difficult for the firm to manipulate orders to get a larger allocation when delivery delays were high.

To address these issues, many firms have moved to integrate the supply chain from customer to raw materials supplier. These policies go by names such as EDI (electronic data interchange), ECR (efficient customer response), and VMI (vendor-managed inventory). These policies have enjoyed broad diffusion in the 1990s as part of the general trend toward lean manufacturing and just-in-time policies. Each attacks a different aspect of the supply chain. EDI reduces the time delays and costs of replenishment ordering so that customers can order smaller batches more frequently, smoothing the flow of materials orders received by suppliers. Other policies, such as ECR, involve additional changes in order fulfillment, distribution, and transportation policies to reduce delivery lead times. These policies include third-party warehousing, continuous replenishment, use of mixed truckload shipping, and so on. Point of sale (POS) data can also be electronically shared with suppliers, eliminating delays and distortions in the information suppliers need to plan production and capacity. Vendor-managed inventory goes further.

Under VMI the supplier manages the entire distribution chain and determines how much to ship to each echelon, eliminating the need for customers to place orders for materials.[6]

CHALLENGE

Reengineering the Supply Chain

Test the effects of different supply chain integration policies using the two-stage supply chain model shown in Figure 18-18. Be sure to consider the effect of each policy on the following variables:

a. The total amplification of the supply chain (the amplification ratio of supplier material deliveries relative to customer orders), a measure of instability in the overall supply chain.

b. The supplier's delivery delay and order fulfillment ratio (measures of the supplier's delivery reliability).

c. The producer firm's delivery delay and order fulfillment ratio (measures of the producer's ability to service its customers).

d. Any other indicators you feel are important, such as materials, WIP, and finished inventory levels at the supplier and producer.

Test the following policies. First, test each policy in isolation, keeping all other policies and parameters in place. In each case, explain why the policy works (or fails) in terms of the feedback structure of the system. Who benefits? Does one partner in the supply chain benefit while the other suffers? What conflicts might the policy create? You should test the response of each policy to a 20% step increase in customer orders and any other test inputs you desire.

1.   Sharing POS data: Assume the supplier bases its forecast of orders on the actual customer order rate instead of the incoming materials order rate. To do so, modify the input to the supplier's forecast of demand to be Customer Orders * Materials Usage per Unit.

2.   EDI and quick response: Assume that by moving to electronic data interchange and making improvements in the order fulfillment process the supplier can reduce the time required to process, ship, and deliver orders. Implement this policy by cutting the supplier's target delivery delay by 50%.

3.   Lean manufacturing: Lean manufacturing policies reduce the amount of inventory a firm requires without compromising its ability to fill orders or meet production schedules. Achieving a well-functioning lean production system is far

---

[6]Simchi-Levi, Kaminsky, and Simchi-Levi (1999) discuss supply chain management in detail.

from trivial and requires changes in many aspects of operations, production scheduling, the layout of plant and equipment on the factory floor, quality improvement and maintenance activity, and others (see Womack and Roos 1991). The supply chain model does not indicate how to achieve a lean production system. Other models would be needed for that. But it can be used to explore how a lean system with dramatically shorter cycle times might affect supply chain performance. To model the effects of a successful transition to lean manufacturing, consider reductions in the manufacturing cycle time (the delay between production starts and completion), minimum inventory coverage, and minimum materials inventory coverage. Consider these changes individually and for the producer alone, the supplier alone, and for both firms.

4. Response to lean manufacturing: Lean manufacturing is more than a reduction in cycle times. In addition to changes in physical delays, consider how various management policies such as the various inventory adjustment times and the sizes of the safety stocks might change once a lean production system is implemented.

5. Phantom orders and lead time gaming: Suppose the producer firm reacts to the unreliability of the supplier by shortening the delay in updating its perception of the supplier delivery delay. What is the impact? Why? What is the effect of eliminating lead time gaming in which firms order farther ahead when supplier lead times stretch out? Implement this policy by changing the response of the expected delivery delay to the perceived delivery delay.

6. Vendor-managed inventory: Suppose the supplier manages the distribution of materials centrally. There are many variants of VMI. One simple treatment is to assume the supplier monitors the producer's materials inventories and ships accordingly. The supplier is then responsible for ensuring the producer always has the materials needed to start production at the desired rate and pays a penalty if it falls short. How would you modify the model to capture such a policy? Implement and test your formulation.

7. Try any other policies you wish. For each, consider how the policy might be implemented in the real world and how that change can be captured in the model.

After considering the effects of each policy in isolation, consider their interactions. In particular, implement the POS and EDI/quick response policies together and then in combination with the lean manufacturing policies you prefer. How does the response of the system to sharing POS data change when the system is lean compared to the base case? Why?

Under what circumstances will different policies for improving supply chain performance work? Are there situations in which some of the commonly recommended policies are likely to fail? Why?

Finally, recommend a combination of policies to stabilize the supply chain and improve customer service. Discuss the challenges firms might face in implementing your preferred policies. Consider in particular which firms bear the costs of each change and which reap the benefits. How might the costs and gains be shared among the partners in a supply chain?

18.3   SYSTEM DYNAMICS IN ACTION: REENGINEERING THE SUPPLY CHAIN IN A HIGH-VELOCITY INDUSTRY[7]

The computer and electronics industry is one of the most dynamic and demanding industries in the world economy today. Competition is intense. Rapid growth, increasing complexity of technology, globalization, and other changes pose enormous challenges for core business processes such as the supply chain and product development. Prices fall at a tremendous rate while speed and functionality grow with each new product generation. Product life cycles of a year or less mean companies have only a few months in which to sell sufficient volume of a new product at high enough margins to generate the profits needed for product development and growth.

"Fast Growth Electronics" (a pseudonym; hereafter referred to as FGE), the client for this system dynamics study, is one of the most successful firms in the industry. In the 5 years prior to the modeling project the number of units shipped grew about 50%/year and revenue grew about 40%/year (revenue growth is slower than shipment growth because computer prices are continually declining). During this period FGE's market share grew steadily. Net income grew about 60%/year.

18.3.1   Initial Problem Definition

On first examination FGE was doing extremely well. But beneath the surface stress was accumulating. Rapid growth had strained FGE's systems for order processing, forecasting, production planning, materials procurement, and other core operations. Quoted delivery dates were typically revised many times. Too often delivery commitments were met through expediting and other last-minute heroics. As in many firms, quarterly revenue targets led to a severe "hockey stick" pattern in which a large fraction of quarterly shipments occurred in the last few days of each quarter as people scrambled to meet the target, disrupting workflow throughout the system. The supply chain and customer service challenge was brought home forcefully in a meeting between FGE's top management and the CEO of one of its largest customers at that time, a large electronics retail chain who said, "You're the best supplier we deal with, but you're first in a race of pigs."

FGE's CEO set aggressive goals to exceed world class benchmarks for a variety of performance metrics. While the potential for improvement was great, the challenge was daunting. Even as FGE grew into a formidable global company, barriers to entry were low and many nimble competitors arose to challenge them.

Internally, FGE's growth had outstripped its own systems for managing the supply chain and the organization could no longer adequately coordinate its many incompatible, overlapping, and undersized systems and processes. For example,

---

[7]I am indebted to "Fast Growth Electronics" and to McKinsey & Company for their permission to present this case and help with its preparation. I particularly thank Damon Beyer (Principal at McKinsey & Co.) and Nathaniel Mass (formerly a principal at McKinsey & Co.; currently Senior Vice President at GenCorp) for their assistance in the preparation of this chapter. I also thank the people I interviewed at FGE.

product complexity was growing exponentially: The number of SKUs (stock keeping units) increased by a factor of 35 in 5 years.

The existing supply chain (including processes for order processing, credit approval, production scheduling, product allocation, shipments and returns, demand forecasting, materials requirements planning (MRP), parts procurement, expediting, supplier qualification, new product launch planning, and product development) had not been designed so much as it evolved from a host of local solutions to local problems caused by the growth and increasing complexity of the business. By the early 1990s, the system was clearly no longer adequate. Product life cycles were 5 to 9 months, yet acquisition times for some key components and materials were over 3 months. The delays were worsened by high turnover in the supplier base as technology changed. Compounding the procurement delays were long delays in FGE's internal planning, forecasting, and purchasing systems. Often 2 to 3 months were required to prepare and revise production plans and order the required components from suppliers. Production planners therefore had to forecast demand for new products well in advance of their introduction to the market and, more importantly, had to ramp down part procurement and production well before the end of the product's life, often just as sales were heating up. Yet, as is typical in such high-velocity industries, the accuracy of demand forecasts over the required planning horizon was low, with typical errors of 50% to 100%. Besides the usual sources of uncertainty such as the state of the economy, forecast accuracy is low because the success of a particular product depends on its price and performance relative to the price and performance of competing products. Delays of even a few weeks in the introduction of a competitor's latest offering will send customers your way, perhaps turning one of your weak sellers into an unexpected success, while introduction of competitor products earlier than expected can turn your strong contender into an also-ran. Predicting the dates of your own product introductions 3 months in advance is difficult enough; anticipating the moves of the competition is even harder.

Product development times often significantly exceeded the life cycles of the products themselves. Advanced development teams were always designing products intended to replace products that hadn't yet been introduced to market. Delays in product introduction could lead to situations where a product was phased out before its successor could be built, leading to gaps in the product line. Though product line gaps were too frequent, on average FGE was caught with an unacceptable level of excess inventory at the end of the product life cycle. Because of the high rate of technological change, old products have low salvage or remaindering value, forcing the sales force to focus a great deal of attention on moving old product to avoid the accumulation of so-called sludge inventory and costly write-downs.

Unanticipated interactions among different functions and between FGE and its customers contributed to forecast error and the buildup of obsolete inventory. The retail chains and corporate resellers that constituted FGE's main distribution channels typically operated on very thin margins. Often the finance department would place customer orders on credit hold, delaying the production planning and procurement process. As the end of the quarter approached, however, finance would come under pressure to lift the credit holds so product groups could meet their quarterly sales objectives. Distribution channel partners quickly learned to withhold their orders until late in the quarter in the hope of receiving more favorable prices or credit terms. Late receipt of orders increased order volatility, decreased forecast accuracy, further strained the procurement system, and eroded trust between FGE and its customers.

Since FGE provided full price protection to their channel partners, resellers and retailers had strong incentives to order aggressively and could freely cancel orders as well. The resulting demand volatility made it harder to deliver reliably to the channel, strengthening beliefs on both sides that the other was unreliable.

There was no lack of ideas to address these problems (Table 18-2). Each policy had its advocates, was supported by a certain logic, and successful examples of each could be found in the business literature. The problem was not generating ideas but evaluating which ideas might work, how they might interact, which would have the highest leverage, and which should be implemented first. Many policies triggered internal conflict: Shrinking procurement lead times conflicted with procedures for supplier qualification and component quality assurance; curtailing expediting decreased marketing flexibility; freezing product introduction dates to prevent holes in the product line stressed the product development organization. Months of traditional analysis by FGE and its consultants revealed no obvious policy recommendations and made it hard to motivate the need for change. After all, the company was undeniably successful. Some in the organization argued away any particular past problem with statements such as "We were just growing too fast," "That was just a bad example . . . [It was the] worst case," or "We solved that one already." Paralysis threatened.

TABLE 18-2
No clear root causes or high leverage policies emerged from traditional analysis.

Key Problems

- Long delivery times and poor delivery reliability
- Surplus inventory
- Low predictability of demand
- Product line gaps
- Quarterly volatility

Suggested Policies

- Dramatically cut restaging delays for long lead time materials
- Cut monthly planning cycle by over 80%
- Improve material positioning at new product introduction
- Improve launch predictability
- Increase component commonality
- Get real-time demand/sales information
- Improve demand forecast accuracy
- Build to order
- Resolve credit holds earlier
- Innovate with manufacturing cells

Source: McKinsey & Co.

18.3.2   Reference Mode and Dynamic Hypothesis

At this point, stimulated by senior managers at FGE, the McKinsey team working to reengineer FGE's supply chain turned to system dynamics. The model was developed by an experienced system dynamics practitioner, Nathaniel Mass, working in close collaboration with the McKinsey and client teams. Building on the data already collected, the modeling team spent about 2 weeks interviewing various members of the client organization, including purchasing managers, materials planners, and others responsible for key decisions in the supply chain. The team also held several 1½-day workshops with key decision makers from the various supply chain functions to elicit information needed to formulate the model. These initial meetings focused on the problem characteristics discussed above: long and variable delivery times, long delays in supply chain response, quarterly volatility, financial pressure to reduce obsolete inventory, etc. The team found that excess inventory at the end of product life was a severe problem whether the product in question was a slow mover or a hot product whose sales greatly exceeded initial expectations. This latter result was unexpected and counterintuitive.

Understanding the source of excess inventory for slow-moving products is straightforward. Sales of such a product, for whatever reason, fall short of the forecasts used to determine initial build volumes and materials commitments. A natural reluctance to reduce the forecasts even as sales fell below expectations, coupled with long lags in the response of the materials planning and production system, caused excess inventories to accumulate.

The accumulation of surplus inventory for hot products, however, was difficult to understand. How is it possible to accumulate surplus inventory for a product whose sales greatly exceed expectations, a product which is flying off the shelves, a product you can't make fast enough? Figure 18-19 shows the typical behavior observed for a hot product, showing how initial backlogs lead to restaging of production and the buildup of excess inventory. Figure 18-20 shows a causal diagram capturing the dynamic hypothesis they developed to explain the inventory buildup.

Prior to product introduction, FGE develops initial sales forecasts and receives initial orders for the product from the distribution channel. The channel partners adjust their orders until the number of units on order with the manufacturer (the channel backlog) equals the channel's desired order backlog, forming the balancing Supply Line Control loop B1.

The manufacturer uses the initial sales forecasts and order backlogs to commit to a product build schedule and initial staging of long lead time components. When a product turns out to be a hot seller, customer purchases rapidly deplete channel inventories. The channel partners must then order more from FGE. These unexpectedly large orders soon deplete FGE's inventories, and shipments fall below requirements (the balancing Availability loop B2 constrains shipments below desired levels). The product is put on allocation and the delivery delay experienced by the channel increases. Further, as shipments fall below requirements the predictability of deliveries also falls—channel buyers and purchasing agents spend a great deal of time trying to get more product and accurate estimates of delivery quantities and timing from their account manager. The channel partners, increasingly desperate to get more of the hot seller, react to the long lead time by Ordering Ahead: When

FIGURE 18-19

Typical dynamics of a hot product

Initial scarcity leads to phantom orders as the distribution channel reacts to rising lead times. The production system responds with a lag to the surge in backorders. As the build rate and shipments rise, lead time falls, leading to cancellation of phantom orders. Lagged response of the supply chain causes excess inventory to accumulate as the backlog of channel orders collapses before the build rate can be ramped down.

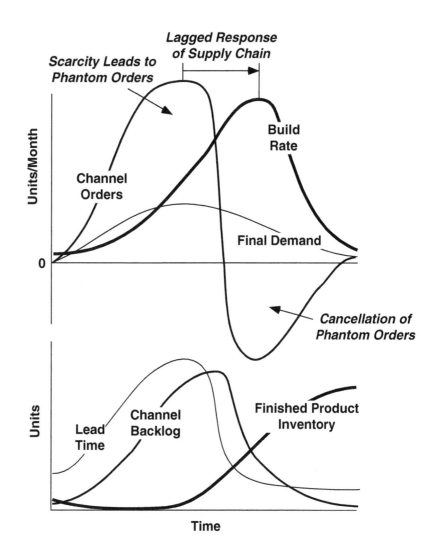

delivery times stretch out from, say, 2 to 4 weeks, the supply line of product on order must grow from 2 to 4 weeks' worth of expected sales. The backlog rises still more, further increasing expected lead time and causing the channel partners to order even more (reinforcing loop R1). Further, as delivery reliability falls, channel purchasing managers react by Ordering Defensively, increasing their desired safety stocks and boosting the backlog still more, which further reduces delivery reliability and closes the reinforcing loop R2. The effect of these two positive feedbacks is to create a surge of "phantom orders" for hot products, orders placed in reaction to the growing scarcity of the product.

From the perspective of FGE's channel partners this behavior is entirely rational. When a hot product becomes scarce, each reseller and retailer must compete against the others for a larger allocation. When the manufacturer informs them that a hot seller is going on allocation each reseller responds by ordering more than it really needs in an attempt to get a larger share of the limited pie of production. The two positive feedbacks caused by Ordering Ahead and Ordering Defensively mean

FIGURE 18-20   Causal loop diagram showing how hot products generate surplus inventory

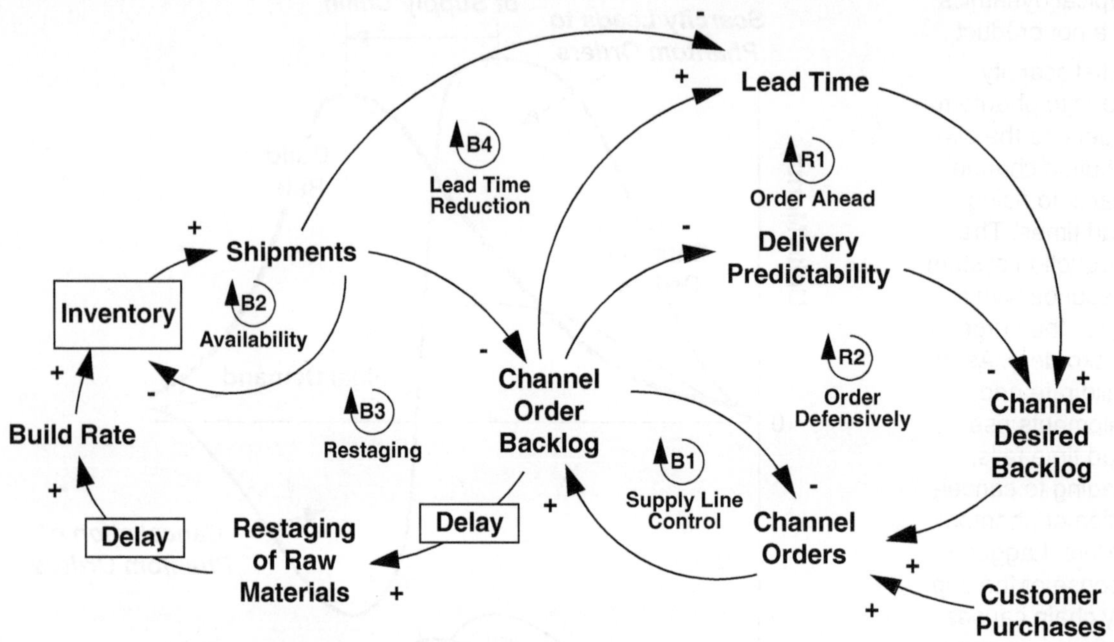

Source: Adapted from a McKinsey and Co. diagram. Used with permission.

that in the near term, reductions in supply actually increase demand, worsening the apparent shortage.

FGE, like many suppliers, could not distinguish real orders from the phantom orders placed in response to product scarcity. Point of sale information on purchases by final customers was not widely available and resellers and retailers were reluctant to share their sales data as they believed it would reduce their ability to control their inventories and hedge against variability in product availability by manipulating their orders. As sales of a hot product led to shortages, channel orders would rise far above final demand, but the customers, if asked, would insist they needed every unit they ordered, and more, to meet the ballooning demand.

Faced with a huge surge in orders, FGE's materials planning and production system would strain to respond, reordering critical components and expediting production. Despite these heroics, revising production targets, restaging parts and materials inventories, and assembling the product take time (note the delays in the links between channel backlog and the build rate).

Eventually, shipments to channel partners increase and the delivery delay experienced by the channel falls. Retailers and resellers find they no longer need to order so far ahead and can reduce their order backlog. Soon the product goes off allocation and channel partners can readily get everything they order.

As soon as customers realize that the product is now fully available with short lead times they cancel the remaining phantom orders, shrinking the backlog. Further, once they can quickly and reliably restock their shelves there is no need for them to carry defensive inventory, so orders fall even further as they liquidate their safety stocks. The reinforcing feedbacks R1 and R2 now reverse: Rising availability reduces channel orders, shrinking the backlog, reducing lead times and increasing delivery reliability, and leading to lower and lower orders. The switch from the vicious cycle of deteriorating order fulfillment and still larger backlogs to the self-reinforcing collapse of the backlog starts at about the point where production has risen enough to match the rate at which new orders arrive. New production plans and materials orders are slashed as product inventory builds, but the long planning delays, along with commitments to suppliers for more components, mean production continues for some time. The lagged response of the supply chain leaves the manufacturer holding a mountain of excess inventory at the end of the product's life.

18.3.3   Model Formulation

Initial model development took about 2 weeks. The team presented the initial model to FGE's senior management team, including the CEO, right away. The model was presented in a workshop format—senior managers could suggest tests and policies that were run immediately and discussed on the spot, helping to build their understanding of and confidence in the model.

Over the course of the next month they revised the model in response to the critiques they received. At each stage they reviewed the interim results in workshops with the senior management team, often including the CEO. In each the model was run live with FGE's executives suggesting tests and policies. Most of these could be simulated and discussed during the workshop; others required changes in model structure and were reported at the next meeting.

The model focused on the dynamic complexity of FGE's supply chain, not the detail complexity. There was no attempt to represent every SKU in the product line. Instead, the model focused on the interdependencies and feedbacks created by the behavior of the actors, particularly interactions between the distribution channel, FGE, and its suppliers. The final model tracked a representative product through its life cycle. The thousands of different components and materials were grouped into seven categories, distinguished by their costs, lead times, and other attributes. The model of the production and assembly process captured the complexity created by multiple configuration options but did not represent every product variation. The model also included the introduction of the next generation product to capture the dynamics of product transitions. The model contained roughly 500 stocks, or state variables, rendering the rich dynamic complexity of the supply chain with sufficient fidelity for the purpose while remaining a manageable size.

18.3.4   Testing the Model

The team tested the model's ability to replicate the history of two actual products, one slow mover and one hot. The purpose of this test was not merely to examine the statistical fit between the model and data nor was it to evaluate the forecasting performance of the model. The FGE managers were sophisticated model users and knew that replication of historical fit alone is a weak test. The model had to be able to replicate the patterns observed for both types of products without any changes to its structure or the parameters characterizing the order processing system. Only the assumed pattern of final demand could vary, from that of a weak seller to that of a strong seller. The model had to generate the right behavior for the right reasons, without the use of fudge factors. Figure 18-21 shows simulations of the full model compared to the actual data (the vertical and time scales have been disguised).

The model tracks the behavior of the slow-moving product well, showing the depletion of the backlog and transition to sludge inventory in the middle of the projected product life cycle. At the time the simulation was made, the slow-moving product had already been withdrawn from the market and the actual data were available. In contrast, the hot product was still on the market at the time of the analysis. Indeed, at the time the simulation was made, there was a large backlog of unfilled orders (net inventory was significantly negative) and the lead time was

FIGURE 18-21
Simulations of the full model compared to history for slow-moving and hot products

Top: Simulation of a slow-moving product. Sales fall short of initial projections; backlog is rapidly depleted and excess inventory accumulates.

Bottom: Simulation of a hot product. Strong sales lead to huge backlog, long delivery delays, and phantom orders by distribution channel. When restaged production eventually shrinks delivery times, channel orders are canceled, leading to excess inventory.

Time periods and vertical scales disguised.

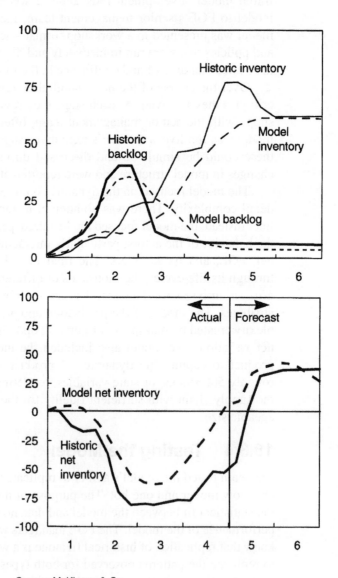

Source: McKinsey & Co.

much longer than normal. The model tracked the buildup of the backlog reasonably well. More importantly, the model suggested that the backlog would soon shift to a large excess inventory, counter to the expectations of many inside the company. Shortly afterward, the backlog collapsed and the firm was left with a large surplus inventory. The ability of the model to replicate these two product histories without extensive parameter adjustment showed FGE's management that the sources of the surplus inventory problem were deeply embedded in the structure of the supply chain and were not the result of bad decisions made by particular managers. The model thus focused attention on redesigning that structure rather than the decisions of the people in the system.

The replication of past experience was not the only test of the model. It is generally quite easy to tune a model to fit a given set of data. Building confidence in a model involves a much broader series of tests, both of the structure and its response to a wide range of circumstances, not only the limited range of historical experience (see chapter 21).

18.3.5 Policy Analysis

To begin policy analysis the team first simulated each major policy initiative in isolation, calculating the change in life cycle profitability. Contrary to the expectations of some, improving forecast accuracy or product launch predictability had only average impact and reducing the severity of the quarterly hockey stick had a weak effect. The stand-alone analysis showed the high leverage point to be reducing the delays in the response of the supply chain to changes in demand. But how would these policies interact? Might they not interfere with one another or suffer diminishing returns? Simulations showed that jointly implementing materials lead time reduction, planning cycle time reductions, and a build-to-order policy generated a substantial synergy. The total impact exceeded the sum of the benefits of the individual policies.

The sources of synergy can be seen in the causal diagram shown in Figure 18-22. The cycle time reduction policies (shown in boxes) create synergy by reducing lead times so the reinforcing feedbacks creating phantom orders operate not as vicious cycles, as they had been, but as virtuous cycles, progressively and cumulatively improving system performance and profitability. As faster order fulfillment and supply chain response reduce the incidence of initial shortages, phantom orders fall and customers require less defensive inventory, stabilizing channel orders. The less volatile the channel orders, the more accurate FGE's demand forecasts become, easing the burden on suppliers and leading to fewer instances of late product restaging, fewer raw material shortages, and more reliable deliveries—reducing phantom orders still more. Further, reduction in late restaging of materials and components leads to higher component quality and lower raw materials and expediting costs. Less expediting and firefighting to get the current product out increase the time available to plan the introduction of the next generation product, reducing launch delays and the risk of holes in the product line. More timely new product introduction prevents the buildup of phantom orders at the start of the next product's life, reducing delivery lead times further. And so on.

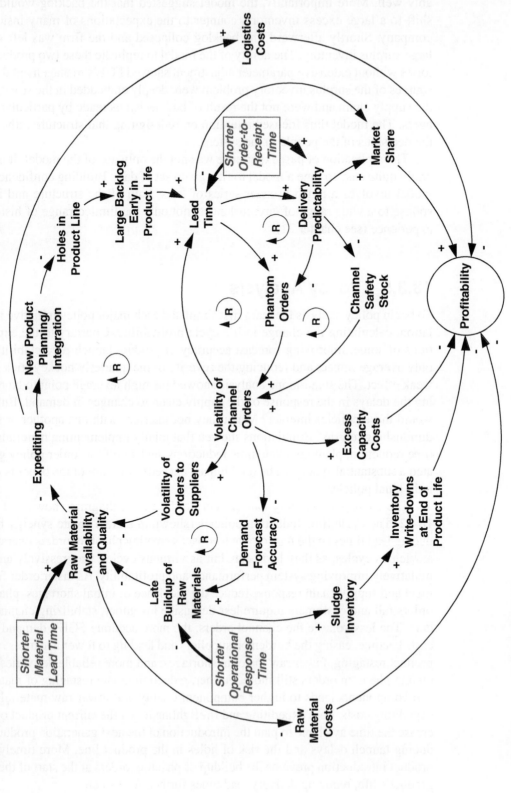

FIGURE 18-22 Causal diagram showing sources of synergy among lead time reduction policies

Policies denoted by rectangles and italics.

Source: Adapted from a McKinsey & Co. diagram.

FIGURE 18-23

Buildup of surplus inventory was self-reinforcing.

Financial pressure to reduce inventory buildup led to more conservative initial materials staging, increasing the chance of shortages that lead to phantom orders, aggressive late restaging of materials, and buildup of even more surplus stock, in a vicious cycle.

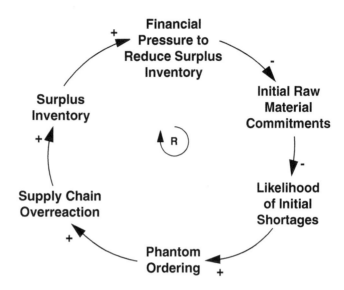

Over time, efforts to reduce inventory had actually made the problem worse, through the feedback shown in Figure 18-23. As the buildup of sludge inventory worsened financial performance, managers throughout the organization came under intense pressure to reduce inventory costs. They reacted by reducing initial staging inventories as each new product was planned. Cutting initial build commitments was rational from their perspective because they viewed demand to be exogenous and unpredictable. From that perspective, smaller initial build volumes reduce the likelihood any given product will be a slow mover. However, demand is not exogenous but is strongly shaped by FGE's own behavior: The lower the initial materials commitments, the greater the chance of initial shortages, triggering phantom orders from customers and forcing the organization to engage in expensive late restaging of critical materials—culminating in even more surplus inventory and still more financial pressure. Unchecked, this positive feedback could act as a death spiral. A key insight emerging from the model was that *larger* initial staging of critical materials could actually *reduce* the buildup of sludge and lower life cycle inventory costs.

18.3.6   Implementation: Sequential Debottlenecking

The model analysis identified a number of high leverage policies and showed how they would generate substantial synergy from joint implementation. The policy recommendations would require complete redesign of the entire order processing, production planning, logistics, supplier management, and production systems—a huge undertaking requiring a phased approach. To put the insights emerging from the model into practice, the modeling team worked with the client to understand the optimal sequencing of policy initiatives. Much of the management literature suggests that improvement activities should focus on finding and relaxing the current bottleneck inhibiting the throughput of any process (see, e.g., Goldratt and Cox 1986). Focusing improvement effort on the current bottleneck immediately boosts throughput, while effort to improve nonbottleneck activities is wasted. The modeling team realized, however, that in the high-growth environment of the computer/electronics industry, relaxing one bottleneck simply enables growth to continue until a new part of the process becomes the bottleneck and threatens the health of the organization. The pace of expansion and the intensity of competition are so great that waiting for each bottleneck to emerge before attacking it could slow the growth of the company and erode its competitiveness.

The team used the model to explore the impact of different implementation sequences. By simulating the effect of implementing one policy, say materials lead time reduction, the team could observe when and how growth improved, putting even more stress on the rest of the system and creating a new bottleneck, say the MRP cycle time. Correcting that bottleneck would enable still more growth, until the next bottleneck emerged, say the assembly and build cycle time. By using the model to anticipate the shifting sequence of bottlenecks, the team was able to design an implementation plan to redesign each aspect of the supply chain before it could choke off throughput and slow growth (Figure 18-24).

The sequential debottlenecking analysis was a critical input to the detailed implementation plan for the supply chain redesign effort, a massive project spanning 3 years and involving at its peak over 150 full-time-equivalent FGE professionals and an army of systems integration, manufacturing, and other consultants.

FIGURE 18-24   Sequential debottlenecking

The bottom curve shows how traditional management practices focus on solving the current problem. Growth resumes, causing a new bottleneck to emerge. Growth slows again. The top curve shows growth when the model is used to anticipate the emergence of bottlenecks so process redesign efforts can eliminate them before they become binding, enabling faster growth, lower volatility, and greater value creation.

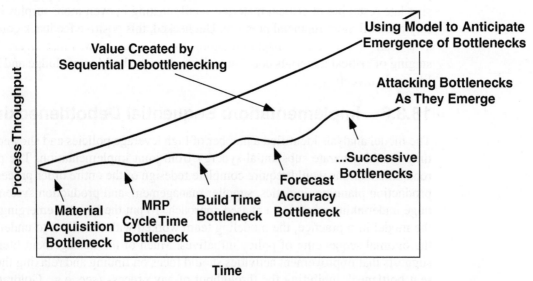

Source: McKinsey & Co.

18.3.7   Results

Just 3 years after the start of the project the results were substantial. As shown in Table 18-3, FGE dramatically reduced its supply chain cycle time, slashed inventory throughout the supply chain, shortened delivery lead times, and improved delivery reliability. These efforts generated more than $3 billion of benefit by 1997.

The modeling process also changed the thinking of many of the people involved. At the start of the system dynamics project, many of the consultants engaged in the reengineering effort were highly skeptical. By the end of the project they had become enthusiastic advocates for the use of system dynamics in such complex projects. FGE itself went on to develop other system dynamics models to consider issues such as product development and overall growth strategy.

TABLE 18-3
Project results

- Order to shipment cycle time by the end of 1996 was 60% below 1993 Q1.
- Backorders were 60% below 1993 Q1.
- Major product transitions improved by $200 million margin.
- Inventory carrying costs fell more than $600 million between 1995 and 1997.
- Inventory turns increased from about 4 per year to more than 12 per year by 1997 Q4 and to 16 per year by 1999.
- $3 billion in cash was generated from the project.

Source: FGE and McKinsey & Co.

18.4   SUMMARY

Supply chains are fundamental to a wide range of systems. This chapter showed how supply chains are built up from linked instances of the stock management structure. The model was used to explain why supply chains in a wide range of industries exhibit oscillation, amplification, and phase lag. These features of supply chain behavior arise even when all actors in the supply chain are locally rational and manage their piece of the system with decision rules that, in isolation, generate smooth and stable responses to unanticipated shocks.

In terms of the modeling process, the model was developed in stages so that the sources of amplification, phase lag, and instability could be identified. Simplifying assumptions were relaxed one at a time. You should build your models in this iterative fashion, beginning with a simple formulation, testing it thoroughly, and adding additional structure only when you fully understand the model.

19

The Labor Supply Chain and the Origin of Business Cycles

The external theories find the root of the business cycle in the fluctuations of something outside *the economic system—in sunspots or astrology, in wars, revolutions, and political events, in gold discoveries, rates of growth of population and migrations, discoveries of new lands and resources, in scientific discoveries and technological innovations.*

The internal theories look for mechanisms within *the economic system itself which will give rise to self-generating business cycles, so that every expansion will breed recession and contraction, and every contraction will in turn breed revival and expansion in a quasi-regular, repeating, never-ending chain.*

—Paul A. Samuelson (1973, p. 257).

Chapter 18 used the stock management structure to model the flow of material through a manufacturing supply chain. This chapter applies the stock management structure to the human resource supply chain. The human resource supply chain is then linked with a manufacturing supply chain, showing how production scheduling and hiring policies can interact to generate instability and oscillation. Challenges invite you to explore policies to enhance stability and responsiveness and extend the structure to include training and on-the-job learning. The chapter closes by considering how interactions of inventory management and the labor supply chain contribute to business cycles in the economy as a whole.

19.1   THE LABOR SUPPLY CHAIN

The manufacturing supply chain models in the previous chapter omitted labor and capital, implying these resources were always ample or infinitely flexible. Neither assumption is correct. This section adapts the stock management structure developed in chapter 17 to represent the provision of labor (Figure 19-1 shows the structure).

19.1.1   Structure of Labor and Hiring

To begin, aggregate the firm's labor force into a single stock, which is increased by the hiring rate and decreased by the attrition rate:

$$\text{Labor} = \text{INTEGRAL}(\text{Hiring Rate} - \text{Attrition Rate}, \text{Labor}_{t_0}) \tag{19-1}$$

The attrition rate includes voluntary quits and retirements. For now, exclude the possibility of layoffs. The attrition rate can be modeled as a first-order process in which employees remain with the firm for the Average Duration of Employment:

$$\text{Attrition Rate} = \text{Labor/Average Duration of Employment} \tag{19-2}$$

FIGURE 19-1   The stock management structure adapted to human resources

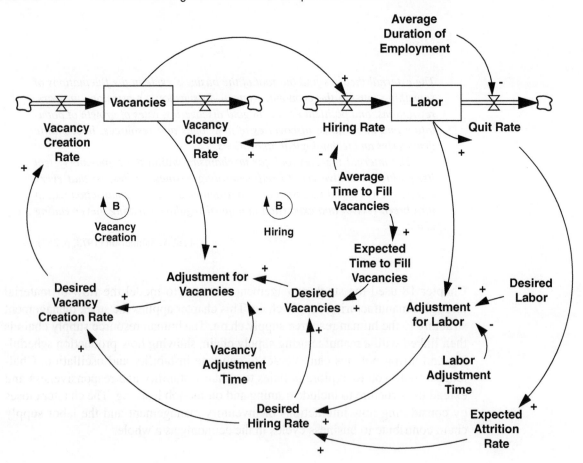

The average duration of employment is strongly affected by the state of the job market. When the economy is robust and unemployment is low, workers can readily find better opportunities, so voluntary attrition rises. During recessions, few good jobs are available and there are many more unemployed competing for them. Workers lucky enough to have jobs tend to keep them and voluntary attrition falls. In a model of a single firm, the state of the economy is exogenous and the average duration of employment might be assumed constant.[1] In a model of a regional or national economy, however, the average duration of employment and the labor market must be modeled endogenously.

The firm cannot instantly hire the workers it needs. Hiring takes time: Positions must be authorized and vacancies must be created. Job openings must be posted and advertised, followed by interviews, background checks, training, and other delays. In the simplest model all these delays are aggregated into a single stock of vacancies. Vacancies are increased by the vacancy creation rate and decreased by the vacancy closure rate, which is equal to the hiring rate. The stock of vacancies is the supply line of orders for workers that have been placed but not yet filled. The Time to Fill Vacancies represents the average delay between creating and filling a vacancy.

$$\text{Hiring Rate} = \text{Vacancies/Time to Fill Vacancies} \tag{19-3}$$

$$\text{Vacancies} = \text{INTEGRAL}(\text{Vacancy Creation Rate} - \text{Vacancy Closure Rate}, \text{Vacancies}_{t_0}) \tag{19-4}$$

$$\text{Vacancy Closure Rate} = \text{Hiring Rate} \tag{19-5}$$

Note that there is no direct physical flow from the stock of vacancies to the labor force. The labor force is a stock of people, while the stock of vacancies, though measured in people, is information. In this simple model, the source for the hiring flow is assumed to be outside the boundary of the model (and hence never constrains the hiring rate). In reality, the pool of unemployed or potentially available workers often limits hiring. In these cases, the delay in filling vacancies will be longer and variable.

Because the labor market is not modeled, the vacancy creation rate is set equal to the desired vacancy creation rate but constrained to be nonnegative (vacancy cancellation will be added later). The desired vacancy creation rate is formulated using the standard stock management structure:

$$\text{Vacancy Creation Rate} = \text{MAX}(0, \text{Desired Vacancy Creation Rate}) \tag{19-6}$$

$$\text{Desired Vacancy Creation Rate} = \text{Desired Hiring Rate} + \text{Adjustment for Vacancies} \tag{19-7}$$

---

[1]Even when the state of the economy is taken to be exogenous, factors internal to the firm such as morale, compensation, and workload may still cause the attrition rate to vary significantly and would have to be modeled endogenously.

The firm seeks to close the gap between desired and actual vacancies over the Time to Adjust Vacancies:

Adjustment for Vacancies
= (Desired Vacancies − Vacancies)/Time to Adjust Vacancies   (19-8)

The desired level of vacancies is the number that will yield the desired hiring rate given the firm's belief about how long it takes to fill a position. Desired vacancies cannot be less than zero:

Desired Vacancies
= MAX(0, Expected Time to Fill Vacancies * Desired Hiring Rate)   (19-9)

Realistically, beliefs about the expected time required to fill positions adjust slowly to changes in the actual time as labor market conditions change. The expected time to fill vacancies could be modeled using an information delay, similar to the gradual adjustment of perceived delivery delay to actual delivery delay in the manufacturing model developed in section 18.2. In this simple model, the Expected Time to Fill Vacancies is assumed to equal the actual time to fill vacancies.

Expected Time to Fill Vacancies = Average Time to Fill Vacancies   (19-10)

The firm attempts to replace those employees who leave and eliminate any discrepancy between the desired and actual number of workers:

Desired Hiring Rate = Expected Attrition Rate + Adjustment for Labor   (19-11)

Expected Attrition Rate = Attrition Rate   (19-12)

Adjustment for Labor = (Desired Labor − Labor)/Time to Adjust Labor   (19-13)

In this simple model, expected attrition is assumed to equal actual attrition. Like the expected time to fill vacancies, it is likely that there is some delay in the response of the organization to changes in the quit rate. In a more complete model the expected attrition rate would adjust to the actual attrition rate with a delay.

19.1.2   Behavior of the Labor Supply Chain

To test the model, the desired labor force is exogenous. The parameters depend strongly on the industry and skill level of the job. For unskilled workers in the fast food industry the time to fill vacancies might be a day or two and the average tenure of employees may be a few weeks to months. Recruiting highly skilled engineers can take months, and the recruiting cycle for MBA students begins in the fall for jobs that start after graduation the following spring.

For illustration, the average duration of employment is assumed to be 100 weeks (2 years) and the average time to fill vacancies is assumed to be 8 weeks. With an arbitrary initial labor force of 1000 people, these parameters define an equilibrium with quits of 10 people/week and 80 vacancies at any given time. The firm is assumed to adjust the number of vacancies to the desired level over a 4-week period, reflecting decision-making and administrative delays in the human resources department. The labor adjustment time is set to 13 weeks, representing the firm's reluctance to alter the labor force too quickly due to the high costs of adding (or cutting) permanent employees.

Figure 19-2 shows the response of the model to a 50% step increase in desired labor in week 5 from an initial balanced equilibrium. The vacancy creation rate immediately rises, both to respond to the increase in the desired hiring rate and to increase the number of vacancies to the new desired level. Soon the stock of vacancies rises roughly to the appropriate level. The hiring rate lags behind the vacancy creation rate. As the labor force grows, the adjustment for labor falls, reducing the desired hiring rate and, gradually, the actual hiring rate. The labor force adjusts in a smooth and stable fashion, settling within 2% of the new target after about 32 weeks.

FIGURE 19-2
Response to unanticipated increase in desired labor

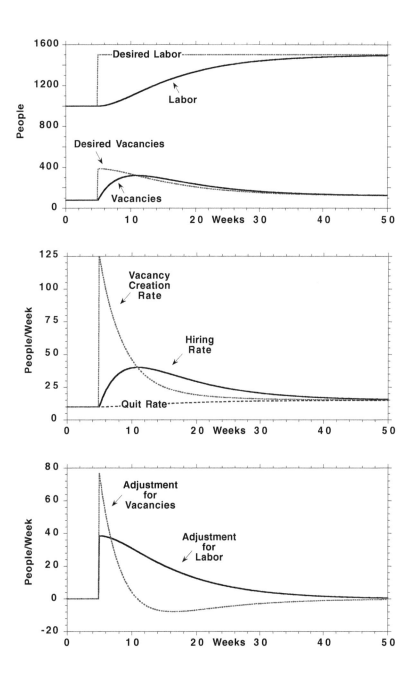

Except for the differences in time constants, the response is identical to the response of the stock management structure adapted for capital investment in chapter 17. Both situations represent examples of the basic stock management system and have identical structure. Note the characteristic amplification generated by the stock management structure: A 50% increase in desired labor causes the vacancy creation rate to rise from 10 people/week to a peak of 125 people/week. Small changes in the desired workforce induce large swings in the load placed on the human resource organization. Of course, if the required rate of activity exceeds the capacity of the human resource organization, the delay in filling vacancies would increase and the quality of new hires might fall.

The behavior of the stock management structure as adapted to labor appears to be reasonable. However, when testing a formulation, it is important to establish its robustness by examining its response to a wide range of inputs. Figure 19-3 shows the response of the model to a 50% *decrease* in desired labor. Now the labor force does not reach its desired level for nearly 2 years. There are two principal reasons for the slow adjustment.

First, the large drop in desired labor means desired hiring becomes negative. Because there are no layoffs, the workforce can fall at most at the rate of attrition. The no-layoff policy introduces an important nonlinearity that causes the response to large increases in the desired stock to differ from the response to large decreases.

Second, note the slow rate of decline of the hiring rate. The large decrease in desired labor causes the desired vacancy creation rate to become negative (it reaches a minimum of negative 48 people/week). However, the actual vacancy creation rate falls at most to zero. Consequently, the stock of vacancies already created continues to be filled. With an 8-week average time to fill vacancies, 80 new people are hired over the next few months even though the firm has far too many employees.

While a firm may choose, as a matter of policy, not to lay off unneeded workers, it is not reasonable to continue to fill all existing vacancies when the firm has far more employees than it needs. The problem cannot be corrected by removing the MAX function that constrains the vacancy creation rate to be nonnegative in equation (19-6). Doing so could, if the surplus work force were large enough, drive the number of vacancies negative, a physical impossibility. The solution is to model the vacancy cancellation process as a separate rate flowing out of the vacancy stock (section 13.3.3).

Existing vacancies cannot be canceled immediately. It takes time for the human resource organization to cancel a vacancy, and some are so far along in the process that they cannot be canceled (for example, those positions for which offers have been made). These considerations define a minimum delay in canceling vacancies. The cancellation rate is therefore the lesser of the Desired Cancellation Rate or the Maximum Cancellation Rate:

Vacancy Cancellation Rate
= MIN(Desired Vacancy Cancellation Rate, Maximum Vacancy Cancellation Rate)

(19-14)

Maximum Vacancy Cancellation Rate
= Vacancies/Vacancy Cancellation Time

(19-15)

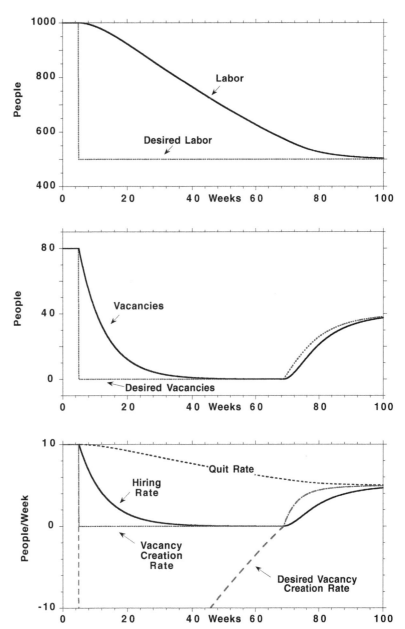

FIGURE 19-3
Response to unanticipated decrease in desired labor

Note: The simulation shows 100 weeks. Compare to 50 weeks shown in Figure 19-2.

The formulation for cancellations ensures that the stock of vacancies can never become negative. If the desired cancellation rate is very large, the actual cancellation rate and stock of vacancies approach zero exponentially with a time constant determined by the Vacancy Cancellation Time.

The desired rate of cancellations is given by the magnitude of the desired vacancy creation rate whenever that rate is negative:

Desired Vacancy Cancellation Rate
= MAX(0, −Desired Vacancy Creation Rate)
(19-16)

The same formulation can be used to model layoffs. Just as it takes time to cancel a vacancy, so too it takes time to terminate employees.

Layoff Rate = MIN(Desired Layoff Rate, Maximum Layoff Rate)   (19-17)

Maximum Layoff Rate = Labor/Average Layoff Time   (19-18)

The Average Layoff Time is the mean time required to terminate employees. The desired layoff rate is the magnitude of the desired hiring rate whenever that rate is negative:

Desired Layoff Rate
= Willingness to Lay Off * MAX(0, −Desired Hiring Rate)   (19-19)

The parameter Willingness to Lay Off represents the firm's layoff policy. If the firm has a no-layoff policy, then Willingness to Lay Off = 0. If Willingness to Lay Off = 1, the firm is just as willing to fire people as to hire people.

Figure 19-4 shows the response of the revised model to the unanticipated 50% decrease in desired labor. The Average Layoff Time is set to 8 weeks, with Willingness to Lay Off = 1. The Vacancy Cancellation Time is 2 weeks.

As soon as desired labor falls, the firm starts to cancel existing vacancies and lay off workers. Vacancies fall to zero after about 6 weeks, compared to more than 30 weeks in the original model. Through layoffs the labor force comes into balance after about a year, compared to nearly 2 years in the original model.

Including explicit vacancy cancellation and layoffs increases the realism and flexibility of the model. The model includes important nonlinearities capturing basic physical constraints (vacancies and the labor force can never be negative). The formulation also enables the modeler to represent important asymmetries in the reaction of a firm to excess labor compared to a situation of insufficient labor.[2] The structure for layoffs and vacancy cancellation can be used in other applications of the stock management structure such as the acquisition of plant and equipment, the return of purchases from a consumer to a supplier, or the transfer of workers between different jobs within a firm (for example, between production and marketing).

19.2   INTERACTIONS OF LABOR AND INVENTORY MANAGEMENT

This section augments the models of production and inventory management developed in chapter 18 by adding labor as an explicit factor of production, using the simple model of the labor supply chain developed above.

---

[2]The speed of layoffs versus hiring can be further differentiated by revising the model so the labor adjustment time LAT depends on whether there is excess or insufficient labor:

$$\text{Labor Adjustment Time} = \begin{cases} \text{LAT}_H & \text{if Desired Labor} \geq \text{Labor} \\ \text{LAT}_L & \text{if Desired Labor} < \text{Labor} \end{cases}$$

where LAT_H is the time constant when the firm seeks to hire and LAT_L is the time constant when the firm needs to fire excess workers. A firm that dislikes layoffs will have $\text{LAT}_H < \text{LAT}_L$; a firm that is quick to fire but slow to hire will have $\text{LAT}_H > \text{LAT}_L$.

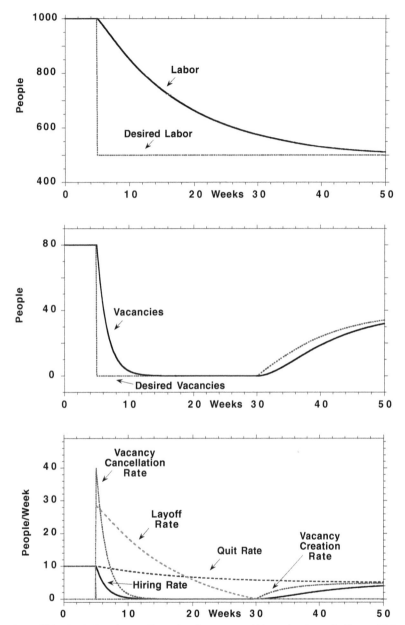

FIGURE 19-4
Response to
unanticipated
decrease in
desired labor
with layoffs
and vacancy
cancellations

Note: This simulation shows 50 weeks. Compare to 100 weeks shown in Figure 19-3.

Consider the first inventory management model described in section 18.1. The model represents stocks of work in process and finished inventory, along with the production scheduling decision. The model includes some strong simplifying assumptions. Customer orders are exogenous. Order backlogs and materials inventories are omitted, as are interactions with suppliers and customers. Most important, production starts always equal desired production starts. In reality, production is determined by the availability of materials, plant and equipment, labor, and other inputs. Section 18.2 relaxed the assumption that materials were always available. This section focuses on the role of labor as a determinant of production. Capital plant and equipment are assumed to be ample. The Production Start Rate then becomes

Production Start Rate = Labor * Workweek * Labor Productivity   (19-20)

Production starts, in widgets per week, are determined by the labor force, the average number of hours these people put in per week, and their productivity (measured in widgets produced per person-hour of effort).

To meet production requirements the firm must adjust its labor force. Desired labor is based on the desired production start rate, the standard workweek, and expected productivity:

Desired Labor
  = Desired Production Starts/(Standard Workweek * Expected Productivity)

(19-21)

Management's estimate of productivity can, and often will, differ from true productivity. For the purposes of this simple model, however, assume the standard workweek is 40 hours and that expected productivity equals actual productivity. These parameters affect only the number of workers needed to produce a widget, not the dynamics of the labor supply chain. For testing, set the actual workweek equal to the standard workweek and set productivity to 0.25 widgets per person-hour.

Figure 19-5 shows the structure of the inventory management and labor sectors. The labor sector includes the structure for layoffs and vacancy cancellation.

CHALLENGE   **Mental Simulation of Inventory Management with Labor**

What is the response of the model shown in Figure 19-5 to an unanticipated 20% step increase in customer orders in week 5? Sketch the pattern of behavior you expect for desired and actual inventory, the flows of orders, shipments, production, production starts, vacancies and labor, and the labor flows. Pay attention to the phase relationships among the variables, that is, the leads and lags of the variables relative to one another.

19.2.1   Inventory–Workforce Interactions: Behavior

Figure 19-6 shows the response of the full system to an unanticipated 20% step increase in customer orders. The parameters for the labor sector are the same as in section 19.1.2. The parameters of the inventory sector are the same as used in section 18.1.6 except the Inventory Adjustment Time has been set to 12 weeks and the WIP adjustment time has been set to 6 weeks.

Adding the labor supply chain means production starts adjust to desired starts with a delay. After the demand shock, inventory therefore falls farther than the no-labor case, boosting production to a higher initial peak and increasing the amplification ratio of production starts relative to customer orders to 2.07, compared to

1.61 for the model without labor. Most important, the system now oscillates vigorously, with a period of about 1 year. The oscillation is quite lightly damped, requiring about 3.5 years for production starts to settle within 2% of the new equilibrium.

19.2.2   Process Point: Explaining Model Behavior

Adding the labor supply chain to the inventory management model introduces important delays in the negative feedbacks through which the firm regulates its inventories. These delays cause the system to oscillate, as you should have predicted.

However, explaining the behavior by saying that production oscillates because the system contains negative loops with delays is not sufficient. Good modelers must strive for a deep understanding of the causes for the behavior observed in their models (whether it is oscillatory or not).

It is seductively simple to develop explanations for model behavior that are flat out wrong. And it is all too easy to make errors in formulations, parameter values, and initial conditions. Many times I've observed people develop intricate theories to explain the behavior of their model, often supported by complicated causal diagrams and argumentation, only to discover that the behavior was an artifact of a poor formulation or even a typographical error. Failure to analyze the behavior of your model in depth increases the chances these errors will go undetected, slowing your learning and reducing the confidence you and your clients can have in your analysis. The antidote to such self-delusion is the rigorous use of sensitivity analysis, extreme conditions testing, and other standard tests designed to uncover flaws in dynamic models (see chapter 21).

Understanding model behavior goes beyond the invocation of simple archetypes such as "the oscillation is caused by negative loops with delays" or "S-shaped growth results from the limits to growth on a reinforcing feedback." While true, these statements don't provide the deep insight into model structure and behavior required to develop your intuition about dynamics or your ability to identify high leverage policies. You should be able to explain why a model does what it does in detail, in terms your client can understand, and without contradicting yourself.

CHALLENGE

Explaining Oscillations

Before continuing, write an explanation for the behavior produced by the step increase in orders shown in Figure 19-6. You may find the explanation emerges naturally as you answer the following questions:

Why isn't the system in equilibrium when inventory first equals desired inventory?

Why isn't the system in equilibrium when production starts first equal orders? When production first equals orders?

Why does production overshoot its equilibrium value?

Why does it undershoot?

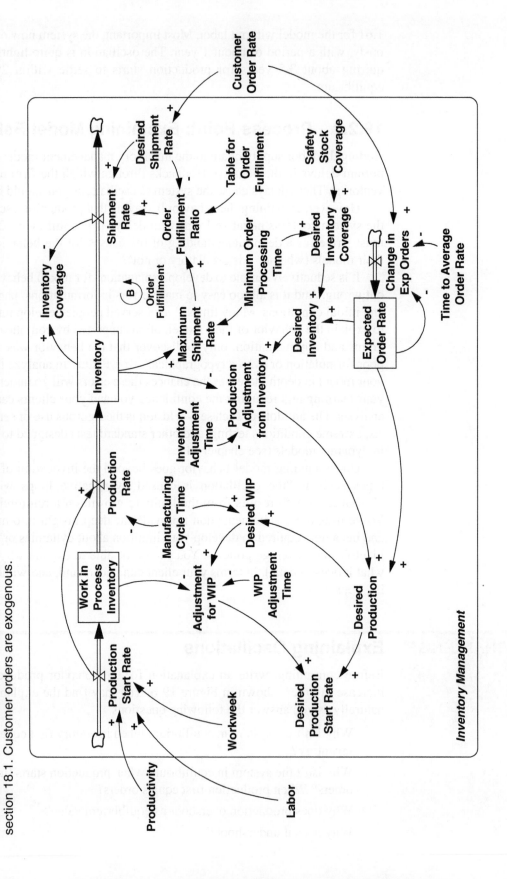

FIGURE 19-5 Inventory–workforce model

Top: Inventory management sector. *Bottom:* Labor supply chain. The two sectors are coupled through Labor (determining the Production Start Rate) and Desired Labor (determined by the Desired Production Start Rate). The inventory management sector is described in section 18.1. Customer orders are exogenous.

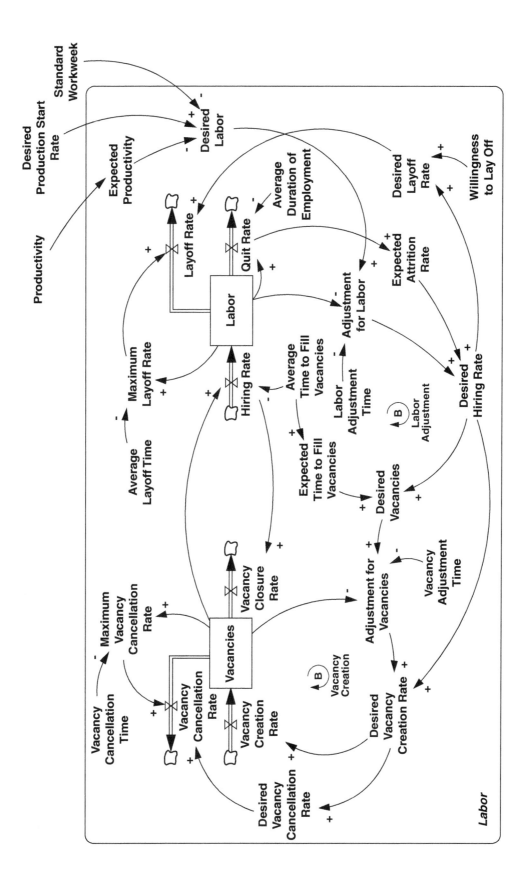

FIGURE 19-6 Cycles generated by the interaction of inventory management with the labor supply chain

Response to unanticipated 20% step increase in customer orders in week 5. Inventory Adjustment Time = 12 weeks; WIP Adjustment Time = 6 weeks.

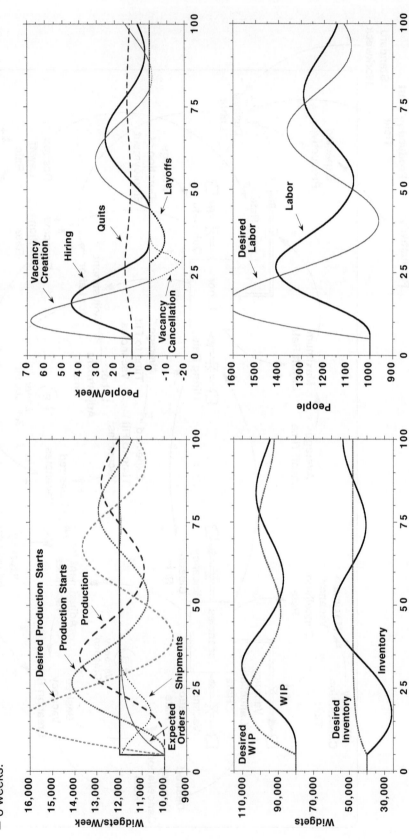

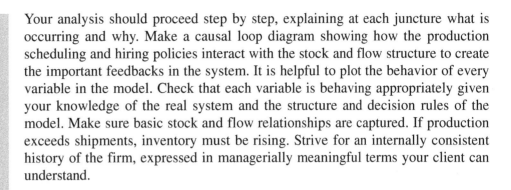

Your analysis should proceed step by step, explaining at each juncture what is occurring and why. Make a causal loop diagram showing how the production scheduling and hiring policies interact with the stock and flow structure to create the important feedbacks in the system. It is helpful to plot the behavior of every variable in the model. Check that each variable is behaving appropriately given your knowledge of the real system and the structure and decision rules of the model. Make sure basic stock and flow relationships are captured. If production exceeds shipments, inventory must be rising. Strive for an internally consistent history of the firm, expressed in managerially meaningful terms your client can understand.

19.2.3 Understanding the Sources of Oscillation

Begin by tracing the effects of the demand shock through the system (Figure 19-6). Immediately after the increase in demand in week 5, the firm tries to boost shipments to the new rate of 12,000 widgets/week. Production, however, remains constant at the initial rate of 10,000. Inventory therefore falls. As inventory falls, and as the firm's demand forecast gradually rises, desired production begins to rise. As it does so too does desired WIP. Desired production starts rise sharply. In the original model without labor actual production starts equal desired starts, so WIP inventory begins to rise immediately. Now, however, the rise in desired starts has no immediate effect on actual starts. Instead, desired labor rises above actual labor. The firm's human resource department struggles to create additional vacancies. The vacancy creation rate rises sharply to a peak nearly 7 times greater than the initial equilibrium rate. These vacancies begin to be filled after a delay, gradually lifting the labor force. By about week 15, enough new people have been hired to boost production starts to the customer order rate. Inventory, however, continues to fall until production is completed.

By week 20, expected orders have nearly adjusted to the new rate of customer orders. Production finally rises to match customer orders in about week 23. Inventory actually reaches its minimum and begins to rise a few weeks earlier, since the low level of inventory has constrained shipments below orders. The inventory gap stops growing, so desired production peaks and starts to decline. As it does, the desired level of WIP inventory also falls. Actual WIP continues to rise since production starts still exceed production. Consequently, desired production starts, and desired labor, fall sharply. By week 24, desired and actual labor meet. Actual labor continues to lag behind the desired level, peaking by week 27 even as desired labor continues to fall. Labor then falls, but remains above the equilibrium level, so production starts continue to exceed production, which in turn exceeds shipments. Therefore WIP and finished inventory keep rising. By week 29, inventory levels have risen enough for desired production starts to fall back to customer orders. Desired labor therefore falls back to its new equilibrium level of 1200 workers. Actual labor still lags behind. Production starts continue to exceed shipments. By week 36 inventory reaches the desired level for the first time since the demand shock. Inventory does not reach equilibrium, however. Labor and production are

FIGURE 19-7

Phase plot for
the inventory–
workforce model

Flow is counter-
clockwise. The
45° line indicates
points where
Production Start
Rate = Desired
Production Start
Rate. The system
begins at the initial
equilibrium of
10,000 widgets/
week and ends at
the new equilib-
rium of 12,000
widgets/week.

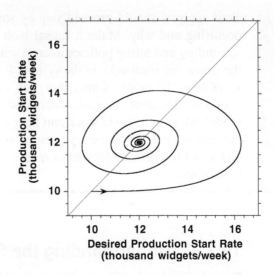

now near their peak values. Goods continue to accumulate, and inventory overshoots the desired level.

Excess inventory now causes desired production starts to drop below customer
orders, forcing desired labor below the equilibrium level. Actual labor, while
falling, still lags behind. Production starts do not drop back to customer orders until week 39, with production falling to customer orders only in week 48. Throughout this period excess inventory continues to accumulate, forcing desired
production starts and desired labor ever lower. The human resource department
finds itself with so many workers that it now scrambles to cancel unfilled vacancies. Layoffs begin around week 28.

After week 39, with labor below equilibrium, shipments exceed production
starts. Aggregate inventory falls. Desired production starts to rise. As before, the
lag in adjusting the workforce means labor continues to fall, reaching its minimum
in week 53. Desired production starts once again reach customer orders in week
55, but actual starts lag behind, so inventory falls farther than desired. By week 63,
inventory is again below the desired level and falling rapidly, the labor force is too
small, and the next cycle begins.

Adding the labor supply chain to the inventory management model does not
change the essential feedback structure of the system. Production starts still respond to the gap between desired and actual inventories. But the hiring process introduces delays in the negative inventory control loop, causing the key state of the
system—inventory—to oscillate around the desired level. The impact of the delay
in adjusting production starts is illustrated in Figure 19-7, a phase plot showing
production starts versus desired starts.

If the firm were able to match actual starts perfectly with desired starts, then
the system's trajectory would always lie along the 45° line. Instead, the system spirals around the equilibrium. With the parameters used here the system is lightly
damped. Starting at the initial equilibrium of 10,000 widgets per week, the demand
shock rapidly increases the desired start rate. When desired starts first reach the
new equilibrium of 12,000 widgets/week, actual starts lag far behind. By the time

actual starts have reached the new equilibrium, inventory is so low that desired starts are near their peak. When desired starts fall back to the equilibrium, actual starts are near their peak, forcing inventory to overshoot and pushing desired starts down. And so it goes—the lag in the adjustment of actual to desired production starts forces the system to chase its tail, spiraling around the equilibrium instead of adjusting smoothly to it.

As discussed in chapter 17, oscillation requires both delays in the negative feedbacks controlling a stock and that the managers' decision rules ignore the supply line of corrective actions in process. The supply line of unfilled orders and work in process inventory in a manufacturing supply chain are easily measured and taken into account (though experiments show people often fail to do so). The decision rules of the model fully account for the supply line of WIP. However, the supply line of corrective actions in process created by the delays in the hiring process is not so obvious. Vacancies and the stock of labor itself represent the potential to produce at a certain rate, not a particular quantity of goods on order or in production. They are not measured in widgets and cannot be compared easily to inventory in the production scheduling decision.

CHALLENGE

Policy Design to Enhance Stability

Now you can begin to use the model to explore policies to stabilize the firm. Before policy analysis is meaningful, however, you must be clear about your objectives.

1.   Instability such as illustrated by the inventory–workforce model is undesirable. The goal of policy analysis here is to identify high leverage policies that can improve stability without degrading other aspects of system performance, particularly the ability of the firm to provide good customer service (to fill 100% of incoming orders), even in the face of unpredictable changes in demand. Provide a brief explanation of what stability means in this context.

2.   To improve the performance of the system as you define it in (1), should the Inventory Adjustment Time and WIP Adjustment Time be increased or decreased? Write down your answer **before** simulating the model.

3.   Test your intuition by simulating the model with Inventory Adjustment Time and WIP Adjustment Time each lengthened or shortened by 50%, according to your prediction in (2). Is your intuition confirmed? Try other values for these parameters until you are satisfied you understand their effects on the behavior. Explain the effect of the change on stability in terms of the feedback structure of the system.

4.   Repeat the analysis in (3) for the other important time constants in the model, including the behavioral parameters (e.g., the Labor Adjustment Time and Vacancy Adjustment Time) and the physical delays (e.g., the Manufacturing Cycle Time and Average Time to Fill Vacancies). Write down your prediction for each parameter before simulating. Briefly explain how each parameter affects the model and why. Do all the parameters have the same effect on stability? Why or why not?

5. What policies would you recommend at this point? You can consider combination policies. Give specifics regarding how each policy might be implemented in reality.

19.2.4   Adding Overtime

So far, the workweek has been constant—workers always produce, whether their output is needed or not. The assumption of constant labor utilization is not a bad approximation for many traditional manufacturing environments, particularly those where performance is evaluated on the basis of overhead absorption, labor utilization, and other metrics designed to maximize gross throughput or those normally operating around the clock. However, in many settings, the workweek varies in response to the need to increase or decrease production.

To introduce the possibility of over-undertime, the workweek becomes a function of schedule pressure, as in section 14.2:

$$\text{Workweek} = \text{Standard Workweek} * \text{Effect of Schedule Pressure on Workweek} \tag{19-22}$$

$$\text{Effect of Schedule Pressure on Workweek} = f(\text{Schedule Pressure}) \tag{19-23}$$

Schedule pressure is the ratio of Desired Production Starts to Standard Production Starts:

$$\text{Schedule Pressure} = \text{Desired Production Starts/Standard Production Starts} \tag{19-24}$$

Standard starts is the rate of starts the firm would attain when the current labor force puts in the standard workweek, given the firm's estimate of productivity:

$$\text{Standard Production Starts} = \text{Labor} * \text{Standard Workweek} * \text{Expected Productivity} \tag{19-25}$$

High schedule pressure means the firm needs to produce more than the standard rate permits; low schedule pressure means there is excess capacity. Now consider the shape of the nonlinear relationship between schedule pressure and the workweek.

To specify the workweek as a function of schedule pressure, note that the reference line Effect of Schedule Pressure on Workweek $= 1$ means the workweek never varies. The 45° reference line, in contrast, represents a situation where the firm always produces at the desired rate. The 45° line entails:

$$\text{Effect of Schedule Pressure on Workweek} = f(\text{Schedule Pressure}) = \text{Schedule Pressure} \tag{19-23a}$$

Substituting this expression in the equation for the workweek,

$$\text{Workweek} = \text{Standard Workweek} * \text{Schedule Pressure} \tag{19-22a}$$

Schedule Pressure is the ratio of desired to standard production starts:

$$\text{Workweek} = \text{Standard Workweek} * \left(\frac{\text{Desired Production Starts}}{\text{Standard Production Starts}}\right) \tag{19-22b}$$

Substituting the definition of standard starts into the equation for workweek yields

FIGURE 19-8
Effect of schedule
pressure on
workweek

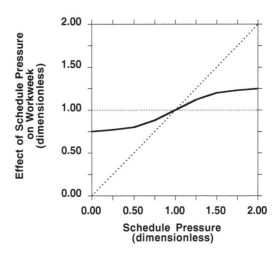

Workweek = Desired Production Starts/(Labor * Expected Productivity)   (19-22c)

Substituting equation (19-22c) into the equation for production starts (19-20) yields

$$\text{Production Start Rate} = \frac{\text{Labor * Productivity * Desired Production Starts}}{\text{Labor * Expected Productivity}} \quad\text{(19-20a)}$$

Assuming the firm has an accurate estimate of productivity, equation (19-20a) reduces to

Production Start Rate = Desired Production Start Rate   (19-20b)

Hence an overtime policy lying along the 45° line would enable the firm to hit its production targets at all times, independent of the workforce.

The workweek function must lie in the area between the two reference lines in Figure 19-8. In the region Schedule Pressure > 1, indicating insufficient capacity, it is not reasonable to assume that the workweek would rise more than needed to lift production starts beyond the desired rate. Likewise, in the region Schedule Pressure < 1, it is not reasonable for the workweek to be cut back so much that production starts fall below the desired rate. Similarly, excess capacity should never cause a firm to schedule overtime and insufficient capacity should never lead to undertime.

The workweek cannot increase indefinitely. The relationship must saturate at a maximum value. A reasonable maximum workweek for the entire workforce might be 50 or 60 hours per week. Figure 19-8 shows workweek rising to a maximum 25% greater than the standard, or to an average of 50 hours per week for the entire workforce when the standard is 40 hours/week. This figure represents an average over the entire labor force: Some workers would be putting in longer hours and some, shorter.[3]

---

[3]Note that the maximum effect of schedule pressure on workweek and the standard workweek are not independent. Given a maximum workweek of 50 hours, the effect saturates at a value of 1.25 when the standard workweek is 40 hours but at 1.43 when the standard workweek is 35 hours.

What happens when there is excess capacity? Many firms are unwilling to reduce the workweek below normal (especially when they are contractually obligated to pay for a full week). Faced with excess capacity, many prefer to stockpile additional units for future sale, waiting for attrition and layoffs to reduce the labor force and eliminate the need for undertime. Firms may also choose to maintain production in the face of low schedule pressure to keep worker skills from eroding. The function shown in Figure 19-8 captures a policy in which the workweek never falls below 75% of normal, or 30 hours/week. The slope of the function is less than 1 in the normal operating region (where schedule pressure is near one), corresponding to a compromise between the pressure to maintain full labor utilization and the need to adjust production starts to the desired rate.

Other workweek policies are possible, including the policy of no undertime (the function is one when schedule pressure is less than one) and a policy in which production starts fall to zero as schedule pressure falls to zero. Under the latter policy, the firm is willing to sacrifice labor productivity to avoid the buildup of excess inventory. In such a firm, the workers may use their extra time in training, maintenance, or process improvement activities.

19.2.5   Response to Flexible Workweeks

Figure 19-9 shows the response of the model with the over/undertime policy to the 20% step increase in orders. The response is dramatically smoother and more stable. Production starts, of course, still overshoot customer orders, but the oscillation is nearly eliminated (the system is almost critically damped). The amplification of production starts relative to customer orders falls from 2.07 without workweek flexibility to 1.52. The need to rebuild inventory still forces the labor force to overshoot its new equilibrium, but the firm is able to prevent the accumulation of excess inventory by cutting the workweek while downsizing through attrition. There is no need for layoffs. Customer service improves as well. Order fulfillment drops only to a low of 93%, compared to 88% in the constant workweek case, and the total number of lost orders is reduced.

The improvement in stability arises because the variable workweek allows production starts to track desired starts better than before. Production starts still fall short of desired starts because the assumed overtime policy has a slope less than 1 (note the smaller variation of the workweek compared to schedule pressure).

Figure 19-10 shows the phase plot for production starts against desired starts. Workweek flexibility means the firm can align actual starts to nearly match desired starts, and, compared to Figure 19-7, the trajectory of the system does lie much closer to the 45° line. Consequently, damping is increased, and the system spirals into the new equilibrium much faster.

Figure 19-11 shows a causal diagram illustrating the feedback structure of the system. The system oscillates because the negative Workforce Adjustment loop involves long delays caused by the hiring process. Workweek flexibility creates a new feedback, the balancing Over-Undertime loop. The overtime and workforce adjustment loops have the same goal: to bring aggregate inventory (finished inventory plus WIP) in line with the desired value. However, the overtime loop

FIGURE 19-9 Effect of workweek flexibility on response to unanticipated increase in orders

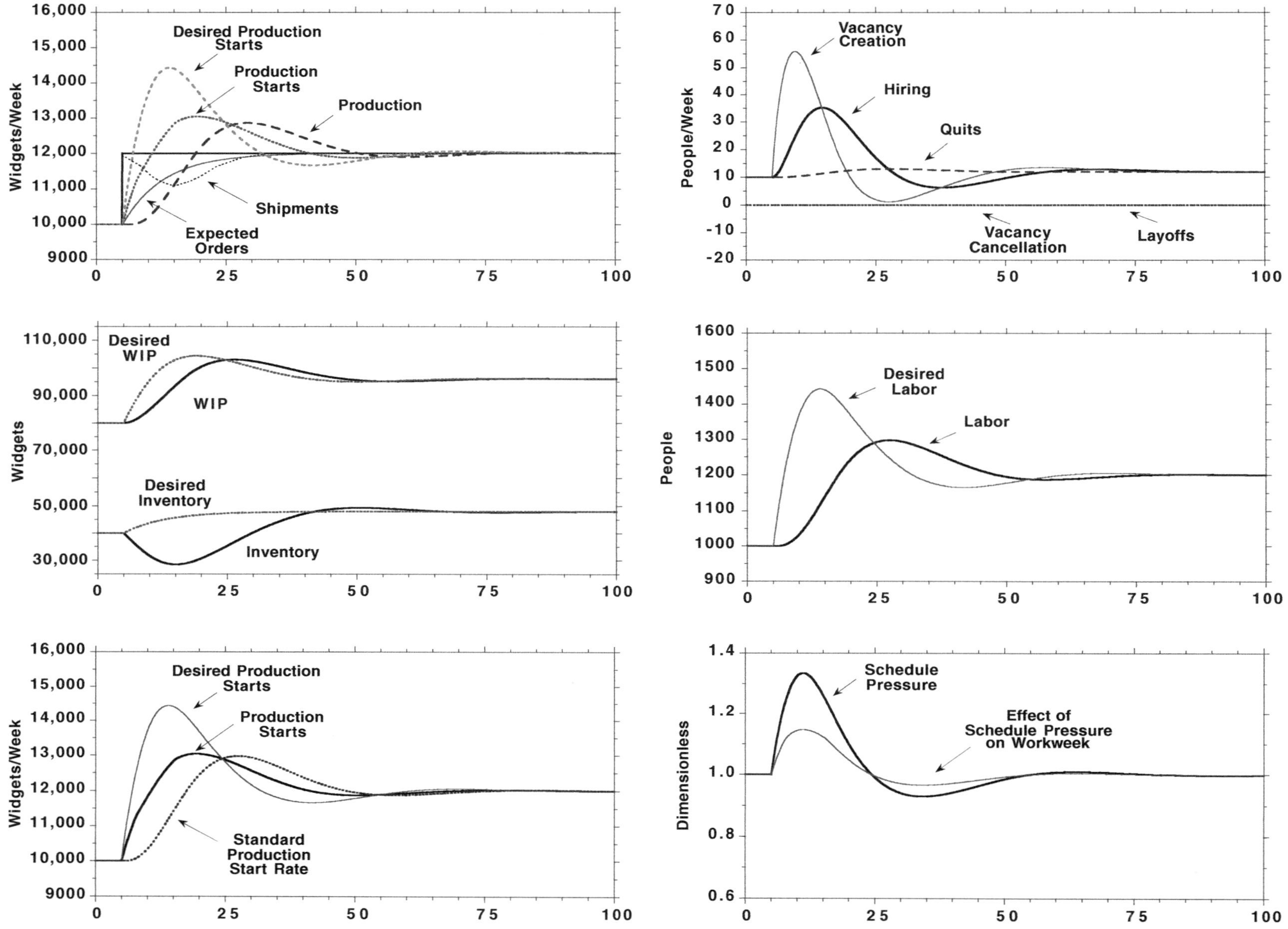

777

FIGURE 19-10
Phase plot for the inventory–workforce model with flexible workweek

Compare to Figure 19-7. Flow is counter-clockwise. The system begins at the initial equilibrium of 10,000 widgets/week and ends at the new equilibrium of 12,000 widgets/week.

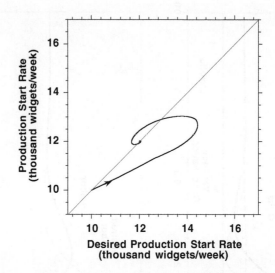

operates with no delay, allowing the system to recover from shocks without generating the cycles seen in the constant workweek case.

The more aggressively the firm uses overtime, the closer production starts track desired starts and the greater the ability to balance inventories without forcing labor above its equilibrium value. The more flexible the workweek, the more dominant the first-order overtime loop becomes, and the less the system must rely on the oscillatory workforce adjustment process to restore inventories to their desired levels. In the limiting case of perfectly flexible workweeks, the inventory sector reduces to the original model in which production starts always equal desired starts and oscillation does not occur because the negative feedbacks controlling aggregate inventory become effectively first-order.

The effect of workweek flexibility illustrates a general principle: The stability of oscillatory systems can always be enhanced by adding or strengthening first-order negative feedbacks that help the system reach its goals without significant delays. As intuition might suggest, adding first-order positive loops to an oscillatory system is destabilizing. As an example of such a positive feedback, consider the effect of schedule pressure on fatigue and error rates (section 14.4.3). If high schedule pressure and long workweeks lead to stress and fatigue, errors may increase, reducing throughput and causing a further increase in schedule pressure. The positive feedback is destabilizing because it pushes the state of the system farther from its goal, forcing larger excursions in the oscillatory workforce adjustment loop.[4]

CHALLENGE

Reengineering a Manufacturing Firm for Enhanced Stability

Using the model with overtime, design an ensemble of policies to enhance the stability of the firm while also improving customer service. Draw on the policies you

---

[4]See Graham (1977) for a good nontechnical discussion of the determinants of stability in oscillatory systems.

FIGURE 19-11   Causal structure of inventory–workforce interactions

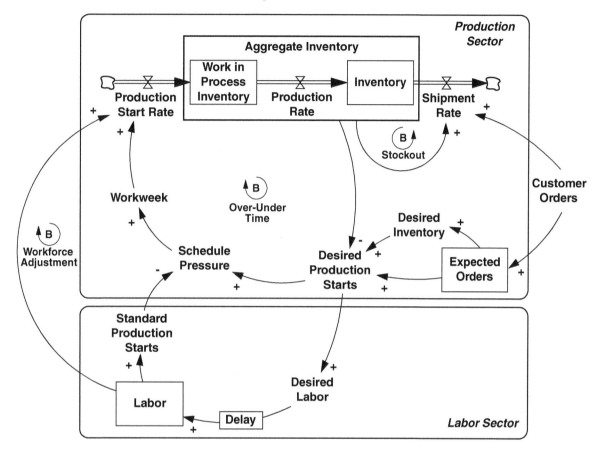

explored in the previous challenge but consider now how these policies may inter-act with a flexible workweek. Once you have arrived at a set of policies you be-lieve can enhance stability and performance, consider again the response of the system to shorter inventory and WIP adjustment times. To boost performance in the reengineered system, should these time constants be increased or decreased? Write down your answer before testing the model. Next, carry out the experiment by altering both these parameters by 50% in the direction you suggested. Was your intuition correct? Why or why not? Compare the impact of shorter inventory and WIP adjustment times in the constant workweek case to their impact in the reengi-neered model with your full suite of policies. Is the effect the same? Explain.

19.2.6   The Costs of Instability

The inventory–workforce model developed so far focuses on the core processes of inventory management and the labor supply chain. To keep it simple the model does not include any accounting or financial variables. While you can examine the impact of various policies on the stability of the system, its period, damping, and so on, you cannot assess the impact of your policies on profitability or cash flow.

Do the benefits of each policy (enhanced use of overtime, accelerated hiring and training, or reduced manufacturing cycle time) outweigh the costs? Without the ability to assess how your policies affect the bottom line, your model will be of little use to your client.

You can easily expand the model to include a full set of financial accounts, including the flow of funds, income statement, and balance sheet. You can also easily model a firm's managerial accounting system, generating variables such as unit direct costs, overhead absorption, and labor utilization variances.[5] However, the model is then likely to underestimate the benefits of enhanced stability. Cost accounting systems do not contain a line item for "Costs of Instability." There is no entry in the income statement for charges against net income due to self-inflicted fluctuations. Yet there is no doubt that instability and oscillation are costly. Modeling the standard accounting system, while necessary to build client confidence in your model, is not sufficient. Indeed, the standard accounting system will be biased against policies that enhance stability, because the costs of implementing the policy will be accounted for while the benefits will not. To properly assess the impact of your policies you need to identify the costs of instability and include them in the analysis.

CHALLENGE   ## The Costs of Instability

List as many costs of instability as you can. Consider the impact of fluctuations in production, inventories, employment, and other variables on all aspects of the performance of a firm. Do not limit yourself to factors that are explicit in the model—consider all possible areas, including operations, suppliers, human resources, customers, management, the financial markets, and others.

For each cost you identify, indicate how you might estimate the impact of improving stability on that cost. That is, how can the costs of instability be measured? For example, an unstable firm experiencing large swings in demand will periodically find itself short of materials and product, requiring expediting and the use of premium freight. You might estimate the savings arising from reduced use of these expensive measures.

CHALLENGE   ## Adding Training and Experience

The model developed above assumes productivity is constant. In reality, many feedbacks cause productivity to vary. These include changes in worker experience, fatigue, and morale effects. The model of the labor supply chain developed so far does not distinguish between new and experienced employees. In most settings, however, new recruits are substantially less productive than experienced workers, as described in section 12.1. Firms that suffer from chronic business cycles go

---

[5]For an example, see Lyneis (1980). Sterman, Repenning, and Kofman (1997) also develop a model with full financial and cost accounting sectors.

through periods of rapid hiring where the average experience of the workforce falls, cutting productivity.

Modify the labor sector of the inventory–workforce model to include the effect of employee experience on productivity. Use the aging chain structure developed in section 12.1 in which new employees are distinguished from experienced employees. Include the structure for the impact of mentoring and on-the-job (OTJ) training on the time experienced workers have available for production.

You will need to modify the aging chain to include the possibility of layoffs from both categories of workers. To keep the model simple assume the probability of layoff is the same for rookie and experienced employees. (How would you formulate layoffs if the firm follows a strict policy of reverse seniority, firing experienced people only after all new employees have been fired?)

Be sure the revised formulation for hiring takes both the rookie and experienced workers into account when assessing the adjustment for labor.

Based on your experience and judgment, select parameters for the time required to become experienced, the rookie attrition rate, and the relative productivity of new employees. To begin, assume rookies do not reduce the time that experienced employees can devote to production.

Next, you will need to modify the formulation for expected productivity. Because there will be some rookie employees in equilibrium (to compensate for those experienced employees leaving the firm), average productivity will be less than the productivity of experienced workers. Referring to section 12.1, derive an algebraic expression for equilibrium productivity. Set expected productivity equal to that expression.

Before running the full model, conduct partial model tests of your revised labor supply chain. In your tests, make desired labor exogenous. Make sure the labor supply chain begins in equilibrium. Then test its response to various shocks to desired labor, including a step up and a step down, both small and large. Examine the responses of the labor force and of productivity, checking for any anomalies or unrealistic responses. Correct any flaws you find.

Once you are satisfied the revised labor supply chain is functioning properly, run the full model. To generate a baseline for comparison, assume rookies are just as productive as experienced employees. In this case, the model should behave nearly the same as the original model without training. Next, set the parameters to reflect lower rookie productivity. How does the inclusion of worker training affect the behavior of the model? Consider the effects on the period and stability of any oscillation. Examine the amplification generated on the production side and in the labor supply chain.

Next, add the effect of mentoring and OTJ training. Select a reasonable value for the impact of rookies on the time experienced workers have available for production. What new feedback loop does the effect create? How does it alter the behavior of the system?

Explore the sensitivity of the model to variations in the parameters of the revised labor supply chain.

What are the implications of your analysis for firms with long training delays and significant OTJ mentoring? Training delays and OTJ learning are particularly important in industries heavily dependent on skilled trades and engineering

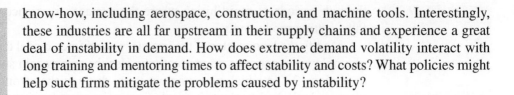

know-how, including aerospace, construction, and machine tools. Interestingly, these industries are all far upstream in their supply chains and experience a great deal of instability in demand. How does extreme demand volatility interact with long training and mentoring times to affect stability and costs? What policies might help such firms mitigate the problems caused by instability?

19.3 INVENTORY–WORKFORCE INTERACTIONS AND THE BUSINESS CYCLE

How realistic is the behavior of the model? With the illustrative parameters used here, the natural period of the cycle is about 1 year. In reality, such a cycle would be entrained with, and probably blamed on, seasonal variations in demand or materials availability. Indeed, many firms experience annual demand cycles and believe these represent externally imposed seasonal variations. There is no doubt that such seasonal fluctuations exist, from the rhythms of agriculture to the winter lull in construction to the December spike in the demand for consumer goods. However, firms often amplify the natural variations in demand, destabilizing operations even as they seek to respond to the seasonal variations. Forrester (1961, appendix N) showed that a firm can mistakenly "learn" that its demand is seasonal and begin to generate strong self-sustaining annual cycles in production, employment, inventories, profit, and orders, even when consumption of the product is perfectly random and has no seasonal cycle at all.[6]

The economy also exhibits cycles with longer periods, including the business cycle, the construction cycle, and the so-called economic long wave (see Forrester 1979 and Sterman 1986). The business cycle has an average period of about 3 to 5 years; the construction cycle has a period in the range of 10 to 20 years, and the long wave period is roughly 50 to 70 years. The business cycle is also highly variable, ranging in the US from as little as 19 months to 8 years or more (see Moore 1983 and Gordon 1986 for details).[7]

What is the role of inventory–workforce interactions in creating or amplifying business cycles? Economists have debated the origin of business cycles for more than a century and there is no agreement yet (for a survey see Zarnowitz 1992). Theories emphasizing the role of lagged responses to demand shocks and, in

---

[6]Forrester's 1961 model of self-generated seasonal cycles constitutes one of the earliest formal models of learning and temporal self-organization.

[7]Empirical assessment of business cycles is difficult. The National Bureau of Economic Research, the official arbiter of business cycles in the US, defines a recession roughly as two consecutive quarters of decline in aggregate economic activity (falling GDP). This definition underestimates the number of cyclical downturns in the economy because it focuses on absolute decline in economic activity. Since the US economy grows at an average rate of 3.4%/year, a downturn in the business cycle may not cause economic activity to fall long enough to meet the definition for a full-fledged recession, even though activity clearly falls against trend. Such "growth cycles" punctuated the long booms of the 1960s, 1980s, and 1990s. When the long-term growth trend in the economy is removed from the data, the remaining cyclical fluctuations have an average period of about 3 years (see Moore 1983).

particular, the role of inventory–workforce interactions have long been central to many business cycle theories.

The model developed in this chapter represents a single firm and omits many important structures, including the full supply chain, plant and equipment, backlogs, consumer demand, labor markets, prices, capital markets, and so on. Hence, the period and damping of the cycle it generates are not typical of the entire economy. System dynamics models incorporating the inventory–workforce structure and other important feedbacks operating at the aggregate level have been developed and calibrated for various industries and for the economy as a whole (e.g., Mass 1975; N. Forrester 1982; Senge 1978; Sterman 1986). Figure 19-12 shows the behavior of the model developed in this chapter when parameterized with values typically estimated in macroeconomic models.[8] Customer demand is random, varying around a constant level with a 5% standard deviation. The behavior of the system is strongly oscillatory. The period of the cycle is now approximately 3 years, quite close to the period of the actual business cycle.

The phase lags in the simulation closely approximate the observed leads and lags in the economy. In the actual economy, vacancies, hiring, and the workweek are leading indicators, peaking before aggregate output (gross domestic product). Employment is a coincident indicator (in phase with production) and inventory is a lagging indicator (peaking after production). As seen in the figure, the model exhibits all these phase relationships. Of course, the correspondence between the model and actual business cycle behavior is not perfect, as expected, given the extreme simplicity of the model. Adding additional structure to capture the important omitted feedbacks in the macroeconomy further enhances the correspondence of the model to the actual business cycle.

The inventory–workforce interaction lies at the core of the short-term business cycle. Business cycles are not caused by the actions of central banks, changes in government fiscal policy, or random shocks such as oil crises, wars, or technological breakthroughs. Rather, the business cycle arises from the fundamental structure of an industrial economy—from the interaction of inventory management and hiring policies with the stock and flow structure of production and employment. The natural period of the inventory–workforce interaction is similar to the observed period of the business cycle but the cycle is highly dissipative—the

---

[8]The parameters, roughly consistent with Senge (1978) and N. Forrester (1982), are Time to Average Order Rate = 26, Manufacturing Cycle Time = 40, Inventory Adjustment Time = 26, WIP Adjustment Time = 40, Minimum Order Processing Time = 8, Safety Stock Coverage = 8, Average Layoff Time = 16, Average Time to Fill Vacancies = 26, Labor Adjustment Time = 16, Vacancy Adjustment Time = 16, Vacancy Cancellation Time = 16, Average Duration of Employment = 150. The Effect of Schedule Pressure on Workweek is (0, 0.83), (0.25, 0.86), (0.5, 0.9), (0.75, 0.95), (1, 1), (1.25, 1.05), (1.5, 1.10), (1.75, 1.14), (2, 1.17). Note that parameter changes alone cannot convert the model into a good representation of the macroeconomy. The level of aggregation captured in a model affects the details of the formulations used. For example, in the model the firm either hires or lays off workers but does not do both at the same time. In the economy, an industry, or even in a large firm, however, labor needs are not perfectly correlated across all firms or sites, so some divisions, firms, and regions are hiring while others are laying workers off. In aggregate models the layoff rate might be formulated as the product of the labor force and a fractional layoff rate, which in turn would equal a normal fractional rate modified by various pressures arising from, e.g., schedule pressure and profitability. See, e.g., Mass (1975).

FIGURE 19-12

Simulating the business cycle

Response of the inventory–workforce model calibrated with parameters typical of macroeconomic models and stimulated by random variations in customer orders (first-order autocorrelated noise with a 4-week correlation time and 5% standard deviation). All variables normalized so their equilibrium value = 100. See note 8 for parameters.

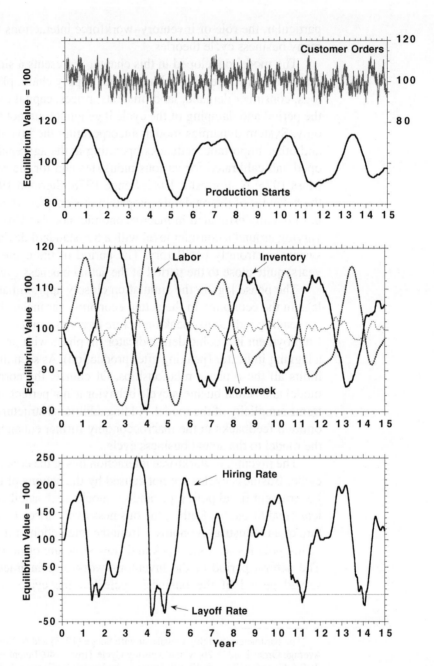

response of the economy to a single shock is highly damped. The business cycle persists because the economy is constantly perturbed by random shocks, as seen in Figure 19-12. These shocks are not the cause of the cycle but the triggering events that elicit the latent pattern of behavior generated by the underlying feedback structure.[9]

---

[9]Economists have debated since at least Frisch (1933/1965) whether the business cycle is a damped oscillation kept alive by random shocks or a self-sustaining cycle requiring no random shocks. Research in the system dynamics tradition suggests the short-term business cycle is damped, while the economic long wave or Kondratiev cycle appears to be a self-sustaining limit

The observation that the business cycle is a highly damped mode of behavior excited by random shocks explains the variability in the duration and details of individual cycles. Both in the economy and in the simulations of the model, the random shocks cause each cycle to have a unique character. Some are longer than average, some are shorter. The amplitude of the fluctuation varies from cycle to cycle. The extent to which the leading and lagging indicators lead and lag varies from cycle to cycle.

19.3.1   Is the Business Cycle Dead?

The hypothesis that the business cycle arises from inventory–workforce interactions and related feedbacks has important implications. It means the business cycle originates in the private sector from the ordinary, everyday decision-making processes of millions of firms and individuals. It also means stabilization of the business cycle through government monetary and fiscal policy is difficult.

Policy levers such as tax and interest rates do not alter the underlying feedbacks or parameters of the inventory–workforce structure and thus are unlikely to alter its inherent oscillatory behavior. Changes in tax and interest rates create shocks that perturb the system and may themselves excite rather than damp out the cycle. Economists across the political spectrum, from Milton Friedman (1956/1973) to A. W. Phillips (1954), have long argued that monetary and fiscal policies intended to stabilize the business cycle may actually be destabilizing. Policies such as raising interest rates when the economy overheats and lowering them when recession threatens are designed to create negative feedbacks whose goal is to counteract variations in unemployment, inflation, or output. However, there are long delays in the measurement and reporting of the data, in the decision to alter monetary and fiscal policies, and in the time required for any changes in interest rates, transfer payments, or tax rates to have their effects. These delays are long relative to the period of the business cycle and may actually destabilize it, counter to the intention of policy makers.

Under rational expectations, well-informed rational agents and central bankers understand the structure of the economy and perfectly account for time delays and feedback effects. In the real world, they don't. Alan Blinder (1997, pp. 9-10), reflecting on his experience as Vice Chairman of the US Federal Reserve, described with refreshing candor how easy it is even for experienced policy makers to underestimate delays using the familiar thermostat-with-time-delay analogy:[10]

---

cycle (see chapter 4 for the distinction and Sterman 1986 for discussion). Though beyond the scope of this chapter, the analysis here raises the question of *entrainment*. Even if individual firms oscillate in response to random shocks, why do these oscillations occur in phase? That is, why is there a business cycle at the level of the macroeconomy rather than a host of individual cycles that cancel out at the aggregate level? Entrainment of individual cycles is common in the natural world, from the entrainment of the orbital and rotational period of the moon (accounting for its dark side) to the beating of your heart (life-threatening fibrillation occurs when this entrainment breaks down) to the synchronized flowering of certain species of bamboo. Haxholdt et al. (1995) discuss entrainment of economic cycles using a simple model. Strogatz (1994) provides an excellent introduction to the mathematics of entrainment.

[10]Compare Blinder's thermostat system to Aftalion's coal-thermostat analogy and the discussion of systems in which people ignore the supply line of corrective actions discussed in chapter 17.

Lags in monetary policy . . . tend to be trivialized or ignored in academia . . . But they pose a huge practical problem for policy makers. Failure to take proper account of lags is, I believe, one of the main sources of central bank error.

One reason is simple . . . All central bankers understand that there are long lags in monetary policy. But when policy is being either tightened or eased, policy makers typically have no usable quantitative estimate of what are often called "pipeline effects," that is, the lagged effects of previous monetary policy actions that have not yet shown through in the data.

The second problem with lags runs much deeper and is, at least in part, psychological. Put plainly, human beings have a hard time doing what *homo economicus* does so easily: waiting patiently for the lagged effects of past actions to be felt. I have often illustrated this problem with the parable of the thermostat. The following has probably happened to each of you; it has certainly happened to me. You check in to a hotel where you are unfamiliar with the room thermostat. The room is much too hot, so you turn down the thermostat and take a shower. Emerging 15 minutes later, you find the room still too hot. So you turn the thermostat down another notch, remove the wool blanket, and go to sleep. At about 3 A.M., you awake shivering in a room that is freezing cold.

The corresponding error in monetary policy leads to a strategy that I call "looking out the window." At each decision point, the central bank takes the economy's temperature and, if it is still too hot (or too cold), proceeds to tighten (or to ease) monetary policy another notch. With long lags, you can easily see how such myopic decision making can lead a central bank to overstay its policy stance, that is, to continue tightening or easing for too long.

. . . I cannot tell you how many times, both at the Federal Reserve and at meetings with foreign central bankers, discussions of future policy were cut short with phrases like "let's see what happens" or "we'll have to wait until next month (or next meeting)."

If activist government policy isn't likely to stabilize the economy, perhaps technological innovations and learning will. Information technology and so-called lean manufacturing techniques should enable firms to integrate their entire supply chain, reduce inventories, anticipate the delays in adjusting resources, and stabilize the cycle.

Changes in production scheduling and hiring policies and changes in the lengths of hiring and production delays can alter the characteristics of the cycle. As seen in the simulations and policy analysis, greater flexibility in workweeks and capacity utilization, by strengthening the first-order negative feedbacks regulating inventories, are stabilizing. Cutting the delays in adjusting production capacity, employment, and training is also stabilizing. Reducing inventory coverage throughout the supply chain can also reduce the period and increase the stability of the cycle. Over the past two decades the lean manufacturing revolution has begun to reduce inventory coverage throughout the economy. Information technology is helping to link partners in a range of supply chains, shortening information reporting and decision-making delays.

These changes should help to stabilize the business cycle. Indeed, the evidence suggests the business cycle was slightly less violent in the late 20th century than in the 19th, at least in the developed economies. However, the impact of these welcome changes should not be overestimated. They may arise simply from the natural evolution toward a service-based economy.

In the 19th century agriculture and manufacturing dominated the economy. Both sectors involve significant inventories, long supply chains, and long delays in adjusting production to changes in demand. Over the past century, the share of GDP and employment arising from these sectors has fallen, while the share arising from services and government has steadily risen. Service industries involve much smaller inventories than manufacturing. As shown in the simulations and policy analysis above, reducing inventory coverage in the supply chain shortens the period and increases the damping of the cycle. Thus the transition to a service economy may reduce the duration and severity of business cycles, independent of any technological progress or learning by firms.

The transition to services, however, is unlikely to eliminate business cycles altogether. Though many service industries do not involve significant physical inventories, the service delivery supply chain often involves long delays. For example, the insurance industry carries no inventories of physical product and no raw materials stocks. Yet the delays between writing insurance policies and the realization of losses, and between losses and the resolution of claims, contribute to the persistent underwriting cycle that has plagued the industry for at least a century (Figure 19-13).

Even in manufacturing, there are limits to lean. Inventory reductions generated by just-in-time (JIT) and lean manufacturing policies implemented by one firm are often offset by increases in inventories held by suppliers or customers. When a manufacturer moves to JIT materials delivery, its suppliers must deliver more frequently and with much higher reliability. To meet these more stringent requirements suppliers often carry additional inventory. Large firms often cut the inventories carried on their balance sheets through third-party warehousing in which materials inventories remain at the producer's site but are still owned by the supplier until they are used. Such policies reduce the inventory levels of individual firms but don't appreciably change inventory levels for the economy as a whole. Figure 19-14 shows aggregate inventory coverage in the US manufacturing sector. As in the model here, inventory coverage fluctuates strongly over the business cycle. From the 1950s through about 1990 coverage oscillated around a relatively constant level of about 1.7 months. Since 1990, as lean production practices

FIGURE 19-13

The insurance underwriting cycle

Underwriting profits fluctuate sharply though there are no physical inventories or raw materials in the insurance supply chain.

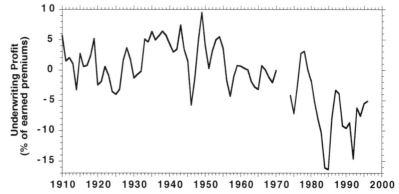

Source: 1910–1970, Stock insurance firms, *Historical Statistics of the US,* Series X-956; 1974–1996, property and casualty/liability firms, *Statistical Abstract of the US,* various years.

FIGURE 19-14

Inventory coverage, US manufacturing

Inventories relative to shipments in US manufacturing industry. Does not include finished inventories held by retailers and other distributors outside the manufacturing sector.

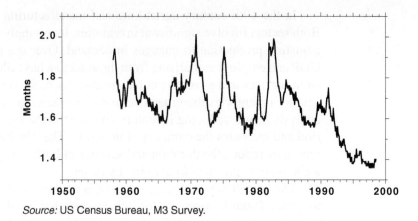

Source: US Census Bureau, M3 Survey.

diffused through the economy, coverage has gradually declined to an average of about 1.4 by the late 1990s, a drop of less than 20%.

No doubt further adoption of lean manufacturing and further developments in information technology will enable inventory coverage to decline still more. Nevertheless, it would be unwise to predict that technological progress spells the death of the business cycle. Over the past century, the business cycle has been pronounced dead many times, usually after long periods of expansion such as the 1920s, 1960s, and 1990s. Each time, the cycle emerged again, often with renewed vigor. Business cycles have existed since the beginning of the industrial age, continuing over more than two centuries, despite unimaginable changes in the products, technologies, markets, transportation and communication technologies, economic institutions, government policies, and dominant nations in the world economy.

The persistence of business cycles despite the complete transformation of every aspect of the global economy testifies to the enduring and fundamental character of the structure underlying the cycle. Though many of the products and technologies used today would be unrecognizable to Adam Smith, manufacturing firms still maintain inventories and still require labor. It still takes time to alter production, acquire materials, and buy new equipment. It still takes time to hire and train workers. An unanticipated increase in demand still causes a drop in inventory, and the only way to rebuild it is to boost production above shipments. Boosting production still requires more resources, including labor. Most of the changes in technology, market structure, products, and so on over the past 200 years, despite their undoubted impact on our lives, can be well represented in the model by modest changes in parameters.

19.4 SUMMARY

This chapter showed how the stock management structure can be applied to the labor supply chain. A simple model of labor acquisition was developed, including vacancy creation, hiring, and layoffs. The model was then linked to the manufacturing supply chain model. The resulting model of inventory–workforce interactions oscillates with characteristics closely resembling the business cycle. The cycle arises from the negative feedbacks through which firms seek to maintain inventories at appropriate levels. Delays in these feedbacks caused by the hiring process mean production cannot be adjusted instantly to desired levels. The delays in these negative loops cause the oscillation.

The chapter also showed how flexibility in the workweek and capacity utilization can help stabilize such oscillations. In general, you can stabilize an oscillatory system by creating first-order negative loops that short-circuit the delays in existing loops that create instability.

In terms of modeling skills, the chapter provided examples of formulating robust decision rules and nonlinear behavioral relationships. Guidelines for analyzing and explaining model behavior were also developed.

20

The Invisible Hand Sometimes Shakes: Commodity Cycles

> *Corrective feedback forces are provided in competitive economies by changing profit possibilities that have tended to direct capital . . . into "appropriate" channels. The implied feedback has been complicated by two human characteristics: the tendency to envisage the future on the basis of linear projections of the recent past, and a follow-the-leader tendency among those who make investment decisions. These characteristics decreed that the economies systematically undershot and overshot . . . , lurching their way through history in perpetual disequilibrium.*
>
> —W. W. Rostow (1993, pp. 14–15)

Up to now the focus has been models of individual firms. Market forces—the feedbacks between price and demand and supply—were omitted. These supply chain models tend to oscillate in response to shocks. Do market forces attenuate or amplify such oscillations? Many industries experience chronic cyclical instability. Most commodities, whether animal, vegetable, or mineral, experience cycles in prices and production with characteristic periods, amplitudes, and phases. Industries with long construction delays and long asset lifetimes such as shipbuilding, paper, chemicals, and real estate likewise exhibit strong cyclical dynamics. Even service industries such as insurance exhibit characteristic cycles in price, profitability, and investment. The diversity of these cycles suggests they arise endogenously within each industry. In these markets the negative feedbacks through which price seeks to equilibrate supply and demand often involve long time delays, leading to oscillation.

This chapter develops a generic commodity market model. Where prior chapters focused on the response of a firm to changes in orders, this chapter adds the role and response of prices and profitability. A formulation for price setting useful in a wide range of market settings is developed and tested. The chapter develops your formulation skills, including principles for formulating decision rules that represent an aggregate industry rather than a single firm, while still grounding the formulations in knowledge of the individual decision makers. Challenges invite you to elaborate the model and to design and test policies to improve performance.

20.1   COMMODITY CYCLES: FROM AIRCRAFT TO ZINC

Commodities include mineral products such as copper, iron, and mercury; forest products such as lumber, pulp, and paper; and agricultural products such as coffee, cocoa, and cattle.[1] Many commodities suffer from persistent cyclical instability in prices, production, profitability, and investment. Instability is costly for the affected industries and their customers. From the cost of your morning coffee and newspaper to the price of steel, commodity prices affect you in countless ways. Many developing nations depend on commodity exports for the bulk of their hard currency. Fluctuations in prices and demand have forced devaluations, plunged whole nations into depression, and triggered political unrest.

A common explanation for commodity cycles is that demand is cyclical. It is of course true that the overall economy rises and falls with the business cycle, and these movements induce some corresponding fluctuation in commodity markets. Yet many commodity markets fluctuate far more than the economy as a whole, exhibit cycles with different periods, and are not entrained to the business cycle, suggesting that a feedback structure endogenous to the particular commodity is responsible.

Figures 20-1 through 20-6 show some typical examples. Hog prices and production (Figure 20-1) fluctuate with roughly a 4-year period, while the cattle cycle averages about 10–12 years (Figure 20-2). Cycles in copper prices are well documented back to at least 1840 (Figure 20-3). The data show rather regular, large amplitude cycles of about 8–10 years around the long-term trend. The trend exhibits the effects of postwar inflation but also shows a long cycle associated with the economic long wave.

Commodity cycles not only arise in raw materials and agricultural products but also in high-tech and highly differentiated products. As an example, Figure 20-4 shows that commercial aircraft orders and production fluctuate with a large amplitude cycle of roughly 10 years. Figure 19-13 presented the insurance underwriting cycle, showing that cyclical instability is not limited to commodities but also plagues highly differentiated service industries.

---

[1]The notion of a commodity implies an undifferentiated product, often supplied by many small, independent producers so that the market is approximately competitive. However, chronic cyclical instability arises also in industries dominated by a small number of large producers and in industries offering highly differentiated products, including commercial aircraft, real estate, shipbuilding, semiconductors, and insurance.

FIGURE 20-1   The hog cycle

Top left: US federally inspected hog slaughter (<1950 in million lbs; scales set for average live weight of 270 lbs). *Top right:* Hog price, wholesale (< 1964 at Chicago; ≥ 1964 at Sioux City). *Middle left:* Frozen pork inventories. *Middle right:* Hog/corn ratio (bushels of #2 yellow corn required to buy 100 lbs live hogs, at Omaha). *Bottom:* US live hog stocks. Note different time scale.

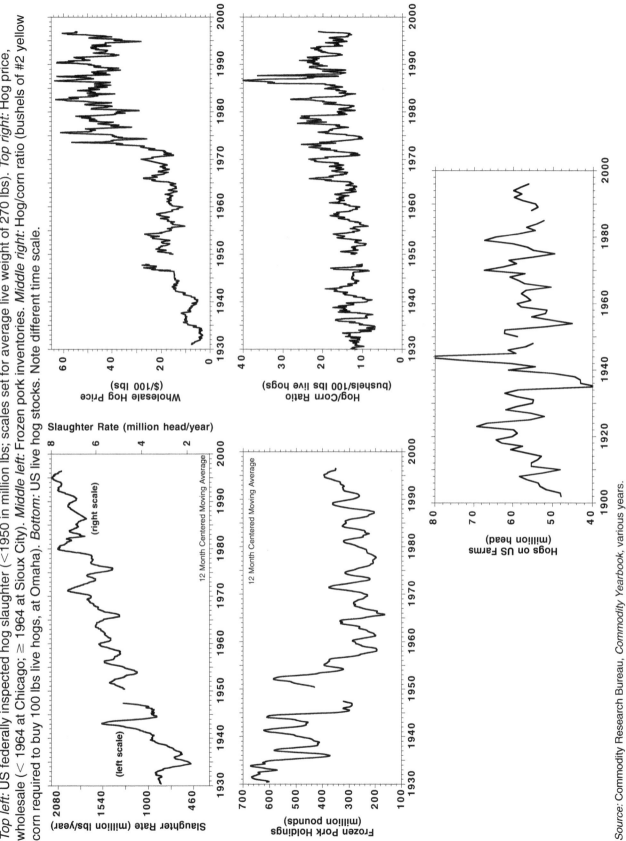

Source: Commodity Research Bureau, *Commodity Yearbook*, various years.

793

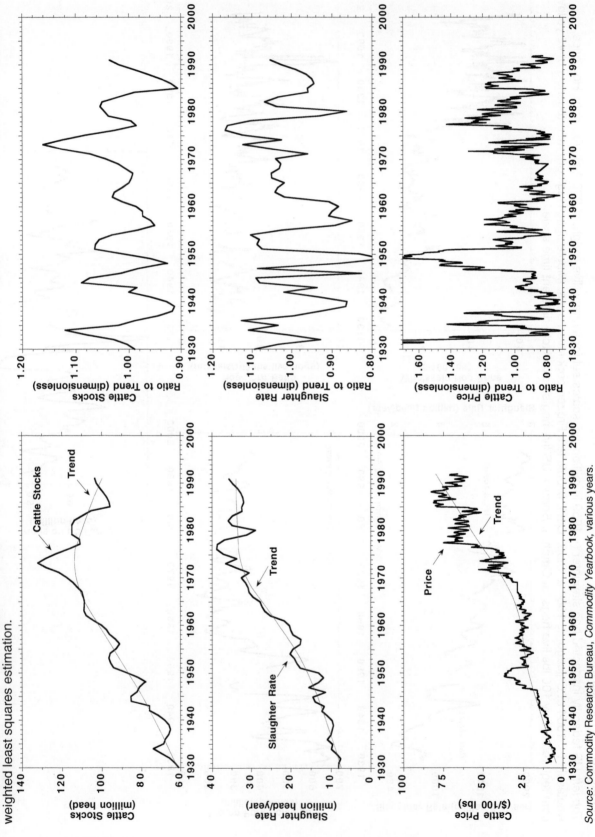

FIGURE 20-2 The cattle cycle

Top: US cattle stocks. *Middle:* Slaughter rate. *Bottom:* Price. Right side shows ratio of variable to the trend. Trends calculated by locally weighted least squares estimation.

Source: Commodity Research Bureau, *Commodity Yearbook*, various years.

FIGURE 20-3 Copper prices and production

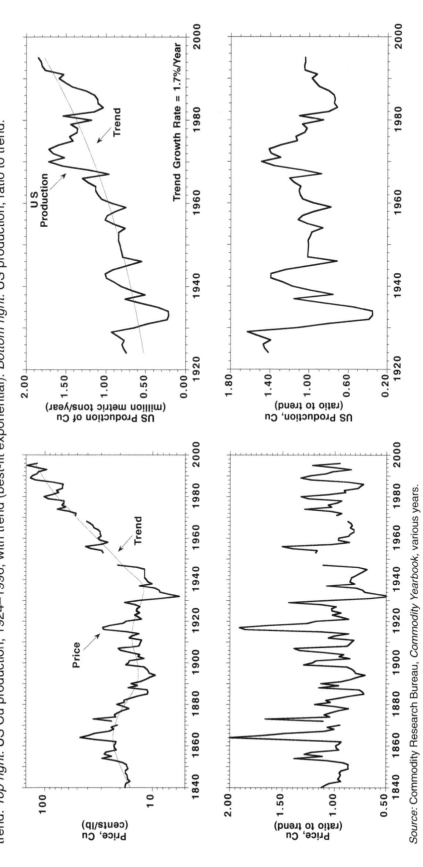

Top left: Copper prices, 1840–1996. Log scale, with trend (calculated by locally weighted least squares). *Bottom left:* Copper prices, ratio to trend. *Top right:* US Cu production, 1924–1996, with trend (best-fit exponential). *Bottom right:* US production, ratio to trend.

Source: Commodity Research Bureau, *Commodity Yearbook*, various years.

FIGURE 20-4

Worldwide aircraft orders

Annual growth rate in orders for commercial aircraft (jets with ≥ 50 seats), commercial air travel (revenue passenger km/year), and GDP weighted by each region's share of world air travel demand. Demand for aircraft exhibits a large amplitude cycle of roughly 10 years.

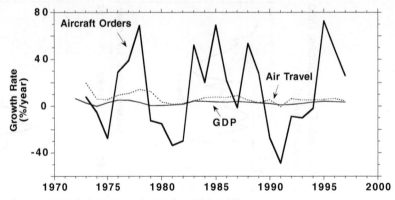

Source: Pugh-Roberts Associates, Cambridge, MA.

FIGURE 20-5

US electric utility capability margin

Capability margin is the margin by which generation capacity exceeds peak summer load.

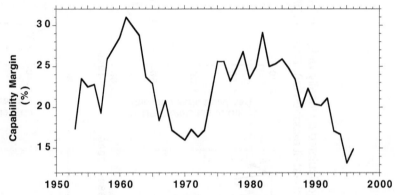

Source: Statistical Abstract of the US, Edison Electric Institute.

As you should expect, these cycles are not perfectly regular and the influence of events external to the markets, such as business cycles, wars, and weather, is clearly discernible (e.g., the price controls on copper during World War II).

Many industries generate at least two distinct cycle periods. As shown in Figure 20-18, the paper industry experiences a roughly 4-year cycle most prominent in inventories, production, and price, and also a longer, 10–15 year cycle most apparent in capacity. Likewise the oil tanker industry (Figure 20-6) exhibits high-frequency cycles of a few years in price but also a large amplitude capacity cycle of roughly 20 years. The amplitude of the short-term cycle in price depends on the phase of the 20-year capacity cycle: Prices are high and volatile when world fleet utilization is high; when there is excess capacity, prices and price variability are low. Real estate markets (Section 17.4.3; Figure 17-14) are similar: Prices and construction activity respond to the pulse of the short-term business cycle but are dominated by a 10–20-year cycle of much larger amplitude. Slade (1982), using spectral analysis, found cycles of 10–14 years in the prices of metals including aluminum, copper, iron, lead, silver, tin, and zinc, along with more rapid fluctuations

FIGURE 20-6 Cycles in the oil tanker industry

Spot rates: Monthly; worldscale units (100 = normal). Trade and capacity: Seaborne trade in crude and petroleum products, billion ton-miles/year. Capacity equals 70% of the theoretical maximum rate given the world fleet. Capacity utilization: Ratio of seaborne trade to capacity. Order, delivery, and scrap rates: Billion ton-miles/year per year.

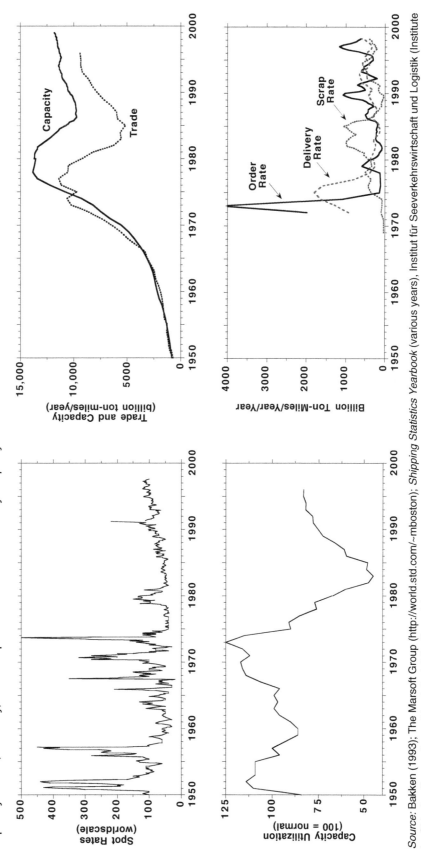

Source: Bakken (1993); The Marsoft Group (http://world.std.com/~mboston); *Shipping Statistics Yearbook* (various years), Institut für Seeverkehrswirtschaft und Logistik (Institute for Shipping Economics and Logistics), http://www.isl.org.

corresponding to the short-term business cycle. A good model of commodity industries must explain the origin of both the short-term inventory cycle and the slower capacity cycles observed in these markets.[2]

20.2   A GENERIC COMMODITY MARKET MODEL

The underlying feedback structure responsible for commodity cycles is shown in Figure 20-7.[3] Building on the basic feedback structure of markets introduced in section 5.5, Figure 20-7 shows the stock and flow structure of commodity production and the perceptual and administrative delays in the main behavioral decision processes. The stock and flow structure for production and inventory at the top of the diagram represents the supply chain for the commodity (such as inventories of copper ore and refined metal); the stock and flow structure for production capacity (such as mines, ore crushers, and smelters) appears at the left.

Consider first the stock and flow structure for production capacity and production. Production capacity is increased by capacity acquisition and decreases as capacity depreciates and is discarded. Capacity acquisition often involves long delays, creating a supply line of capacity on order and under construction. Capacity and capacity utilization determine the production start rate. Production usually takes time, creating a significant supply line of inventory in process. Available inventory of the commodity is increased by production and decreased by consumption.

---

[2]The classical economic theory of commodity cycles is the so-called cobweb model which posits that demand (D) responds to price (P) immediately but supply (S) responds with a lag: $D_t = f_D(P_t)$; $S_t = f_S(P_{t-1})$. You can easily show that the cobweb model oscillates, with a period equal to twice the interval between time periods. First, linearize the supply and demand curves around the equilibrium point: $D_t = d_0 + d_1P_t$; $S_t = s_0 + s_1P_{t-1}$; $s_1 > 0$, $d_1 < 0$. Next, assume the market clears every period and equate demand and supply to yield a single first-order linear difference equation: $P_t = (s_0 - d_0)/d_1 + (s_1/d_1)P_{t-1}$. The solution is $P_t = P_e + [P_0 - P_e](s_1/d_1)^t$, where P_0 is the initial price and $P_e = (s_0 - d_0)/(d_1 - s_1)$ is the equilibrium price. While cobweb models do capture the core structure underlying commodity cycles—the time delay in the negative feedback for the response of supply to price—they are unsuitable for serious modeling of market dynamics. First, they do not represent the stock and flow structure of real markets (including inventories, work in process, and production capacity). Second, they are formulated in discrete time. Discrete time models often generate spurious dynamics, akin to the integration error that arises when differential equation models are simulated with too large a time step (so-called DT error [Appendix A]). Third, the interval between periods is assumed to correspond to the time required to produce the commodity, such as the gestation and maturation time for livestock. However, the observed periods of commodity cycles are much greater than twice the production delays. The gestation–maturation delay for hogs is 11 months, but the period of the hog cycle is 4 years; the construction time for commercial buildings is about 3 years, but the real estate cycle ranges from 10 to 20 years. Fourth, they do not distinguish between production capacity and capacity utilization and so cannot explain the multiple oscillatory periods observed in many industries. Proper commodity cycle models, like all dynamic models, should represent the stock and flow structure, time delays, and behavioral decision processes of the market. The delays should be set to their actual values, not multiples of some arbitrary time period, and the models should be formulated in continuous time.

[3]The models developed in this chapter were inspired by Meadows (1970) who developed an early system dynamics model of commodity cycles and applied it to livestock. See also Weymar (1968). Güvenen, Labys, and Lesourd (1991) provide a good overview of modern commodity models.

FIGURE 20-7   Generic structure of commodity markets

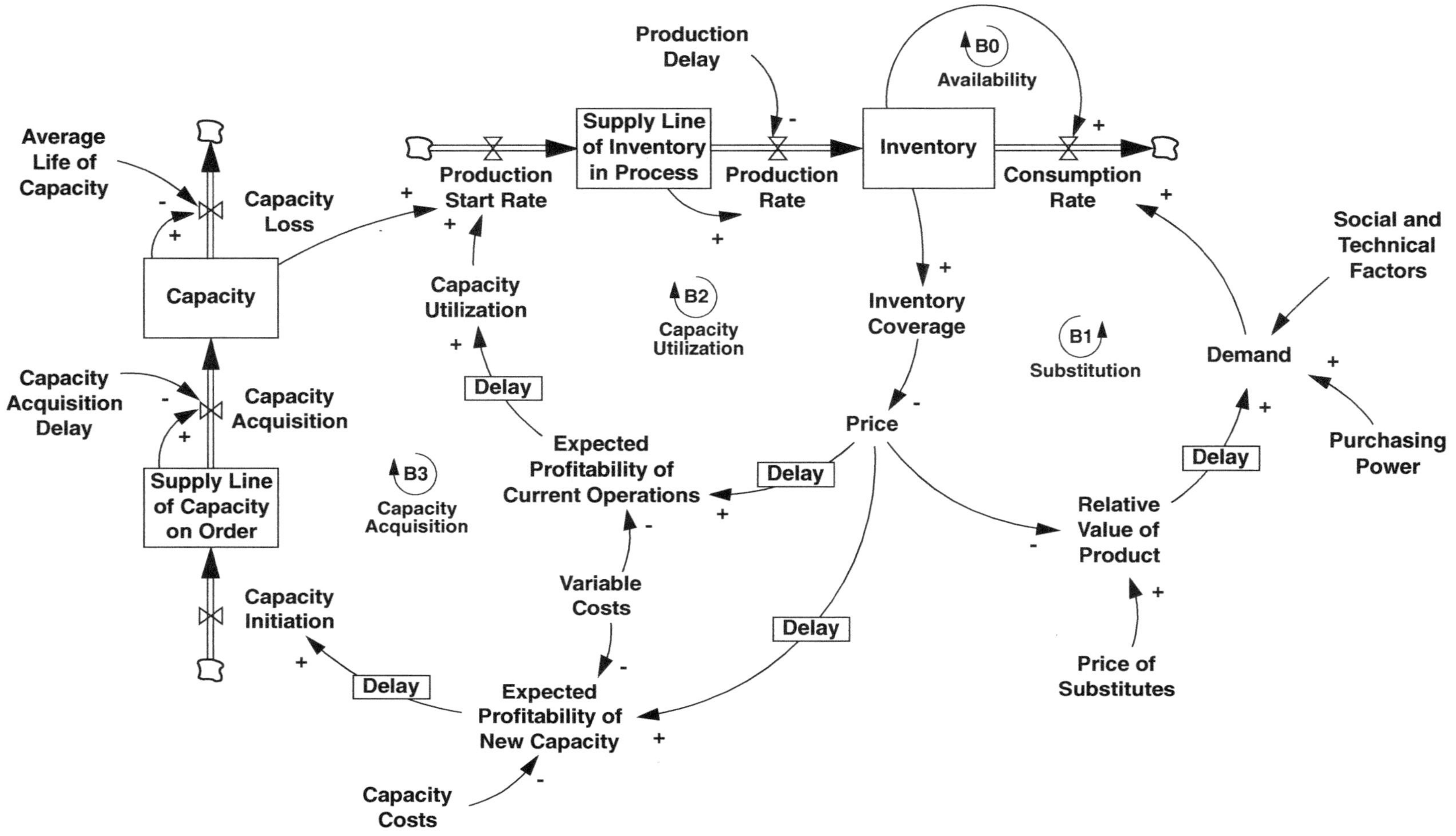

Figure 20-7 shows the three principal feedbacks helping to equilibrate supply and demand. On the demand side, the demand for any commodity depends on its price relative to substitutes, the number and purchasing power of consumers, and social and technical factors unrelated to price (such as a trend toward low-fat diets that might reduce beef consumption). High prices reduce the relative value of the commodity, causing demand to fall through the Substitution loop B1. Substitution often involves substantial delays: While consumers can rapidly switch from beef to pork when pork prices fall, the response of oil demand to price is very slow due to the long lifetimes of oil-consuming capital stocks such as cars and buildings (see Figure 5-11).

On the supply side, higher prices lead to higher utilization of existing capacity (the balancing Capacity Utilization loop B2). If high prices persist, capacity will expand, boosting production through the Capacity Acquisition loop B3. While both utilization and capacity acquisition respond to price, these decisions differ in important ways. The utilization decision responds to the expected profitability of current operations. Expected operating profitability, in turn, depends on the variable costs of operations and the price producers expect to realize when production started today is available for sale. The expected profitability of new investment in contrast depends on the total costs of new capacity, both fixed and variable, and on investors' forecasts of what prices will be over the long term. These may differ from the short-run price expectations used to drive utilization.

The current or spot price of a commodity depends on the balance of supply and demand. The current supply is the available inventory, be it ingots of copper or frozen pork bellies. Demand is the current order rate or order backlog. Prices tend to rise when inventory coverage (the ratio of inventory to consumption) falls. Prices are also influenced by other factors, such as the cost of inventory compared to the costs of storage and risk of spoilage or obsolescence, the degree of competitiveness in the market, beliefs about the costs of substitutes, and so on.

Note also the balancing Availability loop (B0), which limits consumption whenever inventory is inadequate. In many markets, prices, demand, and production usually adjust quickly enough to prevent shortages. But markets do not always clear by price alone. Availability often plays a large role in balancing consumption with production. Shortages are experienced as lengthening delivery delays, products placed on allocation, or simply stockouts. Availability also plays a key role in markets for differentiated products where prices adjust slowly (such as real estate or commercial aircraft) or where social norms for fairness limit price increases when supplies are short (Thaler 1991). Even in commodity markets where prices normally adjust rapidly, extreme conditions such as price controls or a run of panic buying can overwhelm the price feedbacks and force shipments below orders.

The Substitution, Utilization, and Capacity Acquisition loops all involve delays of various types and may therefore cause instability and oscillation. If the production delays are long enough, oscillations may arise as capacity utilization adjusts in response to changes in price. The delays in the capacity acquisition feedback are much longer and may produce even longer cycles. Both supply side loops include physical delays (the capacity acquisition and production lags) and information/perception/decision-making delays (the delays in forming price expectations, assessing expected profitability, and making investment plans).

20.2.1 Production and Inventory

To move from the conceptual model in Figure 20-7 to a formal model, begin with the supply chain for production (Figure 20-8). The supply chain is captured very simply as a two-stock chain with WIP and finished goods inventories. Backlogs and other stages of processing and storage, both upstream and downstream, are omitted. Of course, it is a simple matter to replace the two-stock supply chain used here with one of the more sophisticated versions developed in earlier chapters or with one of your own design. The stock and flow chain is formulated as

$$\text{Inventory} = \text{INTEGRAL}(\text{Production Rate} - \text{Shipment Rate}, \text{Inventory}_{t_0}) \quad (20\text{-}1)$$

$$\begin{aligned}&\text{WIP Inventory}\\&\quad = \text{INTEGRAL}(\text{Production Start Rate} - \text{Production Rate}, \text{WIP}_{t_0})\end{aligned} \quad (20\text{-}2)$$

FIGURE 20-8 Manufacturing supply chain and capacity utilization sectors

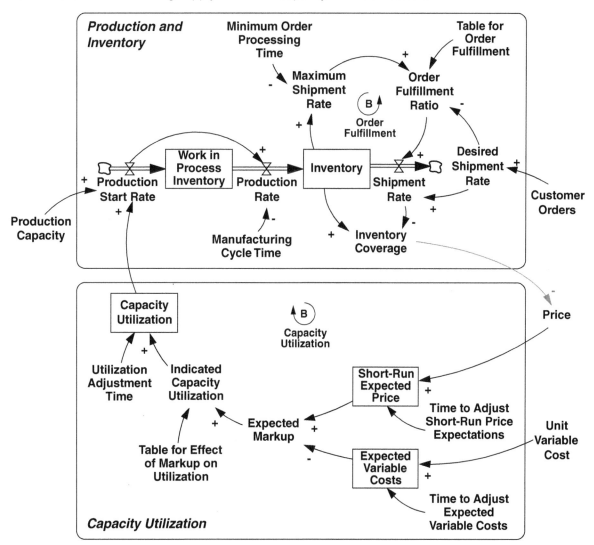

Shipments are determined by customer orders and the Order Fulfillment Ratio:

Shipment Rate = Desired Shipment Rate * Order Fulfillment Ratio   (20-3)

Order Fulfillment Ratio
   = *f*(Maximum Shipment Rate/Desired Shipment Rate)   (20-4)

Maximum Shipment Rate = Inventory/Minimum Order Processing Time   (20-5)

Desired Shipment Rate = Customer Orders   (20-6)

The order fulfillment ratio is the fraction of orders filled and is a function of the Maximum Shipment Rate relative to the Desired Shipment Rate. The maximum shipment rate is determined by inventory and the minimum time required to process and fill an order. The meaning and derivation of the order fulfillment function are described in section 18.1.1. Desired shipments here equal customer orders (backlogs are omitted).

Production is modeled as a delay. A third-order delay provides a reasonable distribution of completions around the average Manufacturing Cycle Time:

Production Rate
   = DELAY3(Production Start Rate, Manufacturing Cycle Time)   (20-7)

Capacity and capacity utilization determine production starts:

Production Start Rate = Production Capacity * Capacity Utilization   (20-8)

Capacity utilization captures variations in the intensity of production above or below the normal rate. Utilization may vary due to deliberate management decisions to respond to current profitability or production pressure or due to undesired factors such as equipment breakdowns, materials shortages, or shortages of storage capacity for output. Labor is not modeled explicitly but is instead implicit in the delay in adjusting utilization to the indicated level.

20.2.2   Capacity Utilization

Utilization depends on producers' expectations regarding the current profitability of operations (Figure 20-9). In reality, utilization also responds to inventory and backlog levels. For example, production of many commodities is constrained by the available storage capacity—when storage capacity is approached, production must be cut back, even if profitability remains high (see Homer 1996 for an example in the chemicals industry). Likewise, shortages will lead to increased utilization at any given level of profitability. The decision structure for these effects is considered in chapters 17–19. For now, the impact of these inventory adjustments on utilization is omitted; the challenge in section 20.3 invites you to add them to the model and explore their impact on market stability.

Utilization cannot generally be changed immediately. It takes time for producers to gather data on costs and profitability. Even when data are available frequently, it takes time to filter out noise and detect changes in the trend. Even after, say, a drop in operating profit is recognized, producers are reluctant to shut down a line or plant, waiting in the hope that profitability will rebound. Once the decision to adjust utilization is made, it takes further time to implement (for example,

FIGURE 20-9
Dependence of indicated capacity utilization on the expected markup

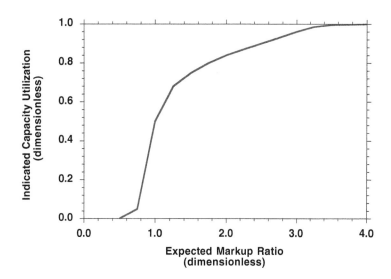

to change the labor force). For simplicity the delay in the adjustment of utilization to the desired level is formulated as first-order exponential smoothing:

Capacity Utilization
$$= \text{SMOOTH}(\text{Indicated Capacity Utilization, Utilization Adjustment Time}) \quad (20\text{-}9)$$

where the Utilization Adjustment Time aggregates the data collection, decision-making, and implementation delays. Indicated utilization depends on the expected profitability of operations, indicated by the Expected Markup Ratio, the ratio of expected price to expected unit variable costs.

Indicated Capacity Utilization $= f(\text{Expected Markup Ratio})$ (20-10)

Expected Markup Ratio
$$= \text{Short-Run Expected Price/Expected Variable Costs} \quad (20\text{-}11)$$

Utilization depends only on variable costs because the decision to run existing capacity depends only on marginal revenue (the price) compared to the marginal cost of an increase in utilization. For the purpose of the utilization decision, capacity is a sunk cost and should not matter.[4]

The effect of expected markup on utilization captures the short-run supply curve for the aggregate industry—how much additional output is generated by an increase in price, given existing capacity. Specifying the shape and likely values of the function requires first considering the utilization decision for an individual plant or piece of equipment and then aggregating over the population of facilities in the industry.

---

[4]In practice, people often fall victim to the sunk cost fallacy, continuing to invest in losing positions in an attempt to recover their prior investment (throwing good money after bad). In the context of capacity utilization, the sunk cost fallacy means producers would continue to operate even when price falls below unit variable costs in an attempt to recover their fixed costs. Cost accounting systems that penalize operators for underrecovery of overhead reinforce the tendency to operate at a loss. To the extent the sunk cost fallacy occurs, capacity utilization will be greater than zero even when the average expected markup ratio is less than 1.

Economic theory suggests firms should operate any equipment for which the markup ratio is greater than 1, that is, as long as price exceeds the variable costs of producing another unit with that equipment. The equipment should be shut down when price falls below unit variable costs.[5] While the theoretical utilization function for a single unit of capacity is sharply discontinuous (reflecting the decision to operate or shut down), the aggregate utilization function for an entire industry will be a smooth curve, rising gradually as the expected markup increases. Why? There is a distribution of productivities and costs—some equipment can operate more cheaply than others. Further, expected prices and expected variable costs represent the average beliefs of all producers. At any moment some will be more optimistic and others will be more pessimistic than average. Thus, as shown in Figure 20-9, utilization is greater than zero even when the average expected markup ratio is less than 1. When the markup is low, only the most efficient plants, and the producers with the most optimistic expectations, find it worthwhile to operate. As the expected markup rises, more and more producers believe their capacity can be operated profitably and utilization rises rapidly. Once most of the facilities have been recruited into production, further increases in expected markup yield diminishing returns, until utilization saturates at 100%. The greater the dispersion in productivity across producers, or the greater the differences of opinion about expected prices and variable costs, the smoother the aggregate utilization curve will be.[6]

Equilibrium markup and utilization will depend on the capital intensity of the particular industry. In capital intensive industries where most costs are fixed, including semiconductors, paper, and chemicals, the equilibrium markup ratio is high, firms will normally operate at high-utilization levels, and utilization will be relatively unresponsive to variations in the markup ratio. In industries where most costs are variable (e.g., some agricultural commodities), equilibrium utilization will be lower and the sensitivity of utilization to markup variations will be greater—the industry will normally operate on the steeper shoulder of the utilization curve represented by Figure 20-9.

The expected markup depends on producers' expectations for price. These short-run price expectations may differ from the long-term price expectations used in the decision to invest in new capacity. As discussed in chapter 16, price expectations in commodity markets and many other settings are characterized well by adaptive expectations (possibly with some trend extrapolation as well). First-order exponential smoothing is assumed for the expectation formation process:

Short-Run Expected Price
= SMOOTH(Price, Time to Adjust Short-Run Price Expectations)   (20-12)

[5]Often it is possible to increase the output of a machine above normal (e.g., through overtime or by speeding up the production process), but these steps usually raise the marginal cost of production and are therefore undertaken only when the markup rises above normal. Such flexibility further spreads out the aggregate short-run supply curve.

[6]The utilization function can be estimated econometrically if utilization, price, and cost data series are available. However, even when data are available, the markup rarely spans the full range over which the function must be specified, so extreme conditions considerations will be important in specifying the function (see chap. 14).

The time constant for the formation of short-run price expectations should be related to the length of the manufacturing supply line and the volatility of demand. The longer the delay in altering production, the longer producers will wait before they decide a change in price is enduring enough to justify a change in utilization. Likewise, the noisier the price, the longer it takes for producers to discern an enduring change in prices amid the temporary variations.

20.2.3   Production Capacity

Production capacity is the rate of output generated at full utilization by existing plant and equipment. In the paper industry, capacity corresponds to the number and productivity of pulp and paper mills. In the copper industry it depends on mine, crusher, and smelter capacity. The acquisition and loss of capacity are modeled by using the standard stock management structure adapted for capital investment (developed and documented in chapter 17). Figure 20-10 shows the capacity sector for the generic model.

Without loss of generality, capacity is measured in arbitrary capacity units, and the productivity of capacity is defined to be one. Hence each capacity unit corresponds to the amount of plant and equipment needed to produce one unit of output per year. The productivity of capacity is, for now, constant.[7]

$$\text{Production Capacity} = \text{Capital Stock} * \text{Capital Productivity} \qquad (20\text{-}13)$$

The supply chain for capacity assumes a first-order discard process and third-order capacity acquisition delay. The Capacity Acquisition Delay and Average Life of Capacity are assumed constant. The stocks are initialized to their equilibrium values.

$$\begin{aligned}&\text{Capital Stock}\\&\quad = \text{INTEGRAL}(\text{Acquisition Rate} - \text{Discard Rate}, \text{Capital Stock}_{t_0})\end{aligned} \qquad (20\text{-}14)$$

$$\begin{aligned}&\text{Capital Stock}_{t_0}\\&\quad = (\text{Reference Demand}/\text{Capacity Utilization}_{t_0})/\text{Capital Productivity}\end{aligned} \qquad (20\text{-}15)$$

$$\text{Discard Rate} = \text{Capital Stock}/\text{Average Life of Capacity} \qquad (20\text{-}16)$$

$$\text{Acquisition Rate} = \text{DELAY3}(\text{Order Rate}, \text{Capacity Acquisition Delay}) \qquad (20\text{-}17)$$

$$\begin{aligned}&\text{Capital on Order}\\&\quad = \text{INTEGRAL}(\text{Order Rate} - \text{Acquisition Rate}, \text{Capital on Order}_{t_0})\end{aligned} \qquad (20\text{-}18)$$

$$\text{Capital on Order}_{t_0} = \text{Discard Rate} * \text{Capacity Acquisition Delay} \qquad (20\text{-}19)$$

The order rate is formulated with the standard stock management structure. Orders are constrained to be nonnegative (for now no order cancellations are allowed):

$$\text{Order Rate} = \text{MAX}(0, \text{Indicated Order Rate}) \qquad (20\text{-}20)$$

---

[7]In reality, the productivity of capital depends on the level of technology embedded in the capital stock, cumulative learning effects, scale economies, and other feedbacks. Structures to model these processes have been described in earlier chapters. For example, embedded technical progress can be modeled with a coflow structure that keeps track of the level of technology and other input requirements associated with each unit of capital from the time it is ordered through construction, startup, aging, and finally discard (see section 12.2).

FIGURE 20-10   Production capacity sector

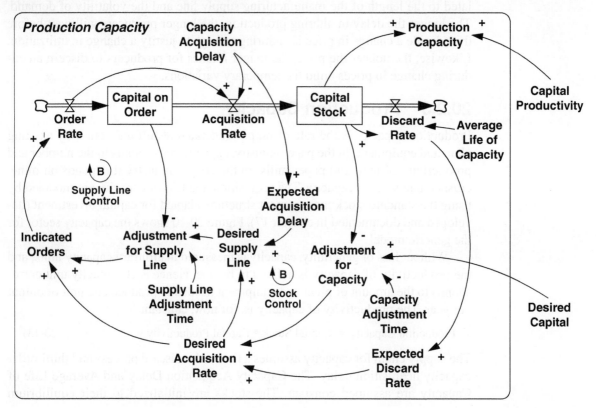

The indicated order rate is the desired acquisition rate adjusted by the adequacy of the supply line. Producers seek to correct the gap between the desired and actual supply line over the Supply Line Adjustment Time.

$$\begin{aligned} &\text{Indicated Order Rate} \\ &\quad = \text{Desired Acquisition Rate} + \text{Adjustment for Supply Line} \end{aligned} \tag{20-21}$$

$$\text{Adjustment for Supply Line} = \frac{(\text{Desired Supply Line} - \text{Capital on Order})}{\text{Supply Line Adjustment Time}} \tag{20-22}$$

The desired supply line is the amount of capital firms must have on order and under construction to yield the desired acquisition rate. By Little's Law, producers must therefore maintain a supply line equal to the expected acquisition delay times the desired acquisition rate. For simplicity, the expected acquisition delay is assumed to equal the actual delay. A more realistic model would capture the delays in the adjustment of producer beliefs about the time required to acquire capacity.

$$\begin{aligned} &\text{Desired Supply Line} \\ &\quad = \text{Expected Acquisition Delay} * \text{Desired Acquisition Rate} \end{aligned} \tag{20-23}$$

$$\text{Expected Acquisition Delay} = \text{Capacity Acquisition Delay} \tag{20-24}$$

The desired acquisition rate, in turn, consists of the replacement of expected discards, adjusted in response to the gap between desired and actual capital stocks. Expected discards, for simplicity, are assumed to equal the actual discard rate.

$$\text{Desired Acquisition Rate}$$
$$= \text{Expected Discard Rate} + \text{Adjustment for Capacity} \tag{20-25}$$

$$\text{Adjustment for Capacity} = \frac{(\text{Desired Capacity} - \text{Capacity})}{\text{Capacity Adjustment Time}} \tag{20-26}$$

$$\text{Expected Discard Rate} = \text{Discard Rate} \tag{20-27}$$

The response of the capacity acquisition sector to test inputs is described in section 17.3.

20.2.4   Desired Capacity

In commodity markets where individual producers are small relative to industry demand, profitability is the chief determinant of investment in new capacity. Existing producers will expand and new players will enter the market when the expected profitability of new investment is high; sustained low profitability leads to contraction and exit. Of course, just as production pressures such as inventories, backlogs, and order rates may affect utilization, so too these direct indicators of demand may affect the decision to invest, particularly in concentrated industries with only a few major producers. Adding these feedbacks is left as an exercise. In the generic model individual producers are assumed to expand or contract their production capacity solely in response to their beliefs about the long-run profitability of new capacity (Figure 20-11).

How much capacity should each producer have? Many economic models calculate optimal capacity based on expected prices and costs and then adjust actual capacity to that level. These formulations implicitly assume producers can solve for optimal capacity and, acting independently, choose targets that, somehow, yield exactly the proper aggregate level of capacity. Such models violate the Baker Criterion (chapter 13). No one knows the long-run equilibrium stock of productive capital in a commodity market. The optimal capital stock depends on highly uncertain factors such as future economic growth, consumer preferences for the commodity, the price elasticity of demand, the development and costs of substitutes, the productivity of capital, and so on. Behavioral decision theory suggests such uncertain factors will have little weight in the capacity decision. In contrast, each producer *can* estimate, albeit imperfectly, whether a new investment is profitable. As long as producers believe new capacity will be profitable, each would like to have more than he or she currently does and new producers will enter the market. When the industry is expected to be unprofitable, producers seek to reduce their capacity and some will exit.

The formulation used here is based on the anchoring and adjustment heuristic commonly used in decision making. Desired capital is anchored to the current level then adjusted up or down based on the expected profitability of new investment.

FIGURE 20-11   Desired capacity sector

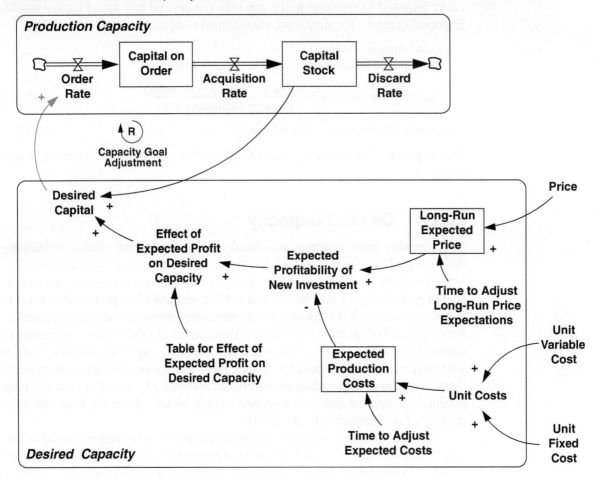

As shown in Figure 20-11, this formulation creates a positive feedback loop, the Capacity Goal Adjustment loop. Producers increase desired capital above current levels when they believe new investment is profitable. Eventually, capital stock rises, and, as long as new investment is still expected to be profitable, producers then reset their aspirations and raise their capital stock goal further. The floating goal for capital stock functions as a hill-climbing heuristic in which capacity grows as long as profits are higher than normal and falls as long as return on investment falls short (section 13.2.12). Thus,

Desired Capital = Capital * Effect of Expected Profit on Desired Capacity   (20-28)

Effect of Expected Profit on Desired Capacity
= f(Expected Profitability of New Investment)   (20-29)

Expected Profitability of New Investment
$$= \frac{(\text{Expected Long-Run Price} - \text{Expected Production Costs})}{\text{Expected Long-Run Price}}$$ (20-30)

FIGURE 20-12
Effect of expected
profitability on
desired capacity

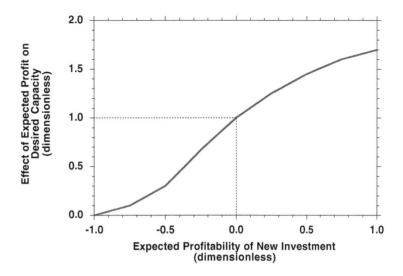

Expected profitability for new investment is the difference between the long-run expected price and expected costs of new capacity (including both fixed and variable costs). Expected costs include the normal return to capital investors require, so that when expected price equals expected cost, producers are earning the normal profit and are just content with the capital they currently have. Expected profitability is normalized by the expected price to provide a dimensionless ratio.

The effect of expected profit on desired capacity is upward sloping. Like the effect of operating margins on utilization, there is a distribution of cost and price expectations in the market. Therefore the function is zero only when profitability is sufficiently negative that even the most efficient producers, with the most optimistic expectations about future price and costs, believe the industry will be so unprofitable in the future that they seek to abandon it altogether. As expected profitability rises, the function rises. The effect eventually saturates at a maximum representing limits on the financing and absorption of new capacity (Figure 20-12).

The steeper the Effect of Expected Profit on Desired Capacity the more responsive desired capital is to a given change in expected profit. The responsiveness of desired capital to expected profit around the equilibrium point depends on two main factors. First, it depends on the responsiveness of individual producers and potential producers to expected profit. Second, it depends on the distribution of costs, prices, and expectations among the population of producers and potential producers. As discussed for the case of capacity utilization, the greater the dispersion in costs and beliefs across the population, the smoother and more gradual the aggregate relationship will be compared to the typical curve for an individual. The responsiveness of desired capital to expected profit for individual producers and potential producers also depends on a variety of factors. These include the availability and reliability of the information about costs and prices needed to assess the profitability of a new investment. Psychological factors play an important role, including the willingness of producers and entrepreneurs to undertake risk, their eagerness to expand when profit beckons and their willingness to contract in the face of losses, and the extent to which they derive nonmonetary satisfaction from participating in the industry. Institutional and structural features of the market can affect their response as well, including access to financing, the scale of the investment required, barriers to entry and exit, and adjustment costs such as startup and decommissioning costs. To expand or enter the market, producers and potential producers must be able to marshal the various resources needed to invest. These resources include financial backing, of course, but also technical know-how, the ability to assemble a qualified team to oversee the project, and, often, political connections and social capital to grease the skids of site selection, line up suppliers, and win commitments from customers.

The formulation for desired capacity represents the aggregate actions of all producers and potential producers in the market. In equilibrium, desired capital equals capital and investment just replaces the loss of old facilities. It is a dynamic equilibrium. New players, with more optimistic expectations than average, will always be entering the market even when there are no excess profits, but these are balanced in equilibrium by the exit of others whose expectations are more pessimistic.

Long-run price forecasts are formed by first-order adaptive expectations. The time constant governing the price expectations driving investment decisions is longer than that used in the utilization decision. Producers must be confident a change in price will persist long enough for investment undertaken today to be profitable when it comes on line.

$$\text{Expected Long-Run Price} = \text{SMOOTH(Price, Time to Adjust Long-Run Price Expectations)} \tag{20-31}$$

Similarly, producers and investors must form expectations regarding the costs of new investment. Due to the long delays in capacity acquisition and long capacity life and to uncertainty about future interest rates, capital costs, and operating costs, these expectations are likely to change only slowly.

$$\text{Expected Production Costs} = \text{SMOOTH(Unit Costs, Time to Adjust Expected Costs)} \tag{20-32}$$

$$\text{Unit Costs} = \text{Unit Variable Costs} + \text{Unit Fixed Costs} \tag{20-33}$$

CHALLENGE   ## Intended Rationality of the Investment Process

Design and execute partial model tests of the desired capacity and capacity acquisition sectors to demonstrate whether the formulation for desired capacity is intendedly rational. Chapter 15 describes partial model testing and provides examples. For the purpose of your tests, link the capacity sector (section 20.2.3) and desired capacity sector (section 20.2.4). Treat price and costs as exogenous inputs. Initialize your model in equilibrium with the capital stock set to an arbitrary level of 100 units and with Price = Unit Costs so that initial expected profit is zero. Confirm that Capital = Desired Capital and that investment just offsets discards.

Next, test the response of the system to various test inputs in price and/or cost. What happens when price rises permanently above unit costs? What happens when price falls permanently below unit costs? Consider the effect of small and large changes in profitability. Explore the sensitivity of the response to the key parameters, including the Effect of Expected Profit on Desired Capacity and the time constants in the stock management structure for capital acquisition. Is the behavior consistent with the intended rationality of the decision process assumed for the individual producers in the market? How do the responsiveness and stability of capacity depend on the parameters?

As discussed above, the responsiveness of desired capital to profitability depends on a variety of factors, including the availability of information, investor attitudes, barriers to entry and exit, and access to financing and other resources. In light of these considerations, evaluate the likely response of desired capital to expected profit for the following industries: Coffee, commercial real estate, copper, hog farming, oil, pulp and paper, and shipbuilding. Rank them from strongest to weakest, that is, from the steepest slope to the smallest. Explain briefly.

How might you estimate the slope of the effect of expected profitability on desired capital for these industries to test your judgmental estimates? Consider both statistical and field-based approaches.

20.2.5   Demand

The demand (order rate) for commodities can be modeled at various levels of detail. A simple demand sector is sufficient for the purposes of the generic model developed here (Figure 20-13).

In modeling particular commodities or industries, it will often be essential to capture the inventories of product in the downstream supply chain and to model the substitution process in more detail. For the purpose of the generic model, however, the essential dynamic feature is that demand falls when prices rise, though possibly with a lag. The adjustment delay aggregates the time required for customers to form price expectations with the delays in their response (finding substitutes, redesigning products to use substitutes, retrofitting or replacing capital stocks dependent on the commodity, etc.).

Customer orders are modeled as the product of an underlying industry demand and the effect of other factors on demand, an exogenous input capturing noise and other short-term variations in demand such as the business cycle.

$$\text{Customer Orders} = \text{Industry Demand} * \text{Other Factors Affecting Demand} \qquad (20\text{-}34)$$

Industry demand adjusts with a lag to the demand indicated by the price of the commodity. In general, the delay may be of high order, but for simplicity, a first-order response is assumed:

$$\begin{aligned}&\text{Industry Demand}\\&\quad = \text{SMOOTH}(\text{Indicated Industry Demand, Demand Adjustment Delay})\end{aligned} \qquad (20\text{-}35)$$

FIGURE 20-13
Demand sector

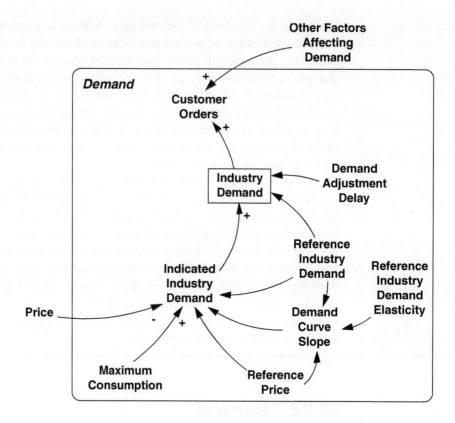

Indicated Industry Demand responds to price relative to a reference price representing the price of substitutes. For simplicity, a linear demand curve is assumed. The demand curve is normalized to generate the Reference Industry Demand at the Reference Price:

$$\frac{\text{Indicated}}{\text{Industry Demand}} = \text{MIN}\left[\begin{matrix}\text{Maximum}\\\text{Consumption,}\end{matrix}\right.$$

$$\left.\frac{\text{Reference}}{\text{Industry Demand}} * \text{MAX}\left(0, 1 + \frac{\text{Demand}}{\text{Curve Slope}} * \left(\frac{\text{Price} - \text{Reference Price}}{\text{Reference Industry Demand}}\right)\right)\right]$$

(20-36)

The MAX function ensures that demand does not fall below zero no matter how high the price. The MIN function ensures that demand remains less than a specified maximum no matter how low the price. Between these limits, the demand curve is linear. The slope of the demand curve is chosen by the modeler by setting the elasticity of demand at the initial equilibrium:[8]

Demand Curve Slope

$$= \left(\frac{-\text{Reference Industry Demand} * \text{Reference Industry Demand Elasticity}}{\text{Reference Price}}\right) \quad (20\text{-}37)$$

---

[8]The demand elasticity e is the fractional change in demand D for a given fractional change in price P: $e = (\partial D/D)/(\partial P/P)$. Since the demand curve slope s is $\partial D/\partial P$, the slope where price and demand equal their reference values P_R and D_R, respectively, is given by $s = e_R D_R/P_R$, where e_R is

The dynamics of the demand sector in isolation are straightforward. A permanent change in price induces a permanent change in indicated industry demand. Actual demand adjusts to that level with some delay. Appropriate choice of the length and order of the delay offers reasonable flexibility in modeling the response of demand to price. If the purpose of the model warrants the extra detail, the demand model can be elaborated to include additional structure, including the distribution channel and consumer stocks of product, cross elasticities with substitute products, and investment in the development of substitutes. The demand adjustment delay can be modeled in more detail. Short-run changes in desired inventory levels can be separated from long-run changes in the input requirements of the consuming sector. As an example, Figure 5-11 provides a causal diagram illustrating the multiple feedbacks affecting the demand for gasoline.

20.2.6   The Price-Setting Process

Price setting offers one of the most difficult formulation challenges in economic modeling. The prices of some goods and services are very stable, while others change from moment to moment. There are as well many different price-setting institutions. One common form is the posted-price system, where one party (usually the seller) posts nonnegotiable prices (price tags) on each item. Seller-posted price is the dominant pricing institution in retail sales (some internet brokers use buyer-posted prices, where buyers state the price they are willing to pay for an item and suppliers respond yea or nay). A variant of posted prices is one-on-one haggling, where an individual buyer negotiates with an individual seller, usually starting from a posted asking price (a system common in real estate and retail auto sales). At the other end of the spectrum, various types of auctions bring multiple buyers and/or sellers together at once. Perhaps the most dramatic is the open outcry double auction, in which multiple buyers and sellers call out bids and offers simultaneously, striking deals whenever they hear a bid or offer they like. Double oral auctions are used in many commodity trading pits and stock markets around the world.

The different price institutions provide different information to the buyers and sellers and involve different decision rules. For example, in an English auction, all bidders know the bids, and often the identities, of their rivals, while in a sealed bid auction they do not. Likewise, prices for many retail and industrial products are set by markup pricing, where the direct costs per item are marked up by a standard ratio to yield the list price. Store or product line managers have limited discretion to adjust prices in response to supply and demand or competitor prices.

The goal of this section is to create a simple and robust model of price setting consistent with the behavioral decision processes of and information available to

---

the demand elasticity at the reference price. Note that the elasticity at other prices differs from e_R: As price rises above the reference level, the elasticity of demand increases, and as price falls below the reference level, the elasticity of demand decreases. The linear demand curve is obviously a simplification but is more robust than the constant elasticity demand curve $D = D_R(P/P_R)^e$, which generates infinite demand when price is zero and gives finite demand for very high prices.

the market makers. The model is generic; detail can easily be added to customize it to particular pricing institutions as the purpose of the model warrants.[9]

In many economic models, price P is formulated as an equilibrium price P^*, adjusted by a function of the current demand/supply balance:

$$P = P^* * f(\text{Demand/Supply}) \tag{20-38}$$

where the function $f()$ is upward sloping. The equilibrium price is constant and is usually the average price over the range of available data. While attractive for its simplicity, a moment's reflection shows the equilibrium price cannot be constant. Imagine a permanent change in the costs of production. The equilibrium price will permanently change, but since the expected equilibrium price is fixed, the market is forced into permanent disequilibrium. In an inflationary environment the equilibrium price will be rising continuously, something the formulation cannot generate without an ever-growing imbalance between demand and supply. Even more fundamentally, assuming market participants know the equilibrium price violates the Baker Criterion. It is necessary to model the process of price discovery—the process by which market participants form expectations about the level of price that would balance demand and supply and clear the market (see section 13.2.12).

Just as investors do not know the equilibrium level of capacity that would clear the market, so too no one knows the true equilibrium price level. If prices rose above current beliefs about the equilibrium price and remained there, traders would gradually begin to revise their estimate of the equilibrium price until it ultimately reached the actual level of prices. In other words, traders' expected price—the level of price they believe will clear the market—adjusts gradually to the actual level of prices. The evidence suggests expectations about prices are strongly conditioned by past prices and can often be modeled well by some form of adaptive expectations, such as exponential smoothing (see chapter 16):

$$P^* = \text{SMOOTH}(\text{Price, Expectation Adjustment Time}) \tag{20-39}$$

Given traders' expected price, how then are actual prices determined? Short-term pressures arising from imbalances of supply and demand or changes in costs or competitor prices will cause traders to bid prices up or down relative to their belief about the equilibrium price. That is, prices are set by an anchoring and adjustment process (section 13.2.10) in which various cues move the price away from the anchor:

$$P = P^* * f_1(\text{Cue}_1) * f_2(\text{Cue}_2) * \cdots * f_n(\text{Cue}_n) \tag{20-40}$$

where the cues represent factors such as demand/supply balance, unit costs, competitor price, and perhaps others that may cause traders to adjust prices. The

[9]Differences in information availability and procedures can affect optimal strategy for buyers and sellers in different price institutions, and experimental studies show that actual behavior often differs from optimal behavior. For example, experimental posted price markets converge more slowly than double auction markets; bidders in experimental sealed bid markets often pay too much for items with uncertain value (the winner's curse); and double auctions often lead to speculative bubbles (see Hogarth and Reder 1987, Thaler 1992, and Smith, Suchanek, and Williams 1988). These features of specific pricing institutions can be modeled explicitly if they are important to the model purpose.

anchor, the expected equilibrium price, itself adjusts to past experience. Prices are anchored to expected prices, and the anchor in turn gradually adjusts to the actual level of prices, closing a positive feedback loop. Like the capacity acquisition process described above, such a price-setting process forms a hill-climbing search procedure in which prices rise as long as demand exceeds supply and fall as long as there is excess capacity (within limits described below). The hill-climbing procedure enables market makers to discover the market clearing price without having to know the preferences of consumers or the cost structure of producers; that is, without having to know the supply and demand curves for the product and all potential or actual substitutes.

The formulation for price developed here incorporates additional structure to ensure robustness and behavioral realism. As shown in Figure 20-14 price is anchored on the Traders' Expected price, representing traders' beliefs about the market-clearing price.[10] Actual price is adjusted up or down from the anchor in response to various pressures. In this simple model, adjustments arise from the demand/supply balance and traders' beliefs about the underlying costs of production.

$$\begin{aligned} \text{Price} = \; & \text{Traders' Expected Price} \\ & * \text{Effect of Inventory Coverage on Price} * \text{Effect of Costs on Price} \end{aligned} \tag{20-41}$$

Other factors may also cause price to adjust away from the equilibrium level, such as news about new technologies, substitute products, changes in the macroeconomy, and so on. In this model these are omitted, though they are easily modeled either as noise or as part of the feedback structure (substitute development will be affected by prices and, in turn, the availability and cost of substitutes may affect prices).[11]

Traders' beliefs about the underlying equilibrium price adjust to past prices. First-order adaptive expectations are assumed, with a time constant given by the Time to Adjust Traders' Expected Price.

$$\begin{aligned} \text{Traders' Expected Price} \\ = \text{INTEGRAL}(\text{Change in Traders' Expected Price}, \text{Price}_{t_0}) \end{aligned} \tag{20-42}$$

$$\begin{aligned} & \text{Change in Traders' Expected Price} \\ = & \frac{(\text{Indicated Price} - \text{Traders' Expected Price})}{\text{Time to Adjust Traders' Expected Price}} \end{aligned} \tag{20-43}$$

$$\text{Indicated Price} = \text{MAX}(\text{Price}, \text{Minimum Price}) \tag{20-44}$$

Note that the expected price adjusts to the Indicated Price, not the actual price. Market makers know that equilibrium prices cannot fall below the minimum costs of bringing product to market. Here the minimum price is set to the expected unit variable cost of production: Price may fall temporarily below variable costs but

---

[10]In the context of a posted-price system such as retail sales, the Traders' Expected Price might represent the list price or manufacturer's suggested retail price (MSRP), with the actual selling price of the goods adjusted above or below list in response to supply and demand, costs, and possibly other pressures.

[11]The model is developed here as a model of the aggregate price of a commodity. When used to represent the pricing decision of an individual firm, other adjustments may be relevant, particularly the price of competitor products.

FIGURE 20-14   Price setting

Compare to Figure 13-7.

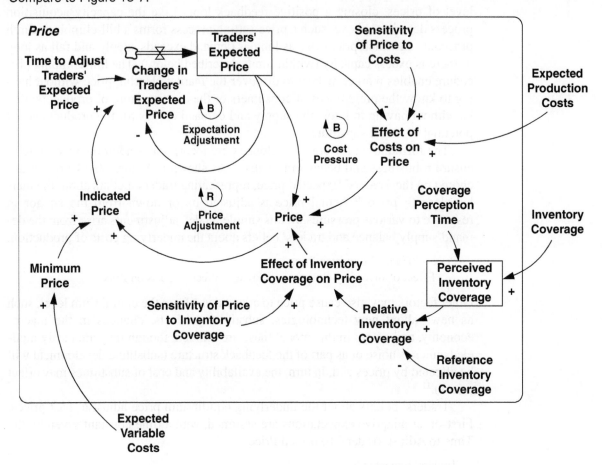

over the long run, production will cease if producers cannot cover their operating costs.

Minimum Price = Expected Variable Costs   (20-45)

In the discussion thus far, prices are assumed to respond to the balance of demand and supply, without specifying how supply and demand are perceived by market participants. There are several possibilities. In commodity markets, producers are most concerned about the level of inventory they must store and finance. On the demand side, consumers are concerned about the ability of sellers to make deliveries in full and on time. Inventory coverage (the ratio of available inventory to shipments) is an excellent measure of both inventory carrying costs for producers and the ability of buyers to receive reliable, timely deliveries. Consistent with many commodity models and substantial empirical evidence, price is adjusted above (below) the expected equilibrium level as inventory coverage falls (rises) relative to a normal, or reference, level.

$$\frac{\text{Effect of Inventory}}{\text{Coverage on Price}} = f\left(\frac{\text{Perceived Inventory Coverage}}{\text{Reference Inventory Coverage}}\right) \qquad (20\text{-}46)$$

Several functional forms for the effect are plausible. A simple and flexible function is given by the power function $y = x^a$ where the exponent a, the Sensitivity of Price to Inventory Coverage, must be negative (higher inventory coverage leads to lower prices):

$$\frac{\text{Effect of Inventory}}{\text{Coverage on Price}} = \left(\frac{\text{Perceived Inventory Coverage}}{\text{Reference Inventory Coverage}}\right)^{\text{Sens of Price to Inv Conv}} \qquad (20\text{-}47)$$

Price depends on perceived coverage, not instantaneous coverage, because the instantaneous shipment rate is not known. It takes time to gather and report data on inventory and shipments. For simplicity, perceived coverage is modeled with first-order smoothing. The Coverage Perception Time would be short in markets with very good data or high sensitivity of storage costs to inventory levels and longer in markets with poor quality data or less sensitivity to storage costs.

$$\begin{aligned}&\text{Perceived Inventory Coverage}\\ &\quad = \text{SMOOTH(Inventory Coverage, Coverage Perception Time)}\end{aligned} \qquad (20\text{-}48)$$

$$\text{Inventory Coverage} = \text{Inventory/Shipments} \qquad (20\text{-}49)$$

In other contexts the demand/supply balance may be indicated by other variables. In modeling an individual manufacturing firm the demand/supply balance is captured well by the ratio of desired production to capacity (schedule pressure), where desired production responds to imbalances in inventories and backlogs. In a service setting where there are no inventories, desired production depends primarily on the backlog of orders or queue of customers, and the demand/supply balance would still be well represented by the ratio of desired to potential output.[12]

Prices are also assumed to respond to changes in traders' beliefs about the costs of production relative to the expected equilibrium price. The strength of the effect is determined by the Sensitivity of Price to Costs.

$$\frac{\text{Effect of Costs}}{\text{on Price}} = 1 + \frac{\text{Sensitivity of}}{\text{Price to Costs}} * \left[\frac{\text{Expected Production Costs}}{\text{Trader's Expected Price}} - 1\right] \qquad (20\text{-}50)$$

---

[12]Novice modelers often use capacity utilization or delivery delay as measures of the demand/supply balance. These variables are not robust, however, and should not be used. Consider utilization. When desired production is high relative to capacity, utilization saturates at its maximum and therefore cannot indicate the magnitude of excess demand faced by the firm or industry. High utilization does not indicate whether demand is 5% or 500% greater than capacity, yet clearly prices would rise farther and faster in the latter case. Similarly, delivery delays cannot fall below the minimum time required to process and ship an order, no matter how large inventories are. Therefore when delivery delay is at its minimum value it is not possible to tell whether inventory coverage is 2 or 10 times the desired level, though the downward pressure on price is greater in the latter case.

If the Sensitivity of Price to Costs = 0, then cost information is ignored in price setting. If Sensitivity of Price to Costs = 1, then traders' beliefs about the equilibrium price are ignored and prices are anchored on expected costs instead. In an aggregate commodity market, unit costs differ from producer to producer. In global markets fluctuating exchange rates further complicate cost assessment. Information about production costs even for a single producer is uncertain and unreliable. Behavioral decision theory suggests such unreliable cues are likely to have less weight in decisions than more certain and reliable cues. Thus in commodity markets the response of price to costs is likely to be weak (Sensitivity of Price to Costs < 1) and expected production costs themselves are likely to adjust slowly to new information (equation (20-32)).

The behavior of the proposed formulation for price can be quite subtle. Consider first the response of price to a change in expected production costs, *assuming demand and supply remain in balance*. The system will always move exponentially to a new equilibrium in which Price = Traders' Expected Price = Expected Production Cost. The adjustment time will depend on the adjustment time for the trader's expected price, of course, but also depends on the sensitivity of price to costs.

To see why, note that as long as expected cost remains greater than the minimum price, the rate of change in expected price reduces to

$$\text{Change in Traders' Expected Price} = dP^*/dt = (P - P^*)/T^e \qquad (20\text{-}43a)$$

where P denotes the price, P^* denotes the Trader's Expected Price, and T^e denotes the Time to Adjust Traders' Expected Price. Assuming inventory coverage is at the normal value and denoting the Effect of Costs on Price as f_C gives

$$\text{Change in Traders' Expected Price}$$
$$= dP^*/dt = (P^* * f_C - P^*)/T^e = P^* * (f_C - 1)/T^e \qquad (20\text{-}43b)$$

Now substitute into this expression the equation for the Effect of Costs on Price, $f_C = 1 + S_C * [(C^*/P^*) - 1]$, where S_C is the Sensitivity of Price to Costs and C^* is Expected Production Cost, and collect terms:

$$\text{Change in Traders' Expected Price} = dP^*/dt$$
$$= P^*(1 + S_C * [(C^*/P^*) - 1] - 1)/T^e$$
$$= S_C * (C^* - P^*)/T^e \qquad (20\text{-}43c)$$
$$= (C^* - P^*)/(T^e/S_C)$$

You should recognize equation (20-43c) as the formulation for a first-order linear negative feedback loop in which the Traders' Expected Price adjusts exponentially to Expected Costs with a time constant equal to (T^e/S_C). As long as $S_C > 0$, the positive Price Adjustment feedback is dominated by the negative Cost Pressure loop and the system converges to the proper equilibrium with Price = Expected Price = Expected Production Costs. The weaker the impact of price on costs, the longer the adjustment will take. Figure 20-15 confirms the results. The figure shows a partial model test in which expected costs suddenly double. Inventory coverage remains constant at the reference value. The adjustment time for expected price is 1 year, and the sensitivity of price to costs is 0.50. Price immediately rises by 50% of the change in costs. In response to the gap between price and

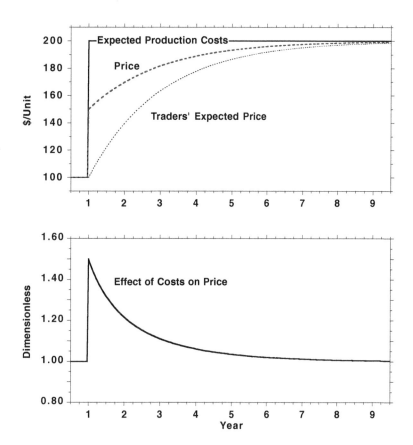

FIGURE 20-15

Response of
price to a change
in costs

Partial model
test. Expected
Production Costs
double in year 1.
Time to Adjust
Traders' Expected
Price = 1 year;
Sensitivity of Price
to Costs = 0.50.

expected price, the expected price starts to rise. As it does, so too does price, but because the ratio of costs to expected price falls as expected price rises, price increases at a slower rate than expected price, until they converge at the new equilibrium. As expected, the time constant for the adjustment is $T^e/S_C = 2$ years (it takes 2 years for expected price to move 63% of the way to the new equilibrium). The response to a decrease in expected costs is symmetric.

Now consider the response of price to imbalances between demand and supply. First, consider the case where the sensitivity of price to cost is zero. Then the equation for the change in the expected equilibrium price becomes

$$\text{Change in Traders' Expected Price}$$
$$= dP^*/dt = (P^* * f_I - P^*)/T^e = P^* * (f_I - 1)/T^e \tag{20-43d}$$

where f_I denotes the Effect of Inventory on Price. You should recognize this expression as the equation for a linear first-order feedback system. If there is insufficient inventory, then $(f_I - 1) > 0$ and the system is dominated by the positive Price Adjustment loop. The expected equilibrium price P^* will grow exponentially at fractional rate $(f_I - 1)/T^e$. If there is excess inventory, then $(f_I - 1) < 0$ and the system is dominated by the negative Expectation Adjustment loop. The expected equilibrium price will decay exponentially at fractional rate $(f_I - 1)/T^e$, until price falls to the minimum level.

Figure 20-16 presents partial model tests for these cases. Before year 1, the system is in equilibrium. In year 1, relative inventory coverage falls to 0.8. The

FIGURE 20-16

Response of price to changes in inventory coverage

Partial model test. Sensitivity of Price to Costs = 0 (no response of price to expected costs). Relative Inventory Coverage falls to 0.8 from year 1 to 3, returns to normal from year 3 to 5, then rises to 1.4. Time to Adjust Traders' Expected Price = 1 year, Sensitivity of Price to Inventory Coverage = −1.

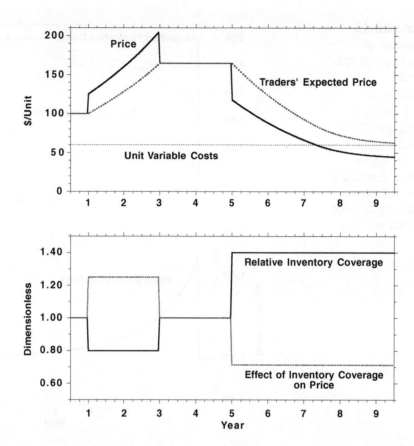

assumed sensitivity of price to inventory coverage is −1, so price immediately rises 25%. Traders gradually begin to revise their expectations about the underlying equilibrium price in the belief that higher prices will clear the market and restore inventory coverage to normal. Instead, the inventory shortage persists, the actual price remains above the expected equilibrium price and traders continue to revise their beliefs about the level of price that will clear the market. The expected equilibrium price chases its own tail in a positive feedback. As long as inventory coverage remains less than normal, prices continue to rise exponentially. In year 3 relative inventory coverage suddenly returns to normal. Price immediately drops to the expected level. Note, however, that the expected equilibrium price has now risen to more than 160. In this test, where costs have no impact on price, price will remain at the new, higher equilibrium until there is another imbalance in inventory. In particular, price cannot fall back toward the initial level unless there is a surplus of inventory. Traders have learned that the higher price is needed to clear the market and will only revise their beliefs if there is new evidence of disequilibrium at that price.

Inventory coverage rises 40% above normal at the start of year 5. Responding to the imbalance, traders immediately adjust prices downward by 29%. The market does not immediately clear, so their beliefs about the equilibrium price now begin to drop. Since inventory coverage remains excessive, price remains lower than the expected equilibrium level and traders reduce their estimate of the market-clearing price still more. Price and the expected equilibrium price decay exponentially.

FIGURE 20-17

Response of
full price sector
to changes
in inventory
coverage

Partial model test.
Relative Inventory
Coverage falls to
0.75 at time 1,
returns to 1 at time
7, and falls to
0.48 at time 12.
Sensitivity of Price
to Costs = 0.50.
Time to Adjust
Traders' Expected
Price = 1 year,
Sensitivity of
Price to Inventory
Coverage = −1.

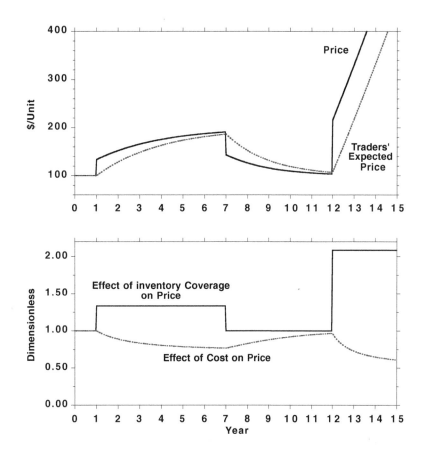

Price continues to fall until the expected price drops to the limit imposed by unit variable costs (assumed to be $60/unit).[13]

What happens when prices respond to both inventory coverage and expected costs? Suppose inventory coverage is less than normal. Prices will start to rise. But as the expected price rises above costs, the effect of cost on price will begin to off-set the effect of inventory. What happens then depends on the functions chosen for the effects of each pressure on price and the magnitude of the assumed inventory shortage. Given the equations and parameters above, small inventory imbalances will eventually be balanced by the cost effect and price will reach equilibrium when it has risen just high enough that the cost effect offsets the inventory effect. The Cost Pressure loop dominates. However, if the effect of inventory on price is large enough, the cost effect will never overcome it. The positive Price Adjustment loop dominates, and price rises exponentially until the inventory imbalance is re-solved. Figure 20-17 illustrates the shift in loop dominance. Inventory coverage

---

[13]Readers familiar with control theory will recognize that the response of expected price to the demand/supply balance is an example of integral control because expected price continues to change as long as there is an imbalance between demand and supply. The response of expected price to costs, in contrast, is an example of a proportional controller. The integral response to the demand/supply balance allows price to adjust to whatever level balances demand and supply. How-ever, integral control can lead to instability because the control action is strongest just when the gap between the desired and actual state of the system is eliminated. See, e.g., Ogata (1997).

falls to 75% of normal in year 1. Prices rise but the cost effect slows the increase. Given the parameters, the system returns to equilibrium when prices double. By year 7 the expected equilibrium price has nearly reached that level. In year 7, inventory coverage returns to normal. Price and expected price now regress toward traders' beliefs about the long-run unit costs. By year 12 the adjustment is nearly complete. In year 12, however, relative inventory coverage falls to 48% of normal. Now the effect of inventory coverage on price is so great that even infinite price cannot generate enough cost pressure to overcome it, and price rises exponentially without bound. In the real world, of course, price could not continue to rise forever since very high prices would trigger production increases and demand reductions that would eventually bring inventory coverage back down.[14]

The rich array of behaviors generated by the price formulation, even in partial model tests, arises from shifts in the dominant feedback loops governing price adjustments. For small inventory imbalances the negative loops dominate and expectations are regressive, tending to return to traders' beliefs about the long-run fundamental value of the commodity. Larger imbalances cause loop dominance to shift to the positive Price Adjustment loop, and the stabilizing impact of beliefs about the fundamental value of the good is overwhelmed. Such behavior may seem unreasonable, but in markets where fundamental value is difficult to assess—or viewed as irrelevant—prices often rise by many orders of magnitude, even after years of comparative calm. As an example, Figure 4-13 showed the bubble in silver prices in the late 1970s. Silver rose by a factor of 700% in just 2 years, before collapsing even faster. Clearly, any notions people may have had about silver's fundamental value or long-run production costs had little if any impact during the speculative frenzy.

The price formulation developed above is quite general. It can represent price setting at the level of an industry or market, as developed here, or modified to represent the price set by individual firms. In that case, the expected price may represent the list price and price may respond to other factors besides cost and the demand/supply balance, such as the price of competitors' products. With suitable parameters, it can represent markets where price expectations and prices change quickly (such as the stock market) or markets where prices are sluggish (e.g., real estate or retail goods). The process by which expected prices are formed can be enriched, for example, by including a term for the expected rate of inflation. You are free to choose different functional forms for the effects of various pressures on price as the case-specific data suggest.

The model provides a formulation for the price discovery process that is robust, generates a rich array of behaviors, and is consistent with the principles of bounded rationality. The two key formulations, price setting as an anchoring and adjustment process and the adaptation of the anchor to past prices, are also supported by a number of studies. Econometric studies routinely show that commodity prices respond to inventory coverage and unit costs. To pick a typical example,

---

[14]As a challenge, derive an analytic expression for the equilibrium price as a function of relative inventory coverage and identify the point at which the equilibrium ceases to exist. Explore how the existence and character of equilibrium depend on the shape of the function defining the effect of inventory coverage on price.

Gerlow, Irwin, and Liu (1993) show that hog prices respond both to the demand/supply balance and to the so-called hog/corn ratio (the price of hogs relative to the price of corn; corn is the primary variable input to hog farming and much more variable in price than other inputs). Although he did not estimate the full price setting model, Williams (1987) found in experimental double auction markets that traders' price expectations were best modeled as adapting to past prices. The data strongly rejected the rational expectations hypothesis that traders optimally and immediately incorporate all relevant information so that their expectations are, on average, correct.

Outside the laboratory, price expectations in many commodity markets have been shown to adjust gradually to past prices and other information such as costs. Chapter 16 presented evidence that expectations for a wide range of variables, including prices, are often formed adaptively, though in some cases such as cattle prices there is evidence of an extrapolative component as well. Frankel and Froot (1987) found that expectations of future currency exchange rates among central bankers, traders, and other participants in foreign exchange markets included both adaptive and regressive components. Expectations adjusted gradually to recent spot exchange rates (just as traders' expected price adjusts to the actual price in the model) but also tended to regress slowly to purchasing power parity (analogous to the gradual adjustment of expected prices to long-run expected unit costs). Typical of many such studies, the data strongly reject rational expectations.

The pricing model has also been applied in a number of cases, with generally good results. Taylor (1999) analyzed the paper industry with a model similar to the one described here. Homer (1996), in modeling a commodity chemical market, noticed that prices tended to rise when inventories were low and fall when inventories were high and showed that a pricing formulation similar to that proposed here worked quite well. Hines (1987) applied the formulation to interest rates. The Traders' Expected Price represented the beliefs of bond traders about the underlying equilibrium interest rate that would balance the supply and demand for funds. Traders then adjust the actual interest rate above or below the expected equilibrium level in response to variations in demand and supply, measured by the free reserves of the banking system. Free reserves are reserve accounts held by banks and other financial institutions in excess of their desired level and represent unexploited lending capacity. Hines estimated the model parameters econometrically from 1959 to 1980, one of the most turbulent periods in US bond market history. The model explained a substantial fraction of the variation in interest rates. The estimated sensitivity of interest rates to free reserves was about -4 (a 1% drop in free reserves caused interest rates to rise about 4% above the underlying equilibrium expectation). The estimated time constant for the expected equilibrium interest rate was 1.4 years. The adjustment time may seem long, but behavioral decision theory suggests that expectations adjust slower when the information causing the adjustments is uncertain. As in the case of inflation expectations (chapter 16), the factors affecting interest rates are numerous, poorly understood, difficult to measure, and hard to forecast. Thus expectations about the underlying rate environment formed during a person's career as a trader or banker are likely to be durable, adjusting slowly and filtering out short-term movements in interest rates caused by temporary swings in liquidity or unpredictable economic and political events. The estimated time constant is approximately the same as the delay in updating inflation expectations estimated in chapter 16.

20.3   APPLICATION: CYCLES IN THE PULP AND PAPER INDUSTRY

The pulp and paper industry provides a typical example of a commodity. As shown in Figure 20-18, the industry is highly cyclical. Production, inventories, capacity utilization, prices, and investment all exhibit a large amplitude cycle of about 3–5 years. The amplitude of the cycle is very large in price, which typically moves from 40% above its average value to 40% below it (there is a long-term declining trend in real prices due to economies of scale, learning, and technical progress in the industry). Inventory coverage fluctuates about ±20% around its average. Capacity utilization averages about 90% and moves comparatively little over the cycle, typically varying between 85% and 95%. Capacity exhibits almost no variations in the 3–5 year range but does exhibit longer, slower movements. The capacity, production, and investment data in Figure 20-18 have been detrended by plotting the ratio of output and capacity to the long-run exponential growth trend. Capacity (and production) both rose relative to the average growth trend between the late 1940s and about 1973. After 1973, the growth rate fell sharply, with capacity and production declining relative to trend. The roughly 60-year rise and fall of paper demand and capacity reflects the impact of the economic long wave (see section 19.3). A close look at the capacity data also reveals an intermediate cycle in capacity. The cycle is most easily seen in the graph of detrended Canadian pulp capacity. Relative to the long-run trend, capacity peaked in 1975 and again in 1992 (17 years). The intermediate cycle is also weakly visible in the US capacity data. Capacity cycles in the 12–20 year range have been noted in a wide range of industries since the 1800s and are also known as construction or Kuznets cycles, after the economist Simon Kuznets, a pioneer of national income accounting who was among the first to study them (see Kuznets 1953).

The generic model can be applied to the pulp and paper industry without any structural changes. On the demand side, Taylor (1999) found a demand elasticity of roughly −0.5 with a 6-month adjustment delay. On the supply side, the paper supply chain is long, progressing from logging through pulping (debarking, chipping, digestion, bleaching, and filtration), paper making (impregnation of pulp with additives and colorants, running pulp through the paper machine), then finishing (coating, drying, rolling, cutting, and packing), and finally into distribution channels. The paper supply chain involves significant inventories of work in process and finished inventories.[15]

---

[15]There are idiosyncracies specific to the paper industry, as in most markets, which would require modifications to the stock and flow structure in a more detailed model. These include the ability to dry, store, and trade pulp and the growing importance of recycled fiber. Taylor (1999) develops a detailed model of the pulp and paper industry that considers these issues. Similarly, paper is not a pure commodity (few goods are), coming in a huge variety of grades and types. Paper products are highly differentiated along dimensions including color, weight, acidity, fiber composition, delivery times, and others. Risch, Troyano-Bermúdez, and Sterman (1995) analyze the strategic implications of differentiation for a major paper supplier. These issues are beyond the scope of this chapter.

FIGURE 20-18 Cyclical behavior of the pulp and paper industry

All data US unless specified otherwise. Capacity, production, and investment: Ratio to long-run exponential trend in production.

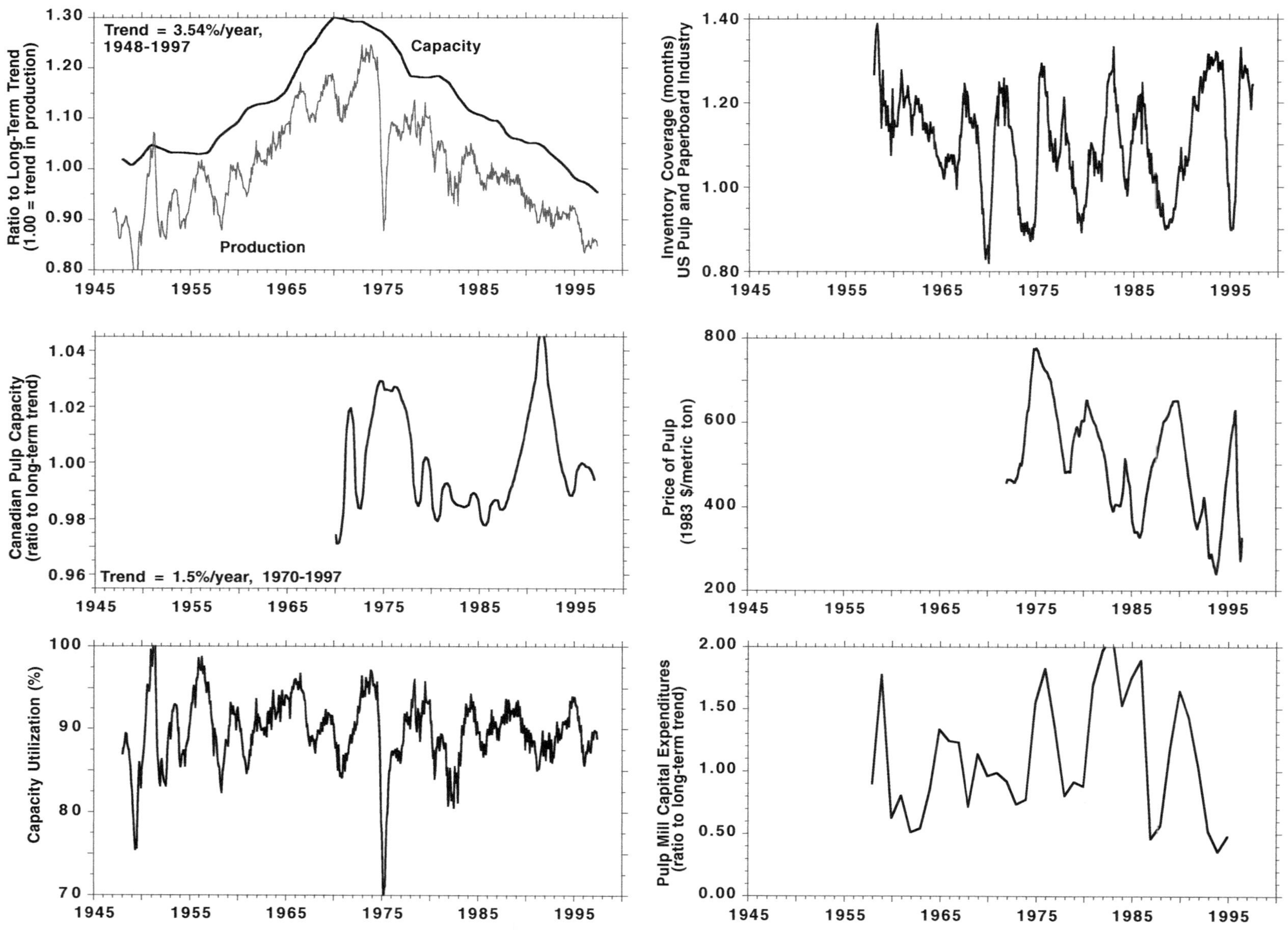

Source: Taylor (1999).

Parameter	Value	Units
Capital Productivity	1	Units/year/capital unit
Average Life of Capacity	20	Years
Capacity Acquisition Delay	4	Years
Capacity Adjustment Time	3	Years
Supply Line Adjustment Time	1	Year
Time to Adjust Long-Run Price Expectations	2	Years
Time to Adjust Expected Costs	2	Years
Reference Inventory Coverage	0.2	Years
Minimum Order Processing Time	0.1	Years
Manufacturing Cycle Time	0.5	Years
Utilization Adjustment Time	0.5	Years
Time to Adjust Short-Run Price Expectations	1	Year
Time to Adjust Expected Variable Costs	1	Year
Initial Variable Cost Fraction	0.4	Dimensionless
Reference Industry Demand Elasticity	0.5	Dimensionless
Demand Adjustment Delay	0.5	Years
Maximum Consumption	∞	Units/year
Sensitivity of Price to Inventory Coverage	−1	Dimensionless
Coverage Perception Time	0.167	Years
Sensitivity of Price to Costs	0.5	Dimensionless
Time to Adjust Traders' Expected Price	1	Year

Capacity acquisition delays are even longer. The capacity acquisition delay for pulp and paper mills is roughly 4 years (including site selection, financing, permitting, and contractor selection, as well as the design and construction process). The average lifetime of the plant and equipment in pulp and paper mills is about 20 years.

Table 20-1 summarizes the parameters used to adapt the generic model to the pulp and paper industry. The nonlinear functions used for utilization and the effect of expected profit on desired capital are the same as shown in Figures 20-9 and 20-12.

Since the focus of this analysis is the cyclical behavior of the industry the model is initialized with demand equal to 100 units/year at the reference price, representing 100% of the long-run trend. Likewise, the price is set to 100 (representing 100% of its initial equilibrium). While the absolute level of initial price and production are unimportant to the dynamics, the mix of costs and the normal capacity utilization level do matter. Paper production involves relatively high fixed costs, roughly 60% of total costs. Due to the high fixed costs, firms seek to run their paper machines continuously. Accounting for normal maintenance downtime, normal utilization is about 90% (as seen in Figure 20-18).

Figure 20-19 shows a simulation of the system with the approximate paper industry parameters. The model is initialized in equilibrium. At the start of year 1, a

FIGURE 20-19

Pulse response of full model with pulp and paper parameters

The system is perturbed by a 25% pulse increase in customer orders at the start of year 1.

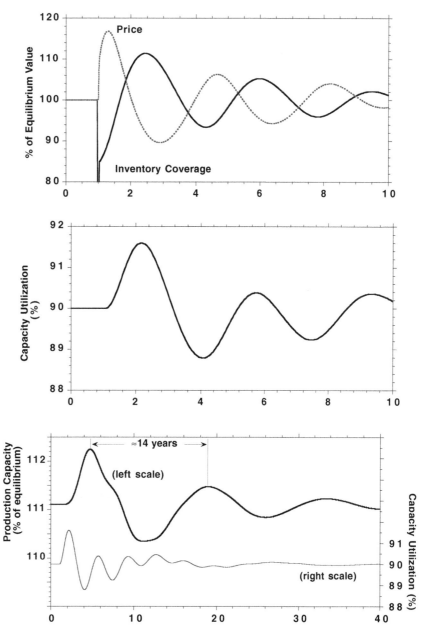

Note: Time scale of top two panels is 10 years to show the 3.6-year cycle caused by the Utilization Adjustment loop. Time scale of bottom panel is 40 years to show the 14-year cycle caused by the Capacity Acquisition loop.

pulse equal to 25% of equilibrium demand is added to customer orders, causing an immediate drop in inventory. The response of the system shows two distinct oscillatory modes. First, inventory, price, utilization, and production oscillate with a period a little less than 4 years. Second, capacity oscillates with a period of about 14 years. The short period is generated by the delays in the negative Capacity Utilization loop (Figure 20-7) and the 14-year period is generated by the longer delays in the negative Capacity Acquisition loop. Note the phase lag between inventory coverage and price: Price is not simply the mirror image of inventory coverage. Rather, price is rising when coverage is at its minimum and continues to rise for a little while even after coverage begins to recover. The phase lag is partly a consequence of the (quite short) time required for traders to perceive changes in coverage and largely a consequence of the price discovery process, in which prices tend to rise as long as inventory coverage is inadequate.[16]

Figure 20-20 shows a more realistic test in which demand begins to vary randomly at the start of year 1, simulating the unpredictable short-term variations in customer orders. The random noise has a standard deviation of 5% and an autocorrelation time constant of 1 year (the noise is introduced through equation (20-34), Other Factors Affecting Demand.

The simulation exhibits the two cyclical modes but with the irregularity you should expect given the random shocks perturbing the system. The capacity utilization loop generates a 3–5 year cycle most apparent in price, utilization, production, and inventory coverage. The capacity acquisition loop, with its longer delays, generates a cycle ranging from about 12–20 years. These periods are consistent with the data for the pulp and paper industry shown in Figure 20-18. The relative amplitudes of the key variables are also consistent with the data. Capacity and capacity utilization vary the least. Utilization generally remains in the 85–95% range and capacity varies roughly ±10% around its equilibrium. Inventory and prices have much larger amplitudes, fluctuating between about 60% and 150% of their equilibrium values. Finally, the capacity acquisition rate, which serves as a proxy for capital expenditures, has the largest amplitude, from about 30% to nearly 200% of its equilibrium value. The phase relationships among the variables are also similar to those observed in the data.

The model is not perfect and no great attempt has been made to calibrate the model parameters (most of which are set to round numbers). The simulated industry is smoother than the actual data because only one source of random variation was included. In reality, not only demand but also utilization, production, investment, costs, and other variables also experience random shocks. Econometric estimation of the parameters and further disaggregation would no doubt improve the correspondence of the model to the data. Nevertheless, the model captures the phase relationships and relative amplitudes of the two different cyclical modes seen in the industry quite well.

CHALLENGE   Sensitivity to Uncertainty in Parameters

Imagine you have just presented the results of your paper industry model to members of your client team. They find your explanation for the cycles in the industry intriguing but wonder how sensitive your results are to your assumptions. Your clients know that the parameter estimates you used are approximate and many are likely to be wrong. For example, how do the periods, relative amplitudes, and

---

[16]Close examination shows that price peaks and begins to fall before coverage returns to normal due to the effect of costs on price, which tends to pull price back to its equilibrium level.

FIGURE 20-20 Behavior of the generic commodity model with pulp and paper parameters

At the start of year 1 demand is modified by a random perturbation with a 5% standard deviation and 1-year autocorrelation time constant. Years 100–150 of the simulation are shown. Note the two distinct cyclical modes generated by the capacity utilization and capacity acquisition responses.

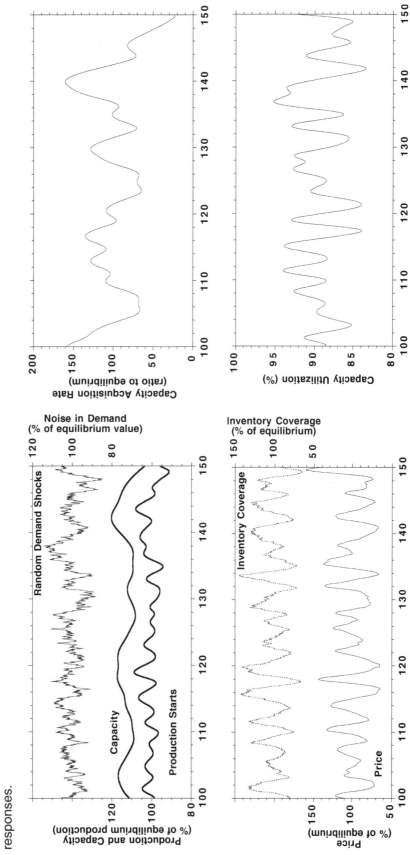

stability of the inventory and capacity cycles (the 3–5 year and 12–20 year cycles) depend on the parameters? Where are the high leverage points for action?

Sensitivity analysis is important for several reasons. First, it helps develop your intuition regarding the relationship between the structure and behavior of complex dynamic systems. Second, sensitivity analysis helps you and your client test the robustness of your conclusions with respect to uncertainty in the estimated parameters. Third, sensitivity analysis guides your data collection efforts. All parameters are uncertain. Most, given enough time and money, can be estimated more accurately. However, you can never estimate parameters perfectly and must always decide which to focus on and when to stop. A parameter that strongly affects the behavior may be a good candidate for additional data collection leading to a better and more reliable estimate. Conversely, for those with but little effect you can be confident that your results are robust even with an approximate estimate, saving time and effort. Modelers often spend too much time refining estimates for parameters that simply do not matter. Finally, parameters that strongly affect the behavior of the model may be high leverage points for policy intervention.

Before running the tests, write down your expectations. What do you predict the impact of each change in parameters will be, and why? Recording your predictions in advance—and the rationale for them—provides a great opportunity for you to improve your intuition. After running the tests, go back and compare the outcome to your expectations. Reformulate your explanation for the effect of each change, and test your new theory with additional experiments. This iterative process of testing will soon develop your ability to understand, explain, and anticipate the behavior of complex systems.

How much should you vary each parameter? One rule of thumb is to estimate the likely range of uncertainty in each parameter and then vary it by more (because people are often overconfident and underestimate the uncertainty in their estimates, whether these are judgmental or statistical. If you thought the uncertainty in a parameter was $\pm 20\%$, you might vary it $\pm 50\%$ or more. An alternative and often highly effective strategy is to try extreme changes. What happens when you zero out an effect, effectively eliminating a feedback from the model? To build your intuition about parameter sensitivity it is important to conduct controlled experiments in which you vary each parameter in isolation, one at a time, so you can be sure any changes in behavior are due to the change in the parameter. A caveat: In complex nonlinear systems, the results of such univariate sensitivity analysis may provide limited guidance to the response of the system to multiple parameter changes. Because real systems (and realistic models of them) are highly nonlinear, the impact of multiple parameter changes is in general not the sum of the impact of the individual changes, and the impact of a 50% change in a parameter is not necessarily twice the impact of the 25% change. In general, you must also conduct multivariate sensitivity analysis to understand the full range of responses of the system. For the purpose of this challenge, though, it is sufficient to conduct univariate tests. Chapter 21 takes up model testing and sensitivity analysis in more detail.

Consider parameter changes in the following sectors of the model:

Capacity utilization and production

1.   Vary the time delays in the Capacity Utilization loop. Consider both the physical delays such as the manufacturing cycle time and the decision-making delays such as the time required to form price expectations or alter utilization.

2.   Vary the slope of the effect of expected markup on utilization. Is the stability of the 3–5 year inventory cycle enhanced if utilization is more responsive to markup or less responsive? What is the impact of increased responsiveness of utilization on the period, stability, and amplitude of the capacity acquisition cycle? Why? To answer this question, you may want to review the impact of the Over/Undertime loop in the inventory–workforce model developed in chapter 19.

Production capacity

3.   Vary the time delays in the Capacity Acquisition loop. Consider both the physical delays such as the capacity acquisition time and the decision-making delays such as the time required to form price expectations.

4.   Vary the slope of the effect of expected profitability on desired capital. Is stability enhanced if desired capital is more or less responsive to expected profit?

Demand

5.   Vary the demand elasticity and demand adjustment time. Given the comparatively short demand adjustment time assumed in Table 20-1, is the negative Substitution feedback stabilizing or destabilizing, and why?

Price setting

6.   Vary the parameters in the price-setting process. What happens if prices are more responsive to inventory coverage? If traders update their beliefs about the underlying equilibrium price faster or slower? If costs are more influential or less?

In each case, explain the results in terms of the feedback structure of the model. How well were you able to anticipate the impact of the parameter changes? What are the high leverage parameters, the parameters that have a large impact on the period, amplitude, and stability of the system? How could these parameters be altered in the real world? That is, what policies could be implemented, either by individual producers or by larger institutions such as governments, to stabilize commodity markets?

CHALLENGE

Sensitivity to Structural Changes

Sensitivity analysis involves more than varying model parameters. All models are approximations—to build a model, every modeler must omit some feedback processes, aggregate different actors and entities, and assume the sources and sinks for the stock and flow structures have unlimited capacity. It is not sufficient to consider the sensitivity of your results to uncertainty in the parameters within the model. You must also examine the sensitivity of your results to plausible alternative structural assumptions, including changes in the model boundary and level of aggregation (chapter 21).

After satisfying your client regarding the sensitivity of your model to uncertainty in parameters, skeptical members of the client team then challenge your results because you have omitted some feedbacks they think might be important. For each of the following, modify the model to incorporate the hypothesized effect. Use your best judgment to estimate the new parameters. To understand the likely effects of the new structures it is helpful to modify your causal diagram of the market to include the new feedbacks. As with parametric sensitivity analysis, write down your expectations regarding the effects of the new feedbacks on the period, stability, and other features of model behavior *before* running the model. Afterward, check to see if your intuition was correct, and continue to test until you understand why the new structure does what it does. You may need to experiment with different parameters for the strengths of the new feedbacks. You can add these effects in isolation to the base case model or add them cumulatively. In either case, be sure you understand the impact of each new structure fully before making additional changes.

1. **Variable capacity lifetime:** The clients point out that in your model the useful life of capacity is fixed. In reality, they say, the useful life of capacity varies with economic conditions in the industry. Producers can decommission existing facilities when profitability is low, and they can keep old plants running longer when there is a shortage of capacity and profits are expected to be high.

    Modify the model to include a variable lifetime of capital. Make the average lifetime of capital equal to a normal lifetime modified by a function of long-run expected profitability (the expected profitability of new investment). Specify the function so that the lifetime of capital equals the normal lifetime in equilibrium. Estimate values for the function using your best judgment and following the guidelines in chapter 14. Explain your choice. Which factors would affect the willingness of producers to accelerate or postpone the decommissioning of existing capacity? Identify any new feedback loops created by the new structure. What effects will the new structure have on the behavior of the system?

    Next, test your hypotheses by comparing the behavior of the revised model to the base case. Consider a variety of test conditions. Were your expectations about the impact of the new structure correct?

2. **Canceling orders for new capacity:** Another member of the client team points out that the model does not allow orders for new capacity to be canceled. Add the possibility of canceling orders for capital in the supply line. Remember that the supply line of capital on order includes both orders for new capacity in the planning stage and the stock of capital under construction. Orders may sometimes be canceled, but projects under

construction rarely are. You may wish to adapt the structure developed in section 19.1 to model layoffs and vacancy cancellation. Select appropriate parameters and justify your choices.

As above, identify any new feedbacks created by order cancellations, and predict their impact on the behavior of the model. Then test your intuition by running the model.

3. **Extrapolative expectations:** Members of the client team point out that you've assumed price expectations are formed adaptively, by smoothing. One says,

    > During market booms a kind of euphoria spreads throughout the industry. Pretty soon, industry analysts and trade publications begin to project continued price increases. *We* never succumb to these pie-in-the-sky forecasts, but many of our competitors are taken in. This leads to overinvestment and worsens the next slump. Then everyone becomes excessively pessimistic, delaying the recovery.

    Recalling chapter 16, you modify the formulation for the long-term expected price to capture the clients' hypothesis that price expectations respond to the recent trend in price:

    Expected Long-Run Price
    = Recent Price * Effect of Trend on Expected Price   (20-31a)

    Recent Price
    = SMOOTH(Price, Time to Adjust Long-Run Price Expectations)   (20-51)

    Effect of Trend on Expected Price
    = f(Expected Trend in Price, Forecast Horizon)   (20-52)

    The Effect of Trend on Expected Price captures the impact of perceived price trends on the forecast of price used in investment decisions. Presumably, the higher the expected inflation rate in price or the longer the forecast horizon (the farther in the future the price trend is projected), the greater the effect.

    The forecast horizon should be related to the time between initiating and realizing investment in new capacity: The longer the capacity acquisition delay, the longer the forecast horizon must be. The expected rate of inflation can be modeled with the TREND function defined in chapter 16:

    Expected Trend in Price = TREND(Price, Price Perception Time,
       Historical Horizon for Price Trend, Time to Perceive Price Trend)   (20-53)

    Here the Price Perception Time is the time required to perceive price and smooth out high-frequency noise, the Historical Horizon for Price Trend represents how far back in history investors look in assessing price trends, and the Time to Perceive Price Trend represents the time required to update beliefs about price trends.

    There are many plausible functions for the Effect of Trend on Expected Price. A simple starting point is the assumption that investors expect the current inflation rate in price to remain constant over the forecast horizon. In that case,

Effect of Trend on Expected Price
$$= \exp(\text{Expected Trend in Price} * \text{Forecast Horizon}) \qquad (20\text{-}52\text{a})$$

If the forecast horizon is zero, the revised formulation reduces to the original model in which long-term expected prices are formed by smoothing actual price.[17]

Implement the formulation for extrapolative expectations. Use your best judgment to select reasonable parameters.

What is the impact of extrapolative price expectations on the stability and other characteristics of the cycle? You may want to start by running the model with a single demand shock to get a feel for the behavior of the forecast and the phase relationships of the forecast and actual price, but be sure to consider the response to random demand as well. Experiment with different parameters for the formation of the expected trend in price and for the forecast horizon. What are the implications for producers and investors?

4. **The long-run supply curve:** The costs of new capacity in the model are constant and independent of the scale of the industry. In economic terms, the long-run supply curve is flat: Capacity could double without any change in marginal costs. In some industries, this is a reasonable assumption. In others, such as many mineral and agricultural commodities, the marginal cost of new capacity rises as industry capacity grows. Expanding copper production means ores of lower quality must be mined; expanding oil production capacity means drilling deeper and in more remote locations; expanding cocoa production means cultivating land that is less productive or more distant from the market.

Modify the model to account for the feedback from production capacity to the marginal cost of new capacity. For simplicity, assume both unit fixed costs and unit variable costs rise by the same proportion as capacity grows. Normalize the function you select so that costs equal their reference levels when capacity equals its reference level. Set the reference level to the initial equilibrium. Select an appropriate shape for the dependence of marginal costs on production capacity. Typically, costs rise slowly at first but at progressively steeper rates as capacity grows.

Identify the new feedbacks introduced by the long-run supply curve and predict the impact of the new feedback structure on the behavior. Design and implement tests to examine the impact of the long-run supply curve.

5. **Separating average and marginal cost:** Adding the feedback from capacity to costs captures the long-run supply curve, but the clients then point out that

---

[17]The assumption that investors believe current trends will continue over the forecast horizon is not likely to hold for very high inflation rates or very long forecast horizons. A more realistic model would replace the exponential function with a function that approximates the exponential for small inflation rates but saturates at a maximum and minimum value at the extremes of very high or low inputs. The saturation nonlinearities capture the idea that investors expect extreme rates of price change to moderate over time.

the model does not distinguish between the marginal cost of new investment and the average costs of operating existing capital. Investors develop the least expensive sources of supply first, turning to more expensive sites only as rising prices justify the added cost. The next copper mine to be opened will have lower grade ore than the average of existing mines, and new paper machines are much more productive than the machines available three decades ago. The decision to invest in a new facility will depend on the fixed and variable costs of new capital, but each producers' decision to operate depends on the variable costs of existing facilities.

Modify the model to distinguish between the unit costs of new investment and the average unit costs of existing capital. To do so you must introduce coflows to keep track of the fixed and variable costs associated with each new unit of capital from the time it is ordered until it is discarded. Section 12.2 describes the relevant structure. Utilization of existing capacity will now depend on average unit variable costs over the stock of existing capacity, not the unit variable costs associated with new investment.

Test the revised model by assuming an exogenous rate of technical progress that lowers the marginal costs per unit of new capacity at some rate, say 5%/year. How does such technical progress affect the dynamics of the market?

The clients also point out that the decommissioning decision depends on the profitability of old capital compared to new capital. Older facilities are less productive and have higher operating costs than new ones. During market upswings, when prices are high, even old, unproductive plants can operate at a profit. During downswings, the least productive plants are shut down first as prices fall. Eventually, a plant becomes so costly that management is forced to scrap it (or invest in expensive retrofitting to boost productivity). The decommissioning decision therefore depends on the profitability of existing capital, which differs from the expected profitability of new facilities. When old capital is much more costly to operate, decommissioning and retrofitting are accelerated. Revise your formulation for the variable lifetime of capital so the life of capital depends on the expected profitability of existing capital rather than the profitability of new investment. What is the impact on the feedback structure and behavior of the model?

6. **Feedback of inventory to capacity utilization:** The clients point out that capacity utilization in the model depends only on the expected markup ratio. They argue instead that utilization is affected directly by the inventory position of the producers. The decision to shut down a facility because it is unprofitable is typically made at corporate headquarters, not by the plant managers. They argue that production schedules at any plant respond primarily to the order and inventory position of the plant. Indeed, as discussed above, shortages of product will stimulate utilization and limits on physical storage capacity can force production to fall when inventories grow too large, no matter how profitable the industry may appear to be.

Taking your high-level causal diagram of the market (Figure 20-7), they redraw it to capture the feedbacks from inventory to utilization (Figure 20-21). The modified diagram shows a new feedback from inventory to utilization, the Inventory Control loop (shown with heavy lines). Indicated capacity utilization in the revised model now responds to both expected markups and Schedule Pressure, defined as the ratio of the desired production start rate to production capacity.

You decide to modify the model to incorporate the direct feedback from inventory to capacity utilization. You decide to use the structure for desired production starts developed in chapter 18. In that structure, shown in Figure 18-5, desired production starts depend on the forecast of customer orders modified by an adjustment to bring inventory in line with desired inventory and a similar adjustment for the work in process inventory. This structure generates the rate of output producers would like to attain based on their aggregate inventory position, including WIP, and taking their forecast of orders into account. Choose appropriate values for the parameters such as the inventory, WIP, and forecast adjustment times. You will have to modify the formulation for capacity utilization and indicated utilization to incorporate both the effects of profitability (expected markup) and schedule pressure. Consider whether the delays in the effects of markup and schedule pressure may differ. Your revised formulation should allow the relative importance of these two factors to be varied in sensitivity tests, from the original formulation with markup as the only input to utilization to the other extreme where schedule pressure is the only input. Be sure your revised model begins in equilibrium.

Implement and test the revised formulation. How does the behavior change when both schedule pressure and markup affect utilization? Also test the extreme condition in which schedule pressure is the only determinant of utilization. What is the effect of the Inventory Control loop on the period, stability, and other properties of the short-term cycle and the capacity acquisition cycle? Explain in terms of the feedback structure of the revised system shown in Figure 20-21.

Finally, critique your new utilization formulation. What defects do you see? How could you reformulate the model to improve the representation of utilization? Under what circumstances would such elaboration be appropriate?

CHALLENGE   ## Implementing Structural Changes— Modeling Livestock Markets

As illustrated in Figures 20-1 and 20-2, the hog and cattle industries experience persistent oscillations. The period of the hog cycle is about 4 years, while the cattle cycle is about 10–12 years.

Adapt the generic commodity model to the livestock industry. In nonagricultural markets production capacity is independent of the manufacturing supply

FIGURE 20-21 Revised causal diagram showing the direct feedback from inventory to utilization

Schedule Pressure is defined as the ratio of Desired Production Starts to Production Capacity (the latter is not shown explicitly).

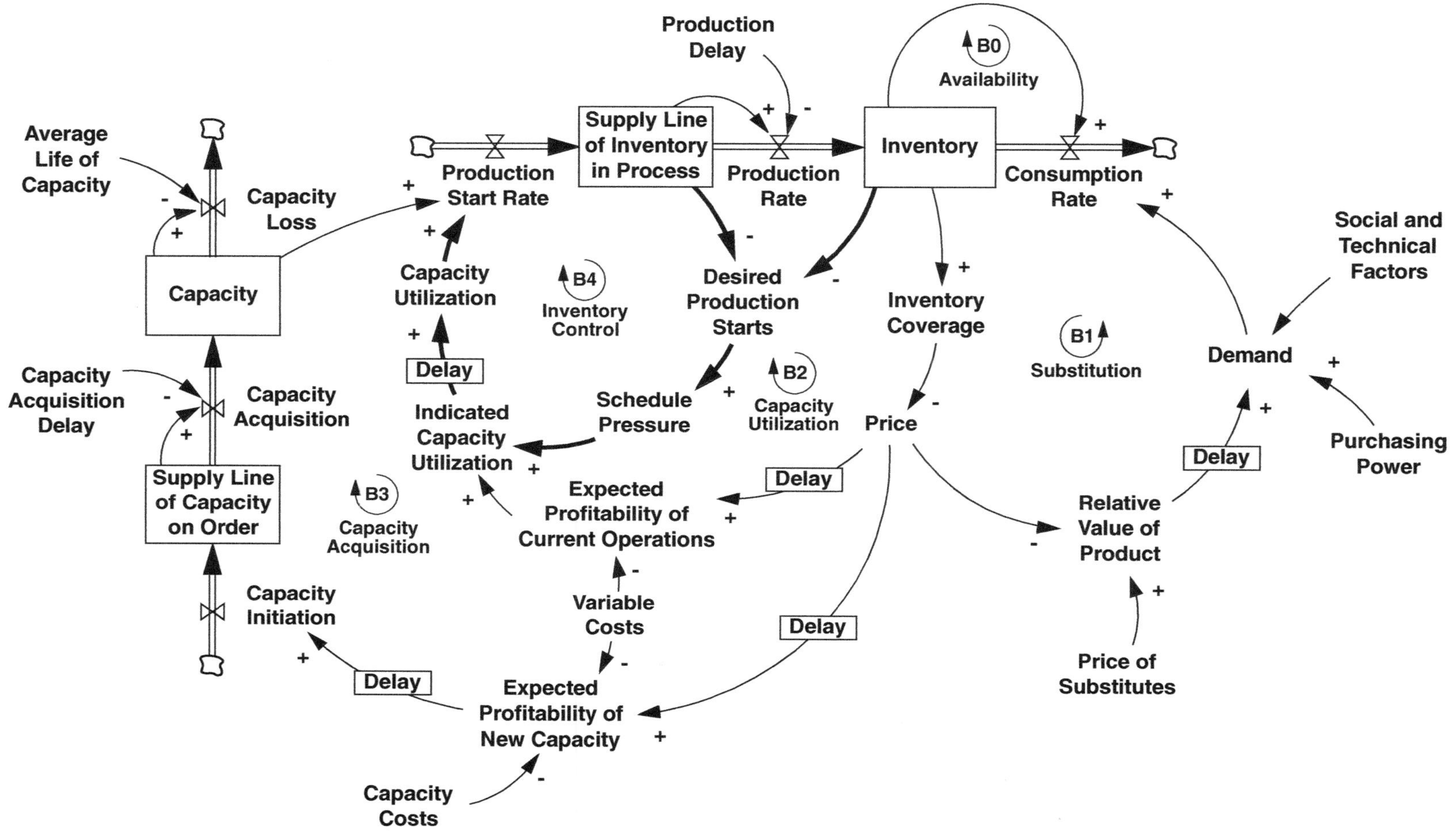

chain: Pulp mills and pulp aren't the same thing. In livestock markets, however, production cannot take place without a breeding stock. Producers must choose whether to send their stock to market now or to keep animals on the farm to increase the future supply. In plain terms, it takes hogs to make hogs. This fundamental biological fact requires the stock and flow structure of production to be altered, as shown in Figure 20-22.

The production supply chain is disaggregated into three categories: the gestation delay, immature stock, and mature stock. For cattle and hogs, mature animals are typically kept on corn feedlots until they reach the optimal weight and will fetch the best price. The key difference between the livestock production process and other commodities, however, is that production starts are not directly controlled by the producer. Production starts correspond to the breeding rate, which depends on the size of the breeding stock (along with the number of litters per year and the average litter size). Producers control the size of the breeding stock. The breeding stock is increased when producers withhold mature animals from market. In adapting the model to livestock you will need to specify the order of each delay in the gestation–maturation process, remembering that your model aggregates all producers (see chapter 11 for guidelines).

The decision to increase the breeding stock, shown in Figure 20-22 as the Indicated Breeding Stock Increase Rate, can be modeled with a variant of the standard stock management structure. Producers need to replace older breeding stock sent to market and adjust the actual breeding stock toward the desired breeding stock. You should model the desired breeding stock as the product of production capacity and indicated capacity utilization. That is, producers will increase their desired breeding stock (to increase future supply) when the expected markup ratio is high and will reduce their breeding stocks when it is low. The total size of the breeding stock is limited by production capacity, representing the capacity of ranches, farms, and feedlots in the industry.

Take care that your reformulated model is robust under extreme conditions: The stocks of animals must remain nonnegative and total breeding stock must remain within the capacity of the industry. The principal parameters for both hogs and cattle are shown in Table 20-2. Use your best judgment and other available information to estimate the other parameters and behavioral relationships in the model.

TABLE 20-2
Parameters for livestock model

Parameter	Hogs	Cattle	Units
Average Litter Size	8.0	1.0	Animals/litter
Litters per Year	2.0	1.0	Litters/animal/year
Gestation Period	0.31	0.83	Years
Maturation Time	0.42	1.67	Years
Mature Stock Feeding Period	0.17	1.0	Years
Average Breeding Period	2.5	2.5	Years

Sources: Meadows (1970); Commodity Research Bureau, *Commodity Yearbook,* various years.

FIGURE 20-22 Modifying the model to represent livestock markets

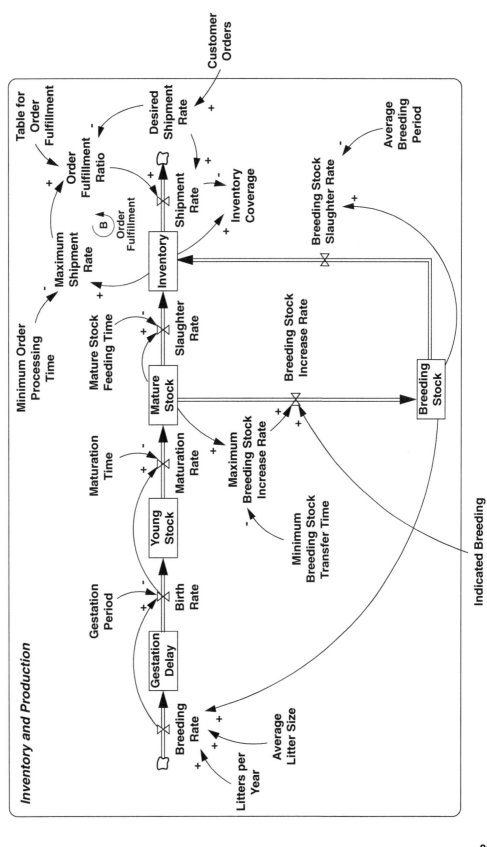

Inventory and Production

Run the model for the case of both hogs and cattle and contrast its behavior against the data. Does the model reproduce the period and other characteristics of the hog and cattle cycles? Explore the sensitivity of your results to parameters.

Because the only way to increase the supply of hogs or cattle in the long run is to withhold some mature animals from market, the short-run response of an increase in the expected markup is a *reduction* in supply. What type of feedback process is created by this biological reality? What effect does this loop have on the stability of the market? Design and execute sensitivity tests to explore the importance of this feedback. Is the effect strongest for the hog or cattle market, and why?

Assume that, from equilibrium, the price of corn suddenly and permanently increases. Design and implement this test in the model. What is the long-run behavior of the market (price, production, breeding stock, etc.)? What is the short-run response? How does the response of the desired breeding stock to the cost increase affect producer profitability in the short run? What are the implications for producers in the livestock markets?[18]

CHALLENGE

Policy Analysis

Commodity cycles result from the interaction of long delays in the response of supply to price with the bounded rationality of producers. Producers and investors form expectations of profitability and price adaptively and do not appear to account adequately for the time delays in the system or the impact of other producers' decisions on future investment, production, and prices.

Can you design policies that improve performance and profitability in cyclical markets? Such policies might involve changes in the information used to form price expectations or make investment decisions or other changes in the investment, utilization, and price expectation formation decisions. Design and test your policies in the model (either the base case model, the enhanced model including the structural changes described in the challenges above, or the livestock version of the model). Contrast the performance of your policies against the original model for a variety of cases, including various one-time demand and cost shocks and random variations in demand. How could these policies be implemented in reality?

Economists often argue that oscillations in commodity markets cannot long endure because they provide arbitrage opportunities. If there were a cycle, savvy investors could make extraordinary profits by timing their investments to buy at cycle troughs and sell at cycle peaks. As more people pursued such countercyclical strategies, their actions would cause the cycle to vanish. Even if people can't learn at all, markets, by transferring wealth from those using poor decision rules to those with superior rules, would quickly cause the population of producers to evolve until all were using (nearly) optimal strategies. While the logic of the argument sounds compelling, the persistence of cyclical movements in so many commodity markets over very long periods (more than a century for many industries) suggests

---

[18]Rosen, et al. (1994), Mundlak and Huang (1996), and Hayes and Schmitz (1987) offer contrasting models and empirical analyses of the livestock markets.

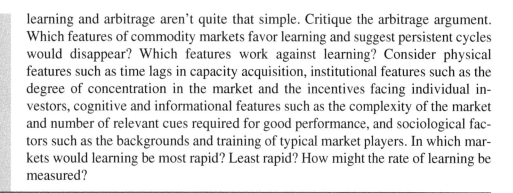

learning and arbitrage aren't quite that simple. Critique the arbitrage argument. Which features of commodity markets favor learning and suggest persistent cycles would disappear? Which features work against learning? Consider physical features such as time lags in capacity acquisition, institutional features such as the degree of concentration in the market and the incentives facing individual investors, cognitive and informational features such as the complexity of the market and number of relevant cues required for good performance, and sociological factors such as the backgrounds and training of typical market players. In which markets would learning be most rapid? Least rapid? How might the rate of learning be measured?

20.4 SUMMARY

This chapter developed models of markets in which price functions to balance supply and demand. The generic industry model introduced several important and useful formulations, including price setting and the response of investment to expected profitability. These formulations are useful across multiple levels of aggregation, from individual firms to the economy as a whole. The model explains the origin of the chronic fluctuations observed in a wide range of commodity industries. Commodity cycles arise from the interaction of the physical delays in production and capacity acquisition with boundedly rational decision making by individual producers and investors. The persistence of cycles in industries from copper to cattle and rubber to real estate suggests learning and market forces that might stabilize the cycles are weak. In market economies price lies in the center of a network of negative feedbacks which act to eliminate imbalances between demand and supply, thus promoting the efficient allocation of resources: the invisible hand. Yet in many markets the reactions of demand and supply to price are very slow. Negative feedbacks with time delays are prone to oscillation and instability: The invisible hand sometimes shakes.

Part VI

Model Testing

How do you know a model is a sound basis for decision making? What tests should you apply? Chapter 21 focuses on the concept of validity, showing that validation in the sense of establishing truthfulness is impossible. The chapter suggests a set of pragmatic questions model clients and model makers should ask to uncover hidden assumptions, biases, and errors. The chapter also describes a wide range of specific tests and procedures you can use to test your models.

21

Truth and Beauty: Validation and Model Testing

A model is a work of fiction.

—Nancy Cartwright (1983, p. 153)

William James used to preach the "will to believe." For my part, I should wish to preach the "will to doubt." . . . What is wanted is not the will to believe, but the wish to find out, which is the exact opposite.

—Bertrand Russell (1928/1961, pp. 104-106)[1]

No I ain't got a witness and I can't prove it
But that's my story and I'm stickin' to it.

—Lee Roy Parnell and Tony Haselden,
"That's my Story," sung by Collin Raye

What makes a good model? As a modeler, how do you know the results can be trusted? As a model consumer, when should you accept a model as the basis for action? What questions should you ask, what evidence should be used, and what standards should be applied? Who decides? This chapter describes model testing and focuses on the process by which you and your clients can build confidence that a model is appropriate for the purpose. Unfortunately, testing is often designed to "prove" the model is "right," an approach that makes learning difficult and

---

[1] *Sceptical Essays*, 1928. 1961 edition, London: Unwin Books.

ultimately erodes the utility of the model and the credibility of the modeler. Worse, many important tests are simply never done. Many modelers focus excessively on replication of historical data without regard to the appropriateness of underlying assumptions, robustness, and the sensitivity of results to assumptions about the model boundary and feedback structure. Modelers often fail to document their work, preventing others from replicating and extending it. Modelers and clients often suffer from confirmation bias, selectively presenting data favorable to their preconceptions, and then stickin' to their story despite the evidence. Model testing should instead be designed to uncover errors so you and your clients can understand the model's limitations, improve it, and ultimately use the best available model to assist in important decisions. The chapter also describes specific tests and procedures you should follow to test the suitability of a model for your purpose, uncover flaws, and improve the chances your model will be used and useful. The tests can be applied by modelers and model consumers and range from examination of model boundary assumptions to quantitative assessment of the model's historical fit. Examples illustrate how the tests can be applied and how failure to do so often results in absurdity or project failure.

21.1 VALIDATION AND VERIFICATION ARE IMPOSSIBLE

Many modelers speak of model "validation" or claim to have "verified" a model. In fact, validation and verification of models is impossible. The word "verify" derives from the Latin *verus*—truth; Webster's defines "verify" as "to establish the truth, accuracy, or reality of." "Valid" is defined as "having a conclusion correctly derived from premises . . . Valid implies being supported by objective truth."

By these definitions, no model can ever be verified or validated. Why? Because all models are wrong. As described in chapter 1, all models, mental or formal, are limited, simplified representations of the real world. They differ from reality in ways large and small, infinite in number. The only statements that can be validated—shown to be true—are pure analytic statements, propositions derived from the axioms of a closed logical system, because, as stated by the philosopher A. J. Ayer (1952, p. 31), "They do not make any assertion about the empirical world, but simply record our determination to use symbols in a certain fashion."

Some modelers have long recognized the impossibility of validation in the sense of establishing truth. Forrester (1961, p. 123) wrote:

> Any "objective" model-validation procedure rests eventually at some lower level on a judgment or faith that either the procedure or its goals are acceptable without objective proof.

Forrester's view, controversial at the time, is now more widely shared among modelers. In an influential assessment of the state of policy modeling in the mid 1970s, Greenberger, Crenson, and Crissey (1976, p. 70-71) concluded that

> No model has ever been or ever will be thoroughly validated . . . "Useful," "illuminating," "convincing," or "inspiring confidence" are more apt descriptors applying to models than "valid."

More recently, Oreskes, Shrader-Frechette, and Belitz (1994, p. 644) wrote, "Models are representations, useful for guiding further study but not susceptible to proof."

The impossibility of validation and verification is not limited to computer models. Any theory that refers to the world relies on imperfectly measured data, abstractions, aggregations, and simplifications, whether the theory is embodied in a large-scale computer model, consists of the simplest equations, or is entirely literary. The differences between analytic theories and computer simulations are differences of degree only.

Many argue that while the truth of a model cannot be established, surely its falsity can. The late Sir Karl Popper's philosophy of *refutationism* or *falsificationism* remains popular among many scientists, modelers, and economists (e.g., Bell and Senge 1980; Redman 1994; McCloskey 1994). While the truth of any empirical statement can never be established, Popper famously argued that it is possible to show a theory to be false. Empirical statements such as "all swans are white" can never be verified. No matter how many swans we find to be white, we can never be sure we've tested them all or that the next swan to hatch will be white. However, observation of a single black swan shows the statement to be false. Popper argued that to be scientific a theory had to be subject to refutation, that is, it had to be possible to falsify it by experiment or other empirical test. Once a theory is falsified empirically it has to be discarded and replaced by some new, more accurate theory. Only those theories that have not yet been refuted should be accepted and that acceptance is always conditional.

The widely taught story of Galileo's experiment at the leaning tower of Pisa provides a classic example. Galileo reportedly dropped cannonballs of different weights from the tower, showing that they hit the ground at the same time. The old theory that heavy objects fall faster than light ones was falsified and replaced with the new theory that gravity causes all objects to accelerate earthward at a constant rate, independent of mass.[2]

Popper called on scientists to seek the "crucial experiment" that, like Galileo's, could falsify their theories. If the proponents of a theory cannot describe an experiment or evidence that would persuade them to abandon their theory, then, Popper argued, it cannot be considered scientific, but must be recognized as a dogma no different in principle from any matter of faith. He pointed to the claims of psychoanalysis, Marxism, and astrology, among others, as prime offenders.

This naïve version of Popper's approach enjoys continued popularity due to its simplicity and intuitive appeal. There are indeed many cases where superstition and ideology cloak themselves in the authority of science. Popper's criterion of falsifiability shows the emperors of these pseudosciences to be naked.

Unfortunately, many people are taught the sound-bite version of refutationism in introductory classes, never digging more deeply into the philosophy of science

---

[2]Actually, Galileo measured the rate at which balls rolled down inclined planes (to slow their acceleration and improve the accuracy of his measurements), and the story of the leaning tower may be apocryphal. Simon Stevin of Bruges was likely the first to carry out the dropped-weight experiment, publishing the results in 1587, prior to Galileo's work (Boyer 1991).

to discover its subtleties and limitations.[3] Most obviously, since all models are wrong, all can be falsified by some test or other. A rock falls faster than a feather, and even Galileo's weights did not all fall to earth at exactly the same time—dense objects consistently fall faster than less dense ones, refuting the theory of constant acceleration. Since all models are false and refutable, which are we to use?

Paradoxically, at the same time that all models are wrong, any particular theoretical proposition can always be rescued from apparent falsification. Accurate measurement shows that objects of different masses and shapes do fall at different rates. Does this falsify the theory? No. As all grade school students are taught, objects *would* fall at the same rate *if* there were no air friction. The theory is saved by invoking an *auxiliary hypothesis*. During a 1971 Apollo 15 moonwalk, astronaut David Scott famously demonstrated the role of air friction by simultaneously dropping a hammer and a feather. Both fell to the surface at the same time. But suppose the feather hadn't fallen as quickly as the hammer. Would physicists around the world have shouted, "The theory has been falsified!" and abandoned the idea that gravitational acceleration is independent of mass? Of course not. They would have invoked auxiliary hypotheses to explain the discrepancy. Perhaps static electricity in Scott's glove slowed the feather's descent. If static electricity were ruled out by subsequent tests, scientists would still not have rewritten the textbooks. Perhaps magnetite in the lunar surface accelerated the hammer's fall. If this were ruled out, we would have postulated some other, unknown force. A favored hypothesis can always be saved by invoking other, auxiliary hypotheses.

Tests of any theory take place at a particular time and place, with particular equipment and instruments. Experiments can never test the theory alone, but only the joint hypothesis consisting of the theory and the auxiliary assumptions that the equipment is properly set up, that the instruments work as expected, and that there are no sources of uncontrolled variation. No matter how carefully an experiment is done an infinite number of possible sources of uncontrolled variation always exist; therefore, there is always an infinite number of auxiliary hypotheses that can be invoked to save any theory from disconfirmation. This realization, known as the Quine-Duhem thesis, means all theories can always be adjusted to accord with any data whatsoever without discarding the core propositions.

The introduction of auxiliary hypotheses to save a favored theory is sometimes a rewarding path to knowledge. After the discovery of Uranus, observations revealed that its orbit did not follow the path predicted by Newton's laws. Instead of discarding or modifying the inverse square law of gravitation, astronomers invoked the auxiliary hypothesis that a more distant planet was perturbing its orbit. Assuming Newton was right, astronomers calculated where the new planet should be and Neptune was indeed found nearby in 1846. In this case, holding fast to Newton's laws despite evidence contradicting the theory was a good strategy.

Most often, however, auxiliary hypotheses serve to insulate a theory from confrontation with unfavorable data. Pre-Copernican astronomers reconciled

---

[3]Lakatos (1976) provides a more sophisticated development of falsificationism.

discrepancies between the Ptolemaic system and observation by invoking ever more complex epicycles. The epicycles preserved the favored hypothesis that the earth reigned supreme at the center of the universe. Postulating yet another epicycle could always eliminate any discrepancies revealed by more accurate observations. Copernicus, working with essentially the same evidence, abandoned the geocentric theory and argued that the planets circled the sun. The evidence did not determine the choice. Indeed, for a long time, the Ptolemaic system provided more accurate predictions than the Copernican.

Invoking auxiliary hypotheses to save a favored theory remains a central tactic in battles between contending worldviews to this day. The most popular theory of the big bang, known as inflation, initially required the total mass of the universe to be much larger than observation suggested. Rather than abandon inflation in the face of this apparent disconfirmation, physicists hypothesized that the universe contains "missing matter" in the form of brown dwarves (unignited stars too dim to see), WIMPS (weakly interacting massive particles undetectable by our instruments), and even the presence of a "cosmological constant"—a mysterious force hypothesized to push all matter apart. Only time will tell whether any of these auxiliary hypotheses will be supported by new data and become the new orthodoxy or whether future physicists will look back on them as foolish errors. Physicists are not alone in their mastery of the auxiliary hypothesis. In the face of laboratory experiments and field data showing that people violate the axioms of rationality and that markets are not perfectly efficient, some economists invoke auxiliary assumptions, epicycles on epicycles, to preserve the core axioms of rationality and equilibrium. Typical moves to save *homo economicus* from extinction include invocation of information asymmetries, transaction costs, search and deliberation costs, limitations on the repertoire of actions available to the agents, unusual utility functions, and so on (see Simon 1984). Rationality and equilibrium are not empirical facts but the central tenets of a deeply felt faith.[4]

Theories built on such nonfalsifiable foundations constitute paradigms in the sense of the late Thomas Kuhn (1970). Paradigms are self-consistent communities of like-minded scientists, sharing a worldview encompassing not only a body of theory and evidence but also methods of inquiry, standards of proof, textbook examples, and heroes. Kuhn argued that different paradigms are fundamentally incommensurable, meaning that rational choice between paradigms based on evidence is not possible and does not drive changes in the dominant scientific theories of an era.

The real significance of Kuhn's paradigms and the Quine-Duhem thesis is this: The decision to abandon a theory is never forced upon us by reality but is always and essentially a human choice. When theory and data clash, we necessarily

---

[4]This discussion is not meant to single out economics. All serious scientific theories include a core of favored beliefs that are not subject to refutation. Try to imagine an experiment or empirical result that could persuade a system dynamics modeler that feedback loops don't exist. See Meadows (1980).

choose between them using nonevidential criteria, such as parsimony, elegance, or conformance to religious, political, or aesthetic beliefs.

Validation is also intrinsically social. The goal of modeling, and of scientific endeavor more generally, is to build shared understanding that provides insight into the world and helps solve important problems. Modeling is therefore inevitably a process of communication and persuasion among modelers, clients, and other affected parties. Each person ultimately judges the quality and appropriateness of any model using his or her own criteria. The physicist turned sociologist of science John Ziman notes, "The objective of Science . . . is a consensus of rational opinion over the widest possible field" (1968, p. 9). C. West Churchman, a pioneer in the management sciences, goes further (1973, p. 12):

> A point of view, or a model, is realistic to the extent that it can be adequately interpreted, understood, and accepted by other points of view.

Recognizing the fundamentally subjective and social nature of model evaluation does not mean model testing is unscientific or that in practice any test or criterion is just as good as any other. Likewise, the Quine-Duhem thesis is not a justification for avoiding empirical tests, ignoring evidence, or stonewalling critics. For those who believe the US government covered up the alleged 1947 crash of an alien spacecraft in Roswell, New Mexico, any government denials are simply further evidence of the conspiracy. These believers are extremely creative in invoking auxiliary hypotheses to interpret any information, no matter how negative, as consistent with the truth as they see it. Whether used in the service of a cult or a scientific theory, such behavior results in an internally consistent worldview sealed off from surprise and immune to evidence. Modelers should focus on tests that can reveal the limitations of our current models, mental and formal. Oreskes et al. (1994) write:

> We must admit that a model may confirm our biases and support incorrect intuitions. Therefore, models are most useful when they are used to challenge existing formulations, rather than to validate or verify them. Any scientist who is asked to use a model to verify or validate a predetermined result should be suspicious.

If validation is impossible and all models are wrong, why then do we bother to build them? As a leader you must recognize that you will be using a model—mental or formal—to make important decisions. Your choice is never whether to use a model but only which model to use. Your responsibility is to use the best model available for the purpose at hand despite its inevitable limitations. The decision to delay action in the vain quest for a perfect model is itself a decision, with its own set of consequences. Experienced modelers likewise recognize that the goal is to help their clients make better decisions, decisions informed by the best available model. Instead of seeking a single test of validity models either pass or fail, good modelers seek multiple points of contact between the model and reality by drawing on many sources of data and a wide range of tests. Instead of viewing validation as a testing step after a model is completed, they recognize that theory building and theory testing are intimately intertwined in an iterative loop. Instead of presenting evidence that the model is valid, good modelers focus the client on the limitations of the model so it can be improved and so clients will not misuse it.

21.2 QUESTIONS MODEL USERS SHOULD ASK— BUT USUALLY DON'T

In most debates over particular models philosophical considerations are like the official ideology an army fights for: great in principle but forgotten in the heat of battle. In practice, models fall on the field of organizational conflict for more mundane and avoidable reasons. Meadows and Robinson (1985) reviewed nine models designed to address various public policy questions in the areas of economic development, resources, and the environment. The models used methods including econometrics, linear programming, and input/output analysis, as well as system dynamics. Though the models were "identified as 'better than average'" by the authors and by "other modelers, clients, and sponsors," Meadows and Robinson (p. 104) found "mismatches of methods with purposes, sloppy documentation, absurd assumptions buried in overcomplex structures, conclusions that do not even follow from model output, and project management strategies that destroy the possibility of influencing actual policy." The record in the world of business models is at least as dismal.

As an antidote, Table 21-1 lists a variety of questions modelers, and especially model users, should ask but usually don't. These questions are designed to assess the overall suitability of the model to your purpose, its conformance to fundamental formulation principles, the sensitivity of results to uncertainty in assumptions, and the integrity of the modeling process.

21.3 PRAGMATICS AND POLITICS OF MODEL USE

Once we recognize that all models are wrong and abandon the black and white dualism of truth and falsification, we can focus on the important questions: Is the model useful? Do its shortcomings matter? To answer these questions you must first ask: Useful for what purpose? Matter to whom?

Model users must critically assess the model's boundary, time horizon, and level of aggregation in light of their purpose. The model boundary determines which variables are treated endogenously, which are treated exogenously, and which are excluded altogether. Factors relevant to the purpose must be captured endogenously. Treating a concept as exogenous, or omitting it, cuts all feedbacks involving that variable. Models with narrow boundaries don't capture the system's responses to policies, leaving the clients to discover them as unforeseen side effects in the real world. Narrow model boundaries are the single greatest source of policy resistance in systems (chapter 1).

Section 21.4 discusses tests to help answer questions about model purpose and boundary, physical and decision-making structure, and sensitivity analysis. This section focuses on the practical and political issues of modeling. There are no value-free theories and no value-free models. Model users must ask about the modelers' biases (and their own). How do these biases, especially those we were not aware of, color the assumptions, methods, and results?

The cost and effort required to run the model also affect the reliability of the results. Large models pose formidable data quality challenges. Simply ensuring that there are no typographical errors in a large model is a daunting task. If it is

TABLE 21-1
Questions model
users should
ask—but
usually don't

Purpose, Suitability, and Boundary

- What is the purpose of the model?
- What is the boundary of the model? Are the issues important to the purpose treated endogenously? What important variables and issues are exogenous, or excluded? Are important variables excluded because there are no numerical data to quantify them?
- What is the time horizon relevant to the problem? Does the model include the factors that may change significantly over the time horizon as endogenous elements?
- Is the level of aggregation consistent with the purpose?

Physical and Decision-Making Structure

- Does the model conform to basic physical laws such as conservation of matter? Are all equations dimensionally consistent without the use of fudge factors?
- Is the stock and flow structure explicit and consistent with the model purpose?
- Does the model represent disequilibrium dynamics or does it assume the system is in or near equilibrium all the time?
- Are appropriate time delays, constraints, and possible bottlenecks taken into account?
- Are people assumed to act rationally and to optimize their performance? Does the model account for cognitive limitations, organizational realities, noneconomic motives, and political factors?
- Are the simulated decisions based on information the real decision makers actually have? Does the model account for delays, distortions, and noise in information flows?

Robustness and Sensitivity to Alternative Assumptions

- Is the model robust in the face of extreme variations in input conditions or policies?
- Are the policy recommendations sensitive to plausible variations in assumptions, including assumptions about parameters, aggregation, and model boundary?

Pragmatics and Politics of Model Use

- Is the model documented? Is the documentation publicly available? Can you run the model on your own computer?
- What types of data were used to develop and test the model (e.g., aggregate statistics collected by third parties, primary data sources, observation and field-based qualitative data, archival materials, interviews)?
- How do the modelers describe the process they used to test and build confidence in their model? Did critics and independent third parties review the model?
- Are the results of the model reproducible? Are the results "add-factored" or otherwise fudged by the modeler?
- How much does it cost to run the model? Does the budget permit adequate sensitivity testing?
- How long does it take to revise and update the model?
- Is the model being operated by its designers or by third parties?
- What are the biases, ideologies and political agendas of the modelers and clients? How might these biases affect the results, both deliberately and inadvertently?

very expensive or time-consuming to run the model, it is a sure bet that adequate sensitivity analysis has not been done, eroding the confidence you can have in the reliability of the results. More insidious, when a model cannot be revised and run quickly, the modelers tend to resist pressures to change it. Often, the modeler will become defensive, arguing that suggested revisions or potential flaws are not important. The consequence of defensiveness is loss of client confidence that the model can be useful, leading to implementation failure.

You should also determine whether the model is being operated by its designers or by third parties. The developers of models are often promoted or move into other responsibilities, leaving their model to be maintained and run by others who may not understand its assumptions or be able to modify it as conditions change.

21.3.1 Types of Data

Forrester (1980) identifies three types of data needed to develop the structure and decision rules in models: numerical, written, and mental data. Numerical data are the familiar time series and cross-sectional records in various databases. Written data include records such as operating procedures, organizational charts, media reports, emails, and any other archival materials. Mental data span all the information in people's mental models, including their impressions, stories they tell, their understanding of the system and how decisions are actually made (as opposed to what is written in procedures manuals), how exceptions are handled, etc. Mental data cannot be accessed directly but must be elicited through interviews, observation, and other methods.

The numerical data contain only a tiny fraction of the information in the written database, which in turn is miniscule compared to the information available only in people's mental models. Most of what we know about the world is descriptive, impressionistic, and has never been recorded. Such information is crucial for understanding and modeling complex systems. Imagine trying to manage a school, factory, or city using only the available numerical data or even the written data. Without the expertise of the participants, the result would be chaos.

Those constructs for which quantitative metrics and numerical data are available are sometimes termed "hard data" or "hard variables." "Soft variables," in contrast, are those for which numerical metrics and data are not available, including factors such as goals, perceptions, and expectations. The term "hard" is intended to show that numerical data are more accurate and real than qualitative data, seen by many as insubstantial and unreliable. In reality, Disraeli was right: There are "lies, damn lies, and statistics"—both hard and soft data can be biased, distorted, and unreliable. Further, no numerical data are available for many of the variables known to be critical to decision making. These might include customers' perceptions of product quality, the level of trust between a manager and subordinates, a purchasing manager's belief about the reliability of a supplier, employee morale, and investor optimism.

Despite the critical importance of qualitative information some modelers restrict the constructs and variables in their models to those for which numerical data are available and include only those parameters that can be estimated statistically. These modelers defend the rejection of soft variables as being more scientific than "making up" the values of parameters and relationships. How, they ask, can the accuracy of estimates about soft variables be tested? How can statistical tests be performed without numerical data?

Omitting structures or variables known to be important because numerical data are unavailable is actually less scientific and less accurate than using your best judgment to estimate their values. "To omit such variables is equivalent to saying they have zero effect—probably the only value that is known to be wrong!" (Forrester 1961, p. 57). Of course, you must evaluate the sensitivity of your results to the uncertainty in your assumptions—whether you estimated your parameters judgmentally or by statistical means.

That said, it is important to use proper statistical methods to estimate parameters and assess the ability of the model to replicate historical data when numerical data are available. Many apparently soft variables such as customer perceptions of quality, employee morale, investor optimism, and political values are routinely quantified with tools such as content analysis, surveys, and focus groups. The quantification of soft variables often yields important insight into the dynamics of a system.[5]

At the same time, the data you need to build and test your model are rarely available without significant cost and effort. Modelers must constantly make judgments about whether the time and cost of additional data gathering are justified. In the earliest phase of modeling it is often worthwhile to use experiential data and estimate parameters judgmentally so you can get the initial model running as soon as possible. Sensitivity analysis of the initial model can then identify those parameters and relationships to which the behavior and policy recommendations are sensitive. Parameters that do not significantly affect the results need not be estimated with high accuracy, allowing you to focus your limited resources on those factors that do matter so they can be modeled and estimated more accurately.

Some modelers go to the other extreme and discount the role of statistical parameter estimation and numerical data in general. They argue that qualitative insights are more important than numerical precision and that model behavior is insensitive to variations in most parameter values. This is a serious error, even when the purpose of a model is insight and when behavior is insensitive to plausible parameter values. Ignoring numerical data or failing to use statistical tools when appropriate is sloppy and lazy. It increases the chance that the insights you derive from your model will be wrong or harmful to the client. Rigorously defining constructs, attempting to measure them, and using the most appropriate methods to estimate their magnitudes are important antidotes to casual empiricism, muddled formulations, and the erroneous insights we often draw from our mental models. Forrester (1961, p. 59), while stressing the importance of experiential data, soft variables, and judgmental parameter estimates, cautions:

> These comments are not to discourage the proper use of the data that are available nor the making of measurements that are shown to be justified . . . Lord Kelvin's

---

[5]Of course, there are subtle measurement issues in survey and related methodologies. Wording and question order can make large differences to responses, and, as observed in the case of the drug use surveys described in section 7.3, self-reports are often systematically biased.

famed quotation, that we do not really understand until we can measure, still stands. But before we measure, we should name the quantity, select a scale of measurement, and in the interests of efficiency we should have a reason for wanting to know.

21.3.2   Documentation

Perhaps the most important pragmatic issue for modelers is documentation. Documentation is an integral part of the modeling process, at once one of the most important and most often neglected activities.

Documentation is required to ensure that your results can be understood, replicated, criticized, and extended by others. Without proper documentation, your work is neither scientific nor useful.

Most important, documentation is essential for *you*. Few things are more frustrating than trying to reconstruct the meaning of or rationale for your own model because you didn't take the time to document your work at the time. Document as you build the model the first time. Don't wait until you are finished with the "more important" work of building the model—by then you may have forgotten why you did what you did. Documenting as you go helps uncover errors that otherwise might not be detected until much later, preventing costly rework. One of the saddest sights I know is the look of panic on a thesis student's face when, on the eve of graduation, we discover an error in the model that early documentation would have revealed. Table 21-2 presents guidelines for documentation. Follow them rigorously.

21.3.3   Replicability

Replication allows others to build on your work, provides an important check that reveals errors, improves the transparency and utility of modeling work, and also uncovers the occasional fraud.

Unfortunately, replication is rarely done in the social and management sciences.[6] Hubbard and Vetter (1991, 1992) examined more than 2700 empirical papers in economics and finance. They found only one pure replication. Only about 4% of journal pages were devoted to replications with extensions of the original work.

The need for replication is great. In a pioneering study, Dewald, Thursby, and Anderson (1986) worked with the *Journal of Money, Credit and Banking* to replicate empirical studies received for consideration. Disturbingly, they found one-third of the authors of previously published papers did not respond to repeated requests to supply their data sets. Half the remainder chose not to submit their data or could not locate them. Response rates were much higher for those whose papers

---

[6]There are many senses of the term "replication" including checking for errors, repeating an experiment or study with exactly the same methods and data, repeating the study with similar experimental conditions or with a new sample of data drawn from the same population, conducting a new study aimed at testing the same hypotheses as the original, and others. For the nuances and different views on replication, see the references cited above and also Collins (1991) and Cartwright (1991); Wulwick (1996) provides a compelling example of the importance of replication.

TABLE 21-2
Guidelines
for model
documentation

Your results must be fully replicable.

- Ensure that independent third parties can replicate all your results using only your written documentation.
- Make your model and its documentation publicly available (for academic research and public policy models). Create a website that allows anyone to download and run your model.
- Make your model available to all members of the client team (for business models where there may be proprietary data). Include all those who will be involved in or affected by implementation, even your critics.

Remember that you are writing for an audience.

- Be sure that your documentation, simulation output, and text conform to high standards for professional communication in the relevant field.
- Describe the assumptions of the model: its structure, boundary, parameter values, data sources, and overall rationale. Documentation is not merely a printout of model equations.
- Organize your documentation by model subsystem.
- Present a structural diagram followed by an equation description for each subsystem or key decision.
- Present and describe your equations in a logical sequence, by subsystem, so that readers do not have to refer to an alphabetical equation listing.
- Use descriptive names or phrases for variable names, not acronyms or symbols. "Production Starts = Labor * Workweek * Productivity" is better than "$P_s = L * W * P$".
- Include for each equation the full name of the variable (if it was abbreviated), the units of measure, a description of the rationale and function of the formulation, and the sources for any parameter values or data.
- Specify the units of measure for every variable and parameter, and make sure all equations are dimensionally consistent.
- Prepare a succession plan. Document the model so others can understand, run, and modify it without having to ask you a lot of questions. Recruit and train others who understand and can use the model. Once you get promoted you won't want to get email from your successor asking how to use the model.

---

were under consideration or just published. Among those who did respond, Dewald et al. found 69 instances of error in or inability to replicate results in 54 data sets. They conclude, "Inadvertent errors in published empirical articles are a commonplace rather than a rare occurrence" and cautioned that "The frequency and magnitude of errors in empirical articles raise serious questions regarding the integrity of the refereeing process of professional journals." In a follow-up article, Anderson and Dewald (1994) were disappointed to find that "A decade after the *JMCB* project, the replication of previous studies as a part of new research seems an infrequent occurrence."

Why is there so little replication? Replicating and extending someone else's study is viewed as uncreative drudge work by most researchers. Of those few replications that are attempted, journals are far more likely to publish those that contradict the original findings, creating incentives for researchers to withhold their data from others. Hubbard and Vetter (1991, 1992) found only 20% of the few replications and extensions in their sample provided full confirmation of the original findings.[7]

Demanding that all models be fully documented and all results be fully replicable also defends against add-factoring—the practice of adding a fudge factor to the *output* of a model so that it squares with the modeler's intuition (Sterman 1988c; chap. 16). Add-factoring allows modelers to generate results they like while avoiding the troublesome bother of actually using the model to reach conclusions from well-documented assumptions.

In one infamous study the Joint Economic Committee of the US Congress (through the politically neutral General Accounting Office) asked the three leading econometric forecasting firms to run their models under different assumptions about monetary policy. Each firm supplied their forecasts and analysis of the different scenarios. In addition, the GAO repeated the simulations using the same models, providing an independent replication test. In a scenario where the money supply was held constant, one firm projected interest rates after a decade to be 7%/year. However, this apparently reasonable value was not the result of the model. The GAO's simulation of the same model yielded an interest rate of 34%/year, a result totally contrary to both economic theory and historical experience. What had happened? Faced with this ridiculous result, the model managers at that firm had not bothered to correct the flaws in the model but simply add-factored the interest rate down by the modest amount of 79%. The other models fared little better (Joint Economic Committee 1982). The GAO's replication test revealed both the inability of the models to yield meaningful results and the extensive ad hoc adjustments made by the forecasters to cover up the flaws in their models.

Add-factoring is fraudulent and deceptive even when the modeler does not keep it secret. Add-factoring allows unethical modelers to sell their mental models, with all their ambiguity, hidden assumptions, and limitations, while at the same time cloaking them in the authority of science. Add-factoring removes all constraints that might provide a check on the modelers' biases and hubris. The late Otto Eckstein, founder of the highly successful econometric forecasting firm Data Resources, Inc., who coined the term "add factor," admitted in a 1983 interview that DRI's forecasts were 60% model and 40% judgment. He conceded that his forecasts sometimes reflected an optimistic view, modestly commenting that "Data Resources is the most influential forecasting firm in the country ... If it were in the hands of a doom-and-gloomer, it would be bad for the country" (*The Wall Street Journal,* 17 February 1983).

---

[7]The low incidence of replication and high rate of nonreplicability are not unique to economics. Indeed, these researchers and journals should be commended for their willingness to undertake and publish studies highlighting the problem.

Despite the continuing need, replication remains rare in the social sciences. The situation in public policy debates and corporate modeling, where feedback from peer review and refereeing are often absent and where models are kept secret to protect their proprietary content, is far worse. The lack of replication and quality control undercuts the effectiveness of all modeling. You should not accept any result generated by a model you can't replicate.

21.3.4   Protective versus Reflective Modeling

Table 21-3 summarizes two polar approaches to model testing and the modeling process. Modelers can use their models in a *protective* fashion, covering up important assumptions, using data selectively to support their prejudices, and acting like an oracle. The protective mode of modeling is self-defeating. It seals the modeler off from learning, weakening the model and reducing the chances of discovering errors. It undercuts the credibility of the model and modelers, ultimately destroying the possibility of successful implementation. Alternatively, modelers can use their modeling in a *reflective* mode in which testing is designed to uncover flaws and hidden assumptions, challenge preconceptions, and expose assumptions for critique and improvement. Paradoxically, a reflective testing process designed to uncover errors helps build confidence in the model and ultimately increases the chances for sustained success.

21.4   MODEL TESTING IN PRACTICE

System dynamics modelers have developed a wide variety of specific tests to uncover flaws and improve models (e.g., Forrester 1973; Forrester and Senge 1980; Barlas 1989, 1990, 1996). These tests help you answer the big-picture questions discussed above and summarized in Table 21-1. Table 21-4 summarizes the main tests, the purpose of each, and the principal tools and methods used in each.

TABLE 21-3
Protective and reflective uses of models

Protective: Models used to	Reflective: Models used to
Prove a point	Promote inquiry
Keep assumptions hidden	Expose hidden assumptions
Use data selectively	Motivate widest range of empirical tests
Support preconceptions and buttress preselected answers	Challenge preconceptions and support multiple viewpoints
. . . and cover up the preselection	. . . and involve the widest community
Promote the authority of the modeler	Promote the empowerment of the clients

Source: Adapted and revised from Isaacs and Senge (1992, p. 191).

TABLE 21-4   Tests for assessment of dynamic models

Test	Purpose of Test	Tools and Procedures
1. Boundary Adequacy	Are the important concepts for addressing the problem endogenous to the model? Does the behavior of the model change significantly when boundary assumptions are relaxed? Do the policy recommendations change when the model boundary is extended?	Use model boundary charts, subsystem diagrams, causal diagrams, stock and flow maps, and direct inspection of model equations. Use interviews, workshops to solicit expert opinion, archival materials, review of literature, direct inspection/participation in system processes, etc. Modify model to include plausible additional structure; make constants and exogenous variables endogenous, then repeat sensitivity and policy analysis.
2. Structure Assessment	Is the model structure consistent with relevant descriptive knowledge of the system? Is the level of aggregation appropriate? Does the model conform to basic physical laws such as conservation laws? Do the decision rules capture the behavior of the actors in the system?	Use policy structure diagrams, causal diagrams, stock and flow maps and direct inspection of model equations. Use interviews, workshops to solicit expert opinion, archival materials, direct inspection or participation in system processes, as in (1) above. Conduct partial model tests of the intended rationality of decision rules. Conduct laboratory experiments to elicit mental models and decision rules of system participants. Develop disaggregate submodels and compare behavior to aggregate formulations. Disaggregate suspect structures, then repeat sensitivity and policy analysis.
3. Dimensional Consistency	Is each equation dimensionally consistent *without* the use of parameters having no real world meaning?	Use dimensional analysis software. Inspect model equations for suspect parameters.
4. Parameter Assessment	Are the parameter values consistent with relevant descriptive and numerical knowledge of the system? Do all parameters have real world counterparts?	Use statistical methods to estimate parameters (wide range of methods available). Use partial model tests to calibrate subsystems. Use judgmental methods based on interviews, expert opinion, focus groups, archival materials, direct experience, etc. (as above) Develop disaggregate submodels to estimate relationships for use in more aggregate models.

(Continued)

TABLE 21-4   *(Continued)*

Test	Purpose of Test	Tools and Procedures
5. Extreme Conditions	Does each equation make sense even when its inputs take on extreme values? Does the model respond plausibly when subjected to extreme policies, shocks, and parameters?	Inspect each equation. Test response to extreme values of each input, alone and in combination. Subject model to large shocks and extreme conditions. Implement tests that examine conformance to basic physical laws (e.g., no inventory, no shipments; no labor, no production).
6. Integration Error	Are the results sensitive to the choice of time step or numerical integration method?	Cut the time step in half and test for changes in behavior. Use different integration methods and test for changes in behavior.
7. Behavior Reproduction	Does the model reproduce the behavior of interest in the system (qualitatively and quantitatively)? Does it endogenously generate the symptoms of difficulty motivating the study? Does the model generate the various modes of behavior observed in the real system? Do the frequencies and phase relationships among the variables match the data?	Compute statistical measures of correspondence between model and data: descriptive statistics (e.g., R^2, MAE); time domain methods (e.g., autocorrelation functions); frequency domain methods (e.g., spectral analysis); many others. Compare model output and data qualitatively, including modes of behavior, shape of variables, asymmetries, relative amplitudes and phasing, unusual events. Examine response of model to test inputs, shocks, and noise.
8. Behavior Anomaly	Do anomalous behaviors result when assumptions of the model are changed or deleted?	Zero out key effects (loop knockout analysis). Replace equilibrium assumptions with disequilibrium structures.
9. Family Member	Can the model generate the behavior observed in other instances of the same system?	Calibrate the model to the widest possible range of related systems.
10. Surprise Behavior	Does the model generate previously unobserved or unrecognized behavior? Does the model successfully anticipate the response of the system to novel conditions?	Keep accurate, complete, and dated records of model simulations. Use model to simulate likely future behavior of system. Resolve all discrepancies between model behavior and your understanding of the real system. Document participant and client mental models prior to the start of the modeling effort.

(Continued)

TABLE 21-4   *(Concluded)*

Test	Purpose of Test	Tools and Procedures
11. Sensitivity Analysis	*Numerical sensitivity:* Do the numerical values change significantly . . . *Behavioral sensitivity:* Do the modes of behavior generated by the model change significantly . . . *Policy sensitivity:* Do the policy implications change significantly . . . . . . when assumptions about parameters, boundary, and aggregation are varied over the plausible range of uncertainty?	Perform univariate and multivariate sensitivity analysis. Use analytic methods (linearization, local and global stability analysis, etc.). Conduct model boundary and aggregation tests listed in (1) and (2) above. Use optimization methods to find the best parameters and policies. Use optimization methods to find parameter combinations that generate implausible results or reverse policy outcomes.
12. System Improvement	Did the modeling process help change the system for the better?	Design instruments *in advance* to assess the impact of the modeling process on mental models, behavior, and outcomes. Design controlled experiments with treatment and control groups, random assignment, pre-intervention and post-intervention assessment, etc.

Source: Adapted and extended from Forrester and Senge (1980).

21.4.1   Boundary Adequacy Tests

Boundary adequacy tests assess the appropriateness of the model boundary for the purpose at hand. The first step is to determine what the boundary is. Helpful tools for this purpose include model boundary charts and subsystem diagrams (chapter 3). If the modeler does not supply these you should construct your own by direct inspection of the model equations. Search the model equations for exogenous inputs to confirm that the list of exogenous variables is complete. Remember that all constants are exogenous but may in fact be variable over the time horizon of interest. You should inspect model diagrams, if provided, or construct causal diagrams from the model equations to identify constants that might properly be considered variable.

Once the model boundary is established, consider whether there are potentially important feedbacks omitted from the model. Of course the list of omitted concepts and variables is infinite. Your concern is whether any feedbacks omitted from the model, if included, might be important given the purpose of the model. Interviews with key participants and outside experts, review of the relevant literature and archival materials, and direct experience with the system may suggest some processes that perhaps should be made endogenous. Construct a dynamic hypothesis suggesting how the inclusion of the candidate feedback might alter the dynamics or policy implications of the model. If review of the data suggests the new structure might matter, you should add it to the model and examine its effects on the behavior (not only for the base case but also for a wide range of sensitivity tests).

If an additional structure has a significant impact on the behavior or policy implications of the model then it must be included. If it has no impact, you can choose to omit it so your model is smaller and easier to explain or retain it if it builds client confidence in the model.

Example: Model Boundary Assumptions in the Debate over NAFTA

During the congressional debate over the North American Free Trade Agreement (NAFTA) in the early 1990s, proponents of NAFTA argued that free trade would boost the incomes and standard of living of all trading partners. The traditional economic theory of comparative advantage suggests trade benefits both parties because each can produce more of what it is best at and trade for the rest, instead of producing all the goods and services it consumes with lower efficiency. NAFTA opponents, however, argued that companies would divert capital investment from the US, with its high wages and comparatively strict environmental regulations, to Mexico, destroying US jobs and harming the environment. They argued that capital mobility would lead to a "race to the bottom" that would drag down wages, safety standards, and environmental quality as different countries competed for factories and jobs.

Dozens of econometric models were used to predict the effects of NAFTA on the health of the US, Canadian, and Mexican economies and their results were used to buttress the arguments in the debate. The vast majority of these models suggested NAFTA would be a boon to all three economies, with little or no short-run costs. The models were used to argue that concerns over capital flight from the US were misplaced.

The Congressional Budget Office (1993) examined 19 models used to make forecasts of the impact of NAFTA. Of the 19 models, 14 did not consider investment flows at all. Of the five that did, four *assumed* there would be no impact on US investment. Implicitly, they assumed all NAFTA-induced investment in Mexico would come from nations other than the US. The one study that treated investment endogenously concluded that NAFTA would transfer $2.5 billion per year in investment from US to Mexico, resulting in a loss of about 375,000 US jobs over 5 years.

Following standard practice since the days of Smith and Ricardo, most NAFTA modelers assumed that capital and labor were fixed and immobile. Goods flowed between nations in trade but capital and labor could not. The theory of comparative advantage works under these conditions. But when capital is mobile, comparative advantage no longer operates because businesses will locate in the region with the greatest absolute advantage. Assuming immobile capital eliminated important feedbacks from the model boundary, feedbacks that changed the outcome of the policy analysis.

This discussion is not to argue that NAFTA was a mistake. Rather, the point is that the results of the models depended on boundary assumptions that were at the very least questionable and that were certainly not made explicit by the modelers. None of the models endogenously treated NAFTA's effect on illegal and legal immigration, the effects of border development on environmental quality, water demand, demographic patterns, and so on. Partisans (on both sides) selected models consistent with their political views and did not make their assumptions available for review. In the debate over NAFTA, as so often in public policy, models were not used honestly as tools of inquiry to build shared understanding but as clubs to beat down the other side.

21.4.2   Structure Assessment Tests

Structure assessment tests ask whether the model is consistent with knowledge of the real system relevant to the purpose. Structure assessment focuses on the level of aggregation, the conformance of the model to basic physical realities such as conservation laws, and the realism of the decision rules for the agents.

In both boundary adequacy and structure assessment testing, you should look for free lunches, inconsistencies, and inappropriate assumptions about the availability, flexibility, and cost of the resources needed for activity to occur. Identify externalities and side effects that should be captured endogenously. Make sure the full costs and benefits of actions are captured. If necessary, create new model structure to account for these costs, even if the accounting systems in the real system do not (see, e.g., the discussion of the costs of instability in chapter 19).

Violations of physical laws such as conservation of matter or energy usually arise because the model does not appropriately capture the stock and flow structure of the system. Other common violations of physical law involve stocks that can become negative. Real quantities such as inventories, populations, and cash balances cannot be negative. Therefore the outflows from all such stocks must approach zero as the stock approaches zero. This means there must be a first-order negative feedback loop that restricts all the outflows from real stocks so that the flow is zero when the stock is zero (section 13.3). These loops must be first-order because any time delay in the loop could cause the rate to continue even after the stock reaches zero, a physical impossibility. You can check for the presence of first-order control by direct inspection of the equations.

Free lunches arise when activities that require important resources in the real system are assumed to occur without those resources in the model. For example, the first supply chain model in chapter 18 assumed production starts equaled the desired production start rate, implying the firm could adjust starts to the desired rate instantly and without cost. Relaxing this assumption significantly alters the dynamics of a supply chain.

Structure assessment tests are carried out using many of the same tools useful in boundary assessment. Subsystem diagrams and stock and flow maps help reveal the level of aggregation. Policy structure and causal diagrams reveal the information cues used in each decision. Direct inspection of the equations reveals the heuristics assumed at each decision point. Partial model tests (chapter 15) can demonstrate the intended rationality of the individual decision rules. In addition, laboratory experiments can reveal how people actually make decisions in situations analogous to those represented in the model (e.g., Sterman 1989a, b). Another technique to test the appropriateness of aggregation assumptions is to develop a more detailed submodel, then compare its behavior to that of the more aggregate formulation. As in boundary adequacy tests, disaggregation of a suspect structure may show that the extra detail is important. When disaggregation does not significantly affect model results and policy implications (relative to the purpose, as always) then the original, simpler model can be retained.

Example: Water Flowing Uphill

The Pecos river originates in New Mexico and also flows through Texas. Beginning in the 1940s both states claimed its water. The dispute led to a series of lawsuits over water rights. Engineering and hydrologic studies of the watershed dating as far back as 1949 were used by both states to plead their case with various courts.

As described by Allison et al. (1994, p. 21), a review in the 1980s revealed that the model used by New Mexico "violated basic physical flow relations . . . For some reaches of the river . . . water would have had to flow upstream to satisfy the hydrological mass balance requirements." The model developers failed to conduct basic tests for conformance to physical laws. Even more remarkably, the error went undetected for years despite the scrutiny applied to expert testimony in an adversarial proceeding. Once the error was discovered it formed a key part of the case for Texas. The US Supreme Court ultimately ruled in favor of the Lone Star state.

Example: Reversing Irreversible Decisions

A linear programming model of the leather market consistently outperformed the actual market. Examining why the model did so much better than real people, the developers discovered that the model made exceptionally good use of its equations describing the supply of leather. During periods of economic downturn, the model simply converted the leather back into cows.[8]

Example: Negative Stocks

Andersen and Sturis (1988) proposed a model of a manufacturing firm to explore chaotic dynamics in a management setting. The model included the following structure for the shipment rate:

$$\text{Inventory} = \text{INTEGRAL}(\text{Production Rate} - \text{Shipment Rate}, \text{Inventory}_{t_0}) \qquad (21\text{-}1)$$

$$\text{Shipment Rate} = \text{Customers} * \text{Average Sales per Customer} \qquad (21\text{-}2)$$

where Average Sales per Customer was constant. The stock of customers was increased by recruitment resulting from sales effort and decreased as customers defected to other suppliers.

$$\text{Customers} = \text{INTEGRAL}(\text{Customer Recruitment} - \text{Customer Defection}, \text{Customers}_{t_0})$$
$$(21\text{-}3)$$

---

[8]*Source:* Prof. Marshall van Alstyne, University of Michigan, personal communication.

The customer loss rate increased dramatically whenever inventory fell below the desired level, as customers responded to low product availability:

$$\frac{\text{Customer}}{\text{Defection}} = \left(\frac{\text{Customers}}{\text{Normal Customer Life}}\right) * \frac{\text{Effect of Availability}}{\text{on Defection}} \tag{21-4}$$

$$\frac{\text{Effect of Availability}}{\text{on Defection}} = f\left(\frac{\text{Desired Inventory} - \text{Inventory}}{\text{Desired Inventory}}\right); f' > 0 \tag{21-5}$$

Inspection of the equations shows the model lacks first-order negative feedback control over the shipment rate (setting inventory to zero does not immediately force shipments to zero). Though zero inventory does cause the stock of customers to fall rapidly, the drop is not instantaneous, allowing inventory to fall below zero. Imagine the case where a fire destroys all inventory one night. The next morning, there has not yet been any change in the stock of customers, so shipments continue though there is no product to ship. Reformulating the model to correct this and other flaws significantly changes its dynamics and stability.

Example: Recovery of the US Economy from Nuclear War

During the Cold War the US government commissioned studies to assess the economic impact of nuclear war. One such model, dubbed the "Economic Recovery Model" (Dresch and Baum 1973) was used to evaluate the effects of different Soviet attacks on the US, including a 500 megaton attack. To put that in perspective, the bomb that destroyed Hiroshima yielded 14 kilotons, 36,000 times less. The model suggested that the gross national product (GNP) of the US would recover to 80% of preattack production after just 9 years—and that's total GNP, not GNP per capita. They also examined the effects of an attack directed at the petroleum sector. Officials feared that a few missiles, by destroying the petroleum sector and causing massive fuel shortages, might cripple the entire economy.[9] The model suggested there was nothing to worry about. Immediately after a 250-megaton attack directed at the petroleum sector, total GNP fell to 22% of the preattack rate. But after 1 year, GNP jumped to 61% of prior output, and after 5 years it reached 94% of preattack output.

The amazing recovery potential suggested by these results means both the US and USSR needed very large arsenals of nuclear weapons to ensure that they could "win" a nuclear war and thus serve as a deterrent. Results such as these were cited by cold warriors as evidence that the US needed still more nuclear weapons.

Sastry, Romm and Tsipis (1987) conducted boundary and structure assessment tests on the model and found a number of unreasonable assumptions. Though ostensibly dynamic, it was actually a general equilibrium input/output model in which the entire economy was assumed to be in equilibrium at all times. The model did not represent stocks of materials, energy, and other resources as dynamic quantities that could affect the ability of industries to function. In equilibrium, stocks are constant, so they are usually omitted from general equilibrium and I/O models, which treat only the steady state flows of goods and services through

---

[9]Destroying the petroleum industry requires targeting oil fields, ports, and refineries (nearly the entire east, west, and Gulf coasts of the US, plus Texas, Oklahoma, Alaska, Ohio, and other states where oil fields and refineries are located), causing a regrettable number of civilian casualties.

the economy. Whether equilibrium is a reasonable assumption for the economy under normal circumstances can be debated. But the notion that the economy immediately returns to equilibrium after a nuclear war, without any shortages of materials, energy, labor, and other resources upon which production depends, beggars belief.

Dresch and Baum (1973), noting the flaws in their own model, commented that the near trebling of GNP in a single year "is largely a consequence of the two-year lag assumed to be required for capital replacement." In their model capital stocks always reached optimal levels in 2 years independent of the capacity of the capital-producing industries, their ability to acquire the necessary raw materials and energy, the availability of liquid fuels to operate construction equipment and ship product to customers, the availability of skilled workers, and the ability of the government to maintain order—in short, without regard to the effects of the very attack their model was designed to evaluate.

Sastry et al. (1987) modified a system dynamics model developed for the Federal Emergency Management Agency to eliminate these free lunches and equilibrium assumptions. In the revised model, small attacks focused on petroleum refineries could cripple the economy through a cascading chain of fuel shortages that shut down production of key industries such as transportation, construction, and manufacturing, thwarting efforts to rebuild the energy sector and causing food shortages that led to starvation and anarchy. The results implied that a very small strategic arsenal provided sufficient deterrent capability and that the strategic missile defense system (so-called star wars) then advocated by the Reagan administration would have to be nearly perfect to protect the US.

21.4.3 Dimensional Consistency

Dimensional consistency is one of the most basic tests and should be among the very first you do. You should always specify the units of measure for each variable as you build your models. Do not wait until afterward to fill in the units and check for consistency. Dimensional inconsistency may reveal nothing more than a typographical error, an inverted ratio, or a missing time constant. More often, units errors reveal important flaws in your understanding of the structure or decision process you are trying to model.

Some simulation software packages for system dynamics now include automated dimensional analysis so you can test for dimensional errors with a single command. However, a model that generates no error messages when you run the dimensional consistency check does *not* necessarily pass the test. Every equation must be dimensionally consistent *without the inclusion of arbitrary scaling factors that have no real world meaning*. The only way you can identify such fudge factors is by direct inspection of the equations. Parameters with meaningless names, strange combinations of units (widgets^2/\$/month^3), or nondimensionless parameters with values of unity are suspect.

21.4.4 Parameter Assessment

Before deciding how a parameter should be estimated or whether its value is reasonable make sure every constant (and variable) has a clear, real-life meaning.

Next you must decide how to estimate the values of each parameter. The basic choice is formal statistical estimation from numerical data, or judgmental estimation.

The estimation of parameter values from numerical data receives a great deal of attention in modeling, particularly the econometric tradition. System dynamics modelers are well advised to study econometrics and other approaches to formal parameter estimation. It is essential to know how the important regression techniques work, what their maintained hypotheses and limitations are, and when each tool is appropriate. The maintained hypotheses are the assumptions about the data and model that must hold for the estimation technique to give reliable and accurate results. The most common method, multiple regression by ordinary least squares (OLS), is often not appropriate in dynamic models. OLS estimates are not accurate in the presence of collinearity (where the variables on the right-hand side are mutually correlated), autocorrelation (where the dependent variable depends on its own past values, that is, where there is feedback), and heteroscedasticity (where the variance of the variables is not constant throughout the sample). Other, more robust estimation methods are available, ranging from relatively simple maximum likelihood and GLS (generalized least squares) methods to sophisticated methods such as Kalman filtering. Each has its strengths and weaknesses; you should know how to select the simplest method that is appropriate to the feedback structure of your model and the statistical properties of the data.[10]

At the same time, limitations on numerical data availability mean it is often impossible to estimate all parameters in a model. You must also develop the ability to estimate parameters judgmentally using expert opinion gleaned from interviews, workshops, archival materials, direct experience, and other methods (see chapter 14). Parameters can also be estimated by developing a disaggregated submodel (see the example below).[11]

In practice, statistical and judgmental methods are used together. Knowledge of the real system constrains the plausible range for many parameters; statistical estimation provides a check on judgmental estimates.

In a large model it is usually impractical to estimate all the critical parameters simultaneously. Even when possible, simultaneous estimation can lead to problems since large models are often underidentified (i.e., more than one set of parameter values fit the data equally well). In these cases judgmental estimates grounded in knowledge of the system are essential in selecting reasonable parameters.

Partial model estimation (Homer 1983b) is also useful for parameter selection. As in partial model testing for intended rationality (chapter 15), the modeler isolates a key structure or decision rule, cutting the feedback loops in the full model. The inputs to each decision rule or formulation are then driven by the actual historical data and the parameters are chosen (judgmentally or formally) so the output

---

[10]Texts such as Berndt (1991) and Greene (1993) provide solid coverage of econometric techniques and applications.

[11]Response surface methods (e.g., Box and Draper 1987) allow you to capture the response of a complex disaggregate model with a few equations. In essence, the behavior of the full model is captured by a polynomial approximation corresponding to the first few terms of the Taylor series expansion of the underlying system in the relevant parameters and policy instruments. The approximation can then be embedded in a larger model.

of the subsystem best fits the data (for examples see Homer 1983b; Fiddaman 1997; Oliva 1996; and Taylor 1999).

A caution: The statistical significance of parameters relating variables in an equation is *not* an indicator of the correctness of the relationship. Statistical significance indicates how well an equation fits the observed data; it does not indicate whether a relationship correctly characterizes causal relationships in the real world. A statistically significant relationship between variables shows only that they are highly correlated and that the apparent correlation is not likely to have been the result of mere chance. Asserting a relationship is causal is a value judgment to be made by considering all the evidence, numerical and qualitative.

Using statistical significance as the test of model validity can also lead modelers to reject equations describing important relationships. A relationship may be statistically insignificant simply because there are too few data points or because the data don't vary enough. When direct knowledge of the system suggests a relationship is real and important, you must include it, using your best judgment to estimate its values even if the numerical data do not allow you to estimate its strength.

Example: Statistical Estimation of Soft Variables

Oliva (1996) developed a model to explore the determinants of service quality in high-contact settings and applied it to retail banking. As discussed in section 14.3, Oliva was able to estimate statistically the response of the workweek and time allocated to each customer to workload. Results showed that loan officers were nearly twice as willing to cut corners by spending less time with each customer than to work overtime when the workload was high. Oliva further hypothesized that loan officers' standards for the time they should spend on each customer inquiry were variable, adjusting over time to the actual time spent. The time spent with each customer correlated highly with the customers' judgment about service quality.

In many models with dynamic goals, norm adjustment is symmetric—norms rise as fast as they fall. Others suggest norm erosion is asymmetric, with quality norms falling more readily than they rise. Oliva tested for asymmetric norm adjustment by estimating the time constants in the nonlinear smoothing structure described in section 11.4.1. Surprisingly, the estimates showed that while quality norms fell quickly when the workload was high, they never rose, even when the workload was light: The estimated value of the time constant for revising the time per customer norm upward was essentially infinite. Further discussions and review of the data showed that the organization did not have any instruments in place to monitor customer satisfaction and feed it back to the managers. Whenever workloads were high, workers reduced the time they spent with each customer to clear the backlog and soon became habituated to the new levels. Without any way to measure the resulting drop in customer satisfaction, management interpreted the drop in quality as an improvement in productivity. When work was slow, the workers felt continuing pressure to meet the organization's new, lower norms for the time spent per customer (appendix B provides further discussion).

The formal estimation process revealed an important feature of the dynamics that prior work had not and motivated additional research that confirmed the results of the statistical estimation process. The combination of formal and judgmental parameter estimation methods, fieldwork, and archival data analysis yielded a more accurate and reliable understanding of the organization's dynamics than any method alone.

Example: Developing a Detailed Submodel

Parameters can often be estimated by statistical or modeling work below the level of aggregation of the model itself. Homer (1999) developed a model designed to improve the performance of a semiconductor equipment manufacturer's field service organization. An important structure in the model relates field service delivery to the availability of technicians and the extent to which technicians are cross-trained on the company's multiple product types. In the real system, there are different technicians in different locations, each with his or her own skills, backlog of work orders, and availability. The full model aggregated these different resources and demands into a simple structure consisting of an aggregate backlog of service requests and an aggregate capacity to provide service, both treated as continuous variables. Service levels were modeled as a simple function of the ratio of the backlog and aggregate capacity, modified by a nonlinear effect of cross-training. To test whether the aggregate structure was appropriate, Homer developed an independent submodel treating the arrival of work and dispatch of technicians using a stochastic, queuing theory framework combined with a linear programming algorithm for period-to-period optimization of service throughput. Individual jobs and technicians were modeled as discrete entities with empirically estimated probabilities for arrival and completion of work for each type of product and job (e.g., repair, preventive maintenance, or engineering change). The detailed submodel showed that the aggregate structure was acceptable for the purpose of the full, strategic model and allowed Homer to derive the shape and values of the nonlinear function governing the effect of cross-training.

21.4.5   Extreme Condition Tests

Models should be robust in extreme conditions. Robustness under extreme conditions means the model should behave in a realistic fashion no matter how extreme the inputs or policies imposed on it may be. Inventories can never drop below zero no matter how large the demand may be. The demand for products must fall to zero when the price rises high enough. Production cannot occur without materials, labor, equipment, and other resources. Extreme condition tests ask whether models behave appropriately when the inputs take on extreme values such as zero or infinity.

Extreme condition tests can be carried out in two main ways: by direct inspection of the model equations and by simulation. You should examine each decision rule (rate equation) in the model and ask whether the output of the rule is feasible and reasonable even when each input to the equation takes on its maximum and minimum values. Be sure to consider the response of the equation when all inputs simultaneously take on their extreme values.

You should also impose extreme conditions as policies in simulations of the model. By using switches that zero out variables and test inputs such as the step and pulse you can simulate conditions such as the complete removal of all workers from the firm or a factor of one billion increase in the price of the firm's product. In the former case, production must immediately go to zero. In the latter case, the demand for the firm's products must immediately drop to zero. Such tests, termed "reality checks" by Peterson and Eberlein (1994), quickly uncover flaws, a great advantage in a large model. In addition, whole model extreme condition tests may reveal subtle flaws that direct inspection may miss. When an extreme condition simulation generates implausible behavior you should examine the equations of the affected formulations to identify the precise source of the flaw.

Example: Extreme Conditions in the Energy System

In 1979 I worked for the US Department of Energy. The department used a variety of models, including system dynamics models, to analyze energy demand, supply, prices, and so on. A critical issue was the feedback between the energy sector and the rest of the economy. Would energy price hikes reduce the gross national product, boost unemployment, and accelerate inflation? What would be the economic consequences of another oil embargo? Lacking an in-house model of energy–economy interactions, the department solicited a proposal from a highly respected macroeconomic forecasting firm, which claimed its model could do the job. I was given the task of evaluating the suitability of the model. The first test I conducted was an extreme condition test. I asked what would happen to the GNP of the United States if all energy sources (oil, gas, coal, nuclear, hydro, etc.) instantly and unexpectedly disappeared. Suddenly deprived of all forms of energy, the GNP must rapidly drop close to zero (as soon as inventories are depleted). Accessing the model via a time-sharing link, I implemented the test. The result: The GNP went up.

Examining the model equations showed that, consistent with its origins as a traditional demand-side Keynesian model, GNP was formulated as depending on aggregate demand. Aggregate demand consists of consumption, investment, government expenditure, and net exports (the famous identity GNP = C + I + G + X familiar from introductory macroeconomics). C, I, and G were formulated as depending on factors such as consumers' incomes, business profitability, interest rates, and so on. Output of goods and services did not require inputs of energy, and a 100% embargo did little. Why then did the GNP go up? Oil imports fell to zero, so net exports increased.

You may object, as the model's developers did, that the test was irrelevant since such extreme conditions could never arise in reality. The model replicated the historical behavior of the economy and the energy sector quite well, so, they argued, it was a reliable guide to their likely behavior in the future. These arguments are mistaken.

The test uncovered limitations of the model that rendered it unusable for our purpose. We needed to know how a physical shortage of oil (caused by possible embargoes) would affect the economy. A model in which production requires no energy cannot answer such questions. The energy sector had been tacked on as a set of ad hoc additions to the original model. Production drove energy consumption in the model but energy availability had no impact on production. Lacking such basic physical realities, the only way the modelers could answer the questions we posed was through still more ad hoc adjustments to model structure, or add-factoring based on their mental models.

The fact that a model replicates historical data well is irrelevant if it fails important extreme condition tests. Models are usually intended to design policies to solve problems, improve performance, or analyze contingencies for which experience provides no guide. The goal of policy design is to move the system outside the limited range of historical experience. Extreme condition tests provide a critical test of the extent to which models capture underlying physical realities and constraints that affect behavior outside the conditions observed in the past.

CHALLENGE   ## Extreme Condition Tests

For each of the following, use extreme condition tests to evaluate the proposed formulations. If you identify any problems, propose a solution and show that your solution passes the extreme condition test.

1.   A firm operates a make-to-order system. Orders accumulate in a backlog until they are shipped. An analyst proposes the following structure to model the firm's orders, shipments, and revenues.

$$\text{Backlog} = \text{INTEGRAL}(\text{Orders} - \text{Shipments}, \text{Backlog}_{t_0}) \tag{21-6}$$

The order rate responds to price; the analyst assumes a constant elasticity demand curve with elasticity $e_d < 0$:

$$\text{Orders} = \text{Reference Orders} * (\text{Price/Reference Price})^{e_d} \tag{21-7}$$

The firm recognizes revenue when the product is shipped:

$$\text{Revenue} = \text{Price} * \text{Shipment Rate} \tag{21-8}$$

Shipments are determined by capacity and capacity utilization:

$$\text{Shipment Rate} = \text{Capacity} * \text{Capacity Utilization} \tag{21-9}$$

$$\text{Capacity Utilization} = f(\text{Desired Production/Capacity}) \tag{21-10}$$

$$\text{Desired Production} = \text{Backlog/Target Delivery Delay} \tag{21-11}$$

Assume the capacity utilization function is well formulated, with $f(0) = 0$, $f(1) = 1$, and $f(\infty) = f_{max} = $ maximum utilization.

2.   In Forrester's (1968) original market growth model production capacity PC was modeled as the accumulation of net production capacity receipts PCR:

$$\text{PC} = \text{INTEGRAL}(\text{PCR}, \text{PC}_{t_0}) \tag{21-12}$$

Net capacity receipts were determined by production capacity orders PCO with a delay given by the production capacity receiving delay PCRD. Forrester assumed a third-order material delay:

$$\text{PCR} = \text{DELAY3}(\text{PCO}, \text{PCRD}) \tag{21-13}$$

The stock of capacity on order accumulated capacity orders less receipts:

$$\text{PCOO} = \text{INTEGRAL}(\text{PCO} - \text{PCR}, \text{PCOO}_{t_0}) \tag{21-14}$$

The firm expands capacity by a net capacity expansion fraction, CEF, per year:

$$PCO = PC * CEF \tag{21-15}$$

The capacity expansion fraction depends on the perceived delivery delay relative to the company's goal, as in chapter 15.

3. Models of competitive dynamics among firms must model the demand for each firm's products as it depends on factors such as price, availability, marketing, quality, and so on. Consider the following formulation:

$$\text{Demand} = a_0 + a_1\text{Price} + a_2\text{Delivery Delay} + a_3\text{Advertising} + a_4\text{Quality} \tag{21-16}$$

The coefficients a_i capture the response of attractiveness to each product attribute. The linear form of the equation facilitates estimation by regression. Estimation results show, as expected, that a_1 and a_2 are negative while a_3 and a_4 are positive.

Consider also the loglinear variant of equation (21-16):

$$\text{Demand} = a_0 * \text{Price}^{a_1} * \text{Delivery Delay}^{a_2} * \text{Advertising}^{a_3} * \text{Quality}^{a_4} \tag{21-17}$$

where, again, $a_1, a_2 < 0$ and $a_3, a_4 > 0$.

4. In a model of a complex product development project, an analyst proposes the following formulation for stock of work remaining and the rate at which work is completed:

$$\text{Tasks Remaining} = \text{INTEGRAL}(\text{New Tasks Assigned} - \text{Completion Rate}, \text{Tasks}_{t_0}) \tag{21-18}$$

$$\text{Completion Rate} = \text{MIN}(\text{Tasks Remaining/DT}, \text{Labor} * \text{Productivity} * \text{Workweek}) \tag{21-19}$$

where DT is the time step used in the simulation. The backlog of tasks remaining aggregates activities including design, prototype fabrication, and testing. The modeler notes that the MIN function in (21-19) prevents the stock of tasks remaining from dropping below zero no matter how large the labor force.

21.4.6   Integration Error Tests

System dynamics models are usually formulated in continuous time and solved by numerical integration. You must select a numerical integration method and time step that yield an approximation of the underlying continuous dynamics accurate enough for your purpose. The results of your models should not be sensitive to the choice of time step or integration method; the wrong time step or integration method can introduce spurious dynamics into your model. Always test for such "DT error" by cutting the time step in half and running the model again. If the results change in ways that matter, the time step was too large. Continue until the results are no longer sensitive to the choice of time step. Likewise run the model with alternate integration methods. The integration error test should be the first simulation test you carry out, since failure here renders all model results meaningless. Appendix A describes the numerical integration process and various integration methods.

Example: Discovering and Correcting Integration Error

Shantzis and Behrens (1973) developed a system dynamics model of the Tsembaga tribe in Papua New Guinea. The Tsembaga, like many indigenous peoples in the region, practiced slash and burn agriculture and also kept pigs, a major source of wealth and status. Every 12 to 15 years they held an elaborate festival during which most of the pigs were slaughtered, followed by the lifting of a taboo against war with neighboring clans. During these wars about 10% of the population was killed. After highly ritualized funerals, a truce was concluded and conflict was prohibited until the next pig festival, at which time unavenged deaths from the last war provided the impetus for the next cycle of conflict. Early western observers found these rituals bizarre and took them as evidence for the savagery of indigenous peoples. In a pathbreaking study, anthropologist Roy Rappaport (1968/1984) showed how pig festivals and wars were triggered by population growth, thus preventing the degradation of land fertility. Instead of a cruel and irrational ritual, the pig–war cycle was actually a finely honed feedback system that kept the human and pig populations within the carrying capacity of the environment, enabling the Tsembaga to live sustainably in their fragile forest ecosystem.

Shantzis and Behrens created a system dynamics model to test Rappaport's theory. One of the earliest formal models integrating biological, agricultural, demographic, and cultural variables, it endogenously represented the human and pig populations, food production, and the quantity and fertility of the land. The pig festivals and wars were triggered endogenously as the pig and human populations began to outstrip food production. The model reproduced the observed behavior of periodic festivals and wars. Shantzis and Behrens showed that the pig festival/war cycle kept Tsembaga society stable. Their policy analysis further showed that the introduction of western culture and technology, such as a ban on war and improved health care, could cause population to outstrip the carrying capacity of the land. Declining land fertility and food production would then lead to starvation, forced migration from their lands, and the destruction of their culture.

Kampmann (1991) analyzed the robustness of these results. The original model was completely documented and fully replicable. However, the model failed the integration error test. The original model used a time step of 1 year. Shortening the time step caused the behavior to change dramatically. With a small time step the model generated a continuous small skirmish rather than an intense war followed by a long truce. Instead of a great pig festival every decade, the daily lunch was a ham sandwich.

The time step in models is not a feature of reality but an artifact of the numerical method used to solve the model. Hence the decision rules in models cannot depend on the time step. Shantzis and Behrens were inadvertently using the long time step as a behavioral parameter to control the duration of the war and the number of casualties. The sensitivity of the results to the time step threw all their results into question.

Kampmann reformulated the model so that the duration and lethality of the festival and war were specified as explicit parameters. He also corrected a number of other formulation errors. The periodic pig–war festivals reemerged in the corrected model. Kampmann's analysis identified a major error, but in the end the reformulated model strengthened the conclusions of the original study.[12]

21.4.7   Behavior Reproduction Tests

Many tools are available to assess a model's ability to reproduce the behavior of a system. Most common are descriptive statistics to assess the point-by-point fit. Point-by-point metrics compute some measure of the error between a data series X_d and the model output X_m at every point for which data exist and then report some sort of average over the relevant time horizon. Table 21-5 lists some of the most common measures of point-by-point fit.

The most widely reported measure of fit is R^2, the coefficient of determination. R^2 measures the fraction of the variance in the data "explained" by the model. If the model exactly replicates the actual series, $R^2 = 1$; if the model output is constant, $R^2 = 0$. R^2 is the square of the correlation coefficient, r, which measures the degree to which two series covary.[13]

The mean absolute error, MAE; mean absolute percent error, MAPE; mean absolute error as a percent of the mean, MAE/Mean; and (root) mean square error, (R)MSE all provide measures of the average error between the simulated and actual series. MAE weights all errors linearly; RMSE weights large errors much more heavily than small ones. Both measure the error in the same units as the variable itself. MAPE should not be used, of course, if the data series includes any points close to zero. In such a case, the MAE divided by the mean of the data provides a more robust dimensionless measure.

Which measures are best? MSE (and RMSE) penalize large errors far more than small ones; usually there is no strong basis for preferring RMSE over MAE. The MAPE and MAE/Mean provide dimensionless metrics for the error, which are easier to interpret. R^2, though it is widely reported and your audience may expect it, is actually not very useful. Two series with the same absolute error can generate very different values for R^2 depending on their common trend. Consider the situation $X_m = X_0 \exp(gt)$; $X_d = X_m + e$. The data and model grow exponentially at the same rate g and the model is perfect except for a random error, e. The higher the growth rate, the greater the correlation r between the model and data and, therefore, the higher the value of R^2, though the error between the model and data is the same in all cases.

It is important to know the sources of error as well as the total size of the error. Large errors may be due to a poor model or a large amount of random noise in the data. The total error may be large if a mode of behavior in the real system is deliberately excluded as irrelevant to the model purpose. While there is ultimately no

---

[12]Kampmann's critique of the Tsembaga model provides an exemplary application of the tests described in this chapter and is well worth consulting, whether your main concern is anthropology, biology, or business (see also chapter 14).

[13]The traditional formula for R^2 used in regression analysis, $R^2 = 1 - \Sigma e^2 / \Sigma (X_m - \bar{X}_d)^2$, where the error $e = X_m - X_d$, assumes that the means of the simulated and actual series are equal (bias = 0). The equivalent formulation $R^2 = r^2$ works even when there is a bias.

TABLE 21-5
Common summary statistics for assessing model fit to data

Metric	Definition	Formula
R^2	Coefficient of determination; the fraction of the variance in the data "explained" by the model (dimensionless). r = correlation coefficient between model and data series	$R^2 = r^2; \ r = \dfrac{1}{n}\sum \dfrac{(X_d - \overline{X}_d)}{s_d} \dfrac{(X_m - \overline{X}_m)}{s_m}$ $\overline{X} = \dfrac{1}{n}\sum X; \ s = \sqrt{\dfrac{1}{n}\sum (X - \overline{X})^2}$
MAE	Mean Absolute Error (units)	$MAE = \dfrac{1}{n}\sum \left| X_m - X_d \right|$
MAPE	Mean Absolute Percent Error (dimensionless)	$MAPE = \dfrac{1}{n}\sum \dfrac{\left| X_m - X_d \right|}{X_d};$ (multiply by 100 for %)
MAE/Mean	Mean Absolute Error as a fraction of the mean (dimensionless)	$MAE/Mean = MAE/\overline{X}_d;$ (multiply by 100 for %)
(R)MSE	(Root) Mean Square Error (RMSE: units; MSE: units^2)	$MSE = \dfrac{1}{n}\sum (X_m - X_d)^2; \ RMSE = \sqrt{MSE}$
Theil's Inequality Statistics	Decomposes MSE into three components: bias (U^M), unequal variation (U^S), and unequal covariation (U^C) (dimensionless); $U^M + U^S + U^C = 1$	$U^M = \dfrac{\overline{X}_m^2 - \overline{X}_d^2}{MSE}$ $U^S = \dfrac{s_m^2 - s_d^2}{MSE}$ $U^C = \dfrac{2(1-r)s_m s_d}{MSE}$

All summations are carried out over the set of data points.

substitute for plotting the simulated and actual data together, several statistical methods help decompose the error into systematic and unsystematic components.

The Theil inequality statistics (Theil 1966) provide an elegant decomposition of the error by dividing the MSE into three components: bias, unequal variation, and unequal covariation. Bias arises when the model output and data have different means. Unequal variation indicates that the variances of the two series differ. Unequal covariation means the model and data are imperfectly correlated, that is, they differ point by point. Dividing each component by the MSE gives the fraction of the MSE due to bias (U^M), the fraction of the MSE due to unequal variation (U^S), and the fraction of the MSE due to unequal covariation (U^C). Since $U^M + U^S + U^C = 1$, the inequality statistics provide an easily interpreted breakdown of the sources of error. Table 21-6 illustrates the interpretation of the Theil statistics for different situations.

A large bias, indicated by *both* a large MSE *and* a large U^M, reveals a systematic error, as seen in case (a). Errors due to bias are potentially serious and are usually due to errors in parameter estimates. Errors due to unequal variance may also be systematic. When unequal variation dominates the MSE, the model and data

TABLE 21-6   Interpretation of the Theil inequality statistics

	Example	U^M	U^S	U^C	Characterization	Interpretation
a.		1	0	0	$X_m = X_d + \text{BIAS}$ Simulated variable equals actual data translated by a bias	Systematic error: bias in model should be corrected by parameter adjustment
b.		0	1	0	$X_m = \overline{X_d} + k(X_d - \overline{X_d})$ Simulated variable is a stretched version of the actual data about their common mean	Systematic error: model and data have different trends
c.		0	1	0	Same as above	Systematic error: model and data have the same phasing but different amplitude fluctuations
d.		0	1	0	$X_m = \overline{X_d}$; $X_d = \overline{X_d} + f(t)$ Simulated variable equals mean of data; actual has noise or cycles. Model and data are uncorrelated because model variance = 0	Systematic error if model purpose involves study of the cycles in the data. Unsystematic if cycles and noise are not relevant to the purpose
e.		0	0	1	$X_d = \overline{X_d} + A\sin(wt)$ $X_m = \overline{X_d} + A\sin(wt - p)$ Model fluctuates with the same mean, amplitude (A), and frequency (w), as data but with a phase shift (p).	Systematic if phasing important to purpose and if model driven by historical data; unsystematic if model driven by random noise
f.		0	a	1 − a	$X_m = f(t)$; $X_d = f(t) + e(t)$ Model tracks actual data except for an error term e(t) with zero mean.	Model has same mean and trends as data but differs from data point-by-point. Unsystematic error unless purpose is to study the cycles in the data

"Data" shown by solid line; "simulation" shown by dashed line.

match on average and are highly correlated but the variation in the two around their common mean differs. One variable is a stretched out version of the other. In case (b), U^S is large because the trend in the two variables is different. Such a case reveals systematic error and directs attention to the assumptions of the model. Systematic error is also the verdict in case (c), in which the model does not capture the magnitude of a cyclical mode in the data, though the phasing is correct. Such a case would direct attention to the factors controlling the amplitude and damping of the cycle.

If both series have the same mean ($U^M = 0$) and either the model or data series is nearly constant, then U^C will be small because the standard deviation s_m or s_d will be small. As shown in case (d), the error would reflect random noise or a cyclic mode in one of the series not present in the other. The interpretation depends on the purpose of the model. If the model is designed to investigate the cycle in the data, failure to generate the cycle would clearly be a systematic error. If the purpose of the model is analysis of long-run behavior that abstracts from short-term movements, failure to capture the cycle is unimportant. The cycle becomes unsystematic noise relative to the model purpose.

If the majority of the error is concentrated in unequal covariation, U^C, the model captures the mean and trends in the data well, differing from the data only point by point (cases e and f). These cases might indicate a fairly constant phase shift of a cyclical mode otherwise reproduced well. More likely, a large U^C indicates the presence of noise or cyclical modes in the data series not captured by the model. When U^C is large the majority of the error is unsystematic; a model should not be faulted for failing to match the random component of the data.

The Theil statistics help you characterize the sources of error. Ideally, the error (indicated by MAPE, RMSE, etc.) should be small and unsystematic (concentrated in U^C). Large errors and large bias or unequal variation fractions indicate systematic error and should lead to questions about the assumptions of the model. The criteria for deciding whether an error is large or systematic depend on the purpose of the model. If the errors arise from modes of behavior excluded from the purpose, then the errors do not compromise the utility of the model for that purpose.

Error measures such as MAPE and R^2 measure the point-by-point correspondence of the model and data. There are several circumstances in which you should not expect your model to correspond to the data on a point-by-point basis. Many systems, including the supply chains and commodity markets examined in chapters 17–20, selectively amplify certain frequencies in the random shocks that constantly perturb them. Since no model can capture all the random variations in the environment, model dynamics can diverge from the data *even if the model is perfectly specified.*[14] Further, in path-dependent systems small differences in random events can dramatically alter the trajectory of the system, including its ultimate equilibrium (see, e.g., Figure 10-25). The data might show a certain product

---

[14]In chaotic systems it is even worse. Because chaotic systems have the property known as sensitive dependence on initial conditions, the model diverges from the true system exponentially even when there are no random shocks, given only a small error in initial conditions.

FIGURE 21-1

Noise destroys
point-prediction
ability

Two simulations
of the inventory–
workforce model in
section 19.2 with
random noise in
labor productivity.
The noise se-
quence in produc-
tivity changes in
week 200.

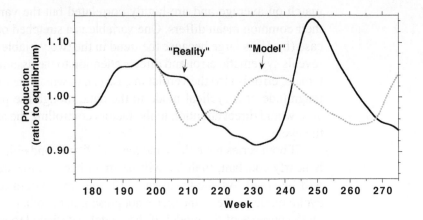

growing to dominate its market. Running the model with different random perturbations might cause that product to win sometimes and lose to the competition
sometimes. The real world that generated the data can be thought of as just one realization of the process; small differences in unobservable perturbations might
have led to a completely different outcome.

In general, the greater the extent to which the model's dynamics are driven by
exogenous inputs, the greater the point-by-point correspondence of the model and
data should be. The exogenous inputs, including their blips and dips, force the
model to dance to a particular beat. In a model that is not forced by any historical
data series it is often necessary to excite the model's latent modes of behavior with
random noise. Even when the random noise is drawn from the correct distribution,
the point-by-point values will differ from historical experience, and so will model
output.

Figure 21-1 illustrates this dynamic with two simulations of the inventory–
workforce model developed in chapter 19. The system is disturbed from equilibrium by a random variation in labor productivity with a standard deviation of 5%
and a correlation time of 4 weeks (see appendix B). These random shocks cause
the system to oscillate irregularly. One simulation can be interpreted as the real
data and the other, as the output of the model. The model is a perfect replica of the
real system—identical structure, initial conditions, and parameters. The trajectories
of the two simulations are identical as long as the "model" is driven by exactly the
same random shocks as the "real system." Beginning in week 200, the random
shocks perturbing the model begin to differ. The random variations are drawn from
the same distribution, with the same variance and correlation time, but differ point
by point. The behavior of the model quickly diverges from the data. The inertia of
the system causes the trajectories to remain close for only a few weeks; after that
there is no point-by-point correspondence between the model and the real system
though the model is perfect. Obviously, point-by-point measures of error such as
R^2, MAPE, or RMSE would be grossly misleading as indicators of the realism and
utility of the model.

Point-by-point error measures are not meaningful when a model is highly sensitive to noise. Instead, a good model should exhibit the same modes of behavior

observed in the data. Fluctuations should have the same frequencies and amplitudes. The phase relationships (leads and lags) among the variables should be the same as observed in the data. The variability of features such as amplitude, frequency, and phase lags should also correspond to the data. The ability of a model to generate the appropriate patterns of behavior can be assessed qualitatively, by judgment, or statistically. Tools such as spectral analysis measure the strength of fluctuations at each frequency. The autocorrelation function quantifies the inertia or persistence in a variable; cross-correlation functions show how one variable depends on current and past values of another. Barlas (1989, 1990) describes how these and related tools can be used to quantify the correspondence of the model and data in terms of relative amplitudes, frequencies, phase lags, and other relationships.

Even when you use statistical measures to assess the correspondence of the model to the data you should always plot the simulated and actual data together. Examine the model to see if it captures asymmetries and other subtle features of the behavior observed in the data.

Beware a modeler who asserts that the model's ability to fit the data indicates that the model is valid or confirms the model. Any such assertion is logically fallacious. Behavior reproduction tests cannot prove a model is correct or reliable. To argue that fitting the data implies that the model must be correct or superior to other models commits the fallacy of affirming the consequence: There may be many models that replicate the data well; observing that one does can never show that the behavior of the real system was generated by any particular structure.

As shown in section 9.3.2, different models can fit a data set equally well yet give radically different forecasts or policy results outside the historical range. Indeed, given any set of data, there always exists an infinite number of models that fit those data to any arbitrary degree of accuracy you care to specify, all yielding different behavior outside the range of experience.[15]

The proper use of the behavior reproduction test is to uncover flaws in the structure or parameters of the model and assess whether they matter relative to the purpose. Instead of showing how well your model fits, you should point out to your clients all the places it doesn't. These discrepancies mark the trails that can guide you to erroneous parameter estimates and inappropriate assumptions you should revise before using the model for policy analysis. Every discrepancy should be discussed. Those discrepancies you believe are significant must lead to model revision, until you and your client agree that the remaining differences between the behavior of the model and the data do not matter to the purpose and need not be corrected. The revisions you undertake to resolve important discrepancies between model behavior and data must also be consistent with all the other formulation principles discussed above. It is not acceptable to introduce fudge factors or exogenous variables whose sole function is to improve the historical fit of the model.

---

[15]This is because any data set can be approximated arbitrarily well by different families of functions, such as the Taylor series or Fourier series, if enough terms are included. Adding additional higher-order terms to these functions changes their behavior outside the range of historical data.

Doing so serves only to lull the client into accepting the model while covering up its underlying flaws.

Example: Capital Punishment

What is the effect of capital punishment on the murder rate? This emotionally charged issue has been the subject of many empirical studies. Often, regression techniques are used to estimate how the murder rate differs between states with and without the death penalty. Leamer (1983) conducted a boundary adequacy test by exploring the robustness of such regressions to different sets of explanatory variables. The dependent variable is the murder rate per 100,000 people, and the explanatory variables include measures of deterrence such as the probability of execution given conviction for murder, the median time served given conviction, and the probability of conviction given arrest. Of course, since the different states vary in more ways than whether they execute convicted murderers, the regressions must include additional explanatory variables in an attempt to control for these other sources of variation. The choice of these "nuisance variables" is a matter of judgment, and different investigators select different explanatory variables based on their ideological perspective. Leamer selected a set of control variables commonly used in such studies, including economic indicators (e.g., median family or personal income, the fraction of households below the poverty line, the unemployment rate, labor force participation) and social variables (e.g., racial composition, the fraction of the population younger than 25, the fraction of the population living in large cities, the fraction of two-parent families).

Selecting different sets of explanatory variables gives wildly different results, all statistically significant: A single execution could deter as many as 29 murders or actually lead to an *increase* of more than 12 murders. The extreme sensitivity of the results to choice of model variables left Leamer (1983, p. 42) "with the feeling that any inference from these data about the deterrent effect of capital punishment is too fragile to be believed."

21.4.8   Behavior Anomaly Tests

Data limitations often mean it is not possible to establish the significance or strength of important relationships or formulations by statistical means. Behavior anomaly tests examine the importance of these structures by asking whether anomalous behavior arises when the relationship is deleted or modified. Anomalous behavior generated by deletion of a relationship provides you with some evidence for its importance.

Loop knockout analysis is a common method to search for behavior anomalies. In loop knockout tests you zero out a target relationship. For example, in decision rules of the form Corrective Action = (Desired State – State)/Adjustment Time, you knock out the loops passing through the corrective action by setting the adjustment time to an essentially infinite value. You can also eliminate loops by setting the delay times in information delays to infinity and by setting nonlinear functions $y = f(x)$ to unity for all values of x. Anomalous behavior resulting from a knockout test suggests the importance of the loop and may help establish a plausible range for the parameters and relationships.

Loop knockout analysis can be revealing when the model is operating under historical conditions but is particularly effective in conjunction with extreme condition tests. Often a loop is not active under normal operating conditions but becomes dominant in unusual circumstances. If a loop knockout test generates bizarre or physically impossible behavior under extreme conditions you have evidence that the relationship is important and must be included, even if it is not normally active and cannot be estimated statistically from the data.

Another form of behavior anomaly test replaces a disequilibrium structure with a simplified structure that assumes a subsystem is in equilibrium. For example, perception and material delays can be eliminated, in effect assuming decision makers can instantly recognize changes in the states of the system and instantly alter those states. Senge (1978, 1980) used behavior anomaly tests as a complement to econometric estimation to show that certain disequilibrium formulations were important in capital investment (section 11.5). For example, assuming manufacturing firms based capital investment only on their forecast of orders, implicitly assuming inventories and backlogs were always in equilibrium, generated implausible behavior under both historical and extreme conditions.

21.4.9   Family Member Tests

The family member test asks whether the model can generate the behavior of other instances in the same class as the system the model was built to mimic. A model of corporate growth should not only explain why one particular company grew but also why some other companies, with different policies and parameters, experience growth punctuated by periodic crises, why some stagnate, and why some fail altogether (Figure 3-6). A model of urban growth such as Forrester's *Urban Dynamics* model, "with appropriate choice of parameters . . . should behave like cities as different as New York, Dallas, . . . Berlin and Calcutta" (Forrester and Senge 1980, p. 221). Chapter 20 showed that the generic commodity model generated the cyclic behavior observed in the pulp and paper industry. It should also generate the appropriate frequencies, amplitudes, phase relationships, and other characteristics observed in commodities such as copper, cocoa, and coffee when the parameters characterizing these commodities are used. With suitable structural changes to represent livestock, the same model should generate the hog cycle when calibrated with hog gestation times, litter sizes, and so forth, and the cattle cycle when calibrated with cattle parameters.

The more diverse the instances of a system a model can represent the more general the theory it embodies. The family member test is particularly helpful when the class of systems the model addresses includes a wide range of different patterns of behavior. You should be suspicious of any model that can exhibit only a single mode of behavior. Consider innovation diffusion. Models such as the Bass diffusion model (chapter 9) can only generate one mode of behavior: S-shaped growth. In reality, many new products and new innovations fail. Others fluctuate as they move in and out of fashion. A general innovation diffusion model should be capable of capturing all these patterns. In contrast to the simple growth models, Homer (1983a, 1987) developed a rich behavioral model for the diffusion of new medical technologies. Besides the basic word of mouth and marketing feedbacks in the Bass model, it included endogenous technological progress, experience dilution and learning curves among clinicians, changes in the indications governing the use of the technology, changes in patient outcomes, and follow-up studies assessing the effectiveness of the new technology. The model successfully replicated very different emergence patterns for several medical innovations ranging from highly successful devices such as the cardiac pacemaker, to failures, to an antibiotic whose sales fluctuated as side effects were discovered and new applications were found. The model has since been used to examine new medical technologies ranging from drugs to artificial skin.

21.4.10   Surprise Behavior Tests

Discrepancies between model behavior and expectation indicate that there are flaws in the formal model, the mental model, or both. Often, of course, discrepancies between model output and your understanding of the system's dynamics indicate defects in the formal model. Occasionally, however, it is your mental model and your understanding of the data that require revision. The surprise behavior test is passed when a model generates a certain behavior, previously unrecognized, and it does indeed occur in the real system. Einstein's theory of general relativity provides a famous example. Einstein suggested that gravity bends the fabric of space-time, causing light to follow what appear to be curved paths. In 1919 the British astronomer Sir Arthur Eddington tested the theory by photographing stars whose light passed near the sun during a total eclipse. General relativity predicted that the light from these stars would curve by a certain amount as it passed close by the sun. Eddington showed that the apparent positions of these stars, briefly visible during the eclipse, were indeed shifted by an amount consistent with the predictions of Einstein's theory. Finding the unexpected behavior gave general relativity a powerful boost.

To take an example from business, Forrester once developed a model for a large automotive components manufacturer. The company had been losing market share for some years despite the technical superiority of their products. Many in the company blamed increasing competition. Most assumed market share was eroding faster during expansions than recessions, reasoning that customers would turn to the competition only when the firm's products were in short supply. However, in the simulations market share fell faster during recessions than booms. Initially, Forrester suspected there was a problem in the way he had captured the firm's inventory management policies. Further testing, however, revealed no errors. The counterintuitive result arose from the firm's extreme aversion to holding inventories. Whenever orders turned down, they slashed part orders and production so aggressively that the product was actually less available during market downturns than during expansions. A close review of the data showed that market share was in fact falling fastest during recessions. This surprising result eventually prompted a change in the firm's production policies (Forrester, personal communication).

Note that the surprise behavior test does not require the model to predict future events such as who will win the Kentucky Derby next year. The sun had been warping space-time all along, but until Einstein suggested the surprising result that gravity could bend light, no one thought to look. So it is with models of less cosmic significance: Until Forrester's model suggested the counterintuitive result that product could actually be less available during recessions than booms, the idea that recessions led to product gluts went unchallenged. We never have all the data, nor the time to search for all the important patterns. A main benefit of modeling is suggesting what to look for.

For the surprise behavior test to be effective you must analyze model behavior closely. Look at the behavior of all variables, not only the major indicators. Track down the sources of all unexpected or anomalous behavior (Mass 1991). Like any good scientist you should keep a laboratory notebook that documents your work. You must also overcome the problems of hindsight bias and reconstructive memory. After you present your analysis it is common for the client or audience to claim that the results are obvious, saying "You don't need a model to figure that out" or "I knew it all along." Because modeling is iterative, learning is often gradual, and people find it hard to remember how they perceived the situation before the project began. To overcome hindsight bias you should carefully document the mental models of the client team prior to the modeling effort (an important part of the process of establishing the purpose of the effort in any case).

21.4.11   Sensitivity Analysis

Since all models are wrong you must test the robustness of your conclusions to uncertainty in your assumptions. Sensitivity analysis asks whether your conclusions change in ways important to your purpose when assumptions are varied over the plausible range of uncertainty.

There are three types of sensitivity: **numerical, behavior mode,** and **policy** sensitivity.

Numerical sensitivity exists when a change in assumptions changes the numerical values of the results. For example, changing the strength of the word of mouth feedback in an innovation diffusion model will change the growth rate for the new product. All models exhibit numerical sensitivity.

Behavior mode sensitivity exists when a change in assumptions changes the patterns of behavior generated by the model. For example, if plausible alternative assumptions changed the behavior of a model from smooth adjustment to oscillation or from s-shaped growth to overshoot and collapse, the model would exhibit behavior mode sensitivity.

Policy sensitivity exists when a change in assumptions reverses the impacts or desirability of a proposed policy. If cutting prices boosted market share and profitability under one set of assumptions but led to ruinous price wars and bankruptcy under another, the model would exhibit policy sensitivity.

The types of sensitivity of concern in any project depend on the purpose of the model. Numerical sensitivity matters a great deal in the models NASA uses to plan the trajectory of the space shuttle. The purpose of these models demands tremendous precision, and there is little uncertainty in model structure or the laws of physics that govern the dynamics. In models of human systems, however, numerical sensitivity may matter little, if at all. The purpose of most business models is not to predict when the next sales slump will come but to redesign the supply chain so sales are more stable; not to predict what profits will be next quarter but to design policies to help the firm become profitable. For most purposes what counts is behavior mode sensitivity and especially policy sensitivity.

Sensitivity analysis requires much more than varying parameters. You must also consider the sensitivity of your results to assumptions about the boundary of the model, to changes in the level of aggregation, and to changes in the way people are assumed to make decisions. The uncertainty in parameter values is important and must be tested. But models are typically much more sensitive to assumptions about the boundary and formulations than to uncertainty in numerical values.

In assessing sensitivity to parametric assumptions you should first identify the plausible range of uncertainty in the values of each parameter or nonlinear relationship. You should then test the sensitivity to those parameters over a much wider range. As discussed in section 8.2.5, people tend to be overconfident in their judgments. Judgmental parameter estimates are likely to be more uncertain than people's intuitive confidence bounds suggest. Overconfidence also arises when parameters are estimated statistically. Formal estimation procedures such as regression yield confidence bounds around the best estimate. The estimated value of, say, the price elasticity of demand might be -0.5, with the 95% confidence bounds ranging from -0.4 to -0.6, indicating that there is only a 5% chance that the true value lies outside this range. These confidence bounds likely underestimate the true uncertainty in the parameter because they account only for one source of uncertainty—sampling error. The confidence bounds estimated in regression do not include the effects of measurement error, faulty specification of the model, or violations of the maintained hypotheses of the regression method. These sources of error are likely to be much larger than the estimated standard errors reported for the regression coefficients, but because they are difficult or impossible to quantify they are often ignored. A good rule of thumb is to test over a range at least twice as wide as statistical and judgmental considerations suggest, though consideration of the sources of uncertainty in particular cases may suggest a much wider range.

Most system dynamics and simulation software packages include automated sensitivity analysis tools. First, you specify which parameters to vary, then provide a range of values for each. The software then runs the model as many times as you like, using the specified values for each parameter, either one at a time (univariate testing) or all at once (multivariate testing).

Comprehensive sensitivity analysis is generally impossible even when restricted to parametric sensitivity. Since most models are significantly nonlinear the impact of combinations of assumptions may not be the sum of the impacts of the assumptions in isolation. Comprehensive sensitivity analysis would require testing all combinations of assumptions over their plausible range of uncertainty. The number of combinations is overwhelming even in models of modest size. Given the limited time and resources in any project, sensitivity analysis must focus on those relationships and parameters you suspect are *both* highly uncertain *and* likely to be influential. A parameter around which no uncertainty exists need not be tested. Likewise, if a parameter has but little effect on the dynamics it need not be

FIGURE 21-2

Best and worst case sensitivity analysis

Simulations of the new-product diffusion model in Figure 9-22.

Best case: Advertising Effectiveness = 0.75 * Base Case; Contact Rate = 0.75 * Base Case; Consumption per Adopter = 2 * Base Case.

Worst case: Advertising Effectiveness = 2 * Base Case; Contact Rate = 1.5 * Base Case; Consumption per Adopter = 0.5 * Base Case.

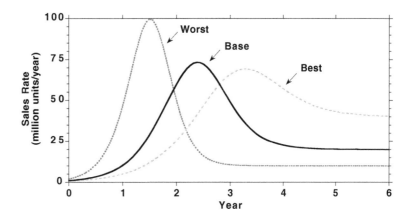

tested even if its value is highly uncertain because estimation errors are of little consequence.

A number of tools help you explore sensitivity efficiently. One common method is to define best and worst case scenarios. In the best (worst) case scenario you set the values of all parameters and relationships to the values most (least) favorable to the outcomes you desire or the policies you want to test. Consider the new-product diffusion model described in Figure 9-22. The model relates sales to advertising, word of mouth, and consumption per capita. Suppose your clients are using the model to plan capacity acquisition. They worry about boom and bust, where sales of a new product initially rise very rapidly only to collapse as the market saturates, leaving them with excess capacity. The worst case scenario to address their concern might assume relatively strong word of mouth and advertising effects and low replacement purchases per capita. The best case scenario might assume weak word of mouth and advertising effects, and high consumption. Figure 21-2 compares these scenarios to the base case. In the base case, the effectiveness of advertising is 0.01/year, the contact rate is 100/year, and consumption per adopter is 0.2 units/year/adopter. The best (worst) case sets advertising effectiveness to 0.0075 (0.02), the contact rate to 75 (150), and per capita consumption to 0.1 (0.4). In the base case, sales fall to about one-third of peak levels when the market saturates. The pattern of behavior in the best and worst cases is the same, but the implications for capacity acquisition are very different. In the best case, slower demand growth and higher replacement consumption mean the drop from the peak is only about 40%. Higher consumption also means the peak sales rate is about the same as the base case. In the worst case, demand peaks after just 1.5 years, then plummets by 90% over the next year. The best and worst cases provide bounds for the behavior the firm is likely to face.

The extreme situations represented by best and worst cases are not the most likely outcomes. Monte Carlo simulations allow you to generate dynamic confidence intervals for the trajectories of the variables in your models. In Monte Carlo analysis, you specify a probability distribution that characterizes the likely values of each parameter. For example, you might assume the values of each parameter

FIGURE 21-3

Dynamic confidence bounds from multivariate sensitivity analysis

Simulation of the new product diffusion model in Figure 9-22, showing the confidence bounds for sales from a sample of 500 simulations. Advertising Effectiveness, Contact Rate, and Consumption per Adopter distributed normally with standard deviations of 25%.

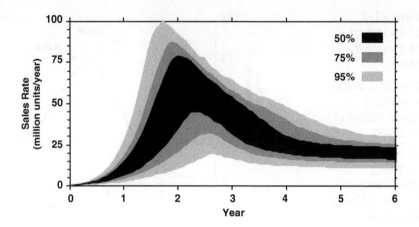

are distributed normally around your best estimates and specify the standard deviation for each. The software randomly draws a value for each parameter from the distributions you choose, then simulates the model. The trajectories generated in a large sample of simulations define dynamic confidence bounds for each variable.

Figure 21-3 shows the results of a Monte Carlo simulation of the product diffusion model. The figure shows the 50%, 75%, and 95% confidence bounds for sales in a sample of 500 simulations. Advertising effectiveness, the contact rate, and per capita consumption are all assumed to be distributed normally and independently with standard deviations of 25% of their base case values.[16] Given these assumptions, there is a 50% chance that sales will be between about 35 and 75 million units/year in year 2 and a 95% chance that sales will be between 10 and 90 million units/year. Note how the confidence intervals widen during the growth phase, then narrow again as the market stabilizes. The uncertainty in sales is much greater during the growth phase because the positive word of mouth feedback dominates. Small changes in the parameters controlling the word of mouth loop compound to yield large differences in peak sales. After the market saturates, word of mouth and advertising no longer matter, and the only remaining uncertainty (in this simple analysis) is in replacement consumption per capita. The interactions of the feedback loops and accumulations in dynamic models mean that the dynamic confidence bounds generated by multivariate sensitivity analysis can be very different from a distribution of a given variance around the base case trajectory.[17]

---

[16]The seemingly natural assumption that each parameter is independently distributed is actually not realistic. Typically, a model is calibrated to data. Varying the parameters independently results in many combinations that significantly degrade historical fit, indicating that these combinations are much less likely than the independence assumption would suggest. Suppose the base case trajectory for sales fit the historical data well. With independent sampling, all three parameters in the sensitivity runs will many times take on high values, leading the model to grossly overestimate historical sales. In reality, if word of mouth were stronger than assumed in the base case the effectiveness of advertising and consumption per capita would have to be smaller than their base case values for the model to correspond reasonably well to the data. Ford (1990) describes how to account for such correlations in multivariate sensitivity analysis.

[17]In interpreting dynamic confidence bounds remember that they represent the envelope of values in a sample of simulations and not a particular trajectory. For example, sales do not follow the path of the upper 95% confidence interval in any of the simulations.

Sensitivity results such as these can help the firm decide how much dedicated capacity to build and how much capacity to lease or outsource so it can meet peak demand while avoiding excess capacity when the market saturates.[18]

Another sensitivity analysis tool, dubbed the "Automated Nonlinear Test" or ANT by Miller (1998), asks whether parameter values can be found that generate anomalous results. ANT analysis is similar to policy optimization. In policy optimization the modeler specifies an objective function such as maximizing the present value of firm profits. The modeler then selects a set of policy instruments, such as the parameters in the decision rules for pricing, marketing expenditure, and capacity planning. The software then finds the set of parameters that maximizes the objective function. Many system dynamics and simulation packages have built in policy optimization capability. In ANT analysis, the modeler specifies an objective function designed to break the model by finding unrealistic behavior.

Miller (1998) demonstrated the ANT using the WORLD3 model (Meadows et al. 1974). The base case of the model generated an overshoot and decline of world population sometime before the year 2100 (see section 12.1.5). By setting the objective function to maximize the world population in the year 2100, the ANT automatically identified combinations of parameters that kept population from declining (within the time horizon). If any of these parameter combinations were plausible, the ANT would call the results of the study into question. The ANT is a very flexible tool. Adding a term to the objective function that reduces the payoff as the square of the number of perturbed parameters increases causes the ANT to find the most influential parameters (with respect to the specified objective function), automating the search for high leverage points. ANTs can also be used to do traditional policy optimization. Any general-purpose optimization method suitable for rugged landscapes with multiple optima can be used in ANTs. Miller compared hill-climbing and genetic algorithms as optimization methods, finding both worked well and significantly outperformed traditional multivariate Monte Carlo analysis.

Miller's analysis of the WORLD3 model showed that the range of populations generated in the year 2100 is wide. The ANTs also found several of the high leverage parameters. The fundamental mode of behavior, however, remained overshoot and collapse, showing that the model exhibits significant numerical sensitivity but low behavior mode sensitivity. Miller did not test for policy sensitivity, though the ANT technique could be used for this purpose.

21.4.12   System Improvement Tests

The ultimate goal of modeling is to solve a problem. System improvement tests ask whether the modeling process helped change the system for the better. To pass the test, the modeling process must identify policies that lead to improvement, those policies must be implemented, and the performance of the system must actually improve. In practice, assessing the impact of a model is extremely difficult. It is hard to assess the extent to which the modeling process changed people's mental

---

[18]In very large models the number of simulations required to explore parameter space using a simple Monte Carlo approach can be prohibitive. Various efficient sampling schemes such as Latin hypercube designs can reduce the number of simulations required. Ford (1990) describes these tools for sensitivity analysis of large models, with examples from the electric utility industry.

models and beliefs. It is rare that clients adopt the recommendations of any model promptly or without modification. When new policies are implemented, it takes a long time for their effects to manifest. Many other variables and conditions change at the same time new policies are implemented, confounding attempts to attribute any results to the policies. Performance improvement following a study does not mean the model-based policies were responsible; the system may have improved for reasons unrelated to the modeling process. Likewise, deteriorating performance after policy implementation does not mean the model failed since the outcome could have been even worse without the new policies.

The keys to successful assessment of a modeling intervention are (1) prospective evaluation, (2) use of multiple data sources, and (3), to the extent possible, adherence to proper experimental protocols. Rigorous follow-up research is essential to build a strong foundation for the refinement and wise use of the tools of system dynamics and systems thinking—a goal of academics and practitioners alike.

First, modeling projects should be designed with evaluation in mind from the beginning. Prospective evaluations are more effective than retrospective studies. After the fact you may discover that the data you need were not collected, memories are distorted by hindsight, and key actors have left the scene. Discuss with your clients how you will know if the project is successful as part of the initial problem definition phase. Resources for assessment should be allocated when budgets, staff, and time lines for the project are set.

Second, modeling interventions can change people's beliefs and attitudes, their behavior, formal organizational policies, and, of course, the actual performance of the system. You should measure change in all these dimensions to assess the extent to which any changes in performance can be attributed to the intervention. Often you will have to create instruments such as interview protocols and surveys to document people's mental models, behavior, and changes in policies (see Doyle 1997).

Third, to the extent possible, design your intervention as an experiment. While most organizational interventions cannot be carried out using the double-blind randomized trials required in the assessment of new medical treatments, you should use these techniques wherever possible. Create control and treatment groups. Look for opportunities to conduct natural experiments, for example, comparing the performance of the intervention to that of business units or companies that did not undertake the modeling process. Consider partnerships with academics and others who can serve as neutral observers to document the impact of your work.

In practice, follow-up studies for any type of management innovation are all too rare. It is understandable that proper design and resources for evaluation and assessment suffer when a new project begins. Identifying potential partner organizations, negotiating entry, building trust, and working with the client team to understand the business is difficult and demanding. Often, clients do not appreciate that follow-up research is not only for academic purposes but also benefits them directly. They are reluctant to provide the resources to support it or to permit basic protocols such as treatment and control groups and randomized assignment.

Nevertheless, as a modeler it is in your best interest and the best interests of the clients to overcome these problems and design assessment into your projects from the start. Without rigorous follow-up research the efficacy of all management interventions remains the province of anecdote. Anecdotes are unreliable because they are not subject to independent confirmation, because people tend to highlight their successes and hide their failures, because people often have a financial or reputational stake in the success of their work, and because even apparently successful interventions may have succeeded due to placebo effects or other factors unrelated to the intervention. Without rigorous follow-up research it is difficult for modelers and clients to learn which tools and processes work or how to improve them. At best, the result is inefficiency; at worst it hurts the organization and the people in it.

Example: Avoiding Proof by Anecdote

Cavaleri and Sterman (1997) evaluated the impact of a system dynamics intervention designed to improve quality and performance in the claims processing unit of a US insurance firm. The intervention, begun in the late 1980s, used tools including group modeling, management flight simulators, and learning laboratories. The intervention was widely cited as a successful application demonstrating the efficacy of these systems thinking tools (see Senge 1990). Through a questionnaire, interviews, and extensive review of company records we established that the intervention did succeed in changing the mental models and behavior of key managers. We found compelling evidence that the managers redesigned policies for hiring and workload management in accordance with the recommendations arising from the modeling process. However, because the original study was not designed with evaluation in mind, it was impossible to find clear evidence that the intervention improved business performance. There were too many confounding changes in the environment. Data needed to test these plausible rival hypotheses were not collected during the original project, weakening claims for project success. Failure to document the impact of the project may also have hurt the company, which is no longer using any of these tools.

It is encouraging that an increasing number of system dynamics interventions have been designed to facilitate evaluation from the start (see, e.g., Vennix 1996 and the papers in Vennix, Richardson, and Andersen 1997). Despite its difficulties rigorous follow-up study is vital if the potential to learn about the efficacy of systems thinking in organizations is to be fully realized.

CHALLENGE   ## Model Testing

Apply the tests described above to the following models. The goal of your testing is to identify problems in the models that render them unsuitable for their purposes. If the purpose of the model is not made explicit by the documentation, then suggest plausible purposes for which the model might be used and evaluate it relative to each of these. Not all tests can be run on all models. For example, quantitative behavior reproduction tests cannot be carried out on an illustrative model that is not calibrated to a particular case.

1. The epidemic and innovation diffusion models described in chapter 9.
2. The model of path dependence and market dominance described in chapter 10.

3. The market growth model described in chapter 15.
4. The supply chain models described in chapters 17–19.
5. The commodity model described in chapter 20.
6. Models in the literature (many are cited in the references).

21.5   SUMMARY

The word validation should be struck from the vocabulary of modelers. All models are wrong, so no models are valid or verifiable in the sense of establishing their truth. The question facing clients and modelers is never whether a model is true but whether it is useful. The choice is never whether to use a model. The only choice is which model to use. Selecting the most appropriate model is always a value judgment to be made by reference to the purpose. Without a clear understanding of the purpose for which the model is to be used, it is impossible to determine whether you should use it as a basis for action.

Models rarely fail because the modelers used the wrong regression technique or because the model didn't fit the historical data well enough. Models fail because more basic questions about the suitability of the model to the purpose aren't asked, because the model violates basic physical laws such as conservation of matter, because a narrow boundary cut critical feedbacks, because the modelers kept the assumptions hidden from the clients, or because the modelers failed to include important stakeholders in the modeling process.

To avoid such problems, whether as a modeler or model consumer, you must insist on the highest standards of documentation. Your models must be fully replicable and available for critical review. Use the documentation to assess the adequacy of the model boundary and the appropriateness of its underlying assumptions about the physical structure of the system and the decision-making behavior of the people acting within it. Consider extreme condition tests and sensitivity to alternative assumptions, including assumptions about model boundary and structure, not only sensitivity to variations in parameter values.

Model testing is iterative and multidimensional and begins at the start of the project. Build into the budget and time line sufficient resources to assess the impact of the work and to document it fully so others can help you improve it.

No one test is adequate. A wide range of tests helps you understand the robustness and limitations of your models. These tests involve direct inspection of equations and simulations of the whole model, the assessment of historical fit, and behavior under extreme conditions.

Use all types of data, both numerical and qualitative. Multiple data sources provide opportunities for triangulation and cross-checking.

Test the robustness of your conclusions to uncertainty in your assumptions. While parametric sensitivity testing is important, model results are usually far more sensitive to assumptions about the model boundary, level of aggregation, and representation of decision making.

Test as you go. Testing is an integral part of the iterative process of modeling. By continuously testing your assumptions and the sensitivity of results as you develop the model you uncover important errors early, avoid costly rework, and generate insights throughout the project, thus involving your clients more deeply and building their—and your—understanding of the problem and the nature of high leverage policies.

Open the modeling process to the widest range of people you can. Implementation success requires changing the clients' mental models. To do so the clients must become partners with you in the modeling process. Ultimately, your chances of success are greatest when you work with your clients to find the limitations of your models, mental and formal, then work together to correct them. In this fashion you and your clients gradually develop a deep understanding of the system and the confidence to use that understanding to take action.

Design assessment into your work from the start so you can determine both the extent to which you meet your goals and how you can improve the process in the future. Work with your clients to collect data that can reveal how your work affected the beliefs, attitudes, and behavior of the people in the system, along with changes in system performance. Track the impact of your work with long-term follow-up studies. A careful testing and assessment process helps you and your clients improve your ability to think systemically in every aspect of your lives, not just in one project.

Part VII

Commencement

Chapter 22 addresses the challenges and opportunities facing the field of system dynamics. It invites you to continue your study of complex systems and apply what you have learned.

22

Challenges for the Future

It is not knowledge, but the act of learning, not possession but the act of getting there, which grants the greatest enjoyment.

—Karl Friedrich Gauss (1777–1855)

This chapter briefly describes the major challenges facing the further development of system dynamics. I discuss five important areas of future development: theory, technology, education, implementation, and applications. The categories are neither mutually exclusive nor exhaustive, and any such list is necessarily subjective, incomplete, and biased.[1] I invite you to develop your own priorities and to work toward their realization.

22.1 THEORY

System dynamics models rest on the theory of nonlinear dynamics, an area in which tremendous progress has been made over the past two decades. Where nonlinear dynamic systems were once largely terra incognita, now there is a large body of theory describing the local and global dynamics of a wide range of complex nonlinear systems. However, important challenges for the future remain, and the mathematical foundations are but one area in which basic research is needed.

- **Theory of nonlinear dynamics and complex systems.** When and how do systems self-organize to produce coherent patterns in both time and space? To what extent are dynamics and complex systems self-similar across different temporal and spatial scales? What determines these scaling

---

[1]Richardson (1996) provides a particularly thoughtful approach to these issues.

relationships? What forces create entrainment of individual subsystems into coherent macrodynamics (e.g., the entrainment of individual firms into coherent aggregate business cycles)? What are the underlying generic structures that create similar dynamics in different domains?

- **Agent-based modeling.** Stimulated by improvements in computer power, applications of agent-based modeling are growing rapidly. In an agent-based model, the individual members of a population such as firms in an economy or people in a social group are represented explicitly rather than as a single aggregate entity. Important heterogeneities in agent attributes and decision rules can then be represented. There are different simulation methods for agent-based modeling, ranging from simple cellular automata to detailed, disaggregate system dynamics models. Though much progress has been made lately, much remains to be learned about the dynamics of agent-based models as well as techniques for analyzing their behavior, for testing their decision rules, and so on. What principles should guide the choice of modeling method and level of aggregation? How should modelers trade off the number of different agents they can represent in the model against the complexity of the individual agents? What rules of interaction, level of rationality, and learning capabilities should be ascribed to the agents?

- **Mental models, dynamic decision making, and learning.** Laboratory research and fieldwork have revealed much about the way people make decisions in complex dynamics environments, but our understanding is still poor. What are the mental models people use in situations of dynamic complexity? How sensitive to the characteristics of the environment are the decision rules people use? Are the misperceptions of feedback (chapter 1) documented in so many cases innate or learned? What types of experience and education might mitigate them and develop our systems thinking capabilities? What incentives, information systems, and organizational structures would catalyze such learning? How can these learning processes be captured in models?

- **Organizational and social evolution.** Even if individuals learn slowly, social structures such as organizations might improve through evolution, as the higher-performing agents prosper and are imitated while the low performers are selected out of the population. Formal modeling of social evolution is growing rapidly, but many questions remain. What are the units of selection? What are the "genes" in an organization? What determines the length of a generation? What rules determine the selection of winners and losers, and what does reproductive success mean in an organization? When can selective pressures reward dysfunctional behavior and perpetuate low performance?

22.2 TECHNOLOGY

Until recently learning about the dynamics of a model proceeded essentially by trial and error, guided by intuition and experience, one simulation at a time. Since complex nonlinear systems can generate a wide range of behaviors, many of which are counter to intuition, developing insight into the dynamics of a complex system has often been difficult.

As computers become ever faster and more capable, simulations will not merely run faster, but the nature of the models, simulation software, and ways of interacting with models will be transformed. Among the tools future simulation software will include are:

- **Automated mapping of parameter space.** Hitting the run button will generate a high-resolution map of model behavior over a user-specified range of parameters and initial conditions.

- **Automated sensitivity analysis.** The software will automatically identify the high-leverage policies and most influential parameters in the model (relative to user-specified criteria).

- **Automated extreme condition testing.** The modeler or client will specify extreme conditions the model must satisfy (e.g., no labor, no production; no inventory, no shipments). The simulation software will automatically implement these "reality checks" and report the results (see Peterson and Eberlein 1994).

- **Automatic, interactive parameter estimation, calibration, and policy optimization.** Modelers can now specify (possibly nonlinear) criteria and weights for different variables and constraints on the plausible values of parameters; the software then finds the best parameter values and confidence bounds around the estimated values (using methods from ordinary least squares to Kalman filtering). However, the process is often tedious and it is difficult to combine quantitative and qualitative information. Future simulation software will automate model calibration, allowing the user to explore the consequences of alternate criteria interactively in real time. Similarly, optimization of system dynamic models has a long history (see, e.g., Coyle 1985, 1998). Currently available software allows the user to specify a (possibly nonlinear) multiattribute objective function and a set of policy instruments (parameters), then searches the policy space for the optimal solution. In the future, this process will be so fast that it can take place interactively and in real time, with the user getting immediate feedback on the consequences of alternative objective functions and policy instruments.

- **Automated identification of dominant loops and feedback structure.** Several methods now exist to identify the dominant loops at any point in a simulation, quantify the contribution of any parameter or loop to a given mode, and show how nonlinearities change the dominant feedback structure (see, e.g., Eberlein 1989; Kampmann 1996; Mojtahedzadeh 1997; and N. Forrester 1982). Future simulation software will automate and speed these computations so that users can get immediate feedback showing the dominant loops in the system and how the influence of parameters and feedback structures waxes and wanes as the dynamics unfold.

- **Automated help.** Through expert systems, pattern recognition software, and other artificial intelligence tools it should soon be possible for simulation software to serve as an automated model-building tutor and guide. The modeling tutor could, for example, examine each equation as it is entered for dimensional consistency, robustness under extreme conditions, and other basic principles of good formulations. The tutor would then suggest improved formulations from a library of standard structures, links to related models and literature, and reasonable parameters. Imagine building, say, a marketing model. The software might tell you that your formulation for customer defection to competitors lacks feedback from the stock of current customers (allowing the customer stock to become negative), suggest an improved formulation, and guide you through a series of questions to help you specify the parameters and nonlinear relationships. Similarly, the software may suggest tests you can conduct and hints to help you better understand the behavior of your model.

A major challenge facing software designers is organizing and presenting the huge masses of data generated by the tools described above. Data presentation and visualization will be a critical arena for future software development, including

- **Visualization of model behavior.** Improvements in graphics and animation are needed to display the global dynamics of complex models with high-dimensional state and parameter spaces.
- **Linking behavior to generative structure.** Computations of dominant structure and parameter sensitivity should automatically be displayed on the structural diagram. Imagine the size, color, and other attributes of the stocks, flows, variables, and loops displayed on the screen changing to indicate shifts in loop dominance or parameter sensitivity as a simulation unfolds, or as you vary input conditions and policies.
- **Data input.** Input devices such as joysticks and data gloves can provide rapid, continuous input of parameter values and control graphical displays. Imagine using a joystick to "fly" over a three-dimensional projection of model behavior as a function of any model parameters you wish to explore.

Linking models with one another and with a wide range of databases is another important area of technological development. At present, finding, checking, and updating data is difficult, expensive, and time-consuming. Incompatibilities abound. Future simulation software will seamlessly integrate data from a variety of sources, automatically identify inconsistencies, and automatically update the model by querying the data servers over public or private networks. Integrating dynamic models with enterprise management software will enable managers to go beyond spreadsheets.

The key challenge is using technology to learn more effectively about the dynamics of our models, to develop tools to aid understanding of complex systems. There are dangers, however. Modelers must resist the temptation to use greater computer power to build bigger and bigger models in the vain belief that the more detailed and comprehensive the model, the better it must be. While computer power grows exponentially, our ability to absorb information remains the same. Larger and larger models may only result in less and less understanding, fewer insights and less implementation success.

22.3 IMPLEMENTATION

Improvements in theory and better technology alone will not improve the chances of successful implementation. Ultimately the client team must still come to a deep understanding of the problem issue and develop enough confidence in model-generated policy insights to act. Despite great strides, successful implementation remains an art. Issues for further research include

- **Communicating modeling insights.** How can models be made transparent and accessible to clients as technology improves and models grow more complex? How do you reach the client when the client is the entire society and your message is filtered by the media (see, e.g., Meadows 1989)?

- **Improving group modeling.** Much progress has been made (e.g., Vennix 1996; Vennix, Richardson, and Andersen 1997; and Morecroft and Sterman 1994) and models have long been used in dispute resolution (see, e.g., section 2.3). How can modeling be used well in the larger groups often required to achieve consensus for implementation? How can modeling be used wisely in adversarial contexts, for example, to promote integrative dispute resolution (see, e.g., Di Stefano 1992; Nyhart and Smarasan 1990; Reichelt and Sterman 1990; Weil and Etherton 1990)?

- **Speeding the process.** Faster communication, shorter product life cycles, and longer work hours are increasing the pressure on managers for fast answers to tough questions. Can the cycle time for the development of a model be reduced? Should it be? Perhaps the modeling process should encourage meditative reflection and prevent knee-jerk reactions.

- **Integrating modeling methodologies.** System dynamics does not stand alone. What synergies can be achieved by integrating dynamic modeling with other modeling approaches, including multiattribute utility assessment, decision analysis, market research methods, and other tools (see, e.g., Reagan-Cirincione et al. 1991)?

- **Creating managerial practice fields.** Rehearsal and practice have long been central to successful team performance in sports and the arts, and simulation has for 50 years been a basic element of military planning and training. Developments in technology and group process now enable managers to develop and use models to create rich, interactive practice fields to design new policies, test new ideas, and explore alternative theories for new phenomena. These management flight simulators will play a vital role in emerging decentralized, networked organizations (Senge et al. 1994). At the same time the research clearly shows how difficult it can be for people to learn effectively from simulations and games (see chapter 1; also Isaacs and Senge 1992; Paich and Sterman 1993). Creating effective practice fields requires much more than exciting and realistic flight simulators.

- **Assessing outcomes.** Some organizations have recently realized that it is in their long-run best interest to share all their experiences with modeling, not only their successes. Too many, however, continue to withhold their experiences, even from their own employees, for fear of revealing proprietary information, the perceived short-run costs of documentation and follow-up, or embarrassment. How can the incentives to carry out rigorous follow-up studies be strengthened?

22.4 EDUCATION

Systems thinking and system dynamics modeling are no longer restricted to advanced study in graduate schools or university courses. Over the past decade many dedicated teachers, administrators, and parents have worked to introduce these concepts and tools in primary and secondary schools. Although exciting experiments in curriculum and pedagogy are underway around the world (see, e.g., Brown 1992; Draper and Swanson 1990; Fisher and Zaraza 1997; Gould 1993; Mandinach and Cline 1994; Roberts and Feurzeig 1999) we are still very early in this process.[2] Much work remains to develop system dynamics curricula appropriate to the K–12 grades, to develop pedagogy for children (and adults) that works, and to develop instruments and methods to assess the long-run impact of these approaches.

Likewise, organizations should devote significant resources to continuing education for all. Few have yet taken the challenge seriously. More commonly, organizations look for the quick fix, faddishly embracing the latest hot management tool, only to abandon it for the next "flavor of the month" program. The result is cynicism and resentment among employees and senior management alike (see, e.g., Sterman and Wittenberg 1999 and Keating et al. 1999 for models of this process). After working intensively with systems thinking and system dynamics for several years, a manager at a US automaker reflected on the prospects for commitment to sustained learning in today's organizations:

> It has taken me a long time to begin to get what this new worldview [system dynamics] is all about. I'm beginning to feel like I felt in my freshman calculus class. After months of confusion, I began to get it. Within a year, I had begun to develop some competence. Within four years, the basic tools and way of thinking were an integrated part of my professional skills... The problem is, if calculus were invented today, our organizations could never learn it. We would send everyone off to the three-day crash course and then tell them to go off and apply it. After three months we'd check if it was working. Since little would have been achieved, we'd conclude that there really wasn't much there, and we'd move on to the next program (Kim and Senge 1994, p. 278).

Forrester, in his prescient paper "A New Corporate Design" (Forrester 1965/1975a, p. 107–108), prescribes

> Some 25 percent of the total working time of all persons in the corporation should be devoted to preparing for their future roles. This means time devoted to competence some five years in the future and does not include the learning that may be a necessary part of the immediate task. Over a period of years this study would cover a wide range—individual and group psychology, writing, speaking, law, dynamics

---

[2]The Creative Learning Exchange serves as a clearinghouse and resource center for people teaching system dynamics in the K–12 setting. See <http://sysdyn.mit.edu/cle/home.html>.

of industrial behavior, corporate policy design, advances in science and engineering, and historical development of political and corporate organizations… The educational program must become an integral part of corporate life, not a few weeks or months once in a lifetime at another institution. The over-all policies of the organization must create incentives that protect the time for education from encroachment by short-term pressures.

For centuries the reductionist program of ever-finer specialization has been very successful, often leading to deep and useful knowledge. Today, most of the problems we face are fundamentally interdisciplinary. As a manager, you won't face marketing problems, financial problems, and human resource problems. As an individual, you don't face economic problems, social problems, and personal problems. You just have problems. We impose these categories on the world to simplify its overwhelming complexity. Some boundaries are necessary and inevitable. But all too often, ignoring what lies outside the familiar walls of our understanding cuts critical feedbacks and breeds arrogance about our ability to control nature and other people. The reductionist program is very powerful, and should not be replaced by vague generalizations about systems and interconnectedness. The challenge is to design an education for ourselves and our children that preserves the power of specialized study while simultaneously teaching practical and rigorous approaches to complexity and cross-disciplinary communication—then using these systems thinking capabilities to address the pressing problems we face in our professional and personal lives.

22.5   APPLICATIONS

System dynamics has been applied to issues from physics to physiology and psychology, from arms races to the war on drugs, from global climate change to organizational change. Yet there are countless problems and issues where understanding is lacking and the dominant theories are event-oriented, exogenous, and static rather than structural, endogenous, and dynamic. The result is policy resistance, the loss of hope for the future, and the feeling of helplessness afflicting so many people today.

CHALLENGE   ## Putting System Dynamics into Action

What are the issues you care most deeply about? What approaches have been tried, with what record of success? Learn what's been done before. Talk to the people living in the system. What feedback structures and dynamics do you see?

Become an expert on the issues. Get involved. Start applying your knowledge and modeling skills to help improve the situation. Build a network of colleagues and decision makers. Be humble about what you know and listen to your critics. Strive always to make a difference. And have fun.

Appendix A

Numerical Integration

System dynamics models are systems of nonlinear ordinary differential equations. Almost all the time, and certainly for any model of moderate realism, analytic solutions cannot be found and the behavior of the models must be computed numerically, a process known as numerical integration. The theory of numerical integration for differential equations is subtle and sophisticated and the literature is large. This appendix focuses on the most common methods and the pragmatics of the process. Which method should you use and in what circumstances? How should the time step be selected? How can you make sure the results of your simulations are not corrupted by errors? Readers interested in the mathematical underpinnings should consult introductory numerical methods texts such as Atkinson (1985), Burden and Faires (1989), or Maron (1987).

As described in chapters 6 and 7, the stocks in a model S accumulate (integrate) their inflows I less their outflows O. The flows, in turn, depend on the stocks, any exogenous variables U, and parameters (constants, C):

$$S_t = \text{INTEGRAL}(I_t - O_t, S_{t_0}) \tag{A-1}$$

$$I_t = f(S_t, U_t, C); \, O_t = g(S_t, U_t, C) \tag{A-2}$$

The initial condition S_{t_0} gives the quantity in any stock today. What will its value be tomorrow? The quantity in the stock tomorrow will be the amount in the stock now, plus the quantity that flows in between today and tomorrow, less the amount that flows out. However, the values of the flows are only known at the current instant, and they usually won't remain constant between today and tomorrow. The challenge is estimating the average flow over the next day (or whatever time interval you use), recognizing that the average over the interval usually won't equal the flow right now.

The simplest assumption is that the rates will remain constant between today and tomorrow. Denoting the time interval between periods as dt (for "delta time"), the assumption the rates remain constant during the next interval implies

$$S_{t+dt} = S_t + dt * (I_t - O_t) \tag{A-3}$$

Equation (A-3) is the most basic technique, known as *Euler integration* after the great mathematician Leonhard Euler (1707–1783). The assumption that the rates remain constant throughout the time interval dt is reasonable if the dynamics of the system are slow enough and dt is small enough. The definitions of "reasonable" and "small enough" depend on the accuracy you require, which in turn depends on the purpose of the model; see below for guidelines for testing the sensitivity of your model to the choice of dt.

As the time step shrinks, the accuracy of Euler's approximation improves. In the limit, when dt becomes an infinitesimal moment of time, equation (A-3) reduces to the exact continuous-time differential equation governing the dynamics of the system:

$$\lim_{dt \to 0} \frac{S_{t+dt} - S_t}{dt} = \frac{dS}{dt} = (I_t - O_t) \tag{A-4}$$

Software packages for system dynamics such as DYNAMO, ithink, Powersim, and Vensim use Euler integration as their default simulation method. The only difference between the numerical and analytic solution of the underlying differential equation system is the size of dt. The differential equation uses an infinitesimal, a true instant. Digital computers must proceed by discrete steps and use a finite time step.

Sample Simulation Sequence

The initial conditions for the stocks, the initial values of any exogenous variables, and the values of the constants allow you to calculate the initial values of the flows. Assuming the flows remain constant throughout the next time step dt allows you to calculate the stock in the next period. From the new value of the stock, the new values of the rates are then calculated and the next value of the stock is determined. Each period the values of the stocks are used to calculate the rates which are then used to update the values of the stocks.

Consider a simple model of a population. The population P is increased by the Birth Rate B and decreased by the Death Rate D. Births and deaths are proportional to population. For simplicity assume the Fractional Birth Rate FBR and Average Lifetime AL are constant, at 4%/year and 80 years, respectively. The initial population is one million. The equations for the system are

$$P = \text{INTEGRAL}(B - D, P_{t_0}) \tag{A-5}$$

$$P_{t_0} = 1e6 \tag{A-6}$$

$$B = \text{FBR} * P \tag{A-7}$$

$$D = P/\text{AL} \tag{A-8}$$

$$\text{FBR} = 0.04 \tag{A-9}$$

$$\text{AL} = 80 \tag{A-10}$$

The model is a linear first-order system and can be solved analytically. The exact solution is

$$P_t = P_{t_0} * \exp[(\text{FBR} - 1/\text{AL}) * t] \tag{A-11}$$

That is, population grows exponentially at the net fractional birth rate FBR − 1/AL (see chapter 8). With these parameters the net fractional birth rate is 2.75%/year.

Table A-1 shows how the dynamics are calculated. The time step is set to 0.25 years.

Time 0.   The value of population at time t = 0 is one million people. The birth rate equals Fractional Birth Rate * Population, or 0.04 * 1e6 = 40,000 people/year. The Death Rate = Population/Average Lifetime = 1e6/80 = 12,500 people/year. The net birth rate is therefore 27,500 people/year. These values are the instantaneous rates of flow at t = 0.

In Euler integration, these rates are assumed to remain constant throughout the time interval defined by dt. The time step dt in this example is 0.25 years, so the total change in the population is dt * Net Birth Rate = 0.25 years * 27,500 people/year = 6875 people. Equivalently, 0.25 years * 40,000 people/year = 10,000 people are born during the first quarter year, and 0.25 years * 12,500 = 3125 people die. The simulated population at t = 0.25 is therefore 1,006,875.

Time 0 + dt.   Given the calculated value of population for t = 0 + dt, the birth rate now equals 0.04 * 1,006,875 = 40,275 people/year. The death rate is 1,006,875/80 = 12,586 people/year. The net birth rate at that instant is 27,689 people/year. Again assuming the rates remain constant over the next quarter year, the quantity added to the population by time t = 0.5 is 0.25 years * 27,689 people/year = 6922 people. Equivalently, 0.25 years * 40,275 people/year = 10,069 people are born, and 0.25 years * 12,586 people year = 3147 people die. The population at t = 0.5 thus equals 1,013,797.

Time 0 + 2dt.   At time t = 0.5, the birth rate is 40,552 people/year and the death rate is 12,672 people/year, yielding an instantaneous net birth rate of 27,880 people/year. Over the next quarter year, assuming that rate remains constant, 6970 people are added, so the population at t = 0.75 years is 1,020,767 people. The simulation continues in this fashion as long as you desire.

Integration Error

The use of a finite time step and resulting approximation to the average rates over the interval introduce error, known as *integration error,* or *dt error.* The magnitude

TABLE A-1   Simulating a model with Euler integration

Time	Population (people)	Birth Rate (people/year)	Death Rate (people/year)	Net Birth Rate (people/year)	People Added (people)
0.00	1,000,000	40,000	12,500	27,500	6875
0.25	1,006,875	40,275	12,586	27,689	6922
0.50	1,013,797	40,552	12,672	27,880	6970
0.75	1,020,767	40,831	12,760	28,071	7018
1.00	1,027,785	41,111	12,847	28,264	7066

TABLE A-2
Integration error
depends on the
time step.

Time Step (dt) (years)	Simulated Population at t = 100 (million people)	% Error (exact solution = 15.643 million)
0.125	15.56	−0.53
0.25	15.49	−0.98
0.5	15.35	−1.87
1.0	15.07	−3.66
2.0	14.54	−7.05
5.0	13.15	−15.94

of integration error depends on how quickly the rates change relative to the time step. The faster the dynamics of the system, or the longer the dt, the greater the integration error will be. Table A-2 compares the simulated values of population after 100 years to the exact, continuous time solution in equation (A-11) for different values of dt.

The exact value of population after 100 years in the continuous time model is 1e6 * exp(0.0275 * 100) ≈ 15.643 million people. The time step is equivalent to the compounding interval for the computation of interest on a bank account. The more often interest is compounded (the smaller the time step), the faster the balance grows, up to the continuous compounding limit. In this example, where the behavior is pure exponential growth, population grows exactly like a bank balance, and the simulated values are always less than the continuous compounding case. For small time steps, the errors are small. With a time step of 0.25 years, the simulation is less than 1% too low after 100 years. Increasing the time step increases the magnitude of the error.

The magnitude of integration error also depends on the stability of the system. The sample model here, a pure positive feedback, is unstable. Small errors grow over time at exponential rates, just as a bank balance of $1001 will eventually exceed a balance of $1000 earning the same interest rate by an arbitrarily large amount, because the extra $1 grows exponentially at the interest rate. In models tending toward a stable equilibrium the integration error would probably be much smaller than shown in Table A-2 and would diminish as the system approached equilibrium.[1]

---

[1]Technically, the population model governed by positive feedback is termed "ill-conditioned" because small errors accumulate with each time step (a process known as error propagation). In the population example the error grows exponentially over time. In "well-conditioned" models errors die away over time. Roughly speaking, a stable system, dominated by negative feedback, tends to be well-conditioned. Since the stability of a system can change within a single simulation as the nonlinearities alter the dominant loops, a particular time step may work well in one part of a simulation and fail in another part. Whether the resulting errors matter depends on the rate at which errors propagate or die away and of course on the purpose of the model.

Selecting an Appropriate Time Step

How should you set the time step? When you need to compare simulation output against data, you should obviously choose a time step that is evenly divisible into the data-reporting interval. It doesn't do to calculate a model with quarterly data using a time step of 0.20 years.

The primary consideration in selecting the time step, however, is the accuracy of the numerical integration process. The smaller the value of dt, the more accurate the assumption that the rates of change remain constant between time steps and the closer to the true continuous time solution your model output will be. However, the smaller the value of dt, the longer it will take your simulation to run. More subtly, the smaller the time step the greater the round-off and truncation error. Round-off and truncation errors arise because computers operate with finite precision arithmetic. The total numerical error in a simulation consists of the integration error and the round-off error. Round-off error means you cannot increase simulation accuracy arbitrarily by shrinking the time step. As some point smaller time steps actually cause the total error to increase as the cumulative effects of round off outweigh the reduction in integration error.

Selecting the time step for your simulations is therefore a matter of trading off integration error against simulation cost and round-off error. As computers become faster, the time step you can select and still simulate quickly is dropping; likewise you can elect to use higher precision without much cost in computation time. The accuracy/simulation time trade-off is easing as technology improves.

A widely used rule of thumb is to set the time step between one-fourth and one-tenth the size of the smallest time constant in your model. However, in a large model it is difficult to estimate all the time constants and select an appropriate time step, so you must always test the sensitivity of your results to the choice of time step (and integration method; see below).

Test for integration error by running your model with your best estimate of an appropriate value for dt. Then cut the value of dt in half and run the model again. If there is no significant change in the behavior—that is, if the behavior does not change in ways that matter to the purpose of the model—then your original choice was fine. If the behavior changes in a significant way, repeat the test with dt cut in half again. Continue until the results no longer differ.

In the population example Euler integration with dt = 0.25 years yields an error of less than 1% after 100 years. The error is far smaller than likely uncertainty in the parameters or initial conditions and far, far smaller than the error caused by the assumption that fractional birth and death rates remain constant over this span.

Round-off error also affects the computation of time in your models. Time is calculated as a stock that increases one time step per time step:

$$\text{Time}_{t + dt} = \text{Time}_t + dt \tag{A-12}$$

In principle, the value of Time n periods of length dt from now should be $\text{Time}_{t_0} + n * dt$. However, if dt cannot be represented exactly with the precision used in the computations, the amount added to Time each period will not be correct. Suppose you selected dt = ⅙ year, or 0.1666.... If you used only the first two digits, truncating the rest, the value of time after three iterations would be only

0.96, not 1 year. Though computers use more than two digits, they still truncate or round, so the problem remains.

Since computers use the binary system you can minimize truncation and round-off error in the calculation of time by choosing a time step that can be represented exactly in base 2 given the precision of your computer. Powers of 2 are most common (e.g., dt = 4, 2, 1, 0.5, 0.25, 0.125, 0.0625, and so on). Setting dt = 0.3 is not a good choice; its base 2 representation is 0.01001001001001 . . . and will be rounded down to a smaller number so that after n time steps the computed value of Time will increase less than n * dt.

Occasionally you will need to select a value of dt that does not meet this criterion. The problem arises most often when time is measured in years and historical data are available monthly. In this case dt must be set to $\frac{1}{12}$ = 0.0833 . . . years to match the data reporting interval. In such cases, enter as many digits for the time step as you can (e.g., 0.08333333333, not 0.083). Still, the computed value of time will eventually fall short as the round-off error accumulates. If the time horizon of the model is not too long, the problem may not arise. Another solution is to measure time in months instead of years, set dt = 1 month, and divide all time constants and other parameters in which time appears by a factor of 12.

Beyond Euler

Euler integration is simple and adequate for many applications. In models of social and human systems the errors in initial conditions, parameters, and especially model specification are large and the data against which you might compare model output are often corrupted by significant measurement error. In such situations, Euler's errors are inconsequential. Spend your time improving the model rather than fine-tuning the numerical integration method. However, there are some systems and some model purposes, particularly in engineering and physics, where Euler is not appropriate, either because the errors it generates are too large or the time step required to gain the needed accuracy slow model execution too much.

There are many more advanced techniques for numerical integration of differential equations. The most popular are the Runge-Kutta methods. Euler's method assumes the rates at time t remain constant over the entire interval to time t + dt, that is, that the average rate over the interval equals the rate at the start of the interval. The Runge-Kutta method finds a better approximation of the average rate between t and t + dt. First, provisional estimates of the stocks at t + dt are calculated by Euler's method. Next the rates at time t + dt are calculated from the Euler estimate of the stocks at time t + dt. The estimated rates at time t and t + dt are averaged and used to calculate the value of the stocks at t + dt. This method, known as second-order Runge-Kutta, gives a more accurate approximation of the actual average rates over the interval [t, t + dt].

Higher-order Runge-Kutta methods work in essentially the same way but estimate the average rate over subintervals within [t, t + dt] to yield a still better approximation. Most simulation packages offer fourth-order Runge-Kutta.

While Runge-Kutta requires more computation per time step, the accuracy of the approximation is much greater than Euler's method. Integration errors for a comparable choice of dt are much smaller and propagate at much smaller rates, allowing the modeler to use a larger time step or gain additional accuracy.

Error Control and Variable Time Step Methods

In nonlinear systems the dominant feedback loops driving the dynamics can change as the system evolves. A system can be changing slowly then suddenly shift to a new regime where change is very fast. In such a system the optimal time step may vary depending on the speed of the dynamics. During calm periods where change is slow a large time step would best trade off integration error, round-off error, and computation time. But that large time step would yield large integration errors during periods of turbulence. Setting the time step to a small value appropriate to the turbulent regime, however, might cause your model to run far too slowly or to generate too much round-off error.

Variable time step methods automate the heuristic test for integration error in which you cut dt in half and ask whether the behavior changes in a significant way. The user specifies an error tolerance and an initial time step. The simulation procedure calculates the next values of the stocks using the initial time step and also calculates them using half the initial step size. If the difference between the two results is too large the time step is cut in half again and the process is repeated until the error falls within the specified tolerance. If the error is very small the time step can be increased (but usually only up to the initial step size). The simulation continues, testing for and controlling the error at each point.[2] Variable step size methods minimize simulation time subject to the constraint on the magnitude of the errors, even as the dynamics speed or slow.[3] Many simulation packages offer variable step size fourth-order Runge-Kutta, an excellent method for situations where high accuracy is required, such as simulations of physical systems where the laws governing the rates, initial conditions, and parameters are known precisely and where small errors matter to the purpose.

Choosing your Integration Method

You can test whether Euler integration is acceptable by running the model with a higher-order integration method (using the same time step or using a variable time step method). If there is no significant change in the results, then Euler integration is fine.

A caveat: Because higher-order methods such as Runge-Kutta perform calculations between the specified time steps, care must be exercised when your models include discontinuous events. System dynamics models are generally formulated

---

[2]These methods only control the local error, that is, the error introduced in the current time step. Modelers, however, are concerned with the global (cumulative total) error between the simulated and exact solutions. Though strictly speaking the global error is unknown, it can be estimated. Reducing it below some tolerance, however, requires going back and resimulating from some earlier point in time. Controlling the local error ensures that the global error also remains within certain tolerances for many but not all systems.

[3]Some systems contain mixtures of very fast and very slow dynamics. For example, prices in a stock market adjust very rapidly to changes in buy and sell orders, while the underlying economic variables that drive changes in corporate earnings change much more slowly. If the differences in time constants governing the fast and slow dynamics are very large, the system is said to be "stiff." Ordinary numerical methods can fail in stiff systems because the time step required to capture the fast dynamics must be so small that the evolution of the slow variables is corrupted by round-off error. The numerical methods texts referenced above discuss stiff system problems and methods specifically designed to solve them.

in continuous time but often include discontinuous elements such as test functions (e.g., a step or pulse), random noise, or queuing-type elements. The implementation of policies can also introduce sudden shocks. These discontinuities create no problems for Euler integration, where the rates now depend only on the current state of the system. Care must be taken, however, that the higher-order integration method you are using does not average out these discontinuous changes. Consult the documentation for your simulation software to see how discontinuous events and random noise are handled in the higher-order methods.

CHALLENGE

Choosing a Time Step

Consider the first-order linear negative feedback system in which the state of the system S adjusts to the desired state S^* with an adjustment time AT:

$$S = INTEGRAL(NCS, S_{t_0}) \qquad\qquad\qquad (A-13)$$

$$NCS = (S^* - S)/AT \qquad\qquad\qquad (A-14)$$

where NCS is the net change in the state of the system.

Assume $S^* = 100$ and $S_{t_0} = 0$. The analytic solution of the system, presented in section 8.3, is

$$S_t = S^* - (S^* - S_{t_0}) * exp(-t/AT) \qquad\qquad\qquad (A-15)$$

Assume the adjustment time is 1 time unit. Simulate the system with Euler integration. What happens when the time step is 1? What happens when it is 2? How small does the time step have to be to give a good approximation to the analytic solution? Implement the analytic solution as an auxiliary variable in the model and create a variable to calculate the fractional error between the simulated and analytic solutions. When the time step is small relative to AT, do the errors grow larger or smaller over time? Repeat the analysis with the fourth-order Runge-Kutta method. How does Runge-Kutta affect the sensitivity of the simulation to the time step? Does it improve on the accuracy of Euler significantly when the time step is small?

SUMMARY

Guidelines for Numerical Integration

- Select a time step for your model that is a power of 2, such as 2, 1, 0.5, 0.25, etc.
- Make sure your time step is evenly divisible into the interval between data points or other periodic exogenous events.
- Select a time step one-fourth to one-tenth as large as the smallest time constant in your model.
- Test for integration error by cutting the time step in half and running the model again. If there are no significant differences (judged relative to your purpose), then the original value is fine. If the behavior changes

significantly, continue to cut the time step in half until the differences in behavior no longer matter.

- Note that Euler integration is almost always fine in models of social and human systems where there are large errors in parameters, initial conditions, historical data, and especially model structure. Test the robustness of your results to Euler by running the model with a higher-order method such as fourth-order Runge-Kutta. If there are no significant differences, Euler is fine.

- Consult a numerical methods text, your software manual, or an expert when in doubt.

Appendix B

Noise

Most variables, such as industrial production (Figure 17-1), often appear to be somewhat "noisy." We see part of the behavior as systematic—for example, the growth trend and cyclical movements in industrial production—and part as noise. What we judge to be a systematic pattern of behavior and what we judge to be meaningless random variation depends on our perspective and purpose. If the purpose of your model were to understand the determinants of long-run economic growth, movements in output other than the growth trend, including the business cycle, might be considered noise and excluded from your analysis. If your concern were the business cycle, your model would explain these cyclical movements, but you might treat the month-to-month movements around the business cycle as noise. An even more detailed model, however, might explain these rapid variations in output as part of the feedback structure. One person's noise is another's signal, depending on the questions in which each person is interested.

The rate equations in system dynamics models capture the decision-making processes of the agents or the physical and biological laws that cause change in system states. Because all models are approximations, the model decision rules do not capture all the sources of change in the actual flows. As explained in section 4.3.2, noise is the label we apply to that part of the actual decision stream our model cannot explain. Noise measures our ignorance.

For example, production starts in the supply chain model developed in chapter 19 depend on the firm's labor force, the workweek, and labor productivity:

$$\text{Production Start Rate} = \text{Labor} * \text{Workweek} * \text{Labor Productivity} \qquad \text{(B-1)}$$

The workweek and productivity might themselves be endogenous variables, dependent on factors such as schedule pressure, worker experience, and equipment quality. The workweek and productivity represent averages: Some workers are more productive than others; some put in more hours than others.

The actual start rate will rarely equal the average value. One worker's baby kept him up all night, so he is less productive today. Another discovers a way to speed up her work, boosting productivity. An unexpected machine problem slashes the productivity of a third. For some purposes, including these variations adds little to the dynamics and only makes it more difficult to understand model behavior. In these cases, the deterministic dynamics are sufficient. Often, however, unpredictable variations around the average values play a critical role in the dynamics and must be modeled. As a general modeling strategy you should first understand the dynamics of your model without noise—even when noise is important. The response of the model to shocks can be assessed through idealized test inputs such as the step function, pulse, ramp, and sine wave. Once you understand how and why the system responds as it does you can consider how more realistic inputs such as noise affect the dynamics.

Variations around the average value of a variable are usually modeled as some type of random process. Noise represents those variables and states of the system we either cannot capture in the model or choose to omit. There are reasons for the variations in productivity not captured by the model, but we don't have the information needed to capture them endogenously. We don't have a way to model when a worker will lose sleep because the baby cried all night.

If the unmodeled variations in productivity were important to the model purpose the formulation for productivity could be modified to include random variations around the average, which itself could be an endogenous or exogenous variable:

$$\text{Productivity} = \text{Average Productivity} * \text{Random Effects on Productivity} \qquad \text{(B-2)}$$

How should the random effects be formulated? You graph the productivity data supplied by your client (Figure B-1) and find productivity varies randomly around a constant level. Next, you plot the distribution of productivity. The values closely approximate a normal distribution with a mean of about 0.25 widgets/person-hour and a standard deviation of 0.0123 widgets/person-hour, about 5% of the mean.

Given the data in Figure B-1 you then specify the random variations in productivity as

$$\begin{aligned}&\text{Random Effects on Productivity}\\&\quad = \text{NORMAL}(1, \text{Standard Deviation in Productivity})\end{aligned} \qquad \text{(B-3)}$$

The NORMAL(Mean, Standard Deviation) function generates, every time step, a value drawn randomly from a normal distribution with the specified mean and standard deviation.[1] You set the mean of the distribution to 1 and the standard deviation to 0.05. Since the random input has a multiplicative effect, productivity will be normally distributed with a mean of 0.25 and standard deviation of 0.0125, as observed in the data.[2]

---

[1] All simulation software packages include built-in functions to generate random variables including the normal and uniform distributions. Because the pseudorandom numbers generated by any software package are not truly random, however, caution must be exercised to ensure that they conform to the required statistical properties. See Hellekalek (1998).

[2] The normal distribution generates values over $[-\infty, \infty]$ so occasionally productivity as specified in equation (B-3) would become negative. A robust formulation requires Random Effects on Productivity ≥ 0. This can be accomplished by truncating the distribution with a MAX function. Alternatively, the random effects could be specified as a lognormal distribution.

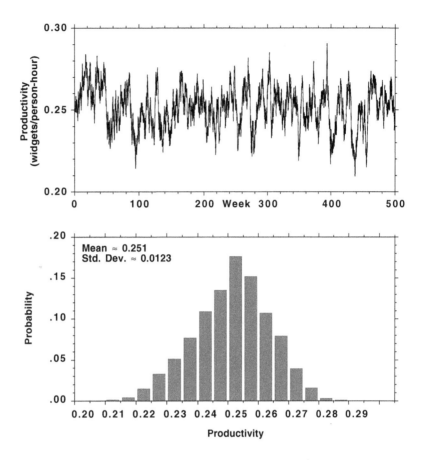

FIGURE B-1

Hypothetical data for labor productivity

Top: Time series.
Bottom: Histogram showing the distribution of productivity.

To your surprise simulated productivity (Figure B-2) looks little like the actual productivity data in Figure B-1. Simulated productivity does conform to the normal distribution with the proper mean and standard deviation but it changes too fast, jumping far too quickly from value to value.

The problem is subtle. Random number generators such as the NORMAL function yield a new value every time step and successive values are independent. History doesn't matter—the values that have come before have no effect on the next value drawn from the distribution, just as the last result on a roulette wheel has no bearing on the next. The values generated by the NORMAL() function are said to be IID—independently and identically distributed. Independence means the next value of the random effect can differ by any amount from the last value. Productivity might be very high right now, but independence means one instant later it could be very low. The time step for the simulation is 0.125 weeks. A new value for productivity, completely independent of the last, is chosen eight times a week. It is this frequent sampling from an independent process that explains why simulated productivity in Figure B-2 jumps around far too fast.

Engineers call the random variations generated by IID processes "white noise." Imagine you have just arrived at a lively party. Each guest is speaking in a perfectly intelligible manner (at least early in the evening), but when all these sounds reach your ear at once, the result is an indecipherable cacophony. Analogously, you can think of noise as the sum of tones of all frequencies, from the

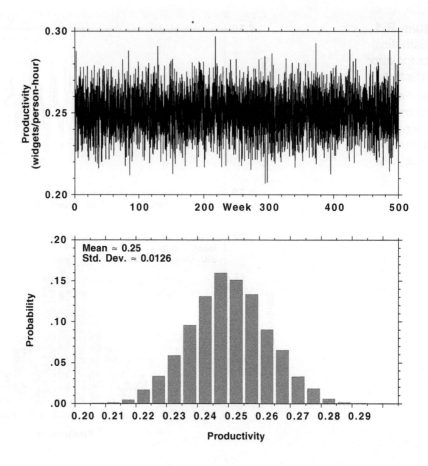

FIGURE B-2

Simulated labor productivity

Top: Time series. *Bottom:* Histogram showing the probability distribution of simulated productivity, generated by equation (B-3).

deepest bass note to the highest high C. Because white noise contains all frequencies in equal measure its current value contains no information about future values, even in the next instant.

While convenient statistically, the white noise assumption of independence does not hold in the real world. Real systems have inertia. Productivity, customer demand, the weather, and all other real quantities cannot change infinitely fast. Suppose a machine breaks down, lowering productivity. Productivity remains depressed at least until the machine can be repaired. The effects of the random shock persist for some period of time. Similar persistence applies, to varying degrees, to all causes of variations in productivity and to all variations in any quantity. The temperature in 1 hour obviously can't be too different from the temperature now. Similarly, the temperature tomorrow, the next day, and a week from now all depend, partially, on the temperature today. Temperature changes only slowly because it depends on the quantity of heat in the air, a stock that, that like all stocks, changes only gradually as it accumulates its inflows and outflows. Similarly, the stock and flow structure of all real processes gives them a certain amount of inertia. Consequently, real noise processes don't contain all frequencies in equal measure. The strength of the high frequencies diminishes above some point, just as a loudspeaker cannot generate sound at frequencies higher than, say, 20,000 cycles/second (Hertz) because the inertia of the mechanical elements in the speaker limits how fast it can vibrate.

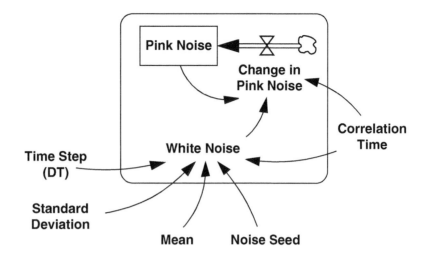

FIGURE B-3
Pink noise:
structure

It is therefore necessary to model noise as a process with inertia, or memory—as a process in which the next value is not independent of the last but depends in some fashion on history. Realistic noise processes with persistence are termed "pink noise." Compared to white noise, which contains all frequencies in equal measure, pink noise filters out the high frequencies at the blue end of the spectrum, leaving more of the reddish frequencies. The challenge is to formulate a simple model of randomness that allows the modeler to specify the degree of persistence, or equivalently, the *power spectrum* of the noise (roughly, the amplitude or strength of each frequency).[3] The statistical properties of the resulting noise should also be insensitive to the choice of the time step (within broad limits).

The inertia in real variables implies the existence of at least one stock in any noise generating process. A simple formulation for pink noise begins with white noise, then smooths it using some type of information delay. The information delay represents the sources of inertia in the noise generating process. The simplest formulation is first-order exponential smoothing. As described in chapter 11, first-order exponential smoothing means the current value is the exponentially weighted sum of all past values of the input. Figure B-3 shows the structure for first-order pink noise, also known as first-order autocorrelated noise.

---

[3]The power of any signal is the energy it contains per time interval and is the integral of the squared signal. The power spectrum is the distribution of the total power by frequency. Pure white noise contains constant power in all frequency ranges. The power contained in the range from 1 Hz to 2 Hz is the same as that in the range from 1001 to 1002 Hz. Since white noise spans all frequencies from 0 to ∞, it contains infinite power, an impossibility. All real processes have finite power, meaning the power per frequency interval must eventually fall to zero as the frequency rises. A *frequency domain* analysis decomposes a time series into sine waves of different frequencies and phases. Frequency domain tools such as Fourier analysis measure the power in each frequency in any time series; other methods such as autocorrelation and cross-correlation functions, ARIMA models, and vector autoregressive models help modelers understand the way current values of a time series depend on its own past values and possibly the past values of other variables. Warner (1998) provides an elementary treatment of spectral analysis; Granger and Newbold (1977) provide a more mathematical approach covering frequency and time domain methods. See also Franses (1998).

Pink noise is formed by first-order exponential smoothing of a white noise input. The delay time is the correlation time constant:

Pink Noise = INTEGRAL(Change in Pink Noise, Mean)   (B-4)

Change in Pink Noise = (White Noise − Pink Noise)/Correlation Time   (B-5)

The white noise input is constructed from a uniform distribution on the interval $[−0.5, 0.5]$, sampled every time step of length dt.[4] The user specifies the mean and standard deviation of the pink noise process, which determines the mean and standard deviation of the white noise input:

White Noise = Mean + Standard Deviation * [(24 * Correlation Time/dt)$^{0.5}$]
        * UNIFORM(−0.5, 0.5, Noise Seed)   (B-6)

where the UNIFORM(Min, Max, Seed) function generates a sequence of values drawn from a uniform distribution on the interval [Min, Max]. The user also specifies the noise seed. By fixing the noise seed, every simulation will generate exactly the same sequence of random values, facilitating comparison of simulations with different policies and parameters. Changing the noise seed changes the realizations of the random process but not its statistical properties. The scaling factor $(24 * \text{Correlation Time/dt})^{0.5}$ adjusts the amplitude of the white noise so that the standard deviation of the pink noise output equals the specified value.[5]

In continuous time, noise can include all frequencies. Since simulations proceed by discrete time steps, the highest frequency in any model variable is twice the time step dt (to complete one cycle of *up-down-up* requires a minimum of two time steps). Exponential smoothing attenuates high frequencies. It is known as a low pass filter because it lets low frequencies pass essentially full strength but progressively attenuates cycle periods near or shorter than the time constant. The longer the correlation time, the greater the attenuation at any frequency. Thus, the longer the correlation time constant, the larger the amplitude of the white noise must be. The less frequently random values are sampled (the larger dt), the smaller

---

[4]This formulation for pink noise assumes the model is solved by Euler integration (appendix A). Higher-order integration methods such as Runge-Kutta change the power spectrum and other properties of noise and should generally be avoided in models with random disturbances.

[5]The pink noise formulation given here smooths a *uniformly* distributed white noise stream. Nevertheless, the distribution of the resulting pink noise is asymptotically *normal*. An alternate formulation smooths a normally distributed white noise signal to yield pink noise that is always Gaussian:

$$\text{White Noise} = M + \left[S^2 * \frac{(2 − (dt/T_c))}{(dt/T_c)} \right]^{0.5} * \text{NORMAL}(0, 1, \text{Noise Seed}) \qquad (B\text{-}6')$$

where M is the mean, S is the standard deviation, T_c is the correlation time constant, and NORMAL(0, 1, Noise Seed) generates a Gaussian distribution with mean 0 and variance 1.

The structure of this alternate pink noise formulation is the same as the one above; the only difference is the distribution of the white noise and the resulting scaling factor to ensure the pink noise has the specified standard deviation. (You can easily derive the scaling factors for each formulation by expanding the Euler integration for the pink noise variable as the weighted sum of the white noise at time t, t − dt, t − 2dt, etc.). If you had strong data showing the unconditional distribution of noise in a process to be Gaussian, the formulation in equation (B-6') would be preferable. In practice, it is unlikely the data would allow you to discriminate between the two forms.

the amplitude of the white noise must be, because less frequent sampling means the power in the white noise is concentrated in lower frequencies that are not attenuated by the smoothing process.

The correlation time constant captures the degree of inertia in the noise process. In first-order pink noise the correlation between current and past values decays exponentially with a time constant equal to the correlation time.[6]

The data shown in Figure B-1 were generated by the pink noise structure with a standard deviation of 5%, correlation time constant of 4 weeks, and time step of 0.125 weeks.

Comparing Figures B-1 and B-2 it is clear that the (unconditional) distributions of the two noise inputs are about the same. The pink noise structure generates a distribution that is essentially normal, with the specified mean and standard deviation (the reported mean and standard deviation differ slightly from the specified values because the sample of data is finite). However, successive values of pink noise are correlated with past values, so the pink noise process does not change as rapidly as the independent, uncorrelated values generated by the normal distribution in equation (B-3).

Does it matter? Yes. Noise consists of signals of various frequencies and amplitudes. Dynamic systems act as filters, selectively attenuating some frequencies while amplifying others. Many systems resonate strongly at certain frequencies. If the noise contains significant power near the resonant frequency, the system will fluctuate, sometimes violently. The Tacoma Narrows bridge, in the state of Washington, vividly demonstrated the power of a system to amplify random noise. Built in 1940, people immediately noticed its tendency to swing in even light winds. On November 7, the bridge, driven by modest winds of about 40 miles per hour, began to oscillate through huge swings. A few hours later it collapsed. Unknown to the designers, the suspension span had a strong resonance near the frequencies in the vortices created as the wind passed around it. A new span was built on the same towers, but this time stiffened so its resonance peak was smaller and far from the frequencies created by the wind. It still stands today. Similar resonance phenomena arise in social and economic systems, as illustrated by the supply chain models in chapters 17–20: Small random variations in customer orders induce large fluctuations in production near the natural frequency of each system.

To illustrate, Figure B-4 and Table B-1 compare simulations of the inventory–workforce model developed in chapter 19 with the two noise inputs in Figures B-1 and B-2.[7] In both simulations, customer orders are constant and the random

---

[6]Occasionally data analysis will show that the autocorrelation function is not well approximated by exponential decay. In these cases, higher-order pink noise formulations may be used, formed by cascading several first-order pink noise delays in series (see chapter 11). The standard deviations of each stage must be scaled appropriately so the output has the proper standard deviation. In practice, it is rarely necessary to use higher-order noise processes. Complex autocorrelations and cross-correlations among the exogenous random effects in your model suggest there is significant feedback and stock and flow structure you should probably be modeling explicitly and endogenously.

[7]The model used in this appendix is identical to the inventory–workforce model developed in chapter 19 except that expected productivity, used in the determination of desired labor, is modeled as a first-order information delay of actual productivity with a time constant of 13 weeks.

FIGURE B-4

Response of inventory–workforce model to white and pink noise

The system resonates near its natural frequency when driven by noise. The noise input in both cases has a standard deviation of 5%. Most of the power in white noise is contained in the high frequencies, which are attenuated by the system. Pink noise contains more power near the system's natural frequency, causing large cycles.

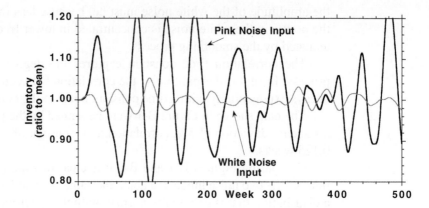

FIGURE B-4

Response of inventory–workforce model to white and pink noise

The system resonates near its natural frequency when driven by noise. The noise input in both cases has a standard deviation of 5%. Most of the power in white noise is contained in the high frequencies, which are attenuated by the system. Pink noise contains more power near the system's natural frequency, causing large cycles.

variations in productivity are the only perturbations disturbing the system. Both noise streams have the same standard deviation and distribution. The only difference is the degree of autocorrelation. The pink noise signal has a correlation time constant of 4 weeks, while the white noise signal is independent (no autocorrelation).

The response of the production system to the two noise streams is very different. Very little happens when the system is perturbed by white noise. There are small variations in inventories, the workforce, and other variables, but the system attenuates nearly all of the noise because most of the power is concentrated in the high frequencies. The independent variations in productivity cause large changes in production starts from dt to dt. Since dt is 1/8 week, this means production starts vary widely from day to day. Low output today is more than likely to be offset by higher than normal values within a few days. Inventory absorbs most of the short-term variations and there is little need for the firm to alter its workforce.

Pink noise, however, means that when output is low today it is likely to remain low for a few weeks. During this time, inventories can fall significantly, forcing the firm to hire workers to expand output and triggering the system's latent oscillatory response to shocks. The variations in productivity are too slow to be absorbed by inventory or filtered out by the hiring delays. The noise contains significant power near the system's natural frequency of about 1 year. Consequently, the system resonates strongly—the standard deviation of production starts is 7.6% of the mean, even though the standard deviation of the noise input is only 5%.

Table B-1 shows the standard deviation as a fraction of the mean value for key variables in both the white noise case and the pink noise case. Under white noise, the system strongly attenuates the random shocks. The standard deviation of inventory is less than 2%, showing how inventory buffers the system from the high frequency variations in production starts caused by the white noise. The standard deviations of production, inventory, and labor are all much less than that of productivity. Only the hiring rate amplifies the white noise input.

Under correlated noise, however, inventory, workforce, and other key variables all fluctuate by more than the variation in productivity. The standard deviation of hiring is six times greater than when the system is driven by white noise and 13 times greater than the standard deviation in productivity.

	Standard Deviation/Mean Pink Noise	Standard Deviation/Mean White Noise	Ratio
Production Starts	0.0760	0.0511	1.49
Production	0.0547	0.0087	6.30
Inventory	0.1055	0.0160	6.59
Labor	0.0591	0.0085	6.99
Hiring Rate	0.6539	0.1097	5.96

TABLE B-1
Autocorrelated noise alters the amplification generated by a system.

Various statistical tools can help you estimate the autocorrelation time constant, if sufficient data are available. Most regression and times series software packages readily compute the autocorrelation function, showing the correlation between the current value of the variable and its values at each interval in the past. From the autocorrelation function you can estimate the time constant for the pink noise function. If numerical data are unavailable, use your best judgment and conduct extensive sensitivity tests.

To illustrate, Oliva (1996) developed a model of a bank's retail loan operation to explore the determinants of service quality (chapters 14 and 21). Customer demand and worker absenteeism, two important inputs to the model, both exhibited small variations around their averages (the standard deviations were less than 4% of the means). To model these random variations Oliva estimated the autocorrelation functions for each, finding a correlation time constant of about 2 weeks for absenteeism and about 1 week for orders. That is, customer orders this week were weakly dependent on orders last week, but absenteeism tended to persist for longer periods. Oliva also found that the random variations in orders and absenteeism were independent of each other, so each could be modeled as a separate pink noise process.[8] Oliva was then able to simulate the effects of various policies affecting service quality while the model system was perturbed with realistic patterns of orders and absenteeism.

Without random noise the loan center remained in equilibrium with demand and capacity in balance and constant service quality. However, when realistic random variations in demand and the workforce were added to the model, quality standards tended to erode over time, even when capacity was sufficient to meet demand on average and even though the random shocks were small. The random

---

[8]Sometimes different noise processes are not independent but are cross-correlated. For example, unpredictable short-run variations in interest rates might be correlated with random shocks in commodity prices. It is a simple matter to incorporate such cross-correlations (e.g., the shocks perturbing a variable can be modeled as an appropriately weighted sum of variable-specific noise and the noise with which it is correlated). Multivariate time series tools such as vector autoregressive models and cross-spectral analysis can help you identify the correlational structure among the variables and their histories (see the references in note 3). However, a complicated set of cross-correlations suggests there is important feedback structure you should probably be modeling explicitly. A good model generates the variances, autocorrelations, and cross-correlations observed in the real system without being forced by too many exogenous inputs.

variations in demand and capacity meant the bank occasionally found itself short of capacity. Loan center personnel responded by spending less time with each customer so they could clear the backlog of work each day. These reductions in time per customer gradually became embedded in worker norms. Management interpreted the reduction in time per customer as improvements in productivity caused by their get-tough management policies, unaware that spending less time with customers reduced service quality, eventually feeding back through customer defections to other banks. Oliva found that reducing the time spent per customer caused a significant reduction in the value of loans issued, directly reducing bank revenue. Lower revenues then fed back to financial pressure leading to staff reductions and still more pressure to spend less time on each customer. The resulting positive feedback, if unchecked, could act as a death spiral for the organization. Small, random variations in capacity and orders elicited the latent self-reinforcing quality erosion created by the policies of the bank and the behavior of its workers and managers.

CHALLENGE

Exploring Noise

Use the inventory–workforce model and pink noise structure to explore the sensitivity of model behavior to the noise correlation time and simulation time step.

1.   Figure B-4 and Table B-1 show that increasing the noise correlation time from 0 (the white noise case) to 4 weeks increases the oscillatory response of the inventory–workforce model. Explore how the system responds to even longer correlation times. Does the amplitude of the production cycle continue to increase? What happens if the correlation time is very long? Why?

2.   In all the simulations above the time step was 0.125 weeks. Explore how the behavior of pink noise and of the inventory–workforce model depend on the time step. Can you correct the problems caused by rapid changes in white noise by using a longer time step? Why/why not?

3.   So far only one source of noise has been considered. Does the behavior of the model change if you also assume customer orders vary randomly? Assume customer orders vary randomly with a small standard deviation around a constant average. Also assume productivity and orders are independent of one another. Assume to start that the correlation time for orders is 13 weeks (one-quarter year) but conduct sensitivity tests. How does the inclusion of multiple sources of noise alter the behavior of the model? Does it alter any of the policy conclusions you reached in chapter 19 regarding ways to improve the stability of the system? Explain.

Summary

Guidelines for the Use of Noise

- It is usually best to omit noise until you understand the dynamics generated by the feedback structure of your model. Use idealized test inputs such as the step, pulse, ramp, and sine wave to develop your understanding of the system's response to shocks, then add more realistic inputs such as noise or historical data as necessary.

- After you understand the dynamics of your model, ask yourself whether random variations in the environment are likely to be important. If so, you must add random variations at key points. You should test the effects of random variations on your conclusions and policy recommendations even if you think they probably won't matter. If they don't matter, you can omit them.

- In principle, effects outside the boundary of your model can perturb every variable. All parameters are candidates for the inclusion of some type of noise, and the reported values of all state variables include some measurement error. You do not need to include noise in every variable and parameter. Decide which are the most important sources of random variation to include. Important sources will be those parameters that are *both* variable in the real system and whose variation matters to the dynamics. There is no point in including noise in a parameter that has little impact on the behavior of the model.

- All real noise sources have inertia and attenuate high frequencies. Never use white noise in your models. Use the pink noise structure to model random shocks. Estimate the distribution, standard deviation, and correlation time constant from the data. Use your best judgment when numerical data are not available.

- If you have multiple sources of noise in your model, consider whether they are independent or correlated. Independence is convenient but not always accurate. Use the available data to estimate the cross-correlations of multiple noise inputs.

- Be sure your results are not sensitive to the choice of time step. As with any structure, the time step should be small relative to the smallest time constant in the model, including the correlation time for any pink noise processes (see appendix A).

- You can compare different sensitivity and policy tests in models with random effects by using the same noise seed in each simulation. Since the sequence of random shocks will be exactly the same in each simulation with the same noise seeds, any differences among them must be due to your policy or parameter changes.

- When using random inputs be sure to run your model long enough, or enough times, to ensure your results are not contingent on the particular realizations of the random processes. Calculate the distributions of the variables over long time periods or over a large sample of simulations. Don't assume any one simulation is representative of all.

- As with any model, conduct extensive sensitivity tests to be sure you assess the robustness of your results to plausible variations in assumptions, including assumptions about the statistical properties of any noise inputs.

References

Aarts, E. and J. Lenstra (eds.) (1997) Local Search in Combinatorial Optimization. Chichester, England: John Wiley and Sons.

Abdel-Hamid, T. and S. Madnick (1989a) Software productivity: Potential, actual, and perceived, System Dynamics Review 5(2), 93-113.

Abdel-Hamid, T. and S. Madnick (1989b) Lessons learned from modeling the dynamics of software project management, Communications of the ACM 32(12), 1426-1438.

Abdel-Hamid, T. and S. Madnick (1989c) Software productivity: Potential, actual, and perceived, System Dynamics Review 5(2), 93-113.

Abdel-Hamid, T. and S. Madnick (1990) The elusive silver lining: How we fail to learn from software development failures, Sloan Management Review 32(1), 39-48.

Abdel-Hamid, T. and S. Madnick (1991) Software Project Dynamics: An Integrated Approach. Englewood Cliffs, NJ: Prentice-Hall.

Achi, Z., A. Doman, O. Sibony, J. Sinha, and S. Witt (1995) The paradox of fast growth tigers, McKinsey Quarterly 3, 4-17.

Adams, H. (1918) The Education of Henry Adams. Boston: Houghton-Mifflin.

Akerlof, G. (1970) The market for lemons: Quality uncertainty and the market mechanism, Quarterly Journal of Economics 84(3), 488-500.

Aldrich, J. and F. Nelson (1984) Linear Probability, Logit, and Probit Models. Newbury Park, CA: Sage Publications.

Alfeld, L. and A. Graham (1976) Introduction to Urban Dynamics. Waltham, MA: Pegasus Communications.

Allen, K. (1993) Maintenance Diffusion at Du Pont: A System Dynamics Perspective. MS thesis, MIT Sloan School of Management, Cambridge MA 02142 (unpublished).

Allison, J., A. Charnes, W. Cooper, and T. Sueyoshi (1994) Uses of modeling in science and society, in Wallace, W. (ed.) Ethics in Modeling. White Plains, NY: Pergamon, 11-36.

Andersen, D. and J. Sturis (1988) Chaotic structures in generic management models: Pedagogical principles and examples, System Dynamics Review 4(1-2), 218-245.

Anderson, E. (1996) VCR battle of the formats model. Memo, MIT Sloan School of Management, Cambridge, MA 02142 (unpublished).

Anderson, E., C. Fine, and G. Parker (1996) Upstream volatility in the supply chain: The machine tool industry as a case study. Working paper, Freeman School of Management, Tulane University, New Orleans, LA. Available through <http://faculty.freeman.tulane.edu/gparker/index.html>.

Anderson, R. (1994) The Croonian lecture, 1994. Populations, infectious disease and immunity: A very nonlinear world, Phil. Trans. of the Royal Society of London B 346, 457-505.

Anderson, R. and W. Dewald (1994) Replication and scientific standards in applied economics a decade after the *Journal of Money, Credit and Banking* project, Federal Reserve Bank of St. Louis Review 76(6), 79-83.

Ando, A. and F. Modigliani (1963) The "life-cycle" hypothesis of saving: Aggregate implications and tests, American Economic Review 53, 55-84.

Angell, J. (1997) Annual and Seasonal Global Temperature Anomalies in the Troposphere and Low Stratosphere, 1958–1996. Air Resources Laboratory, National Oceanic and Atmospheric Administration, Silver Spring, MD 20910. Available through <http://cdiac.esd.ornl.gov/trends/trends.htm>.

Argote, L. and D. Epple (1990) Learning curves in manufacturing. Science 247 (23 Feb) 920-924.

Argyris, C. (1985) Strategy, Change, and Defensive Routines. Boston: Pitman.

Argyris, C., R. Putnam, and D. Smith (1985) Action Science: Concepts, Methods, and Skills for Research and Intervention. San Francisco: Jossey-Bass.

Argyris, C. and D. Schön (1978) Organizational Learning: A Theory of Action Approach. Reading, MA: Addison-Wesley.

Argyris, C. and D. Schön (1996) Organizational Learning II, Reading, MA: Addison-Wesley.

Armstrong, J. (1985) Long Range Forecasting: From Crystal Ball to Computer. New York: John Wiley.

Arrow, K. (1962) The economic implications of learning by doing, Review of Economic Studies 29, 155-173.

Arthur, W. (1994) Increasing Returns and Path Dependence in the Economy. Ann Arbor, MI: University of Michigan Press.

Asch, S. (1951) Effects of group pressure upon the modification and distribution of judgment, in Guetzkow, H. (ed.) Groups, Leadership and Men. Pittsburgh: Carnegie Press.

Asch, S. (1956) Studies of independence and conformity: A minority of one against a unanimous majority, Psychological Monographs 70(9).

Atkinson, K. (1985) Elementary Numerical Analysis. New York: John Wiley.

Axelrod, R. (1976) The Structure of Decision: The Cognitive Maps of Political Elites. Princeton: Princeton University Press.

Ayer, A. (1952) Language, Truth, and Logic. New York: Dover.

Backus, G. (1996) The Dynamics of U.S. Electric Utility Deregulation, U.S. Department of Energy, Office of Utility Technology, Washington, DC, August 1996.

Bahn, P. and J. Flenley (1992) Easter Island, Earth Island. London: Thames and Hudson.

Bakken, B. (1993) Learning and Transfer of Understanding in Dynamic Decision Environments. PhD thesis, MIT Sloan School of Management, Cambridge, MA 02142 (unpublished).

Barabba, V. and N. Pudar (1997) Communication for action: GM's dialogue decision process, Strategic Communication Management 1(1), 24-29.

Barhen J., V. Protopopescu, and D. Reister (1997) TRUST: A deterministic algorithm for global optimization, Science 276 (16 May), 1094-1097.

Barlas Y. (1989) Multiple tests for validation of system dynamics type of simulation models, European Journal of Operational Research 42(1), 59-87.

Barlas Y. (1990) An autocorrelation function-test for output validation, Simulation 55(1), 7-16.

Barlas Y. (1996) Formal aspects of model validity and validation in system dynamics, System Dynamics Review 12(3), 183-210.

Bass, F. (1969) A new product growth model for consumer durables, Management Science 15, 215-227.

Bass, F., T. Krishnan, and D. Jain (1994) Why the Bass model fits without decision variables, Marketing Science 13(3), 203-223.

Becker, G. (1976) The Economic Approach to Human Behavior. Chicago: University of Chicago Press.

Beckhard, R. and R. Harris (1987) Organizational Transitions: Managing Complex Change, 2nd ed. Reading, MA: Addison-Wesley.

Bell, J. and P. Senge (1980) System Dynamics and Scientific Method, in Randers, J. (ed.), Elements of the System Dynamics Method. Waltham, MA: Pegasus Communications.

Berndt, E. (1991) The Practice of Econometrics: Classic and Contemporary. Reading, MA: Addison-Wesley.

Bessler, D. and J. Brandt (1992) An analysis of forecasts of livestock prices, Journal of Economic Behavior and Organization 18(2), 249-263.

Blinder, A. (1997) Distinguished lecture on economics in government: What central bankers could learn from academics—and vice versa, Journal of Economic Perspectives 11(2), 3-19.

Bomberger, W. and W. Frazer (1981) Interest rates, uncertainty and the Livingston data. Journal of Finance 36, 661-675.

Box, G. and N. Draper (1987) Empirical Model Building and Response Surfaces. New York: John Wiley.

Boyer, C. (1991) A History of Mathematics, 2nd ed. New York: John Wiley.

Brehmer, B. (1980) In one word: Not from experience, Acta Psychologica 45, 223-241.

Brehmer, B. (1989) Feedback delays and control in complex dynamic systems, in Milling, P. and E. Zahn (eds.), Computer Based Management of Complex Systems. Berlin: Springer Verlag, 189-196.

Brehmer, B. (1992) Dynamic decision making: Human control of complex systems. Acta Psychologica 81, 211-241.

Brown, G. (1992) Improving education in public schools: Innovative teachers to the rescue, System Dynamics Review 8(1), 83-90.

Brown, L., C. Flavin, and H. Kane (1992) Vital Signs: 1992. New York: W. W. Norton.

Bruner, J. and L. Postman (1949) On the perception of incongruity: A paradigm, Journal of Personality 18, 206-223.

Buchanan, J. and Y. Yoon (1994) The Return to Increasing Returns. Ann Arbor: University of Michigan Press.

Bunn, D. and E. Larsen (eds.) (1997) Systems Modelling for Energy Policy. Chichester, England: John Wiley and Sons.

Bunn, D., E. Larsen, and K. Vlahos (1993) Complementary modelling approaches for analysing several effects of privatisation on electricity investment, Journal of the Operational Research Society 44(10), 957-971.

Burchill, G. and C. Fine (1997) Time versus market orientation in product concept development: Empirically-based theory generation, Management Science 43(4), 465-478.

Burden, R. and J. Faires (1989) Numerical Analysis, 4th ed. Boston, MA: PWS-Kent.

Camerer, C. (1981) General conditions for the success of bootstrapping models, Organizational Behavior and Human Performance 27, 411-422.

Carbone, R. and S. Makridakis (1986) Forecasting when pattern changes occur beyond the historical data, Management Science 32, 257-271.

Carlson, J. (1977) A study of price forecasts, Annals of Economic and Social Measurement 6, 27-56.

Carroll, J., J. Sterman, and A. Marcus (1998) Playing the maintenance game: How mental models drive organizational decisions, in Stern, R. and J. Halpern (eds.), Nonrational Elements of Organizational Decision Making. Ithaca, NY: ILR Press, 99-121.

Cartwright, N. (1983) How the Laws of Physics Lie. Oxford: Clarendon Press.

Cartwright, N. (1991) Replicability, reproducibility and robustness: Comments on Harry Collins, History of Political Economy 23(1), 142-155.

Caskey, J. (1985) Modeling the formation of price expectations: A Bayesian approach, American Economic Review 75, 768-776.

Cavaleri, S. and J. Sterman (1997) Towards evaluation of systems thinking interventions: A case study, System Dynamics Review 13(2), 171-186.

Checkland, P. (1981) Systems Thinking, Systems Practice. Chichester, England: John Wiley and Sons.

Cheng, P. and R. Nisbett (1985) Pragmatic reasoning schema, Cognitive Psychology 17, 391-416.

Churchman, C. (1973) Reliability of models in the social sciences, Interfaces 4(1), 1-12.

Cobb, J. and H. Daly (1989) For the Common Good. Boston, MA: Beacon Press.

Cohen, J. (1995) How Many People Can the Earth Support? New York: W. W. Norton.

Cohen, J. (1998) AIDS therapies—Exploring how to get at and eradicate hidden HIV, Science 279 (20 Mar), 1854-1855.

Collins, H. (1991) The meaning of replication and the science of economics, History of Political Economy 23(1), 123-142.

Commodity Research Bureau (various years) The CRB Commodity Yearbook. New York: John Wiley.

Congressional Budget Office (1993) Estimating the Effects of NAFTA: An Assessment of the Economic Models and Other Empirical Studies. CIS-J932-27.

Conlisk, J. (1996) Why bounded rationality? Journal of Economic Literature 34, 669-700.

Cooley, P., L. Myers, and D. Hamill (1996) A meta-analysis of estimates of the AIDS incubation distribution, European Journal of Epidemiology 12(3), 229-235.

Cooper, K. (1980) Naval ship production: A claim settled and a framework built, Interfaces 10(6), 20-36.

Cooper, K. (1993a) The rework cycle: Why projects are mismanaged, PM Network (Feb), Project Management Institute, Newtown Square, PA 19073, 5-7.

Cooper, K. (1993b) The rework cycle: How it really works . . . and reworks . . . , PM Network (Feb), Project Management Institute, Newtown Square, PA 19073, 25-28.

Cooper, K. (1993c) The rework cycle: Benchmarks for the project manager, Project Management Journal 24(1), 17-21.

Cooper, K. (1994) The $2,000 hour: How managers influence project performance through the rework cycle, Project Management Journal 25(1), 11-24.

Cooper, K. and T. Mullen (1993) Swords and plowshares: The rework cycles of defense and commercial software development projects, American Programmer 6(5), 41-51.

Coyle, R. (1985) The use of optimization methods for policy design in a system dynamics model, System Dynamics Review 1(1), 81-91.

Coyle, R. (1998) The practice of system dynamics: Milestones, lessons and ideas from 30 years of experience, System Dynamics Review 14(4), 343-365.

Croushore, D. (1997) The Livingston survey: Still useful after all these years, Federal Reserve Bank of Philadelphia Business Review (Mar-Apr), 15-26.

Cubbin, J. and P. Geroski (1987) The convergence of profits in the long-run: Interfirm and interindustry comparisons, Journal of Industrial Economics 35(4), 427-442.

Culotta, E. and D. Koshland (1993) Molecule of the year, Science 262 (24 Dec) 1960.

Cusumano, M., Y. Mylonadis, and R. Rosenbloom (1992) Strategic maneuvering and mass-market dynamics—The triumph of VHS over Beta, Business History Review 66(1), 51-94.

Cusumano, M. and R. Selby (1995) Microsoft Secrets: How the World's Most Powerful Software Company Creates Technology, Shapes Markets, and Manages People. New York: Free Press.

Cyert, R. and J. March (1963/1992) A Behavioral Theory of the Firm. Englewood Cliffs, NJ: Prentice Hall, 2nd ed. Cambridge, MA: Blackwell.

David, H. and H. Wright (1971) Abortion legislation: The Romanian experience, Studies in Family Planning 2(10), 205-210.

Davidsen, P. (1988) A Dynamic Petroleum Life Cycle Model for the United States, 1870-2050. Technical Documentation. MIT System Dynamics Group Memo D-3974, Cambridge, MA 02139.

Davidsen, P., J. Sterman, and G. Richardson (1990) A petroleum life cycle model for the United States with endogenous technology, exploration, recovery, and demand, System Dynamics Review 6(1), 66-93.

Davis, H. and R. Hogarth (1992) Rethinking Management Education: A View from Chicago. Selected paper 72, University of Chicago Graduate School of Business.

Dawes, R. (1979) The robust beauty of improper linear models, American Psychologist 34, 571-582.

de Geus, A. (1997) The Living Company. London: Nicholas Brealey Publishing.

Dewald, W., J. Thursby, and R. Anderson (1986) Replication in empirical economics, the *Journal of Money, Credit, and Banking* project, American Economic Review 76(4), 587-603.

Diacu, F. and P. Holmes (1996) Celestial Encounters: The Origins of Chaos and Stability. Princeton: Princeton University Press.

Diehl, E. (1994) Managerial microworlds as learning support tools, in Morecroft, J. and J. Sterman (eds.), Modeling for Learning Organizations. Portland, OR: Productivity Press, 327-338.

Diehl, E. and J. Sterman (1995) Effects of feedback complexity on dynamic decision making, Organizational Behavior and Human Decision Processes 62(2), 198-215.

Di Stefano, J. (1992) Negotiating needs: Using cybernetics and syntonics to rewrite the script. Proceedings of the 1992 International System Dynamics Conference of the System Dynamics Society, Utrecht, the Netherlands: The System Dynamics Society.

Doman, A., M. Glucksman, and N. Mass (1995) The dynamics of managing a life insurance company, System Dynamics Review 11(3), 219-232.

Dörner, D. (1980) On the difficulties people have in dealing with complexity, Simulation and Games 11(1), 87-106.

Dörner, D. (1996) The Logic of Failure. New York: Metropolitan Books/Henry Holt.

Downs, A. (1991) What Have We Learned From the 1980's Experience? Salomon Bros. Real Estate Investment Report (1 July), p.2.

Downs, A. (1992) Stuck in traffic: Coping with peak-hour traffic congestion. Washington, DC: Brookings Institution; Cambridge, MA: Lincoln Institute of Land Policy.

Doyle, J. (1997) The cognitive psychology of systems thinking, System Dynamics Review 13(3), 253-265.

Doyle, J. and D. Ford (1998) Mental models concepts for system dynamics research, System Dynamics Review 14(1), 3-29.

Draper, F. and M. Swanson (1990) Learner-directed systems education: A successful example, System Dynamics Review 6(2), 209-213.

Dresch, F. and S. Baum (1973) Analysis of the US and USSR Potential for Economic Recovery Following a Nuclear Attack. Menlo Park, CA: Stanford Research Institute.

Dreyfus, H. and S. Dreyfus (1986) Mind over Machine. New York: Free Press.

Dyer, W. (1995) Team Building: Current Issues and New Alternatives. Reading, MA: Addison-Wesley.

Eberlein, R. (1989) Simplification and understanding of models, System Dynamics Review 5(1), 51-68.

Eckstein, O. (1981) Core Inflation. Englewood Cliffs, NJ: Prentice-Hall.

Eden, C., S. Jones, and D. Sims (1983) Messing About in Problems. Oxford: Pergamon Press.

Einhorn, H. and R. Hogarth (1978) Confidence in judgment: Persistence of the illusion of validity, Psychological Review 85, 395-476.

Einhorn, H. and R. Hogarth (1986) Judging probable cause, Psychological Bulletin 99, 3-19.

Emmerson, R., R. Fretz, and L. Shaw (1995) Writing Ethnographic Fieldnotes. Chicago: University of Chicago Press.

Epstein, J. and R. Axtell (1996) Growing Artificial Societies: Social Science from the Bottom Up. Washington, DC: Brookings Institution; Cambridge, MA: MIT Press.

Farman, J, B. Gardiner, and J. Shanklin (1985) Large losses of total ozone in Antarctica reveal seasonal ClO/NO$_2$ interaction, Nature 315, 207-210.

Festinger, L. (1957) A Theory of Cognitive Dissonance. Evantson, IL: Row, Peterson.

Fiddaman, T. (1997) Feedback Complexity in Integrated Climate-Economy Models. PhD thesis, MIT Sloan School of Management, Cambridge, MA 02142 (unpublished).

Finan, J. (1993) System Dynamics Analysis of an Ordering System Used for Commercial Aircraft Manufacture. MS thesis, MIT Sloan School of Management, Cambridge, MA 02142 (unpublished).

Fine, P. (1993) Herd immunity: History, theory, practice, Epidemiologic Reviews 15(2), 265-302.

Fisher, D. and R. Zaraza (1997) Seamless integration of system dynamics into high school mathematics: Algebra, calculus, modeling courses. Proceedings of the 15th International System Dynamics Conference: Systems Approach to Learning and Education into the 21st Century, Istanbul, Turkey: Bogazici University Printing Office.

Fisher, I. (1930) The Theory of Interest. New York: MacMillan Press.

Fisher, S. (1986) Stress and Strategy. London: Lawrence Erlbaum Associates.

Ford, A. (1990) Estimating the impact of efficiency standards on the uncertainty of the Northwest electric system, Operations Research 38(4), 580-597.

Ford, A. (1997) System dynamics and the electric power industry, System Dynamics Review 13(1), 57-85.

Ford, A. (1999) Modeling the Environment. Washington, DC: Island Press.

Ford, A. and M. Bull (1989) Using system dynamics for conservation policy analysis in the Pacific Northwest, System Dynamics Review 5(1), 1-16.

Ford, D. and J. Sterman (1998a) Expert knowledge elicitation for improving mental and formal models, System Dynamics Review 14(4), 309-340.

Ford, D. and J. Sterman (1998b) Dynamic modeling of product development processes, System Dynamics Review 14(1), 31-68.

Forrester, J. W. (1961) Industrial Dynamics. Cambridge: MIT Press; Currently available from Pegasus Communications: Waltham, MA.

Forrester, J. W. (1964) Modeling the dynamic processes of corporate growth. Proceedings of the IBM Scientific Computing Symposium on Simulation Models and Gaming.

Reprinted in Forrester, J.W. (1975a) Collected Papers of Jay W. Forrester. Waltham, MA: Pegasus Communications.

Forrester, J. W. (1965) A new corporate design, Industrial Management Review 7(1), 5-17. Reprinted in Forrester, J.W. (1975a) Collected Papers of Jay W. Forrester. Waltham, MA: Pegasus Communications.

Forrester, J. W. (1968) Market growth as influenced by capital investment, Industrial Management Review 9(2), 83-105. Also reprinted in Roberts (1978).

Forrester, J. W. (1969) Urban Dynamics. Waltham, MA: Pegasus Communications.

Forrester, J. W. (1971a) Counterintuitive behavior of social systems, Technology Review 73(3), 52-68.

Forrester, J. W. (1971b) World Dynamics. Waltham, MA: Pegasus Communications.

Forrester, J. W. (1973) Confidence in Models of Social Behavior–With Emphasis on System Dynamics Models. MIT System Dynamics Group Memo D-1967, Cambridge, MA 02139 (unpublished).

Forrester, J. W. (1975a) Collected Papers of Jay W. Forrester. Waltham, MA: Pegasus Communications.

Forrester, J. W. (1975b) Planning and goal creation, in Forrester, J. W. (1975a) Collected Papers of Jay W. Forrester. Waltham, MA: Pegasus Communications, 167-174.

Forrester, J. W. (1977) Growth cycles, De Economist 125(4), 525-543.

Forrester, J. W. (1979) An alternative approach to economic policy: Macrobehavior from Microstructure, in Kamrany, N. and R. Day (eds.), Economic Issues of the Eighties, Baltimore, MD: Johns Hopkins University Press, 80-108.

Forrester, J. W. (1980) Information sources for modeling the national economy, Journal of the American Statistical Association, 75(371), 555-574.

Forrester, J. W. (1983) Innovation and economic change, in Freeman, C. (eds.), Long Waves in the World Economy. London: Butterworths, 126-134.

Forrester, J. W. (1985) "The" model versus a modeling "process," System Dynamics Review 1(1), 133-134.

Forrester, J. W. (1987) 14 obvious truths, System Dynamics Review 3(2), 156-159.

Forrester, J. W. (1992) Policies, decisions, and information sources for modeling, European Journal of Operational Research 59(1), 42-63.

Forrester, J. W., N. Mass, and C. Ryan (1976) The system dynamics national model: Understanding socio-economic behavior and policy alternatives, Technological Forecasting and Social Change 9(1/2), 51-68.

Forrester, J. W. and P. Senge (1980) Tests for building confidence in system dynamics models, in Legasto, A., J. W. Forrester, and J. Lyneis (eds.) (1980) System Dynamics. TIMS Studies in the Management Sciences 14. New York: North-Holland, 209-228.

Forrester, N. (1982) A Dynamic Synthesis of Basic Macroeconomic Theory: Implications for Stabilization Policy Analysis. PhD thesis, MIT Sloan School of Management, Cambridge, MA 02142 (unpublished).

Frankel, J. and K. Froot (1987) Using survey data to test standard propositions regarding exchange rate expectations, American Economic Review 77(1), 133-53.

Franses, P. (1998) Time Series Models for Business and Economic Forecasting. Cambridge, England: Cambridge University Press.

Friedman, M. (1956/1973) Studies in the Quantity Theory of Money. Chicago: University of Chicago Press.

Friedman, M. (1957) A Theory of the Consumption Function. Princeton: Princeton University Press.

Frisch, R. (1933/1965) Propagation problems and impulse problems in dynamic economics, in Economic Essays in Honor of Gustav Cassel. London: George Allen and

Unwin. Reprinted in Gordon, R. and L. Klein (eds.) (1965) Readings in Business Cycle Theory. Homewood, IL: Irwin, 155-185.

Froot, K., D. Scharfstein, and J. Stein (1992) Herd on the street: Informational inefficiencies in a market with short-term speculation, Journal of Finance 47(4), 1461-1484.

Galbraith, C. and G. Merrill (1992) The politics of forecasting: Managing the truth, California Management Review 38(2), 29-43.

Galbraith, J. (1988) The Great Crash, 1929. Boston, MA: Houghton Mifflin.

Gardiner, L. and R. Shreckengost (1987) A system dynamics model for estimating heroin imports into the United States, System Dynamics Review 3(1), 8-27.

Garnett G. and R. Anderson (1996) Sexually transmitted diseases and sexual behavior: Insights from mathematical models, Journal of Infectious Diseases 174 (Supplement), S150-S161.

Garud, R. and M. Rappa (1994) A socio-cognitive model of technology evolution: The case of cochlear implants, Organization Science 5(3), 344-362.

Gentner, D. and A. Stevens (1983) Mental Models. Hillsdale, NJ: Lawrence Erlbaum Associates.

Gerlow, M., S. Irwin, and T. Liu (1993) Economic evaluation of commodity price forecasting models, International Journal of Forecasting 9(3), 387-397.

Gibbs, W. (1997) Transportation's perennial problems, Scientific American (Oct), 54-57.

Gillette, R. (1974) Oil and gas resources: Did USGS gush too high? Science 185 (12 July), 127-130.

Glaser, B. and A. Strauss (1967) The Discovery of Grounded Theory. Chicago: Aldine.

Goldratt, E. and J. Cox (1986) The Goal: A Process of Ongoing Improvement, revised ed. Croton on Hudson, NY: North River Press.

Golüke, U., R. Landeen, and D. Meadows (1981a) A simulation model of drinking behavior, British J. of Addiction 76(3), 289-298.

Golüke, U., R. Landeen, and D. Meadows (1981b) The dynamics of alcoholism, in Paulre, B. (ed.), System Dynamics and the Analysis of Change. Amsterdam: North-Holland (215-231).

Gordon, R., (ed.) (1986) The American Business Cycle: Continuity and Change. National Bureau of Economic Research Studies in Business Cycles Series, Vol. 25. Chicago: University of Chicago Press.

Gould, J., (ed.) (1993) Systems Thinking in Education, System Dynamics Review (special issue) 9(2).

Gould, S. (1990) Wonderful Life. New York: W. W. Norton.

Goulden, M. et al. (1998) Sensitivity of boreal forest carbon balance to soil thaw, Science 279 (9 Jan), 214-217.

Graham, A. (1977) Principles on the Relationship between Structure and Behavior of Dynamic Systems. PhD thesis, MIT, Cambridge, MA 02139 (unpublished).

Graham, A. and P. Senge (1980) A long wave hypothesis of innovation, Technological Forecasting and Social Change 17, 283-311.

Granger, C. and P. Newbold (1977) Forecasting Economic Time Series. New York: Academic Press.

Green, E. and R. Porter (1984) Noncooperative collusion under imperfect price information, Econometrica 52(1), 87-100.

Greenberger, M., M. Crenson, and B. Crissey (1976) Models in the Policy Process. New York: Russell Sage Foundation.

Greene, W. (1993) Econometric Analysis, 2nd ed. New York: Macmillan.

Grinspoon, L. and J. Bakalar (1985) Cocaine: A Drug and Its Social Evolution, revised ed. New York: Basic Books.

Gross, D. and C. Harris (1998) Fundamentals of Queueing Theory, 3rd ed. New York: John Wiley.

Gruber, H. (1992) The learning curve in the production of semiconductor memory chips, Applied Economics 24, 885-894.

Güvenen, O., W. Labys, and J-B Lesourd (1991) International Commodity Market Models: Advances in Methodology and Applications. London: Chapman and Hall.

Halford, G. (1993) Children's Understanding: The Development of Mental Models. Hillsdale, NJ: Lawrence Erlbaum Associates.

Hall, R. (1976) A system pathology of an organization: The rise and fall of the old Saturday Evening Post, Administrative Science Quarterly 21(2), 185-211.

Hamel, G. and C. Prahalad (1993) Strategy as stretch and leverage, Harvard Business Review 71(2), 75-84.

Hamilton, M. (1980) Estimating lengths and orders of delays in system dynamics models, in Randers, J. (ed.), Elements of the System Dynamics Method. Waltham, MA: Pegasus Communications, 162-183.

Hansen, M. (1995) Do new highways generate traffic? Access 7 (Fall), 16-22.

Hardin, G. (1968) The tragedy of the commons, Science 162 (13 Dec), 1243-1248.

Haxholdt, C., C. Kampmann, E, Mosekilde, and J. Sterman (1995) Mode locking and entrainment of endogenous economic cycles, System Dynamics Review 11(3), 177-198.

Hayes, D. and A. Schmitz (1987) Hog cycles and countercyclical production response, American Journal of Agricultural Economics 69(4), 762-70.

Heidenberger K. and M. Roth (1998) Taxonomies in the strategic management of health technology: The case of multiperiod compartmental HIV/AIDS policy models, International Journal of Technology Management 15(3-5), 336-358.

Hellekalek, P. (1998) Good random number generators are (not so) easy to find, Mathematics and Computers in Simulation 46 (5-6), 485-505.

Henderson, R. and K. Clark (1990) Architectural innovation: the reconfiguration of existing product technologies and the failure of established firms, Administrative Science Quarterly 35(1), 9-30.

Hermann, K. and J. Link (1990) The Thoroughbred Horseracing Industry: A System Dynamics Perspective, MS thesis, MIT Sloan School of Management, Cambridge, MA 02142 (unpublished).

Hernandez, K. (1990) Learning in Real Estate: The Role of the Development System in Creating Oversupply. MS thesis, MIT Sloan School of Management, Cambridge, MA 02142 (unpublished).

Hines, J. (1987) Essays in Behavioral Economic Modeling. PhD thesis, MIT Sloan School of Management, Cambridge, MA 02142 (unpublished).

Hogarth, R. (1981) Beyond discrete biases: Functional and dysfunctional aspects of judgmental heuristics, Psychological Bulletin 90, 197-217.

Hogarth, R. (1987) Judgement and Choice, 2nd ed. Chichester, England: John Wiley and Sons.

Hogarth, R. and M. Reder (eds.) (1987) Rational Choice. Chicago: University of Chicago Press.

Holder, H., and J. Blose (1987) Reduction of community alcohol problems: Computer simulation experiments in three counties, Journal of Studies on Alcohol 48(2), 124-135.

Holt, C., F. Modigliani, J. Muth, and H. Simon (1960) Planning Production, Inventories, and Workforce. Englewood Cliffs, NJ: Prentice-Hall.

Homer, J. (1979a) Home insurance in a changing residential community: A system dynamics approach and case study. MIT System Dynamics Group Memo D-3180, Cambridge, MA 02142.

Homer, J. (1979b) INSUR1: A dynamic model of property insurance coverage in an urban neighborhood. MIT System Dynamics Group Memo D-3120, Cambridge, MA 02142.

Homer, J. (1983a) A Dynamic Model for Analyzing the Emergence of New Medical Technologies. PhD thesis, MIT Sloan School of Management, Cambridge, MA 02142 (unpublished).

Homer, J. (1983b) Partial-model testing as a validation tool for system dynamics, Proceedings of the 1983 Intl. System Dynamics Conference, Chestnut Hill, MA: System Dynamics Society.

Homer, J. (1985) Worker burnout: A dynamic model with implications for prevention and control, System Dynamics Review 1(1), 42-62.

Homer, J. (1987) A diffusion model with application to evolving medical technologies, Technological Forecasting and Social Change 31(3), 197-218. Also chapter 9 in Richardson, G. (ed.) (1996) Modeling for Management, Vol. 2. Aldershot, UK: Dartmouth Publishing Co.

Homer, J. (1993) A system dynamics model of national cocaine prevalence, System Dynamics Review 9(1), 49-78.

Homer, J. (1996) Why we iterate: Scientific modeling in theory and practice, System Dynamics Review 12(1), 1-19.

Homer, J. (1997) Structure, data and compelling conclusions: Notes from the field (1997 Jay W. Forrester Award Lecture), System Dynamics Review 13(4), 293-309.

Homer, J. (1999) Macro-and micro-modeling of field service dynamics, System Dynamics Review 15(2), 139-162.

Homer, J., E. Roberts, A. Kasabian, and M. Varrel (1982) A systems view of the smoking problem, Intl. Journal of Biomedical Computing 13, 69-86.

Homer, J, J. Sterman, B. Greenwood, and M. Perkola (1993) Delivery time reduction in pulp and paper mill construction projects: A dynamic analysis of alternatives, in Zepeda, E. and J. Machuca (eds.), Proceedings of the 1993 International System Dynamics Conference, Albany, NY: System Dynamics Society.

Hoyt, H. (1933) One Hundred Years of Land Values in Chicago. Chicago: University of Chicago Press.

Hubbard, R. and D. Vetter (1991) Replications in the finance literature: An empirical study, Journal of Business and Economics 30(4), 70-81.

Hubbard, R. and D. Vetter (1992) The publication incidence of replications and critical commentary in economics, The American Economist 36(1), 29-34.

Hubbert, M. (1962) Energy Resources: Washington: National Academy of Sciences, National Research Council 1000-D. Reprinted as National Technical Information Service PB-222401 (1973).

Hubbert, M. (1975) Hubbert estimates from 1956 to 1974 of U.S. oil and gas, in Grenon, M. (ed.), Methods and Models for Assessing Energy Resources. Oxford: Pergamon.

Institute of Shipping Economics and Logistics (various years) Shipping Statistics Yearbook. Bremen, Germany: ISL.

IPCC (1996) Climate Change 1995. 3 vols. Cambridge: Cambridge University Press. See also <http://www.ipcc.ch/>.

Isaacs, W. and P. Senge (1992) Overcoming limits to learning in computer-based learning environments, European Journal of Operational Research 59(1), 183-196. Also chapter 11 in Morecroft, J. and J. Sterman (1994) Modeling for Learning Organizations. Portland, OR: Productivity Press.

Jacobs, R. and Jones. R. (1980) Price expectations in the United States: 1947-1975, American Economic Review 70, 269-277.

Janis, I. (1982) Groupthink: Psychological Studies of Policy Decisions and Fiascoes, 2nd ed. Boston: Houghton Mifflin.

Joglekar, N. (1996) The Technology Treadmill: Managing Product Performance and Production Ramp-Up in Fast-Paced Industries. PhD thesis, MIT Sloan School of Management, Cambridge, MA 02142 (unpublished).

Johnson, N. and S. Kotz (1977) Urn Models and Their Application. New York: John Wiley.

Johnson-Laird, P. (1983) Mental Models: Toward a Cognitive Science of Language, Inference, and Consciousness. Cambridge, England: Cambridge University Press.

Joint Economic Committee (1982) Three Large Scale Model Simulations of Four Money Growth Scenarios. Prepared for Subcommittee on Monetary and Fiscal Policy, 97th Congress, 2nd Session, Washington, DC.

Jones, A. and N. Repenning (1997) Sustaining Process Improvement at Harley-Davidson. Case study, MIT System Dynamics Group, Cambridge, MA 02142. Available from <http://web.mit.edu/nelsonr/www>.

Jones, P., T. Wigley, and P. Wright (1997) Global and Hemispheric Annual Temperature Variations between 1854 and 1991. Climatic Research Unit, University of East Anglia Norwich, United Kingdom: Available through <http://cdiac.esd.ornl.gov/trends/trends.htm>.

Jorgenson, D., J. Hunter, M. Nadiri (1970) The predictive performance of econometric models of quarterly investment behavior, Econometrica 38, 213-224.

Kahneman, D., J. Knetsch, R. Thaler (1986) Fairness as a constraint on profit seeking: Entitlements in the market, American Economic Review 76(4), 728-41.

Kahneman, D., P. Slovic, and A. Tversky (1982) Judgment Under Uncertainty: Heuristics and Biases. Cambridge, England: Cambridge University Press.

Kampmann, C. (1991) Replication and revision of a classic system dynamics model—critique of "Population-control mechanisms in a primitive agricultural society," System Dynamics Review 7(2), 159-198.

Kampmann, C. (1996) Feedback loop gains and system behavior. Working paper, Technical University of Denmark, Lyngby.

Kampmann, C. and J. Sterman (1998) Feedback complexity, bounded rationality, and market dynamics. Working paper, System Dynamics Group, MIT Sloan School of Management, Cambridge, MA 02142.

Karnopp, D., D. Margolis, and R. Rosenberg (1990) System Dynamics: A Unified Approach. New York: John Wiley.

Kay, J. (1997) Asphalt Nation: How the Automobile Took Over America and How We Can Take It Back. New York: Crown Publishers.

Keating, E., R. Oliva, N. Repenning, S. Rockart, and J. Sterman (1999) Overcoming the improvement paradox, European Management Journal 17(2), 120-134.

Keeling, C. (1997) CO_2 emissions from fossil fuels, Scripps Institution of Oceanography, University of California, La Jolla, California USA 92093-0220: Available through <http://cdiac.esd.ornl.gov/trends/trends.htm>.

Keeling, C. et al. (1997) Atmospheric CO_2 Concentrations—Mauna Loa Observatory, Hawaii, 1958-1996: Available through <http://cdiac.esd.ornl.gov/trends/trends.htm>.

Kermack, W. and A. McKendrick (1927) Contributions to the mathematical theory of epidemics, Proceedings of the Royal Society, 115A 700-721. Reprinted, Bulletin of Mathematical Biology (1991) 53(1-2), 33-55.

Kerr, R. (1998) Signs of past collapse beneath Antarctic ice, Science 281 (3 July), 17-19.

Kestenbaum, D. (1999) Death by the numbers, Science 283 (26 Feb), 1244-1247.

Keyfitz, N. (1977/1985) Applied Mathematical Demography, 2nd ed. New York: Springer Verlag.

Khazzoom, J. (1971) The FPC staff's econometric model of natural gas supply in the United States, Bell Journal of Economics and Management Science 2(1), 51-93.

Kim, D. (1989) Learning laboratories: Designing a reflective learning environment, in Milling, P. and E. Zahn (eds.), Computer-Based Management of Complex Systems. Berlin: Springer, 327-334.

Kim, D. (1992) Systems Archetypes. Toolbox Reprint Series, Waltham, MA: Pegasus Communications.

Kim, D. and P. Senge (1994) Putting systems thinking into practice, System Dynamics Review 10(2–3), 277-290.

Kindleberger, C. (1978) Manias, Panics, and Crashes: A History of Financial Crises. New York: Basic Books.

Kirch, P. (1984) The Evolution of the Polynesian Chiefdoms. Cambridge, MA: Cambridge University Press.

Kirch, P. (1997) Microcosmic histories: Island perspectives on 'global' change, American Anthropologist 99(1), 30-42.

Klayman, J. and Y. Ha (1987) Confirmation, disconfirmation, and information in hypothesis testing, Psychological Review 94, 211-28.

Kleiner, A. and G. Roth (1997) How to make experience your company's best teacher, Harvard Business Review 75(5), 172-177.

Kleinmuntz, D. and J. Thomas (1987) The value of action and inference in dynamic decision making, Organizational Behavior and Human Decision Processes 39(3), 341-364.

Klopfenstein B. (1989) Forecasting consumer adoption of information technology and services—lessons from home video forecasting, Journal of the American Society for Information Science 40(1), 17-26.

Koyck, L. (1954) Distributed Lags and Investment Analysis. Amsterdam: North Holland.

Krugman, P. (1979) Increasing returns, monopolistic competition, and international trade, Journal of International Economics 9(4), 469-79.

Kuhn, T. (1970) The Structure of Scientific Revolutions, 2nd ed. Chicago: University of Chicago Press.

Kurian, G. (1994) Datapedia of the United States, 1790-2000: America Year by Year. Lanham, MD: Bernan Press.

Kuznets, S. (1953) Economic Change. New York: W. W. Norton.

Lakatos, I. (1976) Proofs and Refutations. Cambridge, England: Cambridge University Press.

Lane, D. (1994) With a little help from our friends: How system dynamics and "soft" OR can learn from each other, System Dynamics Review 10(2-3), 101-134.

Langley, P., H. Simon, G. Bradshaw, and J. Zytkow (1987) Scientific Discovery: Computational Explorations of the Creative Processes. Cambridge, MA: MIT Press.

Lant, T. (1992) Aspiration level adaptation: An empirical exploration, Management Science 38(5), 623-644.

Leamer, E. (1983) Let's take the con out of econometrics, American Economic Review 73(1), 31-43.

Ledet, W. (1999) Engaging the entire organization key to improving reliability, Oil and Gas Journal 97(21), p. 54-57.

Lee, E. (1992) Statistical Methods for Survival Data Analysis, 2nd ed. New York: John Wiley.

Levin, G., G. Hirsch, and E. Roberts (1975) The Persistent Poppy: A Computer Aided Search for Heroin Policy. Cambridge, MA: Ballinger.

Levin, G., G. Hirsch, and E. Roberts (1978) Narcotics and the community: A system simulation, in Roberts, E. (ed.), Managerial Applications of System Dynamics. Waltham, MA: Pegasus Communications.

Levine, R. and H. Fitzgerald (1992) Analysis of Dynamic Psychological Systems (2 vols.). New York: Plenum Press.

Lichtenstein, S. and B. Fischoff (1977) Do those who know more also know more about how much they know, Organizational Behavior and Human Performance 20, 159-183.

Lichtenstein, S., B. Fischoff, and L. Phillips (1982) Calibration of probabilities: The state of the art to 1980, in Kahneman, D., P. Slovic and A. Tversky (eds.), Judgment Under Uncertainty: Heuristics and Biases. Cambridge, England: Cambridge University Press.

Liebowitz, S. and S. Margolis (1990) The fable of the keys, Journal of Law and Economics 33 (April).

Lotka, A. (1956) Elements of Mathematical Biology. New York: Dover Publications.

Low, G. (1980) The multiplier-accelerator model of business cycles interpreted from a system dynamics perspective, in Randers, J. (ed.), Elements of the System Dynamics Method. Waltham, MA: Pegasus Communications.

Lucas, R. (1996) Nobel lecture: Monetary neutrality, Journal of Political Economy 104(4), 661.

Lynch, M. (1994) Bias and theoretical error in long-term oil market forecasting, in Moroney, J. (ed.), Advances in the Economics of Energy and Natural Resources. Stamford, CT: JAI Press.

Lyneis, J. (1980) Corporate Planning and Policy Design. Waltham, MA: Pegasus Communications.

MacCoun, R. and P. Reuter (1997) Interpreting Dutch cannabis policy: Reasoning by analogy in the legalization debate, Science 278 (3 Oct), 47-52.

Machiavelli, N. (1979) Discourses, in Bondanella, P. and M. Musa (eds. and trans.), The Portable Machiavelli. New York: Viking Press.

Mahajan, V., E. Muller, and F. Bass (1990) New product diffusion models in marketing: A review and directions for research, Journal of Marketing 54(1), 1-26.

Makridakis, S., et al. (1982) The accuracy of extrapolation (time series) methods: Results of a forecasting competition, Journal of Forecasting 1(2), 111-153.

Makridakis, S., et al. (1984) The Forecasting Accuracy of Major Time Series Methods. Chichester, England: John Wiley and Sons.

Makridakis, S., et al. (1993) The M2 competition: A real time judgmentally based forecasting study, International Journal of Forecasting 9(1), 5-22.

Malakoff, D. (1997) Thirty Kyotos needed to control warming, Science 278 (19 Dec), 2048.

Mandinach, E. and H. Cline (1994) Classroom Dynamics: Implementing a Technology-Based Learning Environment. Hillsdale, NJ: Lawrence Erlbaum Associates.

Mann, C. (1994) Radiation: Balancing the record, Science 263 (28 Jan), 470-473.

March J., L. Sproull, and M. Tamaz (1991) Learning from samples of one or fewer, Organization Science 2(1), 58-70.

Marchetti, C. (1980) Society as a learning system: Discovery, invention, and innovation cycles revisited, Technological Forecasting and Social Change 18, 267-282.

Maron, M. (1987) Numerical Analysis: A Practical Approach, 2nd ed. New York: MacMillan.

Mass, N. (ed.) (1974) Readings in Urban Dynamics, Vol. 1. Waltham, MA: Pegasus Communications.

Mass, N. (1975) Economic Cycles: An Analysis of Underlying Causes. Cambridge, MA: MIT Press.

Mass, N. (1980) Stock and flow variables and the dynamics of supply and demand, in Randers, J. (ed.), Elements of the System Dynamics Method. Waltham, MA: Pegasus Communications.

Mass, N. (1991) Diagnosing surprise model behavior: A tool for evolving behavioral and policy insights, System Dynamics Review 7(1), 68-86.

Masuch, M. (1985) Vicious circles in organizations, Administrative Science Quarterly 30(1), 14-33.

Mayer, T. (1960) Plant and equipment lead times, Journal of Business 33, 127-132.

McCloskey, D. (1994) Knowledge and Persuasion in Economics. Cambridge, England: Cambridge University Press.

McPhee, J. (1989) The Control of Nature. New York: Farrar, Straus Giroux.

Meadows, D. H. (1980) The unavoidable a priori, in Randers, J. (ed.), Elements of the System Dynamics Method. Waltham, MA: Pegasus Communications.

Meadows, D. H. (1982) Whole earth models and systems, CoEvolution Quarterly, Summer, 98-108.

Meadows, D. H. (1989) System dynamics meets the press, System Dynamics Review 5(1), 68-80.

Meadows, D. H., D. L. Meadows, and J. Randers (1992) Beyond the Limits. Post Mills, VT: Chelsea Green Publishing Company.

Meadows, D. H., D. L. Meadows, J. Randers, and W. Behrens (1972) The Limits to Growth. New York: Universe Books.

Meadows, D. H., et al. (1974) Dynamics of Growth in a Finite World. Waltham, MA: Pegasus Communications.

Meadows, D. H., J. Richardson, and G. Bruckmann (1982) Groping in the Dark. Chichester, England: John Wiley and Sons.

Meadows, D. H. and J. Robinson (1985) The Electronic Oracle: Computer Models and Social Decisions. Chichester, England: John Wiley and Sons.

Meadows, D. L. (1970) Dynamics of Commodity Production Cycles. Waltham, MA: Pegasus Communications.

Meadows, D. L., T. Fiddaman, and D. Shannon (1993) Fish Banks, Ltd. A Micro-computer Assisted Group Simulation That Teaches Principles of Sustainable Management of Renewable Natural Resources, 3rd ed. Laboratory for Interactive Learning, University of New Hampshire, Durham, NH 03824.

Meadows, D. L. and D. H. Meadows (eds.) (1973) Toward Global Equilibrium: Collected Papers. Waltham, MA: Pegasus Communications.

Merton, R. (1948/1968) The self-fulfilling prophecy, Antioch Review (Summer), 193-210. Reprinted in Merton, R. K. (1968) Social Theory and Social Structure. New York: Free Press.

Michael, D. (1997) Learning to Plan and Planning to Learn, 2nd ed. Alexandria, VA: Miles River Press.

Miller, G. (1956) The magical number seven, plus or minus two: Some limits on our capacity for processing information, Psychological Review 63, 81-96.

Miller J. (1998) Active nonlinear tests (ANTs) of complex simulation models, Management Science 44(6), 820-830.

Miller, P. (ed.) (1994) The Rational Expectations Revolution: Readings from the Front Line. Cambridge, MA: MIT Press.

Mitchell, B. (1975) European Historical Statistics: 1750-1970. New York: Columbia University Press.

Modis, T. (1992) Predictions. New York: Simon and Schuster.

Mojtahedzadeh, M. (1997) A Path Taken: Computer-Assisted Heuristics for Understanding Dynamic Systems. PhD thesis, Rockefeller College of Public Affairs and Policy, University at Albany, State University of New York, Albany, NY 12222 (unpublished).

Molina, M. and F. Rowland (1974) Stratospheric sink for chlorofluoromethanes: Chlorine atom-catalysed destruction of ozone, Nature 249, 810-812.

Montgomery, M. (1995) "Time to Build" completion patterns for nonresidential structures, 1961-1991, Economics Letters 48, 155-163.

Moore, G. (1983) Business Cycles, Inflation, and Forecasting, 2nd ed. National Bureau of Economic Research Studies in Business Cycles, No. 24. Cambridge, MA: Ballinger.

Morecroft, J. (1982) A critical review of diagramming tools for conceptualizing feedback models, Dynamica 8(I), 20-29.

Morecroft, J. (1983) System dynamics: Portraying bounded rationality, Omega 11(2) 131-142.

Morecroft, J. (1985) Rationality in the analysis of behavioral simulation models, Management Science 31(7), 900-916.

Morecroft, J. and J. Sterman, (eds.) (1994) Modeling for Learning. Portland, OR: Productivity Press.

Mosekilde, E. (1996) Topics in Nonlinear Dynamics: Applications to Physics, Biology and Economic Systems. Singapore: World Scientific.

Mosteller, F. (1981) Innovation and evaluation, Science 211 (27 Feb) 881-886.

Mowry, G. (1958) The Era of Theodore Roosevelt and the Birth of Modern America. New York: Harper and Row.

Moxnes, E. (1992) Positive feedback economics and the competition between "hard" and "soft" energy supplies, Journal of Scientific and Industrial Research 51, 257-265.

Mueller, D. (1977) The persistence of profits above the norm, Economica 44(176), 369-380.

Mueller, D. (1986) Profits in the Long Run. Cambridge, England: Cambridge University Press.

Mullineaux. D. (1978) On testing for rationality: Another look at the Livingston price expectations data, Journal of Political Economy 86, 329-336.

Mundlak, Y. and H. Huang (1996) International comparisons of cattle cycles, American Journal of Agricultural Economics 78(4), 855-868.

Murray, J. (1993) Mathematical Biology, 2nd ed. Berlin: Springer-Verlag.

Muth, J. (1961) Rational expectations and the theory of price movements, Econometrica 29, 315-335.

Naill, R. (1973) The discovery life cycle of a finite resource: A case study of U.S. natural gas, in Meadows, D. L. and D. H. Meadows (eds.), Toward Global Equilibrium: Collected Papers. Waltham, MA: Pegasus Communications, 213-256.

Naill, R. (1977) Managing the Energy Transition. Cambridge, MA: Ballinger Publishing Co.

Naill, R. (1992) A system dynamics model for national energy policy planning, System Dynamics Review 8(1), 1-20.

Naill, R., S. Belanger, A. Klinger, and E. Petersen (1992) An analysis of the cost effectiveness of US energy policies to mitigate global warming, System Dynamics Review 8(2), 111-128.

Neftel, A. et al. (1994) Historical CO_2 Record from the Siple Station Ice Core. Physics Institute, University of Bern, CH-3012: Bern, Switzerland.

Nelson, C. and S. Peck (1985) The NERC Fan: A retrospective analysis of the NERC summary forecasts, Journal of Business and Economic Statistics 3(3), 179-187.

Nelson, R. and S. Winter (1982) An Evolutionary Theory of Economic Change. Cambridge, MA: Belknap Press of Harvard University Press.

Nerlove, M. (1958) Adaptive expectations and the cobweb phenomenon, Quarterly Journal of Economics 72, 227-240.

Nisbett, R and T. Wilson (1977) Telling more than we can know: Verbal reports on mental processes, Psychological Review 84, 231-259.

Nord, O. (1963) Growth of a New Product: Effects of Capacity Acquisition Policies. Cambridge, MA: MIT Press.

Nordhaus, W. (1992a) The "DICE" model: Background and structure of a dynamic integrated climate-economy model of the economics of global warming. Cowles Foundation Discussion Paper No. 1009. New Haven, CT: Cowles Foundation for Research in Economics.

Nordhaus, W. (1992b) An optimal transition path for controlling greenhouse gases, Science 258 (20 Nov), 1315-1319.

Nordhaus, W. (1994) Expert opinion on climatic change, American Scientist 82(1), 45-51.

Northcraft, G. and M. Neale (1987) Experts, amateurs, and real estate: An anchoring-and-adjustment perspective on property pricing decisions, Organizational Behavior and Human Decision Processes 39, 84-97.

Nyhart, J. and D. Smarasan (1990) Generic computer tools as aids in negotiation: The issue of user adoption. Proceedings of the 1990 International Systems Dynamics Conference, Chestnut Hill, MA: International System Dynamics Society.

Ogata, K. (1997) Modern Control Engineering, 3rd ed. Upper Saddle River, NJ: Prentice Hall.

Oliva, R. (1996) A Dynamic Theory of Service Delivery: Implications for Managing Service Quality. PhD thesis, MIT Sloan School of Management, Cambridge, MA 02142 (unpublished).

Oreskes, N., K. Shrader-Frechette, and K. Belitz (1994) Verification, validation, and confirmation of numerical models in the earth sciences, Science 263 (4 Feb), 641-646.

Oskamp, S. (1965) Overconfidence in case study judgments, Journal of Consulting Psychology 29, 261-265. Also in Kahneman, Slovic, and Tversky (eds.), Judgment Under Uncertainty: Heuristics and Biases. Cambridge, England: Cambridge University Press, 287-293.

Packer, D. (1964) Resource Acquisition in Corporate Growth. Cambridge, MA: MIT Press.

Paich, M. and J. Sterman (1993) Boom, bust, and failures to learn in experimental markets, Management Science 39(12), 1439-1458.

Papadopoulos, H. (1993) Queueing Theory in Manufacturing Systems Analysis and Design. New York: Chapman and Hall.

Papert, S. (1980) Mindstorms. New York: Basic Books.

Parker, P. (1994) Aggregate diffusion forecasting models in marketing: A critical review, International Journal of Forecasting 10(2), 353-380.

Parkinson, C. (1957) Parkinson's Law, and Other Studies in Administration. Boston, MA: Houghton Mifflin.

Partee, J. (1993) Heavy Boots. Personal communication from partee@iastate.edu.

Pearce, D. (1979) Comparing survey and rational measures of expected inflation. Journal of Money, Credit, and Banking 11, 447-456.

Peek, J. and J. Wilcox (1984) The degree of fiscal illusion in interest rates: Some direct estimates, American Economic Review 74, 1061-1066.

Pesando, J. (1975) A note on the rationality of the Livingston price expectations, Journal of Political Economy 83, 849-858.

Peterson, D. and R. Eberlein (1994) Reality check: A bridge between systems thinking and system dynamics, System Dynamics Review 10(2-3), 159-174.

Peterson, I. (1993) Newton's Clock: Chaos in the Solar System. New York: W. H. Freeman.

Phelps-Brown, E. (1972) The underdevelopment of economics, The Economic Journal 82 (325), 1-10.

Phillips, A. (1954) Stabilization policy in a closed economy, Economic Journal 64(254), 290-323.

Picardi, A. and W. Seifert (1976) A tragedy of the commons in the Sahel, Technology Review, 78(6), p. 42-51.

Pindyck, R. and J. Rotemberg (1983) Dynamic factor demands and the effects of energy price shocks, American Economic Review 73(5), 1066-1079.

Plous, S. (1993) The Psychology of Judgment and Decision Making. New York: McGraw Hill.

Powers, W. (1973) Feedback: Beyond behaviorism, Science 179 (26 Jan), 351-356.

Prabhu, N. (1997) Foundations of Queueing Theory. Boston, MA: Kluwer Academic Publishers.

Prusiner, S. (1997) Prion diseases and the BSE crisis, Science 278 (10 Oct), 245-251.

Randers, J. (ed.) (1980) Elements of the System Dynamics Method. Waltham, MA: Pegasus Communications.

Rappaport, R. (1968/1984) Pigs for the Ancestors: Ritual in the Ecology of a New Guinea People, revised ed. New Haven: Yale University Press.

Rassekh, F. and B. Wilbratte (1990) The effect of import price changes on domestic inflation: An empirical test of the ratchet effect, Journal of Money, Credit and Banking 22(2), 263-267.

Rayward-Smith, V., et al. (eds.) (1996) Modern Heuristic Search Methods. Chichester, England: John Wiley and Sons.

Reagan-Cirincione, P., S. Schuman, G. Richardson, and S. Dorf (1991) Decision modeling: Tools for strategic thinking, Interfaces 21(6), 52-65.

Redman, D. (1994) Karl Popper's theory of science and econometrics: The rise and decline of social engineering, Journal of Econnomic Issues 28(1), 67-99.

Reichelt, K. and J. Sterman (1990) Halter Marine: A Case Study in the Dangers of Litigation. System Dynamics Group, MIT Sloan School of Management, Cambridge, MA 02142.

Repenning, N. and J. Sterman (1999) Getting quality the old fashioned way: Self-confirming attributions in the dynamics of process improvement, in Scott, R. and R. Cole (eds.), The Quality Movement and Organizational Theory. Newbury Park, CA: Sage.

Richards, J. (1959) A flexible growth function for empirical use, Journal of Experimental Botany 10, 290-300.

Richardson, G. (1983) Heroin addiction and its impact on the community, in Roberts, N. (ed.), Introduction to Computer Simulation, a System Dynamics Approach. Reading, MA: Addison-Wesley.

Richardson, G. (1986a) Problems with causal loop diagrams, System Dynamics Review 2(2), 158-170.

Richardson, G. (1986b) Dominant structure, System Dynamics Review 2(1), 68-75.

Richardson, G. (1991) Feedback Thought in Social Science and Systems Theory. Philadelphia: University of Pennsylvania Press; also Waltham, MA: Pegasus Communications.

Richardson, G. (1995) Loop polarity, loop dominance, and the concept of dominant polarity, System Dynamics Review 11(1), 67-88.

Richardson, G. (1996) Modelling for Management (2 vols.). Aldershot, UK: Dartmouth Publishing Co.

Richardson, G. (1997) Problems in causal loop diagrams revisited, System Dynamics Review 13(3), 247-252.

Richmond, B. (1987) The Strategic Forum: From Vision to Operating Policies and Back Again. High Performance Systems, 45 Lyme Road, Ste. 300, Hanover, NH 03755.

Richmond, B. (1993) Systems thinking: Critical thinking skills for the 1990s and beyond, System Dynamics Review 9(2), 113-134.

Rignot, E. (1998) Fast recession of a West Antarctic glacier, Science 281 (24 July), 549-551.

Risch, J., L. Troyano-Bermúdez, and J. Sterman (1995) Designing corporate strategy with system dynamics: A case study in the pulp and paper industry, System Dynamics Review 11(4), 249-274.

Roberts, C. and B. Dangerfield (1990) Modelling the epidemiological consequences of HIV infection and AIDS: A contribution from operational research, Journal of the Operational Research Society 41(4), 273-289.

Roberts, E. (1977/1978) Strategies for effective implementation of complex corporate models, Interfaces 7(5). Reprinted in Roberts, E. (ed.) (1978) Managerial Applications of System Dynamics. Waltham, MA: Pegasus Communications.

Roberts, E. (ed.) (1978) Managerial Applications of System Dynamics. Waltham, MA: Pegasus Communications.

Roberts, N. (1978) Student performance in the elementary classroom: A system simulation, in Roberts, E. (ed.), Managerial Applications of System Dynamics. Waltham, MA: Pegasus Communications.

Roberts, N. and W. Feurzeig (eds.) (1999) Modeling and Simulation in Precollege Science and Mathematics. New York: Springer Verlag.

Robinson, J. (1988) A Day for the Capital to Consider Its Stars. Boston Globe (Wednesday, 4 May), 1.

Rogers, E. (1995) Diffusion of Innovations, 4th ed. New York: Free Press.

Romer, P. (1990) Endogenous technological change, Journal of Political Economy 98(5, Part 2), S71-S102.

Rosa, R. (1995) Extended workshifts and excessive fatigue, Journal of Sleep Research 4 (Suppl. 2), 51-56.

Rosen, S., K. Murphy, and J. Scheinkman (1994) Cattle cycles, Journal of Political Economy 102(3), 468-92.

Rosenhead, J., (ed.) (1989) Rational Analysis for a Problematic World: Problem Structuring Methods for Complexity, Uncertainty, and Conflict. Chichester, England: John Wiley and Sons.

Rosner, B. (1995) Fundamentals of Biostatistics, 4th ed. Belmont, CA: Duxbury Press.

Ross, L. (1977) The intuitive psychologist and his shortcomings: Distortions in the attribution process, in L. Berkowitz (ed.), Advances in Experimental Social Psychology, Vol. 10. New York: Academic Press.

Rostow, W. (1993) Nonlinear dynamics and economics: A historian's perspective, in Day, R. and P. Chen (eds.), Nonlinear Dynamics and Evolutionary Economics. New York: Oxford University Press, 14-17.

Rowell, D. and D. Wormley (1997) System Dynamics: An Introduction. Upper Saddle River, NJ: Prentice Hall.

Russo, J. and P. Schoemaker (1989) Decision Traps: Ten Barriers to Brilliant Decision-Making and How to Overcome Them. New York: Doubleday.

SAMHSA (1994) National Household Survey on Drug Abuse: Population Estimates (1993) DHHS Publication (SMA) 94-3017, Rockville MD: Substance Abuse and Mental Health Services Administration.

Samuelson, P. (1939) Interactions between the multiplier analysis and the principle of acceleration, Review of Economic Statistics 21, 75-79.

Samuelson, P. (1947) Foundations of Economic Analysis. Cambridge: Harvard University Press.

Samuelson, P. (1973) Economics, 9th ed. New York: McGraw-Hill.

Sanders, N. and K. Manrodt (1994) Forecasting practices in US corporations: Survey results, Interfaces 24(2), 92-100.

Sastry, M. (1997) Problems and paradoxes in a model of punctuated organizational change, Administrative Science Quarterly 42(2), 237-275.

Sastry, M., J. Romm, and K. Tsipis (1987) Nuclear Crash: The U.S. Economy after Small Nuclear Attacks. Report 17, Program in Science and Technology for International Security. MIT, Cambridge, MA 02139.

Sastry, A. and J. Sterman (1993) Desert island dynamics: An annotated guide to the essential system dynamics literature, in Zepeda, E. and J. Machuca (eds.), Proceedings of the 1993 International System Dynamics Conference, Albany, NY: System Dynamics Society.

Schank, R. and R. Abelson (1977) Scripts, Plans, Goals, and Understanding. Hillsdale, NJ: Lawrence Erlbaum Associates.

Schein, E. (1969) Process Consultation: Its Role in Organization Development. Reading, MA: Addison-Wesley.

Schein, E. (1985) Organizational Culture and Leadership. San Francisco, CA: Jossey-Bass.

Schein, E. (1987) Process Consultation, Vol. 2 Reading, MA: Addison-Wesley.

Schein, E. (1988) Process Consultation, Vol. 1 (revised ed.). Reading, MA: Addison-Wesley.

Schneiderman, A. (1988) Setting quality goals, Quality Progress (April), 55-57.

Schön, D. (1983) The Reflective Practitioner. New York: Basic Books.

Schön, D. (1992) The theory of inquiry: Dewey's legacy to education. Curriculum Inquiry. 22(2), 119-139.

Schroeder, W., R. Sweeney, and L. Alfeld (eds.) (1975) Readings in Urban Dynamics, Vol. 2. Waltham, MA: Pegasus Communications.

Senge, P. (1978) The System Dynamics National Model Investment Function: A Comparison to the Neoclassical Investment Function. PhD thesis, MIT Sloan School of Management, Cambridge, MA 02142 (unpublished).

Senge, P. (1980) A system dynamics approach to investment-function specification and testing, Socio-Economic Planning Sciences 14(6), 269-280.

Senge, P. (1990) The Fifth Discipline: The Art and Practice of the Learning Organization. New York: Doubleday.

Senge, P. and J. Sterman (1992) Systems thinking and organizational learning: Acting locally and thinking globally in the organization of the future, European Journal of Operational Research 59(1), 137-150. Also chapter 8 in Morecroft, J. and J. Sterman (eds.) (1994) Modeling for Learning Organizations. Portland, OR: Productivity Press.

Senge, P. et al. (eds.) (1994) The Fifth Discipline Fieldbook. New York: Doubleday.

Shantzis, S. and W. Behrens (1973) Population control mechanisms in a primitive agricultural society, in Meadows, D.L. and D. H. Meadows (eds.), Towards Global Equilibrium: Collected Papers. Waltham, MA: Pegasus Communications.

Shaughnessy, D. (1987) Bogged Down. Boston Globe (Sunday 15 March), 20.

Shewhart, W. (1939) Statistical Method from the Viewpoint of Quality Control. Washington, DC: US Department of Agriculture.

Shiba, S., A. Graham, and D. Walden (1993) A New American TQM: Four Practical Revolutions in Management. Waltham, MA: Pegasus Communications.

Shiller, R. (1989) Market Volatility. Cambridge, MA: MIT Press.

Shreckengost, R. (1991) The dynamic relationship of the cocaine system in the United States, in Schober, S. and C. Schade (eds.), The Epidemiology of Cocaine Use and Abuse. Washington, D. C.: U. S. Government Printing Office, 305-334.

Simchi-Levi, D., P. Kaminsky, and E. Simchi-Levi (1999) Designing and Managing the Supply Chain: Concepts, Strategies and Cases. Chicago: Irwin/McGraw-Hill.

Simon, H. (1957) Administrative Behavior; a Study of Decision-Making Processes in Administrative Organizations, 2nd ed. New York: Macmillan.

Simon, H. (1969) The Sciences of the Artificial. Cambridge, MA: MIT Press, 3rd ed. 1996.

Simon, H. (1979) Rational decision-making in business organizations, American Economic Review 69, 493-513.

Simon, H. (1982) Models of Bounded Rationality. Cambridge, MA: MIT Press.

Simon, H. (1984) On the behavioral and rational foundations of economic dynamics, Journal of Economic Behavior and Organization 5(1), 35-55.

Slade, M. (1982) Cycles in natural-resource commodity prices: An analysis of the frequency domain, Journal of Environmental Economics and Management 9(2), 138-48.

Smith, V., Suchanek, G., and A. Williams. (1988) Bubbles, crashes, and endogenous expectations in experimental spot asset markets, Econometrica 56(5), 1119-1152.

Steadman, D. (1995) Prehistoric extinctions of Pacific Island birds: Biodiversity meets zooarchaeology, Science 267 (4 Feb), 1123-1131.

Sterman, J. (1980) The Use of Aggregate Production Functions in Disequilibrium Models of Energy-Economy Interactions, MIT System Dynamics Group Memo D-3234, Cambridge, MA (unpublished) 02142.

Sterman, J. (1983) Economic vulnerability and the energy transition, Energy Systems and Policy 7(4), 259-301.

Sterman, J. (1984) Appropriate summary statistics for evaluating the historical fit of system dynamics models, Dynamica 10, 51-66.

Sterman, J. (1985a) The growth of knowledge: Testing a theory of scientific revolutions with a formal model, Technological Forecasting and Social Change 28(2), 93-122.

Sterman, J. (1985b) A behavioral model of the economic long wave, Journal of Economic Behavior and Organization 6, 17-53.

Sterman, J. (1986) The economic long wave: Theory and evidence, System Dynamics Review 2(2), 87-125.

Sterman, J. (1987) Expectation formation in behavioral simulation models, Behavioral Science 32, 190-211.

Sterman, J. (1988a) People Express Management Flight Simulator: Software and Briefing Book. Available from the author, Sloan School of Management, MIT, Cambridge, MA 02142. See <web.mit.edu/jsterman/www>.

Sterman, J. (1988b) Modeling the formation of expectations: The history of energy demand forecasts, International Journal of Forecasting 4, 243-259.

Sterman, J. (1988c) A skeptic's guide to computer models, in Grant, L., Foresight and National Decisions. Lanham, MD: University Press of America, 133-169.

Sterman, J. (1989a) Misperceptions of feedback in dynamic decision making, Organizational Behavior and Human Decision Processes 43(3), 301-335.

Sterman, J. (1989b) Modeling managerial behavior: Misperceptions of feedback in a dynamic decision making experiment, Management Science 35(3), 321-339.

Sterman, J. (1989c) Deterministic chaos in an experimental economic system, Journal of Economic Behavior and Organization 12, 1-28.

Sterman, J. (1992) Teaching takes off: Flight simulators for management education, OR/MS Today (October), 40-44.

Sterman, J. , N. Repenning, and F. Kofman (1997) Unanticipated side effects of successful quality programs: Exploring a paradox of organizational improvement, Management Science 43(4), 501-521.

Sterman, J. and G. Richardson (1985) An experiment to evaluate methods for estimating fossil fuel resources, Journal of Forecasting 4(2), 197-226. Reprinted in Richardson, G. (1996) (ed.) Modelling for Management. Aldershot, UK: Dartmouth Publishing Co.

Sterman, J., G. Richardson, and P. Davidsen (1988) Modeling the estimation of petroleum resources in the United States, Technological Forecasting and Social Change 33(3), 219-249.

Sterman, J. and J. Wittenberg (1999) Path dependence, competition, and succession in the dynamics of scientific revolution, Organization Science 10(3), 322-341.

Stewart, I. (1989) Does God Play Dice? The Mathematics of Chaos. Cambridge, MA: Blackwell.

Stolarski, R. and R. Cicerone (1974) Stratospheric chlorine: A possible sink for ozone, Canadian Journal of Chemistry 52, 1610.

Strogatz, S. (1994) Nonlinear Dynamics and Chaos. Reading, MA: Addision-Wesley.

Sturis, J., K. Polonsky, E. Mosekilde, and E. Van Cauter (1991) Computer model for mechanisms underlying ultradian oscillations of insulin and glucose, American Journal of Physiology 260 (Endocrinol. Metab. 23): E801-E809.

Sturm, R. (1993) Nuclear power in Eastern Europe: Learning or forgetting curves? Energy Economics 15(3), 183-189.

Taylor, H. (1999) Modeling Paper Material Flows and Recycling in the US Macro-economy. PhD thesis, Department of Civil Engineering, MIT, Cambridge MA 02139 (unpublished).

Tenner, E. (1996) Why Things Bite Back: Technology and the Revenge of Unintended Consequences. New York: Knopf.

Teplitz, C. (1991) The Learning Curve Deskbook: A Reference Guide to Theory, Calculations, and Applications. New York: Quorum Books.

Thaler, R. (1991) Quasi Rational Economics. New York: Russell Sage Foundation.

Thaler, R. (1992) The Winner's Curse: Paradoxes and Anomalies of Economic Life. Princeton: Princeton University Press.

Theil, H. (1966) Applied Economic Forecasting. Amsterdam: North Holland Publishing Company.

Thomas, L. (1974) The Lives of a Cell: Notes of a Biology Watcher. New York: Viking Press.

Thornton, L. (1992) Real Estate Development Firms as Learning Organizations: Systems Thinking as a Methodology for Strategic Planning. MS thesis, MIT Center for Real Estate Development, Cambridge, MA 02139 (unpublished).

Tversky, K. and P. Kahneman (1974) Judgment under uncertainty: Heuristics and biases, Science 185 (27 Sept) 1124-1131. Reprinted in Kahneman, D., P. Slovic, and A. Tversky (eds.) (1982) Judgment Under Uncertainty: Heuristics and Biases. Cambridge, England: Cambridge University Press.

Ueda, Y. (1992) The Road to Chaos. Santa Cruz, CA: Aerial Press.

Urban, G., J. Hauser, and J. Roberts (1990) Prelaunch forecasting of new automobiles, Management Science 36, 401-421. Also chapter 17 in Richardson, G. (ed.) (1996) Modeling for Management, Vol. 1. Aldershot, UK: Dartmouth Publishing Co.

US Environmental Protection Agency (1994) Health Assessment Document for 2,3,7,8-Tetrachlorodibenzo- p-Dioxin (TCDD) and Related Compounds, Washington, DC: EPA/600/BP-92/001, August 1994.

Van Maanen, J. (1988) Tales of the Field. Chicago: University of Chicago Press.

Van Tilburg, J. (1994) Easter Island: Archaeology, Ecology, and Culture. Washington DC: Smithsonian Institution Press.

Vaupel, J., et al. (1998) Biodemographic trajectories of longevity, Science 280 (8 May), 855-860.

Vennix, J. (1990) Mental Models and Computer Models. PhD thesis. Nijmegen, The Netherlands: Nijmegen Institute for Cognition Research and Information Technology.

Vennix, J. (1996) Group Model Building: Facilitating Team Learning Using System Dynamics. Chichester, England: John Wiley and Sons.

Vennix, J., G. Richardson, and D. Andersen (eds.) (1997) Group model building, System Dynamics Review (special issue) 13(2).

Wagenaar, W. (1978) Intuitive prediction of growth, in Burkhardt, D, and W. Ittelson (eds.), Environmental Assessment of Socioeconomic Systems. New York: Plenum.

Wagenaar, W. and S. Sagaria (1975) Misperception of exponential growth, Perception and Psychophysics 18, 416-422.

Wagenaar, W. and H. Timmers (1978) Extrapolation of exponential time series is not enhanced by having more data points, Perception and Psychophysics 24, 182-184.

Wagenaar, W. and H. Timmers (1979) The pond-and-duckweed problem: Three experiments in the misperception of exponential growth, Acta Psychologica 43, 239-251.

Wallace, W. (ed.) (1994) Ethics in Modeling. White Plains, NY: Pergamon.

Wang, Q. and J. Sterman (1985) A disaggregate population model of China, Simulation 45(1), 7-14.

Warner, R. (1998) Spectral Analysis of Time Series Data. New York: Guilford Press.

Wason, P. and P. Johnson-Laird (1972) Psychology of Reasoning: Structure and Content. Cambridge, MA: Harvard University Press.

Weil, H. and R. Etherton, Jr. (1990) System dynamics in dispute resolution: Proceedings of the 1990 International Systems Dynamics Conference, Chestnut Hill, MA: International System Dynamics Society.

Weymar, H. (1968) Dynamics of the World Cocoa Market. Cambridge, MA: MIT Press.

Williams, A. (1987) The formation of price forecasts in experimental markets, Journal of Money, Credit and Banking 19(1), 1-18.

Wisdom, J. (1987) Urey Prize Lecture: Chaotic dynamics in the solar system, Icarus 72 (Nov), 241-275.

Wolstenholme, E. (1990) System Enquiry—A System Dynamics Approach. Chichester, England: John Wiley and Sons.

Womack, J. and D. Roos (1991) The Machine That Changed the World. New York: Harper Perrenial.

Wulwick, N. (1996) Two econometric replications: The historic Phillips and Lipsey-Phillips curves, History of Political Economy 28(3), 391-439.

Yerkes, R. and J. Dodson (1908) The relation of strength of stimulus to rapidity of habit formation, Journal of Comparative Neurology and Psychology 18, 459-482.

Yin, R. (1994) Case Study Research. Newbury Park, CA: Sage Publications.

Yourdon, E. (ed.) (1993) American Programmer 6(5). Special issue on system dynamics in project management.

Zamudio-Ramirez, P. (1996) The Economics of Automobile Recycling. MS thesis, MIT, Cambridge, MA 02142 (unpublished).

Zangwill, W. and P. Kantor (1998) Toward a theory of continuous improvement and the learning curve, Management Science 44(7), 910-920.

Zarnowitz, V. (1992) Business Cycles: Theory, History, Indicators, and Forecasting, NBER Studies in Business Cycles, Vol. 27. Chicago: University of Chicago Press.

Zenios, S., G. Chertow, and L. Wein (forthcoming) Dynamic allocation of kidneys to candidates on the transplant waiting list, Operations Research.

Ziman, J. (1968) Public Knowledge: An Essay Concerning the Social Dimension of Science. Cambridge, England: Cambridge University Press.

Index